FEATURES AND BENEFITS
PRENTICE HALL ALGEBRA 1

Prentice Hall Algebra 1 provides a comprehensive and cohesive course written to ensure that students master first-year Algebra skills and concepts.

CONTENTS

1 *Comprehensive coverage* begins with Real Numbers and Algebraic Expressions followed by chapters on Solving Linear Equations in One Variable; Inequalities in One Variable; Polynomials; Factoring Polynomials; Rational Expressions; Linear Equations in Two Variables; Relations and Functions; Systems of Linear Equations; Radicals; Quadratic Equations and Functions; Probability and Statistics; and Right Triangle Relationships. (See Contents, pp. iii–x.)

2 *A Capsule Review* in each skill lesson provides a brief review of the prerequisite basic math or Algebra skill needed for the lesson. (See pp. 136, 230.)

3 *Problem Solving Strategy* lessons in each chapter develop critical thinking skills to enable students to choose a successful approach to solve any problem. (See pp. 82, 358.)

4 *Applications* are included in the Practice Exercises in the lessons and as special features in the chapters to underscore the relevancy of Algebra in the real world and in related disciplines. (See pp. 389, 429.)

5 *Calculator and Computer* activities guide students in investigating algebraic concepts and in using technology as a problem solving tool. (See pp. 125, 236.)

6 *Carefully graded Practice Exercises* provide a wealth of practice for students of all ability levels. Although labeled A, B, C for you in the Teacher's Edition to indicate their relative difficulty, they are unlabeled in the Student Text, thereby encouraging students to try all problems. (See pp. 446–449.)

7 *Review and maintenance* features include 2-page Chapter Summary and Reviews, Cumulative Reviews, Maintaining Skills, Extra Practice Exercises, and Preparing for Standardized Tests Reviews. (See pp. 178–184, 224.)

8 *A complete testing program* consists of Test Yourself midway and at the end of each chapter, and a Chapter Test at the end of each chapter. (See pp. 340, 361, 364.)

9 *Special features* include Critical Thinking, Logical Reasoning, Reading and Writing in Algebra, Did You Know?, and Project. (See pp. 40, 553.)

● **The Teacher's Edition** includes a Chapter Overview immediately preceding each chapter, and a complete Lesson Plan for every lesson consisting of background information, teaching suggestions, follow-up activities, and assignment guides to help you plan effectively and efficiently.

● **The Teacher's Resource Book** contains Reteaching, Practice, Enrichment, and Applications organized by chapter, plus Spanish Chapter Summary and Review, Tests, Calculator Tests, Preparing for Standardized Tests, Critical Thinking Activities, Reading and Writing in Algebra Activities, Teaching Aids, Transparencies, Technology Activities (with diskettes), and Answers.

● **The Solution Manual** contains completely worked-out solutions to Student Text exercises.

● **The Computer Test Bank** provides instant tests on all the lessons you teach.

Unforgettable...

Over 3000 Algebra 1 teachers have told us that one of the challenges of teaching is to ensure that skills once learned are not forgotten. *Our approach meets the challenge* by reviewing basic math and Algebra skills right when they are needed.

The Capsule Review at the outset of a lesson reviews the prerequisite basic math or Algebra skills needed for the lesson.

4.2 Solving Equations: Variable on Both Sides

Objective: To solve equations that contain the variable on both sides

In the equations you have solved thus far, the terms containing variables were all on one side of the equation.

Capsule Review

To solve the equations below, you may first have to use the distributive property to remove parentheses before combining like terms.

Solve and check.

1. $2x + 13 = 1$ 2. $29 = 5 - 3y$ 3. $4y - 2y = 16$

4. $-19 = 2a - a - 10$ 5. $2(n - 3) = 14$ 6. $5(4 - b) - 35 = 0$

In equations like $3x + 2 = -x - 2$, you need to place the variable terms all on one side of the equation.

EXAMPLE 1   Solve and check: $3x + 2 = -x - 2$

$$3x + 2 = -x - 2$$
$$3x + x + 2 = -x + x - 2 \qquad \text{Add x to each side.}$$
$$4x + 2 = -2 \qquad\qquad\qquad \text{Combine like terms.}$$
$$4x + 2 - 2 = -2 - 2 \qquad \text{Subtract 2 from each side.}$$
$$4x = -4$$
$$x = -1 \qquad\qquad\qquad \text{Divide each side by 4.}$$

Check: $3x + 2 = -x - 2$

$$3(-1) + 2 \overset{?}{=} -(-1) - 2 \qquad \text{Replace x with } -1.$$
$$-3 + 2 \overset{?}{=} 1 - 2$$
$$-1 = -1 \; \text{✔} \qquad\qquad \text{True}$$

So, the solution is -1.

In Example 1, you might choose to have the variable terms on the right. Then you would begin by subtracting $3x$ from each side of the equation. Solve $3x + 2 = -x - 2$ by first subtracting $3x$ from each side. Do you get -1 for the solution?

140   Chapter 4 More Equations in One Variable

Solid...

The goal of every Algebra 1 teacher is to build a solid foundation of algebraic skills and concepts. The challenge arises in teaching students whose abilities may vary. *Our approach meets the challenge* by systematically developing algebraic skills and concepts and the strategies necessary to select a successful approach to solve any problem.

Some equations have more than one variable term on the same side. To solve these, the first step is to combine like terms that are on the same side.

EXAMPLE 2 Solve and check: $-36 + 2n = -3n + n - 5n$

$$-36 + 2n = -3n + n - 5n$$
$$-36 + 2n = -7n \qquad \text{\textit{Combine like terms on the right side.}}$$
$$-36 + 2n - 2n = -7n - 2n \qquad \text{\textit{Subtract 2n from each side.}}$$
$$-36 = -9n \qquad \text{\textit{Combine like terms.}}$$
$$4 = n \qquad \text{\textit{Divide each side by } -9.}$$

Check:
$$-36 + 2n = -3n + n - 5n$$
$$-36 + 2(4) = -3(4) + (4) - 5(4) \qquad \text{\textit{Replace n with 4.}}$$
$$-36 + 8 = -12 + 4 - 20$$
$$-28 = -28 \; \text{✔} \qquad \text{\textit{True}}$$

At this point, you should be familiar with the following steps for solving an equation.

> **Steps for Solving Equations**
> • Use the distributive property to remove parentheses on each side.
> • Combine like terms on each side.
> • Use the addition or subtraction property for equations so that
>   (a) all variable terms are on one side of the equation, and
>   (b) all numerical terms are on the other side.
> • Use the multiplication or division property for equations.

EXAMPLE 3 Solve: $2y + 3(y - 9) = -(3y - 18) - y$

$$2y + 3(y - 9) = -(3y - 18) - y$$
$$2y + 3(y - 9) = -1(3y - 18) - y$$
$$2y + 3y + 3(-9) = -1(3y) + (-1)(-18) - y \qquad \text{\textit{Distributive property}}$$
$$2y + 3y - 27 = -3y + 18 - y \qquad \text{\textit{Multiplication property for } -1}$$
$$5y - 27 = -4y + 18 \qquad \text{\textit{Combine like terms.}}$$
$$5y + 4y - 27 = -4y + 4y + 18 \qquad \text{\textit{Addition property for equations}}$$
$$9y - 27 = 18$$
$$9y - 27 + 27 = 18 + 27 \qquad \text{\textit{Addition property for equations}}$$
$$9y = 45$$
$$y = 5 \qquad \text{\textit{Division property for equations}}$$

The check is left for you.

Numerous models and examples provide important learning aids while reinforcing the new skill or concept. Solutions to examples are given step-by-step with the reason for each step highlighted in blue type. The use of technology is integrated throughout. Within the lessons, calculators and computers are used in the development of algebraic skills and concepts as problem solving and discovery tools.

Key concepts are boxed in red to highlight their importance.

Relevant...

One of the most frequently asked questions by students is, "Why do I have to learn this?" Our chapter themes, applications at the end of the lessons, and featured applications throughout the text is *the approach that meets the challenge* of underscoring the relevancy of algebraic skills and concepts.

Class Exercises assess students' understanding of lesson concepts and readiness for the Practice Exercises that follow.

The Practice Exercises are labeled A, B, C in the Teacher's Edition to indicate their relative difficulty, but are unlabeled in the Student Text, thereby encouraging students to try all problems.

CLASS EXERCISES

In each case, tell what should be done to get an equivalent equation that has the variable terms on one side and the numerical terms on the other.

1. $7m = -30 + m$
2. $4x + 28 = 7 + x$
3. $6 - z = 2z$
4. $6n = 4(n + 5)$
5. $-7b = 3(4 - 3b)$
6. $2(y - 5) = 15y - 4y$

Solve and check each equation.

7. $3t - 4 = -3t - 4$
8. $8 - 5a = 3a$
9. $4(x + 7) = 7 + x$

For Discussion

10. To solve some equations in Exercises 1–6, you might prefer to get the variable terms on the right side rather than the left. For which equations? Why?

11. Which types of equations might not have a solution. Explain.

PRACTICE EXERCISES

Solve and check.

1. $2y + 5 = -y - 4$
2. $3m + 6 = -m - 6$
3. $3d - 8 = -6 + d$
4. $5a - 14 = -5 + 8a$
5. $4 - 7m = m + 4$
6. $4 - 9j = j + 4$
7. $6n = 4n + 20$
8. $11e = 9e + 14$
9. $5d - 4 = 2d + 6$
10. $2j - 5 = 8j + 7$
11. $-22 - 3d = -2d + d - 3d$
12. $-42 + 4c = -c + 3c - c$
13. $8y + 20 = y + 2y - 5y$
14. $4b - 10 = b + 3b - 2b$
15. $-7f + 2f = -36 + f + 3f$
16. $-5a + 7a = -18 + 3a + 5a$
17. $9y + 2 = 3(y + 4)$
18. $3x - 2 = 4(x - 2)$
19. $3y + 2(y - 5) = -(3y - 35) - y$
20. $4x + 3(x - 2) = -(5x - 20) - x$
21. $5y - 2(y + 5) = -(2y + 15) + y$
22. $2z - 3(z + 1) = -(5z + 3) + z$
23. $6m + 3(m + 2) = -(2m + 7) + m$
24. $9t + 5(t + 3) = -(t + 13) + t$
25. $5f - \frac{1}{2} = 4f + \frac{3}{4}$
26. $2g - \frac{5}{8} = g + \frac{5}{8}$
27. $7(2d - 1) + 5(2 - 3d) = 2d$
28. $3(6e - 2) + 4(1 - 5e) = e$
29. $5(3 - 4y) + 14y = 7(2 - 5y)$
30. $2(5 - 4x) + x = 3(3x - 11)$

31. $6(2n - 5) = -3(7 - 3n) + 2n$

32. $11(3 - 2q) = 3(9 - 7q) + q$

33. $5x - 1 = (4 - 3x)(-2) + 10$

34. $14t - 1 = (1 - 2t)(-3) + 12$

35. $-7y + 3 = -(3y + 5) - 2$

36. $-9m + 5 = -(2m + 8) - 6$

37. $-5(3x - 2) + 6(2 - 2x) = 3x$

38. $-6(6y - 4) + 5(3 - 7y) = -68y$

39. $-6t - [4 - (2 - 3t)] = 4(t + 1)$

40. $-8b - [2(11 - 2b) + 4] = 9b$

41. $4[5y - 4(y - 1)] = 3[4(y + 1)]$

42. $-2[5(2j - 6) - 7j] = 5[3(j - 2)]$

43. $\frac{1}{2}\left[\frac{2}{3}(4d - 1)\right] - (3d - 2) = \frac{5}{9}d$

44. $\left(4 - \frac{1}{2}c\right) - \frac{1}{3}\left[\frac{3}{4}(1 - 2c)\right] = \frac{1}{12}c$

45. $-3[4m + 2(m - 4)] = -5[2(m + 5)]$ **46.** $-2[3k + 3(k - 8)] = -2[3(k + 7)]$

Applications

47. Geometry The area A of a rectangle increased by 4 is equal to 36 decreased by 5 times the area. What is the area of the rectangle?

48. Finance Sally earns $25,000 per year as a computer programmer. Her mother's annual income is twice the amount of Sally's. Her father's total income for 1 year is $\frac{1}{5}$ of Sally's income. What is her family's total income?

ALGEBRA IN TRANSPORTATION

Airplanes are one of the fastest means of transportation today. However, the velocities of different types of airplanes may vary greatly. Propeller planes may travel up to and over 250 mi/h, while a 747 can travel more than 600 mi/h. In 1947, the X-1 flew at the speed of sound, or Mach 1 (about 740 mi/h at sea level). Some years later, the X-15 flew at five times the speed of sound, or Mach 5. Presently, the Concorde provides passenger service at supersonic speeds for thousands of people.

Consider this problem: Two planes, one a propeller plane and one a supersonic transport (SST) travel 3000 mi. The propeller plane travels 1300 mi/h less than the SST. If the SST makes the trip in 2 h and the propeller plane makes it in 15 h, what is the rate of the propeller plane? Use this equation: $2x = 15(x - 1300)$

More support than ever before...

The Teacher's Edition is so easy to use that planning and assessment are never a problem.

A Chapter Overview preceding each chapter capsulizes the key features of the chapter. It includes an Assignment Guide that correlates supplementary materials on a lesson-by-lesson basis to enable you to meet the needs of students of all ability levels.

OVERVIEW · Chapter 4

SUMMARY

In Chapter 4, students expand their understanding of equations containing one variable. Students are introduced to equations in which the variable is contained on both sides of the equals sign. Further, students learn to combine like terms and to take shortcuts to simplify the longer procedures that they have learned up to this point. Four problem solving lessons in this chapter provide ample opportunity to apply algebraic procedures to techniques needed in other fields.

Toward the end of the chapter, students learn the concept of literal equations and its applications. Students recognize that literal equations are familiar to them via several formulas that they have already learned how to use.

CHAPTER OBJECTIVES

- To solve equations by removing parentheses and combining like terms
- To solve equations that contain the variable on both sides
- To solve problems that involve consecutive integers, percent of change, and uniform motion
- To use shortcuts to solve equations
- To use equations for solving simple percent problems and mixture problems involving percent
- To solve literal equations

Problem Solving Strategy

To solve problems by making drawings or tables as two examples of mathematical models

CHAPTER HIGHLIGHTS

The theme of the chapter is transportation. The chapter's special features show how algebra is applied to various means of transportation.

PROBLEM SOLVING AND APPLICATIONS

Problem solving and applications ... each lesson. Students use equa... problems and arrive at solution... fields including sports, science... and other areas of mathematics ... sons 4.3, 4.6, 4.7, 4.9, and 4.10 ... portunity to practice applying ... concrete situations that arise in ...

TECHNOLOGY

Calculator

A calculator can be used in L... check students' answers

RESOURCES

Teacher's Resource Book

- Teaching Aid 4
- Transparencies 6, 7

ASSIGNMENT GUIDE   Meeting Student Needs

STUDENT TEXT				TEACHER'S RESOURCE BOOK		
Chapter Content	**Basic**	**Average**	**Enriched**	**R**	**P**	**E**
4.1 Solving Equations: Combining Like Terms	D: 138/1-23 odd, 48	D: 138/1-39 odd, 48	D: 138/1-47 odd, 48-50	1	2	3
4.2 Solving Equations: Variables on Both Sides	D: 142/1-23 odd, 47 R: 138/12, 18, 22 142/4, 8, 10	D: 142/1-31 odd, 47 R: 138/34, 36, 38 142/6, 12, 18	D: 142/5-45 odd, 47, 48 R: 138/40, 42, 44	4	5	6
4.3 Problem Solving: Consecutive Integers	D: 146/1-15 odd R: 142/16, 20, 24	D: 146/1-21 odd R: 142/18, 22, 30	D: 146/3-27 odd R: 142/18, 22, 38		7	8
4.4 Shortcuts in Solving Equations	D: 150/1-23 odd, 49, 50 R: 146/4, 6, 16 Test Yourself	D: 150/1-39 odd, 49, 51 R: 146/16, 18, 20 Test Yourself	D: 150/3-47 odd, 49, 51, 52 R: 146/22, 24, 26 Test Yourself	9	10	11
4.5 Solving Equations: Percents	D: 154/1-19 odd, 33, 34 R: 150/6, 14, 20 154/6, 8, 12	D: 154/1-27 odd, 33, 35 R: 150/20, 24, 32 154/4, 10, 14, 20	D: 155/7-33 odd, 33-36 R: 150/32, 44, 52	12	13	14
4.6 Problem Solving: Percents	D: 157/1-13 odd R: 154/4, 10, 18 157/2, 4, 6	D: 157/1-27 odd R: 154/10, 16, 20	D: 157/15-31 odd R:154/12, 22, 26		15	16
4.7 Problem Solving: Mixtures	D: 163/1-3 odd R: 157/8, 10, 12	D: 163/1-7 odd R: 157/14, 20, 24	D: 163/5-9 odd R: 157/18, 22, 28		17	18
4.8 Literal Equations	D: 166/1-23 odd, 45 R: 163/2, 4 166/4, 8, 16	D: 163/1-37 odd, 45, 46 R: 163/4, 6 166/2, 14, 20	D: 163/1-43 odd, 45, 46 R: 163/6, 8	19	20	21
4.9 Problem Solving Strategy: Make a Drawing or a Table	D: 170/1-11 odd MPSR: 1-4 R: 166/26, 28, 30, 46	D: 170/1-17 odd MPSR: 1-4 R: 166/32, 36, 38, 46	D: 170/13-17 odd MPSR: 1-4 R: 167/36-42 even, 46		22	23
4.10 Problem Solving: Uniform Motion	D: 175/1-11 odd R: 170/2, 8, 10 Test Yourself	D: 175/1-21 odd R: 170/6, 12, 14 Test Yourself	D: 175/13-23 odd R: Test Yourself		24	25

D = Daily R = Review MPSR = Mixed Problem Solving Review   R = Reteaching P = Practice E = Enrichment

STUDENT TEXT				TEACHER'S RESOURCE BOOK	
Review And Testing	Test Yourself	151	Chapter Test	180	Spanish Chapter Summary and Review	7-8
	Test Yourself	177	Prep. for Stan. Tests	181	• Quizzes	33-36
	Chapter Sum. and Rev.	178	Cumulative Review	182	• Chapter Test (Form A)	37-38
			Extra Practice	658	• Chapter Test (Form B)	39-40
					Calculator Test	7-8
Special Features	Writing in Algebra	139	Algebra in Engineering	159	Applications—Chapter 4	26
	Alg. in Transportation	143	Application	160	Critical Thinking	4
	Math Club Activity	147	Did You Know?	163	Reading and Writing in Algebra	4
	Extra	157	Algebra in Aviation	167	Technology	9
			Project	171		

134B

...To meet the challenges of teaching!

The convenient format accommodates easy-to-read student pages with answers in place. Plus, a wealth of teaching aids appear right next to each student page...where you need them, when you need them.

A Complete Lesson Plan for every lesson helps you meet the challenges of teaching. It includes Background Information, Teaching Suggestions, and...

...Follow-Up Activities with reduced pages from the Teacher's Resource Book that relate to the lesson.

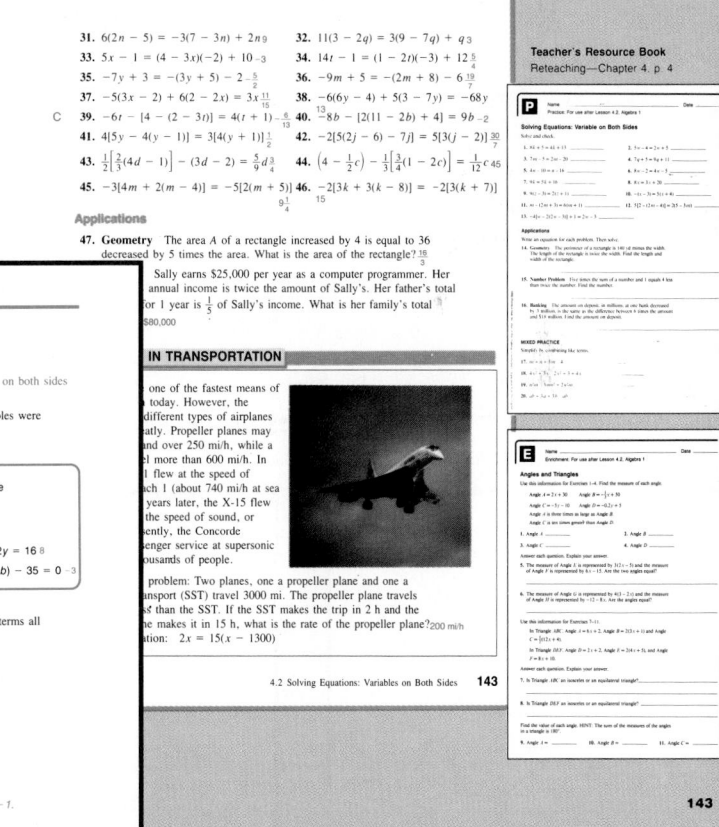

A Solution Manual with completely worked-out solutions to Student Text exercises is also available with this program.

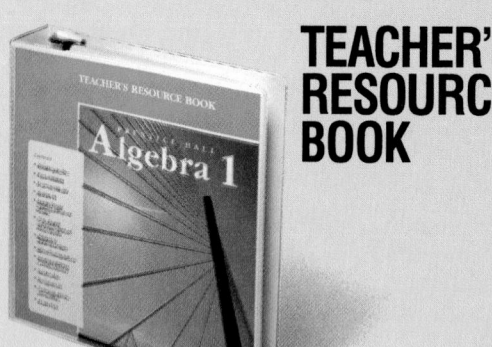

TEACHER'S RESOURCE BOOK

TEACHER'S RESOURCE BOOK

Algebra 1

With a complete teaching package...

Tabbed 3-ring binder contains a wealth of supplementary material organized by chapter, plus special aids and teaching resources including transparencies and computer diskettes.

Follow-Up activities for every lesson aid you in reaching all students.

R Name _____ Date _____
Reteaching: For use after Lesson 4.2, Algebra 1

Solving Equations: Variable on Both Sides

■ **Concept:** Solving equations that contain the variable on both sides

Remember: Use properties of real numbers until one term containing the variable is on one side and all terms that do not contain the variable are on the other side.

Example: Solve: $2 - 3(-x + 2) = 12x - (2x - 3)$

$2 + 3x - 6 = 12x - 2x + 3$ Remove parentheses.
$3x - 4 = 10x + 3$ Combine like terms on each side.
$3x - 3x - 4 = 10x - 3x + 3$ Subtract 3x from each side.
$-4 = 7x + 3$ Combine like terms.
$-4 - 3 = 7x + 3 - 3$ Subtract 3 from each side.
$-7 = 7x$ Combine like terms.
$\frac{-7}{7} = \frac{7x}{7}$ Divide each side by 7.
$-1 = x$ Simplify.

1. Describe the steps in the solution of the equation.
$4x - 6 - 5x = 6 + 2x - 9$
$-6 - x = 2x - 3$ _____
$-6 - x + x = 2x + x - 3$ _____
$-6 = 3x - 3$ _____
$-6 + 3 = 3x - 3 + 3$ _____
$-3 = 3x$ _____
$\frac{-3}{3} = \frac{3x}{3}$ _____
$-1 = x$ _____

Solve and check.

2. $11 - 4x = 5x - 7$ _____
3. $-x + 2 - 3x = -5x - 1$ _____
4. $14 - x = 7x + 4$ _____
5. $-3x - x + 10 + 2x$ _____
6. $-(5x + 6) = 4x + 3$ _____
7. $4x - 8 = -2(-3x - 1)$ _____
8. $4(3x + 4) = 2(5x - 7)$ _____
9. $-(-5x - 6) = -2(-3x + 7) - 3x$ _____

4 Chapter 4

P Name _____ Date _____
Practice: For use after Lesson 4.2, Algebra 1

Solving Equations: Variable on Both Sides

Solve and check.

1. $8k + 5 = 4k + 13$ _____
2. $5w - 4 = 2w + 5$ _____
3. $7m - 5 = 2m - 20$ _____
4. $7g + 5 = 9g + 11$ _____
5. $4x - 10 = n - 16$ _____
6. $8w - 2 = 4w - 5$ _____
7. $9x = 5x + 16$ _____
8. $8x = 3x + 20$ _____
9. $9(z - 3) = 2(z + 1)$ _____
10. $-(x - 3) = 5(x + 4)$ _____
11. $m - (2m + 3) = 6(m + 1)$ _____
12. $5[2 - (2m - 4)] = 2(5 - 3m)$ _____

Applications

Write an equation for each problem. Then solve.

13. **Geometry** The perimeter of a rectangle is 140 yd minus the width. The length of the rectangle is twice the width. Find the length and width of the rectangle.

14. **Number Problem** Five times the sum of a number and 1 equals 4 less than twice the number. Find the number.

15. **Banking** The amount on deposit, in millions, at one bank decreased by 3 million, is the same as the difference between 6 times the amount and $18 million. Find the amount on deposit.

MIXED PRACTICE

Simplify by combining like terms.

16. $m + n + 3m - 4$ _____
17. $4x^2 + 3x - 2x^2 + 3 + 4x$ _____
18. $3m - 3mn^2 + 2n^2m$ _____
19. $ab + 3a + 3b - ab$ _____

Chapter 4 5

E Name _____ Date _____
Enrichment: For use after Lesson 4.2, Algebra 1

Angles and Triangles

Use this information for Exercises 1–4. Find the measure of each angle.

$\angle A = 2x + 30$ $\angle B = -\frac{1}{3}x + 50$
$\angle C = -5y - 10$ $\angle D = -0.2y + 5$
$\angle A$ is three times as large as Angle B.
$\angle C$ is ten times greater than Angle D.

1. $\angle A$ _____
2. $\angle B$ _____
3. $\angle C$ _____
4. $\angle D$ _____

Answer each question. Explain your answer.

5. The measure of $\angle E$ is represented by $3(2x - 5)$ and the measure of $\angle F$ is represented by $6x - 15$. Are the two angles equal?

6. The measure of $\angle G$ is represented by $4(3 - 2x)$ and the measure of $\angle H$ is represented by $-12 - 8x$. Are the angles equal?

Use this information for Exercises 7–14.
In $\triangle ABC$, $\angle A = 6x + 2$, $\angle B = 2(3x + 1)$ and $\angle C = \frac{1}{2}(12x + 4)$.
In $\triangle DEF$, $\angle D = 2x + 2$, $\angle E = 2(4x + 5)$, and $\angle F = 8x + 10$.
Answer each question. Explain your answer.

7. Is $\triangle ABC$ an isosceles or an equilateral triangle? _____

8. Is $\triangle DEF$ an isosceles or an equilateral triangle? _____

Find the value of each angle. HINT: The sum of the measures of the angles in a triangle is 180°.

9. $\angle A =$ _____
10. $\angle B =$ _____
11. $\angle C =$ _____

6 Chapter 4

...in every sense of the word!

Special features support, strengthen, and enrich development in key areas.

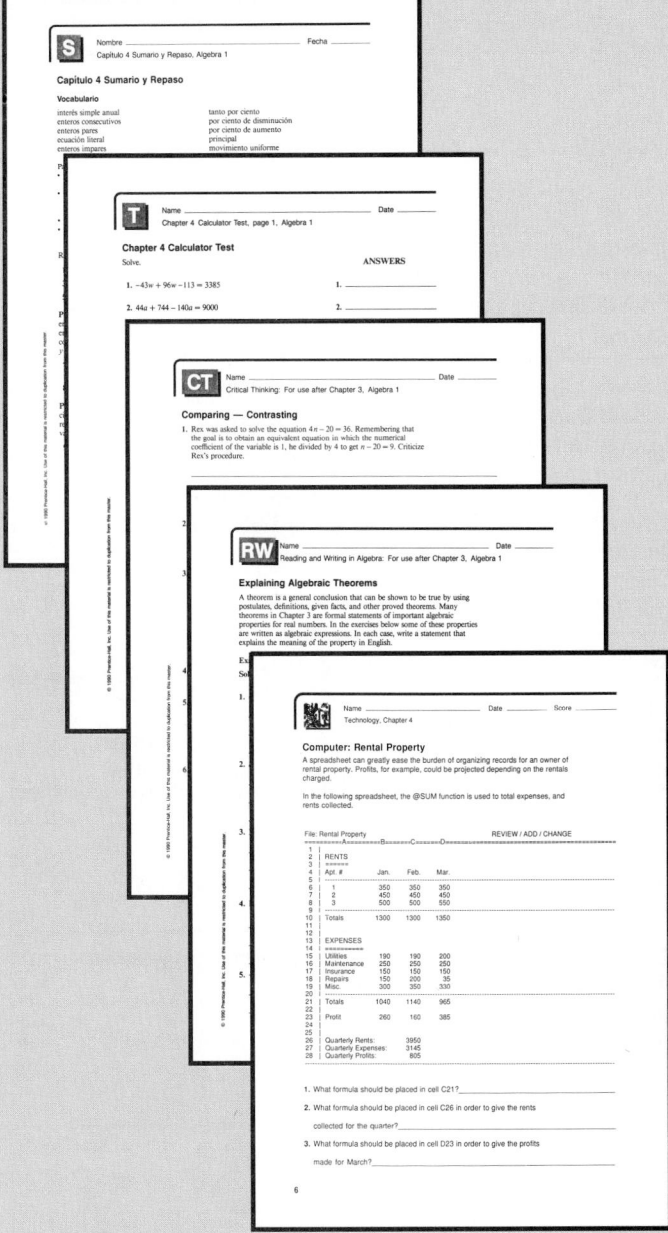

A complete testing program assesses student progress.

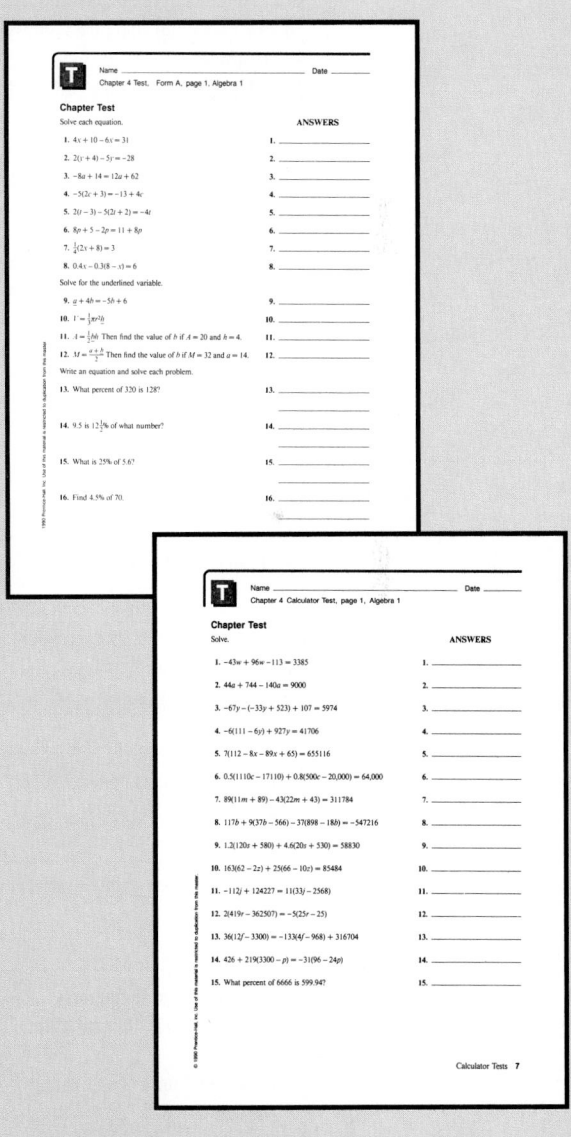

A Computer Test Bank that provides you with instant tests on all the lessons you teach is also available with this program.

The approach that meets the challenge...

	STUDENT TEXT	TEACHER'S EDITION	TEACHER'S RESOURCE BOOK
Unforgettable...	• Capsule Review at the outset of a lesson	• Background information provides suggestions for using the Capsule Review to lead into the lesson	• Reteaching

	• On-going maintenance and review includes:
	  • Chapter Summary and Review
	  • Test-Yourself
	  • Maintaining Skills
	  • Preparing for Standardized Tests
	  • Cumulative Reviews
	  • Extra Practice
		• Quiz for every lesson	• Spanish Chapter Summary and Review
			• Complete Testing Program

Solid...	• Systematic development of problem solving	• Teaching Suggestions to meet classroom needs • Critical Thinking questions and activities	• Practice • Enrichment • Critical Thinking Activities
	• Strategy lessons to help students choose the right approach	• Teaching Suggestions to meet classroom needs • Critical Thinking questions and activities	• Practice • Enrichment • Critical Thinking Activities
	• Numerous models and examples	• Materials/Manipulatives • Additional chalkboard examples • Common Error(s) to identify often-repeated errors	• Transparencies • Teaching Aids
	• Highlighted key concepts	• Lesson Vocabulary	• Reading and Writing in Algebra Activities
	• Use of calculator and computer as problem-solving tools	• Teaching Suggestions for incorporating technology into the lesson	• Technology Activities • Computer diskettes • Calculator Tests
	• A wealth of carefully graded Practice Exercises	• Assignment Guide for different ability levels • Enrichment Problems	• Practice • Enrichment
Relevant...	• Theme-centered chapters • Applications at the end of the lessons • Featured Applications throughout the text • Projects	• Background Information on the chapter's theme • Suggested assignments • Teaching Suggestions	• Follow-Up Applications

For more information, please write: or call TOLL FREE: 1-800-848-9500

PRENTICE HALL
School Division of Simon & Schuster
4343 Equity Drive, P.O. Box 2649
Columbus, OH 43216-2649

Printed in the USA   © by Prentice Hall, Englewood Cliffs, NJ   All rights reserved   ISBN 130-20828-0

TEACHER'S EDITION

PRENTICE HALL
Algebra 1

Jan Fair

Sadie C. Bragg

Prentice Hall
Englewood Cliffs, New Jersey
Needham, Massachusetts

CONTENTS

Pacing Algebra 1		T17
Chapter 1	Overview	1A
Chapter 2	Overview	50A
Chapter 3	Overview	94A
Chapter 4	Overview	134A
Chapter 5	Overview	184A
Chapter 6	Overview	224A
Chapter 7	Overview	268A
Chapter 8	Overview	314A
Chapter 9	Overview	368A
Chapter 10	Overview	410A
Chapter 11	Overview	442A
Chapter 12	Overview	492A
Chapter 13	Overview	542A
Chapter 14	Overview	580A
Chapter 15	Overview	612A
Additional Answers		719

Printed in the United States of America.

ISBN 0-13-021734-4

10 9 8 7 6 5 4 3 2

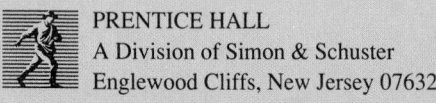

PRENTICE HALL
A Division of Simon & Schuster
Englewood Cliffs, New Jersey 07632

Teachers tackle new and difficult challenges every day, looking to find a better way or wanting to keep up with current trends, but they find few materials to help them get the job done. This Algebra 1 program meets the challenge by providing tools needed to establish a solid base of skills and concepts in first-year Algebra and to ensure that skills once learned are not forgotten.

In this program, students will develop and remember the skills and strategies necessary to select a successful approach to any problem. Our unique four step method to solving problems (*Understand the Problem*, *Plan the Approach*, *Complete the Work*, and *Interpret the Results*) systematically develops their ability to think critically and solve problems with confidence. Problem solving strategies provide students with the tools necessary to attack problems in an organized way. Following is a list of the strategies developed in this program.

Select appropriate notation.

Account for all possibilities.

Make a model.

Write an equation.

Make a drawing or a table.

Write an inequality.

Look for a pattern.

Use polynomial equations.

Solve a simpler problem.

Estimate from graphs.

Use an appropriate formula.

Write a linear system to solve a problem.

Use coordinate geometry.

Use a function.

Draw a diagram.

Check for hidden assumptions.

The flexibility of this program allows you to choose from many approaches to make Algebra work. Real world situations, teaching suggestions involving hands-on activities, and the inclusion of technology are a few of the approaches from which you may choose.

Structure of the Student Text

Prentice Hall Algebra 1 is a comprehensive and cohesive course that prepares students to use algebraic skills and concepts confidently in mathematics, in related disciplines, and in real world situations. When students become proficient in these skills and concepts, they will have acquired the necessary foundation to enjoy more advanced topics.

In order to succeed in mathematics, students must first comprehend the language of mathematics. The Student Text accomplishes this with a readable text that includes the following:

- *Lesson Objective(s)* tell the students at the outset what is expected of them.
- *The Capsule Review* in every skill lesson briefly reviews the prerequisite basic math or Algebra skills needed for the lesson.
- *Highlighted key concepts* are boxed in red to emphasize their importance.
- *Completely worked-out examples* provide important learning aids as students do their homework assignments. Solutions to examples are given step by step with the reason for each step shown in blue type.
- *Class Exercises* assess students' understanding of lesson concepts and readiness for the Practice Exercises that follow.
- *Practice Exercises* encompass a wealth of carefully graded practice including real world applications to underscore the relevancy of the topic.
- *Special Features* at the end of each lesson include Critical Thinking, Logical Reasoning, Reading and Writing in Algebra, Did You Know?, and Project.
- *Applications* are special chapter features that focus on algebraic concepts applied to real world situations.

The complete testing and review program consists of:

- *Test Yourself.* A test midway and at the end of each chapter
- *Chapter Test.* One-page test at the end of each chapter
- *Chapter Summary and Review.* Two-page summary and review of chapter's content including important vocabulary
- *Cumulative Review.* One- to three-page review after all even-numbered chapters
- *Maintaining Skills Review.* One page review of basic math and fundamental Algebra skills after all chapters that do not contain a Cumulative Review
- *Mixed Problem Solving Review.* A review focusing on alternate methods of solving routine and nonroutine problems
- *Preparing for Standardized Tests Review.* A review patterned to reflect the actual competency tests

Structure of the Teacher's Edition

The Teacher's Edition is designed to provide both the experienced and novice Algebra 1 teacher with more features than ever before to plan effectively and assess student understanding. Among the many features is a *Pacing Chart* that suggests how many days might be allocated to each lesson for three possible courses of study in a two-semester course.

Each chapter is preceded by a *Chapter Overview* which includes the following key features.

- *Summary.* A brief description of the chapter's content
- *Chapter Objectives.* A listing of the lesson objectives
- *Chapter Highlights.* Key features contained within the chapter including the chapter theme, problem solving and applications in the chapter, calculator and computer features, and available resources
- *Assignment Guide.* A chart that provides suggested assignments and related resources (found in the Teacher's Resource Book) on a lesson-by-lesson basis, plus review, testing, and other special features in the chapter and in the Teacher's Resource Book.

Throughout the book, nearly full-size student text pages have answers in place, plus teaching aids for every lesson right alongside. These aids include the following:

- *Vocabulary.* A listing of important terms introduced in the lesson

- *Materials/Manipulatives.* Concrete materials that may be used to present lesson concepts
- *Background.* Suggestions for using the Capsule Review
- *Teaching suggestions.* Helpful recommendations on how to present the lesson including Critical Thinking Skills, extra Chalkboard Examples, and Common Errors
- *Follow-Up.* Activities that provide practice and enrichment for each lesson, a quiz on the lesson content, plus reduced pages from the Teacher's Resource Book that relate to the lesson
- *Labeled exercises.* Labels indicating degree of difficulty of exercise sets noted only in the Teacher's Edition

Technology: Using Calculators and Computers

The integration of calculators and computers in the high school mathematics curriculum is a critical issue that concerns teachers. You are the only one who can determine the extent to which technology can be integrated into your classroom. Our approach to using the calculator and computer in developing algebraic concepts provides you with all the options necessary for you to be most effective.

In the Student Text technology is incorporated throughout. Within the lessons, technology is used in the development of algebraic skills and concepts as problem solving and discovery tools. Within the Practice Exercises, technology activities allow students to experiment and apply what they have learned. More detailed development of the use of technology as it applies to algebraic skills and concepts is given in technology lessons within the chapter.

In the Teacher's Edition you are alerted to the use of technology within a chapter in the Chapter Overview immediately preceding the chapter. You will also find references to related Technology Activities that may be found in the Teacher's Resource Book. Also included in the Teacher's Edition are Teaching Suggestions on how to integrate technology within your daily Lesson Plan.

In the Teacher's Resource Book additional activities involving technology are provided in a special section, together with computer diskettes that contain all the programs written exclusively for *Prentice Hall Algebra 1.* These diskettes are duplicable, so you may make as many copies as you wish. Students with no previous programming experience can use the activities along with the diskettes that have been provided for them. Students with some experience can extend these programs using Apple BASIC.

BIBLIOGRAPHY

BOOKLETS AND PERIODICALS

Commission on Standards for School Mathematics, National Council of Teachers of Mathematics. *Curriculum and Evaluation Standards for School Mathematics*. Reston, VA: NCTM, 1988.

National Council of Teachers of Mathematics. *An Agenda for Action: Recommendations for School Mathematics of the 1980's*. Reston, VA: NCTM, 1980.

National Council of Teachers of Mathematics. *The Mathematics Teacher*. Monthly September through May. Reston, VA: NCTM. Annually since 1926.

National Council of Teachers of Mathematics. *The Arithmetic Teacher*. Monthly September through May. Reston, VA: NCTM. Annually since 1926.

BOOKS

Abbott, Edwin A. *Flatland*. New York: Barnes and Noble, 1963.

College Entrance Examination Board. *Academic Preparation in Mathematics: Teaching for Transition from High School to College*. New York: CEEB, 1985.

Eves, Howard. *An Introduction to the History of Mathematics*. New York: Holt Rinehart and Winston, 1976.

Graham, Neill. *Computers and Computing*. St. Paul, MN: West Publishing Company, 1983.

Grinstein, Louise S., and Paul J. Campbell. *Women of Mathematics: A Bibliographic Sourcebook*. Westport, CN: Greenwood Press, 1987.

Historical Topics for the Mathematics Classroom. Thirty-first Yearbook of the National Council of Teachers of Mathematics. Reston, VA: NCTM, 1969.

Jacobs, Harold R. *Mathematics: A Human Endeavor*, 2nd ed. San Francisco: W. H. Freeman & Company, 1982.

James, Glenn, and Robert C. James, eds. *Mathematics Dictionary*. New York: Van Nostrand Reinhold, 1976.

Krulik, Stephen, ed. *Problem Solving in School Mathematics*. 1980 Yearbook of the National Council of Teachers of Mathematics. Reston, VA: NCTM, 1980.

Papert, Seymour. *Mindstorms: Children, Computers, and Powerful Ideas*. New York: Basic Books, 1980.

Perl, T. *Math Equals—Biographies of Women Mathematicians and Related Activities*. Menlo Park, CA: Addison Wesley Publishing Company, 1978.

Polya, George. *How to Solve It: A New Aspect of Mathematical Method*, 2nd ed. Princeton, NJ: Princeton University Press, 1973.

The Ideas of Algebra, K–12. *The 1988 Yearbook of the Council of Teachers of Mathematics*. Reston, VA: NCTM, 1988.

Tobias, Sheila. *Overcoming Math Anxiety*. New York: W. W. Norton Company, 1978.

The following three charts suggest how a total of 170 class days may be allocated by chapter for three different levels of ability.

BASIC COURSE

Chapter	1	2	3	4	5	6	7	8	9	10	11	12	13	14	15
Days	10	12	12	17	13	14	13	16	10	9	14	14	9	7	0
Section	all	all	all	all	all	all	all	all	all	all	all	all	all	all	none

AVERAGE COURSE

Chapter	1	2	3	4	5	6	7	8	9	10	11	12	13	14	15
Days	10	11	11	16	12	14	12	15	9	8	13	15	13	7	4
Section	all	all	all	all	all	all	all	all	all	all	all	all	all	all	15.1 15.2 15.3

ENRICHED COURSE

Chapter	1	2	3	4	5	6	7	8	9	10	11	12	13	14	15
Days	10	11	9	13	12	12	12	13	10	8	12	13	14	9	12
Section	all	all	all	all	all	all	all	all	all	all	all	all	all	all	all

A more detailed pacing chart is provided on the following pages. It is based on the number of days allocated per chapter suggested in the above three charts. Each of the 170 class days is represented (including reviews and tests) with text pages and practice exercises to be assigned.

PACING CHART

Day	Basic Course	Average Course	Enriched Course
1	**1.1** 5/1–19 odd; 43	**1.1** 5/1–35 odd; 43, 44	**1.1** 6/21–41 odd; 43, 44
2	**1.2** 10/1–23 odd; 39–41 R:5/2, 6, 14, 18	**1.2** 10/1–35 odd; 39–43 R:5/6, 10, 24, 34	**1.2** 10/25–37 odd; 39–46 R:6/22, 36, 38, 40
3	**1.3** 15/1–23 odd; 50–52 R:10/4, 8, 14, 22	**1.3** 15/1–39 odd; 50–54 R:10/20, 24, 32	**1.3** 15/25–49 odd; 50–57 R:10/26, 30, 32, 34

R = Review   MPSR = Mixed Problem Solving Review

Day	Basic Course		Average Course		Enriched Course	
4	**1.4**	20/1–21 odd; 35–37 R:15/2, 6, 18, 20	**1.4**	20/1–29 odd; 35–38 R:15/8, 10, 22, 24	**1.4**	20/23–33 odd; 35–39 R:15/26, 30, 40, 42
5	**1.5**	24/1–21 odd; 43–44 R:20/2, 4, 8, 20	**1.5**	24/1–33 odd; 43–46 R:20/10, 16, 22, 26	**1.5**	24/23–41 odd; 45–52 R:20/24, 28, 30, 32
6	**1.6**	29/1–21 odd; 44–46 Test Yourself	**1.6**	29/1–35 odd; 44–47 Test yourself	**1.6**	29/23–43 odd; 44–49 Test Yourself
7	**1.7**	33/1–19 odd; 43 R:29/2, 6, 12, 20	**1.7**	33/1–35 odd; 43, 44 R:29/4, 8, 22, 32	**1.7**	33/21–41 odd; 43, 44 R:29/26, 30, 36, 42
8	**1.8**	38/1–23 odd; 51–54 R:33/4, 6, 12, 18	**1.8**	38/1–41 odd; 51–57 R:33/8, 10, 16, 24	**1.8**	38/25–49 odd; 51–61 R:33/22, 32, 44, 46
9	**1.9**	44/1–9 odd Test Yourself	**1.9**	44/1–13 odd Test Yourself	**1.9**	45/11–15 odd Test Yourself
10		Chapter Summary and Review Chapter Test Maintaining Skills		Chapter Summary and Review Chapter Test Maintaining Skills		Chapter Summary and Review Chapter Test Maintaining Skills
11	**2.1**	53/1–9 odd; 23	**2.1**	53/1–17 odd; 23	**2.1**	Preparing for Standardized Tests 53/1–21 odd; 23
12	**2.2**	57/1–19 odd R:53/4, 6, 8	**2.2**	57/1–39 odd; 46, 48 R:53/10, 12, 14	**2.2**	57/11–45 odd; 46–49 R:53/16, 18, 20
13	**2.2**	57/21–23 odd; 46 R:57/2–6 even; 16–20 even	**2.3**	61/1–27 odd; 33 R:57/30, 34, 36	**2.3**	61/7–31 odd; 33, 34 R:57/38, 40, 44
14	**2.3**	61/1–13 odd; 33 R:57/8, 14, 22	**2.4**	65/7–39 odd R:61/12, 20, 22	**2.4**	65/9–49 odd R:61/18, 24, 30
15	**2.4**	64/1–9 odd R:61/2, 8, 14	**2.4**	65/41–49 odd; 61, 63 Test Yourself	**2.4**	65/51–59 odd; 61–64 Test Yourself
16	**2.4**	64/21–29 odd; 61, 63 Test Yourself	**2.5**	70/7–27 odd; 35, 37, 40 R:65/8, 30, 42	**2.5**	70/11–33 odd; 35–42 R:65/28, 50, 52, 60
17	**2.5**	69/1–17 odd; 35, 39, 41 R:64/2, 10, 24	**2.6**	76/1–19 odd; 22, 23 R:70/14, 20, 22	**2.6**	76/9–19 odd; 21–24 R:70/16, 24, 30
18	**2.6**	76/1–15 odd; 22 R:69/6, 12, 16	**2.7**	80/1–27 odd; 35, 36 R:76/12, 16, 18	**2.7**	81/15–33 odd; 35–37 R:76/16, 18, 20
19	**2.7**	80/1–17 odd; 35 R:76/6, 10, 14	**2.8**	83/1–17 odd; MPSR:1–2	**2.8**	83/3–19 odd; MPSR:1–2
20	**2.8**	83/1–13 odd; MPSR:1–2	**2.9**	87/1–17 odd; 25, 26, 27 Test Yourself	**2.9**	87/13–23 odd; 25–32 Test Yourself
21	**2.9**	87/1–13 odd; 25, 26 Test Yourself		Chapter Summary and Review Chapter Test Cumulative Review		Chapter Summary and Review Chapter Test Cumulative Review

R = Review   MPSR = Mixed Problem Solving Review

T17

Day	Basic Course		Average Course		Enriched Course	
22		Chapter Summary and Review Chapter Test Cumulative Review	**3.1**	98/1–41 odd; 51, 53, 54	**3.1**	Preparing for Standardized Tests 99/11–49 odd; 51–56
23	**3.1**	98/1–23 odd; 51, 53	**3.2**	104/1–37 odd; 45–48 R:98/10, 16, 28, 30, 40	**3.2**	104/11–43 odd; 45–50 R:99/22, 38, 44, 50
24	**3.2**	104/1–27 odd; 45, 46 R:98/4, 6, 12, 20	**3.3**	108/1–15 odd; 35 R:104/10, 12, 30, 32	**3.3**	108/7–33 odd; 35–38 Test Yourself
25	**3.3**	108/1–17 odd; 35 Test Yourself	**3.3**	108/17–23 odd; 35, 36 Test Yourself	**3.4**	111/1–11 odd; MPSR 1–2 R:108/12, 24, 32
26	**3.4**	111/1, 3; MPSR 1–2	**3.4**	111/1, 3, 5; MPSR 1–2 R:108/10, 16, 20	**3.5**	115/1–7 odd; 9–12 R:111/2, 4, 6
27	**3.5**	115/1, 3, 5 R:111/2	**3.5**	115/1–5 odd; 9–11 R:111/2, 4	**3.6**	118/1–11 odd; 13–15 R:115/4, 6
28	**3.5**	115/5, 7, 9, 11 R:115/2, 4	**3.6**	118/1–9 odd; 13, 14 R:115/2, 4	**3.7**	123/1–21 odd; MPSR: 1–5
29	**3.6**	118/1–5 odd; 13 R:115/2, 4, 6	**3.7**	123/1–17 odd; MPSR: 1–5	**3.8**	128/1–19 odd Test Yourself
30	**3.7**	122/1–5 odd; MPSR 1–2 R:118/2, 4	**3.8**	128/1–7 odd R:123/4, 6, 18		Chapter Summary and Review Chapter Test Maintaining Skills
31	**3.7**	122/7–11 odd; MPSR:1–5 R:122/2, 4, 6	**3.8**	128/9–17 odd Test Yourself		Preparing for Standardized Tests
32	**3.8**	128/1–5 odd R:122/8, 10, 12		Chapter Summary and Review Chapter Test Maintaining Skills	**4.1**	138/13–47 odd; 47, 48
33	**3.8**	128/7–13 odd Test Yourself	**4.1**	138/1–39 odd; 48	**4.2**	142/25–45 odd; 47, 48 R:138/40, 42, 44
34		Chapter Summary and Review Chapter Test Maintaining Skills	**4.2**	142/1–23 odd R:138/34, 36, 38	**4.3**	147/17–27 odd R:142/18, 22, 38
35	**4.1**	138/1–23 odd; 48	**4.2**	142/25–31 odd; 47, 48 R:142/6, 12, 18	**4.4**	150/25–39 odd R:147/22, 24, 26
36	**4.2**	142/1–13 odd R:138/12, 18, 22	**4.3**	146/1–21 odd R:142/18, 22, 30	**4.4**	150/41–47 odd; 49–52 Test Yourself
37	**4.2**	142/15–23 odd; 47 R:142/4, 8, 10	**4.4**	150/1–23 odd R:146/16, 18, 20	**4.5**	155/21–31 odd; 33–36 R:150/32, 44, 46
38	**4.3**	146/1–15 odd R:142/16, 20, 24	**4.4**	150/25–39 odd; 49–51 Test Yourself	**4.6**	157/15–31 odd R:154/12, 22, 26

R = Review   MPSR = Mixed Problem Solving Review

Day	Basic Course		Average Course		Enriched Course	
39	**4.4**	150/1–15 odd R:146/4, 6, 16	**4.5**	154/1–19 odd R:150/20, 24, 32	**4.7**	163/5–9 odd R:157/18, 22, 28
40	**4.4**	150/17–23 odd, 49, 50 Test Yourself	**4.5**	154/21–27 odd, 33–35 R:154/4, 10, 14, 20	**4.8**	166/25–43 odd; 45, 46 R:163/6, 8
41	**4.5**	154/1–11 odd R:150/6, 14, 20	**4.6**	157/1–27 odd R:154/10, 16, 20	**4.9**	170/13–17 odd; MPSR:1–4
42	**4.5**	154/13–19 odd; 33, 34 R:154/6, 8, 12	**4.7**	163/1–7 odd R:157/14, 20, 24	**4.10**	175/13–23 odd Test Yourself
43	**4.6**	157/1–5 odd R:154/4, 10, 18	**4.8**	166/1–23 odd R:163/4, 6		Chapter Summary and Review Chapter Test Cumulative Review
44	**4.6**	157/7–13 odd R:157/2, 4, 6	**4.8**	166/25–37 odd; 45.46 R:166/2, 14, 20		Preparing for Standardized Tests
45	**4.7**	163/1–3 odd R:157/8, 10, 12	**4.9**	170/1–17 odd; MPSR:1–4	**5.1**	188/1–23 odd
46	**4.8**	166/1–17 odd R:163/2, 4	**4.10**	175/1–11 odd R:170/6, 12, 14	**5.1**	189/25–39 odd; 40 R:188/12, 20
47	**4.8**	166/19–23 odd; 45 R:166/4, 8, 16	**4.10**	175/1–21 odd Test Yourself	**5.2**	192/7–35 odd; 36–38 R:189/28, 36, 38
48	**4.9**	170/1–11 odd; MPSR:1–4		Chapter Summary and Review Chapter Test Cumulative Review	**5.3**	197/9–35 odd; 37, 38 R:192/20, 32, 34
49	**4.10**	175/1–7 odd R:170/2, 8, 10	**5.1**	188/1–23 odd; 40	**5.4**	200/5–33 odd R:197/22, 26, 28
50	**4.10**	175/9–11 odd Test Yourself	**5.1**	188/25–35 odd R:188/2, 12, 20	**5.4**	201/35–39 odd; 41, 42 Test Yourself
51		Chapter Summary and Review Chapter Test Cumulative Review	**5.2**	192/1–31 odd; 36, 37 R:188/22, 26, 34	**5.5**	205/7–29 odd; 31–33 R:201/28, 36, 40
52	**5.1**	188/1–17 odd	**5.3**	197/1–29 odd; 37 R:193/16, 26, 30	**5.6**	208/19–37 odd; 39–43 R:205/18, 24, 32
53	**5.1**	188/19–23 odd; 40 R:188/4, 8, 18	**5.4**	200/1–19 odd R:197/12, 20, 24	**5.7**	212/17–47 odd; 49, 50 R:208/30, 34, 38
54	**5.2**	192/1–15 odd; 36 R:188/2, 12, 20	**5.4**	200/21–33 odd, 41, 42 Test Yourself	**5.8**	216/3–11 odd; MPSR:1–3 Test Yourself
55	**5.3**	197/1–15 odd; 37 R:192/4, 8, 12	**5.5**	205/1–25 odd; 31, 32 R:200/12, 24, 30		Chapter Summary and Review Chapter Test Maintaining Skills

R = Review   MPSR = Mixed Problem Solving Review

Day	Basic Course		Average Course		Enriched Course	
56	**5.4**	200/1–11 odd R:197/6, 10, 14	**5.6**	208/1–31 odd; 39–41 R:205/14, 22, 26		Preparing for Standardized Tests
57	**5.4**	200/13–19 odd; 41 Test Yourself	**5.7**	212/1–21 odd R:208/22, 26, 28	**6.1**	228/13–43 odd; 44, 45
58	**5.5**	205/1–7 odd R:200/2, 10, 20	**5.7**	212/23–39 odd; 49 R:212/4, 8, 12	**6.2**	233/25–47 odd; 49, 50 R:228/26, 34, 42
59	**5.5**	205/9–15 odd; 31 R:205/2, 4, 6	**5.8**	216/1–9 odd; MPSR:1–3 Test Yourself	**6.3**	236/15–35 odd; 37, 38 R:233/18, 38, 44
60	**5.6**	208/1–23 odd; 39, 40 R:205/4, 10, 16		Chapter Summary and Review Chapter Test Maintaining Skills	**6.4**	239/13–21 odd; 23 Test Yourself
61	**5.7**	212/1–15 odd R:208/12, 16, 20	**6.1**	228/1–29 odd; 44	**6.5**	244/21–31 odd; 33–35 R:239/6, 14, 20
62	**5.7**	212/17–27 odd; 49 R:212/2, 8, 12	**6.2**	232/1–39 odd; 49 R:228/10, 24, 32	**6.6**	247/17–31 odd; 33, 34 R:244/8, 14, 26
63	**5.8**	216/1–7 odd; MPSR:1–3 Test Yourself	**6.3**	236/1–27 odd; 37 R:232/16, 26, 34	**6.7**	249/15–27 odd; 29–33 R:247/24, 26, 30
64		Chapter Summary and Review Chapter Test Maintaining Skills	**6.4**	239/1–7 odd R:236/4, 12, 28	**6.8**	253/29–59 odd; 61–65 R:249/10, 26, 28
65	**6.1**	228/1–20 odd; 44	**6.4**	239/1–17 odd; 23 Test Yourself	**6.9**	258/19–35 odd; 37–40 Test Yourself
66	**6.2**	232/1–23 odd; 49 R:228/6, 16, 2	**6.5**	243/1–27 odd; 33, 34 R:239/4, 8, 14	**6.10**	262/9–15 odd; MPSR 1–2
67	**6.3**	236/1–13 odd; 37 R:232/4, 12, 24	**6.6**	246/1–27 odd; 33 R:243/6, 14, 20		Chapter Summary and Review Chapter Test Cumulative Review
68	**6.4**	239/1–7 odd R:236/2, 10, 12	**6.7**	249/1–23 odd; 29–31 R:246/6, 22, 28		Preparing for Standardized Tests
69	**6.4**	239/9–11 odd; 23 Test Yourself	**6.8**	253/1–27 odd R:249/6, 18, 24	**7.1**	272/17–35 odd; 37–41
70	**6.5**	243/1–15 odd; 33 R:239/2, 10, 12	**6.8**	254/29–47 odd; 61–63 R:253/4, 16, 22	**7.2**	276/21–39 odd; 41–43 R:272/18, 22, 34
71	**6.6**	246/1–15 odd; 33 R:243/4, 10, 12	**6.9**	258/1–17 odd R:254/8, 18, 24	**7.3**	280/31–57 odd; 59–64 R:276/30, 34, 38
72	**6.7**	249/1–13 odd; 29, 30 R:246/4, 12, 14	**6.9**	258/19–29 odd; 37–39 Test Yourself	**7.4**	284/25–41 odd; 43 R:280/36, 38, 40
73	**6.8**	253/1–17 odd R:249/2, 4, 12	**6.10**	262/1–11 odd; MPSR: 1–2	**7.5**	287/25–49 odd; 51–54 Test Yourself

R = Review   MPSR = Mixed Problem Solving Review

Day	Basic Course	Average Course	Enriched Course
74	**6.8** 254/19–27 odd; 61, 62 R:253/6, 12, 14	Chapter Summary and Review Chapter Test Cumulative Review	**7.6** 290/29–51 odd; 52, 53 R:287/32, 34, 38
75	**6.9** 258/1–7 odd R:254/4, 16, 22	**7.1** 272/1–31 odd; 37, 39, 41	**7.7** 294/27–43 odd; 45, 46 R:290/36, 40, 44
76	**6.9** 258/13–17 odd; 37, 38 Test Yourself	**7.2** 276/1–33 odd; 41, 43 **7.3** 280/1–49 odd; 59, 61, 63 R:276/8, 12, 32	**7.8** 298/37–51 odd; 53–56 **7.9** 302/25–47 odd; 49–51 Test Yourself
77	**6.10** 262/1–7 odd; MPSR:1–2	**7.4** 284/1–37 odd; 43 R:280/10, 14, 18	**7.10** 306/11–19 odd; MPSR: 1–4
78	Chapter Summary and Review Chapter Test Cumulative Review	**7.5** 287/1–41 odd; 51, 53 Test Yourself	Chapter Summary and Review Chapter Test Maintaining Skills
79	**7.1** 272/1–15 odd; 37, 39	**7.6** 290/1–47 odd; 52, 53 R:287/14, 16, 18	Preparing for Standardized Tests
80	**7.2** 276/1–19 odd; 41 R:272/4, 6, 12	**7.7** 294/1–37 odd; 45, 46 R:290/18, 24, 28	**8.1** 319/27–45 odd; 47, 48
81	**7.3** 280/1–29 odd; 59, 61 R:276/4, 8, 16	**7.8** 298/1–21 odd R:294/18, 20, 24	**8.2** 322/23–41 odd; 45, 47, 49 R:319/32, 34, 36
82	**7.4** 284/1–23 odd; 43 R:280/4, 6, 14	**7.8** 298/1–43 odd; 53, 55 R:298/4, 12, 18	**8.3** 326/19–39 odd; 40–42 R:322/24, 26, 38
83	**7.5** 287/1–23 odd; 51, 53 Test Yourself	**7.9** 302/1–41 odd; 49, 51 Test Yourself	**8.4** 331/21–39 odd; 41, 42 R:326/24, 30, 36
84	**7.6** 290/1–27 odd; 52 R:287/2, 8, 10	**7.10** 306/1–13 odd; MPSR: 1–4	**8.5** 335/23–39 odd; 41 R:331/22, 24, 26
85	**7.7** 294/1–17 odd R:290/4, 14, 16	Chapter Summary and Review Chapter Test Maintaining Skills	**8.6** 339/25–45 odd; 46, 47 Test Yourself
86	**7.7** 294/19–25 odd; 45 R:294/2, 8, 14	**8.1** 319/1–39 odd; 47, 48	**8.7** 344/21–37 odd; 39 R:339/26, 28, 40
87	**7.8** 298/1–21 odd R:294/10, 18, 20	**8.2** 322/1–35 odd, 43, 45, 47 R:319/22, 24, 26	**8.8** 348/23–37 odd; 39–43 R:344/24, 26, 28
88	**7.8** 298/23–35 odd; 53 R:298/4, 12, 16	**8.3** 326/1–33 odd; 41, 42 R:322/8, 18, 28	**8.9** 352/21–37 odd; 38, 39 R:348/24, 26, 28
89	**7.9** 302/1–23 odd; 49 Test Yourself	**8.4** 331/1–19 odd; 41, 42 R:326/16, 24, 28	**8.10** 357/7–11 odd R:352/22, 26, 28
90	**7.10** 306/1–9 odd; MPSR:1–4	**8.4** 331/21–33 odd; 41, 42 R:331/4, 8, 18	**8.11** 360/7–11 odd; MPSR:1–3 Test Yourself

R = Review   MPSR = Mixed Problem Solving Review

Day	Basic Course		Average Course		Enriched Course	
91		Chapter Summary and Review Chapter Test Maintaining Skills	**8.5**	335/1–31 odd; 41 R:331/10, 22, 30		Chapter Summary and Review Chapter Test Cumulative Review
92	**8.1**	318/1–25 odd; 47	**8.6**	339/1–23 odd R:335/24, 26, 28		Preparing for Standardized Tests
93	**8.1**	319/17–25 odd; 47 R:318/4, 12, 14	**8.6**	339/25–37 odd; 46, 47 Test Yourself	**9.1**	373/25–41 odd; 42–44
94	**8.2**	322/1–20 odd; 43, 45 R:319/2, 6, 8	**8.7**	344/1–31 odd; 39 R:339/20, 24, 34	**9.2**	379/25–39; 40–42 R:373/28, 34, 36
95	**8.3**	326/1–17 odd; 41 R:322/6, 8, 10	**8.8**	348/1–31 odd; 39, 41, 43 R:344/18, 22, 24	**9.3**	382/9–15 odd; MPSR: 1–5
96	**8.4**	331/1–13 odd R:326/6, 8, 14	**8.9**	352/1–19 odd R:348/22, 24, 28	**9.4**	388/25–35 odd R:382/10, 12
97	**8.4**	331/15–19 odd; 41 R:331/2, 8, 14	**8.9**	352/21–31 odd; 38, 39 R:352/2, 10, 16	**9.4**	388/37–41 odd Test Yourself
98	**8.5**	335/1–21 odd; 41 R:331/6, 10, 12	**8.10**	357/1–9 odd R:352/10, 14, 18	**9.5**	394/29–51 odd R:388/26, 30, 34
99	**8.6**	339/1–15 odd R:335/6, 10, 12	**8.11**	360/1–9 odd; MPSR: 1–3 Test Yourself	**9.6**	399/21–37 odd R:394/36, 44, 48
100	**8.6**	339/17–23 odd; 46 Test Yourself		Chapter Summary and Review Chapter Test Cumulative Review	**9.7**	404/23–43 odd Test Yourself
101	**8.7**	344/1–19 odd; 39 R:339/12, 20, 22	**9.1**	373/1–33 odd; 43, 44		Chapter Summary and Review Chapter Test Maintaining Skills
102	**8.8**	348/1–21 odd; 39, 41 R:344/6, 12, 14	**9.2**	379/1–31 odd; 41, 42 R:372/8, 22, 28		Preparing for Standardized Tests
103	**8.9**	352/109 odd R:348/4, 10, 16	**9.3**	381/1–11 odd; MPSR: 1–5	**10.1**	416/13–21 odd; 23–25
104	**8.9**	352/1–19 odd; 38 R:352/2, 4, 8	**9.4**	387/1–23 odd R:381/2, 4, 6	**10.2**	420/23–31 odd; 32, 33 R:416/14, 18, 22
105	**8.10**	357/1–6 odd R:352/10, 12, 14	**9.4**	387/25–35 odd Test Yourself	**10.3**	424/21–35 odd Test Yourself
106	**8.11**	360/1–5 odd; MPSR: 1–3 Test Yourself	**9.5**	394/1–45 odd R:387/18, 24, 30	**10.4**	428/15–27 odd; 29 R:424/28, 32, 34
107		Chapter Summary and Review Chapter Test Cumulative Review	**9.6**	398/1–31 odd R:394/26, 30, 38	**10.5**	432/15–25 odd; 27, 28 R:428/20, 24, 28

R = Review   MPSR = Mixed Problem Solving Review

Day	Basic Course	Average Course	Enriched Course
108	**9.1** 372/1–23 odd; 43	**9.7** 403/1–21 odd R:398/10, 14, 18	**10.6** 436/17–25 odd; MPSR: 1–3 Test Yourself
109	**9.2** 379/1–23 odd; 41 R:372/6, 14, 20	**9.7** 403/23–33 odd Test Yourself	Chapter Summary and Review Chapter Test Cumulative Review
110	**9.3** 381/1–7 odd; MPSR: 1–5	**10.1** 416/9–17 odd; 23, 24	Preparing for Standardized Tests
111	**9.4** 387/1–15 odd R:381/2, 4, 6	**10.2** 420/15–27 odd; 32, 33 R:8, 14, 18	**11.1** 447/31–47 odd; 49–53
112	**9.4** 387/17–23 odd Test Yourself	**10.3** 424/11–25 odd Test Yourself	**11.2** 453/37–47 odd; 50, 51 R:448/22, 34, 40
113	**9.5** 394/1–27 odd R:387/6, 10, 12	**10.4** 428/11–23 odd; 29 R:424/20, 22, 26	**11.3** 457/7–17 odd; MPSR: 1–3
114	**9.6** 398/1–19 odd R:394/10, 14, 18	**10.5** 432/1–7 odd R:428/18, 20, 24	**11.4** 461/27–45 odd; 46–49 R:457/8, 10, 12
115	**9.7** 403/1–11 odd R:398/6, 10, 14	**10.5** 432/7–17 odd; 27, 28 R:432/2, 4, 6	**11.5** 465/19–33 odd; 35, 36 Test Yourself
116	**9.7** 403/13–21 odd Test Yourself	**10.6** 436/11–23 odd; MPSR: 1–3 Test Yourself	**11.6** 469/9–15 odd R:465/28, 30, 32
117	Chapter summary and Review Chapter Test Maintaining Skills	Chapter Summary and Review Chapter Test Cumulative Review	**11.7** 472/11–27 odd R:469/8, 10, 12
118	**10.1** 416/1–11 odd; 23	**11.1** 446/1–29 odd	**11.8** 477/1–14 odd; 21–33 R:472/20, 22, 24
119	**10.2** 420/1–17 odd; 32 R:416/2, 4, 6	**11.1** 446/31–41 odd; 49–52 R:447/6, 14, 22	**11.9** 481/6–21 odd R:447/6, 8, 10
120	**10.3** 424/1–19 odd; Test Yourself	**11.2** 453/1–41 odd; 50, 51 R:447/20, 24, 26	**11.10** 485/17–33 odd; 34, 35 Test Yourself
121	**10.4** 428/1–13 odd; 29 R:424/12, 14, 18	**11.3** 457/1–13 odd; MPSR: 1–3	Chapter Summary and Review Chapter Test Maintaining Skills
	10.5 432/1–7 odd R:428/8, 10, 12	**11.4** 461/1–21 odd R:457/8, 10, 12	Preparing for Standardized Tests
122	**10.5** 432/9–13 odd; 27 R:432/2, 4, 6	**11.4** 461/23–37 odd; 44–48 R:461/8, 10, 18	**12.1** 496/15–33 odd; 35
123	**10.6** 435/1–10 odd R:432/8, 12, 14	**11.5** 465/1–27 odd; 35, 36 Test Yourself	**12.2** 499/17–27 odd; 29, 30 R:496/16, 22, 30
124	**10.6** 436/11–15 odd; MPSR: 1–3 Test Yourself	**11.6** 468/1–15 odd R:465/16, 22, 24	**12.3** 502/17–31 odd; 32 R:499/18, 22, 24

R = Review   MPSR = Mixed Problem Solving Review

T23

Day	Basic Course		Average Course		Enriched Course	
125		Chapter Summary and Review Chapter Test Cumulative Review	**11.7**	471/1–23 odd R:468/6, 8, 12	**12.4**	505/29–49 odd; 51–53 R:502/18, 22, 24
126	**11.1**	446/1–17 odd	**11.8**	476/1–14 odd; 21, 22 R:472/16, 18, 20	**12.5**	511/19–35 odd; 37, 38 R:505/30, 38, 48
127	**11.1**	447/19–29 odd; 49, 50 R:447/4, 12, 14	**11.9**	450/1–19 odd R:476/4, 8, 10	**12.6**	514/21–41 odd; 43–50 Test Yourself
128	**11.2**	453/1–27 odd; 50 R:447/2, 6, 14	**11.10**	485/1–17 odd R:481/16, 18, 20	**12.7**	518/25–41 odd; 43–46 R:514/22, 32, 40
129	**11.3**	457/1–11 odd; MPSR: 1–3	**11.10**	485/19–27 odd; 34, 35 R:486/2, 8, 14 Test Yourself	**12.8**	522/25–41 odd; 42–46 R:518/26, 30, 40
130	**11.4**	461/1–15 odd R:457/2, 4, 6		Chapter Summary and Review Chapter Test Maintaining Skills	**12.9**	526/13–17 odd; 19–24 R:522/26, 34, 40
131	**11.4**	461/17–23 odd; 46, 47 R:461/4, 6, 12	**12.1**	496/1–25 odd; 35	**12.10**	530/13–23 odd; 25 R:526/14, 16
132	**11.5**	465/1–15 odd R:461/2, 8, 10	**12.2**	499/1–23 odd; 29, 30 R:496/4, 12, 14	**12.11**	533/9–17 odd; MPSR: 1–4 Test Yourself
133	**11.5**	465/17–21 odd; 35 Test Yourself	**12.3**	502/1–27 odd; 32 R:499/6, 10, 12		Chapter Summary and Review Chapter Test Cumulative Review
134	**11.6**	468/1–11 odd R:465/2, 4, 10	**12.4**	505/1–27 odd R:502/6, 10, 14		Preparing for Standardized Tests
135	**11.7**	471/1–15 odd R:468/2, 4, 6	**12.4**	505/29–43 odd; 51, 52 R:505/4, 14, 26	**13.1**	545 546/37–47 odd
136	**11.8**	476/1–13 odd; 21 R:471/4, 8, 10	**12.5**	510/1–31 odd; 37, 38 R:505/6, 18, 42	**13.1**	546/49–55 odd; 56 R:546/36, 40, 44
137	**11.9**	480/1–15 odd R:476/2, 4, 6	**12.6**	514/1–19 odd R:510/6, 18, 30	**13.2**	550/25–41 odd; 43, 44 R:546/46, 50, 54
138	**11.10**	486/1–15 odd; 34 Test Yourself	**12.6**	514/21–35 odd; 43–48 Test Yourself	**13.3**	553/25–35 odd R:550/32, 38, 42
139		Chapter Summary and Review Chapter Test Maintaining Skills	**12.7**	518/1–35 odd; 43–45 R:514/6, 16, 34	**13.3**	553/37–41 odd; 43, 44 R:553/28, 32, 36
140	**12.1**	496/1–13 odd; 35	**12.8**	522/1–21 odd R:518/6, 18, 32	**13.4**	555/19–27 odd R:553/34, 38, 42
141	**12.2**	499/1–15 odd; 29 R:496/2, 8, 10	**12.8**	522/1–35 odd; 42–45 R:522/2, 10, 14	**13.4**	556/29–33 odd; 35–41 Test Yourself

R = Review   MPSR = Mixed Problem Solving Review

Day	Basic Course		Average Course		Enriched Course	
142	**12.3**	502/1–15 odd; 32 R:499/2, 4, 6	**12.9**	526/1–15 odd; 19–23 R:522/8, 16, 34	**13.5**	561/9–17 odd R:566/26, 30, 34
143	**12.4**	505/1–15 odd R:502/2, 6, 8	**12.10**	530/1–19 odd; 25 R:526/2, 10, 14	**13.5**	561/19–33 odd; 34, 35 R:561/10, 14, 16
144	**12.4**	505/17–27 odd; 51 R:505/6, 10, 12	**12.11**	532/1–13 odd; MPSR: 1–4 Test Yourself	**13.6**	566/13–23 odd; 25, 26 R:561/24, 28.30
145	**12.5**	510/1–17 odd; 37 R:505/4, 14, 26		Chapter Summary and Review Chapter Test Cumulative Review	**13.7**	570/11–17 odd; MPSR: 1–4
146	**12.6**	514/1–11 odd R:510/6, 12, 16	**13.1**	545/21–31 odd	**13.8**	574/17–29 odd; 30, 31 Test Yourself
147	**12.6**	514/13–19 odd; 43–46 Test Yourself	**13.1**	546/33–45 odd; 56 R:546/18, 22, 26		Chapter Summary and Review Chapter Test Maintaining Skills
148	**12.7**	518/1–23 odd; 43, 44 R:514/2, 10, 18	**13.2**	550/13–29 odd; 43, 44 R:546/36, 40, 44		Preparing for Standardized Tests
149	**12.8**	522/1–23 odd; 42–44 R:518/2, 10, 22	**13.3**	553/17–27 odd R:550/22, 26, 30	**14.1**	585/9–17 odd; 18–20
150	**12.9**	526/1–11 odd; 19–21 R:522/4, 14, 22	**13.3**	553/21–35 odd; 43, 44 R:553/16, 20, 24	**14.2**	588/11–17 odd; 19, 20 R:585/12, 18
151	**12.10**	530/1–11 odd; 25 R:526/2, 8, 10	**13.4**	555/13–21 odd R:553/28, 32, 36	**14.3**	593/5–7 odd; 8, 9 Test Yourself
152	**12.11**	532/1–7 odd; MPSR: 1–4 Test Yourself	**13.4**	555/23–27 odd; 35–39 Test Yourself	**14.4**	599/17–29 odd; 31, 32 R:593/6
153		Chapter Summary and Review Chapter Test Cumulative Review	**13.5**	561/1–11 odd R:555/20, 24, 28	**14.5**	602/5; MPSR: 1–6
154	**13.1**	545/1–27 odd; 56	**13.5**	561/13–27 odd; 34, 35 R:561/2, 8, 10	**14.6**	606/1–17 odd R:602/5
155	**13.2**	549/1–17 odd; 43 R:545/18, 22, 26	**13.6**	566/9–19 odd; 25, 26 R:20, 24, 28	**14.6**	606/19–29 odd; 31, 32 R:606/10, 14, 16 Test Yourself
156	**13.3**	552/1–23 odd; 43 R:549/10, 14, 18	**13.7**	566/9–15 odd; MPSR: 1–4		Chapter Summary and Review Chapter Test Cumulative Review
157	**13.4**	555/1–15 odd; 35, 36 Test Yourself	**13.8**	574/11–23 odd; 30, 31 Test Yourself		Preparing for Standardized Tests
158	**13.5**	560/1–15 odd; 34 R:555/8, 12, 16		Chapter Summary and Review Chapter Test Maintaining Skills	**15.1**	617/13–23 odd; 24, 25

R = Review   MPSR = Mixed Problem Solving Review

T25

Day	Basic Course		Average Course		Enriched Course	
159	**13.6**	566/1–11 odd; 25 R:560/8, 12, 16	**14.1**	584/1–11 odd; 18, 19	**15.2**	621/17–27 odd; 29, 30 R:617/14, 20, 22
160	**13.7**	569/1–9 odd; MPSR: 1–4	**14.2**	588/1–17 odd; 19, 20 R:584/2, 4, 8	**15.3**	625/1–11 odd R:621/18, 22, 26
161	**13.8**	574/1–15 odd; 30 Test Yourself	**14.3**	592/1–7 odd; 8, 9 Test Yourself	**15.3**	626/13–21 odd; 23, 24 Test Yourself
162		Chapter Summary and Review Chapter Test Maintaining Skills	**14.4**	598/1–25 odd; 31, 32 R:592/2, 4, 6	**15.4**	630/13–25 odd; 27 R:625/14, 18, 20
163	**14.1**	584/1–7 odd; 18	**14.5**	602/3; MPSR: 1–6	**15.5**	635/19–27 odd; 28–31 R:630/14, 20, 24
164	**14.2**	588/1–19 odd; 20 R:584/2, 6	**14.6**	606/1–25 odd; 31, 32 Test Yourself	**15.6**	641/11–21 odd R:635/22, 24, 26
165	**14.3**	592/1–3 odd; 8 Test Yourself		Chapter Summary and Review Chapter Test Cumulative Review	**15.6**	641/23–37 odd; 38–41 R:641/12, 16, 20
166	**14.4**	598/1–15 odd; 31 R:592/2	**15.1**	616/1–7 odd	**15.7**	646/1–5 odd R:641/26, 30, 32
167	**14.5**	602/1; MPSR:1–6	**15.1**	616/9–19 odd; 24, 25 R:616/2, 4, 6	**15.7**	641/7–13 odd; MPSR: 1–3 Test Yourself
168	**14.6**	606/1–17 odd; 31 Test Yourself	**15.2**	621/1–25 odd; 29, 30 R:616/6, 10, 18		Chapter Summary and Review Chapter Test Cumulative Review
169		Chapter Summary and Review Chapter Test Cumulative Review	**15.3**	625/1–19 odd; 23–24 Test Yourself		Preparing for Standardized Tests
170		Final Exam		Final Exam		Final Exam

R = Review   MPSR = Mixed Problem Solving Review

PRENTICE HALL
Algebra 1

Jan Fair

Sadie C. Bragg

Prentice Hall
Englewood Cliffs, New Jersey
Needham, Massachusetts

Prentice Hall Algebra 1

Student Text   Teacher's Edition   Teacher's Resource Book
Solution Manual   Computer Test Bank

AUTHORS

Jan Fair
Formerly Chairperson, Mathematics Department
Santa Maria High School
Santa Maria, California

Sadie C. Bragg
Associate Professor of Mathematics
Borough of Manhattan Community College
The City University of New York
New York, New York

REVIEWERS

William E. Cavanaugh
Mathematics Teacher
Elkhart Community Schools
Elkhart, Indiana

Nina L. Ronshausen
Graduate Faculty of the College of Education
Texas Tech University
Lubbock, Texas

Lee V. Stiff
Assistant Professor of Mathematics Education
North Carolina State University
Raleigh, North Carolina

CONSULTANTS

Frederick Bell
Professor of Mathematics Education
University of Pittsburgh
Pittsburgh, Pennsylvania

John M. Erickson
District Mathematics and Science Coordinator
Hopkins Public Schools
Hopkins, Minnesota

Stephen Krulik
Professor of Mathematics Education
Temple University
Philadelphia, Pennsylvania

Mary Dell Morrison
Mathematics Instructor (Retired)
Columbia High School
Maplewood, New Jersey

Jesse A. Rudnick
Professor of Mathematics Education
Temple University
Philadelphia, Pennsylvania

Rex Schweers, Jr.
Professor of Mathematics
University of Colorado
Greeley, Colorado

Harris S. Schultz
Professor of Mathematics
California State University, Fullerton
Fullerton, California

Photo credits appear on page 718

Printed in the United States of America.

ISBN 0-13-021726-3

10 9 8 7 6 5 4 3 2

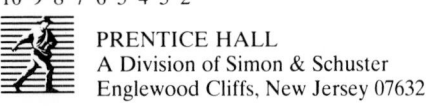

PRENTICE HALL
A Division of Simon & Schuster
Englewood Cliffs, New Jersey 07632

CONTENTS

1   REAL NUMBERS

1.1   Variables and Algebraic Expressions   2
Applications: Travel, Weather

1.2   The Real Number Line   7
Applications: Computer

1.3   Comparing and Ordering Numbers   12
Applications: Meteorology, Health, Navigation, Economics

1.4   Addition on a Number Line   17
Applications: Meteorology, Number Problem, Sports, Economics

1.5   Adding Real Numbers   22
Applications: Meteorology, Sports, Aviation, Finance, Calculator

1.6   Subtracting Real Numbers   27
Applications: Computer

1.7   Multiplying Real Numbers   31
Applications: Weather, Finance

1.8   Dividing Real Numbers   35
Applications: Sports, Statistics, Meteorology, Finance, Calculator

1.9   Problem Solving Strategy: Select Appropriate Notation   42
Featured Application: Meteorology 41
Chapter Summary and Review 46, Chapter Test 48
Preparing for Standardized Tests 49, Maintaining Skills 50

2   ALGEBRAIC EXPRESSIONS

2.1   Simplifying and Evaluating Expressions   52
Applications: Computer

2.2   Exponents and Formulas   55
Applications: !culator

2.3   Properties of Real Numbers   59
Applications: Consumerism

2.4   Combining Like Terms   63
Applications: Number Problems, Geometry

2.5   Simplifying and Evaluating Expressions with Parentheses   67
Applications: Geometry, Calculator

2.6   Translating Phrases to Algebraic Expressions   74
Applications: Sports

2.7   Open Sentences and Solution Sets   78
Applications: Number Problems

2.8	Problem Solving Strategy: Account for All Possibilities	82
2.9	Translating Word Statements to Equations	85

Applications: Consumerism, Geometry

Technology: Introduction to Spreadsheets 72
Chapter Summary and Review 90, Chapter Test 92
Preparing for Standardized Tests 93, Cumulative Review 94

3 EQUATIONS IN ONE VARIABLE

3.1	Solving Equations: Addition and Subtraction Properties	96

Applications: Travel, Number Problems

3.2	Solving Equations: Multiplication and Division Properties	101

Applications: Calculator

3.3	Solving Equations: More Than One Property	106

Applications: Calculator

3.4	Problem Solving Strategy: Make a Model	110
3.5	Algebraic Proof	113

Applications: Language Arts

3.6	Evaluating Formulas	117

Applications: Travel, Geometry

3.7	Problem Solving Strategy: Write an Equation	120
3.8	Problem Solving: Mixed Types	127

Technology: Using Spreadsheets 125
Chapter Summary and Review 130, Chapter Test 132
Preparing for Standardized Tests 133, Maintaining Skills 134

4 MORE EQUATIONS IN ONE VARIABLE

4.1	Solving Equations: Combining Like Terms	136

Applications: Number Problem, Geometry, Hobbies

4.2	Solving Equations: Variable on Both Sides	140

Applications: Geometry, Finance

4.3	Problem Solving: Consecutive Integers	144
4.4	Shortcuts in Solving Equations	148

Applications: Number Problems, Geometry, Sales

4.5	Solving Equations: Percents	152

Applications: Demography, Finance

4.6	Problem Solving: Percents	156

4.7	Problem Solving: Mixtures	161
4.8	Literal Equations	164
	Applications: Sports, Geometry	
4.9	Problem Solving Strategy: Make a Drawing or a Table	168
4.10	Problem Solving: Uniform Motion	172

Featured Application: Messenger Service 160
Chapter Summary and Review 178, Chapter Test 180
Preparing for Standardized Tests 181, Cumulative Review 182

5 INEQUALITIES IN ONE VARIABLE

5.1	Graphing Equations and Inequalities	186
	Applications: Computer	
5.2	Solving Inequalities: Addition and Subtraction Properties	190
	Applications: Number Problems	
5.3	Solving Inequalities: Multiplication and Division Properties	194
	Applications: Number Problems	
5.4	Solving Inequalities: More Than One Property	198
	Applications: Number Problems	
5.5	Combined Inequalities	202
	Applications: Sports	
5.6	Absolute Value Equations	206
	Applications: Number Problems	
5.7	Absolute Value Inequalities	210
	Applications: Meteorology, Sports	
5.8	Problem Solving Strategy: Write an Inequality	214

Featured Application: Marathon Running 218
Chapter Summary and Review 220, Chapter Test 222
Preparing for Standardized Tests 223, Maintaining Skills 224

6 POLYNOMIALS

6.1	Monomials and Multiplying Monomials	226
	Applications: Geometry	
6.2	Dividing Monomials	230
	Applications: Geometry	
6.3	Monomials and Exponents	234
	Applications: Computer, Calculator	

6.4   Scientific Notation   237
Applications: Computer

6.5   Polynomials   241
Applications: Geometry

6.6   Adding and Subtracting Polynomials   245
Applications: Number Problem, Geometry

6.7   Multiplying a Polynomial by a Monomial   248
Applications: Number Problems, Geometry

6.8   Multiplying Polynomials   251
Applications: Number Problems, Geometry

6.9   Multiplying Polynomials: Special Cases   256
Applications: Geometry

6.10   Problem Solving Strategy: Look for a Pattern   260
Featured Application: Fluid Motion 240
Chapter Summary and Review 264, Chapter Test 266
Preparing for Standardized Tests 267, Cumulative Review 268

7   FACTORING POLYNOMIALS

7.1   Factors and Exponents   270
Applications: Computer

7.2   Monomial Factors of Polynomials   274
Applications: Geometry

7.3   Factoring $x^2 + bx + c, c > 0$ 278
Applications: Geometry

7.4   Factoring $x^2 + bx + c, c < 0$ 282
Applications: Gardening

7.5   Factoring $ax^2 + bx + c$ 285
Applications: Geometry

7.6   Factoring: Special Cases   289
Applications: Geometry

7.7   Factoring by Grouping   292
Applications: Geometry

7.8   Factoring Completely   296
Applications: Geometry

7.9   Solving Polynomial Equations by Factoring   300
Applications: Number Problems

7.10 Problem Solving Strategy: Use Polynomial Equations   304

    Featured Application: Agriculture 308
    Chapter Summary and Review 310, Chapter Test 312
    Preparing for Standardized Tests 313, Maintaining Skills 314

8 RATIONAL EXPRESSIONS

8.1 Simplifying Rational Expressions   316
    Applications: Baking

8.2 Multiplying Rational Expressions   320
    Applications: Calculator, Geometry

8.3 Dividing Rational Expressions   324
    Applications: Physics, Manufacturing, Transportation

8.4 Least Common Denominator (LCD)   328
    Applications: Photography, Construction

8.5 Adding and Subtracting Rational Expressions   333
    Applications: Physics

8.6 Mixed Expressions and Complex Rational Expressions   337
    Applications: Statistics, Electricity

8.7 Dividing Polynomials   342
    Applications: Finance

8.8 Ratios and Proportions   345
    Applications: Entertainment, Cartography, Travel

8.9 Solving Rational Equations   350
    Applications: Geometry, Accounting

8.10 Problem Solving: Work and Motion   354
8.11 Problem Solving Strategy: Solve a Simpler Problem   358

    Featured Application: Interest 341
    Chapter Summary and Review 362, Chapter Test 364
    Preparing for Standardized Tests 365, Cumulative Review 366

9 LINEAR EQUATIONS

9.1 Graphing Ordered Pairs   370
    Applications: Chemistry, Transportation, Economics

9.2 Graphs of Linear Equations   375
    Applications: Finance

9.3 Problem Solving Strategy: Estimate from Graphs   380

9.4	Slope	384
	Applications: Geometry, Science	
9.5	Slope-Intercept Form of a Linear Equation	391
	Applications: Computer	
9.6	Equation of a Line	396
	Applications: Chemistry	
9.7	Linear Inequalities in Two Variables	401
	Applications: Computer, Nutrition	

Featured Application: Radio Waves 389
Chapter Summary and Review 406, Chapter Test 408
Preparing for Standardized Tests 409, Maintaining Skills 410

10 RELATIONS, FUNCTIONS, AND VARIATION

10.1	Relations	412
	Applications: Finance, Meteorology	
10.2	Functions and Function Notation	417
	Applications: Finance, Meteorology	
10.3	Linear, Constant, and Composite Functions	422
	Applications: Consumer	
10.4	Direct Variation	426
	Applications: Finance	
10.5	Inverse Variation	430
	Applications: Geometry	
10.6	Problem Solving Strategy: Use an Appropriate Formula	434

Featured Application: Cost Analysis 425
Chapter Summary and Review 438, Chapter Test 440
Preparing for Standardized Tests 441, Cumulative Review 442

11 SYSTEMS OF LINEAR EQUATIONS

11.1	Graphing Systems of Linear Equations	444
	Applications: Calculator, Business, Economics, Geometry	
11.2	The Substitution Method	451
	Applications: Business, Calculator	
11.3	Problem Solving Strategy: Write a Linear System to Solve a Problem	455
11.4	The Addition/Subtraction Method	459
	Applications: Agriculture, Science, Engineering	

11.5	The Multiplication-Addition/Subtraction Method	463
	Applications: Business, Food Preparation	
11.6	Problem Solving: Digit Problems	467
11.7	Problem Solving: Age Problems	470
11.8	Problem Solving: Money and Mixture Problems	474
	Applications: Computer	
11.9	Problem Solving: Wind and Water Current Problems	479
11.10	Graphing Systems of Linear Inequalities	484
	Applications: Office Administration, Agriculture	

Featured Application: Break-Even Point 450
Chapter Summary and Review 488, Chapter Test 490
Preparing for Standardized Tests 491, Maintaining Skills 492

12 RADICALS

12.1	Square Roots	494
	Applications: Physics	
12.2	Irrational Square Roots	497
	Applications: Geometry	
12.3	Decimal Forms of Rational Numbers	500
	Applications: Electricity	
12.4	Simplifying Square Roots	503
	Applications: Physics, Geometry	
12.5	Addition and Subtraction of Radicals	509
	Applications: Geometry	
12.6	Multiplication of Radicals	512
	Applications: Geometry, Number Problems	
12.7	Division of Radicals	516
	Applications: Chemistry, Physics, Number Problems	
12.8	Solving Radical Equations	520
	Applications: Number Problems, Physics	
12.9	The Pythagorean Theorem	524
	Applications: Construction, Physics, Geometry, Sports	
12.10	The Distance Formula	528
	Applications: Computer	
12.11	Problem Solving Strategy: Use Coordinate Geometry	531

Featured Application: Image Formation 507
Chapter Summary and Review 536, Chapter Test 538
Preparing for Standardized Tests 539, Cumulative Review 540

13 QUADRATIC EQUATIONS AND FUNCTIONS

13.1 Quadratic Equations with Perfect Squares   544
Applications: Coordinate Geometry

13.2 Completing the Square   547
Applications: Number Problems

13.3 The Quadratic Formula   551
Applications: Geometry, Number Problem

13.4 Mixed Practice: Solving Quadratic Equations by Any Method   554
Applications: Physics, Construction, Number Problems, Landscaping

13.5 Graphing Quadratic Functions   557
Applications: Business, Physics

13.6 The Discriminant   564
Applications: Engineering, Finance

13.7 Problem Solving Strategy: Use a Function   567

13.8 Sum and Product of the Solutions   572
Applications: Engineering, Business

Featured Application: Physics 562
Chapter Summary and Review 576, Chapter Test 578
Preparing for Standardized Tests 579, Maintaining Skills 580

14 STATISTICS AND PROBABILITY

14.1 Statistics: Measures of Central Tendency   582
Applications: Geography, Business, Education

14.2 Statistics: Graphing Data   586
Applications: Geography, Demography

14.3 Statistics: Measures of Variability   590
Applications: Health, Business

14.4 Simple Probability   596
Applications: Testing, Finance

14.5 Problem Solving Strategy: Draw a Diagram   600

14.6 Probability: Compound Events   603
Applications: Marketing, Finance

Featured Application: Scattergrams 594
Chapter Summary and Review 608, Chapter Test 610
Preparing for Standardized Tests 611, Cumulative Review 612

15 RIGHT TRIANGLE RELATIONSHIPS

15.1   Basic Geometric Figures   614
Applications: Construction, Travel

15.2   Triangles   618
Applications: Hobbies, Forestry

15.3   Congruence   623
Applications: Construction

15.4   Similar Figures   628
Applications: Surveying, Gardening

15.5   Trigonometric Ratios   633
Applications: Navigation, Geometry, Architecture

15.6   Using Trigonometric Ratios   639
Applications: Surveying, Architecture, Engineering, Hobbies

15.7   Problem Solving Strategy: Check for Hidden Assumptions   643

Featured Application: Networks 637
Chapter Summary and Review 648, Chapter Test 650
Preparing for Standardized Tests 651, Cumulative Review 652

Extra Practice   655

Table of Squares and Square Roots   670

Table of Trigonometric Ratios   671

Symbols   672

Answers to Selected Exercises   673

Glossary   698

Index   707

A Letter to the Student

Algebra 1 is going to be your first experience with secondary academic mathematics. This is just the beginning in a series of courses that will interest, excite, and challenge you.

Algebra is the study of numbers and their relationship to each other. The basic skills you learn this year will be your tools for success in other courses in mathematics, science, business, finance, engineering, and many more.

No matter what you do each day, you are involved in some sort of problem solving or decision making situation. Algebra will help you choose a successful approach to solving problems. To help you succeed in solving problems, this text provides completely worked-out examples to follow, strategies to guide you in choosing a successful approach, highlighted key concepts, and plenty of exercises, all written in a language you can read and understand. The applications at the end of every lesson underscore how useful this knowledge can be.

Algebra is different, not difficult. Read carefully, keep up with your assignments, enjoy the challenge, work hard, and above all take satisfaction in your accomplishments. Your hard work and accomplishments will certainly prepare you for your next course in mathematics.

THE AUTHORS

OVERVIEW • Chapter 1

SUMMARY

In Chapter 1 students strengthen their understanding of variables. They learn that a phrase in English may be translated into an algebraic expression and that an algebraic expression may represent a number of different English phrases.

Whole numbers, integers, rational numbers, and irrational numbers are discussed and classified as subsets of the set of the real numbers. The ordering of numbers is related to their placement on the number line.

Students learn about opposites and absolute value, which are used in the development of the four arithmetic operations involving real numbers.

After this chapter has been completed, students should be able to evaluate algebraic expressions involving one operation and operations within grouping symbols for rational number replacements of the variables. Students will find that many exercises serve also to review the arithmetic of fractions and decimals.

CHAPTER OBJECTIVES

- To recognize variables and to write algebraic expressions (of one operation) for word phrases
- To graph real numbers on a number line
- To classify numbers in subsets of the set of real numbers
- To compare and order real numbers
- To use the concepts of opposites and absolute value
- To add numbers by "moves" on a number line
- To perform the four operations of arithmetic upon real numbers
- To evaluate algebraic expressions involving variables and the four operations (with the use of grouping symbols)

Problem Solving Strategy

To solve problems algebraically by reviewing the meaning and usage of algebraic notation

CHAPTER HIGHLIGHTS

The *theme* of the chapter is meteorology. The chapter's *special features* apply skills taught in the lessons to practical situations in meteorology.

PROBLEM SOLVING AND APPLICATIONS

Problem solving and applications form an integral part of each lesson. Students use numerical and algebraic expressions to solve concrete problems and apply formulas in many fields including navigation, economics, finance, sports, and aviation. In Lesson 1.9, the strategy of *Select Appropriate Notation* affords students the opportunity to review the meaning of various algebraic symbols and to practice the correct application of them. This skill will facilitate all subsequent work with algebraic processes.

TECHNOLOGY

Calculator

In Lesson 1.5, students learn to use the sign change key to calculate the sum of positive and negative numbers. In Lesson 1.8, students are shown how to use the reciprocal key to find the reciprocal of any number expressed as a decimal.

Computer

In Chapter 1, students are introduced to the INT and ABS functions on a computer. They learn that INT(X) gives the greatest integer less than or equal to X, while ABS(X) gives the nonnegative value (or absolute value) of X. Students are asked to use both of these functions to determine specific values of X provided in practice exercises.

RESOURCES

Teacher's Resource Book

- Teaching Aid 1
- Transparencies 1, 2, 4

STUDENT TEXT

TEACHER'S RESOURCE BOOK

Chapter Content	Basic	Average	Enriched	R	P	E
1.1 Variables and Algebraic Expressions	D: 5/1-19 odd, 43	D: 5/1-35 odd, 43, 44	D: 6/21-41 odd, 43, 44	1	2	3
1.2 The Real Number Line	D: 10/1-23 odd, 39-41 R: 5/2, 6, 14, 18	D: 10/1-35 odd, 39-43 R: 5/6, 10, 24, 34	D: 6/25-37 odd, 39-46 R: 6/22, 36, 38, 40	4	5	6
1.3 Comparing and Ordering Numbers	D: 15/1-23 odd, 50-52 R: 10/4, 8, 14, 22	D: 15/1-39 odd, 50-54 R: 10/20, 24, 32	D: 15/25-49 odd, 50-57 R: 10/26, 30, 32, 34	7	8	9
1.4 Addition on a Number Line	D: 20/1-21 odd, 35-37 R: 15/2, 6, 18, 20	D: 20/1-29 odd, 35-38 R: 15/8, 10, 22, 24	D: 20/23-33 odd, 35-39 R: 15/26, 30, 40, 42	10	11	12
1.5 Adding Real Numbers	D: 24/1-21 odd, 43-44 R: 20/2, 4, 8, 20	D: 24/1-33 odd, 43-46 R: 20/10, 16, 22, 26	D: 24/23-41 odd, 45-52 R: 20/24, 28, 30, 32	13	14	15
1.6 Subtracting Real Numbers	D: 29/1-21 odd, 44-46 R: Test Yourself	D: 29/1-35 odd, 44-47 R: Test Yourself	D: 29/23-43 odd, 44-49 R: Test Yourself	16	17	18
1.7 Multiplying Real Numbers	D: 33/1-19 odd, 43 R: 29/2, 6, 12, 20	D: 33/1-35 odd, 43, 44 R: 29/4, 8, 22, 32	D: 33/21-4 odd, 43, 44 R: 29/26, 30, 36, 42	19	20	21
1.8 Dividing Real Numbers	D: 38/1-23 odd, 51-54 R: 33/4, 6, 12, 18	D: 38/1-41 odd, 51-57 R: 33/8, 10, 16, 24	D: 38/25-49 odd, 51-61 R: 33/22, 32, 44, 46	22	23	24
1.9 Problem Solving Strategy: Selecting Appropriate Notation	D: 44/1-9 odd R: Test Yourself	D: 44/1-13 odd R: Test Yourself	D: 45/11-15 odd R: Test Yourself		25	26

D = Daily   R = Review   MPSR = Mixed Problem Solving Review   R = Reteaching   P = Practice   E = Enrichment

	STUDENT TEXT				TEACHER'S RESOURCE BOOK	
Review	Test Yourself	30	Chapter Test	48	Spanish Chapter Summary and Review	1-2
And	Test Yourself	45	Prep. for Stan. Tests	49	• Quizzes	5-8
Testing	Chapter Sum. and Rev.	46	Maintaining Skills	50	• Chapter Test (Form A)	9-10
			Extra Practice	655	• Chapter Test (Form B)	11-12
					Calculator Test	1-2
Special	Writing in Algebra	6	Logical Reasoning	26	Applications—Chapter 1	27
Features	Math Club Activity	11	Algebra in Meteorology	34	Critical Thinking	1
	Puzzle	16	Critical Thinking	40	Reading and Writing in Algebra	1
	Biography	21	Application	41	Technology	1-3

1 Real Numbers

Lightning is beautiful, but it can also be dangerous. The temperature inside the channel of a lightning flash is believed to reach 28,000°C. At this temperature, the air expands and produces a tremendous sound wave called thunder.

1

BACKGROUND

Meteorologists study weather by using many mathematical concepts. They work with numerical and algebraic expressions to make various weather predictions. Mathematics is integrated into many professions like meteorology.

Vocabulary
Algebraic expression
Evaluate
Numerical expression
Variable
Variable expression

Materials/Manipulatives
Calculators
*Teacher's Resource Book
Transparency 1*

BACKGROUND

In the Capsule Review, students are introduced to variables by a simple formula for calculating wages. This review prepares students for their work in evaluating algebraic expressions and in writing algebraic expressions for word phrases.

Variables and Algebraic Expressions

Objectives: To evaluate algebraic expressions for given value(s) of the variable(s)
To write algebraic expressions for word phrases

Suppose you work at a weather station where you spent $\frac{3}{4}$ of your time in the office. The rest of the time you work in the field.

The hours worked per week may change, but the fraction of time charged to the office payroll is always $\frac{3}{4} \times n$, where n stands for the total number of hours worked. Out of 8 hours (h), your time in the office is:

$$\frac{3}{4} \times n = \frac{3}{4} \times 8$$

$$= \frac{3}{\overset{1}{\cancel{4}}} \times \frac{\overset{2}{\cancel{8}}}{1} = \frac{6}{1}, \text{ or } 6 \text{ h}$$

Capsule Review

If $6 is the hourly rate of pay and a is the number of hours worked, then $6 \times a$ is the total wages earned.

Use $6 \times a$ to find the pay for each number of hours (h) worked.

1. $\frac{3}{4}$ h $4.50   **2.** $3\frac{1}{2}$ h $21   **3.** 6.8 h $40.80   **4.** 10 h $60

5. How would $6 \times a$ change if the hourly rate became $8? Change to $8 \times a$.

In $\frac{3}{4} \times n$, n is called a *variable*. $\frac{3}{4} \times n$ is a *variable expression*.

A **variable** is a symbol used to represent one or more numbers. Any letter may be used as a variable.

A **variable expression** is an expression that contains one or more variables.

You may not know the number(s) a variable stands for, but the mathematical meaning of a variable expression is clear. Here are different ways to read some expressions.

Addition	Subtraction
$n + 8$	$z - s$
Some number n plus 8	A number z minus another number s
n increased by 8	z decreased by s
The sum of n and 8	The difference between z and s
8 more than n	s less than z

Multiplication	Division
$\frac{2}{3} \times r$	$y \div 3$
$\frac{2}{3}$ times a number r	Some number y divided by 3
The product of $\frac{2}{3}$ and r	The quotient of y and 3
$\frac{2}{3}$ of r	The ratio of y and 3

To **evaluate** a variable expression, substitute a given number for each variable. The result is a **numerical expression** that may contain one or more of the operations of addition, subtraction, multiplication, or division. The number represented by the numerical expression is the value of the variable expression for the value(s) of the variable(s) used.

Both variable and numerical expressions are called **algebraic expressions**. Are 5 and $2xy$ algebraic expressions? Why or why not?

EXAMPLE 1 Evaluate each algebraic expression in the chart above if $n = 17$, $r = 9$, $y = 2.4$, $z = 7.89$, and $s = 0.92$.

Algebraic Expression	Numerical Expression (after substitution)	Value
$n + 8$	$17 + 8$	25
$z - s$	$7.89 - 0.92$	6.97
$\frac{2}{3} \times r$	$\frac{2}{3} \times 9$	$\frac{2}{3} \times 9 = \frac{2}{3} \times \frac{9}{1} = 6$
$y \div 3$	$2.4 \div 3$	$2.4 \div 3 = 0.8$

In algebra, a raised dot or parentheses are often used to indicate multiplication. In variable expressions, multiplication symbols may be omitted. The product of 6 and some number n is given in various ways below.

With a raised dot	With parentheses	With no symbol between
$6 \cdot n$	$(6)(n)$ or $6(n)$	$6n$

1.1 Variables and Algebraic Expressions　**3**

- Place the following expressions on the chalkboard.

$$4 + \square \qquad 17 - \underline{\quad} \qquad ? \div 4$$

Ask students to explain what these three expressions have in common. Ask students what three symbols are used as placeholders and if they remember seeing these placeholders in earlier grades. Relate these earlier forms to the letters used as variables in algebra. The three expressions each contain an unknown number; $\square$, ____, ?
- Some students may have difficulty with the new vocabulary introduced in this lesson. Ask students to explain in their own words and give examples of the following terms: *variable, variable expression, numerical expression, algebraic expression.* Transparency 1, in the *Teacher's Resource Book* may be helpful in introducing new vocabulary.
- Have students use a calculator to evaluate expressions where values are given for the variables. Remind students of the correct order of operations in solving a problem.

CHALKBOARD EXAMPLES

- **For Example 1**
  Evaluate each algebraic expression if $a = 6$, $b = 12.5$, $c = 5.5$, $d = 1.86$, and $e = 7.94$.
  1. $a + 1.2$　7.2
  2. $4 \times b$　50
  3. $c \div 5$　1.1
  4. $e - d$　6.08

- **For Example 2**
  5. Evaluate the algebraic expression mnp if $m = \frac{5}{6}$, $n = \frac{6}{7}$, and $p = 21$.　15

- **For Example 3**
  6. Evaluate $\frac{5}{7}(z + 28)$ if $z = 7$.　25

3

- **For Example 4**

  7. Evaluate $\dfrac{r - s}{t}$ if $r = 16$, $s = 2$ and $t = \dfrac{7}{8}$.   16

- **For Example 5**

  Write an algebraic expression for each phrase.
  8. price of clothing p, less a discount d $p - d$
  9. cost of 5 gallons of gas at price p per gallon $5p$
  10. the total cost t, divided by the number of items n $\dfrac{t}{n}$

Common Errors

- Students often make errors in the order in which they write numbers when translating expressions. The following are some examples.
  1. 6 divided by 18 $\dfrac{1}{3}$
     Students may divide 18 by 6 to get a wrong answer of 3.

  2. a less than b $b - a$
     They may write $a - b$.
- Have students work in pairs. Give each pair the same short list of word phrases to translate. Have students complete the exercises individually and then compare their answers with their partners. Have them consult an answer sheet and try to correct any errors by discussing them. Follow up with class discussion about the errors.
- See *Teacher's Resource Book* for additional remediation.

EXAMPLE 2   **Evaluate the algebraic expression xyz if $x = \dfrac{3}{4}$, $y = 28$, and $z = \dfrac{3}{7}$.**

$$xyz = x \cdot y \cdot z \qquad \textit{xyz means x times y times z.}$$

$$= \frac{3}{4} \cdot \frac{28}{1} \cdot \frac{3}{7} \qquad \textit{Substitute } \tfrac{3}{4} \textit{ for x, 28 for y, and } \tfrac{3}{7} \textit{ for z.}$$

$$= \frac{3 \cdot 28 \cdot 3}{4 \cdot 1 \cdot 7} \qquad \textit{Multiply.}$$

$$= \frac{3 \cdot 3}{1} = 9$$

EXAMPLE 3   **Evaluate $\dfrac{2}{3}(f + 11)$ if $f = 13$.**

$$\frac{2}{3}(f + 11) = \frac{2}{3}(13 + 11) \qquad \begin{cases} \textit{Parentheses mean multiplication.} \\ \textit{Substitute 13 for f.} \end{cases}$$

$$= \frac{2}{3}(24) \qquad \textit{Add within the parentheses.}$$

$$= 16 \qquad \textit{Multiply.}$$

Two operations—addition and multiplication—were needed to evaluate the algebraic expression in Example 3. In all such cases, *operations within the parentheses are done first*.

Division is most often shown in fraction form. $\dfrac{y}{5}$ means *y divided by 5*. In a fraction like $\dfrac{0.011s}{rt}$, the fraction bar creates invisible parentheses around the numerator and the denominator. This means that any operation(s) in the numerator and in the denominator are completed before the division.

EXAMPLE 4   **Evaluate $\dfrac{k - m}{h}$ if $k = 7\dfrac{3}{4}$, $m = \dfrac{1}{4}$, and $h = \dfrac{1}{8}$.**

$$\frac{k - m}{h} = \frac{7\frac{3}{4} - \frac{1}{4}}{\frac{1}{8}} \qquad \textit{Substitute } 7\tfrac{3}{4} \textit{ for k, } \tfrac{1}{4} \textit{ for m, and } \tfrac{1}{8} \textit{ for h.}$$
$$\textit{Subtract.}$$

$$= \frac{7\frac{1}{2}}{\frac{1}{8}} = \frac{15}{2} \cdot \frac{\cancel{8}^{4}}{1} \qquad \textit{Recall the rule for dividing by a fraction.}$$

$$= 15 \cdot 4 = 60$$

4   Chapter 1 Real Numbers

You will often translate word phrases into algebraic expressions.

EXAMPLE 5   **Write an algebraic expression for each phrase.**

  a. The cost of a meal c plus the tax t: $c + t$

  b. The cost of three movie tickets at d dollars per ticket:
  $3d$, or $3 \cdot d$, or $3(d)$

  c. The number of miles traveled m divided by the number of hours
  traveled h: $\frac{m}{h}$, or $m \div h$

CLASS EXERCISES

Identify the variable and describe the operation.

1. $4x$ x; mult.   **2.** $9 - a$ a; subtr.   **3.** $m + 7$ m; add   **4.** $\frac{2}{g}$ g; div.

Evaluate each expression if $a = 1$, $b = 5.4$, and $c = 0.5$.

5. $a + 89$ 90   **6.** $b - c$ 4.9   **7.** $\frac{b}{c}$ 10.8   **8.** cab 2.7

PRACTICE EXERCISES

Evaluate each expression if $n = 12$.

A   **1.** $n + 15$ 27   **2.** $30 - n$ 18   **3.** $\frac{1}{2}n$ 6   **4.** $\frac{5}{6}n$ 10

  5. $n \div 6$ 2   **6.** $\frac{48}{n}$ 4   **7.** $n + n$ 24   **8.** $0 + n$ 12

Evaluate each expression if $a = 15$, $b = 6$, and $c = 3$.

  9. $\frac{ab}{2c}$ 15   **10.** $5abc$ 1350   **11.** $\frac{c}{10ab}$ $\frac{1}{300}$ **12.** $\frac{abc}{25}$ $\frac{54}{5}$

  13. $\frac{1}{3}(a + 3)$ 6   **14.** $\frac{1}{5}(b + c)$ $\frac{9}{5}$ **15.** $\frac{2}{3}c + 5$ 7   **16.** $\frac{5}{3}a + 1$ 26

Write an algebraic expression for each phrase.

17. The sum of 3 and some number x $3 + x$

18. $\frac{3}{2}$ increased by some number y $\frac{3}{2} + y$

19. A number t decreased by 1.07 $t - 1.07$

20. The difference between a number m and 99 $m - 99$

LESSON FOLLOW-UP

Critical Thinking

Identifying Reasons   Although there are no parentheses in the expression $\dfrac{7\frac{3}{4} - \frac{1}{4}}{\frac{1}{8}}$ the subtraction is done before the division. Explain why.   The fraction bar serves as invisible parentheses around the numerator.

Assignment Guide

See p. 1B for assignments.

Writing in Algebra

Exercises 1–3 check students' understanding of the meaning of the terms used in this lesson.

See *Teacher's Resource Book*, for Reading and Writing in Algebra activity, p. 1.

Lesson Quiz

Evaluate each expression for the given value(s) of the variable.
1. $4.82 + r$, $r = 0.37$ 5.19
2. $\frac{4}{7}z$, $z = 28$ 16
3. $\frac{6}{r}$, $r = \frac{15}{4}$ $\frac{8}{5}$
4. $\frac{6m}{pq}$, $m = 18$, $p = 4$, $q = 6$ $\frac{9}{2}$
5. $7(j - h)$, $j = 1\frac{5}{7}$, $h = \frac{3}{7}$ 9

Write an algebraic expression for each situation.
6. The sum of the games won, w, and the games lost, l $w + l$
7. The cost per lb of n lb of kumquats which cost p cents $\frac{p}{n}$

Enrichment

Write an algebraic expression:
The total profit if n items are made for c cents per item and sold for p cents per item. $np - nc$ or $n(p - c)$

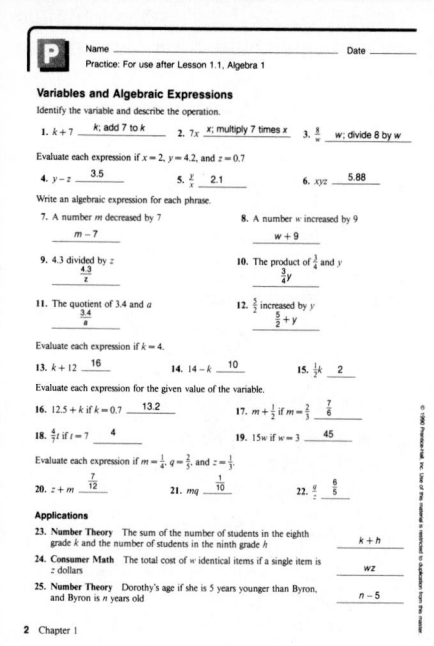

Evaluate each expression if $d = \frac{2}{3}$, $e = \frac{3}{4}$, and $f = \frac{1}{2}$.

B

21. $e \div d$ $\frac{9}{8}$

22. $e - d$ $\frac{1}{12}$

23. $e - f$ $\frac{1}{4}$

24. $\dfrac{de}{f}$ 1

25. $4def$ 1

26. $d - f$ $\frac{1}{6}$

27. $f - f$ 0

28. $d + e + f$ $\frac{23}{12}$

29. $\dfrac{d + e}{f}$ $\frac{17}{6}$

30. $\dfrac{2e - d}{2f}$ $\frac{5}{6}$

31. $3d + 2e + 2f$ $\frac{9}{2}$

32. $\frac{3}{2}d + e + 4f$ $\frac{15}{4}$

Write an algebraic expression for each phrase.

33. The product of $\frac{3}{8}$ and some number j $\frac{3}{8}j$

34. 5 less than z $z - 5$

35. The quotient of 6.4 and some number b $\frac{6.4}{b}$

36. 10 more than x. $x + 10$

Evaluate each expression if $p = 3\frac{5}{8}$, $q = \frac{3}{4}$, $r = 6$, $s = 4$, and $t = 1$.

C

37. $(p - q)8$ 23

38. $(q + r)\frac{1}{3}$ $\frac{9}{4}$

39. $\dfrac{r + s}{r - s}$ 5

40. $\dfrac{r - t + s}{r - q}$ $\frac{12}{7}$

41. $(8q) + \left(\frac{2}{3}r\right) - \left(\frac{1}{2}s\right)$ 8

42. $\frac{7}{10}(r + s) - (4q)$ 4

Applications

Write an algebraic expression for each phrase.

43. Travel   The number of miles traveled m divided by the number of gallons used g $\frac{m}{g}$

44. Weather   The difference between the highest temperature h and the lowest temperature l $h - l$

WRITING IN ALGEBRA

In Exercises 1–4, write one example of each expression.
Answers may vary. Possible answers are given.

1. An algebraic expression that involves multiplication and addition $4a + 6$

2. An algebraic expression that involves division and subtraction $\frac{x}{5} - 4$

3. An algebraic expression that contains parentheses and the operations of addition and multiplication $10(n + 9)$

4. In Exercise 3, what must be known before you can evaluate your algebraic expression? Give in order the arithmetic operations that must be performed. Is this still true if the operations are performed with a calculator?
The value of the variable; operations in parentheses are done first. Yes.

1.2 The Real Number Line

Objectives: To graph real numbers on a number line
To classify numbers in subsets of the set of real numbers

The set of **real numbers** contains all positive numbers, all negative numbers, and zero. The real numbers can be represented as points on a number line.

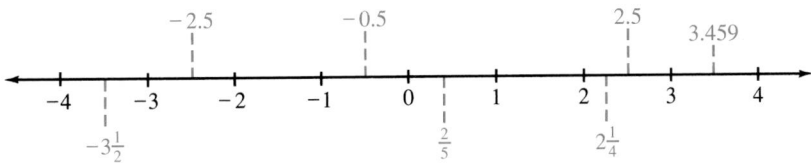

You have made and used number lines in earlier mathematics courses by marking off equal distances from a starting point, labeled 0. The zero point is also called the **origin.** Numbers to the right of 0 are called **positive numbers** and numbers to the left of 0 are called **negative numbers.** Zero (0) is neither positive nor negative.

Capsule Review

On a number line, numbers are associated with points of the line. The number associated with point *J* is +4, or 4.

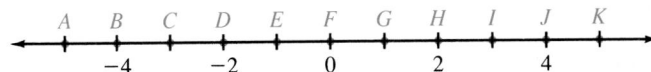

Give the number associated with each point.

1. *H* 2   **2.** *A* −5   **3.** *I* 3   **4.** *F* 0

Name the point associated with each number.

5. −1 *E*   **6.** 5 *K*   **7.** −4 *B*   **8.** 0 *F*

Some sets of numbers, such as {−2, −1, 0, 1, 2, 3}, can be listed. The symbol { } is used to enclose the members of a set. Three dots mean that the numbers of the set go on forever in the same pattern.

The set of all natural (counting) numbers: {1, 2, 3, 4, 5, . . .}
The set of all whole numbers: {0, 1, 2, 3, 4, 5, . . .}
The set of all integers: {. . . , −3, −2, −1, 0, 1, 2, 3, . . .}

1.2 The Real Number Line   **7**

Vocabulary
Coordinate
Graph
Integer
Irrational number
Natural number
Negative number
Origin
Positive number
Rational number
Real number
Whole number

Materials/Manipulatives
Graph paper
Straightedge
Overhead projector
Teacher's Resource Book
   Teaching Aid 1
   Transparency 2

BACKGROUND

- In the Capsule Review, the number line is discussed and points, graphs, and coordinates are reviewed. This review leads into the core of the lesson: graphing real numbers and classifying numbers in subsets of the set of real numbers.
- Some students may want to draw the number line on their paper before doing the exercises. Students should be aware that each interval along the number line represents one unit.

- Remind students that the idea of positive and negative numbers has a basis in the real world. Ask students to give some real-life examples of positive and negative numbers. Temperatures above and below zero, profit and loss, elevations above and below sea level.
- Point out that the arrows at both ends of a number line indicate it can be extended indefinitely in both directions. It may be helpful to use an overhead projector when working with the number lines in this lesson.
- Transparency 2, in the *Teacher's Resource Book*, can be helpful when discussing the examples and the Class Exercises.

Critical Thinking

1. *Observation* On the number line pictured below, the origin occurs at point *A*. Could the origin have been placed elsewhere? *Justify* your answer.

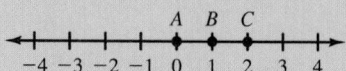

Yes. Positioning of the origin on the number line is arbitrary.

2. *Predicting Outcomes* On the number line above, suppose that coordinates had been assigned to the points so that the coordinates of *B* and *C* are 0 and 1, respectively. *Predict* the effect that this new assignment would have on the number line as pictured. All the points would have different coordinates assigned to them, but the distance between any pair of points would remain the same.

EXAMPLE 1 Graph the integers −4, 2, and 5 on a number line. Label the points *D*, *E*, and *F*, respectively.

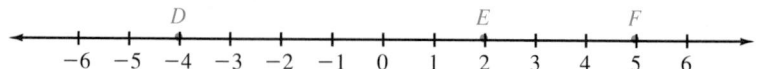

In Example 1, points *D*, *E*, and *F* are called the **graphs** of −4, 2, and 5, respectively. −4, 2, and 5 are called the **coordinates** of points *D*, *E*, and *F*, respectively. This relationship can be written as *D*(−4), *E*(2), and *F*(5).

There are points on the real number line that are *not* integers.

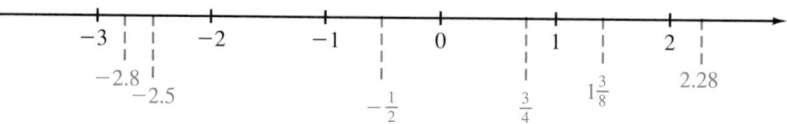

On the number line above, the fractions $-\frac{1}{2}$, $\frac{3}{4}$, and $1\frac{3}{8}$ and the decimals −2.5, 2.28, and −2.8 are graphed. These numbers are part of the set of *rational numbers*.

> A **rational number** is a number that can be written in the form $\frac{m}{n}$, where *m* and *n* are integers and $n \neq 0$.

EXAMPLE 2 Show that the following numbers are rational numbers.

    a. $-3\frac{1}{2}$ **b.** 4   **c.** 5.02   **d.** 0

a. $-3\frac{1}{2} = \frac{-7}{2}$ $m = -7, n = 2$ **b.** $4 = \frac{4}{1}$ $m = 4, n = 1$

c. $5.02 = 5\frac{2}{100} = \frac{502}{100}$ $m = 502, n = 100$ **d.** $0 = \frac{0}{1}$ $m = 0, n = 1$

From Example 2, you can see that the set of rational numbers includes integers, decimals, and fractions.

Some numbers cannot be written in the form $\frac{m}{n}$, where *m* and *n* are integers and $n \neq 0$. These numbers are called **irrational numbers.** Examples of irrational numbers are:

   $\sqrt{2}$ The square root of 2, which is about 1.41

   $\sqrt{3}$ The square root of 3, which is about 1.73

   π Pi, the ratio of the circumference of a circle *C* and its diameter *d*, or $\frac{C}{d}$; π is approximately equal to 3.14.

Irrational numbers are real numbers and can be graphed on a number line, along with the rational numbers.

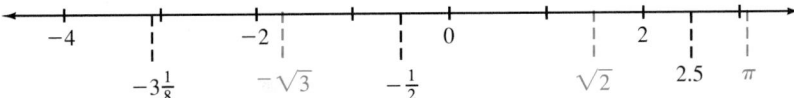

Until a later chapter of the book, most of the real numbers you will work with will be rational numbers.

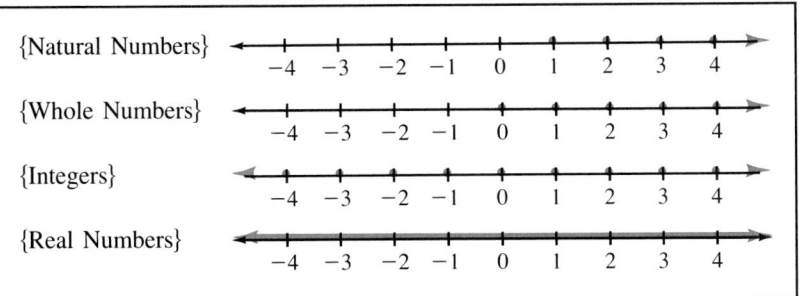

The entire number line is shaded to graph the set of real numbers. Each real number corresponds to exactly one point on the number line. Each point on the number line corresponds to a unique (one and only one) real number.

CLASS EXERCISES

For Exercises 1–8, refer to the number line below.

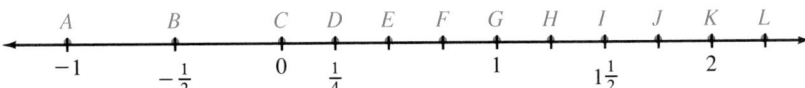

Give the coordinate of each point.

1. E $\frac{1}{2}$ 2. F $\frac{3}{4}$ 3. H $1\frac{1}{4}$ 4. L $2\frac{1}{4}$

State the letter of each coordinate.

5. $\frac{1}{2}$ E 6. $1\frac{3}{4}$ J 7. $-\frac{1}{2}$ B 8. $2\frac{1}{4}$ L

Graph these numbers on a number line. Label the points, as indicated.
See TE side column.

9. $A(-4)$, $B(2)$, $C(-5)$

10. $D\left(-3\frac{1}{2}\right)$, $E(0)$, $F\left(3\frac{1}{2}\right)$

11. $G(-0.5)$, $H(-1.5)$, $J(0.5)$

12. $K\left(-2\frac{3}{4}\right)$, $L\left(1\frac{1}{2}\right)$, $M\left(-4\frac{1}{4}\right)$

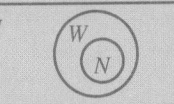
 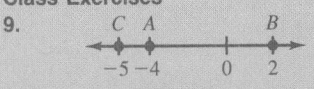

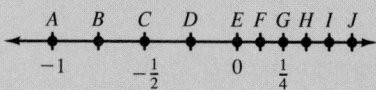
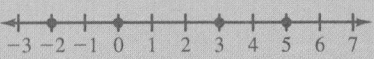
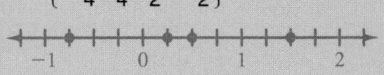
For Exercises 1–16, refer to the number line below.

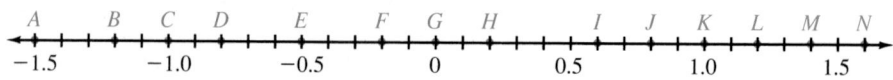

Give the coordinate of each point.

A

1. *C* −1.0 2. *E* −0.5 3. *H* 0.2 4. *J* 0.8
5. *B* −1.2 6. *D* −0.8 7. *L* 1.2 8. *N* 1.6

State the letter of each coordinate.

9. 0 *G* 10. 1.0 *K* 11. −1.5 *A* 12. −0.5 *E*
13. 0.6 *I* 14. 0.2 *H* 15. −0.8 *D* 16. −0.2 *F*

Show that each number is a rational number.

17. $7\frac{7}{1}$ 18. $-5\frac{-5}{1}$ 19. $-3.012\frac{-3012}{1000}$ 20. $2.618\frac{2618}{1000}$

21. $11\frac{3}{4}\frac{47}{4}$ 22. $-6\frac{5}{6}\frac{-41}{6}$ 23. $-1\frac{-1}{1}$ 24. $0\frac{0}{1}$

For each set of numbers, draw a number line and graph the numbers. Use an appropriate scale. See TE side column.

B

25. {−1, 1, 2, 4} 26. {−3, 0, 2, 6} 27. {−4, −1.5, 2, 2.5}
28. {−6.5, −2, 3.5, 7} 29. $\left\{-1\frac{1}{4}, -\frac{1}{2}, \frac{3}{4}, 1\right\}$ 30. $\left\{-2, -\frac{1}{4}, 0, 1\frac{3}{4}\right\}$

Draw this chart and indicate whether the given number belongs in the set.

	Natural Numbers	Whole Numbers	Integers	Rational Numbers	Irrational Numbers	Real Numbers
31. 8	X	X	X	X		X
32. −11			X	X		X
33. $\frac{0}{10}$		X	X	X		X
34. 16.2				X		X
35. $-3\frac{1}{6}$				X		X
36. $-\sqrt{3}$					X	X

C

37. On this number line, is there a point that corresponds to $-\frac{2}{3}$? That corresponds to 100? Explain.
Yes. Both rational and irrational numbers can be graphed on the number line.

A number line with markings −4 −3 −2 −1 0 1 2 3 4

38. The graphs of the natural numbers, the whole numbers, and the integers are a series of points. The graph of the real numbers is a continuous line. Why is this so? See side column.

Applications

Computer The INT function on a computer, INT(X), always gives the greatest INTeger that is less than or equal to X. For example, INT(5.4) = 5, INT(7.9) = 7 and INT(−3.2) = −4. State the value of each expression.

39. INT(71) 71   **40.** INT(−6.1) −7   **41.** INT(4.87) 4

42. INT(1/4) 0   **43.** INT(30/2) 15   **44.** INT(17/2) 8

45. For what values of X does INT(X) = X? when X is an integer

46. For what values of X does INT(X/2) = X? when X is 0 or −1

MATH CLUB ACTIVITY

Copy the number line on your own paper. Locate the points in Exercises 1–3.

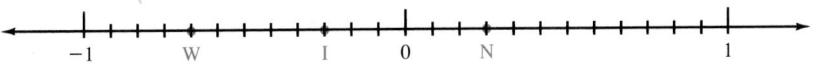

1. The temperature kept decreasing over a period of three hours. It decreased $\frac{1}{3}°$ the first hour and another $\frac{1}{2}°$ the second hour. The average decrease in temperature over a three-hour period was $\frac{1}{2}°$. Represent the temperature change in the third hour. Locate the corresponding point on the number line. Label it W. $-\frac{2}{3}°$

2. Arrange the rational numbers $-\frac{5}{8}$, $-\frac{1}{4}$, $-\frac{5}{16}$ in order from least to greatest. Graph the greatest number on the number line. Label it I. $-\frac{5}{8}, -\frac{5}{16}, -\frac{1}{4}$

3. If water is poured down the mouth of a pipe system and divides evenly at each opening, what fraction of the water moves out of the opening labeled N? Graph the value on the number line. Label it N. $\frac{1}{4}$

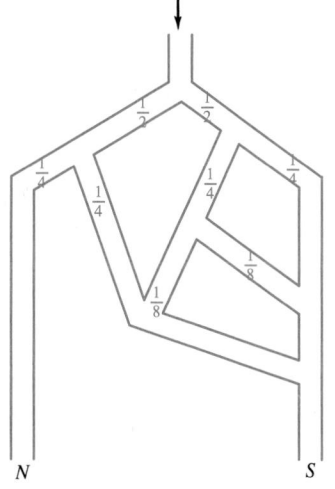

1.2 The Real Number Line   **11**

Teacher's Resource Book
Reteaching—Chapter 1, p. 4

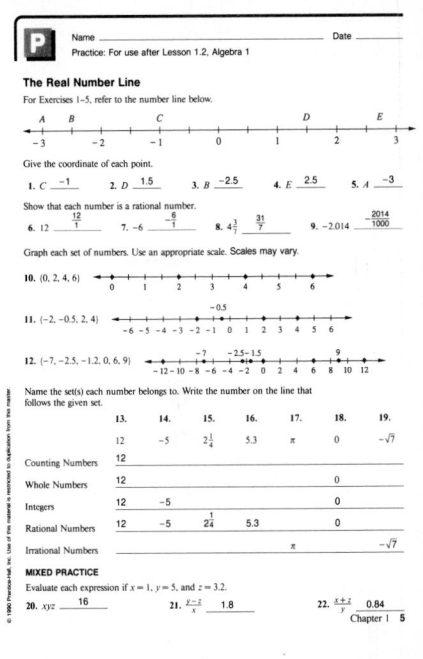

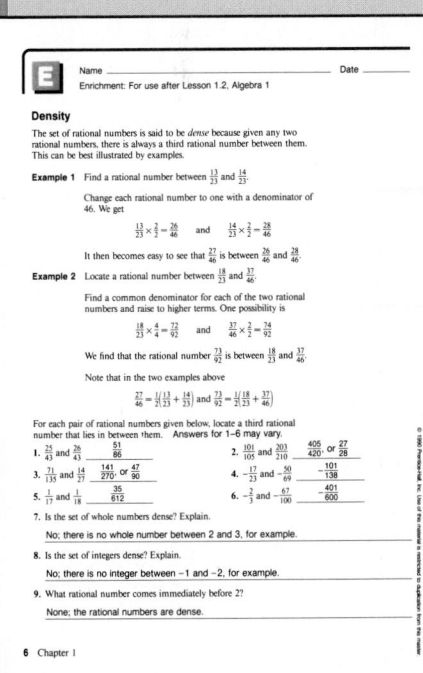

Vocabulary
Absolute value
Opposite
Simplify

Materials/Manipulatives
Graph paper
Straightedge
Teacher's Resource Book
  Transparencies 2, 4

BACKGROUND

- In the Capsule Review, students compare numbers with the use of a number line, which prepares them for their work in comparing and ordering real numbers.
- Remind students that a number is understood to be positive when there is no sign in front of it.
- To help students distinguish between inequality symbols, remind students that the point of the arrow always faces the lesser number.

1.3

Comparing and Ordering Numbers

Objectives: To compare and order real numbers
To use the concepts of opposites and absolute value

Numbers are placed on a number line in increasing order from left to right. Given two numbers on a number line, the number to the left is less. The equal sign, =, and the inequality symbols, < and >, are used to compare numbers.

= means *is equal to*.

< means *is less than*.

> means *is greater than*.

$\frac{3}{2} = 1\frac{1}{2}$ is read "$\frac{3}{2}$ is equal to $1\frac{1}{2}$."

$0 < 2$ is read "0 is less than 2."

$6 > 4$ is read "6 is greater than 4."

Capsule Review

On a horizontal number line:

$-1 < 0$ $\qquad$ -1 is to the left of 0.

$-8 > -9$ $\qquad$ -8 is to the right of -9.

$\frac{1}{2} = 0.5$ $\qquad$ $\frac{1}{2}$ and 0.5 correspond to the same point.

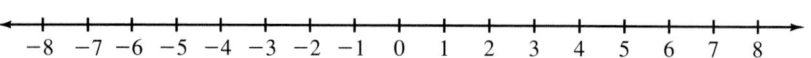

Replace each ? with <, >, or = to make a true statement. Refer to the number line above.

1. $6 \underset{>}{?} -5$ $\qquad$ **2.** $-4 \underset{<}{?} 3$ $\qquad$ **3.** $-1.5 \underset{<}{?} 0$ $\qquad$ **4.** $-2 \underset{=}{?} -2$

5. $-\frac{1}{2} \underset{>}{?} -3$ $\qquad$ **6.** $-1\frac{1}{2} \underset{<}{?} -1$ $\qquad$ **7.** $\frac{2}{3} \underset{<}{?} \frac{3}{4}$ $\qquad$ **8.** $-1.2 \underset{>}{?} -1.25$

A number line can be used to compare or to show the order of two or more numbers.

EXAMPLE 1 Graph the numbers -1, $\frac{1}{2}$, -2, $-\frac{1}{3}$, and $\frac{1}{3}$. Then name them in order from least to greatest.

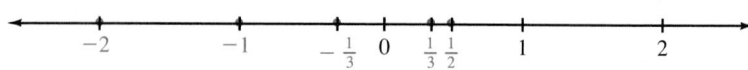

The numbers in order from least to greatest are -2, -1, $-\frac{1}{3}$, $\frac{1}{3}$, and $\frac{1}{2}$.

Every real number has an **opposite** whose graph is the same distance from the origin but in the opposite direction. To use the language of algebra, if n is a real number, then $-n$ is its opposite.

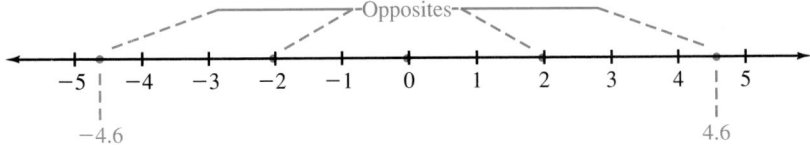

The opposite of 2 is -2; the opposite of -2 is 2.
-4.6 and 4.6 are opposites.
0 is its own opposite. That is, 0 is the opposite of 0.

EXAMPLE 2 **Name the opposite of each number:**
   a. 13   **b.** $\frac{6}{7}$ **c.** -2.75

Number	13	$\frac{6}{7}$	-2.75
Opposite	-13	$-\frac{6}{7}$	2.75

To **simplify** a numerical expression such as $-(-33)$, you should replace the expression with its simplest name. $-(-33)$ means *the opposite of* -33. Therefore, $-(-33) = 33$.

EXAMPLE 3 **Simplify:** **a.** $-(-110)$ **b.** $-[-(-76)]$

   a. $-(-110) = 110$ *The opposite of negative 110 is positive 110.*

   b. $-[-(-76)] = -[76]$ *Remove the parentheses first.*
   $\qquad\qquad\quad = -76$

Positive and negative numbers provide a useful way of representing opposite directions in real-life situations.

16 km above sea level $+16$, or 16   profit of \$11,500 $+11,500$, or 11,500
3 km below sea level -3 loss of \$160 -160

EXAMPLE 4 **A temperature drop of 24.5° C is represented as -24.5. Write the opposite of this number and tell what it represents.**

$$-(-24.5) = 24.5$$

This represents a temperature *rise* of 24.5° C.

TEACHING SUGGESTIONS

- Remind students that one method for comparing fractions is to write them as equivalent fractions with the same denominator.
- You may want to tell students that understanding the concepts of opposite and absolute value will help them later in the chapter when they add and subtract signed numbers. Use Transparency 4, when discussing absolute value.
- Draw a number line on the chalkboard or use Transparency 2, in the *Teacher's Resource Book*. Choose and label a point on the number line and ask a volunteer to describe the number's absolute value in terms of the number line. Then ask the student to identify the opposite of the number.

CHALKBOARD EXAMPLES

- **For Example 1**

  1. Graph the numbers 1, -3, $\frac{4}{5}$, $-\frac{5}{7}$, and 4. Then name them in order from least to greatest. $-3, -\frac{5}{7}, \frac{4}{5}, 1, 4$

- **For Example 2**
  Name the opposite of each number.

  2. 4 -4 **3.** $\frac{1}{2}$ $-\frac{1}{2}$

  4. $-\frac{2}{3}$ $\frac{2}{3}$ **5.** 7.32 -7.32

- **For Example 3**
  Simplify:
  6. $-(-72)$ 72
  7. $-[-(-25)]$ -25

- **For Example 4**
  8. A profit of \$556 is represented as 556. Write the opposite of this number, and tell what it represents. -556; \$556 loss

13

By definition, the graphs of two numbers that are opposites are the same distance from the origin. When mathematicians are interested in distance only, and not direction, they use *absolute value*.

> The **absolute value** of a number is its distance from 0 on a number line. The absolute value of a number n is written $|n|$.

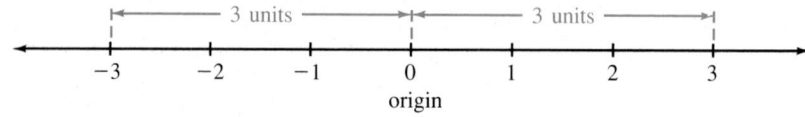

$$|-3| = 3 \qquad\qquad |3| = 3$$

EXAMPLE 5   **Find each absolute value:**   **a.** $|15|$ **b.** $\left|-\frac{3}{4}\right|$ **c.** $|0|$

     a. $|15| = 15$ **b.** $\left|-\frac{3}{4}\right| = \frac{3}{4}$ **c.** $|0| = 0$

Notice that the absolute value of a number is either positive or zero.

EXAMPLE 6   **Simplify:** $-|0.7|$

     $-|0.7| = -(0.7)$ *Find the absolute value first.* $|0.7| = 0.7$
            $= -0.7$ *Then find the opposite. The opposite of 0.7 is -0.7.*

EXAMPLE 7   **Simplify:** $|6| + |-16|$

     $|6| + |-16| = 6 + 16 = 22$

CLASS EXERCISES

1. How many rational numbers are there between 0 and 1? infinitely many

Give the opposite of each number.

2. 19 -19 **3.** -5 5   **4.** $-\frac{2}{3}$ $\frac{2}{3}$ **5.** $\frac{11}{8}$ $-\frac{11}{8}$

Tell whether each statement is *true* or *false*.

6. $6 > 4$ true   **7.** $-3 < 5$ true   **8.** $-3 < -4$ false   **9.** $1 > 1$ false

10. $0 < -2$ false   **11.** $5.8 > 5.82$ false   **12.** $-\frac{7}{8} > -\frac{7}{9}$ false   **13.** $1.3 < 1.36$ true

For Discussion

14. Try the following definition of absolute value for some specific values of x. $|x| = x$ if $x > 0$, $|x| = -x$ if $x < 0$, or $|x| = 0$ if $x = 0$. Does this seem like a good definition of absolute value? Explain.

Yes; if a number is positive or zero then its absolute value is equal to the number itself. If a number is negative then its absolute value is equal to the opposite of the number.

PRACTICE EXERCISES

Graph each group of numbers on a number line. Then list them in order from least to greatest.

A **1.** $-4, 0, 3, 2, -1$ $-4, -1, 0, 2, 3$

2. $5, 3, -3, -2, 1$ $-3, -2, 1, 3, 5$

3. $2\frac{1}{2}, 2, -2\frac{1}{2}, -\frac{1}{2}, 0$ $-2\frac{1}{2}, -\frac{1}{2}, 0, 2, 2\frac{1}{2}$

4. $-1.5, 1.5, -1, -0.5, 0$
$-1.5, -1, -0.5, 0, 1.5$

Replace each ? with <, >, or = to make a true statement.

5. $-1 \underline{?} 0$ $<$

6. $-3 \underline{?} -4$ $>$

7. $\frac{1}{2} \underline{?} \frac{1}{4}$ $>$

8. $\frac{2}{4} \underline{?} \frac{3}{6}$ $=$

9. $\frac{3}{9} \underline{?} \frac{2}{6}$ $=$

10. $-\frac{1}{4} \underline{?} -\frac{1}{8}$ $<$

11. $-\frac{1}{3} \underline{?} -\frac{1}{2}$ $>$

12. $-\frac{3}{5} \underline{?} -\frac{3}{4}$ $>$

Simplify.

13. $-(-3.1)$ 3.1

14. $-(-5.34)$ 5.34

15. $-\left[-\left(-\frac{2}{5}\right)\right]$ $-\frac{2}{5}$

16. $-\left[-\left(-\frac{1}{4}\right)\right]$ $-\frac{1}{4}$

17. $|-6.2|$ 6.2

18. $\left|\frac{1}{2}\right|$ $\frac{1}{2}$

19. $-\left|3\frac{1}{5}\right|$ $-3\frac{1}{5}$

20. $-\left|-\frac{5}{7}\right|$ $-\frac{5}{7}$

21. $|-5| + |8|$ 13

22. $|-15| + |29|$ 44

23. $|-3| + |-2|$ 5

24. $|9| + |-3|$ 12

Write each set of numbers in order from least to greatest.

B **25.** $\left\{\frac{1}{6}, \frac{1}{5}, \frac{1}{7}\right\}$ $\left\{\frac{1}{7}, \frac{1}{6}, \frac{1}{5}\right\}$

26. $\left\{-\frac{3}{5}, -\frac{3}{4}, -\frac{3}{8}\right\}$ $\left\{-\frac{3}{4}, -\frac{3}{5}, -\frac{3}{8}\right\}$

27. $\left\{-1\frac{2}{3}, -\frac{5}{4}, -1\frac{3}{4}\right\}$ $\left\{-1\frac{3}{4}, -1\frac{2}{3}, -\frac{5}{4}\right\}$

28. $\left\{1\frac{5}{6}, \frac{5}{3}, \frac{5}{2}\right\}$ $\left\{\frac{5}{3}, 1\frac{5}{6}, \frac{5}{2}\right\}$

29. $\{-0.104, -0.1, -0.1041\}$
$\{-0.1041, -0.104, -0.1\}$

30. $\{7.88, 7.885, 7.8809\}$
$\{7.88, 7.8809, 7.885\}$

Simplify.

31. $-|-14|$ -14

32. $\left|-4\frac{1}{5}\right|$ $4\frac{1}{5}$

33. $-\left|-\left(-\frac{3}{8}\right)\right|$ $-\frac{3}{8}$

34. $-[-(-5.23)]$ -5.23

35. $-[21]$ -21

36. $-[-50]$ 50

37. $|-3| + |-9|$ 12

38. $5 - |-4|$ 1

39. $2 + |-(+5)|$ 7

1.3 Comparing and Ordering Numbers **15**

Additional Answers
Practice Exercises

1.

2.

3.

4.

15

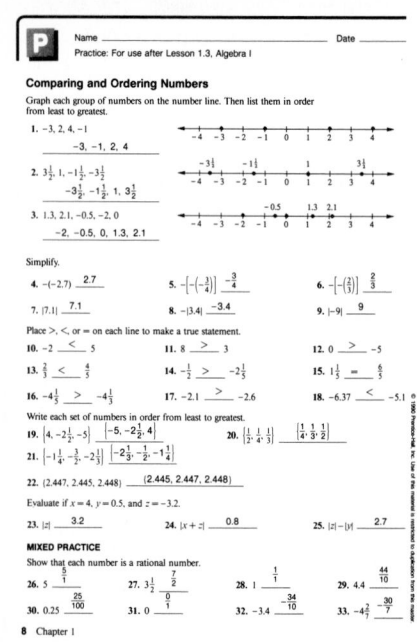

Evaluate if $a = 7$, $b = 2\frac{3}{4}$, and $c = -6.1$.

C **40.** $|c|$ 6.1   **41.** $-|a|$ -7   **42.** $|-c|$ 6.1

43. $-|c|$ -6.1   **44.** $|a + b|$ $9\frac{3}{4}$ **45.** $|c| - |b|$ $3\frac{7}{20}$, or 3.35

For all nonzero real numbers a, tell whether each statement is *true* or *false*.

46. $|a| > 0$ true   **47.** $a > -a$ false   **48.** $|a| = |-a|$ true   **49.** $-(-a) = a$ true

Applications

Use a positive or negative number to give the opposite of each situation. Then tell what the number represents.

50. Meteorology   16° C below freezing
+16; 16° C above freezing

51. Meteorology   20° C above freezing
-20; 20° C below freezing

52. Health   A gain of 6.5 lb
-6.5; loss of 6.5 lb

53. Health   A $3\frac{1}{4}$ lb weight loss
+$3\frac{1}{4}$; $3\frac{1}{4}$ lb weight gain

54. Navigation   120 ft above sea level
-120; 120 ft below sea level

55. Navigation   55 ft below sea level
+55; 55 ft above sea level

56. Economics   A $2560.38 debt
+2560.38; $2560.38 credit

57. Economics   A profit of $785.95
-785.95; loss of $785.95

PUZZLE

The following number pairs form a secret code. Read across the rows.

(19, 0)	(−10, 8)	(−6, −5)	(0, −16)
(−11, −9)	(−21, −19)	(−5, 0)	(−23, −21)
(0, 14)	(−4, 4)	(0, 5)	(−20, −18)
(−2, 0)	(20, −20)	(−8, −9)	(−16, 5)
(−17, 0)	(−8, 23)	(−7, −5)	(−20, 1)
(−21, 20)	(8, 0)	(−8, −5)	(−18, −19)

Why can't the meteorologist work? Here is the decoder. Use it to find the answer. SHE IS UNDER THE WEATHER

First Decoding	Second Decoding			
Use the greater of the two numbers in each pair.	0 = blank space	1 = A	2 = B	3 = C
	4 = D	5 = E	6 = F	7 = G 8 = H
If the greater number is negative, then use its absolute value.	9 = I	10 = J	11 = K	12 = L 13 = M
	14 = N	15 = O	16 = P	17 = Q 18 = R
	19 = S	20 = T	21 = U	22 = V 23 = W
	24 = X	25 = Y	26 = Z	

Addition on a Number Line

1.4

Objective: To add numbers by "moves" on a number line

Positive and negative numbers can be added by using the concept of distance on a number line.

Capsule Review

On the number line below, segments are marked off in 1-unit lengths. The distance between points *A* and *B* is 1 unit, between *F* and *H* is 2 units, and between *J* and *C* is 7 units.

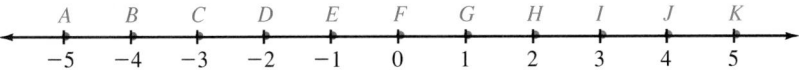

Find the distance between the given points.

1. *G* and *J* 3   **2.** *D* and *E* 1   **3.** *F* and *C* 3   **4.** *K* and *A* 10

5. *H* and *I* 1   **6.** *F* and *B* 4   **7.** *B* and *J* 8   **8.** *D* and *H* 4

Numbers can be represented by "moves" on a number line from one point to another. A move in the positive direction, from left to right, represents a **positive number.** A move in the negative direction, from right to left, represents a **negative number.**

A move of 4 units   A move of 2 units
to the right from −5   to the left from 4

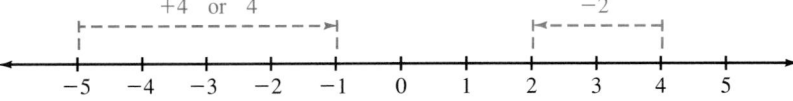

To add two numbers on a number line:

• Start at the origin, 0, and move the number of units and the direction indicated by the first number.
• From there, move the number of units and the direction indicated by the second number.
• The sum is the number that corresponds to the ending point.

LESSON PLAN

Materials/Manipulatives
Graph paper
Straightedge
Overhead projector
Teacher's Resource Book
  Teaching Aid 1
  Transparency 2

BACKGROUND

In the Capsule Review, students find the distance between two points on a number line as preparation for adding positive and negative numbers.

Critical Thinking
Classifying Classify the following sums by their similarities.

a. 5 + (−2)
b. 4 + (+6)
c. −4.5 + (−3.5)
d. $-3 + \frac{5}{2}$
e. −0.5 + 0.5
f. 4.25 + 3.25

Exercises b., c., and f. add numbers with like signs; a., d., and e. add numbers with opposite signs.

- In this lesson students use the number line as a concrete device for adding positive and negative numbers. An overhead projector may be helpful to show students how to solve addition problems on the number line.
- It may help students to think of adding positive and negative numbers as gains and losses. For example, adding $+4$ is a gain of 4 and adding -6 is a loss of 6.
- After Class Exercises 7–12, have students write a generalization about the sign of the sum and determine whether it holds true as they do the Practice Exercises.
- Have students use the number lines provided in the *Teacher's Resource Book* under Teaching Aids 1 to solve several mathematical sentences. You may wish to have the students work through the examples using these number lines.

CHALKBOARD EXAMPLES

- **For Example 1**
  1. Add: $-2 + (-4)$ -6

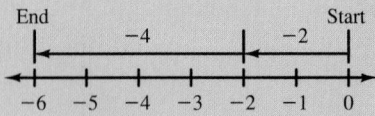

- **For Example 2**
  2. Add: $-5 + 9$ 4

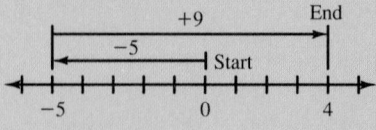

- **For Example 3**
  3. Add: $6 + 0$ 6

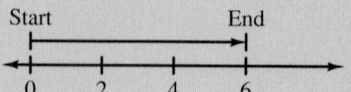

EXAMPLE 1   **Add: $-3 + (-4)$**

Start at 0. Move left to -3. Then move four units to the left.

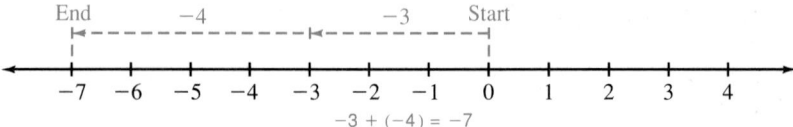

In Example 1, negative 4 is added to negative 3. Notice that parentheses are used so that the negative sign of the number to be added is not confused with the operational symbol ($+$ sign). When a positive number is added, parentheses are not necessary.

EXAMPLE 2   **Add: $-4 + 7$**

Start at 0. Move left to -4. Then move 7 units to the right.

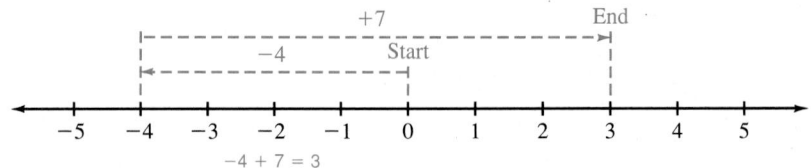

EXAMPLE 3   **Add: $-2 + 0$**

Add 0 means *move no units.*

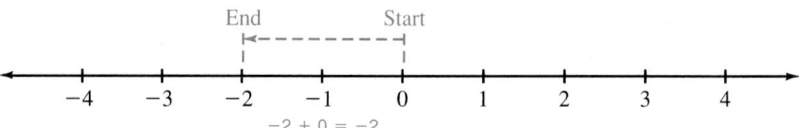

Example 3 illustrates the special property of zero for the addition of real numbers.

Identity Property for Addition

For every real number n, there is exactly one real number 0 such that

$$n + 0 = n$$

and

$$0 + n = n$$

From this you can see that when zero is one of the addends, the sum is the other addend.

18   Chapter 1 Real Numbers

EXAMPLE 4 A weather balloon was reported to be 4.5 mi east of the weather station (+4.5). It then moved 7 mi west from this position. How far from the weather station was the balloon then?

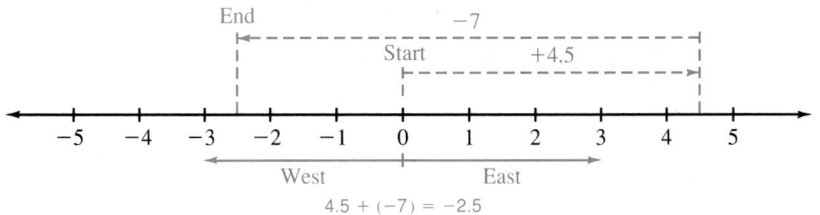

$$4.5 + (-7) = -2.5$$

The balloon was 2.5 mi west of the weather station.

It is possible to add more than two numbers on a number line.

EXAMPLE 5 Add: $5 + (-8) + (-2) + 7$

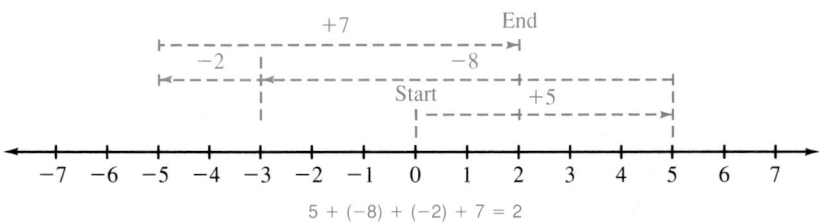

$$5 + (-8) + (-2) + 7 = 2$$

CLASS EXERCISES

Write an addition sentence for each diagram.

1.

$$3 + (-6) = -3$$

2.

$$-2 + 4 = 2$$

3.

$$-4 + (-1) = -5$$

4.

$$3 + 3 = 6$$

5.

$$6 + (-4) = 2$$

6.

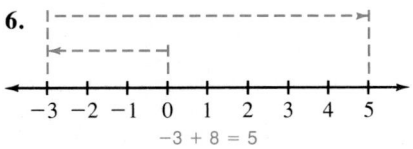

$$-3 + 8 = 5$$

1.4 Addition on a Number Line **19**

• **For Example 4**

4. An airplane was skywriting 1.5 miles west of a city. The pilot then flew 9 miles east. How far from the city was the plane?
7.5 mi east

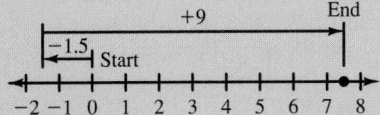

• **For Example 5**

5. Add: $7 + (-3) + (-6) + 8$ 6

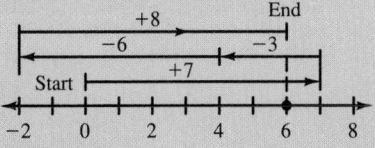

Common Error

• When several numbers are added, as in Example 5, students may become confused by the positive and negative signs. Remind students that these signs should be viewed as direction signals when working with a number line.

• See *Teacher's Resource Book* for additional remediation.

LESSON FOLLOW-UP

Discussion

Compare the operations performed in the two number line diagrams below.

A:

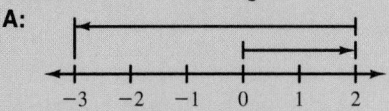

B:

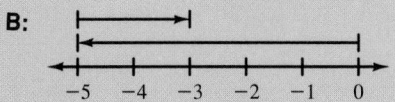

They represent the same sum and illustrate the commutative property of addition.
$2 + (-5) = -3$; $-5 + 2 = -3$

19

Assignment Guide
- See p. 1B for assignments.
- Use Transparency 2, in the *Teacher's Resource Book,* to prepare students for the Practice Exercises.
- Students having difficulty with Exercises 14–30 should first practice with three positive addends. Then they can proceed with Exercises 14–30.

Biography: Carl Friedrich Gauss

This brief sketch of the life of Carl Friedrich Gauss is followed by a discussion of a problem that Gauss tackled at an early age. Encourage students to discuss the illustrated example until they understand the principle and can state it in their own words. Two exercises are included.

Lesson Quiz

Find each sum. Use a number line to help you.

1. $-3 + 5$ 2
2. $\frac{3}{4} + \left(-\frac{1}{2}\right)$ $\frac{1}{4}$
3. $3.4 + (-5.5)$ -2.1
4. $\frac{3}{4} + (-4)$ $-3\frac{1}{4}$
5. $-9 + (-16)$ -25
6. $-8.4 + 5$ -3.4
7. $-3 + (-2) + 7$ 2
8. $4.7 + (-6) + (-3.9)$ -5.2

State whether the sum is positive, negative, or zero.

7. $-4 + (-2)$ neg.
8. $3 + (-9)$ neg.
9. $-1.5 + 2$ pos.
10. $-0.5 + 0.5$ zero
11. $1\frac{1}{2} + \left(-\frac{1}{2}\right)$ pos.
12. $-\frac{2}{3} + \frac{1}{2}$ neg.

PRACTICE EXERCISES

Find each sum. Use the number line below to help you.

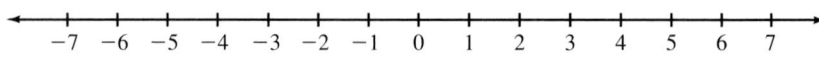

A 1. $-2 + (-3)$ -5 2. $-4 + (-3)$ -7 3. $-4 + (-2)$ -6 4. $-7 + (-14)$ -21

5. $-5 + 6$ 1   6. $-7 + 4$ -3 7. $-3 + (-4)$ -7 8. $-9 + (-8)$ -17

9. $-8 + 0$ -8 10. $0 + (-6)$ -6 11. $1.5 + (-5)$ -3.5 12. $3.7 + (-8)$ -4.3

13. $-4.5 + (-3.5)$ -8.0 14. $5 + (-2) + (-4)$ -1 15. $-3 + 2 + (-5)$ -6

16. $-4 + 3 + (-8)$ -9 17. $-3 + (-2) + 6$ 1   18. $-8 + 2 + (-5)$ -11

19. $8 + (-4) + 2$ 6   20. $8 + (-9) + 3$ 2   21. $-7 + 2 + (-1)$ -6

B 22. $-5 + 7 + (-1)$ 1   23. $-10 + (-2) + (-5)$ -17 24. $-16 + (-3) + (-4)$ -23

25. $-2.5 + (-5.5) + 1.5$ -6.5 26. $1.5 + (-3.5) + 4.5$ 2.5   27. $1\frac{1}{2} + \left(-2\frac{1}{2}\right) + \left(-1\frac{1}{2}\right)$ $-2\frac{1}{2}$

28. $3\frac{1}{4} + \left(-2\frac{1}{4}\right) + 1\frac{3}{4}$ $2\frac{3}{4}$ 29. $\frac{5}{3} + \left(-\frac{2}{3}\right) + \frac{4}{3}$ $\frac{7}{3}$ 30. $\left(-\frac{9}{2}\right) + \left(-\frac{5}{2}\right) + \frac{3}{2}$ $-\frac{11}{2}$

Replace $\underline{\ ?\ }$ with $<$, $>$, or $=$ to make a true statement.

C 31. $-16.5 + (-4.3) + 4.3$ $\underline{\ ?\ }$ $-16.3 + (-4.5) + 4.5$ $<$

32. $0.25 + (-0.9) + 16$ $\underline{\ ?\ }$ $0.9 + (-0.25) + (-16)$ $>$

33. $\left|-\frac{5}{8} + \frac{3}{7}\right|$ $\underline{\ ?\ }$ $\left|-\frac{5}{7} + \frac{3}{8}\right|$ $<$ 34. $\left|\frac{2}{9} + (-1)\right|$ $\underline{\ ?\ }$ $\left|1 + \left(-\frac{2}{9}\right)\right|$ $=$

Applications

Write an addition expression for each situation. Then simplify.

35. **Meteorology** The temperature after a drop of $17°$ from $5°$ C
$5 + (-17) = -12;\ -12°$ C

36. **Number Problem** The floor at which the elevator stopped if the detective followed the suspect into the elevator on the 24th floor and then the elevator went down 11 floors before the door opened $24 + (-11) = 13;$ 13th floor

37. **Sports** The net loss if a football team lost 3 yd on each of 4 successive plays $-3 + (-3) + (-3) + (-3) = -12;$ 12 yd loss

20   Chapter 1 Real Numbers

38. Economics   The net change if Maureen earned $25, spent $12 of it, and then earned $10 more   25 + (−12) + 10 = 23; $23 left

39. Economics   The net change on the stock market for the SUP Corporation if its stock dropped $3\frac{1}{8}$ points on Monday and gained $4\frac{5}{8}$ points on Tuesday $-3\frac{1}{8} + 4\frac{5}{8} = 1\frac{1}{2}$; up $1\frac{1}{2}$ points

BIOGRAPHY: Carl Friedrich Gauss

Carl Friedrich Gauss was born in Brunswick, Germany, on April 30, 1777. Before he was 3 years old, he was demonstrating his genius. At the age of 10, Gauss began to show an unusual ability in arithmetic. As a result of the encouragement and assistance of an able teacher, he was working with proofs in algebra before he was 11 years old.

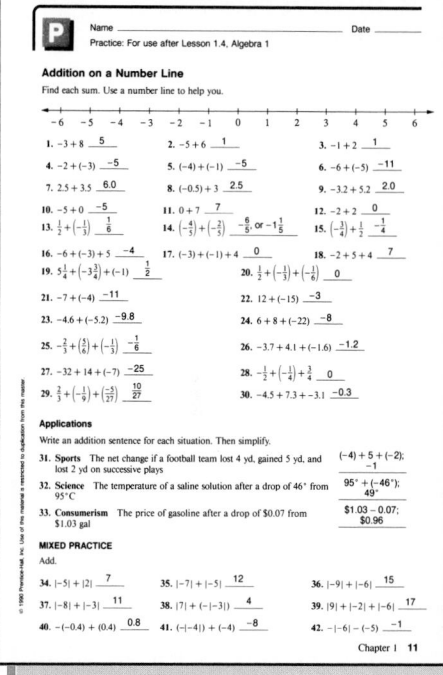

There is a well-known story about Gauss at this age. His arithmetic teacher, hoping to keep the class busy for some time, told the students to find the sum of the first one hundred positive integers. To the teacher's astonishment, young Gauss found the correct answer within a few minutes. His method was something like this:

Write out the sum both forward and backward, lining up the terms.

$$1 + 2 + 3 + \cdots + 98 + 99 + 100$$
$$100 + 99 + 98 + \cdots + 3 + 2 + 1$$

Adding each vertical pair, you get a sum of 101. There are one hundred sums.

$$100(101) \text{ is two times the correct answer.}$$

$$\frac{100(101)}{2} = 50(101) = 5050$$

The answer is 5050.

The system works just as well for adding a million numbers, provided the numbers are all equally spaced.

Use the Gauss method.

1. Find the sum of the first 50 positive integers. 1275

2. Find the sum of the ten positive integers, 31 through 40. 355

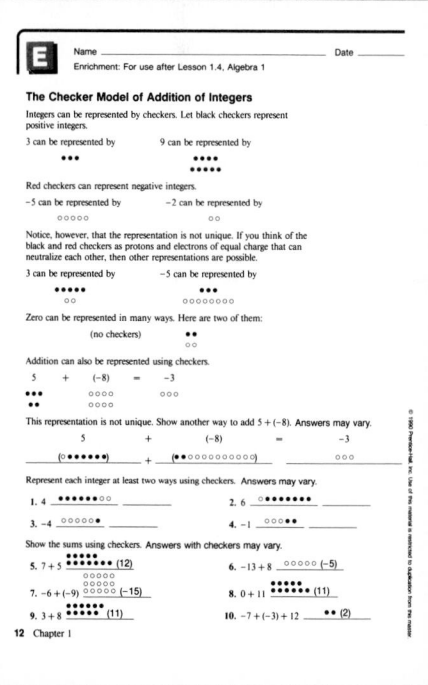

BACKGROUND

In the Capsule Review, the concept of absolute value is reviewed. Deciding which of two absolute value expressions is greater leads into the operation of adding two numbers with opposite signs.

1.5

Adding Real Numbers

Objectives: To add two or more real numbers
To evaluate algebraic expressions involving addition

Sums such as $-436 + 6347$ or $-2\frac{2}{7} + 4\frac{1}{6}$ are not easily found on a number line. If you know the specific rules for adding two or more numbers, a number line is not needed. These rules involve the concept of absolute value.

Capsule Review

The absolute value of a number is its distance from zero on a number line. So, $|15| = 15$, $|-15| = 15$, and $|0| = 0$.

Which absolute value is greater?

1. $|37|$ or $|-38|$ $|-38|$ **2.** $|-6.2|$ or $|6.15|$ $|-6.2|$ **3.** $|0.56|$ or $|0.07|$ $|0.56|$

A rule that can be used to add two positive numbers or two negative numbers is given below.

Addition Rule (Two numbers with the same sign)

To add two numbers that have the same sign, either both positive or both negative:

• Add their absolute values.
• Give the sum the same sign as the sign of each number.

EXAMPLE 1   **Add: $-13 + (-26)$**

Each number is negative. Add the absolute values.

$-13 + (-26)$ $|-13| + |-26| = 13 + 26$, or 39.
$= -39$ *The sum is negative.*

EXAMPLE 2   **Add: $0.3 + 2.634$**

Each number is positive. Add the absolute values.

$0.3 + 2.634$ $|0.3| + |2.634| = 0.3 + 2.634$, or 2.934.
$= 2.934$ *The sum is positive.*

22   Chapter 1 Real Numbers

Absolute value is also used to add two numbers that have different signs.

> **Addition Rule (Two numbers with different signs)**
>
> To add two numbers that have different signs:
>
> - Find their absolute values. Subtract the smaller absolute value from the larger.
> - Give the result the same sign as the sign of the number with the larger absolute value.

EXAMPLE 3 **Add: 14 + (−72)**

Notice that one number is positive, the other is negative.

$14 + (−72)$ *Subtract the absolute values:* $|−72| − |14| = 72 − 14$, *or 58.*
$= −58$ *The sum is negative since* $|−72| > |14|$.

The procedure is the same for other rational numbers.

EXAMPLE 4 **Add: $−\frac{3}{4} + \frac{7}{2}$**

$−\frac{3}{4} + \frac{7}{2}$ *Subtract the absolute values:* $\left|\frac{7}{2}\right| − \left|\frac{3}{4}\right| = \frac{14}{4} − \frac{3}{4} = \frac{11}{4}$.
$= \frac{11}{4}$, *or* $2\frac{3}{4}$ *The sum is positive since* $\left|\frac{7}{2}\right| > \left|−\frac{3}{4}\right|$.

Example 5 shows how to add more than two numbers when some of the numbers are positive and some are negative.

EXAMPLE 5 **Add: −4 + 18 + (−40) + 2**

Add the positive numbers.	*Add the negative numbers.*
$\|18\| = 18$ 18	$\|−4\| = 4$ 4
$\|2\| = 2$ $\underline{+\ 2}$	$\|−40\| = 40$ $\underline{+40}$
20	44
Sum is positive: 20	Sum is negative: −44

Subtract the absolute values: $|44| − |20| = 44 − 20 = 24$. The sum is negative since $|−44| > |20|$. So, $−4 + 18 + (−40) + 2 = −24$.

To add several numbers that have different signs, you can add the positive and negative numbers separately, and then add these two sums. Another method is to add the numbers in the order in which they occur.

TEACHING SUGGESTIONS

- Before introducing the examples you may wish to review Transparency 4, in the Teacher's Resource Book.
- Encourage students to verify the rules for themselves by applying them to simple problems like $−3 + (−2)$, $5 + (−7)$, and $−8 + 4$, which they can also do with a number line.
- The significance of the closure property can be difficult to understand. It might be helpful to name a set that is *not* closed for addition. For example, {0, 1, 2} is not closed since $1 + 2 = 3$ and 3 is not a member of the set.
- You may ask students to use a calculator to check their results for Exercises 27–38.

Critical Thinking

Comparing-Contrasting Compare the worked out Examples in Lesson 1.5 and 1.4. How are they alike and different? In both lessons signed numbers are added. They differ in the methods by which the additions are accomplished. Lesson 1.4 shows the additions using a number line and Lesson 1.5 uses the addition rule for real numbers.

CHALKBOARD EXAMPLES

- **For Example 1**
  Add:
  1. $−10 + (−33)$ −43
  2. $−6 + (−12)$ −18

- **For Example 2**
  Add:
  3. $0.04 + 1.07$ 1.11
  4. $0.03 + 2.10$ 2.13

- **For Example 3**
  Add:
  5. $19.7 + (−37)$ −17.3
  6. $20.2 + (−42)$ −21.8

- **For Example 4**

4. Add: $-\frac{2}{7} + \frac{13}{14}$ $\frac{9}{14}$

- **For Example 5**

5. Add:
   $8.1 + (-2.3) + (-1.5) + 4$ 8.3

- **For Example 6**

6. Evaulate $a + (-27) + b$, if $a = -7$ and $b = 43$.   9

Common Error

- Students are sometimes confused when adding two numbers with opposite signs. Explain that they should verify their answers using a number line.
- See *Teacher's Resource Book* for additional remediation.

LESSON FOLLOW-UP

Discussion

In a graph on the number line, which number, $\left|2\frac{2}{3}\right|$ or $\left|-2\frac{5}{6}\right|$, lies farther to the right? Why? $\left|-2\frac{5}{6}\right|$ because $\left|-2\frac{5}{6}\right| > \left|2\frac{2}{3}\right|$.

Assignment Guide

- See p. 1B for assignments.
- Exercises 43–46 illustrate many applications of adding signed numbers. You may want students to discuss other applications and make up their own.
- See *Teacher's Resource Book*, Technology p. 3.

Logical Reasoning

Students classify statements as always true, sometimes true, or never true. In order to decide which classification is appropriate for each of the given sentences, students should look for specific examples of each statement.

EXAMPLE 6 **Evaluate** $-[5 + x] + y + z$ **if** $x = -\frac{1}{2}$, $y = 3\frac{1}{2}$, **and** $z = -4$.

$$-[5 + x] + y + z$$

$$= -\left[5 + \left(-\frac{1}{2}\right)\right] + 3\frac{1}{2} + (-4) \qquad \text{Substitute} -\frac{1}{2} \text{ for x, } 3\frac{1}{2} \text{ for y, and } -4 \text{ for z.}$$

$$= -\left[4\frac{1}{2}\right] + 3\frac{1}{2} + (-4) \qquad \text{Add within the brackets.}$$

$$= -4\frac{1}{2} + 3\frac{1}{2} + (-4)$$

$$= -1 + (-4) \qquad\qquad -4\frac{1}{2} + 3\frac{1}{2} = -1$$

$$= -5$$

The sum of any two given real numbers is always another real number. Also, the sum is *unique*. That is, there is *one and only one* real number answer. These two ideas are summarized in a special property for real numbers.

> **Closure Property for Addition**
>
> For all real numbers m and n,
>
> $$m + n \text{ is a unique real number.}$$

CLASS EXERCISES

Add, using the method that is easier for you.

1. $38 + (-28) + 15 + (-4)$ 21

2. $-13 + 28 + (-14) + (-5)$ −4

3. $-60 + 22 + (-40) + 72 + 6$ 0

4. $-3\frac{1}{4} + 3\frac{1}{8} + \left(-2\frac{1}{2}\right) + (-6)$ $-8\frac{5}{8}$

For Discussion

5. Can any two real numbers be added by using a number line? Why are rules needed for addition? Yes, but it is cumbersome. Rules may help to simplify the process.

PRACTICE EXERCISES

Add.

A 1. $-199 + (-301)$ −500

2. $-86 + (-127)$ −213

3. $649 + (-1102)$ −453

4. $5851 + (-4998)$ 853

5. $7.08 + (-2.47)$ 4.61

6. $-25.31 + 75.07$ 49.76

7. $-13.689 + 11.98$ –1.709 **8.** $0.234 + (-1.07)$ –0.836 **9.** $\frac{5}{7} + \left(-\frac{9}{7}\right)$ $-\frac{4}{7}$

10. $-\frac{2}{9} + \frac{8}{9}$ $\frac{2}{3}$

11. $-\frac{3}{8} + \left(-\frac{1}{4}\right)$ $-\frac{5}{8}$

12. $-\frac{5}{9} + \left(-\frac{1}{3}\right)$ $-\frac{8}{9}$

13. $-\frac{3}{7} + \frac{1}{2}$ $\frac{1}{14}$

14. $\frac{5}{6} + \left(-\frac{2}{5}\right)$ $\frac{13}{30}$

15. $-17 + 27 + (-10)$ 0

16. $55 + (-19) + 4$ 40

17. $5.2 + (-6.7) + 10.1$ 8.6 **18.** $-20.5 + 4.3 + (-7)$
$\qquad\qquad\qquad\qquad\qquad\qquad\qquad\qquad\qquad\qquad$ –23.2

Evaluate each expression if $a = -5$, $b = 2\frac{1}{2}$, $c = -\frac{1}{2}$, and $d = 15$.

19. $a + (-b) + c$ –8

20. $b + (-d) + (-a)$ $-7\frac{1}{2}$

21. $-a + b + (-c)$ 8

22. $-b + d + a$ $7\frac{1}{2}$

Add.

B **23.** $-\frac{3}{8} + \frac{7}{12} + \frac{1}{2}$ $\frac{17}{24}$

24. $\frac{5}{6} + \left(-\frac{2}{9}\right) + \left(-\frac{1}{3}\right)$ $\frac{5}{18}$

25. $2\frac{3}{25} + \left(-\frac{7}{15}\right)$ $1\frac{49}{75}$

26. $\frac{4}{15} + \left(-3\frac{5}{12}\right)$ $-3\frac{3}{20}$

27. $7.3 + 12.12 + (-3.5) + 8.06$ 23.98

28. $-28.5 + (-11.6) + 5.91 + 9.31$
$\qquad\qquad\qquad\qquad\qquad\qquad\qquad$ –24.88

29. $\frac{2}{3} + \left[3 + \left(-\frac{1}{3}\right)\right]$ $3\frac{1}{3}$

30. $-\left[\frac{7}{8} + (-2)\right] + \frac{3}{8}$ $1\frac{1}{2}$

31. $-(-3 + 11) + [9 + (-14)]$ –13

32. $-[37 + (-15)] + (-8 + 14)$ –16

33. $-|5 + (-7) + (-23)|$ –25

34. $-|13 + (-3) + (-19)|$ –9

C **35.** $82 + [-|8 + (-31)|]$ 59

36. $-|-17 + 28| + (-15)$ –26

37. $|2 + (-6)| + |-30 + 19|$ 15

38. $-|14 + (-30)| + |-17 + 3|$ –2

Evaluate each expression if $r = -22$, $s = 7$, and $t = -8$.

39. $|-r| + [-|t + (-s)|]$ 7

40. $-|s + (-t)| + |r|$ 7

41. $-|t + (-r)| + |s + r|$ 1

42. $|-s + (-r)| + [-|r + (-t)|]$ 1

Applications

For each problem, state a sum. Then answer the question.

43. Meteorology The temperature at 8:00 AM was 19° C. By noon it had risen 6°, but by 4:00 PM it had fallen 8°. What was the temperature at 4:00 PM? $19 + 6 + (-8) = 17$; 17° C

44. Sports On four successive plays, a football team gained 7 yd, lost 11 yd, lost 6 yd, and gained 15 yd. What was the total yardage?
$7 + (-11) + (-6) + 15 = 5$; 5 yd

1.5 Adding Real Numbers **25**

P Name _____ Date _____
Practice: For use after Lesson 1.5, Algebra 1

Adding Real Numbers

Add.

1. $(-412)+(-218)$ __-630__   2. $-81+(-161)$ __-242__   3. $124+(-31)$ __93__

4. $584+(-316)$ __268__   5. $12.03+(-9.02)$ __3.01__   6. $50.25+(-31.70)$ __18.55__

7. $\frac{8}{9}+(-\frac{4}{9})$ __$\frac{4}{9}$__   8. $\frac{2}{3}+(-\frac{1}{6})$ __$\frac{11}{42}$__   9. $(0.034)+(-0.071)$ __-0.037__

10. $54+(-17)+(-22)$ __15__   11. $3.2+(-7.8)+1.1$ __-3.5__

12. $-\frac{1}{2}+\frac{1}{3}+\frac{1}{6}$ __$-\frac{4}{21}$__   13. $\frac{2}{5}+(-\frac{1}{8})+(-\frac{1}{6})$ __$\frac{13}{120}$__

14. $(2+7)+[6+(-3)]$ __12__   15. $-[21+(-7)]+(-9+11)$ __-12__

16. $-|2+(-3)+7|$ __-6__   17. $|(-12)+6|+(-4)|$ __10__

Evaluate each expression if $m=-2$, $p=\frac{3}{4}$, and $k=\frac{1}{4}$.

18. $m+p+k$ __-1__   19. $p+(-k)$ __$\frac{1}{2}$__   20. $-p+(-k)+m$ __-3__

21. $(-m)+(-k)$ __$\frac{7}{4}$, or $1\frac{3}{4}$__   22. $-p+k$ __$-\frac{2}{4}$, or $-\frac{1}{2}$__   23. $-m+k+(-p)$ __$\frac{3}{2}$, or $1\frac{1}{2}$__

24. $(-k)+(-p)+(-m)$ __1__   25. $(-p)+(-k)$ __-1__   26. $m+p+-(k)$ __$-\frac{3}{2}$, or $-1\frac{1}{2}$__

Applications

For each problem, state a sum. Then answer the question.

21. **Economics** The stock of the Xema Corporation sold for $46 on Monday. During the week the price went up $3, down $1, up $4, and then down $5 on Friday. How much was a share of Xema stock worth at closing on Friday?

   $46 + $3 + (-$1) + $4 + (-$5); $47

22. **Finance** Flora had $325.72 in her checking account. She wrote checks for $17.82 and $19.57. She also deposited $14 and $63.17. What is the new balance in her checking account?

   $325.72 + (-$17.82) + (-$19.57) + $14 + $63.17; $365.50

MIXED PRACTICE

Place >, <, or = on each line to make a true statement.

23. $\frac{1}{7}$ __>__ $\frac{1}{9}$ 24. -9.1 __>__ -9.2 25. $2\frac{2}{5}$ __=__ $\frac{12}{5}$

26. $-3\frac{1}{9}$ __<__ $-2\frac{4}{9}$ 27. 0.001 __>__ 0.0001 28. 7.6 __<__ 7.65

14 Chapter 1

E Name _____ Date _____
Enrichment: For use after Lesson 1.5, Algebra 1

Relationships involving Absolute Value

It is sometimes easy to see that certain statements are true. For example, $28 = 28$, $5 < 9$, $-8 < 6$. But what happens if you insert absolute value symbols into the equation or inequality? You can see that $28 = |28|$ and $5 < |9|$, but is $|-8| < 6$? The third statement is not true, because $|-8|$ is 8, which is not less than 6.

If you use a variable in the statement using absolute value, the relationships can sometimes be true and sometimes be false.

Consider the statement $x \le |x|$.

If x is positive, then the absolute value of x is also positive, and the statement is true.

If x is 0, the absolute value is 0, and the statement is true.

If x is negative, the absolute value of x is positive, and the statement is false.

So you can say that the statement is sometimes true.

You can also substitute values for the variable in a relationship to help determine if it is always true, sometimes true, or never true. Consider $|x| + |y| \le |x + y|$.

Evaluate if $x=4$ and $y=0$. __$4 \le 4$__

Evaluate if $x=6$ and $y=-2$. __$8 \not\le 4$__

Evaluate if $x=-1$ and $y=3$. __$4 \not\le 2$__

So the relationship $|x|+|y| \le |x+y|$ is __sometimes__ true.

Tell whether the following relationships are always true, sometimes true, or never true.

1. $-x \le |x|$ __always__   2. $|x| > |-x|$ __never__

3. $|x+y| \le |x|+|y|$ __always__   4. $|x|-|y| \le x-y$ __sometimes__

5. $||x|-|y|| \le |x+y|$ __always__   6. $|x+y+z| \le x+y+z$ __sometimes__

7. $|-x| \cdot 0 = -x$ __never__   8. $0 \ge |-x|$ __sometimes__

9. $||-x|-|-y|| \ge |-x|+|-y|$ __never__   10. $|-x|-|-y| \ge |x-y|$ __sometimes__

11. $|-x| > x$ __sometimes__   12. $|x-y| < |x|-|y|$ __never__

13. Write a relationship using variables and an absolute value that is always true.

   $|x^2| = x^2$ Answers may vary.

Chapter 1 **15**

$1000 + (-60) + 2200 + (-200) + 1700 = 4640; 4640\text{ m}$

45. **Aviation** A powered airplane towed a glider into the air to an altitude of 1000 m and then let it go. The glider dropped 60 m into a thermal (rising bubbles of warm air), which took it up 2200 m. Then it glided down 200 m into another thermal. Then the glider rose 1700 m. What was the altitude of the glider?

46. **Finance** Dee had $300.30 in her checking account. She wrote checks for $35 and $106.15 and deposited $20 and $43.75. What is the new balance in her account?

   $300.30 + (-35) + (-106.15) + 20 + 43.75 = 222.90; $222.90

Calculator The sign change key, $+/-$, is used to enter negative numbers. To find the sum $25 + (-7)$ on a calculator, enter positive 7 first and then the sign change key to make it negative. Then add 25. 18

Find each sum using the sign change key on your calculator.

47. $23 + (-8)$ 15   48. $96 + (-33)$ 63   49. $5.83 + (-0.76)$ 5.07

50. $0.04 + (-98.9)$ -98.86   51. $-29 + 101$ 72   52. $-14.629 + (-9.36)$
   -23.989

LOGICAL REASONING

Three key words in logical reasoning are *always* (every time), *sometimes* (at least once), and *never* (not even once).

Tell whether each of the following sentences is *always true*, *sometimes true*, or *never true*.

1. The sum of two positive numbers is positive. always

2. The sum of two negative numbers is positive. never

3. The sum of a positive number and a negative number is positive. sometimes

4. If two numbers are both positive or both negative, then the absolute value of their sum equals the sum of their absolute values. always

5. If one number is positive and one number is negative, then the absolute value of their sum equals the sum of their absolute values. never

6. If the absolute value of one number is equal to the absolute value of another, then the sum of the two numbers is 0. sometimes

26   Chapter 1 Real Numbers

Subtracting Real Numbers

Objectives: To subtract real numbers
To evaluate algebraic expressions involving subtraction of real numbers

You have learned to add real numbers and to find the opposite of a number. These two concepts together can be used to provide a rule for the subtraction of real numbers.

Capsule Review

Two numbers whose graphs are the same distance from the origin, one number positive and the other negative, are called *opposites*. The opposite of -4.5 is 4.5. The opposite of $2\frac{1}{2}$ is $-2\frac{1}{2}$.

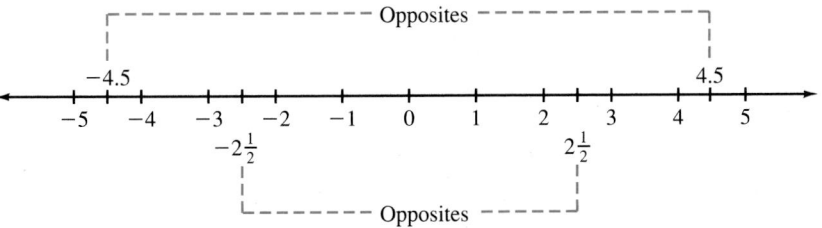

Name the opposite of each number.

1. -6 6   **2.** 15 -15 **3.** $-\frac{1}{4}$ $\frac{1}{4}$ **4.** $-4\frac{1}{3}$ $4\frac{1}{3}$ **5.** 13.09 -13.09

Another name for opposite is **additive inverse.** Notice what happens when a number and its additive inverse are added.

Number	Additive Inverse	Sum
-5	5	$-5 + 5 = 0$
-0.6	0.6	$-0.6 + 0.6 = 0$

Additive Inverse Property

For every real number n, there is exactly one real number $-n$, such that

$$n + (-n) = 0 \quad \text{and} \quad -n + n = 0$$

1.6 Subtracting Real Numbers   **27**

LESSON PLAN

Vocabulary
Additive inverse

Materials/Manipulatives
Graph paper
Straightedge
Teacher's Resource Book,
Teaching Aid 1,
Transparency 2

BACKGROUND

In the Capsule Review, students review the concept of opposites and find the opposites of real numbers, including fractions and decimals. This is a preparation for defining subtraction as the addition of an opposite.

Advise students who are having difficulties to check their answers using the number line. Use Teaching Aid 1 and Transparency 2, in the *Teacher's Resource Book*. For example, to show $6 - 2 = 4$, point out that 2 is 4 units to the left of 6, and to show $3 - 9 = -6$, point out that 9 is 6 units to the right of 3.

CHALKBOARD EXAMPLES

- **For Example 1**
  Simplify:
  1. $-(4.7)$ -4.7 **2.** $-\left(-\dfrac{1}{5}\right)$ $\dfrac{1}{5}$

- **For Example 2**
  3. Subtract: $25 - 47$. -22

- **For Example 3**
  4. Subtract: $7.83 - (-1.41)$ 9.24

- **For Example 4**
  5. Subtract: $-(-14 - 36) - (58 - 42)$ 34

- **For Example 5**
  6. Subtract: $-\dfrac{5}{8} - \left(-\dfrac{3}{4}\right)$ $\dfrac{1}{8}$

- **For Example 6**
  7. Evaluate $c - (4 - d)$ if $c = -7$, $d = 9.1$ -1.9

Common Error

- Students often think that $-x$ must be a negative number. Using specific positive and negative numbers and zero, stress that $-x$ can be negative, positive, or zero.
- See *Teacher's Resource Book* for additional remediation.

The additive inverse of a negative number is a positive number. For example, $-(-4)$ means "the additive inverse of negative 4," which is positive 4, or 4.

EXAMPLE 1   **Simplify: a.** $-(-2.1)$ **b.** $-\left(\dfrac{1}{3}\right)$

a. $-(-2.1) = 2.1$ **b.** $-\left(\dfrac{1}{3}\right) = -\dfrac{1}{3}$

The following definition may be used to subtract real numbers.

> ### Definition of Subtraction
> For all real numbers m and n,
> $$m - n = m + (-n)$$

To subtract a number, add its opposite, or additive inverse. Any subtraction problem may be written as an addition problem. Then the rules for adding numbers are used.

EXAMPLE 2   **Subtract: $3 - 9$**

$3 - 9$ means "positive 3 *subtract* positive 9."

$3 - 9 = 3 + (-9)$ *Change to addition. The additive inverse of 9*
$ = -6$ *is -9.*

The difference is negative since $|-9| > |3|$.

EXAMPLE 3   **Subtract: $5.6 - (-6.02)$**

$5.6 - (-6.02)$ means "positive 5.6 *subtract* negative 6.02."

$5.6 - (-6.02) = 5.6 + 6.02$ *Change to addition. The additive*
$ $ *inverse of -6.02 is 6.02.*
$ = 11.62$ *The difference is positive.*

EXAMPLE 4   **Subtract: $-(12 - 89) - (-9 - 23)$**

Operations within parentheses are done first.

$-(12 - 89) - (-9 - 23) = -[12 + (-89)] - [-9 + (-23)]$
$ = -[-77] - [-32]$
$ = 77 + 32 = 109$

Explain why brackets are needed in Example 4.

EXAMPLE 5 Subtract: $-\frac{2}{3} - \left(-\frac{4}{5}\right)$

$$-\frac{2}{3} - \left(-\frac{4}{5}\right) = -\frac{2}{3} + \frac{4}{5} \qquad \text{Change to addition.}$$

$$= -\frac{10}{15} + \frac{12}{15} \qquad \text{Use a common denominator.}$$

$$= \frac{2}{15} \qquad \text{The difference is positive since } \left|\frac{12}{15}\right| > \left|-\frac{10}{15}\right|.$$

EXAMPLE 6 Evaluate $m - (n - 7)$ if $m = 4.6$ and $n = -3.9$.

$$m - (n - 7) = 4.6 - (-3.9 - 7) \qquad \text{Substitute 4.6 for } m \text{ and } -3.9 \text{ for } n.$$
$$= 4.6 - [-3.9 + (-7)] \qquad \text{Within the brackets, change the}$$
$$= 4.6 - [-10.9] \qquad \text{operation to addition: } -3.9 - 7$$
$$= 4.6 + 10.9 = 15.5 \qquad \text{means } -3.9 + (-7).$$

CLASS EXERCISES

Write each subtraction expression as an addition expression. Then add.

1. $25 - 8$
$25 + (-8) = 17$

2. $9 - 15$
$9 + (-15) = -6$

3. $-6 - 19$
$-6 + (-19) = -25$

4. $17 - (-8)$
$17 + 8 = 25$

Subtract.

5. $-6 - 8 - 15$ -29 **6.** $-14 - 7 - 5 - 6$ -32 **7.** $-2 - (-8) - (+1)$
5

PRACTICE EXERCISES

Simplify.

A **1.** $-(-4.1)$ 4.1 **2.** $-\left(-\frac{3}{4}\right)$ $\frac{3}{4}$ **3.** $-(0.75)$ -0.75 **4.** $-\left(1\frac{2}{3}\right)$ $-1\frac{2}{3}$

Subtract.

5. $10 - 18$ -8 **6.** $110 - 125$ -15 **7.** $6 - 19$ -13 **8.** $23 - 30$ -7

9. $1.4 - (-2.3)$ 3.7 **10.** $2.5 - (-7.4)$ 9.9 **11.** $1.5 - (-8)$ 9.5 **12.** $4.2 - (-1.5)$
5.7

13. $-(10 - 15) - (-12)$ 17 **14.** $-(7) - (-7 - 15)$ 15 **15.** $-(2 - 7) - (-13)$ 18

16. $-(13 - 90) - 10 - 24$ **17.** $-\frac{1}{9} - \left(-\frac{8}{9}\right)$ $\frac{7}{9}$ **18.** $\frac{2}{3} - \left(-\frac{1}{3}\right)$ 1
43

19. $13 - (71 - 104)$ 46 **20.** $-91 - (87 - 215)$ 37 **21.** $-(25 - 88) - 36$ 27

Evaluate each expression if $a = -6.7$, $b = 11.5$, $c = -4.9$, and $d = 15.2$.

B **22.** $a - (b - 10)$ -8.2 **23.** $b - (d - 4)$ 0.3 **24.** $(c - a) - (d - b)$
-1.9

25. $(a - c) - (b - d)$ 1.9 **26.** $[-b - (-d)] - d$ -11.5 **27.** $-c - [a - (-d)]$
-3.6

1.6 Subtracting Real Numbers   **29**

LESSON FOLLOW-UP

Critical Thinking

1. *Generalization* **On** and **off** are opposites so that the opposite of on is off. Now, **not (not on)** means **on**. *Devise* a rule to explain $-(-5)$.   The opposite of the opposite of 5 is 5.

2. *Creative Thinking* *Create* a non-mathematical example to illustrate the opposite of an opposite. Answers may vary. Sample: Up is the opposite of down; the opposite of the opposite of up is up.

Assignment Guide

• See p. 1B for assignments.
• For Exercises 28–39, caution students to watch the operation signs.

Test Yourself

See *Teacher's Resource Book*, Tests, pp. 5–6.

Lesson Quiz

Subtract.
1. $230 - 176$ 54
2. $86 - 94$ -8
3. $-21 - 54$ -75
4. $-4.7 - (-8.9)$ 4.2
5. $32.07 - (-15.19)$ 47.26
6. $-\frac{1}{7} - \frac{4}{7}$ $-\frac{5}{7}$
7. $-(16 - 9) - (24 - 51)$ 20
8. Evaluate $x - (y - z)$ if $x = -3$, $y = 4.2$, and $z = 2$ -5.2

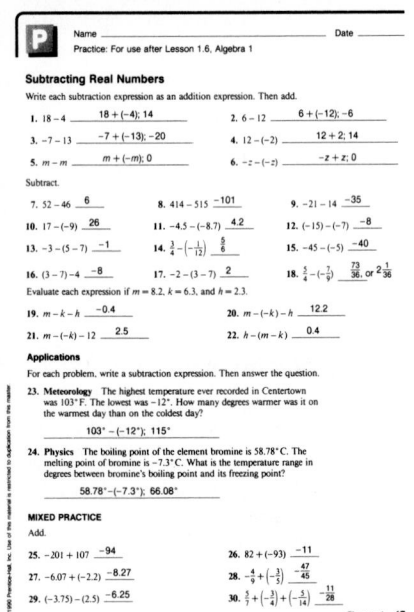

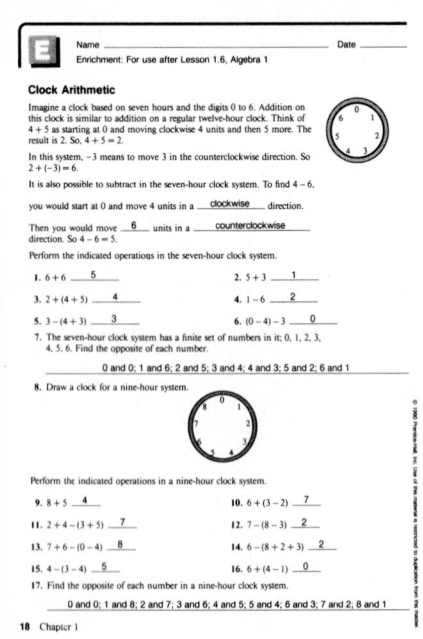

Subtract. When several grouping symbols are used, simplify the expression in the innermost grouping first.

28. $-\frac{1}{2} - \frac{1}{3} - \left(-\frac{1}{3}\right) - \frac{1}{2}$

29. $-\left(\frac{3}{4}\right) - \frac{1}{4} - \frac{5}{8}$ $-\frac{13}{8}$

30. $-0.26 - 5.3 - (-0.87)$ -4.69

31. $-1.9 - 4 - (-0.25)$ -5.65

32. $-5\frac{1}{2} - \left[6 - \left(-1\frac{1}{2}\right)\right]$ -13

33. $\left(7\frac{1}{3} - 5\frac{2}{3}\right) - 16$ $-14\frac{1}{3}$

34. $-\left(9\frac{3}{8} - 1\right) - \left(-\frac{1}{4} - 2\frac{1}{8}\right)$ -6

35. $\left[11\frac{1}{5} - (-14)\right] - \left(3\frac{1}{10} - 8\frac{4}{5}\right)$ $30\frac{9}{10}$

C **36.** $[-7 - \{3 - (-11 - 24)\}]$ -45

37. $-41 - [-(6 - \{(-23) + 5\})]$ -17

38. $|-8 - (-3 + 6)| - |17 + (-2)|$ -4

39. $|28 - (-16)| + |-51 - (-31)|$ 64

Evaluate each expression if $x = -3.2$, $y = 7.8$, and $z = -4.7$.

40. $3 - [(y - x) - (z + 1.4)]$ -11.3

41. $-14.2 - [z - (-y) + (3.8 - x)]$ -24.3

42. $z - |(1.2 - x) - [-(8.5 - y)]|$ -9.8

43. $z - |[x - (-11)] - (13.1 - y)|$ -7.2

Applications

Computer The ABS function on a computer, ABS(X), always gives the nonnegative value of X. For example, ABS(3.4) = 3.4, ABS(−7.05) = 7.05 and ABS(0) = 0. State the value of each expression.

44. ABS(−3) 3

45. ABS(6 − 9) 3

46. ABS(9 − 6) 3

47. −ABS(−5) −5

48. ABS(−6.1 − (−5.7)) 0.4

49. ABS(−6.1) − ABS(−5.7) 0.4

TEST YOURSELF

Evaluate each expression if $a = 0.4$ and $b = 8$.

1. $21.9 + a$ 22.3

2. $2ab$ 6.4

3. $10(b - a)$ 76

1.1

Graph each set of numbers.

4. $\{-3, -2.5, 0, 2.5, 3.5\}$

5. {negative integers}

1.2

Replace each ? with <, >, or = to make a true statement.

6. $-27 \underline{\ ?\ } -28$ >

7. $\frac{5}{8} \underline{\ ?\ } \frac{5}{9}$ >

8. $-0.42 \underline{\ ?\ } -0.425$ >

1.3

Add or subtract, as indicated.

9. $-5.5 + 4.5$ −1

10. $\frac{1}{4} + (-2)$ $-1\frac{3}{4}$

11. $-8 + \left(-2\frac{1}{2}\right) + 15$ $4\frac{1}{2}$

1.4, 1.5

12. $-27 - (-30)$ 3

13. $-0.82 - 3.6$ −4.42

14. $[59 - (-23)] - (-24)$ 106

1.6

30 Chapter 1 Real Numbers

Additional Answers
Test Yourself

4.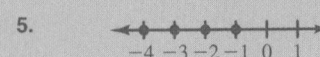

5.

Multiplying Real Numbers

Objectives: To multiply real numbers
To evaluate algebraic expressions involving multiplication of real numbers

LESSON PLAN

Materials/Manipulatives
Calculators
Overhead projector
Teacher's Resource Book,
Transparency 4

A stadium holds 80,000 people. If tickets to a concert in the stadium cost $12.50 each, what is the ticket sales maximum?

$$80,000 \cdot 12.50 = 1,000,000$$

The ticket sales maximum is $1,000,000.

Both 80,000 and 12.50 are positive numbers. The product of any two positive numbers is always a positive number. What happens when you multiply a positive and a negative number or two negative numbers?

BACKGROUND

In the Capsule Review, students multiply whole numbers, fractions, mixed fractions, and decimals. This review is a warm-up that prepares students for multiplying real numbers.

Capsule Review

EXAMPLES   **a.** 12.50 · 80,000 = 1,000,000   **b.** $\dfrac{3}{5} \cdot \dfrac{6}{7} = \dfrac{18}{35}$

   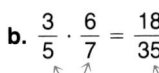

positive   positive   positive positive

Find each product.

1. 56 · 21 1176   **2.** 187 · 100 18,700   **3.** (4.1)(1.5) 6.15   **4.** (0.49)2 0.98

5. 1000(0.04) 40   **6.** $\dfrac{1}{2} \cdot \dfrac{2}{3}$ $\dfrac{1}{3}$ **7.** $7 \cdot 1\dfrac{1}{7}$ 8   **8.** $\dfrac{2}{3} \cdot 2\dfrac{2}{3}$ $\dfrac{16}{9}$

9. $\dfrac{5}{8} \cdot 5\dfrac{2}{6}$ $\dfrac{10}{3}$ **10.** $2\dfrac{1}{2} \cdot \dfrac{6}{9}$ $\dfrac{5}{3}$ **11.** $2\dfrac{4}{7} \cdot 4\dfrac{2}{3}$ 12   **12.** $6\dfrac{3}{4} \cdot 2\dfrac{2}{3}$ 18

Study the addition sentences below. What procedure do they suggest for multiplying a positive number and a negative number?

$$\underbrace{-3 + (-3) + (-3) = -9}_{3(-3)} \qquad \underbrace{-2 + (-2) + (-2) + (-2) = -8}_{4(-2)}$$

> **Multiplication Rule (Two numbers with different signs)**
>
> To multiply a positive and negative number, multiply their absolute values. The product is negative.

- A simple, intuitive lead-in for the positive sign of the product of two negative factors requires the use of the distributive property. You may wish to mention it now or bring it up when the distributive property is studied in Chapter 2. Consider the calculation:

$-5[7 + (-3)]$
$-5[7 + (-3)] = -5[4] = -20$
or
$-5[7 + (-3)] = -5(7) + (-5)(-3)$
$= -35 + (-5)(-3)$

So,
$-20 = -35 + (-5)(-3)$

Therefore, $(-5)(-3)$ must equal $+15$.
- Stress the importance of using parentheses in multiplication problems. Have students use calculators to check their results for Exercises 21–30.

CHALKBOARD EXAMPLES

- **For Example 1**
Multiply:
  1. $-19(28)$ -532
  2. $7.9(-8.2)$ -64.78
  3. $-2\frac{1}{2} \cdot 1\frac{1}{5}$ -3

- **For Example 2**
Multiply:
  4. $-17(-11)$ 187
  5. $-4.3(-0.8)$ 3.44
  6. $-3\frac{2}{3}\left(-\frac{1}{4}\right)$ $\frac{11}{12}$

- **For Example 3**
Multiply:
  7. $3(-2)(-8)(9)$ 432
  8. $-16(0.8)(-0.42)(10)(-5)$
     -268.8

- **For Example 4**
Evaluate each expression if $w = -1$, $x = 9$, $y = -2$, and $z = 4$.
  9. wxy 18
  10. $xy(-z)$ 72
  11. $w(-x)z$ 36

EXAMPLE 1   **Multiply:** $-\frac{1}{5} \cdot \frac{5}{9}$

$-\frac{1}{5} \cdot \frac{5}{9}$ *Multiply the absolute values:* $\left|-\frac{1}{5}\right| \cdot \left|\frac{5}{9}\right| = \frac{1}{\overset{1}{\cancel{5}}} \cdot \frac{\overset{1}{\cancel{5}}}{9} = \frac{1}{9}$

$= -\frac{1}{9}$ *The product is negative since the numbers have different signs.*

A rule for multiplying two positive numbers or two negative numbers is stated below.

> **Multiplication Rule (Two numbers with the same sign)**
>
> To multiply two positive or two negative numbers, multiply their absolute values. The product is positive.

EXAMPLE 2   **Multiply:** $-13(-12)$

$-13(-12)$ *The numbers have the same sign. Multiply the absolute values:* $|-13| \cdot |-12| = 13 \cdot 12 = 156.$

$= 156$ *The product is positive.*

Multiplying a number by 1 does not change its value. The product of any number and 0 is 0.

> **Identity Property for Multiplication**
>
> For every real number n, $n \cdot 1 = n$ and $1 \cdot n = n$.
>
> **Property of Zero for Multiplication**
>
> For every real number n, $n \cdot 0 = 0$ and $0 \cdot n = 0$.

When multiplying more than two numbers, the multiplication can be done in any order.

- If there is an even number of negative numbers, the product is positive.
- If there is an odd number of negative numbers, the product is negative.

EXAMPLE 3   **Multiply:** $-7(-1)(4)(-3)(2)(-5)$

There are four negative numbers. The product is positive.
$-7(-1)(4)(-3)(2)(-5) = 840$

EXAMPLE 4 Evaluate $a \cdot b \cdot c$ if $a = -5$, $b = -2$, and $c = -3$.

$a \cdot b \cdot c = -5(-2)(-3)$ *Substitute* -5 *for a,* -2 *for b, and* -3 *for c.*
$= -30$ *There are 3 negative numbers. The product is negative.*

The product of any two given real numbers is always another real number. Also, the product is *unique*. There is *one and only one* real-number answer.

Closure Property for Multiplication

For all real numbers m and n, $m \cdot n$ is a unique real number.

CLASS EXERCISES

Multiply.

1. $-2 \cdot 1$ -2 **2.** $4(-4)$ -16 **3.** $0.5(-0.6)$ -0.3 **4.** $-19{,}642 \cdot 0$ 0

5. $-\frac{1}{2}\left(-\frac{5}{9}\right)$ $\frac{5}{18}$ **6.** $-\frac{4}{5} \cdot \frac{5}{8}$ $-\frac{1}{2}$ **7.** $-\frac{2}{3} \cdot \frac{1}{9}$ $-\frac{2}{27}$ **8.** $(-36)\left(-\frac{2}{9}\right)$ 8

PRACTICE EXERCISES

Multiply.

A   **1.** $-15 \cdot 2$ -30 **2.** $-12 \cdot 10$ -120 **3.** $-2.34 \cdot 0.2$ -0.468 **4.** $-0.005 \cdot 0.00$ 0

5. $(-5)(-13)$ 65 **6.** $-9(-11)$ 99 **7.** $-0.6(-3.7)$ 2.22 **8.** $-0.02(-0.08)$ 0.0016

9. $-6(10)\left(-\frac{1}{2}\right)$ 30 **10.** $-\frac{3}{5}(-20)(-4)$ -48 **11.** $(-50)\left(-\frac{3}{2}\right)\left(-\frac{3}{5}\right)$ -45 **12.** $-24\left(\frac{0}{6}\right)\left(-\frac{1}{20}\right)$ 0

Evaluate each expression if $a = -4$, $b = 3$, $c = -10$, $d = 5$, **and** $e = -6$.

13. $a \cdot b \cdot c$ 120 **14.** $c \cdot d \cdot b$ -150 **15.** $c \cdot (-a)(-d)$ 200 **16.** $-b(-a)(-d)$ 60

17. $-a(d)(-c)e$ -1200 **18.** $b(-a)(-c)(-d)$ -600 **19.** $c(-b)ed$ -900 **20.** $-e(-b)(-d)$ 90

Multiply.

B   **21.** $-14\left[\frac{3}{7}\left(-\frac{1}{9}\right)(-27)\right]$ -18 **22.** $\left[\frac{4}{5}(-15)\right]\left[\frac{3}{16}(-20)\right]$ 45

23. $-8(-2)(0.5)(3)(-0.25)$ -6 **24.** $32(-0.25)(-0.25)(20)(-10)$ -400

25. $-37{,}037(-1.5)$ $55{,}555.5$ **26.** $-33.67(-0.0132)$ 0.444444

27. $-1.125(0.4)(24{,}691.358)$ $-11{,}111.1111$ **28.** $-5291(-2.1)(0.7)$ 7777.77

29. $-7(0.66)(-48.2)(-7)$ -1558.788 **30.** $0.0156(-3.4)(-5.5)(99)$ 28.88028

1.7 Multiplying Real Numbers   **33**

LESSON FOLLOW-UP

Critical Thinking

Categorical Arguments Judge whether or not $0 \cdot 0$ equals 0. Justify your response. $0 \cdot 0 = 0$ since $n \cdot 0 = 0 \cdot n = 0$ for every real number n, and 0 is a real number.

Assignment Guide

• See p. 1B for assignments.
• Exercises 23–30 are good candidates for calculator solution.

Algebra in Meteorology

Many meteorologists use the expression "With the wind chill factor, the temperature feels . . ." The chart and exercises provide the opportunity to understand what this really means. The use of wind chill factors require students to subtract real numbers.

Lesson Quiz

Multiply:

1. $(-9)(-13)$ 117
2. $-3.56 \cdot 0.4$ -1.424
3. $1\frac{5}{9} \cdot -\frac{11}{14}$ $-\frac{11}{9}$
4. $\frac{1}{2}(-24)(-15)$ 180
5. $-7(-3)(0.8)(-0.15)$ -2.52
6. $14(-0.23)(-0.31)(30)(-20)$ -598.92
7. $-8(0.71)(-54.3)(6)$ 1850.544

Evaluate each expression if $m = -3$, $n = 7$, $p = -\frac{1}{2}$, and $q = 6$.

8. mp 1.5
9. $n(-m)(-p)$ $\frac{21}{2}$
10. $n(-m)p(-q)$ 63

Enrichment

Modify the multiplication rule on p. 32 so that it applies to the product of three numbers, all of them negative. To multiply three numbers, all of them negative:
a. Multiply their absolute values.
b. The product is negative.

33

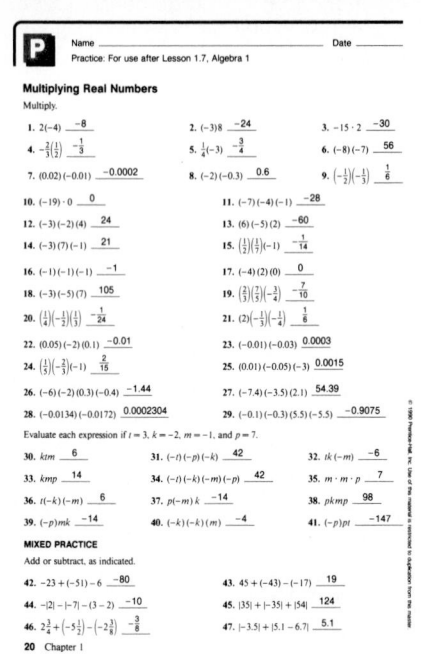

Teacher's Resource Book
Reteaching—Chapter 1, p. 19

P Name _____ Date _____
Practice: For use after Lesson 1.7, Algebra 1

Multiplying Real Numbers

Multiply.

1. $2(-4)$ -8
2. $(-3)8$ -24
3. $-15 \cdot 2$ -30
4. $-\frac{2}{3}\left(\frac{1}{2}\right)$ $-\frac{1}{3}$
5. $\frac{1}{4}(-3)$ $-\frac{3}{4}$
6. $(-8)(-7)$ 56
7. $(0.02)(-0.01)$ -0.0002
8. $(-2)(-0.3)$ 0.6
9. $\left(-\frac{1}{2}\right)\left(-\frac{1}{3}\right)$ $\frac{1}{6}$
10. $(-19) \cdot 0$ 0
11. $(-7)(-4)(-1)$ -28
12. $(-3)(-2)(4)$ 24
13. $(6)(-5)(2)$ -60
14. $(-3)(7)(-1)$ 21
15. $\left(\frac{1}{2}\right)\left(\frac{1}{7}\right)(-1)$ $-\frac{1}{14}$
16. $(-1)(-1)(-1)$ -1
17. $(-4)(2)(0)$ 0
18. $(-3)(-5)(7)$ 105
19. $\left(\frac{2}{5}\right)\left(\frac{7}{5}\right)\left(-\frac{1}{4}\right)$ $-\frac{7}{10}$
20. $\left(\frac{1}{4}\right)\left(-\frac{1}{2}\right)\left(\frac{1}{3}\right)$ $-\frac{1}{24}$
21. $(2)\left(-\frac{1}{3}\right)\left(-\frac{1}{4}\right)$ $\frac{1}{6}$
22. $(0.05)(-2)(0.1)$ -0.01
23. $(-0.01)(-0.03)$ 0.0003
24. $\left(\frac{1}{3}\right)\left(-\frac{2}{5}\right)(-1)$ $\frac{2}{15}$
25. $(0.01)(-0.05)(-3)$ 0.0015
26. $(-6)(-2)(0.3)(-0.4)$ -1.44
27. $(-7.4)(-3.5)(2.1)$ 54.39
28. $(-0.0134)(-0.0172)$ 0.0002304
29. $(-0.1)(-0.3)(5.5)(-5.5)$ -0.9075

Evaluate each expression if $t = 3$, $k = -2$, $m = -1$, and $p = 7$.

30. ktm 6
31. $(-t)(-p)(-k)$ 42
32. $tk(-m)$ -6
33. kmp 14
34. $(-t)(-k)(-m)(-p)$ 42
35. $m \cdot m \cdot p$ 7
36. $t(-k)(-m)$ 6
37. $p(-m)k$ -14
38. $pkmp$ 98
39. $(-p)mk$ -14
40. $(-k)(-k)(m)$ -4
41. $(-p)pt$ -147

MIXED PRACTICE

Add or subtract, as indicated.

42. $-23 + (-51) - 6$ -80
43. $45 + (-43) - (-17)$ 19
44. $-|2| - |-7| - (3 - 2)$ -10
45. $|35| + |-35| + |54|$ 124
46. $2\frac{3}{4} + \left(-5\frac{1}{2}\right) - \left(-2\frac{3}{8}\right)$ $-\frac{3}{8}$
47. $|-3.5| + |5.1 - 6.7|$ 5.1

20 Chapter 1

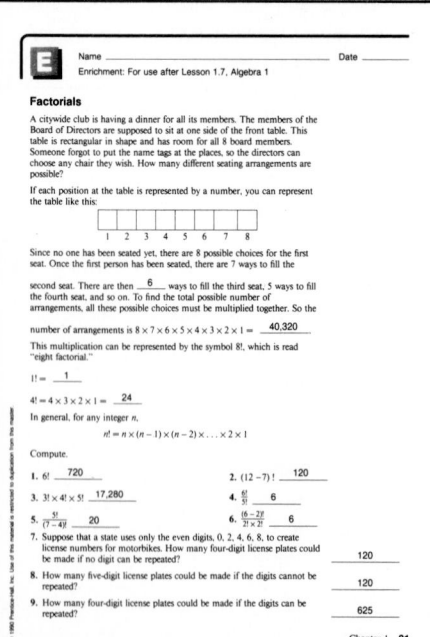

E Name _____ Date _____
Enrichment: For use after Lesson 1.7, Algebra 1

Factorials

A citywide club is having a dinner for all its members. The members of the Board of Directors are supposed to sit at one side of the front table. This table is rectangular in shape and has room for all 8 board members. Someone forgot to put the name tags at the places, so the directors can choose any chair they wish. How many different seating arrangements are possible?

If each position at the table is represented by a number, you can represent the table like this:

| 1 | 2 | 3 | 4 | 5 | 6 | 7 | 8 |

Since no one has been seated yet, there are 8 possible choices for the first seat. Once the first person has been seated, there are 7 ways to fill the second seat. There are then __6__ ways to fill the third seat, 5 ways to fill the fourth seat, and so on. To find the total possible number of arrangements, all these possible choices must be multiplied together. So the number of arrangements is $8 \times 7 \times 6 \times 5 \times 4 \times 3 \times 2 \times 1$ = __40,320__.

This multiplication can be represented by the symbol 8!, which is read "eight factorial."

$1! =$ __1__

$4! = 4 \times 3 \times 2 \times 1 =$ __24__

In general, for any integer n,

$$n! = n \times (n-1) \times (n-2) \times \ldots \times 2 \times 1$$

Compute.

1. $6!$ __720__
2. $(12 - 7)!$ __120__
3. $3! \times 4! \times 5!$ __17,280__
4. $\frac{6!}{5!}$ __6__
5. $\frac{5!}{(7-4)!}$ __20__
6. $\frac{(6-2)!}{2! \times 2!}$ __6__
7. Suppose that a state uses only the even digits, 0, 2, 4, 6, 8, to create license numbers for motorbikes. How many four-digit license plates could be made if no digit can be repeated? __120__
8. How many five-digit license plates can be made if the digits cannot be repeated? __120__
9. How many four-digit license plates could be made if the digits can be repeated? __625__

Chapter 1 21

Evaluate each expression if $r = -6$, $s = -2$, $t = -3$, $v = 10$, and $w = -\frac{1}{2}$.

31. $(rs) - t$ 15
32. $v + (sw)$ 11
33. $(rs) - (vw)$ 17
34. $(tr) - (vs)$ 38
35. $-t(r - s)$ -12
36. $(s - t)vw$ -5
C
37. $-|rw| \cdot st$ -18
38. $r \cdot |w - v|$ -63
39. $|rw| - |st|$ -3
40. $wv|-t - s|$ -25
41. $|w(v + s)|$ 4
42. $vs|(r - v)(-w)|$ -160

Applications

43. **Weather** During a 1 hour and 30 minute period, a drop in temperature of 7° was recorded. Write a numerical expression to show a continuous drop in temperature at the same rate for 3 hours. $(-7) \times 2 = -14°$

44. **Finance** A computer company lost $4.5 million each of the last three years. Use positive and negative numbers to express the total amount lost. $(3)(-4.5) = 13.5$

ALGEBRA IN METEOROLOGY

When you lose body heat, you feel cold. A low temperature can cause a loss of body heat. So can the wind. A combination of low temperature and wind makes it feel colder than the actual temperature. The table shows how cold you feel when a low temperature is combined with a wind.

Wind (mi/h)	Temperature in Degrees Fahrenheit											
	35	30	25	20	15	10	5	0	-5	-10	-15	-20
5	33	27	21	16	12	7	0	-5	-10	-15	-21	-26
10	22	16	10	3	-3	-9	-15	-22	-27	-34	-40	-46
15	16	9	2	-5	-11	-18	-25	-31	-38	-45	-51	-58
20	12	4	-3	-10	-17	-24	-31	-39	-46	-53	-60	-67
25	8	1	-7	-15	-22	-29	-36	-44	-51	-59	-66	-74

Example: The temperature is 25°F. The wind is blowing at 20 mi/h. How cold does it feel to your body?

Solution: Look across the top of the table to find the column for 25°F. Look down the left to find the row for 20 mi/h. At the intersection of the column and the row is the answer, -3°F.

Suppose the temperature drops from 20°F to -10°F while the wind speed remains at 25 mi/h. How many degrees does the actual temperature drop? 30°F How many degrees does your body feel that it has dropped? 44°F

Dividing Real Numbers

Objectives: To divide real numbers
To evaluate algebraic expressions involving multiplication and division of real numbers

Multiplication and division are opposite (or inverse) operations. You will see that the rules for determining the signs for the quotients of real numbers are the same as those for their products.

Capsule Review

The product of two positive numbers is positive. $(2.5) \cdot 3 = 7.5$
The product of two negative numbers is positive. $-3(-16) = 48$
The product of a positive number and a negative number is negative.

$$\left(-\frac{2}{3}\right)\left(\frac{1}{3}\right) = -\frac{2}{9}$$

The product of any number and 0 is 0. $-21 \cdot 0 = 0$

State whether the product is positive, negative, or zero.

1. $-5(-1)$ pos.   **2.** $40(0.256)$ pos.   **3.** $-9 \cdot \frac{1}{9}$ neg.   **4.** $0(3.6)$ zero

5. $\left(\frac{2}{5}\right)\left(-\frac{1}{5}\right)$ neg.   **6.** $-25(-25)$ pos.   **7.** $\left(-\frac{5}{6}\right)\left(-\frac{6}{5}\right)$ pos.   **8.** $-1\frac{1}{3} \cdot 0$ zero

The rules for dividing real numbers involve the mathematical concept of **reciprocals.** Two numbers whose product is 1 are called **reciprocals** or **multiplicative inverses** of each other.

Multiplicative Inverse Property (Reciprocal Property)

For every nonzero real number n, there is exactly one real number $\frac{1}{n}$, such that

$$n \cdot \frac{1}{n} = 1 \quad \text{and} \quad \frac{1}{n} \cdot n = 1$$

n and $\frac{1}{n}$ are reciprocals, or multiplicative inverses, of each other.

Zero does not have a reciprocal since the product of any number and 0 is 0, not 1.

1.8 Dividing Real Numbers   **35**

LESSON PLAN

Vocabulary
Multiplicative inverse
Reciprocal

Materials/Manipulatives
Calculators

BACKGROUND

In the Capsule Review, multiplication is reviewed because of its relationship to the division of real numbers. The exercises focus on the sign of the product rather than the product itself.

- This is probably your students' introduction to addition and multiplication as the two primary operations, with subtraction and division defined as inverse operations.
- Students may have difficulty initially discussing real world applications of dividing real numbers. Point out various applications, such as finding averages of temperatures above and below zero and finding average changes in the stock market. These and other examples are addressed in the Applications.
- Have students use a calculator for several division problems.

Critical Thinking

Categorical Arguments When, if ever, does $n \cdot \dfrac{1}{n}$ not equal 1? *Justify your response.* When $n = 0$, $n \cdot \dfrac{1}{n} \neq 1$ since $\dfrac{1}{n}$ is undefined.

CHALKBOARD EXAMPLES

- **For Example 1**
  Find the reciprocal.
  1. $\dfrac{2}{3}$ $\dfrac{3}{2}$ 2. 7 $\dfrac{1}{7}$
  3. -0.5 -2 4. 1 1

- **For Example 2**
  Divide:
  5. $-\dfrac{117}{9}$ -13
  6. $-\dfrac{120}{-6}$ 20

- **For Example 3**
  Divide:
  7. $2\dfrac{4}{5} \div -\dfrac{2}{7}$ $-\dfrac{49}{5}$
  8. $\dfrac{9.5}{-0.5}$ -19

EXAMPLE 1 **Find the reciprocal of 9, $-\dfrac{1}{3}$, and -0.3.**

Number	Reciprocal	
9, or $\dfrac{9}{1}$	$\dfrac{1}{9}$	$9 \cdot \dfrac{1}{9} = 1$
$-\dfrac{1}{3}$	$-\dfrac{3}{1}$, or -3	$-\dfrac{1}{3}(-3) = 1$
-0.3, or $-\dfrac{3}{10}$	$-\dfrac{10}{3}$	$-\dfrac{3}{10}\left(-\dfrac{10}{3}\right) = 1$

The following definition may be used to divide numbers.

Definition of Division

For all real numbers m and n, $n \neq 0$, $m \div n = m \cdot \dfrac{1}{n}$.

Since division by a number is defined as multiplying by the reciprocal or multiplicative inverse of the number, division can be rewritten as multiplication. Then the rules for multiplying real numbers can be used to decide if the quotient is positive or negative.

EXAMPLE 2 **Divide:** $\dfrac{-81}{3}$

$$-81 \div 3 = -81 \cdot \dfrac{1}{3}$$ *Use the reciprocal of 3 and rewrite as multiplication.*

$$= -\left(|81| \cdot \left|\dfrac{1}{3}\right|\right)$$ *Multiply the absolute values. The quotient is negative.*

$$= -27$$

EXAMPLE 3 **Divide:** $-1\dfrac{1}{2} \div \left(-\dfrac{9}{7}\right)$

$$-1\dfrac{1}{2} \div \left(-\dfrac{9}{7}\right) = \left(-1\dfrac{1}{2}\right)\left(-\dfrac{7}{9}\right)$$ *Rewrite as multiplication.*

$$= \left(\left|-1\dfrac{1}{2}\right| \cdot \left|-\dfrac{7}{9}\right|\right)$$ *Multiply the absolute values. The quotient is positive.*

$$= \left(\dfrac{3}{2} \cdot \dfrac{7}{9}\right)$$

$$= \dfrac{7}{6}$$

The algebraic expression $r[2 \div (-s)]$ involves the operations of multiplication *and* division. After substituting given values for the variables, the operation within the brackets (division) is done first.

EXAMPLE 4 Evaluate $r[2 \div (-s)]$ if $r = 4$ and $s = -3$.

$r[2 \div (-s)]$
$= 4[2 \div 3]$ *Substitute 4 for r and -3 for s.* $-s = -(-3) = 3$.

$= 4\left[2 \cdot \dfrac{1}{3}\right]$

$= 4\left[\dfrac{2}{3}\right]$

$= \dfrac{8}{3}$

Since 0 has no reciprocal, you cannot divide a number by 0. $\dfrac{1}{0}$ is undefined. However, it *is* possible to divide 0 by any real number other than 0. The quotient is always 0.

$$\dfrac{0}{5} = 0 \cdot \dfrac{1}{5} = 0 \qquad 0 \div \left(-\dfrac{1}{6}\right) = 0 \cdot (-6) = 0$$

EXAMPLE 5 Divide, if possible: **a.** $\dfrac{0}{3}$ **b.** $\dfrac{7}{0}$

a. $\dfrac{0}{3} = 0 \cdot \dfrac{1}{3}$ *To divide by 3, multiply by the reciprocal of 3, or $\dfrac{1}{3}$.*

$= 0$

b. $\dfrac{7}{0} = 7 \cdot (?)$ *Zero has no reciprocal.*

It is *not possible* to divide by 0.

CLASS EXERCISES

State whether each quotient will be positive or negative.

1. $-7 \div 1$ neg.   **2.** $1.5 \div 0.5$ pos.   **3.** $\dfrac{119}{7}$ pos.   **4.** $-\dfrac{1}{2} \div \left(-\dfrac{1}{3}\right)$
pos.

Rewrite each division expression as multiplication.

5. $\dfrac{3}{4} \div \dfrac{7}{8}$ $\dfrac{3}{4} \cdot \dfrac{8}{7}$ **6.** $-24 \div \dfrac{4}{5}$ $-24 \cdot \dfrac{5}{4}$ **7.** $\dfrac{132}{-11}$ $132 \cdot \left(-\dfrac{1}{11}\right)$ **8.** $-15 \div \left(-\dfrac{1}{4}\right)$
$-15 \cdot (-4)$

9. $\dfrac{0}{-10}$ $0 \cdot \left(-\dfrac{1}{10}\right)$ **10.** $-\dfrac{2}{3} \div \dfrac{2}{3}$ $-\dfrac{2}{3} \cdot \dfrac{3}{2}$ **11.** $\dfrac{0.8}{5}$ $0.8 \cdot \dfrac{1}{5}$ **12.** $1\dfrac{1}{3} \div \left(-\dfrac{1}{2}\right)$
$1\dfrac{1}{3} \cdot (-2)$

1.8 Dividing Real Numbers   **37**

• **For Example 4**

   9. Evaluate $-3j \div k$ if $j = -5$ and $k = 6$. $\dfrac{5}{2}$

• **For Example 5**
Divide, if possible.

10. $-\dfrac{2}{0}$ not possible

11. $-\dfrac{0}{5}$ 0

Common Errors

• Students may make an error in writing the reciprocal of an integer when it is the divisor in a division problem. In the example:

$$-\dfrac{2}{3} \div (-5) = \left(-\dfrac{2}{3}\right)\left(-\dfrac{1}{5}\right) = \dfrac{2}{15}$$

they may write $-\dfrac{5}{1}$ as the reciprocal of -5 and find an answer of $\dfrac{10}{3}$.

• Sometimes students write the reciprocal of the first number of a division problem, particularly if the first number is a fraction. In the example:

$$\dfrac{3}{4} \div (-9) = \dfrac{3}{4} \cdot \left(-\dfrac{1}{9}\right) = -\dfrac{1}{12}$$

They may multiply -9 by $\dfrac{4}{3}$ and find an answer of -12.

• See *Teacher's Resource Book* for additional remediation.

LESSON FOLLOW-UP

Assignment Guide

• See p. 1B for assignments.
• In Exercises 31–46, students should be encouraged to use calculators to check their answers.
• See *Teacher's Resource Book*, Technology pp. 1–2.

PRACTICE EXERCISES

Find the reciprocal.

A

1. $5\frac{1}{5}$

2. $8\frac{1}{8}$

3. $75\frac{1}{75}$

4. $10\frac{1}{10}$

5. $-\frac{1}{5}$ -5

6. $-\frac{1}{7}$ -7

7. -0.9 $\frac{-10}{9}$

8. -0.6 $\frac{-5}{3}$

Divide, if possible.

9. $\dfrac{84}{-12}$ -7

10. $\dfrac{76}{-19}$ -4

11. $\dfrac{-36}{3}$ -12

12. $\dfrac{-42}{14}$ -3

13. $-1\frac{2}{3} \div \left(\frac{-2}{9}\right)$ $\frac{15}{2}$

14. $-\frac{1}{2} \div \left(\frac{-2}{3}\right)$ $\frac{3}{4}$

15. $-\frac{7}{12} \div \frac{7}{6}$ $-\frac{1}{2}$

16. $-\frac{1}{3} \div \frac{5}{6}$ $-\frac{2}{5}$

17. $\dfrac{0}{5}$ 0

18. $\dfrac{17}{0}$ not possible

19. $9 \div 0$ not possible

20. $0 \div 15$ 0

Evaluate each expression if $a = -8$, $b = -4$, $c = -3$, and $d = \frac{1}{2}$.

21. $\dfrac{a}{b}$ 2

22. $\dfrac{b}{d}$ -8

23. $d \div c$ $-\frac{1}{6}$

24. $d \div a$ $-\frac{1}{16}$

B

25. $\left(\frac{1}{2}d\right) \div b$ $-\frac{1}{16}$

26. $\left(-\frac{3}{2}a\right) \div c$ -4

27. $\dfrac{c - d}{d}$ -7

28. $\dfrac{d}{b - a}$ $\frac{1}{8}$

29. $(-4c) \div (8d)$ 3

30. $\left(-\frac{9}{2}b\right) \div (3c)$ -2

Simplify. *Hint:* The numerator and the denominator of a fraction are each considered to be enclosed within parentheses.

31. $\dfrac{-3 + 5}{-2}$ -1

32. $\dfrac{18}{-11 + 2}$ -2

33. $(-13 - 3) \div (-2 - 6)$ 2

34. $(100 - 16) \div (-14 + 2)$ -7

35. $\dfrac{7(-3)}{-2 - 5}$ 3

36. $\dfrac{-9(4)}{-1 - 2}$ 12

37. $-36.3636 \div 12.5$ -2.909088

38. $789.62 \div 0.52$ 1518.5

39. $\dfrac{(-1.62)(97.87)}{0.27}$ -587.22

40. $\dfrac{-90.81}{(6.25)(-0.025)}$ 581.184

41. $\dfrac{718.3 - 84.7}{3.275 + (-2.923)}$ 1800

42. $\dfrac{7.061 - 33.925}{0.905 + (-0.321)}$ -46

C

43. $\left(3 - 4\frac{1}{3}\right) \div \left(-\frac{2}{3} + \frac{5}{6}\right)$ -8

44. $\left[3 - \left(-\frac{5}{4}\right)\right] \div \left(-5 + \frac{3}{4}\right)$ -1

45. $\dfrac{|(-6)(5)|}{-4}$ $-7\frac{1}{2}$

46. $\dfrac{25 + (-4)}{|11 - 1 - 3|}$ 3

38   Chapter 1 Real Numbers

If *a*, *b*, *c*, and *d* are any nonzero real numbers, with $c \neq d$, tell whether the statements are *true* or *false*.

47. $(a \div b) \div c = (a \div c) \div b$ true

48. $\dfrac{a}{bc} = (a \div b) \div c$ true

49. $\left|\dfrac{ab}{cd}\right| = \left|\dfrac{ab}{cd}\right|$ true

50. $\dfrac{a-b}{c-d} = \dfrac{b-a}{d-c}$ true

Applications

To find the **mean** or **average** of a group of measurements, divide their sum by the number of measurements.

Example $-5.5°$, $-8.2°$, $1.7°$, $3.9°$, $9.7°$, $10.1°$, and $3.0°$ are the 8:00 AM temperature readings in degrees Fahrenheit for a winter week in Minneapolis.
The average temperature at 8:00 AM is:

$$\frac{-5.5 + (-8.2) + 1.7 + 3.9 + 9.7 + 10.1 + 3.0}{7} = \frac{14.7}{7} = 2.1$$

2.1°F is the average 8:00 AM temperature for this week.

51. Sports   A golfer shot 18-hole rounds with scores of 83, 79, 73, and 84. Find the average golf score for these rounds to the nearest whole number. 80

52. Statistics   A student's algebra quiz scores are: 76, 58, 87, 80, and 82. Find the student's average quiz score to the nearest whole number. 77

53. Sports   The heights of the members of the varsity basketball team are: 178 cm, 185 cm, 193 cm, 193 cm, and 201 cm. Find the average height of the players. 190 cm

54. Meteorology   One week the barometric readings were 28.90, 29.10, 30.20, 29.60, 30.10, 29.90, and 30.10. Find the average barometric reading for the week. 29.70

55. Sports   Four friends ride to school on their bikes. The one-way distance for each is: 1.6 km, 0.8 km, 1.2 km, and 2.4 km. What is the average of these distances? Does any one of the riders travel the exact average number of kilometers? 1.5 km; no

56. Finance   The stock market values of NJO stock over a particular week were $62\frac{1}{4}$, $61\frac{1}{2}$, $60\frac{3}{4}$, 61, and $62\frac{1}{2}$. Find NJO's average value for this week. $61\frac{3}{5}$

57. Meteorology   One week the high temperature readings were 82.4°F, 94.1°F, 84.5°F, 89.5°F, 92.6°F, 90.8°F, and 87.9°F. Find the average high temperature reading for the week. 88.8°F

Calculator   Most calculators have a reciprocal key, usually labeled 1/*x* or x^{-1}. This key is used to find the reciprocal of any number, expressed in decimal equivalent form. Find the reciprocal of each number using the reciprocal key on your calculator. Check your answer by division.

57. 17 0.05882   **58.** 100 0.01   **59.** −19 −0.05263   **60.** −0.4 −2.5

CRITICAL THINKING: ANALYSIS

You have seen expressions such as: $\frac{c}{b}$ ($b \neq 0$). This expression means that b can represent any number *except* 0. The following discussion shows logically why you cannot replace b with 0 in the expression $\frac{c}{b}$.

ASSUME   One way to define the division of c by b is to say that for any two numbers c and b, there is one number a such that

$$\frac{c}{b} = a \qquad \text{provided that } a \times b = c.$$

For example, $\frac{6}{3} = 2$, since $2 \times 3 = 6$.

INFER   If division by 0 is possible, then you can divide 6 by 0 and get one number that is the quotient. This means that there is one number a that makes the following number sentence true.

$$\frac{6}{0} = a \qquad \text{provided that } a \times 0 = 6.$$

ANALYZE   Try replacing a in $a \times 0 = 6$ with different numbers. Is there any number that makes the sentence true? Then, is there any number a that will make $\frac{6}{0} = a$ true?

Now try to divide 0 by 0. No value of a makes $\frac{6}{0} = a$ true.

Is there one number a such that $\frac{0}{0} = a$?

Try replacing a in $a \times 0 = 0$ with different numbers. Is there *only one* number that makes the sentence true?
No, any value of a makes $a \times 0 = 0$ true.

CONCLUDE   Explain in your own words why 0 can never be a divisor (a denominator in a rational number). Explain also why $\frac{0}{0}$ is indeterminate (cannot be determined).

APPLICATION:
Meteorology

Did you know that on April 12, 1934, the velocity of the wind reached 231 mi/h at Mount Washington, N.H.? This was the strongest wind ever recorded on the surface of the earth!

Meteorologists measure weather conditions and record and analyze the data. They are stationed around the world and use instruments as basic as the thermometer and as sophisticated as the computer. Meteorologists use the data they gather to prepare forecasts.

State	Station	Date	Temperature Readings (°F)				
			6 AM	10 AM	2 PM	6 PM	10 PM
N. Dak.	Bismarck	1/15	−1.8	0.5	1.5	−2	−2.7

You can use paper and pencil, a calculator, or a computer, to find the average temperature.

$$\frac{\text{Sum of the readings}}{\text{Number of readings}} = \text{Average}$$

$$\frac{(-1.8) + 0.5 + 1.5 + (-2) + (-2.7)}{5} = -0.9$$

```
10 INPUT "HOW MANY NUMBERS ARE YOU
     AVERAGING? ";N:PRINT
20 INPUT "ENTER THE FIRST NUMBER. ;S:
     PRINT
30 FOR I = 2 TO N
40 INPUT "NEXT NUMBER: ";X:PRINT
50 LET S = S + X
60 NEXT I
70 LET A = S / N
80 PRINT "THE AVERAGE IS";A
90 END
```

The average temperature for that day was −0.9°F. Is it possible to use that temperature to predict the temperature for the next day? Explain. Temperatures at a particular time of year are about the same. One day's average temperature will be close to another's.

Solve.

1. The normal daily temperature for Bismarck in January is 8.2°F. How many degrees below normal is −0.9°F? 9.1°F

2. The lowest daily temperature for Bismarck in January was −2.8°F. How many degrees above the lowest temperature is −0.9°F? 1.9°F

3. What is the average of the following readings: 6.2°, −1.8°, 3.6°, 0°, −0.5°? 1.5°F

4. What is the average of the following readings: −2.3°, 0.6°, 5.2°, −4.7°, 3.2°? 0.4°F

Vocabulary
Algebraic notation

Materials/Manipulatives
Overhead projector
Teacher's Resource Book,
  Transparency 1

BACKGROUND

- Solving algebra problems requires
  the correct use of algebraic symbols and operations. This lesson
  develops a foundation for all subsequent problem solving lessons.
  An understanding of the four-step
  problem solving process is essential for student success in learning
  how to solve problems.
- A student's ability to organize information given in a problem so that it
  can be used to solve the problem is
  a key to success in this lesson. To
  determine a student's progress,
  analyze errors in the student's
  work and then classify specific errors.

Error Analysis Classification
1. *Misunderstanding*
   Failed to understand the meaning
   of each step of the problem solving
   process
2. *Misapplied Strategy*
   Did not select the correct notation
   to represent the facts of the problem

Problem Solving Strategy: Select Appropriate Notation

1.9

A problem asks a question for which an answer is not known. The solution
to a problem is the answer to the question. In arithmetic, problems are solved
by using numbers. In algebra, the number or numbers may not be known.
The unknown number (or numbers) is represented by a *variable* whose
specific value is not known until the problem is solved.

The use of variables and other symbols (operation signs, grouping symbols,
and equality and inequality symbols) is called **algebraic notation.**

Algebraic Notation

Letters of the alphabet from a to z are used as variables to represent one or more unknown numbers.	$a = -6 \quad m = 0.89 \quad x = 3\frac{1}{8}$
A raised dot or parentheses is used to represent the operation of multiplication.	$7 \cdot n \quad 4 \cdot x \quad 3(t) \quad -9(y)$
The product of a number and a variable or two or more variables can be expressed without a sign between the number and the variable.	$-3w \quad 16h \quad \frac{2}{3}b \quad 4yz$
The operations of addition, subtraction, and division are represented by the same symbols in algebra and arithmetic.	add: $x + y$ subtract: $5 - n$ divide: $18 \div b$
Division is also indicated by using the fraction form, as in arithmetic.	$\dfrac{3}{4} \quad \dfrac{n}{7} \quad \dfrac{a}{b} \quad \dfrac{25}{f} \quad \dfrac{t-6}{9}$
The symbol { } is used to enclose the members of a set. Three dots mean that the numbers in a set go on forever in the same pattern.	$\{1, 2, 3, 4, 5, 6, \ldots\}$
The equal sign and the inequality symbols are used to compare numbers.	$-5 = -5 \quad -3 < 0 \quad c > -2$
A negative sign before a variable means the opposite of whatever number the variable represents.	If $x = 7$, then $-x = -(7) = -7$. If $x = -4$, then $-x = -(-4) = 4$. If $x = 0$, then $-x = -(0) = 0$.
The absolute value of a number n is written as $\lvert n \rvert$.	$\lvert n \rvert$

Problem solving is a process in which several steps are applied sequentially. Each step consists of a set of skills.

Understand the Problem	**Read the problem.** What facts are given? What is the unknown, that is, what are you asked to find? Review the definitions of all mathematical terms.
Plan Your Approach	**Choose a strategy.** The strategy you choose is your plan of action for solving the problem. Many strategies will be developed in this book to help you plan your approach. In this lesson, the strategy is to use algebraic notation.
Complete the Work	**Apply the strategy.** Use the algebra you know to apply the strategy to solving the problem. Very often, this means using the appropriate algebraic operations. Keep an open mind. Change your strategy if it does not work.
Interpret the Results	**State your conclusion.** **Check your conclusion.** What generalization(s) can you make?

EXAMPLE Maria asked Susan to list all the positive even numbers. Then Maria said she could name them by writing one algebraic expression. What is the algebraic expression Maria is thinking about?

Understand the Problem

What facts are given?
The problem is concerned with the set of positive even numbers.

What are you asked to find?
An algebraic expression that represents all positive even numbers.

Plan Your Approach

Choose a strategy.
Select a variable to use in writing the algebraic expression. Let n represent any counting number.

List the positive even numbers, 2, 4, 6, 8, 10, 12, ...

Observe that every even number is a multiple of 2.

$$2 = 2 \cdot 1 \qquad 4 = 2 \cdot 2 \qquad 6 = 2 \cdot 3$$
$$8 = 2 \cdot 4 \qquad 10 = 2 \cdot 5 \qquad 12 = 2 \cdot 6$$

Problem Solving Strategy: Select Appropriate Notation **43**

43

TEACHING SUGGESTIONS

- Introduce the term *algebraic notation* and illustrate it with the examples given at the beginning of the lesson. An overhead projector may be helpful.
- Use Transparency 1, in the *Teacher's Resource Book,* to point out key word phrases and to prepare students for the exercises.
- Discuss the term *problem* and ask students for their understanding of its meaning. Then introduce and discuss the four-step problem solving process.
- Mention that there is no one way to solve a mathematics problem, but that knowledge of many strategies is useful in solving problems.

CHALKBOARD EXAMPLES

- **For the Example**
  Write each number as a product of its factors.
  1. 3 $1 \cdot 3$ **2.** 21 $3 \cdot 7$
  3. 36 $2 \cdot 2 \cdot 3 \cdot 3$
  4. 40 $2 \cdot 2 \cdot 2 \cdot 5$
  5. 99 $3 \cdot 3 \cdot 11$

  Use algebraic notation to represent each of the following.
  6. The product of a number and itself $n \cdot n$
  7. The area of a football field A
  8. The absolute value of the product of two unknown numbers $|xy|$
  9. The quotient of $n - 2$ and $2 - n$ $\dfrac{n-2}{2-n}$

Common Error

- Students can choose the variable n to be any even number, but it is customary to let n be an integer; then $2n$ is an even integer and $2n + 1$ is odd.
- See *Teacher's Resource Book* for additional remediation.

LESSON FOLLOW-UP

Discussion

- An integer is odd if when divided by 2 the remainder is 1. An integer is even if, when divided by 2, the remainder is 0. Remind students that 0 is an even integer. What remainders can there be in a division problem if the divisor is 3? 0, 1, or 2

Critical Thinking

Reasoning by Analogy   What do the following expressions represent if x is an integer?

1. $2x + 0$ **2.** $2x + 1$
Students should reason that $2x + 0$ is an even integer and $2x + 1$ is an odd integer.

Assignment Guide

- See p. 1B for assignments.

Test Yourself

See *Teacher's Resource Book,* Tests, pp. 7–8.

Project

After the students complete this project, encourage them to discuss how algebra can be applied in other real life situations.

Lesson Quiz

1. Write the product of a and $x + y$ using algebraic notation.
   $a(x + y)$
2. Write the absolute value of $-n$.
   $|-n|$
3. Represent the length of a playing field with a variable. l
4. List the set of counting numbers. $\{1, 2, 3, 4, 5, \ldots\}$
5. If n is even, is $n \cdot n$ odd or even? Give some examples to justify your answers.   even; $2 \cdot 2 = 4$
6. Let p and q represent any two integers. Represent the sum of two odd integers using algebraic notation. $(2p - 1) + (2q - 1)$ or $2(p + q - 1)$

☐ **Complete the Work**   Study the relationships in the list above and observe that any positive even number is 2 times a counting number. Since n represents any counting number, $2n$ represents an even number.

☐ **Interpret the Results**   **State your conclusion.**
If n represents any counting number, the positive even numbers can be represented by the algebraic expression $2n$. You can check by substituting values of n.

CLASS EXERCISES

Use algebraic notation to represent each of the following.

1. An unknown number x
2. The absolute value of an unknown number $|x|$
3. An unknown number less than zero $x < 0$
4. The product of two unknown numbers ab
5. The sum of three unknown numbers $a + b + c$
6. The absolute value of the difference of two unknown numbers $|m - n|$
7. Two times the sum of two unknown numbers $2(r + s)$

PRACTICE EXERCISES

Use algebraic notation to represent each of the following.

A   **1.** Mary's age 2 years ago $m - 2$
    2. One-half the current price $\frac{1}{2}p$
    3. John's salary plus $500 commission $s + 500$
    4. Martha's annual salary less $4500 in deductions $a - 4500$
    5. The price of an item plus 6% sales tax $p + 6\%p$, or $p + 0.06p$
    6. Twenty-five percent of the boys $25\%b$, or $0.25b$
    7. The average of salaries a, b, and c $\frac{a + b + c}{3}$
    8. List the positive multiples of 3. Then write an algebraic expression for any positive multiple of 3.
    $3, 6, 9, 12, \ldots$ x is a positive number, so $3x$ is an expression for the multiples of 3.
    9. List the first 10 even natural numbers. Subtract 1 from each number. Are the resulting numbers odd or even? If x is any natural number, write an algebraic expression to represent the odd natural numbers. odd; $2x - 1$

44   Chapter 1 Real Numbers

B **10.** If p represents the number of pears in a box, does $5p$ represent "5 pears"
or "5 times the number of pears"? Five times the number of pears.

11. If x and y are any two rational numbers, can x and y represent the same
number? Explain. If x and y are any two rational numbers, they can be equal to one another.

12. Write an algebraic expression to represent the negative even integers.
If x is some integer, $-|2x|$ represents a negative even integer.
13. Write an algebraic expression to represent the negative odd integers.
If x is some integer, $-|2x - 1|$ represents a negative odd integer.
C **14.** If a, b, c, and d represent any four integers, is the following equality
true or false? Explain. True only if $b = d$.

$$a + b + c = a + d + c$$

15. If x and y are any two rational numbers, is the following equality true or
false? Explain. Always true because $x - y$ and $y - x$ are opposites; but the absolute
values of opposites are equal.
$$|x - y| = |y - x|$$

16. If a and b are any two nonzero real numbers, and $a + b = c$, is it
possible that $a = c$ or $b = c$? Explain. No, because either a or b would have to be
equal to 0, and it is given that a and b are nonzero rational numbers.

PROJECT

This lesson shows that algebra is *more general* than arithmetic. Use a
dictionary to look up the meaning of the word *general*. Write down the
dictionary definition. Then explain in your own words what you think the
dictionary definition of *general* means as it applies to algebra. Give two or
three examples from this chapter to support your explanation. Answers may vary.

TEST YOURSELF

Add or subtract, as indicated.   1.5–1.6

1. $-21 + (-13)$ -34 **2.** $1.5 + 3.2$ 4.7   **3.** $17 + (-9)$ 8

4. $-\frac{2}{3} + \frac{1}{4}$ $-\frac{5}{12}$ **5.** $-2 + 12 + -10$ 0   **6.** $-\frac{1}{4} - \left(-\frac{3}{5}\right)$ $\frac{7}{20}$

7. $4 - 10$ -6 **8.** $3.2 - (-4.1)$ 7.3   **9.** $-(10 - 15) - (2 - 5)$
 8

Multiply or divide, as indicated.   1.7–1.8

10. $(10)(-15)$ -150 **11.** $-\frac{1}{2} \cdot \frac{2}{9}$ $-\frac{1}{9}$ **12.** $(-2)(-3)(-7)(-2)$ 84

13. $\frac{-36}{4}$ -9 **14.** $-2\frac{1}{3} \div \left(-\frac{1}{2}\right)$ $\frac{14}{3}$ **15.** $\frac{3}{4} \div \frac{2}{4}$ $\frac{3}{2}$

Problem Solving Strategy: Select Appropriate Notation   **45**

P Name _____ Date _____
Practice: For use after Lesson 1.9, Algebra 1

Problem Solving Strategy: Select Appropriate Notation
Represent each of the following with a variable. Answers may vary.

1. The area of a table top ____ t
2. The radius of a circle ____ r
3. The perimeter of a triangle ____ p
4. The interest earned on a savings account ____ i
5. The time it takes to travel from Atlanta to New York ____ t
6. The rate of speed of a car ____ r
7. The weight of a steel ball ____ w
8. The height of a tall building ____ h

Answer each of the following questions *yes* or *no*.

9. Is $x + y$ equal to $y + x$? ____ yes   10. Is $4m$ equal to $m \cdot 4$? ____ yes
11. If z is any real number, can z represent an integer? ____ yes
12. If n is a positive even integer, is $\sqrt{n}$ always a positive even integer? ____ no
13. $|m - n| = |n - m|$ if m and n are integers. ____ yes

Solve each problem by selecting an appropriate algebraic notation and by
using the four-step problem solving process.

14. Write a variable expression to represent any integer. ____ i
15. Write a variable expression to represent any even integer. ____ $2e$
16. Write a variable expression to represent any odd integer. ____ $2p + 1$

MIXED PRACTICE
Simplify.

17. $-4 + 12$ ____ 8   18. $7 + (-3)$ ____ 4   19. $9 - (-1)$ ____ 10
20. $(-6)(-5)$ ____ 30   21. $(-1)(-2)(-3)$ ____ -6 22. $\left(-\frac{2}{3}\right) \div \left(\frac{5}{6}\right)$ ____ $-\frac{4}{5}$

Chapter 1   **25**

E Name _____ Date _____
Enrichment: For use after Lesson 1.9, Algebra 1

Mystery Signs
Look at the equation $5 \# 3 = 8$. Although you do not know the meaning of
the symbol "#," your knowledge of arithmetic tells you that # must mean
to add, because $5 + 3 = 8$.

Now look at the equation $2 \triangle 2 = 4$. If you think that $\triangle$ means to add, you
are right because $2 + 2 = 4$. However, $\triangle$ could also mean to multiply,
because $2 \times 2 = 4$. And, $\triangle$ could also mean "raise to the power of," because
$2^2 = 4$.

In each of the following examples, the signs #, $\triangle$,
@, and * can represent any of the operations
listed in the chart at the right. Once you have
determined the meaning of each "mystery sign,"
rewrite the equation using familiar signs. Unless
indicated, each problem has only one correct
solution.

ADD
SUBTRACT
MULTIPLY
DIVIDE
RAISE TO THE POWER OF ...
TAKE THE SQUARE ROOT OF ...

1. $3 \# 2 = 12$ (Two solutions) ____ $3 \times 2 \times 2 = 12; 3 \times 2^2 = 12$
2. $\triangle (8 * 8) = 4$ ____ $\sqrt{(8 + 8)} = 4$
3. $2 \triangle 3 = 8$ ____ $2^3 = 8$
4. $(3 @ 7) \# m = 10m$ ____ $(3 + 7) \times m = 10m$
5. $(3x \# 6x) * 3 = 3x$ ____ $(3x + 6x) \div 3 = 3x$
6. $30 * 6 \# 5 = 25$ ____ $30 \div 6 \times 5 = 25$
7. $(3 * 9) \# 2 = 25$ ____ $(3 \times 9) - 2 = 25$
8. $4 \# 3 @ 2 = 13$ ____ $4 + 3^2 = 13$
9. $(10n \# 2) + (3n * 3) = 14n$ ____ $(10n \div 2) + (3n \cdot 3) = 14n$
10. $@ 25 * 3 \# 2 \# 1 = 12$ ____ $\sqrt{25} \times 3 - 2 - 1 = 12$
11. $(5x * 2y @ 2x) * 4 = 12x + 8y$ ____ $(5x + 2y - 2x) \times 4 = 12x + 8y$
12. $3 @ (n * 2) = 3n - 6$ ____ $3 \times (n - 2) = 3n - 6$
13. $(4 * 4) \# (2 * 4) \triangle 6 = 18$ (Two solutions) ____ $(4 \times 4) + (2 \times 4) - 6 = 18; (4 + 4) + (2^4) - 6 = 18$

26 Chapter 1

45

- See *Teacher's Resource Book, Spanish Chapter Summary and Review*, pp. 1–2.
- See Extra Practice, p. 655.

CHAPTER 1 SUMMARY AND REVIEW

Vocabulary

absolute value (14)	irrational numbers (8)	positive numbers (7)
additive inverse (27)	multiplicative inverse (35)	rational numbers (8)
algebraic expression (3)	natural numbers (7)	real numbers (7)
average (39)	negative numbers (7)	reciprocal (35)
coordinate of a point (8)	numerical expression (3)	variable (2)
graph of a number (8)	opposite (13)	variable expression (2)
integers (7)	origin (7)	whole numbers (7)

Evaluating Algebraic Expressions   To evaluate an algebraic expression,   **1.1**
substitute the given numbers for the variables and then simplify. Operations
within parentheses are done first.

Evaluate each expression if $w = 4$, $x = 0.5$, $y = 16$, and $z = \frac{2}{3}$.

1. $w - x$ 3.5

2. $\frac{y}{w}$ 4

3. $\frac{3}{4}y$ 12

4. $w \div \frac{1}{2}$ 8

5. $3yz$ 32

6. $4(w - x)$ 14

7. $\frac{8}{4y}$ $\frac{1}{8}$

8. $y - (wx)$ 14

Translating Word Phrases   To translate word phrases to algebraic
expressions, look for key words that indicate operations:

addition (more than, sum)   multiplication (times, product)
subtraction (minus, difference)   division (quotient, ratio)

Write an algebraic expression for each phrase.

9. 18 more than some number x $x + 18$

10. The product of some number n and 22 $22n$

11. The difference of a and b $a - b$

12. The ratio of m and $\frac{2}{3}$ $m \div \frac{2}{3}$

Graphing Numbers   The graph of a number is a point on the   **1.2, 1.3**
number line.

Graph each set of numbers. See side column.

13. $\left\{ -4\frac{1}{2}, -4, 0, 2.5, 3 \right\}$

14. {whole numbers}

15. {odd integers}

Replace each $\underline{\ ?\ }$ with <, >, or = to make a true statement.

16. $-11 \underline{\ ?\ } 10$ <

17. $0 \underline{\ ?\ } -3.5$ >

18. $-1\frac{1}{3} \underline{\ ?\ } -1.5$ >

Additional Answers

13.   −4 −2 0 2 4 6

14.   −2 −1 0 1 2 3

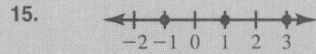

15.   −2 −1 0 1 2 3

Absolute Value and Opposites The absolute value of a number is the
distance the number is from zero on a number line. -2 and 2, $4\frac{1}{3}$ and $-4\frac{1}{3}$
are called opposites. Their graphs are the same distance from the origin.

1.3

Simplify.

19. $-(4.31)$ –4.31   **20.** $|-8|$ 8   **21.** $-|6 + 3|$ –9   **22.** $-\left|-\frac{8}{9}\right|$ $-\frac{8}{9}$

Operations with Real Numbers A number line can be used to find the
sum of real numbers. The rules for addition are given on pages 22–24 and
the rules for multiplication are given on pages 31–33. Subtraction and
division of real numbers are defined *in terms of* addition and multiplication,
respectively.

1.4–1.8

$$m - n = m + (-n) \qquad m \div n = m \cdot \frac{1}{n} \ (n \neq 0)$$

Perform the indicated operations, if possible.

23. $-4.8 + 3.6$ –1.2

24. $-\frac{2}{3} + \left(-\frac{2}{3}\right)$ $-1\frac{1}{3}$

25. $-11 + (-3.6) + 2.9$ –11.7

26. $-18 - (-11)$ –7

27. $-5.9 - 0.02$ –5.92

28. $[-48 - (-48)] - (-9)$ 9

29. $-6(-25)$ 150

30. $-13 \cdot 3 \cdot 0$ 0

31. $\frac{2}{3}(-20)(9)$ –120

32. $\frac{-96}{16}$ –6

33. $0 \div \left(-\frac{1}{3}\right)$ 0

34. $\frac{-4.284}{-2.1}$ 2.04

Problem Solving To solve problems of any type, the four-step
problem-solving approach outlined below may be helpful.

1.9

Understand the Problem	Plan Your Approach	Complete the Work	Interpret the Results

35. The yards gained and lost on eight successive plays by the Lansing High
School football team were as follows: $+6$, -10, $+4$, $+10.5$, -0.5, -9,
-6, $+25$. What was the average yardage for the eight plays? +2.5

36. One carpenter charges \$20 plus \$25 per hour and another charges \$30
per hour. Find how many hours a job must take for both to charge the
same amount. 4 h

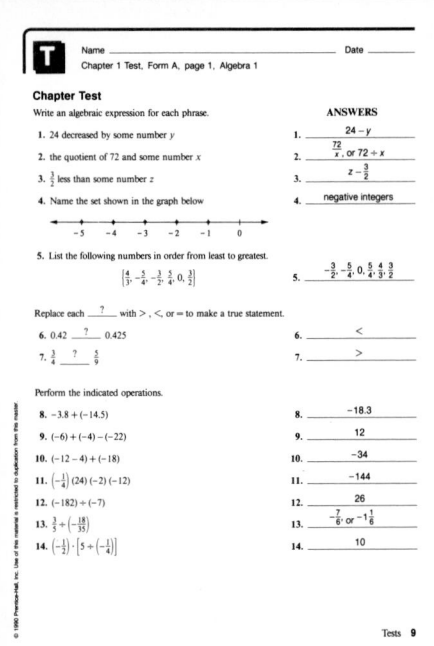

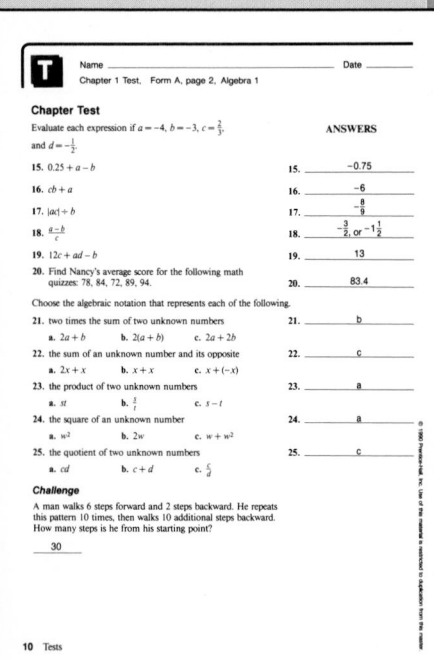

Evaluate each expression if $a = 1.4$, $b = 25$, and $c = \frac{1}{5}$.   **1.1**

1. $0.9 + a$ 2.3

2. abc 7

3. $(5c) - ab$ −34

Write an algebraic expression for each phrase.

4. A number p decreased by 0.85 $p - 0.85$

5. The quotient of a number b and 27 $\frac{b}{27}$

6. $\frac{2}{3}$ less than some number x $x - \frac{2}{3}$

7. The product of w and z wz

Graph each set of numbers. See TE side column.   **1.2**

8. {positive integers}

9. {real numbers}

List the numbers in order from least to greatest.   **1.3**

10. $2.5, -1.5, 0, -2.25, -2, 2.25$
$\{-2.25, -2, -1.5, 0, 2.25, 2.5\}$

11. $0, -\frac{1}{3}, -1\frac{1}{3}, \frac{1}{2}, -1\frac{1}{2}, -3$
$\left\{-3, -1\frac{1}{2}, -1\frac{1}{3}, -\frac{1}{3}, 0, \frac{1}{2}\right\}$

Simplify.

12. $-(-0.3)$ 0.3

13. $-\left|\frac{2}{5}\right|$ $-\frac{2}{5}$

14. $-[-|-9|]$ 9

Perform the indicated operations, if possible.   **1.4–1.8**

15. $-45 + (-132)$ −177

16. $(-8) + 2 + (-9) + (-11) + 6$ −20

17. $3.2 - (-4.07)$ 7.27

18. $(-6 - 5) + (-11)$ −22

19. $0 \div \frac{1}{5}$ 0

20. $-\frac{1}{4}(-5)(24)(-1)(-20)$ 600

21. $-96 \div (-16)$ 6

22. $-1.25 \div 0$ not possible

23. Find the value of each expression if $m = \frac{1}{2}$, $n = \frac{2}{3}$, and $p = \frac{3}{4}$.   **1.7, 1.8**
a. $(np) + m$ 1
b. $-(np) - m$ −1
c. the average of m, n, and p $\frac{23}{36}$

24. One house painter charges \$15 plus \$20 per hour. A second painter charges \$25 per hour. Find out how many hours a job takes for the total charges of the second painter to be the same as the charges of the first painter. 3 h   **1.9**

Challenge

At 10:15 AM a train left Flatfoot, Washington, traveling east at 40 km/h (kilometers per hour). Two hours later, another train left the same station traveling west at 35 km/h. At what time will the trains be 230 km apart? 2:15 PM

48   Chapter 1 Real Numbers

 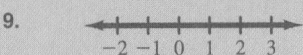

Select the best answer for each and write the appropriate letter.

1. If $a = 3$, $b = 0$, and $c = 2$, then
C $2a + 3b - c$ has a value of

  A. 8   **B.** 6   **C.** 4   **D.** 2   **E.** 0

2. What is the result when the sum
A $[4 + (-5)]$ is subtracted from the
   sum $[9 + (-7)]$?

  A. 3   **B.** -3 **C.** 1   **D.** -1 **E.** 7

3. When simplified, $|7 + (3 - 4)|$ has
B   a value of

  A. 8   **B.** 6   **C.** 0   **D.** -6 **E.** -8

4. If $\frac{4}{3} < k$ and $k < \frac{3}{2}$, then k could
B   be:

  I. $\frac{11}{9}$

  II. $\frac{11}{8}$

  III. $\frac{11}{7}$

  A. I only   **B.** II only

  C. III only   **D.** I, II only

  E. II, III only

5. Which of the following is *not* a
D   multiple of 9?

  A. 2637   **B.** 1008   **C.** 774

  D. 608   **E.** 540

6. $\left(\frac{2}{3}\right)\left(-\frac{3}{5}\right)\left(\frac{4}{5}\right)\left(-\frac{5}{3}\right)\left(-\frac{3}{2}\right)$ equals
B

  A. $\frac{4}{5}$ **B.** $-\frac{4}{5}$ **C.** $\frac{5}{4}$

  D. $-\frac{5}{4}$ **E.** 4

7. 18 is $\frac{2}{3}$ of what number?
D

  A. 6   **B.** 12   **C.** 24   **D.** 27   **E.** 36

8. Which of the following is less than
E $\frac{3}{4}$?

  A. $\frac{49}{64}$ **B.** $\frac{45}{60}$ **C.** $\frac{53}{70}$ **D.** $\frac{51}{67}$

  E. none of the above

9. When $a = 3$ and $b = \frac{2}{3}$, which of
A   the following expressions represents
   the largest value?

  A. $(2a) + (3b)$ **B.** $2(a + b)$

  C. $a + (3b)$ **D.** $(6b) + a$

  E. $(3a) + (6b) - 7$

10. A group of boys pooled their
E   money to buy a new baseball. They
   found they had 19 dimes, 18
   pennies, 17 nickels, and 16
   quarters. How much money did
   they have in all?

  A. $5.83   **B.** $5.93   **C.** $6.03

  D. $6.83   **E.** $6.93

11. A certain type of postage costs 56¢
D   for the first ounce and 17¢ for each
   additional $\frac{1}{2}$ oz or part. At this
   rate, what would be the amount of
   postage on a letter weighing
   2.3 oz?

  A. 90¢   **B.** 97¢   **C.** $1.00

  D. $1.07   **E.** $1.24

The individual comments provided for each problem can be helpful in guiding students to solve these problems.

2. With this type of problem, errors could occur as a result of careless reading of the problem rather than actual mathematical errors.
4. An alternate solution could be to convert each number to its decimal equivalent and then compare the results.
5. Students who are not familiar with simple checks for divisibility should be encouraged to learn and use them.
6. Recognition of a number, its multiplicative inverse, and the fact that their product is 1 is essential.
8. This question offers the opportunity to compare fractions using equivalent forms with either the same numerator or the same denominator and then basing the comparison only on the other part of the fraction.
9. Since both a and b are positive, a little algebra would eliminate choices (b) and (c) immediately [$(2a + 3b) > 2(a + b)$ and $2a + 3b > a + 3b$]. This leaves only the three other choices to be checked out.

See *Teacher's Resource Book,* for Preparing for Standardized Tests.

Maintaining Skills

The following skills and concepts are reviewed:

Multiplication and division of decimals
Addition, subtraction, multiplication, and division of integers
Three-step problems

MAINTAINING SKILLS

Perform the indicated operation.

Example 1

$$3.05 \longleftarrow \text{2 decimal places}$$
$$\times 4.8 \longleftarrow \text{1 decimal place}$$
$$2440$$
$$1220$$
$$14.640 \longleftarrow \text{3 decimal places}$$

Example 2

$$\begin{array}{r} 3.5 \\ 2.4{\overline{)8.4.0}} \\ 72 \\ \hline 120 \\ 120 \end{array}$$

1. 3.81×0.87 3.3147
2. 63.4×0.75 47.55
3. 7.51×5.7 42.807
4. 6.5×9.4 61.1
5. $5.76 \div 6.4$ 0.9
6. $14.7 \div 0.98$ 15
7. $28.12 \div 7.6$ 3.7
8. $135 \div 0.25$ 540
9. 249×0.06 14.94
10. 47.3×2.9 137.17
11. 82.5×3.4 280.5
12. 1.6×0.58 0.928
13. $14.56 \div 5.2$ 2.8
14. $34.3 \div 9.8$ 3.5
15. $62.32 \div 7.6$ 8.2
16. $60.8 \div 6.4$ 9.5
17. 0.0904×5 0.452
18. $0.0904 \div 5$ 0.01808

Example 3 $12 - (-17)$
$12 - (-17) = 12 + 17 = 29$

Example 4 $-36 \div (-9)$
$-36 \div (-9) = 4$

19. $8 - 15$ −7
20. $-9 + 6$ −3
21. -7×4 −28
22. $56 \div (-8)$ −7
23. $5 - (-9)$ 14
24. $-6 \times (-8)$ 48
25. $-7 + (-8)$ −15
26. $-72 \div 9$ −8
27. $-6 - (-2)$ −4
28. $-42 \div (-7)$ 6
29. $7 \times (-6)$ −42
30. $12 + (-8)$ 4

Solve.

Example 5

Gloria typed 24 pages in 2 hours (h).
Jon typed 45 pages in 3 h.
How many more pages per hour did
Jon type than did Gloria?

Step 1 Gloria
$24 \div 2 = 12$

Step 2 Jon
$45 \div 3 = 15$

Step 3 $15 - 12 = 3$
Jon typed 3 more pages per hour.

31. The distance from Dominic's house to the office is 38 mi. How many miles does he travel going to and from the office in a 6-day workweek? 456 mi

32. Sandi bought a stereo for $249 and 5 record albums for $7.98 each. How much did she spend in all? $288.90

33. Harold has 780 packages of pens to pack evenly into 12 boxes. The pens sell for $1.98 a package. How many packages are packed in a box? 65 packages

OVERVIEW • Chapter 2

SUMMARY

In Chapter 2, students are introduced to algebraic expressions and to procedures for simplifying and evaluating them. The order of operations, with and without grouping symbols, and the properties of real numbers are presented in the early lessons of the chapter. These will help students organize their thinking, their approach to a problem, and to its solution. Exponents are introduced, and students learn to simplify expressions containing them. Mathematical formulas are also presented, and students are taught how to evaluate them.

In the final lessons of the chapter, students become familiar with the translation of phrases into algebraic expressions, and of word statements into equations. Such translation facilitates students' understanding of word problems, and also promotes their appreciation of the application of mathematical concepts.

CHAPTER OBJECTIVES

- To simplify numerical expressions by using the rules for order of operations
- To simplify and evaluate expressions containing exponents
- To evaluate formulas for given values of variables
- To identify the commutative, associative, distributive, and identity properties of real numbers and to simplify expressions using these properties
- To simplify algebraic expressions by combining like terms
- To evaluate algebraic expressions containing exponents and/or grouping symbols
- To find solution sets of open sentences from replacement sets
- To translate word phrases and statements into algebraic expressions and equations respectively, and vice versa

Problem Solving Strategy

To account for all possible solutions of a problem for which the solution set is finite

CHAPTER HIGHLIGHTS

The theme of the chapter is computers. The students learn how computers may be used in many practical situations.

PROBLEM SOLVING AND APPLICATIONS

Problem solving and applications form an integral part of each lesson. Students use numerical and algebraic expressions to solve concrete problems and apply formulas in many fields, including geometry, physics, sports, and consumerism. In Lesson 2.8, the strategy of *Account for All Possibilities* affords students the opportunity to practice estimation and the setting of reasonable limits within which the correct solution to a problem may lie.

TECHNOLOGY

Calculator

In Lesson 2.5, students learn to use the memory function when fixing the value of one variable in an algebraic expression.

Computer

In Chapter 2, students are introduced to a spreadsheet and its most basic format and functions. After students are shown how to perform calculations on a spreadsheet, they are then introduced to a program that uses the calculations to solve problems that center around preparing a weekly budget that balances expenses against income.

RESOURCES

Teacher's Resource Book

- Teaching Aid 2
- Transparencies 1, 3

STUDENT TEXT				TEACHER'S RESOURCE BOOK		
Chapter Content	Basic	Average	Enriched	R	P	E
2.1 Simplifying and Evaluating Expressions	D: 53/1-9 odd, 23	D: 53/1-17 odd, 23	D: 53/1-21 odd, 23	1	2	3
2.2 Exponents and Formulas	D: 57/1-23 odd, 46 R: 53/4, 6, 10 57/2-6 even; 16-20 even	D: 57/1-39 odd, 46, 48 R: 53/10, 12, 14	D: 57/11-45 odd, 46-49 R: 53/16, 18, 20	4	5	6
2.3 Properties of Real Numbers Integers	D: 61/1-13 odd, 33 R: 57/8, 14, 22	D: 61/1-27 odd, 33 R: 57/30, 34, 36	D: 61/7-31 odd, 33, 34 R: 57/38, 40, 44	7	8	9
2.4 Combining Like Terms	D: 64/1-29 odd, 61, 63 R: 61/2, 8, 14 Test Yourself	D: 65/7-49 odd, 61, 63 R: 61/12, 20, 22 Test Yourself	D: 65/9-59 odd, 61-64 R: 61/18, 24, 30 Test Yourself	10	11	12
2.5 Simplifying and Evaluating Expressions with Parentheses	D: 69/1-17 odd, 35, 39, 41 R: 64/2, 10, 24	D: 70/7-27 odd, 35, 37, 40 R: 65/8, 30, 42	D: 70/11-33 odd, 35-42 R: 65/28, 50, 52, 60	13	14	15
2.6 Translating Phrases to Algebraic Expressions	D: 76/1-15 odd, 22 R: 69/6, 12, 16	D: 76/1-19 odd, 22, 23 R: 70/14, 20, 22	D: 76/9-21 odd, 21-24 R: 70/16, 24, 30	16	17	18
2.7 Open Sentences and Solution Sets	D: 80/1-17 odd, 35 R: 76/6, 10, 14	D: 80/1-27 odd, 35, 36 R: 76/12, 14, 18	D: 81/15-33 odd, 35-37 R: 76/16, 18, 20	19	20	21
2.8 Problem Solving Strategy: Account for All Possibilities	D: 83/1-13 odd MPSR: 1, 2 R: 80/6, 12, 16	D: 83/1-17 odd MPSR: 1, 2 R: 80/10, 14, 20	D: 83/3-19 odd MPSR: 1, 2 R: 81/22, 30, 34		22	23
2.9 Translating Word Statements to Equations	D: 87/1-13 odd, 25, 26 R: Test Yourself	D: 87/1-11 odd, 25, 26, 27 R: Test Yourself	D: 87/13-23 odd, 25-32 R: Test Yourself	24	25	26

D = Daily   R = Review   MPSR = Mixed Problem Solving Review   R = Reteaching   P = Practice   E = Enrichment

STUDENT TEXT				TEACHER'S RESOURCE BOOK	
Review	Test Yourself	66	Chapter Test	92	Spanish Chapter Summary and Review	3-4
And	Test Yourself	89	Prep. for Stan. Tests	93	• Quizzes	13-16
Testing	Chapter Sum. and Rev.	90	Cumulative Review	94	• Chapter Test (Form A)	17-18
			Extra Practice	656	• Chapter Test (Form B)	19-20
					Calculator Test	3-4
Special	Logical Reasoning	54	Career	77	Applications—Chapter 2	27
Features	Biograpy	58	Did You Know?	81	Critical Thinking	2
	Writing in Algebra	62	Project	84	Reading and Writing in Algebra	2
	Algebra in Geometry	71			Technology	4-6
	Application	72				

2 | Algebraic Expressions

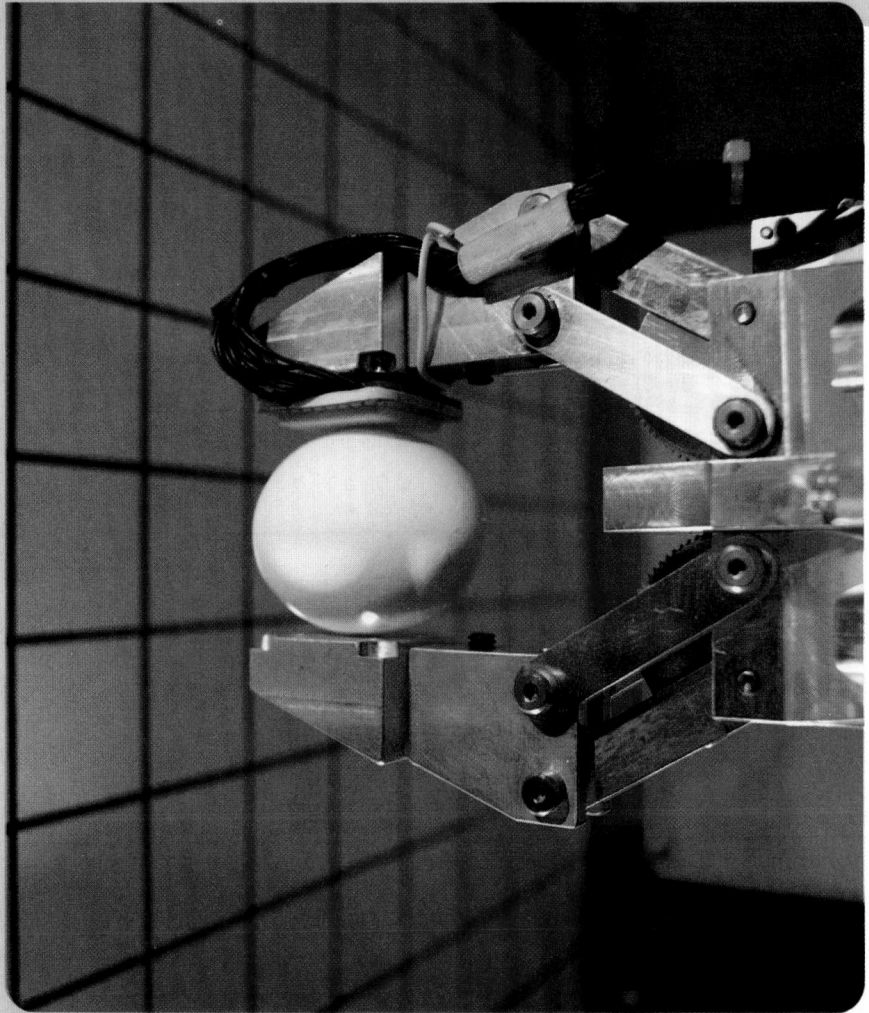

Although computers have been used in the business world for a long time, new advances in technology and research in such areas as artificial intelligence are contributing greatly to new knowledge and productivity.

51

BACKGROUND

Computers play an important role in our society today. They perform various functions, not only for businesses but also for personal use, in less than half the time it would take a human being to complete. Many mathematical expressions and formulas are integrated into the computer field. Often, computer programmers and analysts use a variety of math to successfully complete a program.

BACKGROUND

In the Capsule Review, each exercise involves evaluating simple expressions by substituting given integers for the variables. This review prepares students for their work in simplifying more complex numerical and algebraic expressions according to the rules for order of operations.

Critical Thinking

Observation   How many ways could the expression $4 + 2 \cdot 3 - 1$ be solved if the rules for order of operations did not exist? Without these standardized rules, four different results could be considered correct answers. (8, 9, 12, and 17) The rules for order of operations allow each mathematical expression to have only one unique solution. (9)

TEACHING SUGGESTIONS

- Some students may find it convenient to use the mnemonic expression "Pardon My Dear Aunt Susie" to remember the rules for order of operations. The *P* stands for parentheses, the *M* for multiplication, the *D* for division, the *A* for addition, and the *S* for subtraction.
- Use transparency 3 and Teaching Aid 2, in the *Teacher's Resource Book,* to practice solving expressions using the rules for order of operation. Use a grease pencil to illustrate several examples involving each operation. Use a calculator to check results.

52

2.1

Simplifying and Evaluating Expressions

Objectives: To simplify numerical expressions by using the rules for order of operations
To evaluate algebraic expressions

To *simplify* a numerical expression, replace the expression with its simplest name. To *evaluate* an algebraic expression, substitute given values for the variables and then simplify.

Capsule Review

EXAMPLE   **Evaluate:**   **a.** $-x + z$ if $x = -4$, $z = 2$
b. $3(y - 4)$ if $y = -5$

a. $-x + z = -(-4) + 2$ *Substitute -4 for x and 2 for z.*
$= 4 + 2 = 6$ *Add.*

b. $3(y - 4) = 3(-5 - 4)$ *Substitute -5 for y.*
$= 3(-9) = -27$ *Multiply.*

Evaluate each expression if $a = 2$, $b = -1$, $c = 13$, and $d = -4$.

1. $a + (-b) + c$ 16   **2.** cdb 52   **3.** $a \div b$ -2 **4.** $\dfrac{-b}{-d}$ $\frac{1}{4}$

Operations to be done first are shown within *grouping symbols*. Algebraic grouping symbols include:

parentheses: $(4 + 3) \cdot (8 - 2) = 7 \cdot 6$, or 42
brackets: $8 - [10 - 7] = 8 - 3$, or 5
braces: $\{3 \cdot 2 \cdot 5\} + 3 = 30 + 3$, or 33

fraction bar: $\dfrac{2 + 3}{13 - 3} = \dfrac{5}{10}$, or $\dfrac{1}{2}$

In the expression $14 - 12 \cdot 3 + 2 \div 2$, which operation should be done first? In order to obtain a unique (one and only one) value for this expression, mathematicians use the Rules for Order of Operations.

Rules for Order of Operations

- Perform any operation(s) within parentheses or other grouping symbols.
- Multiply and divide in order from left to right.
- Add and subtract in order from left to right.

---

52   Chapter 2 Algebraic Expressions

EXAMPLE 1 Simplify: $14 - 12 \cdot 3 + 2 \div 2$

$$14 - \underline{12 \cdot 3} + \underline{2 \div 2}$$

$= 14$	$-$	36	$+$	1

Multiply and divide in order from left to right.

$= -22 + 1$ *Add and subtract in order from left to right.*

$= -21$

When several grouping symbols are used in one expression, simplify the expression in the innermost grouping first. Then continue from the innermost to the outermost grouping symbols, using the Rules for Order of Operations.

EXAMPLE 2 Simplify: $\{40 - [3(2 + 4)] \cdot 2\}$

$\{40 - [3(2 + 4)] \cdot 2\}$

$= \{40 - [3(6)] \cdot 2\}$ *Simplify within parentheses.*

$= \{40 - [18] \cdot 2\}$ *Simplify within brackets.*

$= \{40 - 36\}$ *Simplify within braces. Multiply.*

$= 4$ *Subtract.*

EXAMPLE 3 Evaluate: $5a + 6b - \dfrac{2b}{c} + d$ if $a = 4$, $b = -6$, $c = -2$, and $d = 0$

$5a + 6b - \dfrac{2b}{c} + d$

$= 5 \cdot 4 + 6(-6) - \dfrac{2(-6)}{-2} + 0$ *Substitute 4 for a, −6 for b, −2 for c, and 0 for d.*

$= 5 \cdot 4 + 6(-6) - \dfrac{-12}{-2} + 0$ *Multiply in the numerator of the fraction.*

$= 20 + (-36) - 6$ *Multiply and divide.*

$= -16 - 6$ *Add.*

$= -22$ *Subtract.*

CLASS EXERCISES

Simplify each expression.

1. $2 + 6 \cdot 8 \div 4$ 14   **2.** $10 \div 5 \cdot 2 + 6$ 10   **3.** $6 + 8 \div 2 - 3$ 7

Evaluate each expression if $a = 3$, $b = -4$, and $c = 1$.

4. $2a + 1$ 7   **5.** $3b + 1$ −11   **6.** $\dfrac{c}{6 - a}$ $\frac{1}{3}$ **7.** $\dfrac{b + 1}{a}$ −1

PRACTICE EXERCISES

Simplify each expression.

A **1.** $16 - 11 \cdot 2 + 3 \div 3$ −5 **2.** $10 - 13 \cdot 3 + 4 \div 4$ −28   **3.** $21 + 16 \cdot 7 - 6 \div 2$ 130

2.1 Simplifying and Evaluating Expressions **53**

53

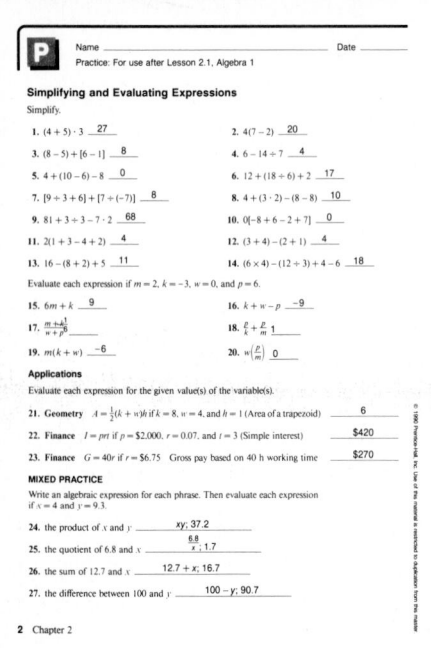

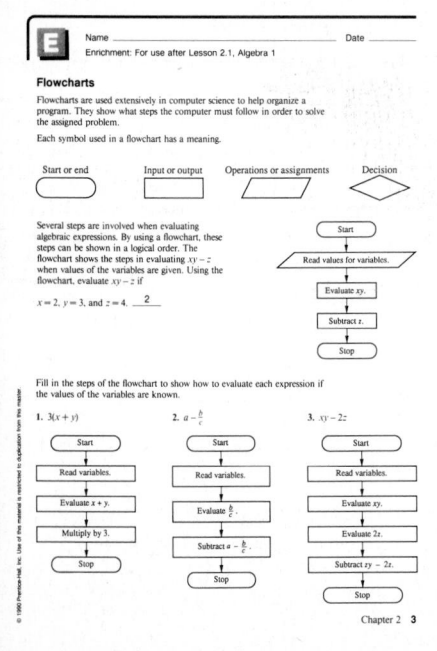

4. $42 + 21 \cdot 9 - 8 \div 4$ 229 **5.** $\{30 - [4(3 + 2)] \cdot 4\}$ −50 **6.** $\{40 - [6(4 + 3)] \cdot 7\}$
−254

Evaluate each expression if $a = 5$, $b = -1$, $c = 0$, and $d = 2$.

7. $4a + 3$ 23   **8.** $2d - b$ 5   **9.** $a - \dfrac{d}{b}$ 7   **10.** $d - \dfrac{c}{b}$ 2

B **11.** $2a - 3b + 4c$ 13   **12.** $-4d + 2b - 3a$ −25   **13.** $\dfrac{7ab - 2d}{6a - b}$ −$\frac{39}{31}$

14. $\dfrac{1 - 16bd}{15a + 1}$ $\frac{33}{76}$ **15.** $8(a + b) - 11bd$ 54   **16.** $-5(2a + d) + 6b$
−66

Simplify each expression.

17. $6 - \{9 + 12(2 + 8) \div 4\}$ −33   **18.** $5 - \{-4[8 - 11(-9 - 1)]\}$ 477

Evaluate each expression if $m = 6$, $n = -2$, $p = 18$, $r = -3$, and $s = 9$.

C **19.** $m + \dfrac{6n + p}{sr - 12}$ $\frac{76}{13}$ **20.** $\dfrac{-r + 7n}{11 - rs}$ −$\frac{11}{38}$

21. $m - (-n)[r - (-s)](m - n)$ −90   **22.** $(p + r)[n - (-m)] - mn$ 72

Applications

Computer If you wanted to open a simple interest savings account, you could use the program below to help you determine which bank would give you the best return for your money (principal).

```
10 INPUT "ENTER THE PRINCIPAL:    ";P
20 INPUT "ENTER THE RATE AS A DECIMAL:    ";R
30 INPUT "ENTER THE TIME IN MONTHS:    ";T: PRINT : PRINT
40 LET I = P * R * (T / 12)
50 PRINT "YOUR RETURN ON $";P;" AT A RATE OF ";R * 100;"%
     FOR ";T;" MONTHS IS $"; INT ((I + 0.005) * 100) / 100
```

23. If bank ABC offers 5% annual interest for a deposit of $500 for 3 months, what interest would you earn? $6.25

LOGICAL REASONING

In each sentence a mathematics term was scrambled. Decode each term.

1. The CALROPICER of x is $\dfrac{1}{x}$, but x cannot be zero. reciprocal

2. Addition and subtraction are mathematical ATOPERONIS. operations

3. Letters that represent numbers are called IBARLEVAS. variables

4. SESTERNAPEH are used as symbols of grouping. parentheses

Exponents and Formulas

2.2

Objectives: To simplify and evaluate expressions containing exponents
To evaluate formulas for given values of the variables

When an automobile makes a turn, it moves in a
curved path. The acceleration (rate at which the car's
velocity changes) can be found if the radius of the
curve and the velocity or speed of the car are known.

Physicists have derived a formula for analyzing
circular motion:

$$a = \frac{v^2}{r} \qquad \begin{aligned} a &= \text{acceleration} \\ v &= \text{velocity} \\ r &= \text{radius of circle} \end{aligned}$$

The expression v^2 means $v \cdot v$, so $a = \dfrac{v^2}{r}$ is
equivalent to $a = \dfrac{v \cdot v}{r}$.

This formula can be evaluated for a if the values of the variables v and r are
known. (See Example 5.)

Capsule Review

EXAMPLE Evaluate: **a.** $m \cdot m \cdot m$ if $m = -3$
b. $2 \cdot 2 \cdot a \cdot a \cdot a \cdot b \cdot b$ if $a = 1, b = -4$

a. $m \cdot m \cdot m$ if $m = -3$ **b.** $2 \cdot 2 \cdot a \cdot a \cdot a \cdot b \cdot b$ if $a = 1, b = -4$
$= -3(-3)(-3) = -27$ $= 2 \cdot 2 \cdot 1 \cdot 1 \cdot 1 \cdot (-4)(-4) = 64$

Evaluate each expression if $x = -2$ and $y = 3$.

1. $y \cdot y \cdot y \cdot y$ 81   **2.** $x \cdot x \cdot x \cdot x$ 16   **3.** $-4 \cdot x \cdot x \cdot x \cdot y \cdot y$
288

When two or more numbers are multiplied, each number is called a **factor.**
An **exponent** is used to show how many times the factor, or **base,** is multiplied.

> If a is any real number and n is any positive integer, then:
> $$a^n = \underbrace{a \cdot a \cdot a \cdot \cdots \cdot a}_{n \text{ factors}}. \qquad \begin{aligned} &n \text{ is the exponent, } a \text{ is the base.} \\ &a^n \text{ is read ``}a \text{ to the } n\text{th power.''} \end{aligned}$$

2.2 Exponents and Formulas   **55**

LESSON PLAN

Vocabulary
Base
Exponent
Factor

Materials/Manipulatives
Calculators
*Teacher's Resource Book,
Teaching Aids 2, 3
Transparency 3*

BACKGROUND

In the Capsule Review, students evaluate simple expressions in which they
must multiply a number by itself two or
more times. This review prepares students to evaluate expressions that
contain exponents.

Critical Thinking
Observation What is the relationship between a number and the product of that number multiplied by itself
for a whole number? a proper fraction? Students should conclude that
when the number is a whole number, the
product is greater than the whole number.
When the number is a proper fraction, the
product is less than the number.

TEACHING SUGGESTIONS

- In the previous lesson, the Teaching Suggestions included a mnemonic device for remembering the rules for the order of operations. Explain that this can be modified to "Please Excuse My Dear Aunt Susie" where E stands for exponents. See Example 2.
- Explain how the power key on a calculator, usually labeled y^x, can be used to simplify expressions with exponents.

CHALKBOARD EXAMPLES

- **For Example 1**
  Simplify:
  1. 4^1 4   2. 3^3 27
  3. 1^7 1   4. $\left(\frac{1}{8}\right)^2$ $\frac{1}{64}$

- **For Example 2**
  Simplify:
  5. $-(5)^2$ -25 6. $-(-5)^2$ -25
  7. -5^2 -25 8. $(-5)^2$ 25

- **For Example 3**
  Simplify:
  9. $3(6 + 2)^2$ 192
  10. $(3^3 - 20)^2$ 49

- **For Example 4**
  Evaluate:
  11. $3x^2y^3$ if $x = 4$ and $y = -1$ -48
  12. $5m^3 + n^2$ if $m = -2$ and $n = 8$ 24

- **For Example 5**
  13. Evaluate $A = \pi r^2$ for A if $\pi \approx 3.14$ and $r = 4$.   50

Common Error

- Students often make the mistake of multiplying the exponent and the base. They may also multiply a coefficient times the base first before raising it to a power. Have these students identify the base and write the expressions in expanded form before multiplying.
- See *Teacher's Resource Book* for additional remediation.

EXAMPLE 1 Simplify: **a.** 5^2 **b.** $\left(\frac{1}{2}\right)^3$ **c.** 3^1 **d.** 1^5

	Read	Base	Exponent	Value
a. 5^2	5 squared	5	2	$5 \cdot 5 = 25$
b. $\left(\frac{1}{2}\right)^3$	$\frac{1}{2}$ cubed	$\frac{1}{2}$	3	$\frac{1}{2} \cdot \frac{1}{2} \cdot \frac{1}{2} = \frac{1}{8}$
c. 3^1	3 to the first	3	1	3
d. 1^5	1 to the fifth	1	5	$1 \cdot 1 \cdot 1 \cdot 1 \cdot 1 = 1$

When the exponent is 1, it is not necessary to write the exponent.

EXAMPLE 2 Simplify: **a.** -3^2 **b.** $(-3)^2$ **c.** $-(3)^2$ **d.** $-(-3)^2$

a. $-3^2 = -(3 \cdot 3) = -9$ **b.** $(-3)^2 = (-3)(-3) = 9$

c. $-(3)^2 = -(3 \cdot 3) = -9$ **d.** $-(-3)^2 = -[(-3)(-3)] = -9$

To simplify expressions with exponents, simplify the exponent first.

$$3 \cdot 2^4 = 3 \cdot (2 \cdot 2 \cdot 2 \cdot 2) = 48$$

The order of operations introduced on page 52 is thus extended to include exponents:

- Perform any operation(s) within grouping symbols.
- Simplify any exponents.
- Multiply and divide in order from left to right.
- Add and subtract in order from left to right.

EXAMPLE 3 Simplify: **a.** $2(3 + 4)^2$ **b.** $(4 - 2^3)^2$

a. $2(3 + 4)^2$
    $= 2(7)^2$ *Simplify within parentheses.*
    $= 2 \cdot 7 \cdot 7$ *Simplify the exponent.*
    $= 98$ *Multiply.*

b. $(4 - 2^3)^2$
    $= [4 - (2)(2)(2)]^2$ *Simplify $(4 - 2^3)$.*
    $= [4 - 8]^2$
    $= [-4]^2$ *Multiply.*
    $= (-4)(-4) = 16$

EXAMPLE 4 Evaluate: **a.** $5x^3y^2$ if $x = 2$, $y = 3$
                  b. $2x^2 - y^3$ if $x = -1$, $y = -4$

Substitute values for x and y. Then simplify.

a. $5x^3y^2$ if $x = 2$, $y = 3$
    $= 5 \cdot 2^3 \cdot 3^2$
    $= 5 \cdot 2 \cdot 2 \cdot 2 \cdot 3 \cdot 3$
    $= 360$

b. $2x^2 - y^3$ if $x = -1$, $y = -4$
    $= 2(-1)^2 - (-4)^3$
    $= 2(-1)(-1) - (-4)(-4)(-4)$
    $= 2 - (-64)$
    $= 2 + 64 = 66$

EXAMPLE 5 Evaluate $a = \dfrac{v^2}{r}$ for a if $v = 35$ and $r = 200$.

$$a = \frac{v^2}{r}$$

$$= \frac{35^2}{200} \qquad \text{Substitute 35 for } v \text{ and 200 for } r.$$

$$= \frac{35 \cdot 35}{200} \qquad \text{Simplify the exponent.}$$

$$= \frac{1225}{200} = 6.125$$

CLASS EXERCISES

Simplify.

1. 10^2 100 **2.** $\left(\frac{2}{3}\right)^3$ $\frac{8}{27}$ **3.** -2^2 -4 **4.** $2 \cdot 5^2$ 50 **5.** $-(-2-3)^3$ 125

Evaluate each expression if $x = 2$ and $y = 3$.

6. $x^2 y$ 12 **7.** $-x^2 y$ -12 **8.** $x^3 + y^2$ 17 **9.** $(xy)^2$ 36 **10.** $-(x - y)^2$ -1

PRACTICE EXERCISES

Simplify each expression.

A **1.** 5^2 25 **2.** 7^2 49 **3.** $\left(\frac{1}{2}\right)^2$ $\frac{1}{4}$ **4.** $\left(\frac{1}{5}\right)^3$ $\frac{1}{125}$ **5.** -4^2 -16

6. -6^2 -36 **7.** $(-4)^2$ 16 **8.** $(-6)^2$ 36 **9.** $-(4)^2$ -16 **10.** $-(6)^2$ -36

11. $-(-4)^2$ -16 **12.** $-(-6)^2$ -36 **13.** $2(4 + 3)^2$ 98 **14.** $3(2 + 3)^2$ 75 **15.** $(2 - 7^2)^2$ 2209

16. $(3 - 5^3)^2$ 14884 **17.** $3(7 + 4)^2$ 363 **18.** $4(6 + 3)^2$ 324 **19.** $(4 - 6^3)^2$ 44944 **20.** $(7 - 3^2)^2$ 4

Evaluate each expression for the given value(s) of the variables.

21. $2m^2 n^3$ if $m = 2$, $n = 3$ 216 **22.** $3r^3 s^2$ if $r = 2$, $s = 3$ 216

23. $3b^3 - c^2$ if $b = -2$, $c = -3$ -33 **24.** $6d^2 - e^3$ if $d = -2$, $e = -3$ 51

Simplify.

B **25.** $(0.3)^2$ 0.09 **26.** $(0.5)^2$ 0.25 **27.** $(0.001)^3$ 0.000000001 **28.** $(0.001)^2$ 0.000001

29. $2^2(2 + 3)^2$ 100 **30.** $3^2(4 + 2)^2$ 324 **31.** $5^2(1 - 3)^2$ 100 **32.** $4^2(1 - 5)^2$ 256

Evaluate each expression if $c = 4$, $d = 3$, and $e = -2$.

33. $-c + d^2$ 5 **34.** $-d + e^2$ 1 **35.** $3c^2 - e^3$ 56 **36.** $e^3 - 2c^2$ -40

37. $c^3(d + e)^2$ 64 **38.** $(e - d)^2 c^2$ 400 **39.** $(2c + 4d)^2$ 400 **40.** $(e - 2d)^3$ -512

2.2 Exponents and Formulas **57**

Critical Thinking

Observation What do you observe about the value of a when r increases in the formula $a = \dfrac{v^2}{r}$, if the value of v is fixed at 35? When v is fixed, the value of a decreases as r increases.

Assignment Guide

- Before assigning the practice exercises, use Transparency 3 and Teaching Aid 2, in the *Teacher's Resource Book* to review several examples involving exponents. Use a grease pencil to insert exponents and operations.
- See p. 50B for assignments.
- You may wish to use Teaching Aid 3, in order for students to become familiar with formulas and symbols.

Lesson Quiz

Simplify.

1. $\left(-\frac{3}{5}\right)^2$ $\frac{9}{25}$ **2.** $(2 - 9)^2$ 49

3. $-(4 - 7)^3$ 27

4. $4 \cdot 3^4 \cdot 5$ 1620

Evaluate each expression.

5. m^4 if $m = 4$ 256

6. $-4r^2 s^2$ if $r = -1$, $s = 3$ -36

Simplify.

7. $5\left(\frac{-1}{5}\right)^3$ $-\frac{1}{25}$

8. $(0.4)^2$ 0.16

9. $(0.05)^2$ 0.0025

10. Evaluate $3x^2 - y^3$ if $x = 2$, $y = -1$. 13

Enrichment

Have students work with the formula $d = 16t^2$ [where d represents distance (in feet) of a fallen object and t represents time (in seconds)] to determine a relationship between d and t.

If $t = 2$ s, $d = ?$ 64 ft
If $t = 3$ s, $d = ?$ 144 ft
If $t = 4$ s, $d = ?$ 256 ft

For every additional second of time that passes, an object falls faster.

57

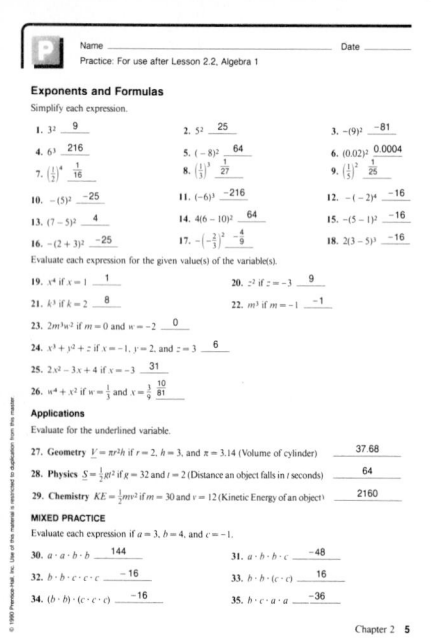

Evaluate each expression for the given value(s) of the variables.

C **41.** $\dfrac{m^4 - n^4}{(m - n)^4}$ if $m = -1$, $n = -2$ -15 **42.** $\dfrac{x^3 + y^3}{(x - y)^3}$ if $x = 1$, $y = -1$ 0

43. $a^3 \div [b^2 - c^2 - (-d)^2]$ if $a = -3$, $b = 4$, $c = 3$, $d = 2$ -9

44. $[r^3 - s^3 + (-t)^3]u^3$ if $r = 3$, $s = -2$, $t = 1$, $u = 4$ 2176

45. $-a^4 + b^2[c^2 - 2d^2] \div 2$ if $a = -1$, $b = 5$, $c = 0$, $d = 3$ -226

Applications

Calculator The Power Key on your calculator, usually labeled y^x, can be used to simplify expressions with exponents.

Simplify the following expressions.

46. 9^4 $6{,}561$ **47.** 6^5 $7{,}776$ **48.** $(-7.1)^6$ $128{,}100.2839$ **49.** -3.9^4 -231.3441

BIOGRAPHY

Srinivasa Ramanujan was born in southern India in 1887. Although he had no formal schooling, he had an uncanny manipulative ability in arithmetic and algebra. When a mathematician said that he had just ridden in a taxi that was labeled with the "dull" number 1729, Ramanujan disagreed that the number was dull. He immediately pointed out that 1729 is the least number that can be represented in two different ways as the sum of two cubes:

$$1^3 + 12^3 = 1729 \text{ and } 9^3 + 10^3 = 1729$$

Ramanujan spent much of his life developing ways of calculating pi. The formulas found in his "Notebooks" never contained proofs. Also, computer algorithms were anticipated by Ramanujan, though he knew nothing about computer programming. Today, with our supercomputers, we are able to verify the accuracy of the work Ramanujan did by hand.

Use books about the history of mathematics or other reference books to answer the following questions.

1. Our system of numeration for integers is called the Hindu-Arabic system. What is the origin of the system?
Invented in India and transmitted by the Arabs to western Europe.

2. Why is Srinivasa Ramanujan often called the "formula man"?
He discovered many important algebra formulas.

58   Chapter 2 Algebraic Expressions

Properties of Real Numbers

Objectives: To identify the commutative, associative, distributive, and identity properties of real numbers
To simplify expressions using the properties of real numbers

Properties of real numbers are statements that are true for all real numbers. These properties help you perform arithmetic and algebraic calculations.

Capsule Review

Some of the statements below are examples of the properties of real numbers; others are just false statements.

In each case, tell whether the statement is *true* or *false*.

1. $-3 + 5 = 5 + (-3)$ true

2. $7 - 11 = 11 - 7$ false

3. $-4 + (12 + 9) = (-4 + 12) + 9$ true

4. $6 + (2 - 15) = (6 + 2) - 15$ true

5. $-\dfrac{3}{4}(16) = 16\left(-\dfrac{3}{4}\right)$ true

6. $18 \div \dfrac{3}{5} = \dfrac{3}{5} \div 18$ false

The sum of 0 and any real number a is equal to the number a. That is, $a + 0 = a$, so 0 is called the **additive identity.**

The product of 1 and any real number a is equal to the number a. That is, $a \cdot 1 = a$, so 1 is called the **multiplicative identity.**

The commutative properties state that the order in which you add or multiply two numbers does not change the sum or the product.

Commutative Property for Addition

For all real numbers a and b, $\quad a + b = b + a$.

Commutative Property for Multiplication

For all real numbers a and b, $\quad a \cdot b = b \cdot a$.

The associative properties state that when you add or multiply more than two numbers, the grouping of the numbers does not change the result.

2.3 Properties of Real Numbers **59**

LESSON PLAN

Vocabulary
Additive identity
Multiplicative identity
Properties

Materials/Manipulatives
Calculators

BACKGROUND

In the Capsule Review, students should recognize statements that are true from their previous study of real-number properties. Those students who have difficulty should evaluate the expressions on both sides of the equals sign to see if the statement is true or false. This review is a warmup that prepares students for the properties of real numbers.

- In this lesson, the word *property* is used in place of *axiom* or *postulate*. Students are asked to name the property that justifies a given statement. They then use the properties of real numbers to simplify expressions. This is valuable preparation for the two-column proofs they will study later in geometry.
- Explain how using the parentheses' keys on a calculator can facilitate calculations involving the distributive property.

CHALKBOARD EXAMPLES

- **For Example 1**

  Simplify:
  1. $(54 + 9) + 91$ 154
  2. $\frac{2}{5} \cdot \left(\frac{1}{3} \cdot \frac{5}{2}\right)$ $\frac{1}{3}$

- **For Example 2**

  Simplify by using the distributive property:
  3. $46(100 + 23)$ 5658
  4. $\left(\frac{3}{7} - \frac{1}{5}\right)\frac{7}{3}$ $\frac{8}{15}$

Common Error

- Students often confuse the commutative and associative properties. To help students distinguish between them, use the following real world analogies. Compare the word *commutative* to "commuting" back and forth from home to school or to taking a "commuter" train to work and back. The word *associative* can be thought of in terms of three students standing next to each other. Without changing position, the middle student can "associate" with the student on the left or with the one on the right.
- See *Teacher's Resource Book* for additional remediation.

| Associative Property for Addition |
| For all real numbers a, b, and c, $(a + b) + c = a + (b + c)$. |

| Associative Property for Multiplication |
| For all real numbers a, b, and c, $(a \cdot b) \cdot c = a \cdot (b \cdot c)$. |

EXAMPLE 1 **Simplify: a.** $(13 + 2) + 98$ **b.** $\frac{5}{7} \cdot \left(\frac{2}{3} \cdot \frac{7}{5}\right)$

a. $(13 + 2) + 98 = 13 + (2 + 98) = 13 + 100$, or 113

b. $\frac{5}{7} \cdot \left(\frac{2}{3} \cdot \frac{7}{5}\right) = \frac{5}{7} \cdot \left(\frac{7}{5} \cdot \frac{2}{3}\right) = \left(\frac{5}{7} \cdot \frac{7}{5}\right) \cdot \frac{2}{3} = 1 \cdot \frac{2}{3}$, or $\frac{2}{3}$

How did the *order* or the *grouping* of the numbers change? How did these changes make the computation easier?

Multiplication is said to be *distributive over addition* (or *subtraction*). The distributive property allows you to simplify an expression such as $5(11 + 7)$ in two different ways:

$$5(11 + 7) = 5(18) \qquad \text{or} \qquad 5(11 + 7) = 5(11) + 5(7)$$
$$= 90 \qquad\qquad\qquad\qquad = 55 + 35$$
$$\qquad\qquad\qquad\qquad\qquad = 90$$

| Distributive Property |
| For all real numbers a, b, and c, |
| $a(b + c) = a \cdot b + a \cdot c$ and $(b + c)a = b \cdot a + c \cdot a$ |
| $a(b - c) = a \cdot b - a \cdot c$ and $(b - c)a = b \cdot a - c \cdot a$ |

EXAMPLE 2 **Simplify by using the distributive property:**

a. $43(100 + 2)$ **b.** $\left(\frac{2}{5} - \frac{1}{9}\right)5$

a. $43(100 + 2) = 43 \cdot 100 + 43 \cdot 2 = 4300 + 86 = 4386$

b. $\left(\frac{2}{5} - \frac{1}{9}\right)5 = \frac{2}{5} \cdot 5 - \frac{1}{9} \cdot 5 = 2 - \frac{5}{9} = 1\frac{4}{9}$

In your work in algebra, you will often use the following properties of equality.

Properties of Equality

For all real numbers a, b, and c:

Reflexive Property	$a = a$
Symmetric Property	If $a = b$, then $b = a$.
Transitive Property	If $a = b$ and $b = c$, then $a = c$.

CLASS EXERCISES

Which property of real numbers justifies each statement?

1. $3 + [5 + (-2)] = (3 + 5) + (-2)$ **2.** $6 \cdot 13 = 13 \cdot 6$ commut. prop. mult.
assoc. prop. addit.

3. $4(3 + 7) = 4 \cdot 3 + 4 \cdot 7$ distrib. prop.   **4.** $1.4 + 0 = 1.4$ ident. prop. addit.

5. $\frac{8}{7} \cdot \frac{4}{9} \cdot \frac{7}{8} = \frac{8}{7} \cdot \frac{7}{8} \cdot \frac{4}{9}$ commut. prop. mult. **6.** $4 + (-1 + 9) = [4 + (-1)] + 9$
assoc. prop. add.

For Discussion

7. Is subtraction commutative? For all real numbers a and b, does
$a - b = b - a$? Justify your answer by giving a numerical example.
no; $3 - 2 \neq 2 - 3$

8. Is division associative? For all real numbers a, b, and c, does
$a \div (b \div c) = (a \div b) \div c$? Justify your answer by giving a numerical
example. no; $8 \div (4 \div 2) \neq (8 \div 4) \div 2$

PRACTICE EXERCISES

Simplify.

A   **1.** $(10 + 3) + 55$ 68   **2.** $(16 + 7) + 32$ 55   **3.** $98 + (27 + 9)$ 134

4. $53 + (30 + 29)$ 112   **5.** $\frac{2}{3} \cdot \left(\frac{1}{7} \cdot \frac{3}{2} \right)$ $\frac{1}{7}$ **6.** $\frac{7}{8} \cdot \left(\frac{1}{4} \cdot \frac{8}{7} \right)$ $\frac{1}{4}$

Simplify by using the distributive property.

7. $10(500 + 13)$ **8.** $12(200 + 10)$ **9.** $25(98 - 5)$ **10.** $36(53 - 12)$
5130   2520   2325   1476

11. $(1 - 100)0.25$ **12.** $(1000 + 30)1.5$ **13.** $\left(\frac{2}{3} - \frac{8}{21} \right)7$ 2   **14.** $\left(\frac{2}{5} - \frac{7}{8} \right)5$ $-\frac{19}{8}$
-24.75 1545

Left sidebar reproduction (Practice worksheet)

Left sidebar reproduction (Enrichment worksheet)

Main content

Which property of real numbers justifies each statement?

B

15. $-3(a + 2) = -3(a) + (-3)(2)$ distributive
16. $(5 + y)(-2) = 5(-2) + y(-2)$ distributive
17. $8 - 7xy = 8 - 7yx$ commutative
18. $8(4b) = (8 \cdot 4)b$ associative
19. If $12 = 3x$, then $3x = 12$. symmetric
20. If $y + 4 = 9$ and $9 = 5 + 4$, then $y + 4 = 5 + 4$. transitive property

Rewrite each expression, using the distributive property.

21. $2(3x - 11)$
    $(2)(3x) - (2)(11)$
22. $(6 + 2y)7$
    $(7)(6) + 7(2y)$
23. $-\frac{3}{4}\left(\frac{2}{3}x - 8\right)$
    $\left(-\frac{3}{4}\right)\left(\frac{2}{3}x\right) - \left(-\frac{3}{4}\right)(8)$
24. $(-5j + 20)\left(-\frac{3}{5}\right)$
    $\left(-\frac{3}{5}\right)(-5j) + \left(-\frac{3}{5}\right)(20)$
25. $12a - 3a$
    $a(12 - 3)$
26. $19b + 11b$
    $b(19 + 11)$

Is the property true with respect to the given operation(s) for all real numbers? If not, give a statement to show that it is false.

C

27. Associative; subtraction
    false; $(2 - 3) - 4 \neq 2 - (3 - 4)$
28. Commutative; division
    false; $2 \div 4 \neq 4 \div 2$
29. Distributive; division over multiplication false; $12 \div (6 \cdot 2) \neq (12 \div 6)(12 \div 2)$
30. Distributive; multiplication over division false; $2(8 \div 4) \neq (2 \cdot 8) \div (2 \cdot 4)$
31. Distributive; subtraction over division false; $2 - (10 \div 5) \neq (2 - 10) \div (2 - 5)$
32. Distributive; multiplication over multiplication false; $3 \cdot 7 \cdot 5 \neq (3 \cdot 7)(3 \cdot 5)$

Applications

Use the properties of real numbers to find the total cost.

33. **Consumerism** Flour—3 bags @ 99¢ per bag; Cereal—3 boxes @ $2.19 per box; Juice—3 bottles @ $1.31 per bottle $13.47

34. **Consumerism** Envelopes—10 boxes @ 89¢ per box; Ballpoint pens—5 boxes @ $1.59 per box; Staples—10 boxes @ $2.59 per box $42.75

WRITING IN ALGEBRA

On a separate piece of paper, write a brief description of each term. For example:

Variable: A letter or symbol used to represent unspecified number(s)

1. absolute value
2. additive inverse
3. grouping symbol
4. multiplicative inverse
5. rational number
6. real number
7. operation
8. zero
9. inequality symbol

Additional Answers · Writing in Algebra
1. a number's distance from the origin on a number line
2. When it is added to its own opposite, the sum is zero.
3. indicates the order in which mathematical operations are to be performed
4. a number n such that the product of $\frac{1}{n}$ and n is 1
5. can be written as $\frac{m}{n}$, where m and n are integers

See Additional Answer section beginning p. 719.

Combining Like Terms

Objective: To simplify algebraic expressions by combining like terms

LESSON PLAN

Vocabulary
Like terms
Numerical coefficient
Unlike terms

Materials/Manipulatives
*Teacher's Resource Book,
Teaching Aid 2,
Transparency 3*

A *term* of an expression is a number, a variable, or a product or quotient of numbers and variables. Examples of terms are 13, x, $5y^2$, $6ab$, and $\frac{x}{7}$.

The expression $6x^2 + x - 6$ consists of three terms: $6x^2$, x, and -6. The **numerical coefficient** or **coefficient** of the term $6x^2$ is 6. The coefficient of x is 1, since $x = 1x$.

BACKGROUND

In the Capsule Review, some of the properties taught in Lesson 2.3 are reviewed in preparation for combining like terms. You may want to point out that in Exercise 4 there are two factors, 9 and $(3x - 7)$.

Capsule Review

> $5a + 11a = 11a + 5a$ by the commutative property for addition
> $5a + 11a = (5 + 11)a$ by the distributive property

Use the property listed to write an expression equivalent to $4x^2 + 3x^2$.

1. commutative property for addition
$3x^2 + 4x^2$

2. distributive property $(4 + 3)x^2$

Use the property listed to write an expression equivalent to $9(3x - 7)$.

3. distributive property $9 \cdot 3x - 9 \cdot 7$

4. commutative property for multiplication
$(3x - 7)9$

Algebraic expressions such as $5a + 11a$ and $4x^2 + 3x^2$ contain *like terms*.

> **Like** (or **similar**) **terms** are terms that are exactly the same or differ only in their numerical coefficients. Terms that are not like terms are called **unlike terms.**

EXAMPLE 1 **Name the terms and tell whether they are like or unlike:**
a. $4x^2y + 3x^2y$ **b.** $-6a^2b + 3ab^2$ **c.** $m - 3m$ **d.** $3d + 6$

Expression	**Terms**	**Like or Unlike**
a. $4x^2y + 3x^2y$	$4x^2y$, $3x^2y$	Like terms
b. $-6a^2b + 3ab^2$	$-6a^2b$, $3ab^2$	Unlike terms
c. $m - 3m$	m, $-3m$	Like terms
d. $3d + 6$	$3d$, 6	Unlike terms

Explain why the terms in (a) are called like terms and the terms in (b) are called unlike terms.

2.4 Combining Like Terms **63**

- Note that any variable x has a numerical coefficient of 1 and an exponent of 1; that is, x can be written as $1x^1$.
- For Example 1, be sure students can explain why the terms in a. and c. are called like terms—that is, they differ only in their numerical coefficients. The terms in b. and d. are called unlike terms because they do not have the same corresponding exponents.
- For Example 3a, point out that according to the rules for order of operations the distributive property must be used first. Some students may want to add 4 and 2 as a first step.
- Use Transparency 3 and Teaching Aid 2, in the *Teacher's Resource Book,* to illustrate the distributive property. Use a grease pencil to insert parentheses where needed.

CHALKBOARD EXAMPLES

- **For Example 1**
  Name the terms and tell whether they are like or unlike:
  1. $3pg + 7p^2q$
  $3pg, 7p^2q$; unlike
  2. $g + 7g$ $g, 7g$; like
  3. $-11ab^2 + 3ab^2$
  $-11ab^2, 3ab^2$; like
  4. $9c + 9$ $9c, 9$; unlike

- **For Example 2**
  Simplify:
  5. $3x + 9x$ $12x$
  6. $8c + 7c + 4c^3 - 2c^3$
  $15c + 2c^3$
  7. $9 + 7c - 3d + 5c - 5d - 3$
  $6 + 12c - 8d$

- **For Example 3**
  Simplify:
  8. $8z + (2z - 3)3 + 15$
  $14z + 6$
  9. $5a^3b^2 + 2a^2b^3$
  Unlike terms cannot be combined.

Some algebraic expressions can be simplified by using the distributive property to combine like terms, such as $4y + 7y$:

$$4 \cdot y + 7 \cdot y = (4 + 7)y, \text{ or } 11y$$

EXAMPLE 2 **Simplify:** **a.** $x + 6x$ **b.** $8z + 5z + 4z^2 - 3z^2$
c. $-4 + 3a - 2b + 5b - 6 - 7a$

a. $x + 6x$
$= 1x + 6x$
$= (1 + 6)x$
$= 7x$

b. $8z + 5z + 4z^2 - 3z^2$
$= (8z + 5z) + (4z^2 - 3z^2)$
$= (8 + 5)z + (4 - 3)z^2$
$= 13z + 1z^2, \text{ or } 13z + z^2$

c. $-4 + 3a - 2b + 5b - 6 - 7a$
$= (3a - 7a) + (-2b + 5b) + (-4 - 6)$
$= -4a + 3b + (-10)$
$= -4a + 3b - 10$

EXAMPLE 3 **Simplify:** **a.** $4 + 2(3x + 1) + 5x$ **b.** $4mn^2 + 3m^2n$

a. $4 + 2(3x + 1) + 5x$
$= 4 + 6x + 2 + 5x$
$= (6x + 5x) + (4 + 2)$
$= 11x + 6$

b. $4mn^2 + 3m^2n$
Unlike terms cannot be combined.

CLASS EXERCISES

For each expression; state the number of terms, name each term, and give its numerical coefficient.

1. $3x + y$
2; $3x, y$; 3, 1

2. $-4xy^3$
1; $-4xy^3$; -4

3. $3a + a + 5a + 4$
4; $3a, a, 5a, 4$; 3, 1, 5

4. $xy^2 + x^2y$
2; xy^2, x^2y; 1, 1

For each expression, tell whether the terms are like or unlike.

5. $6 + 5m$ unlike   **6.** $4xy - 5xy$ like   **7.** $3r^2s^3 - 6r^2s^3$ like   **8.** $u^3 + u^2$ unlike

Simplify.

9. $3x + 8x$ $11x$ **10.** $5y + 4y$ $9y$ **11.** $-4a^2 + 11a^2$ $7a^2$ **12.** $16m^2 - 3m^2$ $13m^2$

PRACTICE EXERCISES

For each expression, tell whether the terms are like or unlike.

A **1.** $4xy^2z - xy^2z$ like   **2.** $r^2st - 12r^2st$ like   **3.** $7a^2b + 3ab^2$ unlike

4. $8m^2n^2 + 3mn^2$ unlike   **5.** $2x + 6x$ like   **6.** $8a + 3a$ like

64   Chapter 2 Algebraic Expressions

7. $2 + 5m$ _{unlike} **8.** $7y - 6$_{unlike} **9.** $t^2 - t$_{unlike}

10. $x - x^2$_{unlike} **11.** $4a + a$_{like} **12.** $b + 3b$_{like}

Simplify.

13. $3x + 5x$ _{8x}

14. $2y + 8y$ _{10y}

15. $-9t - 3t$ _{−12t}

16. $-2q - 5q$ _{−7q}

17. $9 + 2t + 6$ _{2t + 15}

18. $8 + 3x + 7$ _{3x + 15}

19. $15g^2 - 3g^2$ _{12g²}

20. $12m^3 - 9m^3$ _{3m³}

21. $5x + 2x + 6x^2 + x^2$ _{7x² + 7x}

22. $3y^3 + 2y^3 + 8y - y$ _{5y³ + 7y}

23. $-2 + 5g - 4h + 3h + 4 + 7g$
_{12g − h + 2}

24. $-1 - 4x + 6y + 3 - 4x - 6y$
_{−8x + 2}

25. $3ab + 6ab$ _{9ab}

26. $10rs + 13rs$ _{23rs}

27. $3ab^2 + 2ab^2$ _{5ab²}

28. $6m^2n + 3m^2n$ _{9m²n}

29. $1 + 6(m + 2) - 2m$ _{4m + 13}

30. $-2 + 3(2b - 8) + 4b$ _{10b − 26}

B **31.** $2 + 3x - 4y + 11y - 6 - 9x$
_{7y − 6x − 4}

32. $6m - 19 + 27 - 11n + 4m - 11n$
_{10m − 22n + 8}

33. $3(x + 2) + 5$ _{3x + 11}

34. $2(x + 1) + 3$ _{2x + 5}

35. $3r + 2(r - 1)$ _{5r − 2}

36. $6s + 3(s - 2)$ _{9s − 6}

37. $4 + 3(2x + 1)$ _{6x + 7}

38. $3 + 4(3x + 2)$ _{12x + 11}

39. $3(5c) - 15c^2 + c$ _{16c − 15c²}

40. $9b^2 + 4(5b) - 8b^2$ _{b² + 20b}

41. $4(2x^3 + x^2) - 5x^2$ _{8x³ − x²}

42. $-8b^3 + 5(b^2 - 4b^3)$ _{−28b³ + 5b²}

43. $(10 + 5r)13 + (11 + 6r)15$ _{295 + 155r}

44. $(6p - 22)5 + (7p - 25)4$ _{58p − 210}

45. $4(m + n) + 3(m + n)$ _{7m + 7n}

46. $6(a + b) + 7(a + b)$ _{13a + 13b}

47. $2(x^2 - y) + 4(x^2 - y)$ _{6x² − 6y}

48. $7(g^3 - h) + 3(g^3 - h)$ _{10g³ − 10h}

49. $2(t - t^2) + 5(t + t^2)$ _{3t² + 7t}

50. $5(b^2 + b) + 8(b^2 - b)$ _{13b² − 3b}

C **51.** $3(x^2y + xy^2) + 6(x^2y^2 - 2xy^2)$
_{3x²y − 9xy² + 6x²y²}

52. $7(3mn - mn^2) + 5(mn^2 - m^2n)$
_{21mn − 2mn² − 5m²n}

53. $\frac{1}{2}(4a + 2b) + \frac{1}{3}(6a - 3b)$ _{4a}

54. $\frac{1}{4}(8v + 4w) + \frac{1}{2}(10w - 12v)$
_{−4v + 6w}

55. $\frac{1}{4}\left(y - \frac{1}{2}\right) + \left(y + \frac{1}{3}\right)\frac{3}{8}$ _{5/8 y}

56. $\frac{3}{10}(a - 10) + \left(\frac{3}{4}a - 6\right)\frac{2}{5}$ _{3/5 a − 27/5}

57. $6[5c + 4(d - 2c)] - 5c$ _{−23c + 24d}

58. $4[2a + 3(2b - a)] + 8b$ _{−4a + 32b}

59. $0.69[b + 2(0.6b - 0.5)]$ _{1.518b − 0.69}

60. $0.4[2.54(a + 0.2) - a]$
_{0.616a + 0.2032}

2.4 Combining Like Terms **65**

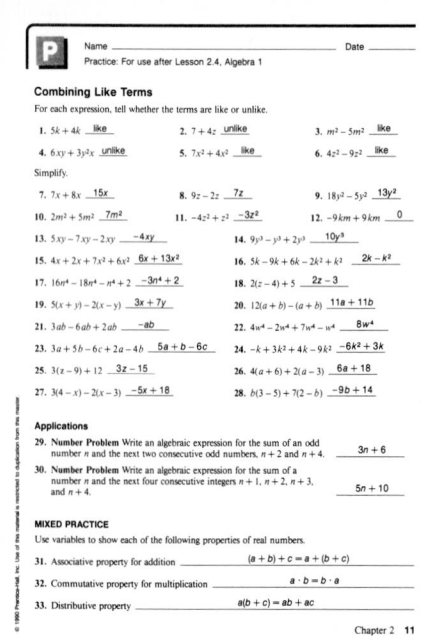

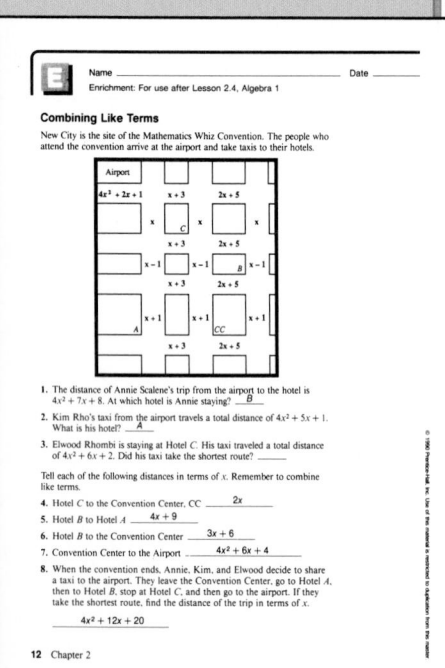

Applications

61. Number Problem Write an algebraic expression for the sum of a number n and the next two consecutive numbers, $n + 1$ and $n + 2$. Simplify the expression. $n + (n + 1) + (n + 2); 3n + 3$

62. Number Problem Write an algebraic expression for the sum of an even number n and the next two consecutive even numbers, $n + 2$ and $n + 4$. Simplify the expression. $n + (n + 2) + n + 4; 3n + 6$

Geometry The area of a rectangle is found by multiplying length times width. Find the total area of each set of figures.

63.

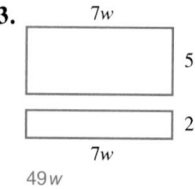

$49w$

64.

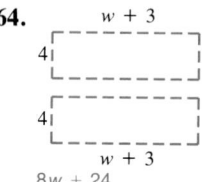

$8w + 24$

TEST YOURSELF

Simplify each expression. 2.1

1. $9 - 6 \cdot 3$ -9 **2.** $-1 + 7(4 + 4)$ 55 **3.** $8 \div 16 \cdot 2$ 1

Evaluate each expression if $x = -2$, $y = 0$, and $z = 3$. 2.2

4. $5x + 3$ -7 **5.** $2x - 3y + 4z$ 8 **6.** $x + \dfrac{y + z}{y - z}$ -3

7. Simplify $3 \cdot 2^4 \cdot 4$. 192

8. Evaluate $-m^2 + n$ if $m = -3$ and $n = -2$. -11

9. Evaluate $V = \pi r^2 h$ for V if $\pi \approx 3.14$, $r = 3$, and $h = 2$. 56.52

Which property of real numbers justifies each statement? 2.3

10. $m + (-n) = (-n) + m$
commut. prop. addit.

11. $[2(6.5)] \cdot 10 = 2[(6.5) \cdot 10]$
assoc. prop. mult.

12. $8\left(\dfrac{3}{8}x - 1\right) = 3x - 8$
distrib. prop.

13. $\dfrac{2}{3} + \left(-\dfrac{4}{5}\right) + \dfrac{5}{6} = \dfrac{5}{6} + \dfrac{2}{3} + \left(-\dfrac{4}{5}\right)$
commut. prop. addit.

Simplify each expression. 2.4

14. $-4y^2 + y + 3y^2$ $-y^2 + y$ **15.** $5hk - 5hk^2 + 6hk - 5h^2k$
$11hk - 5hk^2 - 5h^2k$

16. $3(a^2 - 1) + 4(a^2 - 2)$ $7a^2 - 11$ **17.** $5(x^2 + 2) - 3(x^2 + 1)$ $2x^2 + 7$

66 Chapter 2 Algebraic Expressions

Simplifying and Evaluating Expressions with Parentheses

Objective: To simplify and evaluate algebraic expressions containing grouping symbols

In mathematics, science, and situations that arise daily, it is often necessary to find the value of an algebraic expression where the numerical values of the variables are given.

For example, when the local weather forecaster states, ''The current temperature downtown is 5°C.'' You can estimate the Fahrenheit temperature by doubling the Celsius temperature and adding 32. The actual Fahrenheit temperature can be found by evaluating the algebraic expression $(1.8 \cdot C) + 32$.

$$(1.8 \cdot C) + 32$$
$$\downarrow \quad \downarrow \quad \quad \downarrow$$
$$= (1.8 \cdot 5) + 32$$
$$= 9 + 32$$
$$= 41$$

The Fahrenheit temperature is 41°.

Capsule Review

To evaluate $x - 2y$ if $x = 2$, $y = -3$, substitute the given values for the variables, and then simplify the result.

$$x - 2y$$
$$= 2 - 2(-3)$$ *Substitute 2 for x and −3 for y.*
$$= 2 + 6$$ *Multiply.*
$$= 8$$ *Then add.*

Evaluate each expression if $x = 2$ and $y = -3$.

1. xy -6 **2.** $2xy$ -12 **3.** $2x + y$ 1 **4.** $x + 2y$ -4

5. $x - y$ 5 **6.** $y - x$ -5 **7.** $3x - y$ 9 **8.** $2y - 2x$ -10

One way to simplify an expression such as $-(3x - 2)$ is to apply the property of -1 for multiplication.

Property of −1 for Multiplication

For every real number a,

$$-1 \cdot a = -a \text{ and } a \cdot -1 = -a$$

2.5 Simplifying and Evaluating Expressions with Parentheses   **67**

LESSON PLAN

Materials/Manipulatives
Calculators
Overhead projector
Teacher's Resource Book,
  Teaching Aid 2,
  Transparency 3

BACKGROUND

In the Capsule Review, as preparation for using grouping symbols, students evaluate algebraic expressions without grouping symbols using real numbers. If students are having difficulty, you may want to review the rules for operations with real numbers and rules for order of operations.

Critical Thinking

Observation What are the advantages of simplifying the algebraic expression first and then evaluating? Students should observe that the simplified algebraic expression requires fewer substitutions for the variable and the resulting numerical computation is easier.

- When you explain the property of −1 for multiplication, you may want to review the different meanings of the minus sign; for example, subtraction, additive inverse, or opposite.
- In Example 1, students should realize the second method shown is the preferred method. As students get proficient, more steps can be done mentally.
- This lesson is a natural follow-up to the previous lesson. You may have to remind students that in Example 2 they are distributing −3, not 3 over $2x + 4$.
- For Exercises 11–28, have students review using the parentheses' and exponent keys on a calculator to solve each expression. Have students use the memory key to evaluate Exercises 39–44.

CHALKBOARD EXAMPLES

- **For Example 1**
  Simplify:
  1. $5z + 4 − (2z + 3)$ $3z + 1$

- **For Example 2**
  Simplify:
  2. $−2(7a + 3) − (15a − 13)$
  $−29a + 7$

- **For Example 3**
  Simplify:
  3. $−(3yz^3) − 2(4y^3z) − 5yz^3$
  $−8yz^3 − 8y^3z$

- **For Example 4**
  Simplify: Then evaluate if $a = 2$ and $b = 4$.
  4. $−(a^3 + b^2)$ $−24$
  5. $−(a^2 − b^3)$ 60

- **For Example 5**
  Simplify: Then evaluate if $b = 1.5$.
  6. $5 + 3[4 − 2(3 − b) + 6b]$
  35

To apply this property to $−(3x − 2)$, think of $(3x − 2)$ as a real number a.

$$\overset{a}{\overbrace{−(3x − 2)}}$$

$$= −1(3x − 2) \qquad −a = −1 \cdot a$$

$$= −1(3x − 2) \qquad \text{Use the distributive property.}$$

$$= −1 \cdot 3x + (−1)(−2)$$

$$= −3x + 2$$

Because the terms in $−3x + 2$ are unlike, it is not possible to simplify the expression further.

EXAMPLE 1   Simplify: $2a − 3 − (a + 2)$

$$2a − 3 − (a + 2)$$
$$= 2a − 3 + (−1)(a + 2) \qquad −(a + 2) = −1(a + 2)$$
$$= 2a − 3 + (−1)(a) + (−1)(2)$$
$$= \underline{2a + (−1a)} + \underline{(−3) + (−2)} \qquad \text{Group like terms.}$$
$$= \quad 1a \quad + \quad (−5) \qquad \text{Combine like terms.}$$
$$= a − 5$$

Here is another way to simplify $2a − 3 − (a + 2)$. Compare it with the steps shown in Example 1.

$$2a − 3 − (a + 2)$$
$$= 2a − 3 − 1(a + 2) \qquad \text{Omit the step using the } + \text{ symbol.}$$
$$= 2a − 3 − a − 2 \qquad \text{Use the distributive property mentally.}$$
$$= a − 5 \qquad \text{Combine like terms without showing the grouping.}$$

EXAMPLE 2   Simplify: $(16x − 11) − 3(2x + 4)$

$$(16x − 11) − 3(2x + 4)$$
$$= 16x − 11 − 6x − 12 \qquad \text{Remove parentheses.}$$
$$= 16x − 6x − 11 − 12$$
$$= 10x − 23 \qquad \text{Combine like terms.}$$

In Example 2, $(16x − 11) = 1(16x − 11)$ by the identity property for multiplication. The parentheses are removed by distributing 1 over $(16x − 11)$.

EXAMPLE 3   Simplify: $−(2xy^2) − (3xy^2 + 4x^2y)$

$$−(2xy^2) − (3xy^2 + 4x^2y)$$
$$= −2xy^2 − 3xy^2 − 4x^2y$$
$$= −5xy^2 − 4x^2y$$

EXAMPLE 4 Simplify: $-(r + s^2)$. Then evaluate if $r = 3$ and $s = -2$.

$$-(r + s^2)$$
$$= -r - s^2$$

$$-r - s^2$$
$$= -(3) - (-2)^2 \qquad \textit{Substitute 3 for r and } -2 \textit{ for s.}$$
$$= -3 - (4)$$
$$= -3 - 4$$
$$= -7$$

When an expression contains more than one set of grouping symbols, begin with the innermost grouping and work toward the outermost grouping.

EXAMPLE 5 Simplify: $3 + 2[-4(p - 4) + 8p]$. Then evaluate if $p = 0.5$.

$$3 + 2[-4(p - 4) + 8p]$$
$$= 3 + 2[-4p + 16 + 8p] \qquad \textit{Remove parentheses. Use the distributive property.}$$
$$= 3 + 2[4p + 16] \qquad \textit{Combine like terms within brackets.}$$
$$= 3 + 8p + 32 \qquad \textit{Remove brackets. Use the distributive property.}$$
$$= 8p + 35 \qquad \textit{Combine like terms.}$$

$$= 8 \cdot 0.5 + 35 \qquad \textit{To evaluate } 8p + 35, \textit{ substitute 0.5 for p.}$$
$$= 4 + 35$$
$$= 39$$

CLASS EXERCISES

Simplify.

1. $-(x + 3)$ $-x - 3$
2. $-(y - 7)$ $-y + 7$
3. $-(-a + 4)$ $a - 4$
4. $-(-b - 3)$ $b + 3$
5. $-(2m^2 + 3)$ $-2m^2 - 3$
6. $-(5n^2 - 6)$ $-5n^2 + 6$
7. $-(-f^2 + f)$ $f^2 - f$
8. $-(-2g^2 - g)$ $2g^2 + g$
9. $-(ab^2) - (ab^2)$ $-2ab^2$
10. $-(2rs) - (rs)$ $-3rs$
11. $2x - 4 - (x - 5)$ $x + 1$
12. $y - 7 - (4 + 2y)$ $-y - 11$

Simplify. Then evaluate if $a = 6$ and $b = -5$.

13. $-(b - a^2)$ $-b + a^2; 41$
14. $-4[2(b + 3) - a]$ $4a - 8b - 24; 40$

PRACTICE EXERCISES

Simplify.

A 1. $2g - 4 - (g + 4)$ $g - 8$
2. $4 + 5m - (3 + m)$ $1 + 4m$

2.5 Simplifying and Evaluating Expressions with Parentheses **69**

Common Error
- When using the property of -1 for multiplication, students may distribute the -1 only over the first term in the parentheses. For example, $-1(3x - 2)$ may be written as $-1 \cdot 3x - 2$ or as $-3x - 2$. For these students, you may want to require that they use arrows whenever there are parentheses; for example, $-\overset{\frown}{1(3x} - 2)$.
- See the *Teacher's Resource Book* for additional remediation.

LESSON FOLLOW-UP

Critical Thinking
Comparing-Contrasting Compare and contrast the lesson objectives of Lessons 2.1 and 2.5. In what major ways are Lessons 2.5 and 2.1 alike? different? In both lessons, the objective is to simplify and evaluate algebraic expressions. In both, grouping symbols are used, and the rules for order of operations are the same. In terms of contrast, students should observe that in Lesson 2.1 the expressions to be simplified are numerical or become numerical expressions when values of the variables are substituted. In Lesson 2.5, the expressions to be simplified and evaluated are algebraic and are first simplified algebraically and then evaluated.

Assignment Guide
- See p. 50B for assignments.
- In exercises like Exercise 21, some students may distribute the -3 but forget to distribute the 2.
- When using the formula for the area of a trapezoid, students should realize that sometimes it is easier to take $\frac{1}{2}$ of the height first. Other times, it may be easier to find the product of the height and the sum of the bases first. Either method will yield a correct answer.
- See *Teacher's Resource Book*, Technology, pp. 4–5.

3. $(3a + 4) - (5a - 9)$ $13 - 2a$
4. $(2h - 5) - (7h + 5)$ $-5h - 10$
5. $(5t^2 - 2) - (2t^2 + 7)$ $3t^2 - 9$
6. $(9p^2 - 1) - (3p^2 + 2)$ $6p^2 - 3$
7. $(x + 5) - 3(x + 2)$ $-2x - 1$
8. $(y + 3) - 2(y + 7)$ $-y - 11$
9. $-(ab^2c) - (3abc^2 - 2ab^2c)$
  $ab^2c - 3abc^2$
10. $-(a^2bc) - (-a^2bc^2 - a^2bc)$ a^2bc^2

Simplify each expression. Then evaluate for the given value(s) of the variables in Exercises 11–18 and 25–28.

11. $-(a + b^2)$ if $a = 2$ and $b = -5$ -27
12. $-(m + n^2)$ if $m = 3$ and $n = -7$
  -52
13. $-(x - y^2)$ if $x = 4$ and $y = -1$ -3
14. $-(r - s^2)$ if $r = 1$ and $s = -5$ 24
15. $8 + 3[-2(p - 3) + 2p]$ if $p = 0.3$ 26
16. $5 + 2[-1(z - 7) + 4z]$ if $z = 0.2$
  20.2
17. $13 - 4[3(q + 1) - 2q]$ if $q = -1$ 5
18. $10 - 3[4(a + 2) - 3a]$ if $a = -3$
  -5

B

19. $x^2yz - (-x^2yz^2 - x^2yz)$ $2x^2yz + x^2yz^2$
20. $x^2yz^2 - (-xyz^2 - x^2yz^2)$
  $2x^2yz^2 + xyz^2$
21. $2 + 2[-3(x - 2)]$ $-6x + 14$
22. $7 + 3[-2(x - 1)]$ $-6x + 13$
23. $(5r - 9) + (r - 9)16$ $21r - 153$
24. $(x - 11)12 + (x + 13)$ $13x - 119$
25. $-(m - n^2); m = 4, n = -5$
  $-m + n^2; 21$
26. $-(y - z^2); y = -6, z = 7$
  $-y + z^2; 55$
27. $5 - 6[10(x^2 + 2x) + 3x]; x = -2$
  $5 - 60x^2 - 138x; 41$
28. $11 - [4y + 3(y^2 - 5y)]8; y = 2$
  $-24y^2 + 88y + 11; 91$

Simplify.

C

29. $4 - \{m + [5(m + 1) - m]\}$ $-5m - 1$
30. $2 - \{g + [3(g - 1) + g]\}$ $-5g + 5$
31. $1 - \{a - [a + (a - 3)]\}$ $a - 2$
32. $1 - \{q - [q - (q + 4)]\}$ $-q - 3$
33. $5 - 4\{13 + [3(2x - 7 + x)]\}$
  $-36x + 37$
34. $7 + 9\{11 - [4(3z + 6 - z)]\}$
  $-72z - 110$

Applications

The formula for finding the area A of a trapezoid is

$$A = \frac{1}{2}h(b_1 + b_2)$$

where h is the height and b_1 and b_2 are the lengths of the two parallel bases.

35. **Geometry** Find the area of a trapezoid if its height is 3 cm and the lengths of its bases are 5 cm and 7 cm. 18 cm^2

36. **Geometry** Find the area of a trapezoid if its dimensions are: height, 14 ft, and bases, 10 ft and 12 ft. 154 ft^2

Geometry Write an expression for the perimeter of each figure. Simplify the expression.

$2(x + 2) + 2 \cdot 2 + 2(x + 4) + x;\ 5x + 16$

37.

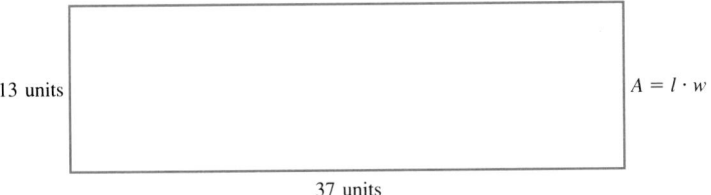

$3a$ $3a$

$a + 6$ $a + 6$

$3a$ $3a$

$4(3a) + 2(a + 6);\ 14a + 12$

38.

$x + 4$ $x + 4$

2 2

$x + 2$ $x + 2$

x

Calculator One way to evaluate $4(p - 3) + p^2$ if $p = 0.3$ is to use the Memory Key on your calculator. Store the value 0.3 in Memory. Then evaluate as usual, except press Memory Recall Key when p is needed.

You may find that the following exercises can be worked more quickly by using a calculator.

Evaluate each expression for the given value of the variable.

39. $10 - (y - 2) + y^2;\ y = 1.7$ 13.19   **40.** $9 + (2x - 3) + x^2;\ x = 3.1$ 21.81

41. $(a - 4)12 + (a + 6)13;\ a = -1$ 5   **42.** $10(b + 9) - 3(b - 8);\ b = -2$ 100

43. $(m - 6)^2 + 3(m - 6);\ m = -2$ 40   **44.** $\frac{1}{2}(x - x^2) + \frac{1}{3}(x^2 - 1);\ x = 6$ $-\frac{10}{3}$

ALGEBRA IN GEOMETRY

1. The perimeter of a figure is the sum of the lengths of its sides. If the sides measure n, $n + 1$, $n + 2$, and $n + 3$, find the perimeter of the figure in terms of n. What is the least integral sum that the perimeter can be? $4n + 6;\ 10$

2. The rectangle below measures 37 units by 13 units. Its area is 481 square units.

13 units $A = l \cdot w$

37 units

The number $481 = (37)(13)$. Express the factor 37 as the sum of two squares. How many 6 by 6 squares can fit into the rectangle? How many 1-unit squares are left? $37 = 6^2 + 1^2;\ 13;\ 13$

2.5 Simplifying and Evaluating Expressions with Parentheses   **71**

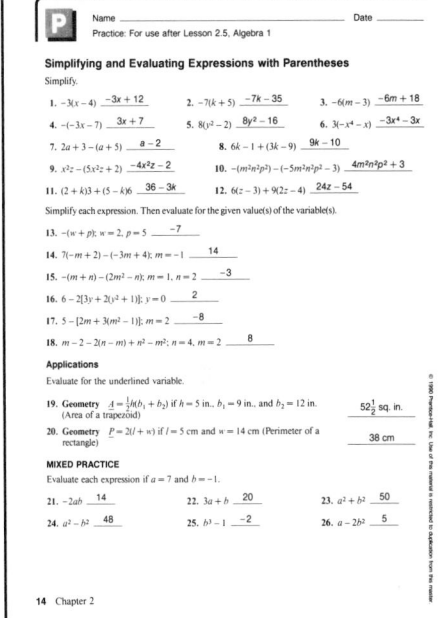

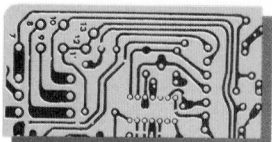

TECHNOLOGY:
Introduction to Spreadsheets

One of today's most widely used computer software applications programs is a spreadsheet. A **spreadsheet** is a table of information that is organized into rows and columns.

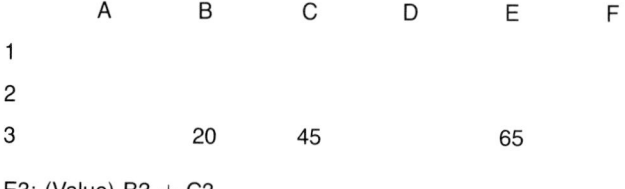

The intersection of a row and a column is a **cell.** A cell is named by the column-row (letter-number) that forms it. The cell indicated above is C3.

Each cell can contain two types of data:

- Labels: letters or words such as R or JOB
- Values: numbers such as 7 or \$4.25 or expressions such as 28 + 72 or B3 + D3

The second expression above, B3 + D3, tells the computer to add the contents of cells B3 and D3. The sum will be displayed in the same cell where the expression is located.

	A	B	C	D	E	F
1						
2						
3		20	45		65	

E3: (Value) B3 + C3

When you enter an expression or formula into a spreadsheet, the spreadsheet will calculate and display the results in various cells in certain ways. If you change the information in any cell, the program can recalculate every other cell that uses that information. A spreadsheet performs calculations using the same rules for order of operations that you use when making calculations in mathematics.

A feature of spreadsheets is the "what if" speculating it allows you to do. Suppose you wanted to see how best to use your money. You might set up a spreadsheet like the one below.

```
File: Money                          REVIEW/ADD/CHANGE

========= A ========= B ========= C ========= D ========= E =========
 1:
 2: WEEKLY INCOME
 3:    BALANCE                    $15.45
 4:    ALLOWANCE
 5:    JOB
 6:    MISCELLANEOUS
 7:
 8:    TOTAL INCOME
 9:
10:
11: WEEKLY EXPENSES
12:    CLOTHES
13:    TAPES
14:    FOOD
15:    MOVIES:
16:    MISCELLANEOUS
17:
18:    TOTAL EXPENSES
19:
20:
21: MONEY FOR SAVINGS
C8: (Value)
```

If you enter values in the INCOME categories for a given week, you can then experiment by putting various values in the EXPENSES categories for the same time span.

Many functions available in a spreadsheet are shortcuts for certain kinds of arithmetic. The @SUM function, for example, totals a group of values and presents the result in a cell where the function appears. You will learn more about this function later.

Solve. Use cell names to state the formula that you would use for:

1. C8 C3 + C4 + C5 + C6   **2.** C18   **3.** C21 C8 – C18
                                    C12 + C13 + C14 + C15 + C16
4. Use a spreadsheet to project your monthly savings based on your weekly income and expenses. Answers may vary. Possible answer is C18 *4.

5. If you want to save $100 a month toward the cost of a new stereo, how could you adjust your income and expenses to meet that goal? Answers may vary.

6. If you planned on saving the same amount of money each week, what expression could you put in C23 if it represents how much money you save in a year? C18 *52

7. If in a given week you received an additional $25 that you do not usually get, use the "what if," capability of the spreadsheet to see how you could spend the $25 and still save the amount you usually do. Answers will vary.

BACKGROUND

In the Capsule Review, students translate simple word phrases to algebraic expressions involving only one operation. This review prepares students for their work in translating more complex word phrases into algebraic expressions.

2.6

Translating Phrases to Algebraic Expressions

Objectives: To translate a word phrase to an algebraic expression
To write word phrases for algebraic expressions

You can use algebra as a tool for applying mathematical logic to real-life situations and solving problems. In order to do so, you must be able to translate simple English word phrases into *algebraic expressions*.

Capsule Review

EXAMPLE   Translate each word phrase to an algebraic expression.

x decreased by y	$x - y$	**a less than z**	$z - a$
p divided by q	$\dfrac{p}{q}$	**u more than y**	$y + u$

Translate each word phrase to an algebraic expression.

1. The sum of a and b $a + b$ **2.** x decreased by d $x - d$

3. The product of e and f ef **4.** g divided by h $\dfrac{g}{h}$

5. i less than j $j - i$ **6.** k more than l $l + k$

7. The quotient of m and n $\dfrac{m}{n}$ **8.** The difference of o and p $o - p$

9. Two minus y $2 - y$ **10.** r times 4 $4r$

EXAMPLE 1   Translate each word phrase to an algebraic expression.

    a. Pedro's age in 4 years if p is his age now

    b. 3.14 times the square of the length of the radius r

    c. The sum of two consecutive numbers if n is the first number

    a. $p + 4$ **b.** $3.14 \cdot r^2$, or $3.14r^2$ **c.** $n + (n + 1)$, or $2n + 1$

When you need to translate a word phrase to an algebraic expression but the variable is not given, the following steps may apply:

1. Assign a variable to one of the unknown quantities.

2. Write an expression for any other unknown quantities in terms of the same variable.

74   Chapter 2 Algebraic Expressions

EXAMPLE 2 **Translate each word phrase to an algebraic expression.**

    a. Twice the sum of a number and 3
    b. Woodrow's age 7 years ago
    c. A given length subtracted from 3 times that length

    a. Let x = the number. $2(x + 3)$

    b. Let w = Woodrow's age now. $w - 7$

    c. Let l = length.
       Then $3l$ = 3 times the length. $3l - l$

Explain why $2x + 3$ is not a correct translation of the word phrase in Example 2a.

EXAMPLE 3 **Translate to an algebraic expression: The amount of money Della has (in cents) if she has 6 more dimes than Felix.**

    Let d = number of dimes Felix has.
    Then $d + 6$ = number of dimes Della has.
    The value of $d + 6$ dimes is $10(d + 6)$ cents.

    So, Della has $10(d + 6)$ cents.

Working backwards can be a helpful strategy when translating word phrases to algebraic expressions.

EXAMPLE 4 **Write two word phrases for each algebraic expression:**
    a. $k - 5$ **b.** $5n + 25$

  a. A number k decreased by 5   **b.** 5 times a number n increased by 25
     5 less than some number k The sum of $5n$ and 25

CLASS EXERCISES

Translate each word phrase to an algebraic expression.

1. Six more than a number $n + 6$ **2.** A number decreased by 2 $n - 2$

3. One-half of a number $\frac{1}{2}n$ **4.** The quotient of a number and 6 $\frac{n}{6}$

5. Two less than 5 times a number $5n - 2$ **6.** Five more than 2 times a number
                                                $2n + 5$

7. The product of 5 and a number squared $5n^2$

8. The quotient of a number squared and 3 $\frac{n^2}{3}$

9. Four times the sum of a number and 9 $4(n + 9)$

10. Twice the difference of a number and 7 $2(n - 7)$

TEACHING SUGGESTIONS

- This lesson focuses on the skill of translating phrases and sentences to algebraic expressions. You may want to point out that this is a necessary skill in many problem-solving lessons later in the book.
- This lesson lends itself to having students work in groups. As students discuss the phrases or sentences, understanding may come more easily.

Critical Thinking

Generalizing State the different phrases that imply addition, subtraction, multiplication, or division. Formulate a generalization that states whether the order in which terms are written makes a difference. Students should state that for subtraction and division, the order in which terms are presented makes a difference.

CHALKBOARD EXAMPLES

For Exercises 1–5, translate each word phrase to an algebraic expression.

- **For Example 1**
  1. The sum of two consecutive even numbers if n is the first number
     $n + (n + 2)$ or $2n + 2$
  2. 6 times the square of the length of a rectangle l $6l^2$
  3. Mickey's age 3 years ago if a is his age now $a - 3$

- **For Example 2**
  4. The difference between the square of a radius and the radius $r^2 - r$
  5. The product of 3 and a number cubed $3n^3$

- **For Example 3**
  6. The amount of money Donald has (in cents) if he has 3 fewer quarters than Daisy $25(q - 3)$

• **For Example 4**

Write two word phrases for each algebraic expression.

7. $r + 3$ A number r increased by 3;
3 more than some number r

8. $\frac{p}{4}$ The quotient of p and 4; a
number p divided by 4

Common Error

• When a phrase calls for the operation of subtraction or division, students often make an error in the order in which they write the terms in the expression. Emphasize the importance of reading each word phrase or sentence several times. Review Transparency 1, in the *Teacher's Resource Book,* to distinguish between operations.

• See *Teacher's Resource Book* for additional remediation.

LESSON FOLLOW-UP

Assignment Guide

See p. 50B for assignments.

Lesson Quiz

Translate each word phrase to an algebraic expression.
1. 17 more than a number $n + 17$
2. A number decreased by 6 $n - 6$
3. The difference between twice a number and 5 $2n - 5$
4. Four times the quotient of a number and 9 $4 \cdot \frac{n}{9}$ or $\frac{4}{9} n$
5. The amount of money Diane has (in cents) if she has 9 more dimes than David $10(d + 9)$

Answer each question with an algebraic expression. Let s be Sarah's age now.
6. What was her age 4 years ago? $s - 4$
7. How old is Courtney now if she is 3 years older than Sarah? $s + 3$
8. How old was Courtney 4 years ago? $(s + 3) - 4$, or $s - 1$

76

Write two word phrases for each algebraic expression. Answers may vary.
See below.
11. $2n + 3$ **12.** $9 - 3c$ **13.** $r^2 + 1$ **14.** $10d^2 + 60$

PRACTICE EXERCISES

Translate each word phrase to an algebraic expression.

A **1.** Seven less than a number $n - 7$ **2.** A number decreased by 6 $n - 6$

3. Five more than a number $n + 5$ **4.** A number increased by 6 $n + 6$

5. One less than 8 times a number $8n - 1$ **6.** Nine more than 1 times a number $1n + 9$, or $n + 9$

7. The product of 5 and a number squared $5n^2$

8. The product of 6 and a number squared $6n^2$

9. The quotient of a number squared and 3 $\frac{n^2}{3}$

10. The quotient of a number squared and 2 $\frac{n^2}{2}$

11. Six times the sum of a number and 3 $6(n + 3)$

12. Twice the sum of 3 and a number $2(3 + n)$

Write two word phrases for each algebraic expression. Answers may vary.
See side column.
13. $3d - 5$ **14.** $7d + 6$ **15.** $w(w + 3)$

Answer each question with an algebraic expression.

B **16.** Let s be Sumi's age now.
  a. What was Sumi's age 4 years ago? $s - 4$
  b. Hiko is 2 years older than Sumi. Represent Hiko's age now. $s + 2$
  c. What was Hiko's age 4 years ago? $s - 2$

17. Let m be Mike's age now.
  a. What was Mike's age 4 years ago? $m - 4$
  b. Tina is 4 years younger than Mike. Represent Tina's age now. $m - 4$
  c. What was Tina's age 4 years ago? $m - 8$

Solve. Use $A = lw$ to find the area and $P = 2l + 2w$ to find the perimeter.

18. Let w be the width of a rectangle whose length is 4 units more than its width.
  a. What is the width? w **b.** What is the length? $w + 4$
  c. Find the area. $w(w + 4) = w^2 + 4w$ **d.** Find the perimeter. $4w + 8$

19. Let l be the length of a rectangle whose width is 7 units less than its length.
  a. What is the length? l **b.** What is the width? $l - 7$
  c. Find the area. $l(l - 7) = l^2 - 7l$ **d.** Find the perimeter. $4l - 14$

76   Chapter 2 Algebraic Expressions

Additional Answers
Class Exercises
11. two times a number plus three; two times a number increased by three
12. nine decreased by three times a number; the difference of nine and three times a number
13. a number squared increased by one; one more than a number squared
See Additional Answer section beginning page 719.

C **20.** Tony buys baseball pennants at 3 for *a*¢ and sells them all at 5 for *b*¢. Represent Tony's profit on each pennant. $\frac{b}{5} - \frac{a}{3}$ assuming $3b > 5a$

21. Sadie bought several items at the record store. A tape costs $12 less than a disc, and the same amount as a record. If a tape costs *t* dollars, what is the cost of 4 tapes, 3 discs, and 2 records? How much change did Sadie receive if she paid for these items with 11*t* dollars?
$9t + 36$ dollars; $2t - 36$ dollars

Applications

Write an algebraic expression for one unknown in terms of the other.

22. Sports The Los Angeles Dodgers have won twice as many World Series as the Chicago Cubs. $d = 2c$

23. Sports If the Pittsburgh Pirates win one more series, they will have won 3 times as many series as the Chicago Cubs. $p + 1 = 3c$

24. Sports Baseball trivia.
  a. Joe DiMaggio hit 3 more home runs than Yogi Berra. $d = b + 3$
  b. If Babe Ruth had hit 2 more home runs, he would have hit twice as many as Yogi Berra. $r + 2 = 2b$
  c. If Hank Aaron had hit 1 more home run, he would have hit 40 more than twice as many as Yogi Berra. $a + 1 = 2b + 40$

CAREER

For a computer to be useful, information must be input into the computer and processed information must be retrieved from it. Computer software is of two types: programs and data. Programs are sets of instructions; data are collections of organized information. Software is generally stored on disks.

If you are interested in computers, you may find a career as a **computer software developer** to be both rewarding and lucrative.

William Gates started a computer programming company in 1970 when he was in the 10th grade. One of his programs was written to schedule classes in schools.

In 1975 William Gates and a friend, Paul Allen, started a computer software company and they became multimillionaires from the company's profits.

Conduct research and list at least two other people who have been successful in the field of computers since 1975.

2.6 Translating Phrases to Algebraic Expressions **77**

Vocabulary

Empty set
Equation
Inequality
Open sentence
Replacement set
Solution
Solution set

BACKGROUND

In the Capsule Review, students are asked to evaluate formulas for given values of the variables. This review leads into the content of the lesson: finding solution sets of open sentences from given replacement sets.

Critical Thinking

Classification Classify the statement 2 = 5 by considering the questions: Is the statement an equation? Why? Is the statement true or false? Students should be able to conclude that the statement is an equation because it is a statement of equality for two numbers; that is, two numerical expressions. The statement is false, however. Students should conclude further that the truth or falsehood of a statement does not necessarily deny its classification as an equation.

2.7

Open Sentences and Solution Sets

Objective: To find solution sets of open sentences from given replacement sets

Usually you see lightning flash and then listen for the thunder. The thunder often occurs within 10 seconds. Sometimes it is possible to tell the distance to the thunderstorm. A science reference book indicates that the formula $d = \frac{1}{5}s$ can be used to find the distance from the thunderstorm.

d = distance, in miles, of storm from observer
s = time in seconds

$$d = \frac{1}{5}s$$

$$= \frac{1}{5} \cdot 10 = 2 \text{ mi}$$

Capsule Review

Find the value of A for the given values of the variables.

EXAMPLE

$w = 3$

$l = 5$

$A = lw$
$\quad = 5 \cdot 3$
$\quad = 15$
$A = 15$ square units

1. $l = 8$ and $w = 6$ 48   **2.** $l = 11.1$ and $w = 5$ 55.5   **3.** $l = \frac{1}{2}$ and $w = 7$ $\frac{7}{2}$

Find the distance d for the given values of the rate r and the time t.

4. $r = 10$ and $t = 2$ 20   **5.** $r = 50$ and $t = 3$ 150   **6.** $r = 26$ and $t = \frac{1}{2}$ 13

Some of the most powerful tools of mathematics are *equations* and *inequalities*. They are often used in solving problems in daily life.

> An **equation** is a mathematical sentence in which the symbol = (equals) connects two numerical or variable expressions.
>
> An **inequality** is a mathematical sentence in which the symbol < (less than), > (greater than), or ≠ (is not equal to) is used.

78   Chapter 2 Algebraic Expressions

An equation such as $x - 5 = 1$ or an inequality such as $x - 3 < 4$ that contains a variable is neither true nor false until you replace the variable with a number. Such equations and inequalities that contain variables are called **open sentences.**

A **solution** of an open sentence is any value of the variable that makes the open sentence a true statement.

The **replacement set** of an open sentence is the set of numbers that may be substituted for the variable.

The **solution set** of an open sentence is the set of all of the numbers from the replacement set that make the open sentence true.

EXAMPLE 1 Find the solution set of $1 - 6g = -1$. The replacement set is $\left\{-1, 0, \frac{1}{3}\right\}$.

Replace g with -1.

$$1 - 6g = -1$$
$$1 - 6(-1) = -1$$
$$1 + 6 = -1$$
$$7 = -1 \quad \text{False}$$

Replace g with 0.

$$1 - 6g = -1$$
$$1 - 6(0) = -1$$
$$1 - 0 = -1$$
$$1 = -1 \quad \text{False}$$

Replace g with $\frac{1}{3}$.

$$1 - 6g = -1$$
$$1 - 6\left\{\frac{1}{3}\right\} = -1$$
$$1 - 2 = -1$$
$$-1 = -1 \quad \checkmark \text{ True}$$

$\frac{1}{3}$ makes $1 - 6g = -1$ true. The solution set is $\left\{\frac{1}{3}\right\}$.

EXAMPLE 2 Find the solution set of $x - 5 < -4$. The replacement set is $\{-1, 0, 1\}$.

Replace x with -1.

$$x - 5 < -4$$
$$-1 - 5 < -4$$
$$-6 < -4 \quad \checkmark \text{ True}$$

Replace x with 0.

$$x - 5 < -4$$
$$0 - 5 < -4$$
$$-5 < -4 \quad \checkmark \text{ True}$$

Replace x with 1.

$$x - 5 < -4$$
$$1 - 5 < -4$$
$$-4 < -4 \quad \text{False}$$

-1 and 0 make $x - 5 < -4$ true. The solution set is $\{-1, 0\}$.

When no number from the replacement set makes an open sentence true, the solution set is the **empty set,** $\{\ \}$. Another symbol for the empty set is $\emptyset$.

2.7 Open Sentences and Solution Sets **79**

Common Error

Common Error

- Some students may mistakenly change an inequality symbol to an equal sign when *solving* inequalities. Remind these students that we are using replacements sets and that the inequality symbols should be maintained.
- See *Teacher's Resource Book* for additional remediation.

LESSON FOLLOW-UP

Assignment Guide

See p. 50B for assignments.

Did You Know?

Find out additional information about Colossus I and compare it in several ways to modern computers.

Lesson Quiz

Find the solution set of each sentence. The replacement set is $\{-2, 0, 2\}$.

1. $m + 4 = 2$ $\{-2\}$
2. $z + 3 \neq 1$ $\{0, 2\}$
3. $y + 5 < 6$ $\{-2, 0\}$
4. $3d + 10 = 10$ $\{0\}$
5. $8x - 1 > 4$ $\{2\}$

Find the solution set of each sentence. The replacement set is $\left\{-\frac{1}{2}, 0, 1, 1\frac{1}{2}\right\}$.

6. $2r + 1 = -2$ $\emptyset$ or $\{\ \}$
7. $1 < 4 - 4m$ $\left\{-\frac{1}{2}, 0\right\}$
8. $2 = b \cdot b$ $\emptyset$ or $\{\ \}$

Enrichment

Write examples of open sentences for which the solution set is (a) all numbers, (b) one and only one solution, (c) exactly two numbers, and (d) the empty set. Use the real numbers as the domain. Answers may vary. Possible answers are: $x + 2 = x - (-2)$, {all real numbers}; $x + 3 = 4$, $\{1\}$; $x^2 = x$, $\{0, 1\}$; $x = -\frac{1}{x}$, $\emptyset$.

EXAMPLE 3 Find the solution set of $-2 > y - 3$. The replacement set is $\left\{1, 1\frac{1}{2}, 2\right\}$.

$-2 > y - 3$	$-2 > y - 3$	$-2 > y - 3$
$-2 > 1 - 3$	$-2 > 1\frac{1}{2} - 3$	$-2 > 2 - 3$
$-2 > -2$ False	$-2 > -1\frac{1}{2}$ False	$-2 > -1$ False

The solution set is $\emptyset$.

EXAMPLE 4 Solve: $x \neq \dfrac{1}{x}$. The replacement set is $\{-1, 1, 2\}$.

$x \neq \dfrac{1}{x}$ is read as "*x is not equal to* $\dfrac{1}{x}$."

$x \neq \dfrac{1}{x}$	$x \neq \dfrac{1}{x}$	$x \neq \dfrac{1}{x}$
$-1 \neq \dfrac{1}{-1}$	$1 \neq \dfrac{1}{1}$	$2 \neq \dfrac{1}{2}$
$-1 \neq -1$ False	$1 \neq 1$ False	$2 \neq \dfrac{1}{2}$ ✔ True

The solution set is $\{2\}$.

CLASS EXERCISES

Classify each sentence as *true* or *false*.

1. $3 \cdot 4 - 8 = 10$ F
2. $-5 \cdot 6 < -7$ T
3. $-9 \cdot \dfrac{1}{9} \neq 9\left(-\dfrac{1}{9}\right)$ F

Find the solution set of each sentence. The replacement set is $\{-1, 0, 1\}$.

4. $a + 3 = 0$ $\emptyset$
5. $3m < 0$ $\{-1\}$
6. $g - 2 \neq -1$ $\{-1, 0\}$
7. $q + q = 2$ $\{1\}$
8. $n + 1 > 0$ $\{0, 1\}$
9. $x + 2 = 0$ $\emptyset$

PRACTICE EXERCISES

Find the solution set of each sentence. The replacement set is $\{-1, 0, 1\}$.

A
1. $5 - 4x = 1$ $\{1\}$
2. $2 - 3z = 5$ $\{-1\}$
3. $n + 3 = 3$ $\{0\}$
4. $m + 2 = 1$ $\{-1\}$
5. $y - 1 < 2$ $\{-1, 0, 1\}$
6. $x + 1 > -2$ $\{-1, 0, 1\}$
7. $a - 0 \neq 0$ $\{-1, 1\}$
8. $b - 1 \neq 0$ $\{-1, 0\}$
9. $3y + 5 = 5$ $\{0\}$
10. $2x + 1 = 3$ $\{1\}$
11. $2x + 3 > 0$ $\{-1, 0, 1\}$
12. $1 - 6h < 7$ $\{0, 1\}$
13. $3g = -3$ $\{-1\}$
14. $-5d = -5$ $\{1\}$
15. $-4 > 2y - 5$ $\{-1, 0\}$

Find the solution set. The replacement set is $\left\{-2,\, -1,\, 0,\, \frac{1}{2}\right\}$**.**

16. $-6 < 3 - 3m$ $\left\{-2,\, -1,\, 0,\, \frac{1}{2}\right\}$ **17.** $-x - 3 = 5x$ $\emptyset$ **18.** $-n - 4 = 6n$ $\emptyset$

B   **19.** $9c = 7c + 1$ $\left\{\frac{1}{2}\right\}$ **20.** $d^2 - 2 = 2$ $\{-2\}$ **21.** $f^2 - 3 = -2$ $\{-1\}$

22. $2d \cdot 2d = 0$ $\{0\}$ **23.** $1 = m \cdot m$ $\{-1\}$ **24.** $-x = \dfrac{4}{x}$ $\emptyset$

25. $\dfrac{1}{a} = -1$ $\{-1\}$ **26.** $5x - 2 \neq 2 - 5x$ $\left\{-2,\, -1,\, 0,\, \frac{1}{2}\right\}$ **27.** $-7y - 6 \neq -6 - 7y$ $\emptyset$

**Write two different open sentences for which each of the following is the
solution set. The replacement set is** $\{-2,\, -1,\, 0,\, 1,\, 2\}$**.** Answers may vary.
Some possible answers are shown.

C   **28.** $\{1\}$ **29.** $\{-2, 2\}$ **30.** $\{-2, -1, 0, 1, 2\}$ **31.** $\{0, 2\}$
     $x - 1 = 0;\ 3x = 3$ $x^2 - 4 = 0;\ 3x^2 = 12$ $x < 3;\ 2x = 2x$ $x^2 - 2x = 0;\ 3x^2 = 6x$

**If possible, find a number that can replace x in each open sentence to
make it a true statement. If no such number can be found, explain why.**

32. $\dfrac{7}{x} = 3\dfrac{7}{3}$ **33.** $\dfrac{6}{x} < 0$ **34.** $x^2 + 2x \neq x + (x^2 + x)$
                       any negative number   no such number; left side
                                                    and right side always have
                                                        same value

Applications

Number Problems   Translate each open sentence into words.

35. $-5 > -7$ **36.** $4 > -11$ **37.** $a - 6 > 0$
     Negative five is greater   Positive four is greater than   Six subtracted from a is
     than negative seven.   negative eleven.   greater than zero.

DID YOU KNOW?

Did you know that the first successful electronic computer, Colossus 1, was
built in England in 1943? It was designed for a single purpose—to crack
secret codes during World War II. The main designer of Colossus 1 was an
Englishman named Alan Turing (1912–1954). His theory of how a computer
should work earned him the honor of being called "the father of computers."

COLOSSUS

COUNTERS

2.7 Open Sentences and Solution Sets   **81**

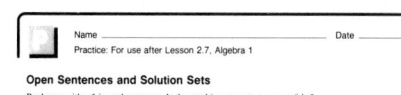
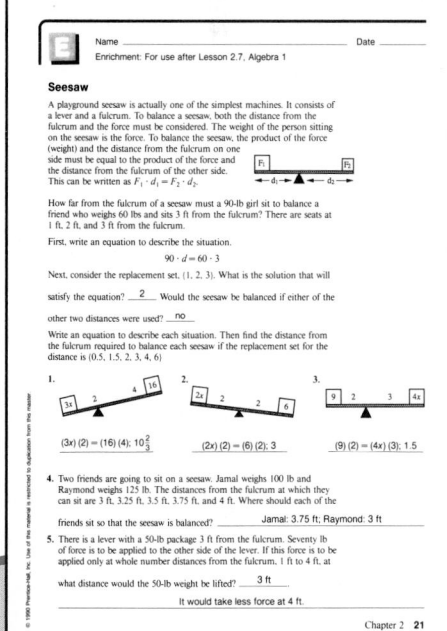

BACKGROUND

A student's ability to organize information given in a problem, so that it can be used to solve the problem, is a key to success in this lesson. To determine a student's progress, analyze errors in the student's work and then classify specific errors.

Error Analysis Classification

1. *Misunderstanding*
   Failed to understand that the solution set has a very large number of possible solutions or is an infinite set

2. *Misapplied Strategy*
   Wrote an incorrect model to find the possible solutions
   Listed the possible solutions incorrectly
   Made error(s) in checking the possible solutions

TEACHING SUGGESTIONS

* Discuss the meaning of the term *finite* as being a countable number of elements in a set.

* Point out that computers, which are able to check thousands of possible solutions quickly, have enabled scientists to solve problems that were not solvable in the recent past.

2.8

Problem Solving Strategy: Account for All Possibilities

The problem solving strategy of accounting for all possibilities means that every possible solution to a problem is identified and checked to see if it is actually a solution. This strategy can be used if the number of possible solutions is **finite,** meaning you can count the number of possible solutions.

The replacement set of the variable lists the possible solutions for a given open sentence. You can find the solution by replacing the variable with each number in the replacement set. When a number from the replacement set makes an open sentence a true statement, that number is a solution. A false statement indicates that the possible solution was not a solution.

If the replacement set of a variable is **infinite,** then the strategy of accounting for all possibilities cannot be used.

EXAMPLE 1 Erik weighs w lb and his sister, Lauren, weighs 12 lb less. The sum of their weights is 158 lb. Find the weight of Erik and of Lauren.

▢ Understand the Problem

Read the problem.

It is given that Erik weighs w lb and Lauren weighs 12 lb less. The sum of their weights is 158 lb.
You are asked to find the weights of Erik and of Lauren.

▢ Plan Your Approach

Assign symbols.

Let w represent Erik's weight.
Let $w - 12$ represent Lauren's weight.

Write an equation.

$$w + (w - 12) = 158$$

The solution of the equation can be found by using the strategy of accounting for all possibilities. The number w must be less than 90, since $90 + (90 - 12) = 168$. Also, w is greater than 80, since $80 + (80 - 12) = 148$.
Thus, w is a number between 80 and 90.

82 Chapter 2 Algebraic Expressions

Complete the Work	Try the possible whole number solutions for w, starting with 81.
	$81 + (81 - 12) = 150$ *No*
	$82 + (82 - 12) = 152$ *No*
	$83 + (83 - 12) = 154$ *No*
	$84 + (84 - 12) = 156$ *No*
	$85 + (85 - 12) = 158$ *Yes*

Interpret the Results	**State your conclusion.**
	Erik weighs 85 lb and Lauren weighs $85 - 12$, or 73 lb.
	Check your conclusion.
	$85 + 73 = 158$ ✔

LASS EXERCISES

1. Explain the meaning of the word *finite*. Finite means a limited number.
2. Is an open sentence true, false, or neither? Explain. An open sentence is either true or false.
3. Does a solution to an equation or inequality make it true or false? Explain. true
4. Explain the meaning of the word *infinite*. Infinite means unending.

RACTICE EXERCISES

For each equation, find the solution set. In each case, the replacement set is the set of integers from -5 to $+5$, inclusive.

1. $x + 4 = 11$ ∅
2. $y - 2 = 3$ {5}
3. $n + 4 = 4$ {0}
4. $-t + 5 = 9$ {-4}
5. $2k - 4 = -8$ {-2}
6. $3(b - 2) = 0$ {2}
7. $m \div 3 = -1$ {-3}
8. $z \div 5 = 0$ {0}
9. $2(a + 1) = 4$ {1}

Solve each equation by checking the possible solutions.

10. Lois has d dimes and $10(d + 6) = 140$. 8
11. Bob is n years old and $2n + 4 = 34$. 15
12. Ken worked w weeks and $\frac{w}{2} - 1 = 24$. 50
13. Suzanne edited p pages and $5 + \frac{1}{3}p = 16$. 33

Write an equation for each problem. Solve the equation by checking the possible solutions.

14. Helen weighs x pounds. Her sister weighs 9 lb more. The sum of their weights is 229 lb. How much do Helen and her sister weigh?
$x + (x + 9) = 229$; 110 lb, 119 lb

B **15.** Carmen has 2 times as much money as Bill. She has $50 more than he has. How much money does each one have? $m + 50 = 2m$; $50, $100

16. Harry and Beth each have some quarters. Harry has 5 more quarters than Beth. The combined value of their quarters is $4.75. How many quarters does each person have? $25q + 25(q + 5) = 475$; 7, 12

17. The sum of a number and six more than that number is -8. Find the number. $n + (n + 6) = -8$; -7

C **18.** Is it possible to list the solutions of the inequality $x + 4 < -3$ if the replacement set for x is the set of all integers greater than -100? Explain.
$-100 < x < -7$

19. The area of a rectangle is 252 ft^2. The perimeter of the rectangle is 64 ft. Find the length and width of the rectangle.
$l(32 - l) = 252$; $w = 14$ ft; $l = 18$ ft

Mixed Problem Solving Review

1. A submarine made a dive of 419 ft and then came up 212 ft. What was the final depth of the submarine? 207 ft.

2. Write an equation for each word sentence. Solve the equation, using $\{-3, -2, -1, 0, 1, 2, 3\}$ as the replacement set.
  a. a number increased by 2 is -1. $x + 2 = -1$ $\{-3\}$
  b. Twice a number less -3 is 7. $2x - (-3) = 7$ $\{2\}$
  c. The quotient of 9 and a number is -3. $\frac{9}{x} = -3$ $\{-3\}$
  d. The difference between a number and 16 is -1. $x - 16 = -1$ no solution

PROJECT

Review the properties of real numbers discussed in Lesson 2.3. For each property, write its name and the replacement set for the variable or variables.

Are the replacement sets finite or infinite sets? Can you check if the properties are true by using the strategy of accounting for all possibilities? Explain your answer in writing.

Use a dictionary to look up the meaning of the words *assumption* and *postulate*. Do you think that every fact in arithmetic and algebra is a property? That is, do we just assume that all mathematical facts are true? If not, how can we tell true statements from false statements? See below.

Additional Answers
Project
Commutative Property for Addition, Commutative Property for Multiplication, Associative Property for Addition, Associative Property for Multiplication, and the Distributive Property, all have D: {all real numbers}; infinite sets; The Strategy of Accounting for all possibilities cannot be used since the replacement set is infinite; Answers may vary.

Translating Word Statements to Equations

Objectives: To translate a word statement to an equation
To write word statements for equations

The skills you acquire in your study of algebra have many useful applications. Various approaches can be used to solve application-type problems. One approach that is often useful is to translate a word statement into an equation and then solve the equation. The solution of the equation will lead to an answer to the question(s) asked in the problem.

To write an equation, you translate word phrases to algebraic expressions.

Capsule Review

Word Phrase	Algebraic Expression
Four times the length of a side s of a square	$4s$
The value in cents of a given number of dimes d	$10d$
The quotient of a number n and 2 less than the number	$\dfrac{n}{n-2}$

Translate each word phrase to an algebraic expression.

1. The sum of a number x and twice that number $x + 2x$

2. The quotient of a number j and 5 times that number $\dfrac{j}{5j}$

3. The value in cents of a given number of half dollars $50n$

4. Zachary's age 9 years ago $z - 9$

Write a word phrase for each algebraic expression.

5. $r + 2$ two more than a number r
6. $30 - x$ thirty decreased by a number x
7. lw product of l and w
8. $p + 8p$ a number p increased by 8 times that number

EXAMPLE 1 **Write an equation for each word sentence.**
a. The difference between x and y is 6.
b. Nineteen is 7 more than twice z.
c. The sum of 3 times a and 2 is 4.
d. Three times the sum of a and 2 is 4.

The difference between x and y is 6.

a. $x - y = 6$ **b.** $19 = 2z + 7$ **c.** $3a + 2 = 4$ **d.** $3(a + 2) = 4$

2.9 Translating Word Statements to Equations **85**

Materials/Manipulatives
Teacher's Resource Book, Transparency 1

BACKGROUND

In the Capsule Review, the exercises involve writing word phrases and algebraic expressions. If students are having difficulty with the exercises, you may want to refer them to Lesson 2.6.

Critical Thinking

Observation How are the skills developed in Lesson 2.6 related to those being taught in this lesson? Students should observe that the skill of translating word phrases into algebraic expressions (2.6) is used in this lesson (2.8) to set up equations. Both lessons involve a translation process.

- Emphasize the importance of reading each question carefully several times and then thinking about its meaning. Students should identify what they are looking for and choose a variable to represent it.
- Some students may want to solve some of the equations. Remind them that the point of this lesson is not to find the answer but to learn a skill that will help them throughout the course.
- You may want to set up a "Puzzle For Today" board on which you would write an equation or a word statement and then challenge students to translate it.
- Use transparency 1, in the *Teacher's Resource Book*, to review key words in writing an algebraic expression. Add on to the list by using a grease pencil.

CHALKBOARD EXAMPLES

- **For Example 1**

  Write an equation for each word sentence.
  1. Three more than x is 21.
     $x + 3 = 21$
  2. Five less than 11 times g is 28.
     $11g - 5 = 28$
  3. The sum of 4 and 5 times a number is 12. $4 + 5n = 12$
  4. The quotient of a number and two less than the number is 4.

     $\dfrac{n}{n - 2} = 4$

- **For Example 2**

  Use the first sentence to set up the algebraic expression. Write an equation for the second sentence.
  5. Robin is r years old and Marion is 3 years older than him. The sum of their ages is 15.
     $r + (r + 3) = 15$

Writing an equation becomes more challenging when the variable represents a specific number.

EXAMPLE 2 **Use the first sentence to set up an algebraic expression. Write an equation for the second sentence.**

John weighs p lb, and his brother weighs 17 lb more. The sum of their weights is 207 lb.

$p = $ John's weight (lb)
$p + 17 = $ brother's weight (lb)

$$\underbrace{\text{Sum of their weights}}\ \ \underbrace{\text{is}}\ \ 207 \text{ lb}$$
$$p + (p + 17) \qquad = \qquad 207$$

By solving $p + (p + 17) = 207$, you would find John's weight, and then you would be able to find his brother's weight. In later chapters, you will solve equations of this type.

EXAMPLE 3 **Write an equation using the first and second sentence.**

Mineko has 4 times as much money as Tony. She has $15 more than he has.

$m = $ amount of Tony's money (in dollars)
$4m = $ amount of Mineko's money

$$\underbrace{\text{Mineko's money}} \qquad \underbrace{\text{15 more than Tony's}}$$
$$4m \qquad = \qquad 15 + m$$

If you solve the equation $4m = 15 + m$, you would know how much money Tony has, and you could find out how much money Mineko has (4 times as much).

EXAMPLE 4 **Write an equation using the information given.**

Loida and Rosita each have some quarters. Rosita has 6 more than Loida. The combined value of their quarters is $5.50.

$q = $ number of quarters Loida has
$q + 6 = $ number of quarters Rosita has

The value of Loida's quarters in cents is $25q$.
The value of Rosita's quarters in cents is $25(q + 6)$.

$$\underbrace{\text{Combined value}}\ \text{is}\ \underbrace{\$5.50, \text{ or } 550\cancel{c}}.$$
$$25q + 25(q + 6) = 550$$

To improve your ability to translate word statements into equations, it is helpful to practice working backward. Note that there may be many ways to translate a given equation into a word statement.

EXAMPLE 5 **Write a word statement for each equation.**

    a. $w(w + 5) = 14$ **b.** $x^2 = 144$

    a. The product of a number and five   **b.** The square of a number
        more than that number is 14.   is 144.

CLASS EXERCISES

Copy the sentence. Let n = the unknown number and write an equation.
Use arrows to show how the word statement and the equation are related.

1. Two times a number is 14. $2n = 14$ **2.** A number decreased by 12 is 7.
                                                 $n - 12 = 7$
3. One-half of a number is 34. $\frac{1}{2}n = 34$ **4.** The quotient of a number and 6 is $\frac{2}{3}$.

5. Six less than twice a number is 5. $2n - 6 = 5$ $\frac{n}{6} = \frac{2}{3}$

6. The product of 5 and a number squared is 45. $5n^2 = 45$

PRACTICE EXERCISES

Let x = an unknown number. Write an equation for each sentence.

A   **1.** Three less than a number is 18.   **2.** A number decreased by 12 is 4.
        $x - 3 = 18$ $x - 12 = 4$
     3. Four more than a number is 27.   **4.** A number increased by -7 is 2.
        $x + 4 = 27$ $x + (-7) = 2$
     5. Two less than 5 times a number is 18. $5x - 2 = 18$

     6. One more than twice a number is -13. $2x + 1 = -13$

     7. The product of a number squared and 8 is 56. $8x^2 = 56$

     8. The product of 8 times a number and 7 is 79. $8x \cdot 7 = 79$

     9. The quotient of 5 and 3 times a number is 10. $\frac{5}{3x} = 10$

   10. The quotient of 5 and a number squared is 100. $\frac{5}{x^2} = 100$

   11. Six times the sum of a number and 9 is 132. $6(x + 9) = 132$

   12. Three times the sum of a number and 3 is -18. $3(x + 3) = -18$

Write an algebraic expression. Then write an equation for the variable
indicated for the last sentence.

   13. Let b be Bonnie's age now.
       a. What was her age 6 years ago? $b - 6$
       b. If Clyde is 1 year younger than Bonnie, represent his age now. $b - 1$
       c. What was Clyde's age 6 years ago? $b - 7$
       d. If 6 years ago the sum of their ages was 35, write an equation to
         represent this. $(b - 6) + (b - 7) = 35$

- **For Example 3**
  Write an equation for the second sentence.
  6. Cleo has $27 more than Petra. He has 3 times as much money as Petra. $p + 27 = 3p$

- **For Example 4**
  Write an equation for the last sentence.
  7. Irwin and Louise have a lot of dimes. Louise has 13 more dimes than Irwin. The combined value of their dimes is $3.70. $10d + 10(d + 13) = 370$

- **For Example 5**
  Write a word statement for each equation.   Answers may vary. A possible answer is given.
  8. $x^2 - 3 = 172$ Three less than a number squared is 172.
  9. $(2w + 3)w = 113$ The area of a rectangle is 113. The length is 3 more than twice the width.

LESSON FOLLOW-UP

Assignment Guide

- See p. 50B for assignments.
- When solving exercises similar to Exercise 13, students should be encouraged not to give up too quickly. Rereading the problem several times, both before and after solving it, should be encouraged.

Lesson Quiz

Let n = an unknown number. Write an equation for each sentence.

1. A number decreased by 7 is 15.
   $n - 7 = 15$
2. Eight more than 3 times a number is −21. $3n + 8 = -21$
3. Six less than 4 times a number is 18. $4n - 6 = 18$
4. The product of 3 and a number squared is 12. $3n^2 = 12$
5. Five times the sum of the number and eight is 95. $5(n + 8) = 95$
6. The number of dimes that Penny has equals $4.50. $10n = 450$

Let j be Jose's age now. Write algebraic expressions.

7. What was his age 5 years ago? $j - 5$
8. Consuella is 7 years younger than Jose. Represent her age now. $j - 7$
9. What was Consuella's age 5 years ago? $j - 7 - 5$ or $j - 12$
10. Write an equation to represent this statement: Five years ago Jose was 3 times as old as Consuella. $j - 5 = 3(j - 12)$

14. Let j be Jesse's present age.
    a. What will Jesse's age be in 9 years? $j + 9$
    b. If James is 15 years younger than Jesse, represent his present age. $j - 15$
    c. What will James's age be in 9 years? $j - 6$
    d. If in 9 years Jesse will be 2.5 times as old as James, write an equation to represent this. $j + 9 = 2.5(j - 6)$

B 15. Let n be the number of $45 monthly payments made to purchase a VCR.
    a. What is the total value of these payments? $45n$
    b. If a $35 down payment was made, represent the total cost. $45n + 35$
    c. If the VCR cost $485, write an equation to represent this. $45n + 35 = 485$

16. Let n be the number of $55 monthly payments made to buy a stereo.
    a. What is the total value of the monthly payments? $55n$
    b. If there was a down payment of $65, represent the total cost. $55n + 65$
    c. If the stereo cost $670, write an equation to represent this. $55n + 65 = 670$

Write a word statement, or statements, for each equation. Answers may vary.

17. $3n - 7 = 32$

18. $w - 3 = 4w$

19. $w(w + 6) = 48$

20. $2(l - 5) + 2l = 128$

Write an equation for each situation.

C 21. Joan's brother is now 3 times as old as she. In five years, his age will be twice hers. Let j = Joan's age now. $3j + 5 = 2(j + 5)$

22. Paolo's mother is twice old as he. Fourteen years ago, her age was 4 times his age. Let p = Paolo's age now. $2p - 14 = 4(p - 14)$

23. Ernesto has a number of coins, all quarters. Laura has 6 more coins than Ernesto. Her coins are all dimes. The combined value of their coins is $2.35. Let e = number of coins Ernesto has. $25e + 10(e + 6) = 235$

24. Tony has a certain number of quarters and 11 more nickels than quarters. The total value of his coins is $2.65. Let q = number of quarters Tony has. $25q + 5(q + 11) = 265$

Applications

Write an equation for the underlined sentence. Tell what question(s) can be answered if the equation is solved. Answers may vary.

25. **Consumerism** Tom's new car cost $150 more than twice as much as his old one. <u>The cost of the new car was $13,250.</u>

26. **Geometry** The length of a rectangle is 10 mm less than twice its width. <u>The area of the rectangle is 208 mm^2.</u>

88 Chapter 2 Algebraic Expressions

Additional Answers

17. Three times a number decreased by seven equals thirty-two.
18. Three less than w equals four times w.
19. w times the sum of w and six equals forty-eight.
20. Two times the difference of l and five plus the product of two and l equals one hundred and twenty-eight.
25. $2x + 150 = 13,250$; What was the cost of the old car?
26. $(2w - 10)w = 208$; What is the length and width of the rectangle?

27. Consumerism Leila paid \$35 down and made 5 equal monthly payments on her prom dress. <u>The prom dress cost \$110.</u> See below.

28. Geometry The length of a rectangle is 25 in. longer than three times its width. <u>The perimeter of the rectangle is 130 in.</u> See below.

29. Consumerism Sheila paid \$100 more than twice the amount Howard paid in tuition for college courses. <u>Howard paid \$1200 in tuition.</u> See below.

30. Consumerism Jim purchased a compact disc player. He paid \$65 down and made 12 equal monthly payments. <u>The total cost of his compact disc player was \$245.</u> See below.

31. Geometry The height of a triangle is 2 cm more than 4 times the length of the base. <u>The area of the triangle is 55 cm^2.</u> See below.

32. Geometry Two sides of a triangle have the same length. The third side is 12 cm less than 3 times the length of the equal sides. <u>The perimeter of the triangle is 23 cm.</u> See below.

TEST YOURSELF

Simplify each expression.   2.5

1. $2r - 4(r + 3)$ $-2r - 12$
2. $(y - 6) - 2(y + 2)$ $-y - 10$
3. Simplify $-(m^2 - n)$. Then evaluate if $m = -3$ and $n = -2$. $-m^2 + n; -11$

Translate each word phrase to an algebraic expression.   2.6

4. Seven times the sum of a number and 3 $7(n + 3)$
5. Eight less than the quotient of a number and 9 $\frac{n}{9} - 8$

Write two word phrases for each algebraic expression. Answers may vary. See below.

6. $10d - 6$ 7. $\frac{y}{4} + 6$

Find the solution set of each sentence. The replacement set is   2.7
$\{-2, -1, 0, 1, 2\}$.

8. $m + 4 = 3$ $\{-1\}$ 9. $z - 2 > 1$ $\emptyset$ 10. $2x + 1 \neq x$
                                                                      $\{-2, 0, 1, 2\}$

Write an equation for each sentence.   2.8

11. A number decreased by -2 is -11. $n - (-2) = -11$
12. Two more than 5 times a number is 25. $5x + 2 = 25$

2.9 Translating Word Statements to Equations   **89**

Additional Answers
27. $5x + 35 = 110$ **28.** $2w + 2(3w + 25) = 130$
29. $s = 2400 + 100$ **30.** $12x + 65 = 245$
31. $\frac{1}{2}(b)(4b + 2) = 55$ **32.** $2s + 3s - 12 = 23$

6. Ten times d less six; the product of ten and d decreased by six.
7. One fourth y increased by six; the product of one-fourth and y plus six.

Teacher's Resource Book
Reteaching—Chapter 2, p. 24

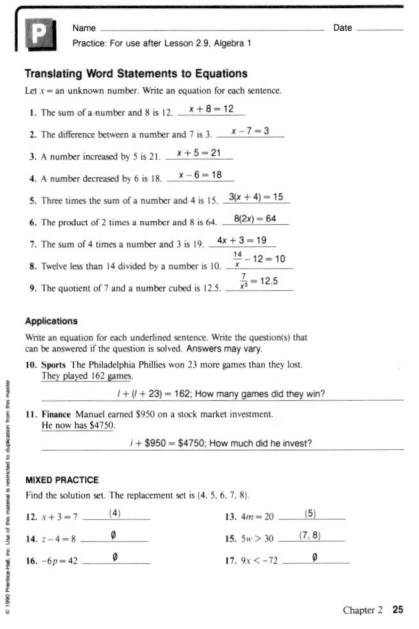

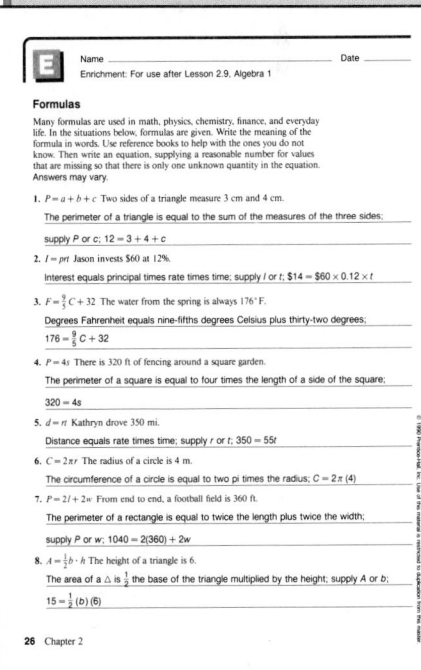

89

Vocabulary

additive identity (59)	factor (55)	properties of real numbers (59)
base (55)	inequality (78)	replacement set (79)
coefficient (63)	like terms (63)	solution (79)
empty set (79)	multiplicative identity (59)	solution set (79)
equation (78)	open sentence (79)	unlike terms (63)
exponent (55)	power (55)	

Rules for Order of Operations

- Perform any operation(s) within grouping symbols.
- Simplify exponents.
- Multiply and divide in order from left to right.
- Add and subtract in order from left to right.

Simplify each expression.   2.1, 2.2

1. $-2(5-8) + 18 \div 3$ 12   **2.** $4\left(\frac{1}{2}\right)^4$ $\frac{1}{4}$ **3.** -0.01^2 -0.0001 **4.** $5(2^4 - 3^3)$ -55

Evaluate each expression if $a = -1$, $b = 4$, and $c = 2$.

5. $c + \dfrac{b-a}{c+a}$ 7   **6.** $(c-b)^3$ -8

Properties of Real Numbers

Commutative:	$-7 + 12 = 12 + (-7)$;	$r \cdot 5 = 5 \cdot r$
Associative:	$(-3 + 8) + 14 = -3 + (8 + 14)$;	$(-9b)c = -9(bc)$
Distributive:	$13(10 + 5) = 13 \cdot 10 + 13 \cdot 5$;	$a(21) - a(5) = a(21 - 5)$

Which property of real numbers justifies each statement?   2.3

7. $-5(29) + (-5)1 = -5(29 + 1)$
distrib. prop.
8. $4kl = 4lk$
commut. prop. mult.
9. $(2x + 3y) + 7y = 2x + (3y + 7y)$
assoc. prop. add.
10. $-2 + [5 + (-x)] = (-2 + 5) + (-x)$
assoc. prop. add.
11. $(13x)y = 13(xy)$
assoc. prop. mult.
12. $(x + y)5 = 5x + 5y$
distrib. prop.

Combining Like Terms   Like terms may be combined by adding or subtracting their numerical coefficients: $-2t + 7t^2 - t^2 = -2t + 6t^2$.

Simplify.   2.4

13. $-3c + c + 5 + 4c^2$ $-2c + 5 + 4c^2$ **14.** $-8x + 3(x - 5)$ $-5x - 15$

15. $mn^2 - mn + 3mn^2 - 2mn$ $4mn^2 - 3mn$ **16.** $4(5 - 3r) - 10r$ $20 - 22r$

90   Chapter 2 Algebraic Expressions

Property of −1 $-(5a - 1) = -1(5a - 1) = -1(5a) - (-1)(1)$
$$= -5a + 1$$

Simplify.   2.5

17. $-(-2h^2 + h) + h$ $2h^2$ **18.** $8t^3 - (4t^2 + t^3)$ $7t^3 - 4t^2$

19. Simplify $-3[2(4 - 5p) + p] - p$. Then evaluate if $p = 2$. $-24 + 26p$; 28

Translating Phrases to Algebraic Expressions

Word Phrase	**Algebraic Expression**
The product of -7 and a number	$-7 \cdot n$, or $-7n$
4 times the difference of a number and 6	$4(a - 6)$

Translate each word phrase to an algebraic expression.   2.6

20. The quotient of 11 and a number $\frac{11}{n}$

21. Twice the sum of a number and -2 $2[n + (-2)]$

22. 8 less than the product of a number and 12 $12n - 8$

23. The number of cents in a given number of nickels $5n$

Finding Solution Sets   The solution set of an open sentence is the set of all numbers from the replacement set that make the open sentence true.

Find the solution set. The replacement set is $\{-2, -1, 0, 1, 2\}$.   2.7

24. $5 + x = 5$ {0}   **25.** $2y - 1 = 3$ {2}   **26.** $v + 2 < -1$ ∅

27. $1 - 3h > 4$ {−2}   **28.** $2w - 1 \neq -1$ **29.** $x^2 = 1$ {−1, 1}
                                     {−2, −1, 1, 2}

Translating Statements to Equations

The product of some number and 5 reduced by 14 is 6.

Let n = some number.   Then: $n(5) - 14 = 6$, or $5n - 14 = 6$

The perimeter of an equilateral triangle is 96 cm.

Let s = length (cm) of a side.   Then: $3s = 96$

Let x = an unknown number. Write an equation for each sentence.   2.8

30. Two times a number is -15. $2x = -15$

31. Two less than twice some number is 1. $2x - 2 = 1$

32. Carla has a number of \$5 bills. Juan has 4 fewer \$5 bills. The total value of their \$5 bills is \$160. $5x + 5(x - 4) = 160$

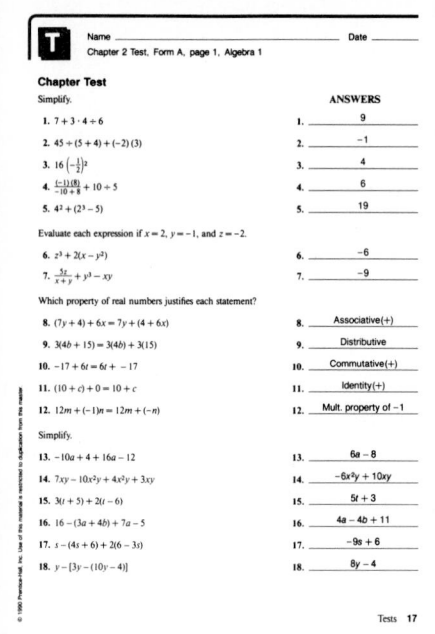

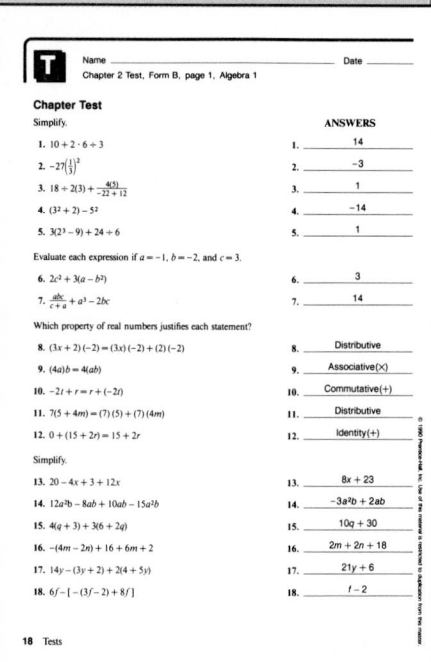

CHAPTER 2 TEST

Simplify each expression.

1. $-3 \cdot 2 + 27$ 21   **2.** $24 \div (8 - 5) + (-2)$ 6   **3.** 2^4 16   **4.** $9\left(\frac{1}{3}\right)^3$ $\frac{1}{3}$

Evaluate each expression if $a = -1$, $b = 4$, and $c = -2$.

5. $\dfrac{a + b}{c}$ $-\frac{3}{2}$ **6.** $\dfrac{b - 2c}{a + b}$ $\frac{8}{3}$

Which property of real numbers justifies each statement?

7. $3(10t + u) = 3(10t) + 3u$ distrib. prop.   **8.** $4d + 11d = (4 + 11)d$ distrib. prop.

9. $(ha)t = h(at)$ assoc. prop. mult.   **10.** $-6f + 5 = 5 + (-6f)$ commut. prop. add.

Simplify.

11. $-7q + 5 - q + q^2$ $-8q + 5 + q^2$ **12.** $-9rt + r^2t - rt + 2rt^2$ $-10rt + r^2t + 2rt^2$

13. $4(x - 2) + x$ $5x - 8$ **14.** $7 - (3 - 2j)$ $4 + 2j$

15. $-5[2 - 3(2t + 7) - t]$ $35t + 95$ **16.** $y - [2y + 3(y - 1)]$ $-4y + 3$

Translate each word phrase to an algebraic expression.

17. Five less than a number $a - 5$

18. The perimeter of a square if the length of one side is l $4l$

Find the solution set. The replacement set is $\{-2, -1, 0, 1\}$.

19. $x - 2 = -1$ $\{1\}$ **20.** $r^2 = 1$ $\{-1, 1\}$ **21.** $1(k) = k$ $\{-2, -1, 0, 1\}$

22. $2x + 1 = 0$ $\emptyset$ **23.** $z - 1 > -2$ $\{0, 1\}$ **24.** $y + 0 \neq y$ $\emptyset$

Write an equation for each sentence.

25. Three more than half a number is 25. $\frac{1}{2}x + 3 = 25$

26. Billy's father is twice Billy's age. Eleven years ago, Billy's father was 3 times Billy's age. (*Hint:* Translate the second sentence to an equation using algebraic expressions from the first sentence.) $2b - 11 = 3(b - 11)$

Challenge

1. Simplify: $3 - \{x - [x - 3(x - 3)]\}$ $-3x + 12$

2. Write an equation for this situation:

Annie Oakley was 14 years younger than Buffalo Bill. When she became the star attraction in his Wild West Show, she was two-thirds his age. $b - 14 = \frac{2}{3}b$

Select the best answer for each and write the appropriate letter.

1. Simplify the following:
D $(3a + b - 2c) + (a - 2b + c)$

  A. $2a - b - c$
  B. $2a - b - 2c$
  C. $3a - 2b - 2c$
  D. $4a - b - c$
  E. $4a - b - 2c$

2. Find the value of $a^2 + b^2$ when
B $a = 3$ and $b = 4$.

  A. 27 **B.** 25 **C.** 14
  D. 7   **E.** 5

3. An algebraic expression for "seven
A less than twice a certain number" is

  A. $2x - 7$ **B.** $2x + 7$ **C.** $7 - 2x$
  D. $x - 14$ **E.** $14 - x$

4. Which of the following would be
E the best *estimate* of 6832×19.81?

  A. 12,000 **B.** 14,000 **C.** 60,000
  D. 120,000 **E.** 140,000

5. Which of the following is a
E multiple of 4?

  A. 2874   **B.** 4315   **C.** 7982
  D. 13,410 **E.** 16,056

6. Find the value of $2[3(x^2 - 4) + 5y]$
B when $x = 3$ and $y = 1$.

  A. 22 **B.** 40 **C.** 12
  D. 56 **E.** 55

7. Which of the following is less than
D 0.45 but more than 0.35?

  A. $\frac{1}{2}$ **B.** $\frac{1}{3}$ **C.** $\frac{2}{7}$
  D. $\frac{4}{9}$ **E.** $\frac{8}{25}$

8. If the replacement set is $\{-5, 5,$
B $12, -12\}$, the solution set of the
equation $x + 7 = 19 - 7$ is

  A. $\{-5\}$ **B.** $\{5\}$ **C.** $\{-12\}$
  D. $\{12\}$ **E.** $\{19\}$

9. If k is an integer, and $2k < 60$,
E then k *cannot* be

  A. 7   **B.** 12 **C.** 23
  D. 28 **E.** 32

10. Alex has one more math test to
B take before grades are averaged. So
far, he has scores of 96, 85, 79,
91, and 89. What must his score be
on this last test to maintain his
present average?

  A. 86 **B.** 88 **C.** 91
  D. 93 **E.** 95

11. Alice and Betty spent their vacation
B doing yardwork. If their earnings
were in the ratio $2:3$, respectively,
how much had Betty earned when
Alice had earned $14.70?

  A. $29.40   **B.** $22.05
  C. $19.60   **D.** $17.15
  E. It cannot be determined from
     the information given.

The individual comments provided for the problems listed below can be helpful in guiding students to solve these problems.

4. The techniques of estimating are too often neglected or omitted entirely. Estimating should be included as often as possible and used almost automatically in problem solving.
5. Divisibility is an elementary number theory topic which is often quite useful in problem solving. Students not familiar with simple checks for divisibility should be encouraged to learn and use them.
7. Estimating the decimal approximations of simple fractions should be encouraged over actually carrying out the division.

See *Teacher's Resource Book,* for Preparing for Standardized Tests.

CUMULATIVE REVIEW (CHAPTERS 1–2)

Write the numbers in order from least to greatest. 1.3

1. $2.5, -1, 0, -1.5, 2$ $_{-1.5, -1, 0, 2, 2.5}$ **2.** $-2, 1\frac{1}{2}, -\frac{1}{2}, 1, -1$ $_{-2, -1, -\frac{1}{2}, 1, 1\frac{1}{2}}$

3. Graph $3, -2, -\frac{1}{2}, 0, 1$ on a number line.

$-3 \quad -2 \quad -1 \quad 0 \quad 1 \quad 2 \quad 3$

Perform the indicated operation. 1.5–1.8

4. $-12 + 8$ $_{-4}$ **5.** $(-0.2)(-4)$ $_{0.8}$ **6.** $9(-7)$ $_{-63}$ **7.** $\frac{3}{4} - \left(-\frac{3}{4}\right)$ $_{1\frac{1}{2}}$

8. $-36 \div (-4)$ $_{9}$ **9.** $6 - (-8)$ $_{14}$ **10.** $\frac{1}{2} \div \left(-\frac{3}{4}\right)$ $_{-\frac{2}{3}}$ **11.** $-5 - (-0.9)$ $_{-4.1}$

12. $-\frac{5}{6} \cdot \frac{3}{5}$ $_{-\frac{1}{2}}$ **13.** $-3.2 - 0.8$ $_{-4}$ **14.** $-5.4 \div 9$ $_{-0.6}$ **15.** $\frac{5}{8} + \left(-\frac{3}{8}\right)$ $_{\frac{1}{4}}$

Simplify. 1.3, 2.1, 2.4, 2.5

16. $-\left|-\left(-\frac{3}{4}\right)\right|$ $_{-\frac{3}{4}}$ **17.** $9 + 21 \div 3$ $_{16}$ **18.** $6 + 24 \div (8 - 2)$ $_{10}$

19. $-2[12 - 3(5 + 2)]$ $_{18}$ **20.** $[6 - (-2)^2]^3$ $_{8}$ **21.** $4x - 3y + 2x$ $_{6x - 3y}$

22. $m^2 - 2m^2 + m$ $_{-m^2 + m}$ **23.** $3(a + 2) - 5a$ $_{-2a + 6}$ **24.** $p - (5 - 2p)$ $_{3p - 5}$

25. $(5c + 2) - (3c - 6)$ $_{2c + 8}$ **26.** $-2st^2 - (-3st^2 + 1)$ $_{st^2 - 1}$

Evaluate each expression if $a = 3$, $b = \frac{2}{3}$, and $c = 4$. 1.1, 2.1, 2.2

27. $ab - 5$ $_{-3}$ **28.** $3b - ac$ $_{-10}$ **29.** abc $_{8}$

30. $|a - 2c|$ $_{5}$ **31.** $(5a - 6b)c$ $_{44}$ **32.** $\frac{2a - c}{b}$ $_{3}$

33. $5[b \div (2a + c)]$ $_{\frac{1}{3}}$ **34.** $\dfrac{3a + 1}{b + \frac{c}{a}}$ $_{5}$ **35.** $2a^2 - c$ $_{14}$

Translate each word phrase to an algebraic expression. 2.6

36. Karl's age in 5 years if x is his age now $_{x + 5}$

37. Three less than twice a number $_{2n - 3}$

38. Five times the sum of a number and 3 $_{5(n + 3)}$

39. The length of a rectangle is 1 cm more than twice the width $_{l = 2w + 1}$

40. 14 lb more than 3 times Eva's weight $_{3w + 14}$

OVERVIEW • Chapter 3

SUMMARY

In Chapter 3, students begin to solve simple linear equations requiring use of only one or two of the properties for equations. The equation solving skills learned are applied to formulas as well. Students are introduced to an important problem solving strategy—translating an English statement into an equation. They should see that this strategy is a key to solving many simple problems.

The terms used in formal proofs are defined, and two-column algebraic proofs are shown and explained. Students are expected to complete the proofs.

After this chapter has been completed, students should be able to solve simple linear equations in one variable. They should also be able to solve simple problems in which statements are translated into such equations.

CHAPTER OBJECTIVES

- To solve linear equations of the form $ax + b = c$ by using the properties for equations

- To write an equation from a word statement

- To identify postulates, theorems, and proofs

- To prove simple algebraic statements

- To solve for any variable in a formula when values of the other variables are given

- To use formulas to solve simple word problems

- To use equations to solve various types of word problems

Problem Solving Strategy

To create mathematical models as useful and appropriate problem solving tools, and to write equations from word statements

CHAPTER HIGHLIGHTS

The *theme* of the chapter is school activities. The chapter's special features show how algebra may be applied in a variety of school settings.

PROBLEM SOLVING AND APPLICATIONS

Problem solving and applications form an integral part of each lesson. Students use equations and mathematical models to solve problems and arrive at solutions to problems in many fields including travel, language arts, and other areas of math. The problem solving Lessons 3.4, 3.7, and 3.8 afford students the opportunity to practice applying algebraic methods: models and equations to concrete problem situations that arise in a variety of fields.

TECHNOLOGY

Calculator

The emphasis of calculator activities in this chapter is on preparing algebraic equations for solution by a calculator. Students learn that an equation must be expressed in terms of the variable before students enter numerical equivalents into the calculator.

Computer

The computer feature in Chapter 3 introduces students to the **SUM** function of a spreadsheet which enables the user to indicate to the computer what cells it is to add together. Students are shown a spreadsheet containing data about test scores, and are then shown how the **SUM** function may be used to determine what additional test score is needed to result in a desired overall grade (average).

RESOURCES

Teacher's Resource Book

- Teaching Aid 4
- Transparency 5

STUDENT TEXT

TEACHER'S RESOURCE BOOK

Chapter Content	Basic	Average	Enriched	R	P	E
3.1 Solving Equations: Addition and Subtraction Properties	D: 98/1-23 odd, 51, 53	D: 98/1-41 odd,51, 53, 54	D: 99/11-49 odd, 51-56	1	2	3
3.2 Solving Equations: Multiplication and Division Properties	D: 104/1-27 odd, 45, 46 R: 98/4, 6, 12, 20	D: 104/1-37 odd, 45-48 R: 98/10, 16, 28, 30, 40	D: 104/11-43 odd, 45-50 R: 99/22, 38, 44, 50	4	5	6
3.3 Solving Equations: More Than One Property	D: 108/1-17 odd, 35 R: Test Yourself	D: 108/1-23 odd, 35, 36 R: 104/10, 12, 30, 32 Test Yourself	D: 108/7-33 odd, 35-38 R: Test Yourself	7	8	9
3.4 Problem Solving Strategy: Make a Model	D: 111/1, 3 MPSR: 1, 2 R: 108/4, 8, 12	D: 111/1, 3, 5 MPSR: 1, 2 R: 108/10, 16, 20	D: 111/1-11 odd MPSR: 1, 2 R: 108/12, 24, 32		10	11
3.5 Algebraic Proofs	D: 115/1, 3, 9, 11 R: 111/2 115/2-4 even	D: 115/1-5 odd, 5, 9-11 R: 111/2, 4	D: 115/1-7 odd, 9-12 R: 111/4, 6, 12	12	13	14
3.6 Evaluating Formulas	D: 118/1-5 odd, 13 R: 115/2, 4, 6	D: 118/1-9 odd, 13, 14 R: 115/2, 4	D: 118/1-11 odd, 13-15 R: 115/4, 6	15	16	17
3.7 Problem Solving Strategy: Write an Equation	D: 122/1-11 odd MPSR: 1-5 R: 118/2 122/2, 4, 6	D: 123/1-17 odd MPSR: 1-5 R: 118/4, 6	D: 123/1-21 odd MPSR: 1-5 R: 118/4, 6, 8		19	20
3.8 Problem Solving: Mixed Types	D: 128/1-13 odd R: 122/8, 10, 12 Test Yourself	D: 128/1-17 odd R: 123/4, 16, 18 Test Yourself	D: 128/1-19 odd R: Test Yourself		21	22

D = Daily   R = Review   MPSR = Mixed Problem Solving Review   R = Reteaching   P = Practice   E = Enrichment

STUDENT TEXT

TEACHER'S RESOURCE BOOK

Reviewing	Test Yourself	109	Chapter Test	132	Spanish Chapter Summary and Review	5-6
And	Test Yourself	129	Prep. for Stan. Tests	133	• Quizzes	25-28
Testing	Chapter Sum. and Rev.	130	Maintaining Skills	134	• Chapter Test (Form A)	29-30
			Extra Practice	657	• Chapter Test (Form B)	31-32
					Calculator Test	5-6
Special	Puzzle	100	Technology	125	Applications—Chapter 3	23
Features	Writing in Algebra	105, 119	Logical Reasoning	116	Critical Thinking	3
	Project	112, 124			Reading and Writing in Algebra	3
					Technology	7-8

Equations in One Variable

Colleges use various criteria for selecting their students. For example, in addition to evaluating a student's high school academic record, many admissions officers look for involvement in school activities.

BACKGROUND

Extra curricular activities such as Math Clubs, Computer Clubs, the Marching Band and athletic teams provide many rewarding experiences among students. These outside activities can often lead to success in college education and in the business world.

95

Vocabulary
Equivalent equations
Inverse operations

Materials/Manipulatives
Balance scale
Gram weights
Calculators

BACKGROUND

In the Capsule Review, Exercises 1–2 illustrate that addition and subtraction are inverse operations. Exercises 3–8 prepare students for use of the addition or subtraction properties in solving equations of the type $x - b = c$ or $x + b = c$.

3.1 Solving Equations: Addition and Subtraction Properties

Objective: To solve equations using the Addition and Subtraction Properties for Equations

Suppose you are given directions for walking from the bus stop to the aquarium. To walk back from the aquarium to the bus stop, you would need to change a direction such as "Walk 10 blocks north" to its opposite, "Walk 10 blocks south."

Inverse (opposite) operations are used in mathematics as an efficient way to solve equations. Adding and subtracting the same number are inverse operations. One operation "undoes" the other.

Capsule Review

Recall what it means to add two numbers such as $5 + 4$.

$$\text{Start with } 5 \longrightarrow \text{add } 4 \longrightarrow 5 + 4.$$

To undo this, work backwards:

$$\text{Start with } 5 + 4 \longrightarrow \text{subtract } 4 \longrightarrow \text{to get back to } 5.$$

Simplify.

1. $4 - 4$ 0 **2.** $-39 + 39$ 0 **3.** $y - 1.5 + 1.5$ y **4.** $2\frac{1}{8} + x - 2\frac{1}{8}$ x

Tell what must be done to get the variable x by itself.

5. $x + 6$ subtract 6 **6.** $x - 21$ add 21 **7.** $\frac{4}{5} + x$ subtract $\frac{4}{5}$ **8.** $-2.1 + x$ subtract (-2.1)

In Chapter 2, you found the solutions of equations by substituting numbers from a given replacement set. From now on, you may assume that the replacement set is the set of real numbers unless otherwise stated.

Equivalent equations are equations that have the same solution(s) for the same replacement set. The equations $x + 2 = 10$ and $x = 8$ are equivalent; in each case, the solution is 8.

Adding or subtracting the same real number to each side of an equation produces an equivalent equation.

Addition Property for Equations

For all real numbers a, b, and c if $a = b$, then $a + c = b + c$.

Subtraction Property for Equations

For all real numbers a, b, and c if $a = b$, then $a - c = b - c$.

In the equation $x - 1.4 = 9.2$ below, 1.4 has been subtracted from some number x. The addition property for equations can be used to obtain an equivalent equation that has x alone on one side of the equation.

EXAMPLE 1 **Solve and check:** $x - 1.4 = 9.2$

$$x - 1.4 = 9.2$$
$$x - 1.4 + 1.4 = 9.2 + 1.4 \qquad \textit{Add 1.4 to each side of the equation.}$$
$$x + 0 = 10.6 \qquad \textit{-1.4 + 1.4 = 0}$$
$$x = 10.6 \qquad \textit{0 is the additive identity, so x + 0 = x.}$$

Check:
$$x - 1.4 = 9.2$$
$$10.6 - 1.4 \overset{?}{=} 9.2 \qquad \textit{Replace x with 10.6.}$$
$$9.2 = 9.2 \ \text{✔} \qquad \textit{True}$$

The solution is 10.6.

The solution of the equation is 10.6. Its *solution set* is {10.6}. When asked to solve an equation, you may give the solution without using set notation.

EXAMPLE 2 **Solve:** $8 = y + 4\frac{1}{5}$

$$8 = y + 4\frac{1}{5}$$

$$8 - 4\frac{1}{5} = y + 4\frac{1}{5} - 4\frac{1}{5} \qquad \textit{Subtract } 4\frac{1}{5} \textit{ from each side of the equation.}$$

$$\frac{40}{5} - \frac{21}{5} = y + 0 \qquad \textit{8} = \frac{40}{5}; 4\frac{1}{5} = \frac{21}{5}$$

$$\frac{19}{5} = y$$

$$y = \frac{19}{5}, \text{ or } 3\frac{4}{5}$$

The solution is $\frac{19}{5}$, or $3\frac{4}{5}$. How do you *check* the solution?

3.1 Solving Equations: Addition and Subtraction Properties   **97**

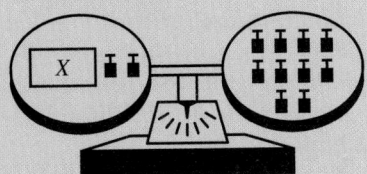
97

- **For Example 1**

  Solve and check:

  1. $x - 1.9 = 8.5$ 10.4

  2. $-10.3 = k + 1.8$ -12.1

- **For Example 2**

  Solve:

  3. $5 = b - 1\frac{2}{3}$ $6\frac{2}{3}$

  4. $x + 3\frac{1}{4} = 7$ $3\frac{3}{4}$

- **For Example 3**

  Solve:

  5. $x - (-47) = 19$ -28

  6. $-32 = y - (-26.1)$ -58.1

- **For Example 4**

  Solve:

  7. $-0.95 + x = -6.713$ -5.763

  8. $-1\frac{5}{8} + d = -\frac{3}{8}$ $1\frac{1}{4}$

Common Errors

- Some students fail to perform the same operation on both sides of an equation. For example, in $x + 4 = 7$, some students may subtract 4 from the left side and add 4 to the right side, getting 11 as the solution. You may want students to set up equations using the following method.

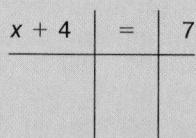

- Some students may put all the terms on one side of the equation. For example, in $x + 4 = 7$, some students may subtract 7 from both sides and get -3 as the solution.
- Emphasize that the goal is to get the variable alone and that whatever is done to one "side" of the equation must be done to the other.
- See *Teacher's Resource Book* for additional remediation.

The equation $a - (-52) = 25$ may be solved by removing parentheses and then using the subtraction property for equations.

EXAMPLE 3 Solve: $a - (-52) = 25$

$$a - (-52) = 25$$
$$a + 52 = 25 \qquad \text{\textit{To subtract} -52, \textit{add its opposite}, 52.}$$
$$a + 52 - 52 = 25 - 52 \qquad \text{\textit{Subtract} 52 \textit{from each side of the equation.}}$$
$$a = -27$$

Check: $a - (-52) = 25$
$$-27 - (-52) \overset{?}{=} 25 \qquad \text{\textit{Replace} a \textit{with} -27.}$$
$$-27 + 52 \overset{?}{=} 25$$
$$25 = 25 \; \checkmark \qquad \text{\textit{True}}$$

The solution is -27.

EXAMPLE 4 Solve: $-6.9 + z = -9.75$

$$-6.9 + z = -9.75$$
$$-6.9 + z + 6.9 = -9.75 + 6.9 \qquad \text{\textit{Add} 6.9 \textit{to each side of the}}$$
$$z = -2.85 \qquad\qquad\qquad \text{\textit{equation.}}$$

Is -2.85 the solution? Check to be sure.

CLASS EXERCISES

Tell what operation you would perform on each side of the equation to get x alone on one side.

1. $x + 4 = -6$ 　 **2.** $x - 2 = 10$ 　 **3.** $-2 = -1 + x$ 　 **4.** $x - 4 = -4$
subtract 4 　　　 add 2 　　　　 add 1 　　　　 add 4
5. $x - (-15) = 17$ **6.** $9 = x - 11$ 　 **7.** $24 = x + 24$ 　 **8.** $-35 + x = 50$
subtract 15 　　 add 11 　　　 subtract 24 　　 add 35

Solve and check.

9. $a - 7 = 24$ 31 　 **10.** $x + 21 = -25$ -46 　 **11.** $12 + d = -15$ -27

12. $r - (-7) = 13$ 6 　 **13.** $-2 = -15 + n$ 13 　 **14.** $33 = -14 + c$ 47

PRACTICE EXERCISES

Solve and check.

A 　 **1.** $x - 3.4 = 9.61$ 13.01 　 **2.** $a - 12.5 = 13.9$ 26.4 　 **3.** $y + 1.9 = 10.2$ 8.3

　 4. $z + 2.4 = 5.3$ 2.9 　 **5.** $m - 3.6 = 4.5$ 8.1 　 **6.** $t - 5.3 = 2.3$ 7.6

　 7. $9 = x + 2\frac{1}{3}$ $6\frac{2}{3}$ 　 **8.** $11 = z + 3\frac{2}{5}$ $7\frac{3}{5}$ 　 **9.** $4 = m + 1\frac{1}{3}$ $\frac{8}{3}$, or $2\frac{2}{3}$

10. $8 = s + 4\frac{1}{2}$ $3\frac{1}{2}$

11. $3 = t - 1\frac{2}{3}$ $4\frac{2}{3}$

12. $5 = y - 1\frac{1}{4}$ $6\frac{1}{4}$

13. $a - (-60) = 30$ -30

14. $b - (-25) = 24$ -1

15. $x - (-5) = 10$ 5

16. $m - (-2) = 12$ 10

17. $z - (-6) = 50$ 44

18. $t - (-9) = 41$ 32

19. $-2.3 + x = -5.9$ -3.6

20. $-5.3 + m = 10.2$ 15.5

21. $-3.4 + s = -9.5$ -6.1

22. $-8.2 + t = -12.4$ -4.2

23. $-5.3 + r = -12.3$ -7

24. $-2.5 + a = -5.5$ -3

B
25. $y - 7.01 = 12.009$ 19.019

26. $x - 3.12 = 5.23$ 8.35

27. $z - 0.032 = 1.03$ 1.062

28. $4 = n + 3\frac{1}{2}$ $\frac{1}{2}$

29. $5 = a + 2\frac{1}{3}$ $2\frac{2}{3}$

30. $8 = x + 3\frac{1}{4}$ $4\frac{3}{4}$

31. $45 - (-a) = 50$ 5

32. $17 - (-x) = 22$ 5

33. $52 = 25 - (-a)$ 27

34. $-5.8 = a - 2.75$ -3.05

35. $-8.3 = x - 2.5$ -5.8

36. $-3.9 = b - 5.1$ 1.2

Solve and check. The replacement set is the set of positive integers.

Hint: Solve the equation. If the result is not a positive integer, then write *no solution*.

37. $-15 + y = -15$
no solution

38. $x - 12 = -12$
no solution

39. $\frac{1}{2} + y = 5\frac{1}{2}$ 5

40. $-\frac{4}{5} + x = -\frac{8}{5}$
no solution

41. $\frac{2}{3} + y = -\frac{1}{2}$
no solution

42. $-\frac{3}{4} + x = 1\frac{1}{4}$ 2

Complete each sentence.

C
43. If $a - 12 = 15$, then $a - 1 = $ ___?___ . 26

44. If $8 = t + 3$, then ___?___ $= t - 17$. -12

45. If $7 - 2x = 8$, then $11 - 2x = $ ___?___ . 12

46. If $-3n - 5 = 17$, then $-3n + 5 = $ ___?___ . 27

Find the solution set of each equation. Check your answer.

Example $y - 2 = |-5|$
$y - 2 = 5$
$y = 7$ The solution set is {7}.

Check: $y - 2 = |-5|$
$7 - 2 \stackrel{?}{=} |-5|$
$5 = 5$ ✔ True

47. $x = |3|$
{3}

48. $y = |-4|$
{4}

49. $x - 6 = |-3|$
{9}

50. $|z| = |-4| - |-6|$
∅

3.1 Solving Equations: Addition and Subtraction Properties   **99**

LESSON FOLLOW-UP

Discussion
Explain why addition and subtraction are inverse operations.   One operation "undoes" the other.

Assignment Guide
• See p. 94B for assignments.
• In Exercises 37–42, emphasize that the replacement set is the set of positive integers only.

Puzzle
In the feature, students are asked to organize information presented in the statements, in a systematic way, in order to reach the desired conclusion/ solution.

Lesson Quiz
Solve and check.
1. $m - 1.6 = 8.3$ 9.9
2. $7 = x + 3\frac{1}{9}$ $3\frac{8}{9}$
3. $b - (-34) = 17$ -17
4. $y - 1\frac{9}{10} = 4\frac{3}{10}$ $6\frac{1}{5}$
5. $-5.9 + a = 3.75$ 9.65

Enrichment
Describe how you could solve the equation $-x = -13$, if you have not yet learned an algebraic method but could translate the equation into a statement using the word "opposite" and then find the solution readily.
The opposite of x is -13, so x must be 13.

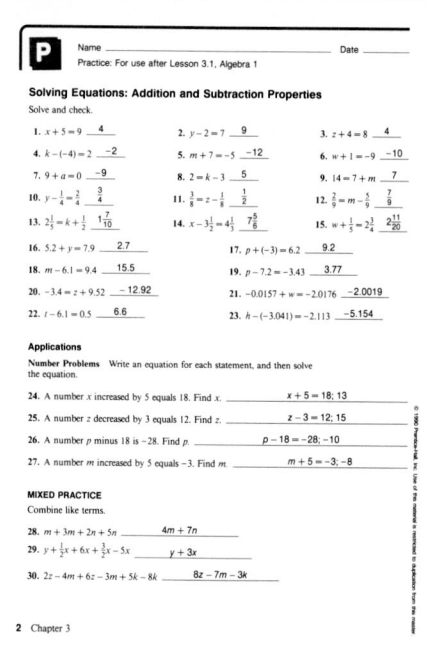

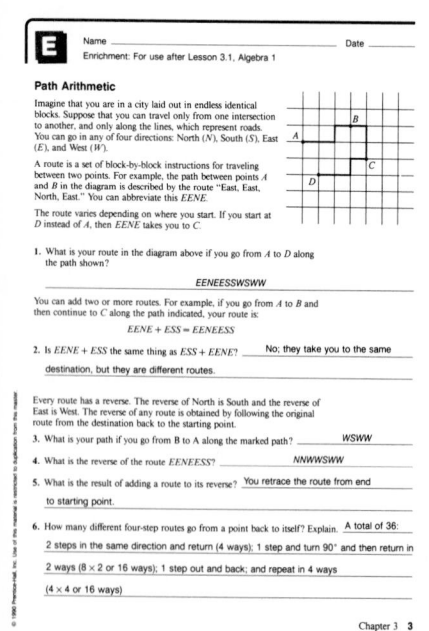

Applications

The directions to go from school to the aquarium are given. State the directions from the aquarium to school.

51. Travel Go 7 blocks south, 3 blocks east, 2 blocks south, and 1 block west. See below.

52. Travel Drive 6 mi west on Rt. 117 and 2 mi north on Rt. 9 to the third traffic light. Make a left at the third traffic light and go 2 blocks. See below.

Write an equation for each statement. Then solve the equation.

53. Number Problem A number n increased by 25 equals 11. Find n.
$n + 25 = 11; -14$

54. Number Problem The sum of -43 and some number t is -18. Find t.
$-43 + t = -18; 25$

55. Number Problem Find a number x if x decreased by 29 equals -7.
$x - 29 = -7; 22$

56. Number Problem Find a number r if the difference between r and 11 is -58. $r - 11 = -58; -47$

PUZZLE

Everett, Toni, Alice, and Enid are students at Lanier High School. Each takes part in one extracurricular activity. One plays the tuba in the school orchestra, one has the leading role in the school play, one is on the cycling team, and one is a cheerleader.

Everett and Alice were in the audience when the orchestra gave its concert. Enid and Toni tried out for the cycling team but did not make it. Everett is the cheerleader's best friend, but he does not know the cyclist. Enid and the cheerleader are cousins. Which student participates in which activity?
Toni: cheerleader; Enid: tuba player; Everett: school play; Alice: cycling team

100   Chapter 3 Equations in One Variable

Additional Answers
51. Go 1 block east, 2 blocks north, 3 blocks west, and 7 blocks north.
52. Drive 2 blocks east, make a right, drive 2 mi south on Rt. 9, and drive 6 mi east on Rt. 117.

Solving Equations: Multiplication and Division Properties

Objective: To solve equations using the Multiplication and Division Properties for Equations

Laura gave Steve a copy of her favorite recipe. She told him that she had doubled the measure of each ingredient. To determine the original recipe, Steve had to "undo" Laura's doubling process. He had to divide each measure by 2.

LESSON PLAN

Materials/Manipulatives
Calculators

BACKGROUND

In the Capsule Review, Exercises 1–2 illustrate that multiplication and division are inverse operations. Exercises 3–8 prepare students for use of the multiplication or division property in solving equations of the type $ax = b$.

Capsule Review

Multiplying and dividing by the same number are inverse operations. One operation "undoes" the other.

$$\text{Start with } x \longrightarrow \text{divide by 3} \longrightarrow \frac{x}{3}.$$

To undo this, work backwards:

$$\text{Start with } \frac{x}{3} \longrightarrow \text{multiply by 3} \longrightarrow \text{to get back to } x.$$

Simplify.

1. $\dfrac{1}{4} \cdot 4$ 1 **2.** $\dfrac{-5}{-5}$ 1 **3.** $\dfrac{r}{5} \cdot 5$ r **4.** $-\dfrac{1}{8} a \cdot (-8)$ a

Tell what operation to perform to get the variable x by itself.

5. $\dfrac{x}{9}$ multiply by 9 **6.** $-15x$ divide by -15 **7.** $\dfrac{x}{-3}$ multiply by -3 **8.** $2.9x$ divide by 2.9

Multiplying or dividing each side of an equation by the same nonzero real number produces an equivalent equation.

Multiplication Property for Equations

For all real numbers a, b, and c, $c \neq 0$, if $a = b$, then $ac = bc$.

Division Property for Equations

For all real numbers a, b, and c, $c \neq 0$, if $a = b$, then $\dfrac{a}{c} = \dfrac{b}{c}$.

- In Example 2, point out that the equation $5 = -x$ has not been solved. x alone is needed on one side of the equation.
- In Example 3, $\frac{x}{5} = -7$ is solved in two ways. Point out that $\frac{x}{5}$ and $\frac{1}{5}x$ are equivalent.
- You may wish to demonstrate the greater convenience of the reciprocal method for operations, used in Example 4, by showing the division method as well.
- It is very important that students put equations into *calculation-ready form* before using the calculator. Unless this is done you will find that with more complicated equations, some students will use the calculator to transform the equation, one arithmetic step at a time. This is not efficient, and, more importantly, will not promote real facility with the calculator.

Critical Thinking

Comparing-Contrasting How are the solution processes for solving the following equations alike? How are they different? $2x = 8$; $x + 4 = 8$ Students should observe that in each the goal is to reach an equation with the variable (with a coefficient of one) alone on one side of the equation. Each type requires the use of one property for equations. The division property is used to solve the first equation; the subtraction property is used for the second equation.

In Example 1, each side of the equation is divided by -16, since $\frac{-16}{-16} = 1$.

EXAMPLE 1 **Solve and check: $-16x = 96$**

$$-16x = 96$$

$$\frac{-16x}{-16} = \frac{96}{-16} \qquad \textit{Divide each side by } -16.$$

$$x = -6$$

Check: $\qquad -16x = 96$

$$-16(-6) \overset{?}{=} 96 \qquad \textit{Replace x with } -6.$$

$$96 = 96 \ \rlap{/}{} \qquad \textit{True}$$

The solution of the equation is -6.

Example 2 illustrates a special case in which a property is used to solve an equation. Remember that you must obtain an equivalent equation in which the variable has a numerical coefficient of 1. The goal is an equation such as $x = 4$ or $-28 = x$, not $-x = 17$ or $-56 = -x$.

EXAMPLE 2 **Solve: $5 = -x$**

$$5 = -x$$

$$5 = -1x \qquad \textit{-x = -1x by the property of -1 for multiplication.}$$

$$\frac{5}{-1} = \frac{-1x}{-1} \qquad \textit{Divide each side of the equation by -1.}$$

$$-5 = x$$

The solution of the equation is -5. Check the solution.

To solve an equation, find an equivalent equation in which the variable (with a numerical coefficient of 1) is alone on one side of the equation. In Example 3, this is done by multiplying each side of the equation by 5.

EXAMPLE 3 **Solve and check: $\frac{x}{5} = -7$**

$$\frac{x}{5} = -7$$

$$5 \cdot \frac{x}{5} = -7 \cdot 5 \qquad \textit{Multiply each side of the equation by 5.}$$

$$x = -35 \qquad 5 \cdot \frac{x}{5} = \frac{\overset{1}{\cancel{5}}}{1} \cdot \frac{x}{\underset{1}{\cancel{5}}} = 1x, \textit{ or } x$$

Check: $\dfrac{x}{5} = -7$

$\dfrac{-35}{5} \overset{?}{=} -7$ *Replace x with −35.*

$-7 = -7\checkmark$ *True*

The solution of the equation is −35.

The equation $\dfrac{x}{5} = -7$ can also be solved by using reciprocals. Recall that the product of a number and its reciprocal is 1.

$\dfrac{x}{5} = -7$

$\dfrac{1}{5}x = -7$ *$\dfrac{x}{5}$ means $\dfrac{1}{5} \cdot x$.*

$5 \cdot \dfrac{1}{5}x = 5(-7)$ *Multiply each side of the equation by 5, the reciprocal of $\dfrac{1}{5}$.*

$x = -35$ *$5 \cdot \dfrac{1}{5} = 1$*

EXAMPLE 4 **Solve:** $\dfrac{3}{5}c = 6$

$\dfrac{3}{5}c = 6$

$\dfrac{5}{3} \cdot \dfrac{3}{5}c = \dfrac{5}{3} \cdot 6$ *Multiply each side of the equation by $\dfrac{5}{3}$, the reciprocal of $\dfrac{3}{5}$.*

$c = 10$ *$\dfrac{5}{3} \cdot \dfrac{3}{5}c = 1 \cdot c$, or c*

The solution of the equation is 10. How do you check the solution?

A calculator can be a very useful tool in solving equations. In order to use a calculator effectively, first write the equation in *calculation-ready form*. That is, write the equation with the variable alone on one side so that the computations are easily recognizable. Save the computations until the end.

EXAMPLE 5 **Write the equation $\dfrac{3a}{17} = 11.3$ in calculation-ready form.**

$\dfrac{3a}{17} = 11.3$

$\dfrac{3}{17}a = 11.3$ *$\dfrac{3a}{17}$ means $\dfrac{3}{17}a$.*

$\dfrac{17}{3} \cdot \dfrac{3}{17}a = 11.3 \cdot \dfrac{17}{3}$ *Multiply each side of the equation by $\dfrac{17}{3}$, the reciprocal of $\dfrac{3}{17}$.*

$a = 11.3 \cdot \dfrac{17}{3}$ *Calculation-ready form*

3.2 Solving Equations: Multiplication and Division Properties **103**

Critical Thinking

Discovering Relationships Are $x + 4 = 8$ and $2x = 8$ equivalent equations? Why or why not? Give other equations equivalent to $x - 3 = 7$.
Yes, the equations have the same solution set. Examples: $3x = 30$, $x + 5 = 15$

Assignment Guide

• See p. 94B for assignments.
• For Exercises 45–50 have students round their answers to the nearest hundredth.

Writing in Algebra

The feature emphasizes the students' need to be able to "read" and "translate" statements from English to math and vice-versa. See *Teacher's Resource Book,* Reading and Writing in Algebra activity, p. 3.

Lesson Quiz

Solve and check.
1. $-6y = 54$ -9
2. $\dfrac{b}{-6} = -1$ 6
3. $\dfrac{4}{9}x = -16$ -36
4. $-z = \dfrac{4}{5}$ $-\dfrac{4}{5}$
5. $\dfrac{-m}{8} = 0.6$ -4.8
6. $-0.4m = -1.24$ 3.1
7. $\dfrac{t}{0.1} = 8.7$ 0.87
8. $3 = \dfrac{-6}{9}c$ $-\dfrac{9}{2}$

Enrichment

The equation $\dfrac{21}{3}x = 14$ can be solved in many different ways. Discover as many methods of solution as possible. Answers may vary. Some possible solutions are: start by multiplying both sides by 3 or $\dfrac{3}{21}$; start by dividing both sides by 21; and so on.

CLASS EXERCISES

Tell what must be done to each side of the equation so the variable will be alone on one side. Then solve and check.

1. $5x = 30$
divide by 5; 6

2. $-6y = 48$
divide by -6; -8

3. $\dfrac{a}{5} = -4$
multiply by 5; -20

4. $6 = -\dfrac{1}{3}t$
multiply by -3; -18

5. $-24 = -y$
divide by -1; -24

6. $\dfrac{2}{3}x = 1$
multiply by $\dfrac{3}{2}$; $\dfrac{3}{2}$

7. $-1.01b = 6.06$
divide by -1.01; -6

8. $\dfrac{x}{-6} = 5$
multiply by -6; -30

PRACTICE EXERCISES

Solve and check.

A
1. $-9t = 72$ -8
2. $-17t = 51$ -3
3. $-8a = 56$ -7
4. $-2x = 12$ -6
5. $-24r = 120$ -5
6. $-5p = 75$ -15
7. $3 = -x$ -3
8. $15 = -z$ -15
9. $7 = -x$ -7
10. $\dfrac{c}{25} = -1$ -25
11. $\dfrac{x}{7} = -3$ -21
12. $\dfrac{t}{3} = -12$ -36
13. $\dfrac{a}{4} = -3$ -12
14. $\dfrac{m}{2} = 10$ 20
15. $\dfrac{s}{5} = 11$ 55
16. $\dfrac{1}{2}e = 2$ 4
17. $\dfrac{3}{5}a = 12$ 20
18. $\dfrac{1}{4}x = 9$ 36
19. $\dfrac{1}{8}n = 3$ 24
20. $\dfrac{2}{3}m = 4$ 6
21. $\dfrac{3}{7}t = 15$ 35

Write the following equations in calculation-ready form.

22. $\dfrac{a}{12} = 11.5$ $a = 11.5 \cdot 12$
23. $\dfrac{m}{15} = 10.5$ $m = 10.5 \cdot 15$
24. $\dfrac{2x}{7} = 21.2$ $x = \dfrac{21.2 \cdot 7}{2}$
25. $\dfrac{5t}{11} = 55.5$ $t = \dfrac{55.5 \cdot 11}{5}$
26. $\dfrac{-2s}{3} = 33.5$ $s = \dfrac{33.5 \cdot 3}{-2}$
27. $\dfrac{-5r}{6} = 24.6$ $r = \dfrac{24.6 \cdot 6}{-5}$

Solve and check.

B
28. $\dfrac{x}{5} = -1\dfrac{1}{10}$ $-5\dfrac{1}{2}$
29. $\dfrac{m}{8} = -2\dfrac{1}{4}$ -18
30. $\dfrac{y}{9} = -\dfrac{5}{3}$ -15
31. $\dfrac{z}{3} = -\dfrac{9}{3}$ -9
32. $\dfrac{7}{9}d = \dfrac{14}{3}$ 6
33. $\dfrac{2}{3}a = \dfrac{4}{9}$ $\dfrac{2}{3}$
34. $-4.027m = 50.1$ -12.441
35. $-7.850n = 0.929$ -0.118
36. $-\dfrac{x}{5} = -2.5$ 12.5
37. $-\dfrac{z}{2} = -4.6$ 9.2

Complete each sentence.

C **38.** If $3a = -11$, then $12a = \underline{\ ?\ }$ -44 **39.** If $2c = -5$, then $-8c = \underline{\ ?\ }$ 20

Find the solution set of each equation. Check your answer.

40. $|a| = 30$ {30, −30}

41. $-12|x| = -144$ {12, −12}

42. $\dfrac{|c|}{3} = 15$ {−45, 45}

43. $-6|2t| = -8$ $\left\{-\dfrac{2}{3}, \dfrac{2}{3}\right\}$

44. True or false: Every equation in this lesson can be solved using the multiplication property for equations exclusively. Explain your answer.
True by mult. by the reciprocal of the number.

Applications

Calculator Write each equation in calculation-ready form. Then solve the equation and state your answer to the nearest hundredths.

45. $\dfrac{m}{4.5} = 33$
$m = 4.5 \cdot 33$; 148.5

46. $\dfrac{r}{29} = 1.1$
$r = 29 \cdot 1.1$; 31.9

47. $\dfrac{1}{6}y = 0.89$
$y = 6 \cdot 0.89$; 5.34

48. $17.25x = 50.59$
$x = 50.59 \div 17.25$; 2.93

49. $81.23m = 62.4$
$m = 62.4 \div 81.23$; 0.77

50. $\dfrac{x}{5.023} = -2.98$
$x = 5.023(-2.98)$; −14.97

WRITING IN ALGEBRA

Write one example of each of the expressions 1–5. See below.

1. An algebraic expression involving subtraction of negative numbers.

2. An algebraic expression involving addition of negative numbers.

3. An algebraic expression involving subtraction of a negative number and multiplication of a positive number.

4. An algebraic expression containing parentheses and the operations of subtraction and multiplication.

5. An algebraic expression containing parentheses and the operations of addition and division.

6. In Exercises 4 and 5, explain what must be known before you can evaluate the expressions. Identify the order of the operations that would be used to evaluate each expression.

7. Write your own explanation of the procedures to be used in *evaluating* an algebraic expression.

Additional Answers
1. $m - (-2)$ 2. $4x + (-3)$ 3. $2c - (-5)$
4. $(t - 6) \cdot 3$ 5. $(s + 3) \div 2$
6. The value of the variable is needed to evaluate the expression. In the expression for Exercise 4, first subtract and then multiply. In Exercise 5 first add and then divide.
7. First do whatever operation is indicated in parenthesis and then multiply, divide, add and subtract from left to right.

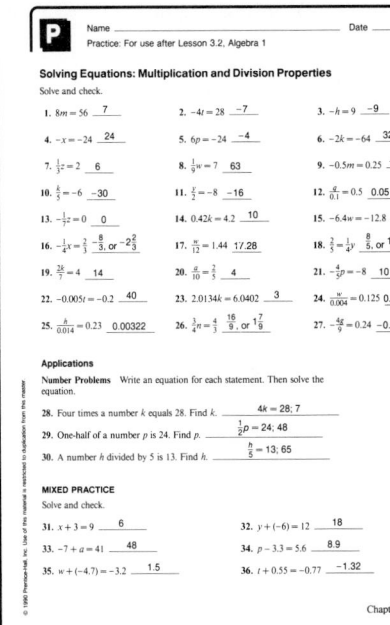

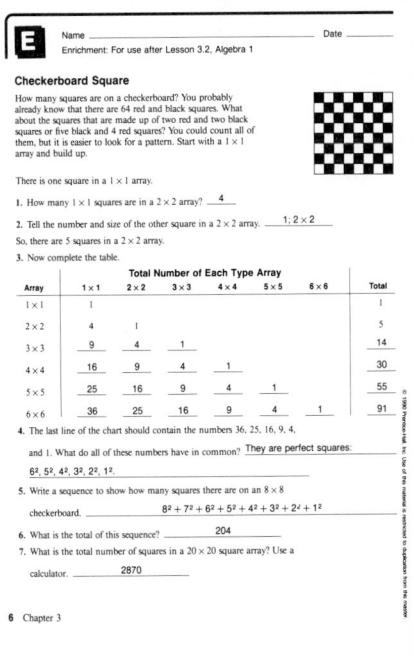

In the Capsule Review, each exercise requires that two operations be performed to obtain an isolated variable. The lesson will expand students' understanding of the equation properties by combining any two of the four equation properties in each expression.

3.3 Solving Equations: More Than One Property

Objective: To solve equations using more than one equation property

Louisa asked Jesse what time the math contest started on Saturday morning. In typical contest fashion, Jesse replied, "If you multiply the time by 3 and then add 6, the result is 33." Louisa made the following diagram:

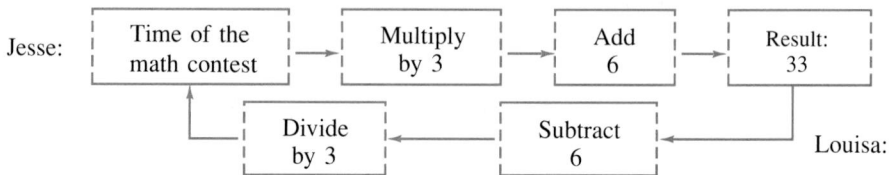

By "undoing" Jesse's steps, $(33 - 6 = 27; 27 \div 3 = 9)$, Louisa determined that the time of the math contest was 9:00 AM.

Capsule Review

To obtain n from the expression $4n - 20$, follow these steps:

(1) Add 20.
$4n - 20 + 20 = 4n + 0 = 4n$

(2) Divide by 4.
$4n \div 4 = 1n$, or n

Tell what operations to perform to get the variable n by itself.   add 18; multiply by $\frac{3}{2}$

1. $3n + 2$
subtract 2; divide by 3

2. $-4n + 24$
subtract 24; divide by -4

3. $\frac{n}{4} - 3$
add 3; multiply by 4

4. $\frac{2}{3}n - 18$

To solve an equation when more than one equation property is required, first simplify the equation and then use the addition or subtraction property for equations. Then you are ready to use the multiplication or division property for equations.

EXAMPLE 1   **Solve and check:** $4n - 20 = 36$

$$4n - 20 = 36$$
$$4n - 20 + 20 = 36 + 20 \qquad \textit{First add 20 to each side of the equation.}$$
$$4n = 56$$

$$\frac{4n}{4} = \frac{56}{4} \qquad \textit{Then divide each side of the equation by 4.}$$
$$n = 14$$

106   Chapter 3 Equations in One Variable

Check:
$$4n - 20 = 36$$
$$4 \cdot 14 - 20 \stackrel{?}{=} 36 \qquad \textit{Replace n with 14.}$$
$$56 - 20 \stackrel{?}{=} 36$$
$$36 = 36 \; \checkmark \qquad \textit{True}$$

The solution of the equation is 14.

In the next equation, $4(x - 3) = -24$, a number is decreased by 3 and the result is multiplied by 4. To solve equations of this type, the distributive property is used to simplify and then the inverse operations—addition and division—are used. It is important to simplify an equation first, then solve for the variable.

EXAMPLE 2   Solve: $4(x - 3) = -24$

$$4(x - 3) = -24$$
$$4x - 12 = -24 \qquad \textit{Use distributive property.}$$
$$4x - 12 + 12 = -24 + 12 \qquad \textit{Add 12 to each side of the equation.}$$
$$4x = -12$$
$$\frac{4x}{4} = \frac{-12}{4} \qquad \textit{Divide each side of the equation by 4.}$$
$$x = -3$$

The solution of the equation is -3. How do you check the solution?

EXAMPLE 3   Solve: $-\dfrac{8}{15} = \dfrac{6}{15} - \dfrac{2}{3}x$

$$-\frac{8}{15} = \frac{6}{15} - \frac{2}{3}x$$
$$-\frac{8}{15} - \frac{6}{15} = \frac{6}{15} - \frac{2}{3}x - \frac{6}{15} \qquad \textit{Subtract } \frac{6}{15} \textit{ from each side of the equation.}$$
$$-\frac{14}{15} = -\frac{2}{3}x$$
$$-\frac{3}{2}\left(-\frac{14}{15}\right) = -\frac{3}{2}\left(-\frac{2}{3}x\right) \qquad \textit{Multiply each side of the equation by } -\frac{3}{2}, \textit{ the reciprocal of } -\frac{2}{3}.$$
$$\frac{7}{5} = x$$

The solution of the equation is $\dfrac{7}{5}$. Check the solution.

3.3 Solving Equations: More Than One Property   **107**

TEACHING SUGGESTIONS

- Emphasize that to solve equations of the form $ax + b = c$ and $\dfrac{x}{a} + b = c$, students must perform two operations.
- At this stage, most students need to write out all the equation solving steps.
- Students may be confused when an equation has 0 on one side. Emphasize that an equation such as $15 - 1.3x = 0$ is a perfectly valid equation. (See Class Exercises 8 and 18.)

CHALKBOARD EXAMPLES

- **For Example 1**
  Solve and check:
  1. $3n - 15 = 33$ 16
  2. $8p - 1.2 = -2.8$ -0.2

- **For Example 2**
  Solve:
  3. $3(y - 6) = -30$ -4
  4. $5(x + 3) = 40$ 5

- **For Example 3**
  Solve:
  5. $-\dfrac{3}{4}x + \dfrac{1}{8} = -\dfrac{7}{8}$ $\dfrac{4}{3}$
  6. $7 - \dfrac{3}{8}y = 13$ -16

Common Error

- Some students may have difficulty organizing the steps for solving equations that require two operations. Encourage students to work systematically, writing out each step in the equation solving process to minimize errors and help them organize their thinking.
- See *Teacher's Resource Book* for additional remediation.

108

LESSON FOLLOW-UP

Discussion

Why should the addition or subtraction property be used first, then the multiplication or division property. *To simplify the equation so that no fractions are involved as to facilitate calculations.*

Critical Thinking

Causal Explanation To solve the equation $4n - 20 = 36$, why is the first step to add 20 to each side of the equation? *Students should conclude that the primary goal in solving an equation is to isolate the variable on one side of the equation.*

Assignment Guide

- See p. 94B for assignments.
- You may wish to review *calculation-ready form* before assigning Exercises 35–38.

Test Yourself

See *Teacher's Resource Book*, Tests, pp. 25–26.

Lesson Quiz

Solve and check.
1. $4a - 5 = 11$ 4
2. $4m + 13 = 29$ 4
3. $2(x + 4) = 14$ 3
4. $5(y - 6) = -60$ −6
5. $\dfrac{y}{12} - 48 = -22$ 312
6. $6 - \dfrac{2}{5}y = 14$ −20

Enrichment

The problem in the lesson introduction requires students to solve the equation $3x + 6 = 33$. Ask students to formulate a word problem or puzzle which requires solving the equation $2x + 5 = 21$. *Answers may vary. One possible solution is: How many chairs are in a row if twice the number of chairs increased by 5 is 21? 8 chairs*

CLASS EXERCISES

Tell what must be done to each side of the first equation in order to get the second equation.

1. $-7b + 8 = -6$; $-7b = -14$ subtract 8
2. $2x - 15 = -9$; $2x = 6$ · add 15
3. $-19 + \dfrac{5}{4}y = 26$; $\dfrac{5}{4}y = 45$ add 19
4. $-17 = 11 + \dfrac{t}{7}$; $-28 = \dfrac{t}{7}$ subtract 11

Tell what must be done to each side of the equation to get x alone.

5. $2x - 3 = 8$
   add 3; divide by 2
6. $3x + 7 = 17$
   subtract 7; divide by 3
7. $11 - 4x = 1\dfrac{1}{2}$
   subtract 11; divide by −4
8. $15 - 1.3x = 0$
   subtract 15; divide by −1.3
9. $4x + 28 = 28$
   subtract 28; divide by 4
10. $-4.7 + \dfrac{3}{4}x = 1.8$
    add 4.7; multiply by $\dfrac{4}{3}$
11. $3x - 15 = 33$
    add 15; divide by 3
12. $\dfrac{1}{2}x - 20 = 20$
    add 20; multiply by 2
13. $-24 = 2 - x$
    subtract 2; divide by −1

Solve each equation by changing it to an equivalent equation as described. Check each answer to see if it makes the original equation true.

14. $7m + 5 = 26$ Subtract 5; divide by 7. 3
15. $-11h - 7 = -18$ Add 7; divide by −11. 1
16. $\dfrac{2}{3}x - 9 = 17$ Add 9; multiply by $\dfrac{3}{2}$. 39
17. $-10 = \dfrac{3}{8}y + 14$ Subtract 14; multiply by $\dfrac{8}{3}$. −64
18. $\dfrac{x}{5} + 15 = 0$ Subtract 15; multiply by 5. −75
19. $-8 - x = 11$ Add 8; divide by −1. −19

PRACTICE EXERCISES

Solve and check.

A
1. $3a - 1 = 7$ $\dfrac{8}{3}$
2. $2y - 18 = 44$ 31
3. $3x - 1 = 8$ 3
4. $20 - 5y = 45$ −5
5. $25 - 3c = 36$ $-\dfrac{11}{3}$
6. $14 - 2x = 18$ −2
7. $2(x - 4) = 26$ 17
8. $5(3 - x) = 40$ −5
9. $\dfrac{1}{4}(x - 24) = 13$ 76
10. $\dfrac{1}{3}(x + 27) = 4$ −15
11. $-7(3 + 2x) = 84$ $-\dfrac{15}{2}$
12. $6(5 - 3x) = 84$ −3

13. $-\dfrac{3}{4} = \dfrac{12}{4} - \dfrac{1}{2}x$ $\tfrac{15}{2}$ **14.** $-\dfrac{5}{6} = \dfrac{5}{6} - \dfrac{2}{3}x$ $\tfrac{5}{2}$ **15.** $\dfrac{2}{9} = \dfrac{1}{3} - \dfrac{4}{9}x$ $\tfrac{1}{4}$

16. $\dfrac{1}{2} = \dfrac{5}{4} - \dfrac{3}{2}x$ $\tfrac{1}{2}$ **17.** $\dfrac{1}{5} = \dfrac{2}{3} + \dfrac{3}{5}x$ $-\tfrac{7}{9}$ **18.** $\dfrac{1}{8} = \dfrac{3}{4} + \dfrac{1}{8}x$ -5

B   **19.** $49w - 186 = 5351$ 113   **20.** $44x - 728 = 1736$ 56

21. $\dfrac{x}{3} + 3 = 42$ 117   **22.** $\dfrac{f}{34} + 16 = 35$ 646

23. $-\dfrac{7}{12} = \dfrac{5}{12} - \dfrac{2}{3}x$ $\tfrac{3}{2}$ **24.** $\dfrac{-3}{24} = \dfrac{5}{24} - \dfrac{4}{12}x$ 1

Solve and check.

25. $2|x| - 7 = 1$ 4, -4 **26.** $3|n| + 6 = -3$ no solution   **27.** $5|t| - 10 = 0$ 2, -2

28. $9|x| - 7 = 7$ $\tfrac{14}{9}, -\tfrac{14}{9}$ **29.** $-5|x| + 7 = 2$ 1, -1 **30.** $-7|r| - 8 = -1$ no solution

Complete each sentence.

C   **31.** If $4x + 2 = 14$, then $2x + 1 = \underline{\ ?\ }$.   7

32. If $3x - 1 = 17$, then $6x - 2 = \underline{\ ?\ }$.   34

33. If $x + 7 = 8$, then $7 - x = \underline{\ ?\ }$.   6

34. If $2x + 5 = 21$, then $8x = \underline{\ ?\ }$.   64

Applications

Calculator   The calculation ready form of $23x - 1.7 = 1.2$ is: $x = \dfrac{1.2 + 1.7}{23}$. Write each equation below in calculation ready form. Then solve the equation and state your answer to the nearest hundredth.

35. $583r + 23.58 = 2.79$
$r = \dfrac{2.79 - 23.58}{583}; \approx -0.04$

36. $-51.5 = 29m - 4.06$
$m = \dfrac{-51.5 + 4.06}{29}; \approx -1.64$

37. $\dfrac{x}{0.24} - 0.03 = -0.14$
$x = (-0.14 + 0.03)0.24; -0.03$

38. $\dfrac{a}{2.5} + 11.9 = 0.02$
$a = (0.02 - 11.9)2.5; -29.7$

TEST YOURSELF

Solve each equation. Check your answer.

1. $y + 11 = 4$ -7 **2.** $-7.6 = x - 1.4$ -6.2 **3.** $-\dfrac{3}{4} + z = \dfrac{5}{2}$ $\tfrac{13}{4}$ **3.1**

4. $9t = 30$ $\tfrac{10}{3}$ **5.** $24 = -\dfrac{2}{5}m$ -60 **6.** $\dfrac{x}{7} = -3.15$ -22.05 **3.2**

7. $6k + 5 = 23$ 3   **8.** $5 - \dfrac{j}{12} = 1$ 48   **9.** $-7.13 = 0.15p - 7.13$ 0   **3.3**

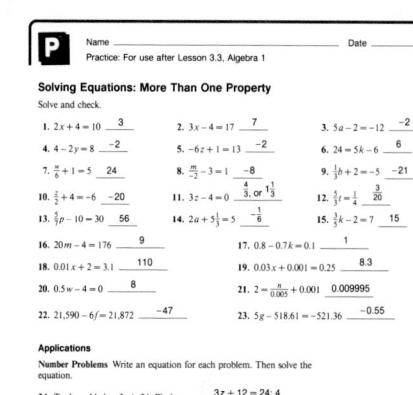

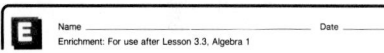

3.4 Problem Solving Strategy: Make a Model

BACKGROUND

- A student's ability to construct a mathematical model is critical to solving problems in algebra.
- A student's ability to organize information given in a problem so that it can be used to solve the problem is a key to success in this lesson. To determine a student's progress, analyze and classify specific errors in the student's work.

Error Analysis Classification

1. *Misunderstanding*
   Failed to understand how to set up a word equation
2. *Misapplied Strategy*
   Selected an inappropriate model
   Translated the word equation into an algebraic equation incorrectly

TEACHING SUGGESTIONS

- Stress the idea that mathematics is used to solve many different kinds of problems in science, medicine, business, economics, and so on, provided these problems can be expressed in mathematical terms.
- Note that the use of mathematical models is most effective if students learn to choose the most appropriate model for the problem they are trying to solve. For example, often when a lot of data is presented in a problem, a table is the best model to use. Ask students to suggest other examples and the models appropriate to solve them. You might list their suggestions on an overhead projector.

Many real-world problems can be solved by constructing and analyzing *mathematical models*. A **mathematical model** represents the known parts of a problem. Many different kinds of models may be used to solve problems in algebra. For example, a drawing, figure, graph, or table can be constructed as a model. Other models may include a formula, pattern, equation, or an inequality. This lesson presents writing an equation as a model.

EXAMPLE 1 Janice bought a number of cassette tapes for $8 each. She then spent $3 more for a magazine. If she spent a total of $35, how many tapes did she buy?

Understand the Problem Janice bought a number of cassette tapes at $8 each and spent $3 for a magazine. The total cost was $35.

You are asked to find how many cassette tapes Janice bought.

Plan Your Approach **Choose a strategy.**
A successful strategy to solve a problem is to set up a mathematical model. An appropriate model for this problem is an equation.

Write a word equation.

| Number of dollars spent for tapes | + | Cost of magazine | = | Total amount spent |

Assign variables.
Let x represent the number of tapes bought.
Then $8x$ represents the total amount spent for the tapes.

Translate the word equation into an algebraic equation.

Number of dollars spent for tapes	*plus*	Cost of magazine	*equals*	Total amount spent
↓	↓	↓	↓	↓
$8x$	$+$	3	$=$	35

Complete the Work **Solve the equation.**
$$8x + 3 = 35$$
$$8x + 3 - 3 = 35 - 3$$
$$\frac{8x}{8} = \frac{32}{8}$$
$$x = 4$$

110 Chapter 3 Equations in One Variable

Interpret the Results	**State your conclusion.** Janice bought 4 cassette tapes.	

Check your conclusion.

$$8x + 3 = 35$$
$$8(4) + 3 \stackrel{?}{=} 35$$
$$32 + 3 \stackrel{?}{=} 35$$
$$35 = 35 \quad \checkmark$$

CLASS EXERCISES

Identify a mathematical model for each situation described. The model may be a geometric figure, a formula, table, or an algebraic expression.

1. The number of books in a box which holds 64 books if the box is n books short of being filled. $64 - n$

2. The area of a rectangular floor in order to calculate the number of floor tiles needed to cover it. $A = lw$

3. The shortest distance from one point on a map to another point. line segment

4. The receipts from the sale of 95 tickets if each ticket costs d dollars. $95d$

5. The distance an automobile travels in a given time if its speed is 35 mi/h. $d = rt$, or $d = 35t$

PRACTICE EXERCISES

Identify a mathematical model for each problem. Then use the model to solve the problem.

A 1. Jane bought a number of records for $7 each. She then spent $3 more for a poster. If she spent a total of $24, how many records did she buy? $7x + 3 = 24$; 3 records

2. Robert and Jeanine are having a dinner party. There are 24 guests to be expected. If there are 4 tables seating an equal number of guests, how many guests will each table accommodate? $4x = 24$; 6 guests

3. John works for a shipping department where he packs an equal number of books into boxes. John has 40 books and 5 boxes. How many books did John pack into each box? How many books were left over? $5x = 40$; 8 books; 0 left over

B 4. At a graduation dinner, an equal number of people were seated at 8 tables. The host invited 35 people and 3 guests arrived late. A new table was set up for the late guests. How many people were seated at each of the other tables? $8p + 3 = 35$; 4 people per table

5. Lois worked part time after school and 4 h on Saturday. One Saturday, her boss paid her $25 for the day, which included a $5 tip. How much does Lois earn per hour? $4e + 5 = 25$; $5 per hour

111

P Name _____ Date _____
Practice: For use after Lesson 3.4, Algebra 1

Problem Solving Strategy: Make a Model

Write an equation that is a mathematical model for the problem, then solve the equation.

1. Tony works in a shipping department where he packs canisters of tennis balls into boxes. For an order of 85 canisters, he packed the canisters equally into 10 boxes with 5 canisters left over. How many canisters did Tony pack into each box? $10c + 5 = 85$; 8

2. At a brunch for a group of students, an equal number of people were seated at each of 12 tables. The host invited 100 students and 4 students arrived late. A new table was set up for the late students. How many people were at the other tables? $12s + 4 = 100$; 8

3. Helen works part time at a hospital and is paid by the hour. How much does she earn per/h if her pay was $73.00 and she worked 20 h? $20w = 73; $3.65

4. The equation for the circumference of a circle is $C = 2\pi r$. Find the radius of a circle whose circumference is 36 in. $36 = 2\pi r$; approx 5.7 in.

Write the name of a geometric figure that can serve as a mathematical model for each situation.

5. You want to study the revolution of a record on a stereo. ___ circle

6. You want to calculate the volume of a volleyball. ___ sphere

Write a problem that can be described by each equation. Answers may vary.

7. $2x + 4 = 1$;
   Tim's age is twice his cousin Sandy's age plus 4 yr. Find Sandy's age.

8. $5x - 3 = 17$
   Rene has 17 cookbooks. This is 3 less than 5 times the number of cookbooks Amelia has. How many does Amelia have?

MIXED PROBLEM SOLVING REVIEW

1. Mia has $762.42 in her checking account. She wrote checks for $75 and $236.79 and deposited $372.40 and $31. What is the new balance in her account? $854.09

2. In a bowling tournament Kerri scored 136, 186, 174, 142, 146 and 129. What was her average for the tournament?   152

3. Sean and Ashley are saving money to go skiing. Ashley has saved 10 dollars more than Sean. If their combined savings is $230, how much has each saved? $110, $120

10   Chapter 3

E Name _____ Date _____
Enrichment: For use after Lesson 3.4, Algebra 1

Making a Model: Consumer Price Index

Mathematical models are often used to describe changes or situations that affect society. One such model is the Consumer Price Index(CPI). The CPI is a measure of the average change in prices over time for various types of goods and services.

The CPI measures changes in prices from a fixed reference date, 1967. Prices during that year are designated as 100.0, for $100. An increase in prices of 70% over 1967 would be recorded as 170.0. A change in prices of 150% would be recorded as 250.0.

The chart below shows the CPI for the years 1979–1983. *Commodities* refers to food, fuel, clothing, and other necessary items. *Services* refers to dentists, doctors, lawyers, plumbers, electricians, and so on.

YEAR	COMMODITIES	SERVICES	HOUSING	ALL ITEMS
1979	208.4	234.2	227.6	217.4
1980	233.9	270.3	263.3	246.8
1981	253.6	305.7	293.5	272.4
1982	263.8	333.3	314.7	289.1
1983	270.9	342.6	322.0	297.1

1. Between which two consecutive years did the cost of housing increase the most? What was the increase?
   Between 1979 and 1980; 35.7

2. From 1979 to 1983, which of the three groups of items, commodities, services, and housing, increased the most? Which increased the least? What were these increases?
   Most: services—108.4; least: commodities—62.5

3. If a bag of groceries cost $10.00 in 1967, what would the same bag of groceries cost in 1980? $23.39

4. A corporation wants to give raises based on the increase in consumer prices. If the raises are based on the CPI for all items, in which year will raises be the greatest?   1983

5. If a lawyer charged $50/h in 1967, how much would she probably charge in 1981? $152.85/h

6. An apartment that cost $500/month to rent in 1980 would cost how much to rent in 1983? (HINT: make a ratio.) $611.47

Chapter 3   11

---

6. Juan enjoys solving mathematics problems. A friend gave him this problem to solve: Seven times a number increased by five is 33. What is the number? $7n + 5 = 33$; 4

Write a word problem for which the equation or inequality is a mathematical model. Answers may vary. See below.

C   7. $\frac{1}{2}b = 8$ 8. $5y - 14 = 27$ 9. $a - 3 < 7$ 10. $\frac{m}{7} + 1 > 19$

11. Select a model and then describe the procedure you would follow to explain how our place-value numeration system works. See p. 719.

12. Select a model and show how you can measure exactly 4 quarts when you have only a 3-quart measure and a 5-quart measure to use. See p. 719.

Mixed Problem Solving Review

1. An investor in the stock market had the following gains and losses on the sale of 6 different stocks: +$400, -$700, +$1,000, +$200, -$500, +$100. What is the total gain or loss? What is the average gain or loss for the 6 stocks? $500 gain; +$83, to the nearest dollar

2. Write an equation for each word sentence. Then solve the equation, using the set of whole numbers from 0 through 10 as the replacement set.
   a. The product of a number and 2, increased by 5, is 11. $2n + 5 = 11$; 3
   b. A number less 8 is the first positive even number. $n - 8 = 2$; 10
   c. The quotient of 20 and a number equals 4. $\frac{20}{a} = 4$; 5
   d. The sum of a number and nine times the number equals 10. $b + 9b = 10$; 1

PROJECT

A table is a useful problem-solving model. A table shows numerical information, called *data* (plural of *datum*). Tables are used to organize data and answer questions about the data.

Construct a table to record the amount of time you spend studying each of your school subjects each day for 30 consecutive days. Record the time to the nearest 5 minutes.

At the end of 30 days, find the total time for each subject and divide by 30. Your answer will be the average number of minutes you study each subject each day for 30 days.

By analyzing the data in your table, identify three other conclusions that can be made. What does this project tell you about your study habits? Check students' work.

112   Chapter 3 Equations in One Variable

Additional Answers

7. The product of one half and *b* equals eight.
8. Five times *y* less fourteen equals twenty-seven.
9. *a* less three is less than seven.
10. One seventh times *m* plus one is greater than nineteen.

Algebraic Proof

Objectives: To identify postulates, theorems, and proofs
To prove simple algebraic statements

LESSON PLAN

Vocabulary
Conclusion
Direct proof
Hypothesis
Postulate
Theorem

Materials/Manipulatives
Overhead projector
*Teacher's Resource Book,
Teaching Aid 4,
Transparency 5*

Many properties about the sums and products of real numbers are stated earlier in this book. You have used them in computations and in solving equations. Some of these properties are also called *postulates*. **Postulates** are statements that are accepted as true without requiring a proof.

Capsule Review

Name the property of real numbers illustrated by each statement.

1. $5 + 9 = 9 + 5$ Commut. Prop. Addit.

2. $6\left(\frac{2}{3} + 4\right) = 6 \cdot \frac{2}{3} + 6 \cdot 4$
Distributive Prop.

3. $3 + (7 + x) = (3 + 7) + x$
Assoc. Prop. Addit.

4. $8 \cdot 1 = 8$ Identity Prop. Mult.

5. $10 + (4 + 0) = 10 + 4$
Identity Prop. Addit.

6. $7 \cdot 3 + 7 \cdot 2 = 7(3 + 2)$
Distributive Prop.

A summary follows of some of the definitions and properties of real numbers. These definitions and properties will be useful in doing algebraic proofs.

Properties of Operations with Real Numbers		
	Addition	**Multiplication**
Commutative	$a + b = b + a$	$a \cdot b = b \cdot a$
Associative	$a + (b + c) = (a + b) + c$	$a \cdot (b \cdot c) = (a \cdot b) \cdot c$
Inverse	$a + (-a) = 0$ and $-a + a = 0$	$a \cdot \frac{1}{a} = 1$ and $\frac{1}{a} \cdot a = 1, a \neq 0$
Identity	$a + 0 = a$ and $0 + a = a$	$a \cdot 1 = a$ and $1 \cdot a = a$
Distributive property		$a(b + c) = ab + ac$ and $(b + c)a = ba + ca$
Property of 0 for multiplication		$a \cdot 0 = 0$ and $0 \cdot a = 0$
Property of -1 for multiplication		$-1(a) = -a$ and $a(-1) = -a$
Definition of subtraction		$a - b = a + (-b)$
Definition of division		$a \div b = a \cdot \frac{1}{b}, b \neq 0$

BACKGROUND

In the Capsule Review, students are required to identify and use the properties of real numbers studied previously. A summary of all of the properties is presented below the Capsule Review. A clear understanding of the properties is necessary if students are to comprehend and complete algebraic proofs.

Critical Thinking

Comparing-Contrasting Compare and contrast postulates and theorems. Students should classify both as mathematical statements or propositions; however, postulates are accepted as true without proof; theorems are accepted as true only after proof.

TEACHING SUGGESTIONS

- Few students have been exposed to formal proofs before. You may wish to give an informal proof for the examples before discussing the formal proofs.
- You may want to present formal proofs of the examples on an overhead projector. Use Transparency 5 and Teaching Aid 4 to work through several examples.
- Students who have trouble with the Capsule Review should be asked to give numerical examples illustrating each property in the summary.

CHALKBOARD EXAMPLES

- **For Example 1**
  1. Prove: For all real numbers a, b, and c, if $a = b$, then $a - c = b - c$. Fill in the missing statements and reasons.

Statements	Reasons
1. $a = b$	1. Given
2. $a - c = a - c$	2. Reflex. prop.
3. $a - c = b - c$	3. Subst. prop.

- **For Example 2**
  2. Prove: For all real numbers x, y, and z, if $x = y$, then $x + z = y + z$. Fill in the missing statements and reasons.

Statements	Reasons
1. $x = y$	1. Given
2. $x + z = x + z$	2. Reflexive prop.
3. $x + z = y + z$	3. Substitution prop.

The following properties of equality for all real numbers a, b, and c are also used in algebraic proofs.

Properties of Equality	
Reflexive	$a = a$ (A number is equal to itself.)
Symmetric	If $a = b$, then $b = a$.
Transitive	If $a = b$ and $b = c$, then $a = c$.
Substitution	If $a = b$, then a may replace b or b may replace a in any statement.

A **theorem** is a general conclusion that is shown to be true by using postulates, definitions, given facts, and other proved theorems. The reasoning that takes you from the **hypothesis** (the given statement) to the **conclusion** (the final statement) is called a **direct proof**.

EXAMPLE 1   **Prove: For all real numbers a, b, and c, if $a = b$, then $ac = bc$.**

If $\underline{a = b}$ then $\underline{ac = bc}$.

hypothesis (given)   conclusion

Proof:

Statements	Reasons
1. $a = b$	1. Given
2. $ac = ac$	2. Reflexive property
3. $ac = bc$	3. Substitution property

Therefore, if $a = b$, then $ac = bc$.

Notice that the theorem proved in Example 1 is a formal statement of the Multiplication Property for Equations.

EXAMPLE 2   **Prove: For all real numbers a and b, $-(a - b) = b - a$.**

Proof:

Statements	Reasons
1. $-(a - b) = -[a + (-b)]$	1. Definition of subtraction
2. $\quad\quad\quad = -1[a + (-b)]$	2. Property of -1 for multiplication
3. $\quad\quad\quad = (-1)a + (-1)(-b)$	3. Distributive property
4. $\quad\quad\quad = (-a) + (b)$	4. Property of -1 for multiplication
5. $\quad\quad\quad = b + (-a)$	5. Commutative property for addition
6. $\quad\quad\quad = b - a$	6. Definition of subtraction

Therefore, for all real numbers a and b, $-(a - b) = b - a$.

114   Chapter 3 Equations in One Variable

CLASS EXERCISES

Write the missing statements or reasons for each step of the proof.

Prove: For all real numbers a and b, $a + b + (-b) = a$.

Proof:

Statements	Reasons
1. $(a + b) + (-b) = a + [b + (-b)]$	1. ___?___ Associative prop. add.
2. $\qquad\qquad = a + \underline{\ ?\ }\ 0$	2. ___?___ Inverse prop. add.
3. $\qquad\qquad = a$	3. ___?___ Identity prop. add.

PRACTICE EXERCISES

Write the missing statements or reasons in each proof.

A **1.** Prove: For all real numbers a, b, and c, if $a = b$ and $c \neq 0$, then $\dfrac{a}{c} = \dfrac{b}{c}$.

Proof:

Statements	Reasons
1. $a = b,\ c \neq 0$	1. ___?___ Given
2. $\dfrac{a}{c} = \underline{\ ?\ }\ \dfrac{a}{c}$	2. Reflexive property
3. $\dfrac{a}{c} = \underline{\ ?\ }\ \dfrac{b}{c}$	3. ___?___ Substitution prop.

2. Prove: For all real numbers x and y, $-(x - y) + (y - x) = 2(y - x)$.

Proof:

Statements	Reasons
1. $-(x - y) + (y - x)$	1. Definition of subtraction
$\quad = -[x + (-y)] + (y - x)$	
2. $= -1[x + (-y)] + (y - x)$	2. ___?___ Property of -1 for multiplication
3. $= (-1)(x) + (-1)(-y) + (y - x)$	3. ___?___ Distributive property
4. $= -x + y + (y - x)$	4. ___?___ Property of -1 for multiplication
5. $= y + y - x - x$	5. Commutative property for addition
6. $= 2y - 2x$	6. ___?___ Combine like terms
7. $2(y - x)$	7. Distributive property

Prove. Assume that all variables represent real numbers. See side column.

3. If $a = b$ then $a - c = b - c$.

4. If $x = y$ then $z - x = z - y$

B **5.** $a + [b + (-a)] = b$

6. $x + [-(x + y)] = -y$

C **7.** If $a = b$, then $a - d = -(d - b)$.

3.5 Algebraic Proof   **115**

Additional Answers

3. Proof:

Statements	Reasons
1. $\qquad a = b$	1. Given
2. $a - c = a - c$	2. Reflexive prop.
3. $a - c = b - c$	3. Substitution prop.

See Additional Answer section beginning p. 719.

Common Error

- Writing the reasons formally and using the names of the properties are difficult for many students. You may wish to accept "add 0 to both sides of the equation" for "addition property for equations" until students become comfortable using the names of properties.
- See *Teacher's Resource Book* for additional remediation.

LESSON FOLLOW-UP

Discussion

You may wish to ask students to distinguish between a direct proof, a hypothesis, and a conclusion. A direct proof is the reasoning that takes you from the hypothesis to the conclusion. The hypothesis is the given statement and the conclusion is the final statement.

Assignment Guide

See p. 94B for assignments.

Logical Reasoning

The feature introduces a simple probability problem that students can solve by playing the game that is presented. You may wish to create or have students create other simple problems that students can solve in the same fashion.

Lesson Quiz

Write the missing statements or reasons in the proof below.

1. Prove: If $a \neq 0$, then $\dfrac{1}{a}(ab) = b$.

Statements	Reasons
1. $\dfrac{1}{a}(ab)$	1. Assoc. prop. for mult.
$\quad = (\dfrac{1}{a} \cdot a)b$	
2. $= 1 \cdot b$	2. Inv. prop. for mult.
3. $= b$	3. Ident. prop. for mult.

115

P Name _____ Date _____
Practice: For use after Lesson 3.5, Algebra 1

Algebraic Proof
Write the missing reasons in each proof.

1. Prove: For all real numbers a, b, and c if $a = b$, then $a + (-c) = b + (-c)$.

Statements	Reasons
1. $a = b$	1. Given
2. $a + (-c) = a + (-c)$	2. Reflexive property for equality
3. $a + (-c) = b + (-c)$	3. Substitution property of equality

2. Prove: For all real numbers a, b, and c, $a(b + c) = (b + c)a$.

Statements	Reasons
1. $a(b + c) = ab + ac$	1. Distributive property
2. $ = ba + ca$	2. Commutative property for multiplication
3. $ = (b + c)a$	3. Distributive property

3. Prove: For all real numbers x, y, and z if $x = y$, then $x(-z) = y(-z)$.

Statements	Reasons
1. $x = y$	1. Given
2. $y(-z) = y(-z)$	2. Reflexive property for equality
3. $x(-z) = y(-z)$	3. Substitution property of equality

MIXED PRACTICE
Solve each problem by writing and solving an equation.

4. Eighteen times a number is −1008. Find the number. $18n = -1008;\ -56$

5. A case of a dozen video cassette tapes costs $191.40. Find the cost of a single tape. $12t = \$191.40;\ \$15.95$

6. If you add two-fifths of a number to the number itself, you get 56. What is the number? $n + \frac{2}{5}n = 56;\ 40$

7. A number divided by 12 is 51. Find the number. $\frac{n}{12} = 51;\ 612$

Chapter 3 **13**

14 Chapter 3

E Name _____ Date _____
Enrichment: For use after Lesson 3.5, Algebra 1

Cairnpit Island
Professor Defoe is an authority on the naming practices of Cairnpit Island. Everyone on the island has a last name of either Smith, Jones, Robinson, Crusoe, or Friday.

This chart shows how they determine their children's names. Whenever a man and a woman with the same name marry, they name their children Smith. When someone named Smith marries anyone, their children are given the latter's name. It is possible for anyone to have a child with a different name. The scheme is shown in the chart at the right.

Only the initial of the last name is given. The woman's name appears at the top of the chart, the man's name on the left, and the children's in the body of the chart.

	S	J	R	C	F
S	S	J	R	C	F
J	J	S	F	R	C
R	R	C	S	F	J
C	C	F	J	S	R
F	F	R	C	J	S

1. The present ruler of Cairnpit Island is Queen Friday. Neither of her parents were named Smith or Jones. What were their names?
Crusoe and Robinson

2. While visiting Cairnpit Island, Professor Defoe stayed at the house of a man named Smith. Smith told the professor that three of his grandparents were named Robinson. What was the name of Smith's fourth grandparent?
Robinson

3. Smith's three sons married women named Robinson, Crusoe, and Friday. They all have children, none of whom are named Smith. Smith's wife is not a Smith either. What is her name?
Jones

4. A brother and sister named Crusoe married two people who were also brother and sister. The children of the two families have different names, neither of which is Robinson. What are the names of the other parents and the children?
Mr. Crusoe and Miss Robinson had Joneses; Miss Crusoe and Mr. Robinson had Fridays.

5. There is a legend that once everyone on the island was named either Smith or Friday. Then someone named Crusoe arrived, whose son, King Jones, became the first ruler. What can you conclude from this account?
The first Crusoe must have been a woman.

Complete the proof.

8. Prove: For all real numbers a, $(a)(0) = 0$.

Proof:

Statements	Reasons
1. a is a real number	1. _?_ Given
2. $a + 0 = a$	2. _?_ Identity prop. add.
3. $a(a + 0) = (a)(a)$	3. _?_ Mult. prop. for equations
4. $(a)(a) + (a)(0) = (a)(a)$	4. _?_ Distributive prop.
5. $(a)(a) + (a)(0) - (a)(a) = 0$	5. _?_ Subtraction prop. for equations
6. $(a)(a) - (a)(a) + (a)(0) = 0$	6. _?_ Commutative prop. for add.
7. $0 + (a)(0) = 0$	7. _?_ Additive inverse prop.
8. $(a)(0) = 0$	8. _?_ Identity prop. add.

Applications

Language Arts The reflexive, symmetric, and transitive properties are true for the equality relationship. Which of these properties are true for the given relationship of the replacement set of all family members?

9. is a brother of transitive; symmetric

10. is younger than transitive

11. is married to symmetric

12. is a cousin of symmetric

LOGICAL REASONING

Sprouts is a game for two people to play. It begins with a fixed number of sprouts (or dots) on paper. To play, each player must (1) draw a branch from one sprout to another or to the same sprout, and (2) make an additional sprout anywhere on the branch drawn. The object is to cut off sprouts with branches so no moves are possible. The rules of the game follow.

Rules: No sprout may have more than three branches. Branches may not intersect. The person who draws the last branch is the winner.

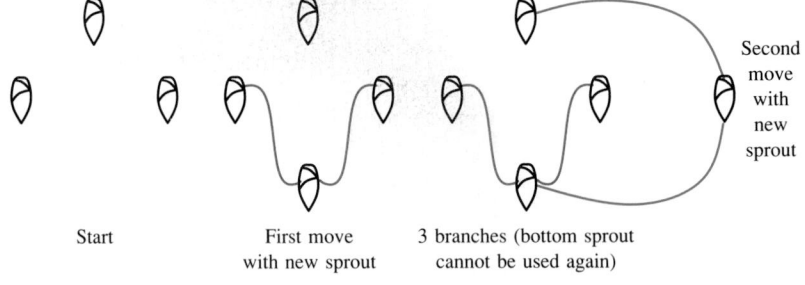

Start | First move with new sprout | 3 branches (bottom sprout cannot be used again) | Second move with new sprout

What is the least number of moves needed to determine a winner? 6

3.6

Evaluating Formulas

Objectives: To solve for any variable in a formula when the values of the other variables are given
To use formulas to solve simple word problems

A **formula** is an equation that expresses a relationship among two or more quantities. The formula $P = 2l + 2w$ states a relationship involving the perimeter P, length l, and width w of a rectangle. If any two of the quantities are known, you can find the third.

You solve for variables in formulas in the same way as you do in other equations.

Capsule Review

EXAMPLES Solve: $27 = \dfrac{2}{3}r$ 　　　　Solve: $3a + 6 = 27$

$$27 = \frac{2}{3}r$$

$$\frac{3}{2} \cdot 27 = \frac{3}{2} \cdot \frac{2}{3}r$$

$$40\frac{1}{2} = r$$

The solution is $40\frac{1}{2}$.

$$3a + 6 = 27$$
$$3a + 6 - 6 = 27 - 6$$
$$3a = 21$$
$$\frac{3a}{3} = \frac{21}{3}$$
$$a = 7$$

The solution is 7.

Solve each equation for x.

1. $-49 = 7x$ _–7_ 　　　　**2.** $\dfrac{1}{2}x = -35$ _–70_ 　　　　**3.** $\dfrac{x}{5} + 6 = 11$ _25_

4. $-4x - 9 = 31$ _–10_ 　　　　**5.** $13 - 13x = 0$ _1_ 　　　　**6.** $\dfrac{1}{3}x - 9 = -6$ _9_

7. $16.2 = 2x + 6.2$ _5_ 　　　　　　**8.** $0.7x - 5.6 = 0$ _8_

To solve a formula for one variable when values of other variables are given:

• Replace each variable by its given value.

• Solve the resulting equation, using the properties for equations.

In Example 1, a formula is used to find the length of a rectangle when its perimeter and width are known.

Vocabulary
Formula

Materials/Manipulatives
*Teacher's Resource Book,
Teaching Aid 3*

BACKGROUND

In the Capsule Review, students solve equations for one variable. This is an appropriate way to prepare students to solve multivariable formulas by substituting values for all but one variable, and solving for it.

Critical Thinking

Judging Ideas　What is the validity of the statement: If every formula is an equation, then every equation is a formula?　The statement is false. The two parts of the statement are not equivalent.

TEACHING SUGGESTIONS

Point out that the variables solved for in formulas such as, $d = rt$, must be expressed in corresponding (commensurate) units; thus, distance in miles, time in hours, and rate in miles per hour—or distance in feet, time in minutes, and rate in feet per minute.

CHALKBOARD EXAMPLES

• **For Example 1**
　1. Given the formula $P = 2b + 2c$, find the value of b, when $c = 19.2$ and $P = 73.6$.　17.6

• **For Example 2**
　2. Evaluate $V = \dfrac{1}{3}\pi r^2 h$ for h if
　$V = 616$ in.^{3}, $\pi = \dfrac{22}{7}$, and $r = 7$ in.　12 in.

EXAMPLE 1 Given the formula $P = 2l + 2w$, find the length l of a rectangle when its perimeter P is 18.2 units and its width w is 3.6 units.

$$P = 2l + 2w$$
$$18.2 = 2l + 2(3.6)$$ *Replace P with 18.2 and w with 3.6.*
$$18.2 = 2l + 7.2$$ *Solve the equation for l.*
$$18.2 - 7.2 = 2l + 7.2 - 7.2$$
$$11 = 2l$$
$$\frac{11}{2} = \frac{2l}{2}$$
$$5.5 = l$$

The length of the rectangle is 5.5 units.

Example 2 uses the formula for the volume of a cylinder.

EXAMPLE 2 Evaluate $V = \pi r^2 h$ for h if $V = 9420$ ft^3, $\pi \approx 3.14$, and $r = 10$ ft.

$$V = \pi r^2 h$$
$$9420 = 3.14(10^2)h$$
$$9420 = 3.14(100)h$$
$$9420 = 314h$$
$$30 = h$$

The height of the cylinder is 30 ft.

CLASS EXERCISES

1. *Area of triangle:* $A = \dfrac{1}{2}bh$ Find the value of h if $A = 16$ and $b = 4$. 8

2. *Amount in savings account:* $A = p + prt$ Evaluate $A = p + prt$ when $p = \$800$, $r = 0.04$, and $t = \dfrac{1}{4}$. $808

3. *Sum of n terms of arithmetic series:* $S = \dfrac{n}{2}(a + l)$ Find the value of n if $S = 52$, $a = -4$, and $l = 12$. 13

4. *Volume of rectangular prism:* $V = lwh$ Find the value of l if $V = 3.6$, $w = 0.8$, and $h = 3$. 1.5

5. *Temperature conversion:* $F = \dfrac{9}{5}C + 32$ Find the value of C when $F = -31°$. $-35°$

PRACTICE EXERCISES

A   1. Given the formula $P = 2l + 2w$, find the length l of a rectangle when its perimeter P is 15.5 units and its width w is 4.25 units. $l = 3.5$ units

2. Given the formula $P = 2l + 2w$, find the width w of a rectangle when its perimeter P is 17.6 units and its length l is 3.3 units. $w = 5.5$ units

118   Chapter 3 Equations in One Variable

3. Evaluate $V = \pi r^2 h$ for h if $V = 168$, $\pi \approx 3.14$, and $r = 3$. $h = 5.9$

4. Evaluate $V = \pi r^2 h$ for h if $V = 235.5$, $\pi \approx 3.14$, and $r = 5$. $h = 3$

B

5. Using the distance formula $d = rt$, find the value of r if $d = 28$ and $t = 4$. $r = 7$

6. Using the distance formula $d = rt$, find the value of t if $d = 45$ and $r = 5$. $t = 9$

7. Given the formula for the volume of a rectangular prism $V = lwh$. Find the value of h, if $V = 36$, $l = 4$, and $w = 3$. $h = 3$

8. Given the formula $V = lwh$, find the value of w if $V = 120$, $l = 5$, and $h = 3$. $w = 8$

In each formula, find the value of the indicated variable.

9. $P = 2l + 2w$; find w when $P = 240$ and $l = 10$. $w = 110$

10. $P = 2l + 2w$; find l when $P = 360$ and $w = 6$. $l = 174$

C

11. $A = \dfrac{b}{2} + i - 1$; find b when $A = 15$ and $i = 10$. 12

12. $V = \pi r^2 h$; find h when $V = 420$, $\pi \approx 3.14$, and $r = 3$. $h = 14.9$

Applications

13. **Travel** A train takes $3\frac{1}{2}$ h to go a distance of 334.25 km. Find its average speed. 95.5 km/h

14. **Travel** If a bicycle goes 219.8 cm in one turn of the wheels, what is the length of a radius of the wheels? ≈34.98 cm

15. **Geometry** The floor of one of the classrooms in a new school has a perimeter of 34.6 m. Find the area if the length is 10.6 m. 71.02 m²

WRITING IN ALGEBRA

Answers may vary. See below for possible answers.
1. Write an equation whose solution is found by using the addition and the division properties for equations.
2. Write an equation whose solution is found by using the subtraction and the multiplication properties for equations.
3. Write a short paragraph to explain how to check a solution for an equation.
4. Dan claims that to solve an equation like $3b - 2 = 19$, it is just as easy to use the division property before the addition property. Rosita insists that it is easier to use the addition property first. Show how each would solve the equation $3b - 2 = 19$. Which method is easier? Explain.

3.6 Evaluating Formulas **119**

Teacher's Resource Book
Reteaching—Chapter 3, p. 15

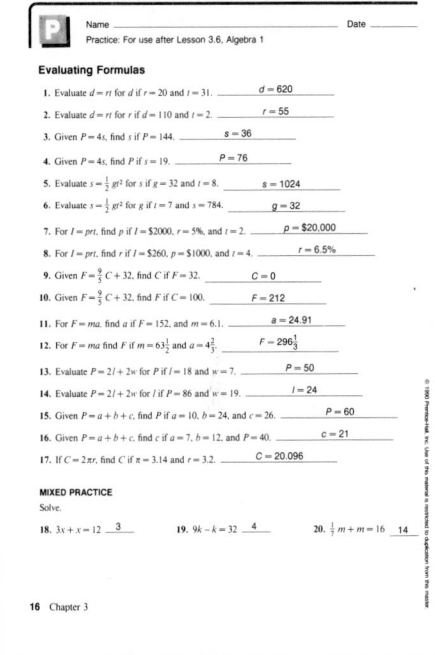

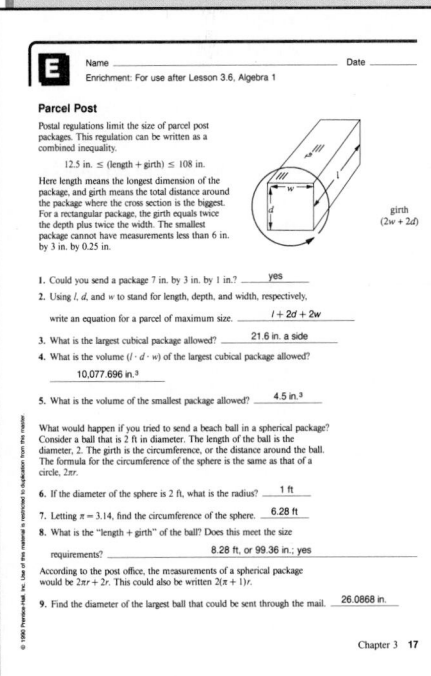

Additional Answers

1. $3c - 2 = 4$ 2. $\dfrac{n}{2} + 2 = 6$

3. To check a solution for an equation, substitute the value of the variable obtained back into the equation. If the result is correct no more work needs to be done. If the result is incorrect go back and redo the problem.
See Additional Answer section beginning p. 719.

BACKGROUND

Students' success with problem solving is a function of the parameters of the problem and their knowledge of relevant information prior to encountering the problem. These two factors determine the approach that a given student takes in a specific problem solving situation. To determine a student's progress, analyze errors in the student's work and then classify specific errors.

Error Analysis Classification

1. *Misunderstanding*
   Failed to identify the necessary mathematical relationships
   Failed to understand how to set up the word equation
2. *Misapplied Strategy*
   Selected an incorrect model
   Translated the word equation incorrectly into an algebraic equation
   Made errors in solving the equation
   Stopped short in the process and gave an incomplete answer

3.7

Problem Solving Strategy: Write an Equation

Equations serve as mathematical models for many situations in social sciences, physical sciences, and business. Before attempting to write an algebraic equation to solve a problem, it is helpful to write a *word equation*, as shown in Example 1.

EXAMPLE 1 Scientists use facts about how parts of the body relate to each other to study the human body. For example, it is a fact that the length of a woman's radius bone is about $\frac{1}{7}$ of her height. The radius bone connects the elbow and the wrist. If a scientist knows that the radius bone of a woman is 9 in. long, then about how tall is the woman?

■ **Understand the Problem**

Read the problem.
It is given that the length of a woman's radius bone is about $\frac{1}{7}$ of her height. It is also given that the radius bone of a woman is 9 in. long. You are asked to find the approximate height of the woman.

■ **Plan Your Approach**

Choose a strategy.
The word *is* implies that the length of the radius bone *equals* $\frac{1}{7}$ of a woman's height. Try the strategy of writing an equation.

Write a word equation.
The phrase "$\frac{1}{7}$ *of* her height" means "$\frac{1}{7}$ *times* her height," thus

$$\text{length of radius bone} = \frac{1}{7} \times \text{height}$$

Translate the word equation into an algebraic equation.
Let *h* represent the height of a woman whose radius bone measures 9 in.

$$9 = \frac{1}{7}h$$

■ **Complete the Work**

Solve the equation.

$$9 = \frac{1}{7}h$$

$$7 \cdot 9 = 7 \cdot \frac{1}{7}h \qquad \textit{Multiply each side of the equation by 7.}$$

$$63 = h$$

120   Chapter 3 Equations in One Variable

| Interpret the Results | **State your conclusion.** |
| | The woman is approximately 63 in., or 5 ft 3 in. tall. |

Check your conclusion.

Is the length of the radius bone (9 in.) equal to $\frac{1}{7}$ of the woman's height (63 in.)?

$$9 = \frac{1}{7}h$$

$$9 \overset{?}{=} \frac{1}{7} \cdot 63 \qquad \textit{Replace h with 63.}$$

$$9 = 9 \text{ } \checkmark \qquad \textit{True}$$

Is 63 in. a reasonable height for a woman?

EXAMPLE 2   If twice the weight of a truck is increased by 1500 lb, it will weigh 9000 lb. Find the weight of the truck.

Understand the Problem	You are asked to find the actual weight of the truck after a certain number of pounds is added to twice the weight of the truck.
Plan Your Approach	Let w represent the weight of the truck.
	Twice the weight increased by 1500 lb equals 9000 lb.

$$2w + 1500 = 9000$$

| Complete the Work | |

$$2w + 1500 = 9000$$
$$2w + 1500 - 1500 = 9000 - 1500$$
$$2w = 7500$$
$$\frac{2w}{2} = \frac{7500}{2}$$
$$w = 3750$$

| Interpret the Results | The weight of the truck is 3750 lb. Is 9000 lb equal to twice the equal to twice the weight of the truck increased by 1500 lb? |

$$2w + 1500 = 9000$$
$$2(3750) + 1500 \overset{?}{=} 9000$$
$$7500 + 1500 \overset{?}{=} 9000$$
$$9000 = 9000 \text{ } \checkmark$$

Problem Solving Reminders

- Write a word equation to express the relationships in a problem before you write an algebraic equation.
- Be sure that your solution to a problem *meets the conditions of the problem* and checks in the equation.

- Encourage students to develop a systematic approach to solving word problems. The four-step plan presented in this lesson is recommended. You may wish to review Teaching Aid 6 in the *Teacher's Resource* Book when discussing the examples.
- One of the aims of this lesson is to facilitate the development of *translation skills.* In setting up a mathematical model, students must translate the problem solving situation into their own words (word equation) and then translate the word equation into abstract form (algebraic equation).
- To sharpen the focus on translation skills, present several exercises, for which students are asked to write the equation that fits the problem. They should not be required to solve the equation or answer the question(s) that appear in the problem.
- Special emphasis should be placed on Step 4 of the problem solving plan, *Interpret the Results.* Students need to recognize that their solution must check in the original equation. Equally important, the answer they obtain must agree with all of the conditions stated in the problem.

CHALKBOARD EXAMPLES

- **For Example 1**

  1. Mr. McNulty's car is worth $2\frac{1}{2}$ times as much as his son Brian's car. If Mr. McNulty's car is worth $6500, how much is Brian's car worth? $2600

  2. If Susan deposits $39.85 in her bank account, her new balance will be $758.68. What is her present balance? $718.83

- **For Example 2**
  3. If 38 is added to four times a number the result is 374. Find this number. 84
  4. A poster is in the shape of a triangle with two equal sides and whose perimeter is 29 in. If the base is 7 in., how long is each of the equal sides? 11 in.

Common Error

- Some students are overwhelmed by the "words" in a problem. Provide some in-class practice where students are asked to read problems aloud while they, or other student(s), write down the relevant information.
- See *Teacher's Resource Book* for additional remediation.

LESSON FOLLOW-UP

Discussion

Explain why it is helpful to write a word equation before attempting to write an algebraic equation to solve a problem. It allows students to see the association between Key phrases and the necessary mathematical symbols.

Critical Thinking

Discovering Relationships Write a word equation for which the translated algebraic equations are as follows:

a. $11x - 20 = -185$
b. $15 = 2c - 3$
Possible answers to illustrate the relationship:
a. When the product of a number and 11 is decreased by 20, the result is −185.
b. The profit, $15, is $3 less than twice the cost.

CLASS EXERCISES

Complete each of the following exercises.

1. A number reduced by 59 gives −85. If n represents the original number, __?__ represents the number reduced by 59. $n - 59$
   Complete the equation: __?__ = −85 $n - 59$

2. Traveling for a number of hours at an average speed of 47 mi/h, Jon travels 564 mi. t represents the number of hours Jon travels.
   Complete the equation: $47t =$ __?__ 564

3. The cost of an item is $1.59; n represents the number of these items purchased; $20.67 is the total cost. Complete the equation: __?__ = 20.67 $1.59n$

4. The perimeter of a square is 148 cm. Let s represent the length in cm of one side of the square. Complete the equation: $4s =$ __?__ 148

Solve each problem by writing and solving an equation.

5. The sum of a number and −32 is 79. Find the number. $n + (-32) = 79$; 111

6. Sue has $1809.46 in her savings account. This is $14.95 more than three times the amount Charles has in his account. How much money does Charles have in his savings account? $3x + 14.95 = 1809.46$; $598.17

For Discussion

7. Name two types of open sentences. equation, inequality

8. What is a number called that makes an open sentence a true statement? a solution

9. What word in a written sentence implies a relationship of equality? is

10. What is a mathematical term for a relationship of equality? equation

11. Are equations and inequalities examples of mathematical models? Explain. Yes; they express relationships and display information algebraically.

PRACTICE EXERCISES

Write an appropriate equation, but do not solve.

A
1. If $\frac{1}{3}$ of the money Jason earns each week consists of tips, how much money did he earn one week when he received $10 in tips? $\frac{1}{3}x = 10$

2. Mary saves $\frac{1}{4}$ of her pay each week so she can purchase a bicycle. This week she saved $25. How much did she earn? $\frac{1}{4}x = 25$

3. If twice the weight of an elephant is increased by 3 tons, it will weigh 7 tons. Find the weight of the elephant. $2w + 3 = 7$

4. If three times the weight of a Shot Put is increased by 2 lb, it will weigh 18 lb. What is the weight of the Shot Put? $3w + 2 = 18$

Solve each problem by writing and solving an equation.

5. Decreasing a number by 92 gives -28. What is the number? 64

6. Decreasing a number by 47 gives -15. What is the number? 32

7. The product of a number and 11 is -165. Find the number. -15

8. The product of a number and 15 is -240. Find the number. -16

9. A number increased by 7.13 is 2.09. Find the original number. -5.04

10. A number increased by 4.12 is 3.15. Find the original number. -0.97

11. Tom's age is $\frac{2}{5}$ of his mother's age. Tom is 16 years old. How old is his mother? 40 yr

12. Dan's brother is $\frac{1}{2}$ his father's age. His brother is 22. How old is his father? 44 yr

13. If 11 is added to 3 times a number, the result is 50. Find the number. 13

14. If 14 is added to 5 times a number, the result is 129. Find the number. 23

15. The perimeter of a rectangle is 54 cm. The width is 12 cm. What is the length? 15 cm

16. What must the length of the two equal sides of an isosceles triangle be if the perimeter is 56 mm and the length of the third side is 18 mm? 19 mm

17. Hester paid $245.97 for a VCR. This was $\frac{3}{5}$ of its original price. What is the original price? $409.95

18. Christy paid $25 for a sweater. This was $\frac{1}{2}$ of its regular price. What is the regular price? $50

19. At the local movie theater, children's tickets cost $2.50 each and adults' tickets cost $4.50 each. If 117 children's tickets were sold, and the total sales were $733.50, how many adults' tickets were sold? 98

20. A cheetah can sprint for short distances at a rate of 70 mi/h. At that rate, how many minutes should it take a cheetah to sprint 2.1 mi? 1.8 min

21. Mr. Sangupta invested $\frac{1}{2}$ of his money in land, $\frac{1}{10}$ in stock, and $\frac{1}{20}$ in machinery. The remainder, $35,000, is in a savings account. What is the total amount of money that Mr. Sangupta saved or invested? $100,000

3.7 Problem Solving Strategy: Write an Equation **123**

Assignment Guide
See p. 94B for assignments.

Mixed Problem Solving Review
• The following skills and concepts are reviewed:
 Operations with real numbers (Ex. 1)
 Use of the formulas for perimeter and area of a rectangle (Ex. 2)
 Translation of a word phrase into an algebraic expression (Ex. 3)
• The following problem solving strategy may be appropriate:
 Drawing a diagram (Ex. 2)

Project
The feature asks students to compile and organize scientific data that should lead them to be able to draw mathematical conclusions.

Lesson Quiz
Solve each problem by writing and solving an equation.

1. If Ira has $\frac{3}{4}$ as much money as his sister and he has $1500, how much money does his sister have? $2000

2. A school ordered 157 books this year. This is 13 more than twice the number of books that were ordered last year. How many were ordered last year? 72

3. Increasing a number by 42 gives -4. What is the number? -46

Enrichment
A man's radius bone is approximately $\frac{2}{3}$ the length of his femur (thigh bone), and his femur is approximately $\frac{1}{5}$ of his total height. If his radius bone measures 9 in., approximately how tall is the man? $9 = \left(\frac{2}{3}\right)\left(\frac{1}{5}\right)h$; $9 = \frac{2}{15}h$; $h = 67.5$; 67.5 in. tall

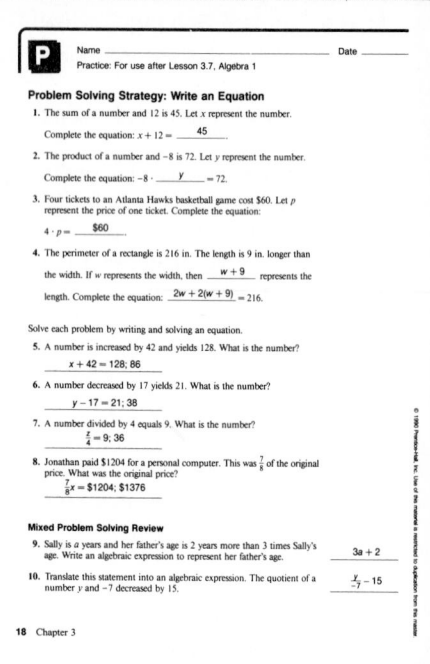

P Name _____ Date _____
Practice: For use after Lesson 3.7, Algebra 1

Problem Solving Strategy: Write an Equation

1. The sum of a number and 12 is 45. Let *x* represent the number.

   Complete the equation: $x + 12 = \underline{45}$

2. The product of a number and −8 is 72. Let *y* represent the number.

   Complete the equation: $-8 \cdot \underline{y} = 72$.

3. Four tickets to an Atlanta Hawks basketball game cost $60. Let *p* represent the price of one ticket. Complete the equation:

   $4 \cdot p = \underline{\$60}$

4. The perimeter of a rectangle is 216 in. The length is 9 in. longer than the width. If *w* represents the width, then $\underline{w + 9}$ represents the length. Complete the equation: $\underline{2w + 2(w + 9)} = 216$.

Solve each problem by writing and solving an equation.

5. A number is increased by 42 and yields 128. What is the number?

   $\underline{x + 42 = 128; 86}$

6. A number decreased by 17 yields 21. What is the number?

   $\underline{y - 17 = 21; 38}$

7. A number divided by 4 equals 9. What is the number?

   $\underline{\frac{z}{4} = 9; 36}$

8. Jonathan paid $1204 for a personal computer. This was $\frac{7}{8}$ of the original price. What was the original price?

   $\underline{\frac{7}{8}x = \$1204; \$1376}$

Mixed Problem Solving Review

9. Sally is *a* years and her father's age is 2 years more than 3 times Sally's age. Write an algebraic expression to represent her father's age. ___ $3a + 2$

10. Translate this statement into an algebraic expression. The quotient of a number *y* and −7 decreased by 15. ___ $\frac{y}{-7} - 15$

18 Chapter 3

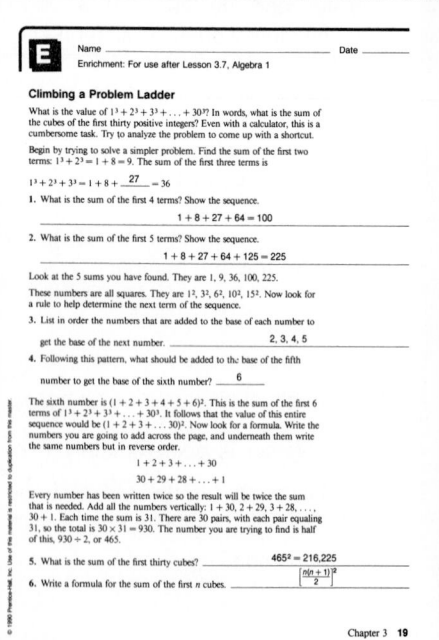

E Name _____ Date _____
Enrichment: For use after Lesson 3.7, Algebra 1

Climbing a Problem Ladder

What is the value of $1^3 + 2^3 + 3^3 + \ldots + 30^3$? In words, what is the sum of the cubes of the first thirty positive integers? Even with a calculator, this is a cumbersome task. Try to analyze the problem to come up with a shortcut.

Begin by trying to solve a simpler problem. Find the sum of the first two terms: $1^3 + 2^3 = 1 + 8 = 9$. The sum of the first three terms is

$1^3 + 2^3 + 3^3 = 1 + 8 + \underline{27} = 36$.

1. What is the sum of the first 4 terms? Show the sequence.

   $1 + 8 + 27 + 64 = 100$

2. What is the sum of the first 5 terms? Show the sequence.

   $1 + 8 + 27 + 64 + 125 = 225$

Look at the 5 sums you have found. They are 1, 9, 36, 100, 225.

These numbers are all squares. They are $1^2, 3^2, 6^2, 10^2, 15^2$. Now look for a rule to help determine the next term of the sequence.

3. List in order the numbers that are added to the base of each number to

   get the base of the next number. ___ 2, 3, 4, 5

4. Following this pattern, what should be added to the base of the fifth

   number to get the base of the sixth number? ___ 6

The sixth number is $(1 + 2 + 3 + 4 + 5 + 6)^2$. This is the sum of the first 6 terms of $1^3 + 2^3 + 3^3 + \ldots + 30^3$. It follows that the value of this entire sequence would be $(1 + 2 + 3 + \ldots 30)^2$. Now look for a formula. Write the numbers you are going to add across the page, and underneath them write the same numbers but in reverse order.

$1 + 2 + 3 + \ldots + 30$
$30 + 29 + 28 + \ldots + 1$

Every number has been written twice so the result will be twice the sum that is needed. Add all the numbers vertically: $1 + 30, 2 + 29, 3 + 28, \ldots, 30 + 1$. Each time the sum is 31. There are 30 pairs, with each pair equaling 31, so the total is $30 \times 31 = 930$. The number you are trying to find is half of this, $930 \div 2$, or 465.

5. What is the sum of the first thirty cubes? ___ $465^2 = 216,225$

6. Write a formula for the sum of the first *n* cubes. ___ $\left[\frac{n(n+1)}{2}\right]^2$

Chapter 3 **19**

Mixed Problem Solving Review

1. The weekly change in stock prices for the Pueschner Health Food Company was recorded as follows: Mon, $+3\frac{1}{8}$; Tue, $+2\frac{1}{4}$; Wed, -3; Thur, $-3\frac{3}{8}$; Fri, $+1\frac{1}{4}$. What was the net change for the week? $+\frac{1}{4}$

2. A square mat extends 2 in. beyond each side of a 12 in. × 12 in. photograph.
   a. Find the outer perimeter of the mat. 64 in.
   b. Find the area of the mat surrounding the photograph. 112 in.^{2}

3. Eduardo's age is *a* years and his mother's age is 1 year more than 3 times Eduardo's age. Write an algebraic expression to represent Eduardo's mother's age. $3a + 1$

4. This is a diagram of the Smiths' new swimming pool. Each end is a semicircle. Mr. Smith needs to know its perimeter in order to purchase a special reflecting tape for the edge. If the dimension *x* is 22 ft and the dimension *y* is 28 ft, what is the pool's perimeter? 125.1 ft

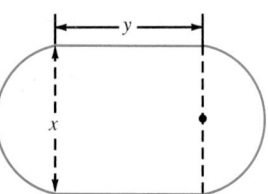

5. $r + s = 24$. If *r* and *s* are integers, what is the maximum value of *rs*? 144

PROJECT

Conduct a study of your classmates to determine if the following statement is true of your class.

> A girl's radius bone (bone that connects the elbow and the wrist) is approximately $\frac{1}{7}$ of her height.

- Talk to at least five female students who are willing to provide the necessary data.
- Record data for each volunteer—length of radius bone and height.
- Find the ratio (as a decimal to the nearest thousandth) of the length of the radius bone to height for each person.
- Find the average of the ratios you obtain.
- Compare the results that you obtain to the ratio $\frac{1}{7}$ (≈ 0.143) in Example 1. Using the average ratio you find, rewrite the equation in Example 1.
- Analyze your results. Would your results be different if the size of your sample of volunteers had been greater?

Conduct a study of your male classmates to determine if an adult male is approximately four times as tall as the length of his tibia bone (the bone that goes from the ankle to the knee). Answers may vary.

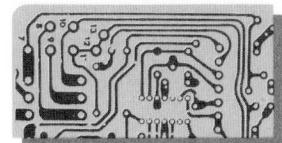

TECHNOLOGY:
Using Spreadsheets

Technology

Students learn how to use spreadsheets to facilitate computations. The spreadsheet introduces the SUM function to the students and illustrates how more than one cell can be added to another. This may generate some discussion and suggestions for alternative spreadsheets.

See *Teacher's Resource Book, Technology, p. 7.*

Most spreadsheets have special functions that enable you to do specific calculations. One very helpful function is the SUM function. This enables you to indicate what cells you would like the computer to add.

If the formula

Function Name   Range of Cells

@SUM(C6. . .C11)

appears in cell C13, it means that the computer will SUM the data in cells C6 through C11 and put the result in cell C13. The following spreadsheet uses the SUM function.

```
File: Grades                REVIEW/ADD/CHANGE
======A======== B ========C=======:D ========
 1|        GRADES—FALL SEMESTER
 2|
 3|                      Possible      Actual
 4|Description            Points       Points
 5|
 6|TEST 1                   100          85
 7|QUIZ 1                    10           9
 8|HOMEWORK P. 6              5           5
 9|HOMEWORK P. 10            5           5
10|QUIZ 2                    10           8
11|TEST 2                   100
12|                      _____
13|                         230         112
14|Score needed for an A     90
15|CURRENT GRADE IS       86.15384
16|
   _____
C15:
```

Solve.

1. What formula would the display area show for cell D13 if you wanted the sum? @SUM(D6. . .D10)

2. If the formula in cell C15 is +D13/@SUM(C6. . .C10), what would it represent? percentage grade

3. Use the spreadsheet to determine if it is possible for the student to get an A after taking TEST 2. yes, a score of 95 on TEST 2

This spreadsheet is designed to compute a personal budget.

```
File: Budget                                      REVIEW/ADD/CHANGE
======A======B======C======D======E======F======G======
 1|                        PERSONAL BUDGET
 2|
 3|                                SEPT.   OCT.   NOV.   DEC.
 4|AMOUNT FROM LAST MONTH                                 .9
 5|ALLOWANCE                                              20
 6|                                                      ____
 7|MONEY AVAILABLE THIS MONTH                            20.9
 8|
 9|EXPENSES:
10|  LUNCHES                                              10
11|  GAS                                                   5
12|  TAPES                                                 0
13|  DATES                                                 0
14|  CLOTHES                                               0
15|  FAMILY                                              5.9
16|                                                      ____
17|TOTAL MONEY SPENT                                     20.9
18|                                            _____
--------------------------------------------------------------
G17:
```

Solve.

4. What formula should the display area show for cell G7? +G4 + G5

5. What formula should be in the cell for G17? @SUM(G10...G15)

6. During the summer Joe saved $800. During the school year he receives an allowance of $10.00 per week. His expenses for September, October, and November are as follows:

	Sept.	Oct.	Nov.
Lunches	$65	$60	$50
Gas	20	25	22
Tapes	7	0	18
Dates	0	20	30
Clothes	100	0	25
Family	10	12	0

Joe has set a spending limit of $150 for the holidays. Can he continue to spend at the above rates for the remainder of the school year? Yes

7. Revise the spreadsheet to reflect your answer for Exercise 6. Check students' work.

Problem Solving: Mixed Types

Objective: To use equations to solve various types of word problems

LESSON PLAN

Materials/Manipulatives
Teacher's Resource Book
   Teaching Aid 6

The following exercises include different types of problems presented in this chapter. First, review the four-step approach to solving word problems.

Problem Solving Steps

Understand the Problem

Read the problem.
   What is given?
   What are you asked to find?
Identify important mathematical ideas.
Draw a diagram.

Plan Your Approach

Assign symbols. Label your drawing.

Write a word equation.

Translate the word equation into an algebraic equation.

Complete the Work

Solve the equation.
   Apply algebraic operations as needed.
   Keep an open mind.
   Change your approach if necessary.

Interpret the Results

State your conclusion.

Check your conclusion.

BACKGROUND

As students learn how to solve various types of word problems it is helpful to frequently review them. Students should learn how to classify the problems, such as number problems, simple age problems, geometry, money and formulas. Once a problem has been classified then an approach can be planned to obtain a solution.

Error Analysis Classification

1. *Misunderstanding*
   Failed to identify all the given information stated in the problem
2. *Misapplied Strategy*
   Translated the word equation incorrectly into an algebraic equation

Keep in mind that some problems are easier to solve than others. All problems, however, can be solved by first carefully reading the information and understanding what you are being asked to find before proceeding.

CLASS EXERCISES

Solve each problem.

1. The sum of 8 times a number and 12 is -84. What is the number? -12

2. Two-thirds of a number decreased by 7 equals 27. Find the number. 51

3. The perimeter of a square is 196 m. How long is each side of the square? 49 m

4. In the freshman class, $\frac{8}{9}$ of the students are taking Algebra. Find the total number of students in the class if 160 are taking Algebra. 180

PRACTICE EXERCISES

Solve each problem.

A 1. Twelve increased by 3 times a number is 21. Find the number. 3

2. Fifteen increased by 3 times a number is 54. Find the number. 13

3. Five times a number, decreased by 1, is −26. Find the number. −5

4. Three times a number, decreased by 3, is −18. Find the number. −5

5. The product of a number and 0.5 divided by 3 equals 1.5. Find the number. 9

6. The product of a number and 2.4 divided by 6 equals 12. Find the number. 30

7. One-fifth of a number, decreased by 8, equals 7. Find the number. 75

8. One-fourth of a number, decreased by 5, equals 10. Find the number. 60

9. A sweater is on sale for $16. The sale price is $5.98 less than the original price. What was the original price of the sweater? $21.98

10. The cost of a shirt plus a sales tax of $0.87 equals $16.86. Find the cost of the shirt. $15.99

11. Eight less than twice Lisa's age is 36 yr. Find Lisa's age. 22 yr

12. Ten less than three times Tony's age is 50. Find Tony's age. 20 yr

13. If the quotient of a number and 5 is decreased by 15, the result is −100. Find the number. −425

14. If the quotient of a number and 7 is decreased by 14, the result is −150. Find the number. −952

B 15. If the difference of a certain number and 7 is multiplied by 6, the result is 4.2. Find the number. 7.7

16. If the difference of a certain number and 12 is multiplied by 8, the result is 9.2. Find the number. 13.15

17. The perimeter of a rectangle is 64 m. If the length of the rectangle is 14 m, find its width. 18 m

18. The perimeter of a rectangle is 96 m. If the width of the rectangle is 12 m, find its length. 36 m

19. Find the time it will take a cyclist to travel 40 mi at average speed of 12.5 mi/h. 3.2 h

20. Find the average speed of a runner who runs a distance of 2.5 mi in 20 min. 7.5 mi/h

21. A pentagon, a five-sided figure, has two sides of equal measure and three sides measuring 12 in., 9 in., and 13 in. Find the lengths of the equal sides if the perimeter is 56 in. 11 in.

22. A hexagon, a six-sided figure, has three equal sides and three sides measuring 15 cm, 20 cm, and 25 cm, respectively. Find the length of one of the equal sides if the perimeter is 150 cm. 30 cm

C 23. A man invested one-half as much money in stock for National Computing, Inc. as he did in stock for Gateway Airlines. If his total investment was $4500, how much did he invest in stock for Gateway Airlines? $3000

24. The distribution of grades in a class was 5 more B's than A's and twice as many C's as B's. If there are 35 students in the class, how many received each letter grade? 5 A's, 10 B's, 20 C's

25. The formula $F = \frac{9}{5}C + 32$ can be used to convert a given Celsius temperature, C, to an equivalent Fahrenheit temperature, F. If the thermometer reads $-20°C$, find what the corresponding Fahrenheit reading would be. $-4°F$

26. The formula $C = \frac{5}{9}(F - 32)$ can be used to convert a given Fahrenheit temperature, F, to an equivalent Celsius temperature, C. If the thermometer reads $59°F$, find what the corresponding Celsius reading would be. 15°C

TEST YOURSELF

1. The quotient of a number and -6 is 36. What is the number? -216

2. Daphne paid $360 for a video cassette player. This was $30 less than 3 times the amount Barbara paid. How much did Barbara pay? $130

3. Prove: For all real numbers m, n, r ($n \neq 0$), if $m = r$, then $\frac{m}{n} = \frac{r}{n}$.
See p. 719.

4. Evaluate $P = 4s$ for s if $P = \frac{1}{4}$. $s = \frac{1}{16}$

5. Evaluate $A = \frac{1}{2}h(a + b)$ for h if $A = 40$, $a = 5.5$, and $b = 2.5$. $h = 10$

3.8 Problem Solving: Mixed Types **129**

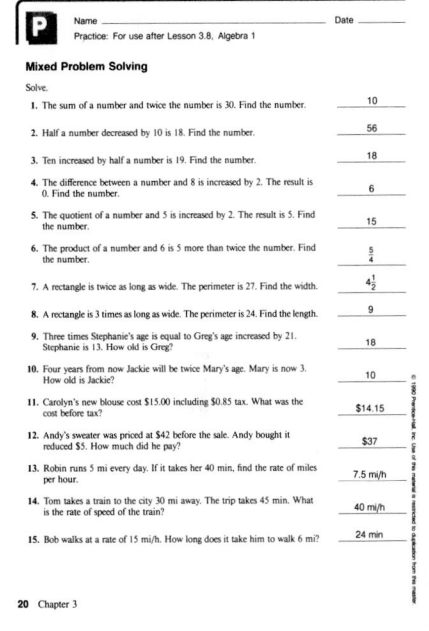

- See *Teacher's Resource Book, Spanish Chapter Summary and Review*, pp. 5–6.
- See Extra Practice, p. 657.

CHAPTER 3 SUMMARY AND REVIEW

Vocabulary

conclusion (114)
direct proof (114)
equivalent equations (96)
formula (117)
hypothesis (114)

inverse operations (96)
mathematical models (110)
postulate (113)
theorem (114)

Steps for Solving Equations

3.1–3.3

a. Use the Addition or Subtraction Property for Equations.

b. Use the Multiplication or Division Property for Equations.

c. Check your solution in the original equation.

Solve and check.

1. $x + 7 = 28$ 21
2. $y - 11 = -38$ –27
3. $-27 = a + 5$ –32
4. $3.1 = -5.8 + b$ 8.9
5. $9a = 45$ 5
6. $\frac{1}{3}t = -15$ –45
7. $-18 = -\frac{5}{2}x$ $\frac{36}{5}$
8. $-22y = -121$ 5.5
9. $3a + 4 = 19$ 5
10. $8 = 5x - 12$ 4
11. $-5(y + 7) = 25$ –12
12. $13a + 7 = 7$ 0
13. $15.8 = 16 - 0.2d$ 1
14. $4.9w - 18.6 = 535.1$ 113
15. $0 = 1\frac{3}{5} - \frac{1}{5}y$ 8
16. $\frac{1}{2} + \frac{3}{4}p = \frac{1}{4}$ $-\frac{1}{3}$

Evaluating Formulas
To use a formula as an equation, you must know the value of all variables but one.

3.6

17. $P = 2l + 2w$ If $P = 72$ and $l = 28$, find w.   w = 8
18. $A = \frac{1}{2}h(a + b)$ If $A = 16$, $a = 3\frac{1}{4}$, and $b = 2$, find h.   h = $6\frac{2}{21}$
19. $A = p + prt$ If $A = \$896$, $p = \$800$, and $t = 3$, find r.   r = 0.04
20. $C = 2\pi r$ If $C = 16.956$ and $\pi \approx 3.14$, find r.   r = 2.7

Algebraic Proof To prove statements about real numbers, use postulates, definitions, given facts, and other proved theorems.

21. State the Addition Property for Equations using real numbers x, y, and z.
For all real numbers x, y, and z, if $x = y$, then $x + z = y + z$.

22. Complete the unfinished statement and give the reason for each step of this proof.

Prove: If $x = y$, then $x - z = y - z$.

Proof:

Statements	Reasons
1. $x = y$	1. __?__ Given
2. $x - z = x - z$	2. __?__ Reflexive property
3. $x - z = \underset{y-z}{\underline{\quad?\quad}}$	3. __?__ Substitution property

Problem Solving Steps

Understand the Problem	Plan Your Approach	Complete the Work	Interpret the Results

Write an equation for each problem. Then solve the equation.   3.4, 3.7

23. Three times the weight of a truck increased by 500 lb equals 12,200 lb. Find the weight of the truck. $3x + 500 = 12,200$; 3900 lb

24. The product of a number and $-\frac{3}{8}$ is -24. Find the number. $-\frac{3}{8}(x) = -24$; 64

25. Alison has $809.45 in her savings account. This is $14.95 more than two times the amount Eric has in his account. How much money does Eric have in his account? $2x + 14.95 = 809.45$; $397.25

26. If Roberto's age is $\frac{3}{4}$ of his brother's age and Roberto is 45 years old, how old is his brother? $\frac{3}{4}(x) = 45$; 60

27. The perimeter of a rectangle is 54 cm. If the width is 12 cm, what is the length? $54 = 2(12) + 2(x)$; 15 cm

28. If Eli can average 37.5 mi/h, how long will it take him to drive 93.75 mi? $37.5(x) = 93.75$; 2.5 h

29. Sarat weighs twice as much as his sister Brenda. If Sarat weighs 210 lb, how much does Brenda weigh? $2(x) = 210$; 105 lb

30. If Greg can walk 3.5 mi/h, how long will it take Greg to walk 5.25 mi? $3.5(x) = 5.25$; 1.5 h

Summary and Review   **131**

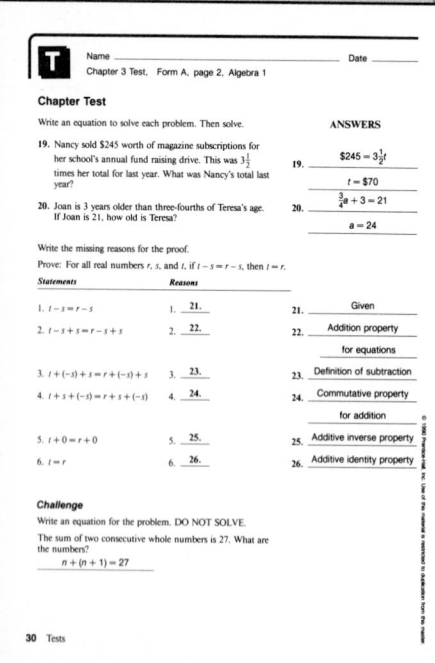

CHAPTER 3   TEST

Solve and check.

1. $b - 2.7 = 2.5$ 5.2

2. $7 = y + 3\frac{2}{5}$ $3\frac{3}{5}$

3. $-\frac{1}{2}(y - 8) = 7$ −6

4. $3t + 13 = -11$ −8

5. $-\frac{5}{7}x = 35$ −49

6. $-11 = a + 2$ −13

7. $6d + \frac{3}{4} = -\frac{3}{4}$ $-\frac{1}{4}$

8. $\frac{3}{4}(t + 8) = -6$ −16

9. If $P = 2l + 2w$, $l = 15$, and $P = 80$, find w. w = 25

10. If $d = rt$, $d = 1140$, and $t = 4\frac{3}{4}$, find r. r = 240

11. Prove: For all real numbers x, y, and z, if $x = y$, then $xz = yz$.
See below.

12. Prove: For all real numbers a, b, c, and d, then $ab + cb + d = d + b(a + c)$
See p. 719.

Write an equation for each problem. Then solve the equation.

13. Anne Marie bought a number of shirts at $8 each. She also bought a pair of socks for $3. How many shirts did she buy if her total cost was $27.
8n + 3 = 27; 3

14. If the product of a number and −3 is −87, find the number. −3n = −87; 29

15. A bag of a dozen bagels cost 34¢ less than twelve individual bagels. If the price of the bag of bagels is $3.50, find the price of one individual bagel. 350 = 12p − 34; 32¢

Challenge

Write an equation for each problem. Do not solve.

1. A 35 ft long wire is cut so that one piece is $9\frac{1}{2}$ ft longer than the other. What is the length of the shorter piece? $l + \left(l + 9\frac{1}{2}\right) = 35$

2. A computer system consisting of a monitor, a keyboard, and a computer with a hard disk costs $1800. The monitor costs $300 more than the keyboard, and the computer costs $600 more than the monitor. Find the cost of the keyboard. 1800 = k + (k + 300) + (k + 900)

Additional Answers
11. Proof:

Statements	Reasons
1. $x = y$	1. Given
2. $xz = xz$	2. Reflexive prop.
3. $xz = yz$	3. Substitution prop.

In each item you are to compare a quantity in Column 1 with a quantity in Column 2. Write the letter of the correct answer from these choices:

A. The quantity in Column 1 is greater than the quantity in Column 2.
B. The quantity in Column 2 is greater than the quantity in Column 1.
C. The quantity in Column 1 is equal to the quantity in Column 2.
D. The relationship cannot be determined from the given information.

Notes: Information centered over both columns refers to one or both of the quantities being compared. A symbol that appears in both columns has the same meaning in each column. All variables represent real numbers.

Column 1	Column 2
1. 0.63 B	$\dfrac{17}{25}$
2. $-\dfrac{2}{7}$ A	$-\dfrac{2}{5}$
3. $\dfrac{0}{-1}$ C	$\dfrac{0}{1}$
4. $10 + 4 \div 2$ A	$5 \cdot 6 \div 3$
5. $\dfrac{1}{5}$ of \$640 C	$\dfrac{1}{3}$ of \$384

$$P = 2l + 2w$$

Column 1	Column 2
6. $l = 10 \quad w = 5$ B	$l = 12 \quad w = 4$
7. $-(a - b)$ C	$b - a$
8. $\dfrac{ab}{3}$ D	$-\dfrac{3a}{b}$
9. $2(2^2 + 3^2)$ A	$(2 + 3)^2$

$$5x - 8 = 12$$
$$15 - 4y = 7$$

Column 1	Column 2
10. x A	y
11. The sum of 2 B $\quad$ times a number and 3	2 times the sum of a number and 3

The product of

Column 1	Column 2
12. $\dfrac{55}{154}$ and $\dfrac{42}{70}$ B	$\dfrac{65}{78}$ and $\dfrac{54}{126}$

Use this problem to answer Exercises 13–15.

Ann's age is $\dfrac{2}{3}$ her mother's age.

Ann's age is $\dfrac{1}{2}$ her father's age.

Ann is 24.

Column 1	Column 2
13. father's age A	mother's age
14. 30 B	mother's age
15. father's age C	48

The individual comments provided for each problem can be helpful in guiding students to solve these problems.

1. It is important for students to be readily able to change familiar fractions to their decimal equivalents.
2. Students should recognize that when both fractions are negative and their numerators are equal, the fraction with the greater denominator is the greater fraction.

See *Teacher's Resource Book,* for Preparing for Standardized Tests.

Maintaining Skills
The following skills and concepts are reviewed:
Using the distributive property
Combining like terms
Changing percents to decimals
Changing decimals to percents
Changing fractions to percents
Changing percents to fractions
Using a formula to solve a problem

MAINTAINING SKILLS

Simplify.

Example 1 $8a - 3(a - 9) - 12$
$= 8a - 3a + 27 - 12$ *Distribute* -3.
$= 5a + 15$ *Combine like terms.*

1. $7(b + 5) - 9b$ $-2b + 35$

2. $6x + 5(x - 2) + 4$ $11x - 6$

3. $5y + 3 - (4y - 2)$ $y + 5$

4. $-2(3c + 9) + 4c$ $-2c - 18$

5. $m - 5 + (-5m + 9)$ $-4m + 4$

6. $-(8 - 3n) + 6(2n - 12)$ $15n - 80$

Change each percent to a decimal. Change each decimal to a percent.

Example 2 $5\% \rightarrow 0.05 \rightarrow 0.05$ *Divide by 100.*

Example 3 $0.585 \rightarrow 0.58.5\% \rightarrow 58.5\%$ *Multiply by 100.*

7. 20% 0.20

8. 42% 0.42

9. 6% 0.06

10. 12.5% 0.125

11. 10% 0.1

12. 30.3% 0.303

13. 0.75 75%

14. 0.18 18%

15. 0.07 7%

16. 0.01 1%

17. 0.385 38.5%

18. 0.065 6.5%

Change each fraction to a percent. Change each percent to a fraction.

Example 4 $\dfrac{5}{8}$ $8)\overline{5.000}$ = 0.625 $0.625 \longrightarrow 62.5\%$

Example 5 $41\dfrac{2}{3}\%$ means $\dfrac{41\frac{2}{3}}{100} = \dfrac{\frac{125}{3}}{100} = \dfrac{125}{3} \cdot \dfrac{1}{100} = \dfrac{5}{12}$

19. $\dfrac{1}{4}$ 25%

20. $\dfrac{2}{5}$ 40%

21. $\dfrac{7}{10}$ 70%

22. $\dfrac{1}{2}$ 50%

23. $\dfrac{3}{8}$ 37.5%

24. $\dfrac{2}{3}$ $66\frac{2}{3}\%$

25. 35% $\dfrac{7}{20}$

26. 80% $\dfrac{4}{5}$

27. $37\dfrac{1}{2}\%$ $\dfrac{3}{8}$

28. 75% $\dfrac{3}{4}$

29. $8\dfrac{1}{3}\%$ $\dfrac{1}{12}$

30. 36% $\dfrac{9}{25}$

Use the formula given to solve each word problem.

31. Miriam lives 75 mi from Albany. How long would it take her to drive to Albany if she averages 50 mi/h? ($d = rt$) $1\frac{1}{2}$h

32. The length of a rectangular garden is 12 m. The distance around the garden (P) is 42 m. What is the width? ($P = 2l + 2w$) 9 m

33. The Celsius (C) thermometer reads 35°. Find the temperature in degrees Fahrenheit. $\left(F = \dfrac{9}{5}C + 32\right)$ 95°F

OVERVIEW • Chapter 4

SUMMARY

In Chapter 4, students expand their understanding of equations containing one variable. Students are introduced to equations in which the variable is contained on both sides of the equals sign. Further, students learn to combine like terms and to take shortcuts to simplify the longer procedures that they have learned up to this point. Five problem solving lessons in this chapter provide ample opportunity to apply algebraic procedures to techniques needed in other fields.

Toward the end of the chapter, students learn the concept of literal equations and its applications. Students recognize that literal equations are familiar to them via several formulas that they have already learned how to use.

CHAPTER OBJECTIVES

- To solve equations by removing parentheses and combining like terms

- To solve equations that contain the variable on both sides

- To solve problems that involve consecutive integers, percent of change, and uniform motion

- To use shortcuts to solve equations

- To use equations for solving simple percent problems and mixture problems involving percent

- To solve literal equations

Problem Solving Strategy

To solve problems by making drawings or tables as two examples of mathematical models

CHAPTER HIGHLIGHTS

The theme of the chapter is transportation. The chapter's special features show how algebra is applied to various means of transportation.

PROBLEM SOLVING AND APPLICATIONS

Problem solving and applications form an integral part of each lesson. Students use equations to solve practical problems and arrive at solutions to problems in many fields including sports, science, demography, finance, and other areas of mathematics. Problem solving Lessons 4.3, 4.6, 4.7, 4.9, and 4.10 afford students the opportunity to practice applying algebraic equations to concrete situations that arise in a variety of fields.

TECHNOLOGY

Calculator

A calculator can be used in Lessons 4.4 and 4.5 to check students' answers.

RESOURCES

Teacher's Resource Book

- Teaching Aid 5

- Transparencies 6, 7, 24

STUDENT TEXT

TEACHER'S RESOURCE BOOK

Chapter Content		Basic	Average	Enriched	R	P	E
4.1	Solving Equations: Combining Like Terms	D: 138/1-23 odd, 48	D: 138/1-39 odd, 48	D: 138/1-47 odd, 48-50	1	2	3

4.2	Solving Equations: Variables on Both Sides	D: 142/1-23 odd, 47
		R: 138/12, 18, 22
		    142/4, 8, 10
			D: 142/1-31 odd, 47
			R: 138/34, 36, 38
			    142/6, 12, 18
				D: 142/5-45 odd, 47, 48
				R: 138/40, 42, 44
					4	5	6

4.3	Problem Solving: Consecutive Integers	D: 146/1-15 odd R: 142/16, 20, 24	D: 146/1-21 odd R: 142/18, 22, 30	D: 146/3-27 odd R: 142/18, 22, 38		7	8
4.4	Shortcuts in Solving Equations	D: 150/1-23 odd, 49, 50 R: Test Yourself	D: 150/1-39 odd, 49, 51 R: Test Yourself	D: 150/3-47 odd, 49, 51, 52 R: Test Yourself	9	10	11

4.5	Solving Equations: Percents	D: 154/1-19 odd, 33, 34
		R: 150/6, 14, 20
		    154/6, 8, 12
			D: 154/1-27 odd, 33, 35
			R: 150/20, 24, 32
			    154/4, 10, 14, 20
				D: 155/7-33 odd, 33-36
				R: 150/32, 44, 52
					12	13	14

4.6	Problem Solving: Percents	D: 157/1-13 odd R: 154/4, 10, 18 157/2, 4, 6	D: 157/1-27 odd R: 154/10, 16, 20	D: 157/15-31 odd R:154/12, 22, 26		15	16
4.7	Problem Solving: Mixtures	D: 163/1-3 odd R: 157/8, 10, 12	D: 163/1-7 odd R: 157/14, 20, 24	D: 163/5-9 odd R: 157/18, 22, 28		17	18

4.8	Literal Equations	D: 166/1-23 odd, 45
		R: 163/2, 4
		    166/4, 8, 16
			D: 163/1-37 odd, 45, 46
			R: 163/4, 6
			    166/2, 14, 20
				D: 163/1-43 odd, 45, 46
				R: 163/6, 8
					19	20	21

4.9	Problem Solving Strategy: Make a Drawing or a Table	D: 170/1-11 odd MPSR: 1-4 R: 166/26, 28, 30, 46	D: 170/1-17 odd MPSR: 1-4 R: 166/32, 36, 38, 46	D: 170/13-17 odd MPSR: 1-4 R: 167/36-42 even, 46		22	23
4.10	Problem Solving: Uniform Motion	D: 175/1-11 odd R: Test Yourself	D: 175/1-21 odd R: Test Yourself	D: 175/13-23 odd R: Test Yourself		24	25

D = Daily   R = Review   MPSR = Mixed Problem Solving Review   R = Reteaching   P = Practice   E = Enrichment

---

STUDENT TEXT

TEACHER'S RESOURCE BOOK

Review And Testing	Test Yourself	151	Chapter Test	180
	Test Yourself	177	Prep. for Stan. Tests	181
	Chapter Sum. and Rev.	178	Cumulative Review	182
			Extra Practice	658
Special Features	Writing in Algebra	139	Algebra in Engineering	159
	Alg. in Transportation	143	Application	160
	Math Club Activity	147	Did You Know?	163
	Extra	155	Algebra in Aviation	167
			Project	171

Teacher's Resource Book	
Spanish Chapter Summary and Review	7-8
• Quizzes	33-36
• Chapter Test (Form A)	37-38
• Chapter Test (Form B)	39-40
Calculator Test	7-8
Applications—Chapter 4	26
Critical Thinking	4
Reading and Writing in Algebra	4
Technology	9

4 | More Equations in One Variable

Manufacturers and designers of transportation systems must be able to solve equations involving variables. Such equations can aid in development of more efficient means of transportation.

135

BACKGROUND

Automotive designers have become increasingly concerned with greater fuel efficiency. The introduction of such features as aerodynamic styling, lighter engine materials, synthetic lubricants, and improved tire design, has resulted in better performing cars. Measurements of a car's performance can be found by examining the distance d a car travels in relation to the time t it takes and at what speed r it moves. Solving for fuel efficiency f includes measuring the car's fuel consumption g. Engineers working with equations such as $d = rt$ and $\frac{d}{g} = f$ can easily determine these values.

BACKGROUND

In the Capsule Review, students are required to simplify expressions by combining like terms that are both numerical and algebraic. Since simplifying expressions is the first step to solving equations containing like terms this review is an appropriate warm-up exercise.

Critical Thinking

Analyzing Whole-Part Relationships
Look at the model introduced in the lesson development. Interpret what the variables $2n$ and $3n$ represent.
Students should observe that $2n$ is the cost of bus fares for n students and $3n$ is the cost of admissions for n students.

Solving Equations: Combining Like Terms

4.1

Objective: To solve equations by removing parentheses and combining like terms

Some ninth graders are planning a trip to the Maritime Museum. The bus fare is $2 per student; admission to the museum is $3 per student.

If the variable n represents the number of students going on the trip, the entire cost can be thought of as $2n + 3n$.

Another way is to use the fact that the total cost per student is $5. Then $5n$ also expresses the entire cost of the trip. That is, $2n + 3n = 5n$.

Capsule Review

One of the key procedures needed in solving equations with the same variable is to combine like terms. Recall that $-5y$ and $3y$ are like terms but $3y$ and $3y^2$ are not like terms.

Combine like terms to simplify.

1. $7n + n - 2$ $8n - 2$ **2.** $5a^2 - b^2 + 8b^2$ $5a^2 + 7b^2$ **3.** $-5n - 6n - 1$
$-11n - 1$
4. $-6 - 5 + 8x$ $-11 + 8x$ **5.** $3b + (-9b) - 8b^2$ **6.** $0 - 3w + 3$ $-3w + 3$
$-6b - 8b^2$

EXAMPLE 1   It will cost each student $2 for bus fare and $3 for admission to the Maritime Museum. How many students plan to go on the trip if the total expense is $75?

Let n = number of students going on the trip.

$$2n + 3n = 75$$
$$5n = 75 \qquad \textit{Combine like terms.}$$
$$\frac{5n}{5} = \frac{75}{5} \qquad \textit{Divide each side by 5.}$$
$$n = 15$$

So, 15 students plan to go on the trip.

EXAMPLE 2 Solve and check: $28 - a + 4a = 7$

$$28 - a + 4a = 7$$
$$28 + 3a = 7 \qquad \text{\textit{Combine like terms: } } -1a + 4a = 3a$$
$$28 - 28 + 3a = 7 - 28 \qquad \text{\textit{Subtract 28 from each side.}}$$
$$3a = -21$$
$$\frac{3a}{3} = \frac{-21}{3} \qquad \text{\textit{Divide each side by 3.}}$$
$$a = -7$$

Check:
$$28 - a + 4a = 7$$
$$28 - (-7) + 4(-7) \overset{?}{=} 7 \qquad \text{\textit{Replace a with } } -7.$$
$$28 + 7 - 28 \overset{?}{=} 7$$
$$7 = 7 \quad \text{✔} \qquad \text{\textit{True}}$$

So, the solution is -7.

The commutative and associative properties for addition allow you to add and group terms in any order. In Example 3, notice how these properties are used to solve the equation $y + (y + 3) + (2y - 5) = 10$.

EXAMPLE 3 Solve and check: $y + (y + 3) + (2y - 5) = 10$

$$y + (y + 3) + (2y - 5) = 10$$
$$(y + y + 2y) + [3 + (-5)] = 10 \qquad \text{\textit{Group like terms.}}$$
$$4y + (-2) = 10 \qquad \text{\textit{Combine like terms.}}$$
$$4y - 2 + 2 = 10 + 2 \qquad \text{\textit{Add 2 to each side.}}$$
$$4y = 12$$
$$\frac{4y}{4} = \frac{12}{4} \qquad \text{\textit{Divide each side by 4.}}$$
$$y = 3$$

Check:
$$y + (y + 3) + (2y - 5) = 10$$
$$3 + (3 + 3) + [(2 \cdot 3 - 5)] \overset{?}{=} 10 \qquad \text{\textit{Replace y with 3.}}$$
$$3 + 6 + 1 \overset{?}{=} 10$$
$$10 = 10 \quad \text{✔} \qquad \text{\textit{True}}$$

So, the solution is 3.

In the equation $4n - 7(n - 9) = 42$, parentheses are used to indicate multiplication. In such cases, use the distributive property to multiply before combining like terms and using the equation properties.

4.1 Solving Equations: Combining Like Terms **137**

TEACHING SUGGESTIONS

- Emphasize that the students should combine like terms within equations before using the equation properties. Point out that this will simplify the equation and that as a result students will have fewer variables to keep track of in subsequent steps.
- Point out that sometimes, as in Example 3, work may be simplified by combining like terms mentally.
- Stress the importance of removing parentheses according to the order of operations before combining like terms.

CHALKBOARD EXAMPLES

- **For Example 1**
  1. Each student who attended the freshman class picnic purchased a $5 food voucher and a $1 beverage voucher. If all the money collected from voucher sales was $486, how many students attended the picnic? 81

- **For Example 2**
  Solve and check:
  2. $17 + b - 4b = -4$ 7
  3. $-44 = 10x - x + 1$ −5

- **For Example 3**
  Solve and check:
  4. $x + (x + 2) + (x + 4) = 9$ 1
  5. $(5x - 1) + (2x + 3) = -12$ −2

- **For Example 4**
  Solve and check:
  6. $m + 3(m - 5) = 21$ 9
  7. $(7y - 1) - (4y + 3) = 2$ 2

Common Error

- In equations similar to Example 4, students may fail to multiply each term in the parentheses by -7. Review removing parentheses and combining like terms as well as the distributive property.
- See *Teacher's Resource Book* for additional remediation.

137

EXAMPLE 4   Solve: $4n - 7(n - 9) = 42$

$$4n - 7(n - 9) = 42$$
$$4n + (-7)(n - 9) = 42 \qquad \textit{Definition of subtraction}$$
$$4n + (-7)(n) + (-7)(-9) = 42 \qquad \textit{Distribute } -7.$$
$$4n - 7n + 63 = 42$$
$$-3n + 63 = 42 \qquad \textit{Combine like terms.}$$
$$-3n + 63 - 63 = 42 - 63 \qquad \textit{Subtract 63 from each side.}$$
$$-3n = -21 \qquad \textit{Divide by } -3.$$
$$n = 7$$

So, the solution is 7. The check is left for you.

CLASS EXERCISES

Use the distributive property to find each product.

1. $3(a + 2)$ $3a + 6$
2. $5(1 - 2b)$ $5 - 10b$
3. $4(-3y - 8)$ $-12y - 32$

4. $-3(-7 - 4x)$ $21 + 12x$
5. $1.4(2m - 1)$ $2.8m - 1.4$
6. $-1(-1 + 3a)$ $1 - 3a$

Solve and check.

7. $a + 3a = 8$ 2
8. $7x + 2x - x = 30$ $\frac{15}{4}$

9. $5x - 3x - 6 = 6$ 6
10. $x + x - 5 = 4$ $\frac{9}{2}$

11. $5 - t - t = -1$ 3
12. $3(b + 5) = 21$ 2

13. $4(y - 2) = 16$ 6
14. $-3(-6 - 5m) = -12$ -2

15. $(7x - 3) - (4x + 2) = 13$ 6
16. $(5y + 4) + (3y - 9) = 11$ 2

PRACTICE EXERCISES

Solve and check.

A
1. $6y + 2y = 16$ 2
2. $4x - 2x = 18$ 9
3. $4a + 3a - 7 = 21$ 4

4. $7b - 2b = 30$ 6
5. $3 - 6t - 5t = -19$ 2
6. $5 - 8x - 2x = -25$ 3

7. $-13 = 2x - x - 10$ -3
8. $7x + 4 - 15x = 36$ -4
9. $1 - 6y - 4y = 1$ 0

10. $-5 = -6 - 3s + s + 1$ 0
11. $c + (c + 2) + (c + 4) = 27$ 7

12. $(2y + 5) - (y + 3) + (7y - 3y) = 17$ 3

13. $x + (x + 3) + (x + 2) + (x + 7) = 40$ 7

14. $(x + 7) + (x - 3) + (2x + 11) = 45$ $7\frac{1}{2}$

15. $2(n - 3) = 12$ 9
16. $3(b + 4) = 24$ 4
17. $8(x - 1) = -24$ -2

18. $3(5 - r) = 18$ -1
19. $-2(3 - m) = 14$ 10
20. $-5(3 - d) = 25$ 8

21. $6(7 - 2t) = 30$ 1
22. $4(5x - 5) = 0$ 1
23. $-2(3x + 5) = 2$ -2

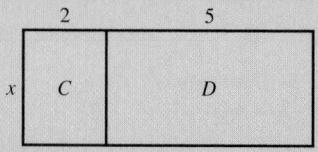

B

24. $4x - 7(x - 9) = 42$ _7_

25. $3n + 4(n - 9) = -78$ _-6_

26. $-5(t - 7) + 5 = -5$ _9_

27. $2(7 - a) - 4 = 0$ _5_

28. $0.5d - 0.7d = 0.8$ _-4_

29. $1.5c + 7.5c = 1.8$ _0.2_

30. $3z + z + z = 3.2$ _0.64_

31. $-4.5 = 5n - n - n$ _-1.5_

32. $3(a - 5) = 4$ _$\frac{19}{3}$_

33. $-2(b + 4) = 11$ _$-\frac{19}{2}$_

34. $x - 3(6 - x) = -14$ _1_

35. $6 - 22(p + 6) = 2$ _$-\frac{64}{11}$_

36. $-4 - (7 + 3y) = 7$ _-6_

37. $-9 - (8 - 5t) = 18$ _7_

38. $\frac{1}{3}(x - 9) = -6$ _-9_

39. $\frac{2}{5}(y + 10) = 0$ _-10_

C

40. $1 - \frac{3}{4}a - 9 = 2$ _$-\frac{40}{3}$_

41. $\frac{1}{5}b - 6 + 11 = 1$ _-20_

42. $\frac{2}{3} + 3(2 - m) = -2$ _$\frac{26}{9}$_

43. $-2(4 + n) - \frac{5}{8} = \frac{7}{8}$ _$-\frac{19}{4}$_

44. $4.67y - 3.6y + 8.42 = 2$ _-6_

45. $0.02 - 0.05x - 0.3x = -0.68$ _2_

46. $2[x + 3(x - 1)] = 18$ _3_

47. $4(2k - 7) + 3(k - 1) = 46$ _7_

Applications

Write an equation for each problem. Then solve the problem.

48. Number Problem   Five times a number subtracted from 3 times the number equals 20. Find the number. $3n - 5n = 20$; -10

49. Geometry   The length of a rectangular sign is 10 ft less than twice its width. Its perimeter is 118 ft. Find the length and width of the sign.
$2(2w - 10) + 2w = 118$; length: 36 ft; width: 23 ft

50. Hobby   Jane, Jasmine, and Jocelyn have record collections. Jane has 3 times as many records as Jocelyn has. Jasmine has 2 more than twice the number Jocelyn has. Together the three girls have 56 records. How many records does each girl have? $3r + r + (2r + 2) = 56$; Jocelyn, 9; Jane, 27; Jasmine, 20

WRITING IN ALGEBRA

Write an equation for each statement. By using operations and properties of numbers, think of a solution or solutions for each equation.

1. The sum of two numbers x and y is the same as their product.
$x + y = xy$; $x = 0$, $y = 0$; $x = 2$, $y = 2$

2. A number n and its reciprocal are equal. $n = \frac{1}{n}$; $n = 1$

3. The difference of two numbers r and s is the same as their sum.
$r - s = r + s$; $r = 1$, $s = 0$

4. The quotient of two numbers c and d is the same as their product. $\frac{c}{d} = cd$; $c = 0$, $d = 1$

5. The sum of a number m and its reciprocal is 2. $m + \frac{1}{m} = 2$; $m = 1$

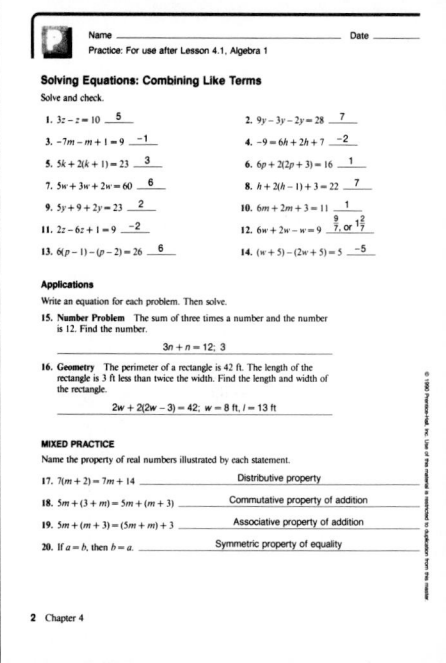

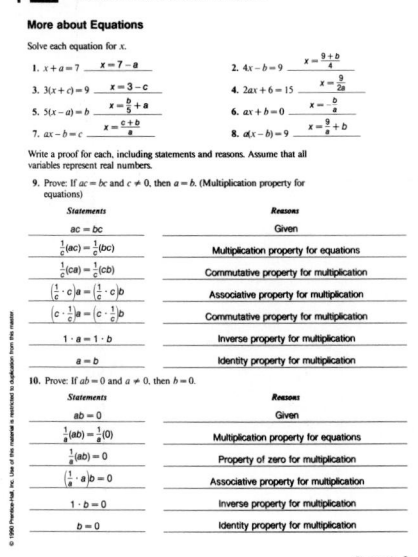

BACKGROUND

In the Capsule Review, Exercises 1–6 provide students with the opportunity to solve several types of equations in which the variable is contained on one side of the equal sign. Simplifying expressions using the properties of equations helps prepare students for the task of combining like terms by moving the variable from one side of the equation to the other.

Critical Thinking

Predicting Consequences Examine the paragraph preceding Example 1. The text says that "you need to place the variable terms all on one side of the equation." Explain why it is desirable to have the variable terms all on one side of the equation. With the variable terms combined on one side, the equation would then be in a form with which they are already familiar, and, more importantly, in a form that is solvable.

4.2

Solving Equations: Variable on Both Sides

Objective: To solve equations that contain the variable on both sides

In the equations you have solved thus far, the terms containing variables were all on one side of the equation.

Capsule Review

To solve the equations below, you may have to use the distributive property to remove parentheses first, before combining like terms.

Solve and check.

1. $2x + 13 = 1$ $\,-6$ **2.** $29 = 5 - 3y$ $\,-8$ **3.** $4y - 2y = 16$ $\,8$

4. $-19 = 2a - a - 10$ $\,-9$ **5.** $2(n - 3) = 14$ $\,10$ **6.** $5(4 - b) - 35 = 0$ $\,-3$

In equations like $3x + 2 = -x - 2$, you need to place all the variable terms on one side of the equation.

EXAMPLE 1   **Solve and check:** $3x + 2 = -x - 2$

$$3x + 2 = -x - 2$$
$$3x + x + 2 = -x + x - 2 \qquad \textit{Add x to each side.}$$
$$4x + 2 = -2 \qquad\qquad \textit{Combine like terms.}$$
$$4x + 2 - 2 = -2 - 2 \qquad \textit{Subtract 2 from each side.}$$
$$4x = -4$$
$$x = -1 \qquad\qquad \textit{Divide each side by 4.}$$

Check: $3x + 2 = -x - 2$
$$3(-1) + 2 \stackrel{?}{=} -(-1) - 2 \qquad \textit{Replace x with } -1.$$
$$-3 + 2 \stackrel{?}{=} 1 - 2$$
$$-1 = -1 \ \vee \qquad\qquad \textit{True}$$

So, the solution is -1.

In Example 1, you might choose to have the variable terms on the right. Then you would begin by subtracting $3x$ from each side of the equation. Solve $3x + 2 = -x - 2$ by first subtracting $3x$ from each side. Do you get -1 for the solution?

Some equations have more than one variable term on the same side. To solve these, the first step is to combine like terms that are on the same side.

EXAMPLE 2   **Solve and check:** $-36 + 2n = -3n + n - 5n$

$$-36 + 2n = -3n + n - 5n$$
$$-36 + 2n = -7n \qquad \text{\textit{Combine like terms on the right side.}}$$
$$-36 + 2n - 2n = -7n - 2n \qquad \text{\textit{Subtract } 2n \text{ \textit{from each side.}}}$$
$$-36 = -9n \qquad \text{\textit{Combine like terms.}}$$
$$4 = n \qquad \text{\textit{Divide each side by } -9.}$$

Check: $-36 + 2n = -3n + n - 5n$
$$-36 + 2(4) = -3(4) + (4) - 5(4) \qquad \text{\textit{Replace } n \text{ \textit{with 4.}}}$$
$$-36 + 8 = -12 + 4 - 20$$
$$-28 = -28 \; \checkmark \qquad \text{\textit{True}}$$

At this point, you should be familiar with the following steps for solving an equation.

Steps for Solving Equations

- Use the distributive property to remove parentheses on each side.
- Combine like terms on each side.
- Use the addition or subtraction property for equations so that
  (a) all variable terms are on one side of the equation, and
  (b) all numerical terms are on the other side.
- Use the multiplication or division property for equations.

EXAMPLE 3   **Solve:** $2y + 3(y - 9) = -(3y - 18) - y$

$$2y + 3(y - 9) = -(3y - 18) - y$$
$$2y + 3(y - 9) = -1(3y - 18) - y$$
$$2y + 3y + 3(-9) = -1(3y) + (-1)(-18) - y \qquad \text{\textit{Distributive property}}$$
$$2y + 3y - 27 = -3y + 18 - y \qquad \text{\textit{Multiplication property for } -1}$$
$$5y - 27 = -4y + 18 \qquad \text{\textit{Combine like terms.}}$$
$$5y + 4y - 27 = -4y + 4y + 18 \qquad \text{\textit{Addition property for equations}}$$
$$9y - 27 = 18$$
$$9y - 27 + 27 = 18 + 27 \qquad \text{\textit{Addition property for equations}}$$
$$9y = 45$$
$$y = 5 \qquad \text{\textit{Division property for equations}}$$

The check is left for you.

4.2 Solving Equations: Variables on Both Sides   **141**

TEACHING SUGGESTIONS

- Stress that for equations like Example 2, students should first combine like terms.
- Have students illustrate the four equation solving steps by solving the Chalkboard Examples given for Example 3. This will enable you to anticipate the difficulties that students may have with similar equations. You can use an overhead projector to illustrate the equation solving steps.
- For Example 3, the check is left for the student to complete. You may want students to do this before beginning the Class Exercises.

CHALKBOARD EXAMPLES

- **For Example 1**
  Solve and check:
  1. $2k - 3 = k + 4$ 7
  2. $-r = -4r + 2$ $\frac{2}{3}$

- **For Example 2**
  Solve and check:
  3. $-b - 3b + 5b = 2b + 15$ -15
  4. $56 - 3x = x - 3x + 6x$ 8

- **For Example 3**
  Solve:
  5. $5(2z + 4) = 5z$ -4
  6. $-2.5w = -5.5(w - 0.6)$ 1.1

Common Error

- With some of the more involved equations, students may ignore the equal sign and try to combine the variables on the left side with the variables on the right side. Emphasize the left and right sides of an equation by drawing a vertical line through the equals sign to avoid this confusion.
- See *Teacher's Resource Book* for additional remediation.

Critical Thinking

Observation In Example 3, why would a check be not necessarily valid if 5 was substituted for *y* in one of the simpler, later equations. Errors could have been made when the simpler equivalent equations were written.

Assignment Guide

- See p. 134B for assignments.
- You may want students to check their answers using calculators.

Algebra in Transportation

In the feature, students are asked to solve a problem involving aviation. Students are shown how algebraic equations are integrated into real world situations. This feature familiarizes students with the terminology used in Lesson 4.10.

Lesson Quiz

Solve and check.
1. $-5z = 3z - 16$ 2
2. $7 - m = 5 + 3m$ $\frac{1}{2}$
3. $-r = -4r + 2$ $\frac{2}{3}$
4. $-4(y + 6) = -20$ -1
5. $3p - 2(p - 7) = -(4p - 8) - p$
   -1

Enrichment

What is the solution set for the equation $\frac{2}{3x} = \frac{2}{3x}$? $\{x: x \neq 0\}$

CLASS EXERCISES

In each case, tell what should be done to get an equivalent equation that has the variable terms on one side and the numerical terms on the other.
See below.

1. $7m = -30 + m$
2. $4x + 28 = 7 + x$
3. $6 - z = 2z$
4. $6n = 4(n + 5)$
5. $-7b = 3(4 - 3b)$
6. $2(y - 5) = 15y - 4y$

Solve and check each equation.

7. $3t - 4 = -3t - 4$ 0
8. $8 - 5a = 3a$ 1
9. $4(x + 7) = 7 + x$ -7

For Discussion

10. To solve some equations in Exercises 1–6, you might prefer to get the variable terms on the right side rather than the left. For which equations? Why? For equations in Ex. 3 and 6. To avoid dividing by a negative.

11. Which types of equations might not have a solution. Explain. Some possible answers are absolute value equations, rational equations, or equations which involve division by zero.

PRACTICE EXERCISES

Solve and check.

A
1. $2y + 5 = -y - 4$ -3
2. $3m + 6 = -m - 6$ -3
3. $3d - 8 = -6 + d$ 1
4. $5a - 14 = -5 + 8a$ -3
5. $4 - 7m = m + 4$ 0
6. $4 - 9j = j + 4$ 0
7. $6n = 4n + 20$ 10
8. $11e = 9e + 14$ 7
9. $5d - 4 = 2d + 6$ $\frac{10}{3}$
10. $2j - 5 = 8j + 7$ -2
11. $-22 - 3d = -2d + d - 3d$ 22
12. $-42 + 4c = -c + 3c - c$ 14
13. $8y + 20 = y + 2y - 5y$ -2
14. $4b - 10 = b + 3b - 2b$ 5
15. $-7f + 2f = -36 + f + 3f$ 4
16. $-5a + 7a = -18 + 3a + 5a$ 3
17. $9y + 2 = 3(y + 4)$ $\frac{10}{6}$ or $\frac{5}{3}$
18. $3x - 2 = 4(x - 2)$ 6
19. $3y + 2(y - 5) = -(3y - 35) - y$ 5
20. $4x + 3(x - 2) = -(5x - 20) - x$ 2
21. $5y - 2(y + 5) = -(2y + 15) + y$ $-\frac{5}{4}$
22. $2z - 3(z + 1) = -(5z + 3) + z$ 0
23. $6m + 3(m + 2) = -(2m + 7) + m$ $-\frac{13}{10}$
24. $9t + 5(t + 3) = -(t + 13) + t$ -2

B
25. $5f - \frac{1}{2} = 4f + \frac{3}{4}$ $\frac{5}{4}$
26. $2g - \frac{5}{8} = g + \frac{5}{8}$ $\frac{5}{4}$
27. $7(2d - 1) + 5(2 - 3d) = 2d$ 1
28. $3(6e - 2) + 4(1 - 5e) = e$ $-\frac{2}{3}$
29. $5(3 - 4y) + 14y = 7(2 - 5y)$ $-\frac{1}{29}$
30. $2(5 - 4x) + x = 3(3x - 11)$ $\frac{43}{16}$

Additional Answers
Class Exercises
1. Subtract *m* from each side
2. Subtract *x* from each side; subtract 28 from each side
3. Add *z* to each
4. Distribute 4 on the right side; Subtract 4*n* from each side
5. Distribute 3 on the right side; Add 9*b* to each side
6. Distribute 2 on the left side; Combine like terms; Subtract 2*y* from each side

31. $6(2n - 5) = -3(7 - 3n) + 2n$ 9

32. $11(3 - 2q) = 3(9 - 7q) + q$ 3

33. $5x - 1 = (4 - 3x)(-2) + 10$ -3

34. $14t - 1 = (1 - 2t)(-3) + 12$ $\frac{5}{4}$

35. $-7y + 3 = -(3y + 5) - 2$ $\frac{5}{2}$

36. $-9m + 5 = -(2m + 8) - 6$ $\frac{19}{7}$

37. $-5(3x - 2) + 6(2 - 2x) = 3x$ $\frac{11}{15}$

38. $-6(6y - 4) + 5(3 - 7y) = -68y$ 13

C **39.** $-6t - [4 - (2 - 3t)] = 4(t + 1)$ $-\frac{6}{13}$

40. $-8b - [2(11 - 2b) + 4] = 9b$ -2

41. $4[5y - 4(y - 1)] = 3[4(y + 1)]$ $\frac{1}{2}$

42. $-2[5(2j - 6) - 7j] = 5[3(j - 2)]$ $\frac{30}{7}$

43. $\frac{1}{2}\left[\frac{2}{3}(4d - 1)\right] - (3d - 2) = \frac{5}{9}d$ $\frac{3}{4}$

44. $\left(4 - \frac{1}{2}c\right) - \frac{1}{3}\left[\frac{3}{4}(1 - 2c)\right] = \frac{1}{12}c$ 45

45. $-3[4m + 2(m - 4)] = -5[2(m + 5)]$ $9\frac{1}{4}$

46. $-2[3k + 3(k - 8)] = -2[3(k + 7)]$ 15

Applications

47. Geometry The area A of a rectangle increased by 4 is equal to 36 decreased by 5 times the area. What is the area of the rectangle? $\frac{16}{3}$

48. Finance Sally earns $25,000 per year as a computer programmer. Her mother's annual income is twice the amount of Sally's. Her brother's total income for 1 year is $\frac{1}{5}$ of Sally's income. What is her family's total income? $80,000

ALGEBRA IN TRANSPORTATION

Airplanes are one of the fastest means of transportation today. However, the velocities of different types of airplanes may vary greatly. Propeller planes may travel up to and over 250 mi/h, while a 747 can travel more than 600 mi/h. In 1947, the X-1 flew at the speed of sound, or Mach 1 (about 740 mi/h at sea level). Some years later, the X-15 flew at five times the speed of sound, or Mach 5. Presently, the Concorde provides passenger service at supersonic speeds for thousands of people.

Consider this problem: Two planes, one a propeller plane and one a supersonic transport (SST) travel the same distance. The propeller plane travels at a rate of 1300 mi/h less than that of the SST. If the SST makes the trip in 2 h and the propeller plane makes it in 15 h, what is the rate of the propeller plane? Use this equation: $2x = 15(x - 1300)$, where x is the rate of the SST. 200 mi/h

4.2 Solving Equations: Variables on Both Sides **143**

Teacher's Resource Book
Reteaching—Chapter 4, p. 4

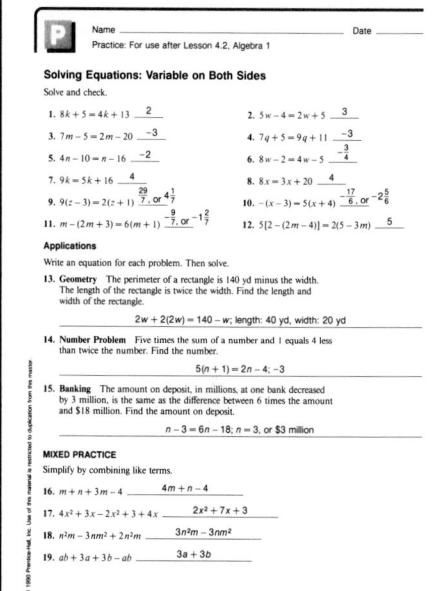

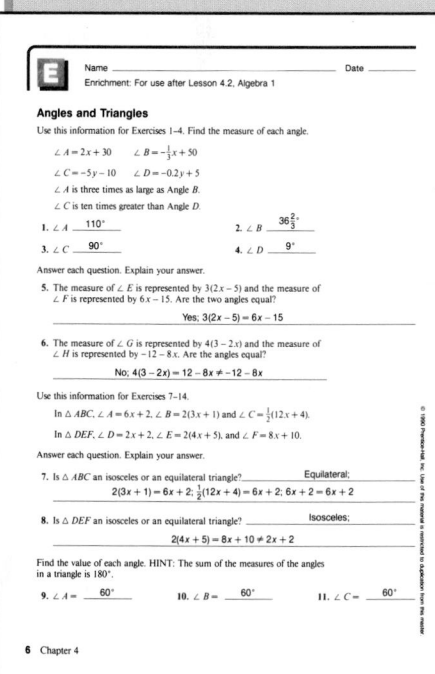

BACKGROUND

A student's ability to organize information given in a problem, so that it can be used to solve the problem, is a key to success in this lesson. To determine a student's progress, analyze errors in the student's work and then classify specific errors.

Error Analysis Classification
1. *Misunderstanding*
    Failed to understand the underlying concept of the problem
    Was unable to understand important mathematical ideas
    Selected an incorrect strategy
2. *Misapplied Strategy*
    Ignored some relevant information in the problem
    Wrote an incorrect equation
    Made error(s) in the solution process
    Stopped short in the process so that the answer given for the problem was incomplete
    Made error(s) in checking

Problem Solving: Consecutive Integers

4.3

Objective: To solve problems that involve consecutive integers

Consecutive integers are integers that differ by one. For example, 3, 4, and 5 are consecutive integers; -3, -2, and -1 are also consecutive integers.

If x is an integer, a general representation of three consecutive integers is x, $x + 1$, $x + 2$.

EXAMPLE 1 **Find three consecutive integers whose sum is 75.**

Understand the Problem   You are told that the sum of three consecutive integers is 75. You are asked to find the integers.

Plan Your Approach   Let $x =$ the first integer. Then $x + 1 =$ the second integer and $x + 2 =$ the third integer. The equation is:

$$x + (x + 1) + (x + 2) = 75$$

1st	x	?
2nd	$x + 1$	?
3rd	$x + 2$	?
Sum	$3x + 3$	75

Complete the Work   Solve: $x + (x + 1) + (x + 2) = 75$

$$(x + x + x) + (1 + 2) = 75 \qquad \textit{Group like terms.}$$
$$3x \qquad + \quad 3 \quad = 75$$
$$3x + 3 - 3 = 75 - 3 \qquad \textit{Subtract 3 from each}$$
$$3x = 72 \qquad \textit{side.}$$
$$x = 24 \qquad \textit{Divide each side by 3.}$$

Then $x + 1 = 25$ and $x + 2 = 26$.

Interpret the Results   Are 24, 25, and 26 three consecutive integers with a sum of 75?

$$24 + 25 + 26 \stackrel{?}{=} 75$$
$$75 = 75 \; \checkmark \qquad \textit{True}$$

Even integers are exactly divisible by 2. Beginning with an even integer and counting by twos gives consecutive even integers. For example, beginning with -8, four consecutive even integers are -8, -6, -4, and -2. If n is an even integer, then four consecutive even integers are n, $n + 2$, $n + 4$, and $n + 6$.

144   Chapter 4 More Equations in One Variable

EXAMPLE 2 **The sum of four consecutive even integers is -148. Find the integers.**

◻ Understand
the Problem

This is an addition problem for which the sum is known; there are four consecutive addends, each divisible by 2.

◻ Plan Your
Approach

Let n = the first even integer.
Then $n + 2$ = the second even integer,
$n + 4$ = the third even integer,
and $n + 6$ = the fourth even integer.

The equation is $n + (n + 2) + (n + 4) + (n + 6) = -148$.

◻ Complete
the Work

$4n + 12 = -148$
$4n = -160$ *Subtract 12 from each side.*
$n = -40$ *Divide each side by 4.*

Then $n + 2 = -40 + 2 = -38$,
$n + 4 = -40 + 4 = -36$,
and $n + 6 = -40 + 6 = -34$.

◻ Interpret
the Results

The four consecutive even integers whose sum is -148 are -40, -38, -36, and -34. The check is left for you.

Odd integers are not exactly divisible by 2. Beginning with an odd integer and counting by twos gives consecutive odd integers. For example, three consecutive odd integers are 17, 19, and 21. If t is an odd integer, then four consecutive odd integers are t, $t + 2$, $t + 4$, and $t + 6$.

EXAMPLE 3 **Find five consecutive odd integers if the sum of the first and the fifth is 1 less than 3 times the fourth.**

◻ Understand
the Problem

Let the five consecutive odd integers be t, $t + 2$, $t + 4$, $t + 6$, and $t + 8$.

◻ Plan Your
Approach

The equation is $t + (t + 8) = 3(t + 6) - 1$.

◻ Complete
the Work

$2t + 8 = 3t + 18 - 1$
$2t + 8 = 3t + 17$
$8 = t + 17$ *Subtract 2t from each side.*
$-9 = t$ *Subtract 17 from each side.*

◻ Interpret
the Results

If $t = -9$, counting by twos gives the five consecutive odd integers: -9, -7, -5, -3, and -1. Check the solution in Example 3.

4.3 Problem Solving: Consecutive Integers   **145**

Common Error

- In problems like Example 2, students may tend to write -42 as the next consecutive even integer after -40. Stress that 2, not -2, is added to get the next consecutive even integer. The next consecutive even integer after -40, therefore, is $-40 + 2$, or -38.
- See *Teacher's Resource Book* for additional remediation.

LESSON FOLLOW-UP

Critical Thinking

Observation Determine the inaccuracy of letting n and $n + 2$ represent two consecutive even integers whose sum is 75. They should recognize that the corresponding equation, $n + (n + 2) = 75$, has a solution of 36.5, which is not an integer. Students should be able to conclude that $n + (n + 2) = 75$ has no solution within the set of integers.

Assignment Guide

See p. 134B for assignments.

Math Club Activity

Some students may not find it necessary to solve these problems algebraically. Students should be encouraged to use all reasoning methods to solve problems.

Lesson Quiz

1. The sum of four consecutive even integers is 388. Find the integers. 94, 96, 98, 100
2. Find five consecutive odd integers whose sum is -35. $-11, -9, -7, -5, -3$
3. Four brothers were born in two-year intervals. The sum of their ages is 36. Find the age of each. 6 yr, 8 yr, 10 yr, 12 yr
4. The sum of four consecutive integers is equal to 10 more than twice the greatest integer. Find the four integers. 5, 6, 7, 8

CLASS EXERCISES

Complete the table where possible.

Begin with	Write the next three consecutive integers.	Write the next three consecutive even integers.	Write the next three consecutive odd integers.
1. 2	$\underline{?}$ 3, 4, 5	$\underline{?}$ 4, 6, 8	$\underline{?}$ cannot be done
2. 0	$\underline{?}$ 1, 2, 3	$\underline{?}$ 2, 4, 6	$\underline{?}$ cannot be done
3. -109	$\underline{?}$ $-108, -107, -106$	$\underline{?}$ cannot be done	$\underline{?}$ $-107, -105, -103$

PRACTICE EXERCISES

Write an equation for each problem. Then solve the problem.

A 1. Find three consecutive integers whose sum is 99. $x + (x + 1) + (x + 2) = 99; 32, 33, 34$

2. Find four consecutive integers whose sum is 26.
$x + (x + 1) + (x + 2) + (x + 23) = 26; 5, 6, 7, 8$
3. The sum of four consecutive even integers is -124. Find the number.
$x + (x + 2) + (x + 4) + (x + 6) = -124; -34, -32, -30, -28$
4. The sum of four consecutive even integers is -36. Find the number.
$x + (x + 2) + (x + 4) + (x + 6) = -36; -12, -10, -8, -6$
5. Find five consecutive even integers if the sum of the first and fifth is 2 less than 3 times the fourth. $x + (x + 8) = 3(x + 6) - 2; -8, -6, -4, -2, 0$

6. Find four consecutive odd integers if the sum of the first and fourth is 3 less than 3 times the second. $x + (x + 6) = 3(x + 2) - 3; 3, 5, 7, 9$

Write an equation for each problem. Then solve the problem.

7. The sum of two consecutive integers is 105. Find the integers.
$x + (x + 1) = 105; 52, 53$
8. The sum of two consecutive integers is -35. Find the integers.
$x + (x + 1) = -35; -18, -17$
9. Find three consecutive integers whose sum is -354.
$x + (x + 1) + (x + 2) = -354; -119, -118, -117$
10. Find four consecutive integers whose sum is 50.
$x + (x + 1) + (x + 2) + (x + 3) = 50; 11, 12, 13, 14$
11. The sum of two consecutive even integers is -54. Find the integers.
$x + (x + 2) = -54; -28, -26$
12. The sum of three consecutive even integers is 312. Find the integers.
$x + (x + 2) + (x + 4) = 312; 102, 104, 106$
13. The sum of three consecutive odd integers is -45. Find the integers.
$x + (x + 2) + (x + 4) = -45; -17, -15, -13$
14. The sum of four consecutive even integers is 180. Find the integers.
$x + (x + 2) + (x + 4) + (x + 6) = 180; 42, 44, 46, 48$
15. Find four consecutive integers if the sum of the second and fourth is 48.
$(x + 1) + (x + 3) = 48; 22, 23, 24, 25$
16. Find three consecutive integers. The sum of the first and third is -34.
$x + (x + 2) = -34; -18, -17, -16$

B 17. Find two consecutive odd integers if twice the larger, increased by the smaller, equals 85. $2(x + 2) + x = 85; 27, 29$

18. Find three consecutive even integers if their sum, decreased by the third, equals -22. $x + (x + 2) + (x + 4) - (x - 4) = -22; -12, -10, -8$

19. The ages in years of three brothers are consecutive. The sum of their ages is 39 decreased by the age of the youngest. What are their ages? $x + (x + 1) + (x + 2) = 39 - x; 9, 10, 11$

20. The sum of three consecutive even integers is 50 more than the third integer. Find the integers. $x + (x + 2) + (x + 4) = 50 + (x + 4); 24, 26, 28$

21. The sum of three consecutive integers is equal to 9 less than 4 times the least of the integers. Find the three integers. $x + (x + 1) + (x + 2) = 4x - 9; 12, 13, 14$

22. When the sum of four consecutive even integers is divided by 7, the result is 4. Find these integers. $\dfrac{x + (x + 2) + (x + 4) + (x + 6)}{7} = 4; 4, 6, 8, 10$

C 23. Find four consecutive multiples of 5 whose sum is 90. $x + (x + 5) + (x + 10) + (x + 15) = 90; 15, 20, 25, 30$

24. Find three consecutive multiples of 3 if the sum of the first and the third is 12. $x + (x + 6) = 12; 3, 6, 9$

25. Find three consecutive integers if twice the middle integer is equal to the sum of the first and the third. $2(x + 1) = x + x + 2;$ any three consecutive integers

26. Find two consecutive odd integers whose sum is 0. $x + (x + 2) = 0; -1, 1$

27. Find four consecutive integers such that the sum of the two largest subtracted from three times the sum of the two smallest is 70. $3[x + (x + 1)] - [(x + 2) + (x + 3)] = 70; 18, 19, 20, 21$

28. Find four consecutive odd integers such that the sum of the two smallest added to four times the largest is 92. $x + (x + 2) + 4(x + 6) = 92; 11, 13, 15, 17$

MATH CLUB ACTIVITY

1. The sum of two consecutive integers is 2165. What is their difference? 1

2. Find four consecutive even integers if the sum of the first and the third is 8 less than the sum of the second and the fourth. no solution

3. Find six consecutive multiples of 13 whose sum is 39. $-26, -13, 0, 13, 26, 39$

4. Find three consecutive even integers if the first is $\frac{2}{5}$ of their sum. $-12, -10, -8$

5. A sequence of four integers begins with two consecutive even integers and contains the next two consecutive odd integers. Their sum is 18. What are the four integers? 2, 4, 5, 7

4.3 Problem Solving: Consecutive Integers **147**

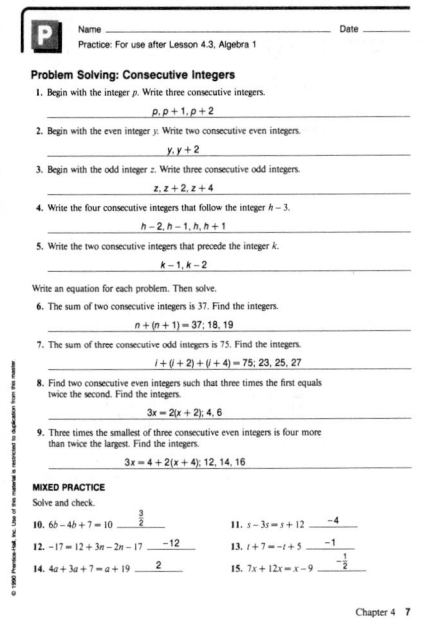

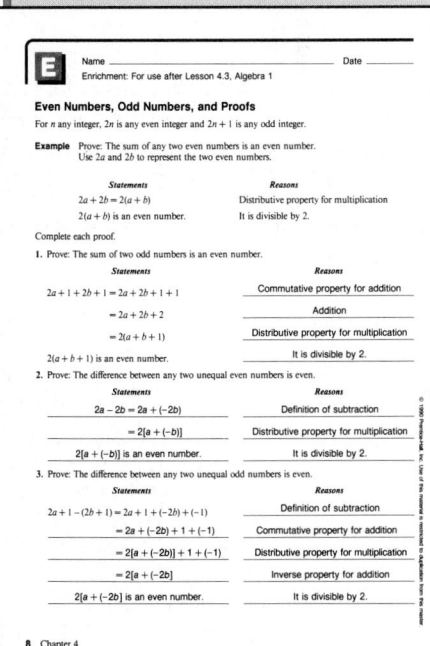

BACKGROUND

In the Capsule Review, the exercises make use of a familiar shortcut, the multiplication of decimals by powers of 10, as it is applied to numerical calculations. This is an appropriate exercise for introducing students to similar shortcuts that may be applied when solving algebraic equations.

Critical Thinking

Judging Ideas Shortcuts for solving equations are generally taught after learning the basic techniques. Judge the alternative of learning the shortcuts first. It is important to master the basic techniques first, since these provide the foundation for the shortcuts. It then becomes easier to understand the relationship between the complete procedure and the shortcut.

4.4

Shortcuts in Solving Equations

Objective: To use shortcuts to solve equations

Yasmin was asked to solve the equation $0.2x - 0.5x - 0.7 = 0.3 + 0.2x$. She knew that she could combine the two x-terms on the left side and then apply the equation properties. However, she noticed that there was a $0.2x$ term on each side of the equation. "Wouldn't it be simpler to subtract $0.2x$ from each side first?" she wondered. She tried it.

$$0.2x - 0.5x - 0.7 = 0.3 + 0.2x$$

$0.2x - 0.2x - 0.5x - 0.7 = 0.3 + 0.2x - 0.2x$ *Subtract 0.2x from each side.*

$$-0.5x - 0.7 = 0.3$$ *Add 0.7 to each side.*

$$-0.5x = 1$$ *Divide each side by -0.5.*

$$x = -2$$

Yasmin checked -2 in the original equation and found that it was correct.

Capsule Review

Multiplying a decimal by a power of 10 such as 10, 100, 1000 changes the place value of the digits. This can be thought of as "moving the decimal point."

EXAMPLE   **a.** $100(0.73) = 0_\smile 73_\smile$ or 73   **b.** $1000(3.8) = 3_\smile 800_\smile$ or 3800

                            2 places   3 places

Multiply.

1. $10(42.8)$ 428   **2.** $8.75(100)$ 875   **3.** $1000(-0.635)$ -635 **4.** $7.001(10,000)$
                                                                        70,010

State the power of 10 that gives the product at the right.

5. $(?)(0.041) = 41$ 10^3 **6.** $(?)(32.08) = 3208$ 10^2 **7.** $(?)(0.00032) = 32$ 10^5

Equations with decimal coefficients can be simplified by multiplying each side of the equation by a power of 10. Consider the following:

$$0.11y = 1.5 + 0.1y$$

Since the greatest number of digits to the right of either decimal point is two, you can multiply each side of the equation by 100 to clear all decimals.

148   Chapter 4 More Equations in One Variable

EXAMPLE 1 **Solve and check:** $0.11y = 1.5 + 0.1y$

$$0.11y = 1.5 + 0.1y$$
$$(100)(0.11y) = 100(1.5 + 0.1y) \qquad \textit{Multiply each side by 100.}$$
$$11y = 100(1.5) + 100(0.1y) \qquad \textit{Distribute 100.}$$
$$11y = 150 + 10y$$
$$11y - 10y = 150 + 10y - 10y \qquad \textit{Subtract 10y from each side.}$$
$$y = 150$$

Check: $\qquad 0.11y = 1.5 + 0.1y$
$$(0.11)150 \overset{?}{=} 1.5 + 0.1(150) \qquad \textit{Replace y with 150.}$$
$$16.5 \overset{?}{=} 1.5 + 15$$
$$16.5 = 16.5 ✔ \qquad \textit{True}$$

So, 150 is the solution.

The equation $9a = 3(a - 2)$ can be simplified by distributing the 3, but note that both $9a$ and $3(a - 2)$ are divisible by 3.

EXAMPLE 2 **Solve and check:** $9a = 3(a - 2)$

$$9a = 3(a - 2)$$
$$\frac{9a}{3} = \frac{3(a - 2)}{3} \qquad \textit{Divide each side by 3.}$$
$$\qquad\qquad \frac{3(a-2)}{3} = \frac{3}{3} \cdot \frac{a-2}{1} = a - 2$$
$$3a = a - 2$$
$$3a - a = a - a - 2 \qquad \textit{Subtract a from each side.}$$
$$2a = -2$$
$$a = -1$$

So, -1 is the solution. The check is left for you.

You need not always use shortcuts, but be aware that they frequently make solving equations much simpler.

CLASS EXERCISES

Identify an appropriate shortcut operation. Then give the resulting equation. Do not solve. See below.

1. $4(3 - x) = 16$ **2.** $18 = -6(y + 5)$ **3.** $33 - 4a = 11a - 4a$

4. $-7(b + 4) + 5 = 5$ **5.** $0.3 - 0.1c = 1.5$ **6.** $2.1 + 0.3d = 0.33d$

7. $5(2m - 3) = 15m$ **8.** $5(p - 6) - 8 = 45 - 8$

4.4 Shortcuts in Solving Equations   **149**

For Discussion

9. If each side of the equation $0.4(0.2q + 5.1) = -7.2$ is multiplied by 10, what equation results? $4(0.2q + 5.1) = -72$

10. In Exercise 8 above, two shortcut operations are possible. What are they? After the two shortcuts are used, what is the resulting equation?
First add 8 to both sides, then divide each side by 5; $p - 6 = 9$

PRACTICE EXERCISES

Solve and check. Use shortcuts where possible.

A
1. $0.2y - 0.4 = 1.5$ 9.5
2. $0.8x + 0.3 = 59.7$ 74.25
3. $1.80 - 0.02j = 1.32$ 24
4. $3.21 - 4.27k = 7.48$ -1
5. $23.4 - d = 0.25d$ 18.72
6. $82.6 - e = 0.18e$ 70
7. $6a = 2(a + 3)$ $\frac{3}{2}$
8. $15x = 5(x + 4)$ 2
9. $2(5 - a) = 4$ 3
10. $-18 = 9(t - 4)$ 2
11. $(b + 7)(-12) = 36$ -10
12. $(5 + c)(-13) = 65$ -10
13. $5 + 7r = -25r + 7r$ $-\frac{1}{5}$
14. $-8t - t = 24 - t$ -3
15. $-8 + 5f = 3f - 11 + 5f$ 1
16. $-13 + 7g = 4g - 23 + 7g$ $\frac{5}{2}$
17. $-7(2x - 7) = 21(3x - 5)$ 2
18. $-8(4y - 6) = 16(2y - 5)$ 2
19. $-35(14 - 2r) = -5(8 + r)$ 6
20. $-36(7 - 3t) = -6(2 + 2t)$ 2
21. $3(2y - 1) + y = y - 3$ 0
22. $4(3x - 5) - x = -x + 16$ 3
23. $962.5 = 805 + 1.5a$ 105
24. $178.5 = 310 + 2.5b$ -52.6

B
25. $0.045p = 0.06(2000 - p) + 27$ 1400
26. $0.075v = 0.03(50 - v) + 3$ 42.857
27. $0.2q + 0.07(q + 4) = 0.01q$ -1.077
28. $0.8r + 0.09(r + 3) = 0.08r$ $-0.33\overline{3}$
29. $0.1a + 0.05(2 - a) = 0.08$ -0.4
30. $0.7b + 0.15(5 - b) = 0.2$ -1
31. $-4.5n + 0.02n = 19.2 - 4.5n$ 960
32. $5.36m - 0.4m = 26.8 - 0.4m$ 5
33. $8(3x - 4) + 16(x + 3) = -112$ $-\frac{16}{5}$
34. $9(2y + 3) + 27(y + 2) = -36$ $-\frac{13}{5}$
35. $2(3 - 4f) - 4(6 - f) = 4$ $-\frac{11}{2}$
36. $10(2 - g) - 5(1 - 3g) = 30$ 3
37. $4.85(2 - b) + 0.2b = 4.85(2 - b)$ 0
38. $7.1(c - 11) + 3.4c = -7.1(11 - c)$ 0
39. $6a - 3(2a - 3) + 9(3 - a) = 12$ $2\frac{2}{3}$
40. $-5b - 15(1 - 2b) + 30(b - 2) = 60$ $2\frac{5}{11}$

C
41. $0.1y - 0.05(y + 2) = 0.1y + 0.03(3 - 2y)$ 19
42. $3.86x - 5.4(2x + 5) = 3.86x + 1.8(6 + 3x)$ $-2.3\overline{3}$

43. $0.31t - 0.1(0.02 - 0.2t) = 0.064$ 0.2

44. $0.73w - 0.3(0.15 - 0.3w) = -5.785$ –7

45. $-0.6x - 0.1[4 - (2 - 3x)] = 0.4(x + 1)$ ≈−0.46

46. $3.2y - 0.5[7 - (4 - 5y)] = 0.6(2y + 2)$ –5.4

47. $7.03(2 - 5v) = 0.2[2v - (1 - v)] + 3.2v$ ≈0.37

48. $-2.25(3 - 2z) = -0.5[-6z - (1 - 2z)] + z$ 4.83̄

Applications

49. Number Problem Three times the sum of a number x and -5 equals -6 times the sum of x and -2. Find x. 3

50. Number Problem The product of -4 and a number y is equal to 20 times the sum of 7 and 3 times y. Find y. $-2\frac{3}{16}$

51. Geometry If the perimeter of the rectangle shown is 84 m, find its length and width. 26 m, 16 m

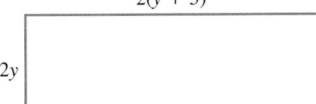
$2(y + 5)$

$2y$

52. Sales Charles sold bottles of juice at a football game for $1.25 each. At the end of the game, he had $86.25. This included the $7.50 he had started with. How many bottles of juice did Charles sell? 63 bottles

TEST YOURSELF

1. Solve: $x + (x + 1) + (x + 2) = 45$ 14   4.1

2. Solve: $-9 = 6m - (2 - m)$ –1

3. The sum of a number and 2 more than twice the number is 8. Find the number. 2

4. Solve: $8y - 3 = -7 + 6y$ –2   4.2

5. Solve: $2 - 3r = -3(1 + 2r)$ $-\frac{5}{3}$

6. Solve: $-8j + 5 = 4(11 - 2j)$ no solution

7. If i is an even integer, write the next two consecutive even integers. $i + 2, i + 4$ 4.3

8. If $d - 1$ is an integer, write the next three consecutive integers. $d, d + 1, d + 2$

9. Find four consecutive odd integers whose sum is 56. 11, 13, 15, 17

10. Solve using a shortcut: $3t - 2t = 18 + 3t$ –9   4.4

11. Solve using a shortcut: $0.01 + 0.2x = 7.0$ 34.95

12. Solve using a shortcut: $-8k = 16(k - 1)$ $\frac{2}{3}$

4.4 Shortcuts in Solving Equations   **151**

Teacher's Resource Book
Reteaching—Chapter 4, p. 9

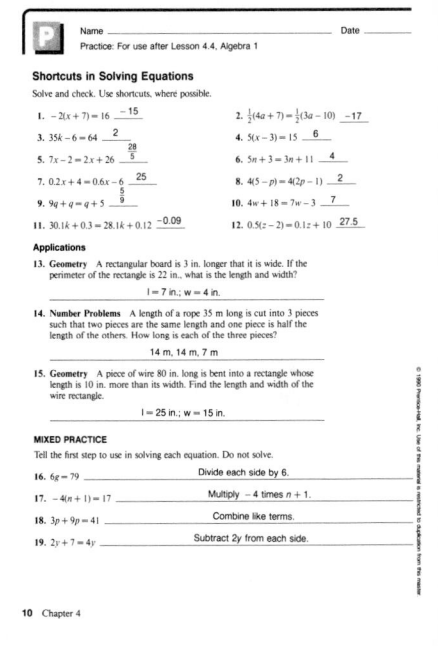

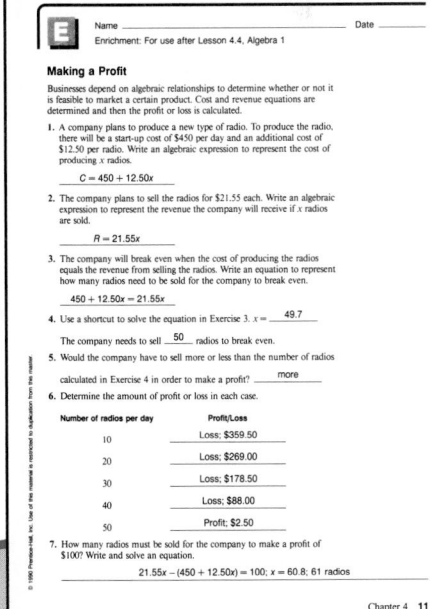

BACKGROUND

In the Capsule Review, students are asked to change percents to decimals and decimals to percents. Since these are necessary steps in solving problems involving percents, this review is an appropriate warm-up exercise.

4.5

Solving Equations: Percents

Objective: To use equations for solving simple percent problems

Number relationships are often expressed in terms of percent, as in these newspaper headlines. **Percent** (%) means per hundred or hundredth. For example, one way of thinking about an unemployment rate of 8% is to say 8 out of 100 people are out of work. Likewise, a 5% increase in gasoline prices translates into a 5-cent increase for every $1.00 spent. It is helpful to be able to use algebraic techniques to solve problems involving percent.

Gasoline prices
up 5%

Unemployment at 8%

Capsule Review

EXAMPLE   12.5% = 0.12.5   Move the decimal point two places to the left.

Express each percent as a decimal.

1. 29% 0.29   **2.** 3.1% 0.031   **3.** 100% 1   **4.** 280% 2.80   **5.** 0.02% 0.0002

EXAMPLE   0.82 = 0.82.%   Move the decimal point two places to the right.

Express each decimal as a percent.

6. 0.05 5%   **7.** 0.13 13%   **8.** 2.0 200%   **9.** 0.4115 41.15%   **10.** 15 1500%

Any situation that involves percent can be expressed in the general form:

$$a \text{ is } b\% \text{ of } c$$

Since there are three quantities involved here, there are three types of percent problems. If you know any two of the three quantities, the third can be found. These three types of percent problems are often referred to as the "three cases of percent."

CASE I   Find a percent of a number.

CASE II   Find what percent one number is of another.

CASE III Find a number when a percent of it is known.

EXAMPLE 1   **What number is 25% of 700?**

Let n = the number.

n is 25% of 700.   **CASE I**

$n = 0.25(700)$ *25% = 0.25; "of" means times.*

$n = 175$

EXAMPLE 2   **1 is what percent of 3?**

Let r = the percent.

1 is what percent of 3?   **CASE II**

$1 = r(3)$

$\frac{1}{3} = r$ *Divide each side by 3.*

$r = 0.33\overline{3}$, or $33\frac{1}{3}\%$ *Change $\frac{1}{3}$ to a decimal and a percent.*

EXAMPLE 3   **33 is $37\frac{1}{2}\%$ of what number?**

Let t = the number.

33 is 37.5% of t.   **CASE III**

$33 = (0.375)t$

$33,000 = 375t$ *Multiply each side by 1000.*

$88 = t$ *Divide each side by 375.*

To solve percent problems, usually it is most efficient to change percents to decimals. However, it may be just as easy to work with fractions.

EXAMPLE 4   **$12\frac{1}{2}\%$ of what number is 30?**

Let m = the number.

$12\frac{1}{2}\%$ of m is 30.   **CASE III**

$0.125 \cdot m = 30$

$\frac{1}{8}m = 30$ *$0.125 = \frac{125}{1000} = \frac{1}{8}$*

$m = 240$ *Multiply each side by 8; $8 \cdot \frac{1}{8}m = m$.*

4.5 Solving Equations: Percents   **153**

TEACHING SUGGESTION

Point out that in each case of percent problems there is a direct translation of the general form, *a* is *b*% of *c*. In the three cases of percent problems, the word *of* indicates multiplication and the word *is* indicates equality.

CHALKBOARD EXAMPLES

- **For Example 1**
  1. What is 75% of 600?   450
  2. What is $37\frac{1}{2}\%$ of 250?   93.75

- **For Example 2**
  3. 1 is what percent of 6? $16\frac{2}{3}\%$
  4. What percent of 4 is 6?   150%

- **For Example 3**
  5. 19 is $12\frac{1}{2}\%$ of what number?   152
  6. 100% of what number is 9.1?   9.1

- **For Example 4**
  7. $33\frac{1}{3}\%$ of what number is 60?   180
  8. 700 is $87\frac{1}{2}\%$ of what number?   800

- **For Example 5**
  9. Bob's bank pays $6\frac{1}{2}\%$ annual simple interest on his savings account of $650. How much interest will the account earn in one year? $42.25

Common Error

- In problems like Examples 3 and 4, some students may forget to change the fraction or decimal to a percent. Encourage students to read each problem carefully.
- See *Teacher's Resource Book* for additional remediation.

Observation Determine the error in the following.

$3\frac{1}{4}\% = 3\% + \frac{1}{4}\%$

$\qquad = 0.03 + 0.25 = 0.28$

Students should observe that $\frac{1}{4}\%$ was not converted to the proper decimal. $\frac{1}{4}\% = 0.25\% = 0.0025$, and so $3\% + \frac{1}{4}\% = 0.03 + 0.0025 = 0.0325$. Alternately, $3\frac{1}{4}\% = 3.25\% = 0.0325$.

Assignment Guide
- See p. 134B for assignments.
- Some students may have trouble with exercises like Exercise 12. Point out that $62\frac{1}{2}\%$ does not equal 62.5. Students should be encouraged to check their solutions using a calculator.

Extra
The feature presents equations involving percents that can be used to form a magic square. The entertaining aspect of this feature may help eliminate some of the stress experienced by students who have difficulty with fractions and decimals.

Lesson Quiz
1. What is 35% of 700? 245
2. 2 is what percent of 3? $66\frac{2}{3}\%$
3. 200% of what number is 8? 4
4. $62\frac{1}{2}\%$ of what number is 25? 40
5. You earned $131.25 in annual simple interest on an investment of $1500. What annual rate of interest was paid?

   8.75%, or $8\frac{3}{4}\%$

Enrichment
What is $a\%$ of $b\%$ of $c\%$ of 1,000,000? *abc*

In Example 5, this formula is used to compute annual simple interest.

$$\underbrace{\frac{\text{Annual}}{\text{Simple Interest}}}_{i} = \underbrace{\text{Principal}}_{p} \times \underbrace{\frac{\text{Annual}}{\text{Interest Rate}}}_{r} \times \underbrace{\frac{\text{Time}}{\text{(in years)}}}_{t}$$

Explain how this relationship shows another case of "*a* is *b*% of *c*."

EXAMPLE 5   **Dierdre earned $65.25 in simple interest for one year on an investment of $900. What annual rate of interest was paid?**

Let r = the annual interest rate.

$65.25 is what percent of $900?   **CASE II**

$65.25 = 900r(1)$

$6525 = 90{,}000r$ *Multiply each side by 100.*

$0.0725 = r$ *Divide each side by 90,000.*

So, the annual rate of interest was 0.0725, or 7.25%.

CLASS EXERCISES

For each exercise, first give a word statement in the form *a* is *b*% of *c*. Then write it as an algebraic equation.

	a.	b.	c.	
1.	?	25%	32	*a* is 25% of 32; *a* = (0.25)(32)
2.	150	?	200	150 is *b*% of 200; 150 = (*b*)(200)
3.	30	15%	?	30 is 15% of *c*; 30 = (0.15)(*c*)
4.	?	35%	400	*a* is 35% of 400; *a* = (0.35)(400)
5.	16	?	48	16 is *b*% of 48; 16 = (*b*)(48)
6.	8	4%	?	8 is 4% of *c*; 8 = (0.04)(*c*)

PRACTICE EXERCISES

A
1. What number is 2% of 49? 0.98
2. What number is 65% of 130? 84.5
3. Find 37.5% of 1000. 375
4. Find 6% of 248. 14.88
5. 5 is what percent of 25? 20%
6. 35 is what percent of 35? 100%
7. 6 is what percent of 9? $66\frac{2}{3}\%$
8. 30 is what percent of 80? 37.5%
9. 0.75 is 5% of what number? 15
10. 8.9 is 100% of what number? 8.9
11. 80% of what number is 28? 35
12. $62\frac{1}{2}\%$ of 480 is what number? 300

13. $87\frac{1}{2}\%$ of $4000 is what amount? $3500   **14.** 150% of what number is 60? 40

15. 0.8 is what percent of 32? 2.5%   **16.** What percent of 75 is 2.4? 3.2%

17. 36 is $66\frac{2}{3}\%$ of what number? 54   **18.** $33\frac{1}{3}\%$ of what number is 75? 225

19. What percent of 1.4 is 3.5? 250%   **20.** 30 is what percent of 25? 120%

B **21.** $16\frac{2}{3}\%$ of what number is 1.2? 7.2   **22.** 12.5% of what number is 1.5? 12

23. What percent of 9 is 12? $133\frac{1}{3}\%$ **24.** 15 is what percent of 5? 300%

25. What amount is $1\frac{1}{2}\%$ of $6000? $90   **26.** What amount is $8\frac{1}{4}\%$ of $720? $59.40

27. What amount is $\frac{1}{2}\%$ of $5000? $25   **28.** 10 is what percent of 4000? 0.25%

C **29.** $0.16a$ is what percent of $2a$? 8%   **30.** What percent of $0.3b$ is $5b$? $1666\frac{2}{3}\%$

31. $y\%$ of what number is y? 100   **32.** $x\%$ of what number is $3x$? 300

Applications

33. Demography   Of 625 people surveyed, 44% agreed with the mayor. How many people agreed with the mayor? 275

34. Finance   Ben's bank pays $6\frac{3}{4}\%$ annual simple interest on his account of $440. How much interest will the account earn in one year? $29.70

35. Finance   Sara's investment of $1572 earned $129.69 in annual simple interest. What was the annual interest rate? 8.25%

36. Demography   The population of Andropolis is now 25,868. This is 145% of what it was ten years ago. What was the earlier population? 17,840

EXTRA

Draw a square like the one shown. Write the value of each variable in the appropriate space to form a magic square (the sum of the numbers in each row, each column, and each diagonal are all the same).

1. a is 5% of 80.   **2.** $4\frac{1}{2}\%$ of 200 is b.

3. 4 is 200% of c.   **4.** d is 15% of 20.

5. $\frac{1}{2}\%$ of 1000 is e.   **6.** $33\frac{1}{3}\%$ of 21 is f.

7. g is 12% of $66\frac{2}{3}$.   **8.** $\frac{1}{3}\%$ of 300 is h.

9. $90 is $i\%$ of $1500.

$a = 4$	$b = 9$	$c = 2$
$d = 3$	$e = 5$	$f = 7$
$g = 8$	$h = 1$	$i = 6$

4.5 Solving Equations: Percents   **155**

Teacher's Resource Book
Reteaching—Chapter 4, p. 12

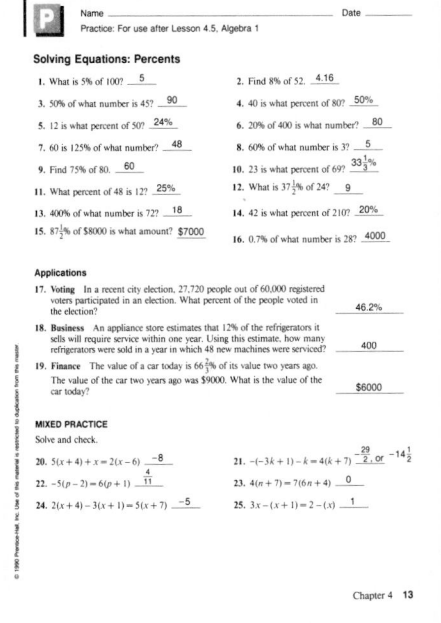

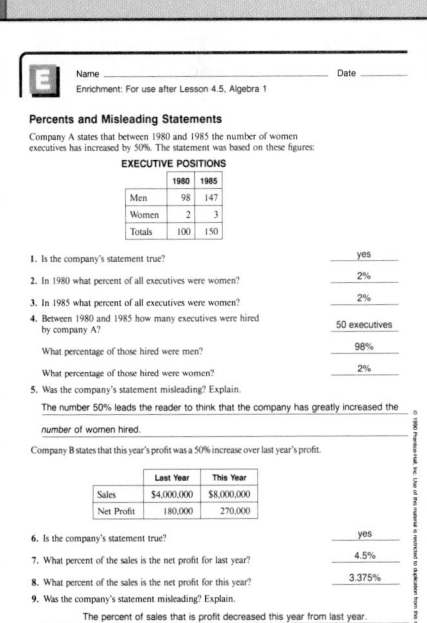

4.6

Problem Solving: Percents

Objective: To solve percent of change problems

If you are thinking about taking a trip to the West Coast, this newspaper ad might be of interest to you.

The 30% mentioned is a *percent of change*. In this case, it is a **percent of increase.** The change will be 30% of the original price.

LAST WEEK
REDUCED FLIGHT RATES
ROUND TRIP TO WEST COAST   **$299**
BEGINNING SUNDAY RATES WILL
INCREASE BY 30%

EXAMPLE 1   **If the price of a $299 round-trip plane ticket is increased by 30%, find the new price.**

☐ **Understand the Problem**   Given: The original price is $299. The increase is 30%.
Find: The new price.

☐ **Plan Your Approach**   What is 30% of the original price?
Let x = the dollar change in price.

☐ **Complete the Work** $x = 0.30(299)$ *Write an equation.*
$x = 89.7$ *The change in price is $89.70.*

☐ **Interpret the Results** $89.70 is 30% of the original price, $299.00.
The new (higher) price is the sum of the original price and the increase: $299.00 + $89.70 = $388.70

So, $388.70 is the new price.

Percent of change can involve a decrease as well as an increase. If you know an original value and a new lower value, you can find the **percent of decrease.**

EXAMPLE 2   **The population of Warrensville has decreased from 696 to 580. Find the percent of decrease.**

☐ **Understand the Problem**   Given: The change (the decrease): $696 - 580 = 116$
Find: What percent the decrease is of the original.

	Plan Your Approach	Let r = percent of decrease. 116 is what percent of 696?

	Complete the Work	$116 = r(696)$

$$\frac{116}{696} = r \qquad \text{Divide each side by 696.}$$

$$r = \frac{1}{6} \qquad \qquad \frac{116}{696} = \frac{1}{6}$$

$$= 0.16\overline{6} \text{ or } 16\tfrac{2}{3}\%$$

	Interpret the Results	So, the population has decreased by $16\tfrac{2}{3}\%$, or approximately 16.7%. How can you check this answer?

CLASS EXERCISES

Copy and complete the table.

	Original Price	New Price	Change (Inc/Dec)	% Change (Inc/Dec)
1.	$36	$24	__?__ $12 (dec)	__?__ $33\tfrac{1}{3}$% (dec)
2.	$72	__?__ $88	$16 (inc)	__?__ 22.2% (inc)
3.	__?__ $52	$64	$12 (inc)	__?__ 23.1% (inc)
4.	$75	__?__ $50	__?__ $25 (dec)	$33\tfrac{1}{3}$% (dec)
5.	__?__ $150	__?__ $135	$15 (dec)	10% (dec)

PRACTICE EXERCISES

Copy the table and find the missing entries in each row. Round amounts to the nearest cent, or to the nearest tenth of a percent.

A

	Original Price	New Price	Change (Inc/Dec)	% Change (Inc/Dec)
1.	$196	__?__ $147	$49 (dec)	__?__ 25% (dec)
2.	$144	__?__ $168	__?__ $24 (inc)	$16\tfrac{2}{3}$% (inc)
3.	__?__ $82.86	__?__ $111.86	$29 (inc)	35% (inc)
4.	__?__ $1092	$1028	$64 (dec)	__?__ 5.9% (dec)
5.	$883	$909	__?__ $26 (inc)	__?__ 2.9% (inc)
6.	$684	__?__ $720	$36 (inc)	__?__ 5.3% (inc)
7.	$84	__?__ $78.75	__?__ $5.25 (dec)	$6\tfrac{1}{4}$% (dec)
8.	__?__ $496	$514	$18 (inc)	__?__ 3.6% (inc)

Assignment Guide
- See p. 134B for assignments.
- You may wish to encourage students to use calculators for many of these exercises.
- See *Teacher's Resource Book, Technology*, p. 9.

Algebra in Engineering

Exercises 2–4 are Case 1 percent problems similar to Example 1 in this lesson, but they contain extraneous information. Have students identify any unnecessary information before proceeding.

Lesson Quiz

1. Last year the computer that Ms. Brady wanted cost $1640. With an increased memory and a different drive, this year's model costs 15% more. How much would Ms. Brady have to pay for the new model? $1886

2. Ed's weekly income increased from $480 to $508.80. Find the percent of increase. 6%

3. If the number of viewers watching MZQ has dropped from 118,000 to 97,232, what is the percent of decrease? 17.6%

4. The original price of a CD player is $146. Crazy Cal's is offering a closeout price of 25.5% off the original. Find the closeout price. $108.77

Enrichment

If an item that cost $100 first had its price decreased by 5% and then increased by 5%, what would the final price of the item be? $99.75

9. When Marya began her new job in marketing, she was told that if her work was satisfactory she would receive a 15% increase after six months. If her starting salary was $19,500, what could she hope to earn after six months? $22,425

10. If oil prices decline by $12\frac{1}{2}\%$, what will be the price of oil now selling for $48 per barrel? $42

11. The number of subscribers to *ACE Magazine* fell from 810,153 to 708,417. What percent of decrease does this drop represent? 12.6%

12. Jane bought shares of stock in MARTCO for $78.90 per share. Now each share is worth $84.95. By what percent has the value of MARTCO stock risen? 7.7%

13. Over the last five years, the popoulation of Chowan increased by 1084 people. The earlier population was 9785. By what percent has Chowan's population risen? 11.1%

B 14. Razi weighs 135 lb. In order to qualify for his wrestling division, he must lose 9 lb. What percent weight decrease does this loss represent? 6.7%

15. In Dawn City, the number of registered voters fell by 115. Now there are 7826 registered voters. What percent of decrease is this change? 1.4%

16. Sneakers at a local sports store cost $48.50. This is $6.75 more than they cost last year. By what percent has the price increased? 16.2%

17. The price of a cheese stick at Dairy Heaven has gone up by $16\frac{2}{3}\%$, or 10¢. What was the old price and what is the new? old price: 60¢; new price: 70¢

18. This year, 7 fewer students tried out for Lesterville High School's football team than tried out last year. This is a 14% decrease. How many students tried out last year? This year? 50; 43

19. By buying last year's model, Mr. D'Andrea saved 20% on the sticker price of a new automobile. If the sticker price is $12,998, what did he actually pay? $10,398.40

20. At the Hairways Beauty Salon, women's haircuts cost $18.50. If the price increases by 15%, what will the new price be? $21.28

21. At the supermarket, Laura found that the price of tomatoes had risen from 89¢/lb to $1.19/lb. By what percent had the price increased? 33.7%

22. Last year, the cost of Julio's dance lessons was $21.95 per week. If the price has increased by $8\frac{1}{3}\%$, what is the cost of the lessons this year? $23.78

23. In order to promote its new bagels, Bagel King plans to sell them initially at 25% less than the regular price of 88¢. What is the promotion price? 66¢

24. This year's assessment of the Mehtas' home is $189,000, an increase of $19,000 over last year's assessment. What percent increase does the new assessment represent? 11.2%

25. The value of Ari's car, bought last year, has depreciated by $1850. If it is now worth $8990, by what percent did its value decrease? 17.1%

26. This week at Record World, records by Girl Jill cost $1.10 less than usual. This is a 20% decrease. What is the current price? $4.40

27. At one service station the price of super unleaded gasoline is 20¢ per gal higher, or 26% higher than that of regular unleaded gasoline. What does super unleaded gasoline cost? 96.9¢

C 28. Pet World has reduced the price of angelfish by 30%. If they now cost $2.75 each, what did they cost before? $3.93

29. The number of students who signed up for a museum tour is 19% more than the number that went last year. If 88 plan to go this year, how many went last year? 74 students

30. Breathless Cosmetics now offers 24 shades of eye shadow, 20% more than last year. How many shades were offered last year? 20 shades

31. After the price of T-shirt dresses was reduced by 39%, they sold for $13.98. What was the earlier price? $22.92

ALGEBRA IN ENGINEERING

Drag force is a vehicle's resistance to moving through air. When designing automobiles, engineers try to reduce drag force because 60% of an automobile's power may be needed to overcome it. Decreasing the surface area of the front of an auto and recessing bumpers and door handles helps to reduce drag force.

1. Rank these vehicles from 1 (best) to 5 (worst) at overcoming drag force.
1(C); 2(B); 3(A); 4(D); 5(E)

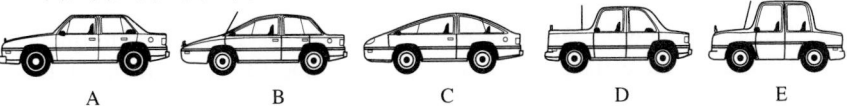

   A   B   C   D   E

2. A 19% reduction in drag force will result in a 4.25% increase in gas mileage. If the previous mileage was 36.5 mi/gal, find the new mileage after the drag force has been reduced. 38.1 mi/gal

3. Luggage on top of a car increased the drag force by 19%, and caused a 4.5% decrease in gas mileage. Without luggage, mileage was 28.0 mi/gal. What was the gas mileage with luggage? 26.7 mi/gal

4. With a 15 mi/h tail wind, the gas mileage from Pittsburgh to Harrisburg was 43.0 mi/gal. With a head wind of 25 mi/h, the mileage was reduced by 9%. What was the mileage with the head wind? 39.1 mi/gal

4.6 Problem Solving: Percents   **159**

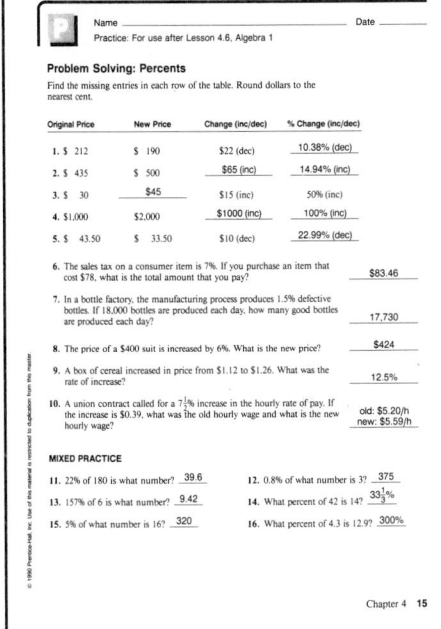

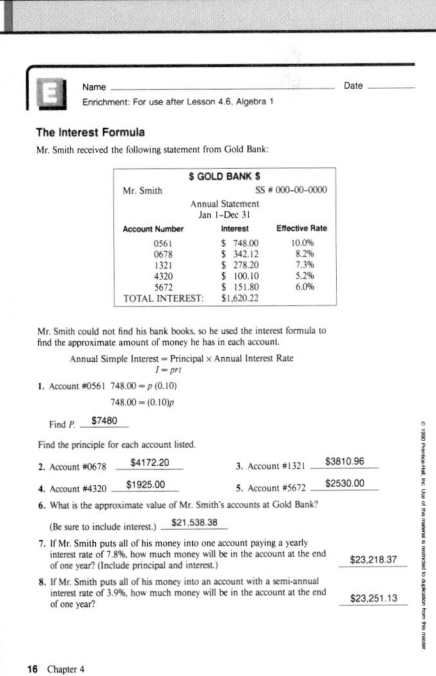

APPLICATION:
Messenger Service

Bicycles are used throughout the world as a means of transportation. In large cities, messengers use bicycles because they can get in and out of traffic quickly. The messenger earns a percent of the amount of money the customer pays for the delivery. The percent increases each year he or she works for the service.

The table below gives the rates for a typical messenger service.

MESSENGER SERVICE

Location	Zone 1	Zone 2	Zone 3	Zone 4	Zone 5
Cost of Service	$6.00	$12.00	$18.00	$24.00	$30.00
Messengers' Earnings					
1st year	$3.00	$6.00	$ 9.00	$12.00	$15.00
2nd year	3.30	6.60	9.90	13.20	16.50
3rd year	3.60	7.20	10.80	14.40	18.00

Look for a pattern to find a formula for earnings in the first year.

Each amount in the first year is $\frac{1}{2}$ or 50% of the cost of the service.

Let c = cost of the service   Then e_1 = 50% of c
e_1 = earnings the first year $e_1 = 0.5 \cdot c$

Solve.

1. Use guess and check to find a formula for the earnings in the second year. 55% of c $e_2 = 0.55(c)$

2. Use guess and check to find a formula for the earnings in the third year. 60% of c $e_3 = 0.60(c)$

3. The deliveries Jack made on Monday cost $228. This is his second year as a messenger. What were his earnings for the day? $125.40

4. The deliveries Ann makes on an average day cost $240. This is her third year as a messenger. How much does she earn in a 5-day week? $720.00

5. Sue is in her second year as a messenger. If she earned $90 in 1 day, what was the cost of the service to her customers for that day? $163.64

6. One week during Tom's third year as a messenger, he earned $132. What was the cost of the service to his customers for that week? $220.00

Problem Solving: Mixtures

4.7

Objective: To solve mixture problems involving percents

A type of problem that chemists and pharmacists often encounter is the need to change the concentration of solutions or other mixtures. In such problems, the amount of a particular ingredient in the solution or mixture is often expressed as a percent of the total.

Suppose a solution of salt in water has a salt concentration of 15%. Then in 100 g of this solution there are 15 g of salt (and 85 g of water). If you have 20 g of this solution, it contains 0.15(20) or 3 g of salt.

EXAMPLE 1   A 50 mL solution of acid in water contains 25% acid. How much water would you add in order to make a 10% acid solution?

Understand the Problem   50 mL of 25% acid solution is to be changed to a 10% acid solution. Water is to be added. The number of milliliters of pure acid does not change.

Plan Your Approach   Let x = number of milliliters of water to be added. Make a chart.

	Substance	Total No. mL	No. mL Pure Acid
Start with	25% acid solution	50	0.25(50)
Add	water	x	0
Finish with	10% acid solution	$x + 50$	0.10($x + 50$)

Since the number of milliliters of pure acid stays the same, the first and third entries of the last column are equal.

$$0.25(50) = 0.10(x + 50)$$

Complete the Work
$$0.25(50) = 0.10(x + 50)$$
$$100(0.25)(50) = 100(0.10)(x + 50) \quad \textit{Multiply each side by 100.}$$
$$25(50) = 10(x + 50)$$
$$1250 = 10x + 500$$
$$750 = 10x$$
$$75 = x$$

Materials/Manipulatives
Graduated cylinder
Gram weights
Salt
Teacher's Resource Book,
Teaching Aid 5,
Transparency 7

BACKGROUND

Many mathematical situations can be analyzed by using a chart. A chart can help to organize information and provide a better understanding of a problem.

- Organizing the given information by making a chart and understanding the chart entries so that they can be used correctly in devising an equation are keys to success in this lesson

Error Analysis Classification
1. *Misunderstanding*
   Failed to understand the underlying concept of the problem
   Failed to understand the significance of the column entries
2. *Misapplied Strategy*
   Failed to complete table correctly
   Wrote an incorrect equation
   Made errors in the solution process
   Made errors in checking

Critical Thinking
Causal Explanation Suppose you have a solution of salt in water. Determine two ways that the salt concentration of the solution can be increased. Students may reason that 1. More salt could be added to the solution, or 2. The solution could be boiled to reduce the amount of water it contains.

- You may wish to use a graduated cylinder, gram weights, and salt to demonstrate Chalkboard Example 2.
- Stress the importance of setting up and correctly labeling a chart when solving mixture problems. Use Teaching Aid 5, and Transparency 7, in the *Teacher's Resource Book,* to help set up charts involving mixture problems.

CHALKBOARD EXAMPLES

- **For Example 1**
  1. You have 40 g of a 50% solution of acid in water. How much water must you add to make a 10% acid solution?   160 g

- **For Example 2**
  2. How many grams of salt must be added to 30 g of a solution that is 20% salt to make a solution that is 25% salt?   2 g

LESSON FOLLOW-UP

Assignment Guide
See p. 134B for assignments.

Did You Know?
Have students discuss the efficiency of the Egyptian number system in comparison to the Arabic system.

Lesson Quiz
1. Alix has 15 L of a 24% acid solution. How much water should she add in order to dilute the solution so that it is 8% acid?   30 L
2. How many mL of acid must be added to 50 mL of a 10% acid solution in order to produce a 20% acid solution?   6.25 mL

Enrichment
If 2 L of a 15% acid solution is mixed with 3 L of a 25% acid solution, how much water must be added to make the solution 10% acid?   5.5 L

Interpret the Results   Check to see if 75 mL is a correct answer. Is the number of mL of pure acid, $0.25 \cdot 50$, equal to 10% of the total number of milliliters in the new solution, $0.10(75 \text{ mL} + 50 \text{ mL})$ or 125 mL?

$$12.5 \overset{?}{=} 0.10(125)$$
$$12.5 = 12.5 \; \text{✔} \qquad \textit{True}$$

So, 75 mL of water must be added.

EXAMPLE 2   To increase the sugar concentration of a solution from 15% to 40%, how many ounces of pure sugar must be added to 80 oz of the 15% solution?

Understand the Problem   An 80 oz solution which has a sugar concentration of 15% is to be changed to a solution with a 40% sugar concentration.

Plan Your Approach   Let x = number of ounces of pure sugar to be added. Make a chart.

	Substance	Total No. Oz	No. Oz Pure Sugar
Start with	15% sugar solution	80	0.15(80)
Add	100% pure sugar	x	1.00(x), or x
Finish with	40% sugar solution	$80 + x$	0.40(80 + x)

In the last column, the number of ounces of pure sugar in the 15% solution plus the number of ounces of pure sugar added equals the number of ounces of pure sugar in the 40% solution.

Complete the Work
$$0.15(80) + x = 0.40(80 + x)$$
$$100(0.15)(80) + 100x = 100(0.40)(80 + x) \qquad \textit{Multiply each}$$
$$15(80) + 100x = 40(80 + x) \qquad \textit{side by 100.}$$
$$1200 + 100x = 3200 + 40x$$
$$60x = 2000 \qquad \textit{Use the subtraction property.}$$
$$x = 33.\overline{3} \text{ or } 33\frac{1}{3}$$

Interpret the Results   So, $33\frac{1}{3}$ oz of pure sugar must be added. How would you check this answer?

CLASS EXERCISES

Copy and complete the table. Do not simplify.

Substance	Total Amount of Solution	Amount of Substance in the Solution
1. 25% acid solution	150 mL	0.25(__?__) mL 150
2. 35% alcohol solution	250 oz	__?__ oz 0.35(250)
3. pure acid	540 g	__?__ g 540
4. 15% salt solution	185 g	__?__ g 0.15(185)

162   Chapter 4 More Equations in One Variable

PRACTICE EXERCISES

A 1. Steven added 25 mL of water to 125 mL of a 20% salt solution in water. What is the salt concentration of the new solution? $16\frac{2}{3}\%$

2. Mary added 2 L of water to 8 L of a 48% nitric acid solution. What is the acid concentration of the new solution? 38.4%

3. Jorge added 15 g of sugar to 210 g of a 5% sugar solution in water. What is the percent of sugar in his new solution? $11.\overline{3}\%$

B 4. Rita added 1 qt of alcohol to 4 qt of a solution that is 20% alcohol in water. What is the percent of alcohol in her new solution? 36%

5. If you wish to increase the percent of acid in 50 mL of a 15% acid solution in water to 25% acid, how much pure acid must you add? 6.7 mL

6. How many ounces of alcohol should be added to 125 oz of a 45% solution of sugar in alcohol in order to produce a 30% sugar solution? 62.5 oz

C 7. In order to increase the concentration of 25 g of 5% salt solution in water to 15% salt, how much salt must be added? 2.9 g

8. How many gallons of milk that is $3\frac{1}{2}\%$ butterfat must be added to 80 gal of 1% butterfat milk to make milk that is 2% butterfat? 53.3 gal

---

DID YOU KNOW?

Ancient Egyptians developed a base-ten system that used special symbols for powers of ten.

Our Symbols	1	10	100	1000	10,000	100,000
Egyptian Symbol						

Our number 2345 can be written in expanded form as:

$$(2 \times 1000) + (3 \times 100) + (4 \times 10) + (5 \times 1)$$

In some Egyptian writings found on stone tablets, the order of their number symbols in comparison to ours was reversed. The Egyptians wrote their number for 2345 as:

‖‖‖	∩∩∩∩	999	££
five units	four tens	three hundred	two thousands

1. Use Egyptian symbols to write five large numbers.  Answers may vary.

2. Conduct research to find out how the Egyptians performed the operations of addition and multiplication. Could they solve equations? Explain.

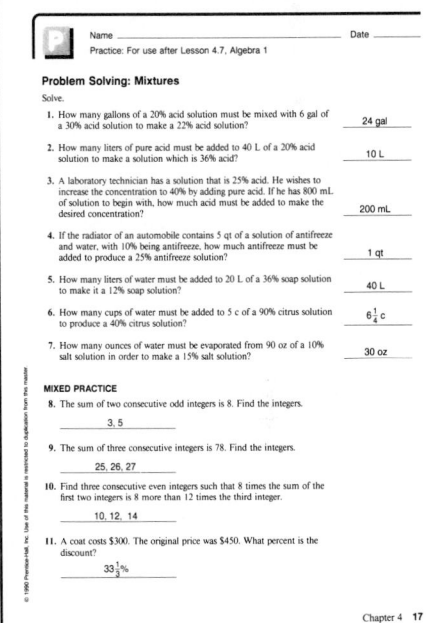

Problem Solving: Mixtures

Solve.

1. How many gallons of a 20% acid solution must be mixed with 6 gal of a 30% acid solution to make a 22% acid solution? — 24 gal

2. How many liters of pure acid must be added to 40 L of a 20% acid solution to make a solution which is 36% acid? — 10 L

3. A laboratory technician has a solution that is 25% acid. He wishes to increase the concentration to 40% by adding pure acid. If he has 800 mL of solution to begin with, how much acid must be added to make the desired concentration? — 200 mL

4. If the radiator of an automobile contains 5 qt of a solution of antifreeze and water, with 10% being antifreeze, how much antifreeze must be added to produce a 25% antifreeze solution? — 1 qt

5. How many liters of water must be added to 20 L of a 36% soap solution to make it a 12% soap solution? — 40 L

6. How many cups of water must be added to 5 c of a 90% citrus solution to produce a 40% citrus solution? — $6\frac{1}{4}$ c

7. How many ounces of water must be evaporated from 90 oz of a 10% salt solution in order to make a 15% salt solution? — 30 oz

MIXED PRACTICE

8. The sum of two consecutive odd integers is 8. Find the integers. — 3, 5

9. The sum of three consecutive integers is 78. Find the integers. — 25, 26, 27

10. Find three consecutive even integers such that 8 times the sum of the first two integers is 8 more than 12 times the third integer. — 10, 12, 14

11. A coat costs $300. The original price was $450. What percent is the discount? — $33\frac{1}{3}\%$

Chapter 4 **17**

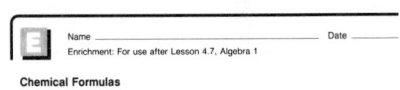

Chemical Formulas

A chemist can analyze substances to determine which elements it contains and how much of each element. She can use this information to determine the chemical formula for the substance.

Example To determine the formula for water, start with a sample of 100 grams. Suppose you find that it contains 11 g of hydrogen (H) and 89 g of oxygen (O). Divide each amount by the atomic weight* of the element. Divide 11 by 1 and 89 by 16. You get 11.0 and 5.56, the relative amounts of H and O. To calculate the ratio that compares the two elements, divide each relative amount by the smaller relative amount. $11 \div 5.56 = 1.98$, ≈ 2, and $5.56 \div 5.56 = 1$. The relative amount of water is H_2O; 2 parts hydrogen to 1 part oxygen.

1. Find the chemical formula for table salt. It is composed of sodium (Na) and chlorine (Cl).

	100-g Sample	Atomic Weight	Relative Amount	Ratio
Na	39.6 g	23	1.72	1
Cl	60.4 g	35	1.72	1

Chemical formula __NaCl__ Atomic weight of the compound __58__

2. Find the chemical formula for sulfuric acid. It is a compound of hydrogen (H), sulfur (S), and oxygen (O).

	100-g Sample	Atomic Weight	Relative Amount	Ratio
H	2 g	1	2	2
S	32.7 g	32	1	1
O	65.3 g	16	4	4

Chemical formula __H_2SO_4__ Atomic weight of the compound __49__

3. Find the chemical formula for calcium chloride, a compound of calcium (Ca) and chlorine (Cl).

	100-g Sample	Atomic Weight	Relative Amount	Ratio
Ca	36.4 g	40	0.91	1
Cl	63.6 g	35	1.82	2

Chemical formula __$CaCl_2$__ Atomic weight of the compound __75__

* The atomic weight of an element is the average weight of an atom of the element, based on $\frac{1}{12}$ the weight of the carbon-12 atom.

18 Chapter 4

BACKGROUND

In the Capsule Review, Exercises 1–8 review the properties used to solve equations. Point out that the Properties for equations will be used in this lesson to solve equations with more than one variable.

Critical Thinking

Classifying Point out that previous experiences in mathematics have explored equations that can be called "literal equations"; for example, $A = \pi r^2$ is such an equation, which gives the area of a circle. Give two more such equations that may be classified as "literal equations," and tell the purpose of each one. Students will probably reason by analogy that geometry formulas are literal equations and will give other examples.

4.8

Literal Equations

Objective: To solve literal equations

A **literal equation** is one in which the constants or the coefficients of a variable are expressed by letters. Formulas are literal equations.

For the spring concert:
  a = number of adult tickets sold
  s = number of student tickets sold

The total revenue from ticket sales may be represented by:

$$t = 5a + 2s$$

The formula $t = 5a + 2s$ is a *literal equation*. You say that *t is solved in terms of a and s* because if you substitute values for a and s, the value of t can be found. The equation properties can be used to solve literal equations.

Capsule Review

EXAMPLE	$2r - 7 = 3$	
	$2r - 7 + 7 = 3 + 7$	*Addition property for equations*
	$2r = 3 + 7$	

Name the equation property used to derive the second equation from the first.

1. $3 + y = 8$
$y = 8 - 3$
Subtr. Prop.

2. $4a = 8 - 12$
$a = 2 - 3$
Division Prop.

3. $s - 9 = 6$
$s = 15$
Addit. Prop.

4. $4 = w - 3$
$4 + 3 = w$
Addit. Prop.

5. $3p = 16$
$p = \dfrac{16}{3}$
Division Prop.

6. $\dfrac{q}{4} = 17$
$q = 68$
Mult. Prop.

7. $3r + 11 = 6$
$3r = -5$
Subtr. Prop.

8. $5y + 25 = 7$
$5y = 7 - 25$
Subtr. Prop.

To solve a literal equation for one variable, the variable must be isolated on one side of the equation. In Example 1, the subtraction and multiplication properties are used.

EXAMPLE 1 **Solve each equation for the underlined variable in terms of the other variable(s).**

a. $\underline{x} + 11 = y$
$x + 11 - 11 = y - 11$
$x = y - 11$

b. $\dfrac{K}{m} = t$
$m \cdot \dfrac{K}{m} = m \cdot t$
$K = mt$

164 Chapter 4 More Equations in One Variable

To solve some literal equations for a given variable, more than one of the properties may be needed.

EXAMPLE 2   Solve the equation $2x + 4a = 10$ for x.

$$2x + 4a = 10$$
$$2x + 4a - 4a = 10 - 4a \qquad \textit{Subtract 4a from each side.}$$
$$2x = 10 - 4a$$
$$\frac{2x}{2} = \frac{10 - 4a}{2} \qquad \textit{Divide each side by 2.}$$
$$x = \frac{10}{2} - \frac{4a}{2}$$
$$x = 5 - 2a$$

So, in terms of a, $x = 5 - 2a$.

Solving a literal equation may require combining like terms.

EXAMPLE 3   Solve the equation $ay - b = 3d + 7b$ for y, assuming a is not zero.

$$ay - b = 3d + 7b$$
$$ay - b + b = 3d + 7b + b \qquad \textit{Add b to each side.}$$
$$ay = 3d + 8b \qquad \textit{Combine like terms: } 7b + b = 8b$$
$$y = \frac{3d + 8b}{a} \qquad \textit{Divide each side by a.}$$

Do you see why you needed to know that a is not zero?

In still other literal equations, it may be necessary to remove parentheses.

EXAMPLE 4   Solve $G = 3(t - s)$ for s. Then find the value of s when $G = 12$ and $t = -1$.

$$G = 3(t - s)$$
$$G = 3t - 3s \qquad \textit{Distribute 3 on the right side.}$$
$$G - 3t = -3s \qquad \textit{Subtract 3t from each side.}$$
$$\frac{G - 3t}{-3} = s \qquad \textit{Divide each side by } -3.$$
$$s = \frac{G - 3t}{-3}$$
$$s = \frac{12 - 3(-1)}{-3} \qquad \textit{Replace G with 12 and t with } -1.$$
$$s = \frac{12 + 3}{-3} = \frac{15}{-3} = -5$$

TEACHING SUGGESTIONS

- It may be helpful for Example 2 to compare solving $2x + 4 = 10$ and $2x + 4a = 10$, both for x, showing that the steps are almost analogous.
- In solving equations such as Example 4, many students are unaware that expressions such as 1. $\frac{G - 3t}{-3}$, 2. $\frac{3t - G}{3}$ and 3. $t - \frac{G}{3}$ are all equivalent and all perfectly satisfactory. Students should be made aware that 2. and 3. will be the forms most often encountered.

CHALKBOARD EXAMPLES

- **For Example 1**

  Solve each equation for the underlined variable.
    1. $\underline{a} - 19 = b \quad a = b + 19$
    2. $t = \underline{s} + p \quad s = t - p$

- **For Example 2**

    3. $pq\underline{m} = n \quad p = \frac{n}{qm}$
    4. $\frac{4}{3}\underline{d} = -e \quad d = -\frac{3}{4}e$

- **For Example 3**

    5. $3\underline{x} - 6b = 12 \quad x = 2b + 4$
    6. $4d - 2\underline{y} = 9 \quad y = \frac{4d - 9}{2}$, or
       $y = 2d - \frac{9}{2}$

- **For Example 4**

    7. $c\underline{x} + 3t = 2s - t$
       $x = \frac{2s - 4t}{c}$

LESSON FOLLOW-UP

Discussion

Consider these two equations: (1) $y = 3x$ and (2) $y = mx$ in which m and x can be any real number. Classify one of these equations as belonging to the class or group defined by the other.   1. belongs to the class defined by 2.; since 3 is just one of the values m may have, 2. is more general.

Assignment Guide

See p. 134B for assignments.

Algebra in Aviation

Point out while discussing this feature that literal equations are used in many disciplines of science and technology.

Lesson Quiz

Solve each literal equation for the underlined variable.
1. $r = \underline{t} + 4$ $t = r - 4$
2. $\dfrac{3\underline{a}}{b} = c$ $a = \dfrac{bc}{3}$
3. $18 = 3\underline{x} - 6a$ $x = 6 + 2a$
4. $c\underline{w} + b = -4b + 3d$

$w = \dfrac{3d - 5b}{c}$

5. Solve $P = 2(l + w)$ for w. Then find the value of w when $P = 64$ and $l = 10$. $\dfrac{P - 2l}{2} = w; w = 22$

CLASS EXERCISES

Solve each literal equation for the variable indicated.

1. $x - 7 = y$, for x
$x = y + 7$

2. $pq = -12$, for q $q = -\dfrac{12}{p}$

3. $\dfrac{3}{4}r = st$, for r $r = \dfrac{4}{3}st$

4. $l = 2m + n$, for m
$m = \dfrac{l - n}{2}$

5. $3a = 2b + 2c$, for b
$b = \dfrac{3}{2}a - c$

6. $3d + 14 = 7e - 4d$, for d $d = e - 2$

PRACTICE EXERCISES

Solve each literal equation for the underlined variable. Assume that all other literal coefficients are not zero.

A

1. $\underline{x} + 10 = y$ $x = y - 10$
2. $\underline{a} + 13 = b$ $a = b - 13$
3. $\underline{c} - 3 = d$ $c = d + 3$

4. $y + \underline{z} = -8$ $z = -8 - y$
5. $2y = \underline{d}a$ $d = \dfrac{2y}{a}$
6. $a\underline{x} = c$ $x = \dfrac{c}{a}$

7. $\dfrac{3}{4}\underline{n} = 2k$ $n = \dfrac{8}{3}k$
8. $\dfrac{3}{2}\underline{l} = -4m$ $l = -\dfrac{8}{3}m$
9. $j = \dfrac{1}{2}kl\underline{m}$ $m = \dfrac{2j}{kl}$

10. $t = \dfrac{3}{4}\underline{p}sr$ $p = \dfrac{4t}{3sr}$
11. $3x + 4\underline{y} = 12$ $y = \dfrac{12 - 3x}{4}$
12. $\underline{j} + 3m = -2$
$j = -2 - 3m$

13. $\underline{y} - 4t = 0$ $y = 4t$
14. $6 = \underline{z} - 7p$ $z = 6 + 7p$
15. $-7 = 3\underline{a} + 11b$
$a = \dfrac{-11b - 7}{3}$

16. $5\underline{p} - b = r$ $p = \dfrac{r + b}{5}$
17. $h = 2(l - 2\underline{m})$ $m = \dfrac{2l - h}{2}$
18. $-3(2a - \underline{b}) = c$
$b = \dfrac{6a + c}{3}$

Solve each literal equation for the underlined variable. Then find the value of the variable for the given values of the other variables.

19. $A = l\underline{w}$ Find w if $A = 63$, $l = 9$. $w = \dfrac{A}{l}$; 7

20. $V = lw\underline{h}$ Find h if $V = 64$, $l = 10$, and $w = 2$. $h = \dfrac{V}{lw}$; 3.2

21. $p = 2a + \underline{b}$ Find b if $p = 74$ and $a = 27$. $b = p - 2a$; 20

22. $P = 2\underline{l} + 2w$ Find l if $P = 30$ and $w = 6$. $l = \dfrac{P - 2w}{2}$; 9

23. $V = \underline{b}h$ Find b if $V = 260$ and $h = \dfrac{3}{4}$. $b = \dfrac{V}{h}$; $346\dfrac{2}{3}$

24. $C = 2\pi\underline{r}$ Find r if $C = 81.64$ ($\pi \approx 3.14$). $r = \dfrac{C}{2\pi}$; 13

Solve each literal equation for the underlined variable. Assume that all literal coefficients are not zero.

B

25. $3x - 4\underline{y} = 10x + 14z$ $y = \dfrac{-7x - 14z}{4}$
26. $5a + 9 = 2a - 3\underline{b}$ $b = -a - 3$

27. $0.02q + 2.1\underline{r} = 3.16 - 0.2r$ $r = \dfrac{158 - q}{115}$
28. $3.5s - 0.12\underline{t} = 4.5 - 5.12t$ $t = \dfrac{9 - 7s}{10}$

29. $-3(4t - \underline{w}) = 4t$ $w = \dfrac{16}{3}t$
30. $-a = (\underline{j} - 3a)7$ $j = \dfrac{20a}{7}$

31. $\dfrac{1}{3}(v - 2\underline{q}) = 2v + 3$ $q = \dfrac{-5v - 9}{2}$
32. $\dfrac{1}{2}(3\underline{p} - t) = t - 8$ $p = \dfrac{3t - 16}{3}$

33. $\frac{3}{4}(l - \underline{h}) = l - 4j$ $h = \frac{16j - l}{3}$ **34.** $6 - 5m = \frac{3}{2}(\underline{n} + 2)$ $n = \frac{6 - 10m}{3}$

35. $F = \frac{9}{5}\underline{C} + 32$ if $F = -4$ $C = \frac{5F - 160}{9}; \frac{}{-20}$ **36.** $G = 3(t - \underline{s})$ if $G = 18$ and $t = 8$

                                                                          $s = \frac{3t - G}{3}; 2$

37. $A = p + pr\underline{t}$ if $p = 800$, $A = 1000$, and $r = 0.05$ $t = \frac{A - p}{pr}; 5$

38. $V = \pi r^2 \underline{h}$ if $V = 6458.98$ and $r = 11$ $(\pi = 3.14)$ $h = \frac{V}{\pi r^2}; 17$

C   **39.** $L = a + (\underline{n} - 1)d$ **40.** $A = \frac{1}{2}h(a + \underline{b})$ **41.** $S = \frac{1}{2}n(a + \underline{l})$

   $n = \frac{L - a + d}{d}$ $b = \frac{2A - ha}{h}$ $l = \frac{2s - na}{n}$

42. $C = \frac{5}{9}(\underline{F} - 32)$ **43.** $\frac{a + 2b}{3\underline{c}} = 4b$ $c = \frac{a + 2b}{12b}$ **44.** $\frac{\underline{x}}{n} - y = 5 - \frac{x}{2}$

   $F = \frac{9C + 160}{5}$ $x = \frac{2y + 10}{3}$

Applications

Write a literal equation for each and solve for the desired variable. Then find the value of this variable for the given values of the other variables.

45. Sports In a Walk-a-thon, Terry walked 18 km in $3\frac{1}{2}$ h. What was her average speed? $d = rt; r = \frac{d}{t}; 5.14$ km/h

46. Geometry The length of a rectangular room is 14 ft. If the perimeter is 42 ft, how wide is the room? $P = 2l + 2w; w = \frac{P - 2l}{2}; 7$ ft

ALGEBRA IN AVIATION

In the formula $R = \frac{s^2}{A}$, R is the aspect ratio of a hang glider and indicates its ability to glide and soar. The area of the wing is A and the length of the wingspan is s.

If a hang glider has a wing area of 36 ft² and a wingspan of 10 ft, its aspect ratio is:

$$R = \frac{s^2}{A}$$

$$R = \frac{(10)^2}{36} = \frac{100}{36} = 2.78$$

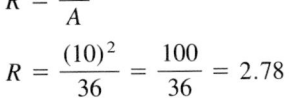

1. Solve the aspect ratio formula for A. $A = \frac{s^2}{R}$

Use the formula $R = \frac{s^2}{A}$ **to find the values of the missing variables.**

2. $R = 3$, $s = 9$ ft, $A = $ ___?___ 27 ft²   **3.** $s = 12.2$ ft, $A = 30.5$ ft², $R = $ ___?___

                                                        4.88

4. $R = 4.50$, $A = 32$ ft², $s = $ ___?___   *Hint:* $s^2 = s \cdot s$ 12 ft

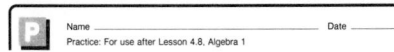

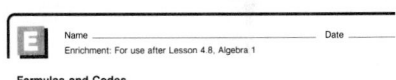

BACKGROUND

- Many mathematical situations can be analyzed by using a drawing or a table. These mathematical models help to organize information and can make the essential relationships or a problem clear. Many students are helped by using visual aids such as drawings or tables.
- To determine a student's progress, analyze errors in the student's work and then classify specific errors.

Critical Thinking

Observation What information can be obtained from the drawing below?

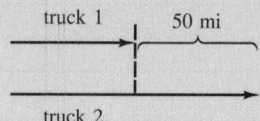

Truck 2 has traveled 50 mi farther than Truck 1.

Error Analysis Classification

1. *Misunderstanding*
   Did not understand the conditions of the problem
2. *Misapplied Strategy*
   Made an incorrect drawing. Did not organize the information given in the problem correctly in a table

---

4.9 Problem Solving Strategy: Make a Drawing or a Table

A very effective strategy to use in solving some problems is to make a simple drawing or sketch to illustrate the conditions of the problem. The use of a table can serve the same purpose, and drawings and tables are often used together.

Drawings are used to help solve problems involving motion. For example, if two cars leave a city traveling along the same road and travel the same distance, a drawing can show this situation.

The distance each car travels is the same and can be represented by d.

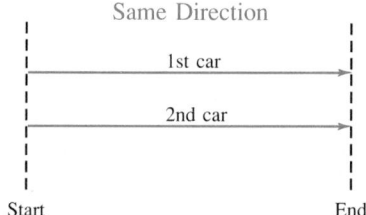

If two hikers leave from the same camp and walk in opposite directions, the drawing would look like this.

The distances may or may not be equal.

Opposite Directions

West   Camp   East

A car making a round trip to the beach can be shown in this way.

Round Trip

Since this is a round trip, the distances are equal.

Going
Home

Returning   Beach

A table can also be used in solving motion problems. The formula for uniform motion is $d = rt$, where d is distance, r is rate or speed, and t is time.

XAMPLE Two buses leave from the same station at different times. Bus 2 leaves 2 h later than Bus 1. Bus 1 is traveling at 40 mi/h and Bus 2 is traveling at 60 mi/h. How long will it take Bus 2 to overtake Bus 1?

Understand the Problem

What are the given facts?
What are you asked to find?

You already know a great deal about the problem from the discussion above. You are asked to find how long it will take for Bus 2 to overtake Bus 1.

Plan Your Approach

Choose a strategy.

Use the first drawing on the previous page and a table.

Bus 1 travels $40t$ mi
Bus 2 travels $60(t - 2)$ mi

	Rate	× Time	= Distance
Bus 1	40	t	$40t$
Bus 2	60	$t - 2$	$60(t - 2)$

Since the distances the buses travel are equal, $40t = 60(t - 2)$.

Complete the Work

Solve the equation.
$$40t = 60(t - 2)$$
$$40t = 60t - 120$$
$$0 = 20t - 120$$
$$120 = 20t$$
$$6 = t \quad \text{Bus 1's time: } t = 6 \text{ h, Bus 2's time: } t - 2 = 6 - 2, \text{ or 4 h}$$

Interpret the Results

Conclusion: Bus 2 overtakes Bus 1 in 4 h.

Bus 1 travels 6 h at 40 mi/h for 240 mi.
Bus 2 travels 4 h at 60 mi/h for 240 mi.

CLASS EXERCISES

1. Make a drawing to show that one car has traveled twice as far as another. Answers may vary. See below.
2. Make a drawing to show that two planes have traveled the same distance in opposite directions. Answers may vary. See below.

3. Make a drawing to show that a train has traveled from Boston to New York City and back to Boston again. Answers may vary. See below.

4. If t represents the number of hours a car has traveled, how would you represent the time of a car that has traveled 1 h longer? $t + 1$

5. If t represents the number of hours an airplane has flown, how would you represent the time of a plane that has flown $\frac{1}{2}$ h less? $t - \frac{1}{2}$

6. If $d = 45t$ and $d = 55(t + 1)$ and the distances are equal, write an equation involving t only. $45t = 55(t + 1)$

4.9 Problem Solving Strategy: Make a Drawing or a Table **169**

Additional Answers

1.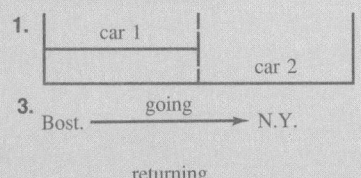

2.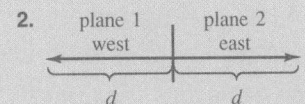

3.
Bost. —going→ N.Y.

Bost. ←returning— N.Y.

TEACHING SUGGESTIONS

- Stress that a drawing must reflect the conditions of a problem accurately and must be labeled correctly if it is to be useful in solving the problem. You may wish to show several examples on the overhead projector.
- Make sure students understand that the distance Bus 1 and Bus 2 both travel when Bus 2 overtakes Bus 1 is the same, and is therefore denoted by the same variable, namely d.

CHALKBOARD EXAMPLES

- **For the Example**
  Two trucks leave the same warehouse on a Friday. One truck leaves at 9 A.M. and travels 50 miles per hour. The second truck leaves at 10:30 A.M. and travels at 65 miles per hour along the same route. How long will it take the second truck to pass the first truck?
  5 h

Common Errors

- Students have difficulty expressing the time variables correctly in distance problems such as those given in the lesson. Suggest that students check that all of their time variables are in the same unit. For example, if one car travels for $1\frac{1}{2}$ h and another car travels for 45 min, the students should convert both times to the same units of measure.
- Students make errors applying the basic distance formula to situations relating the motion of two vehicles. Suggest that students carefully draw a diagram of the problem and observe whether they are looking for the total distance in opposite directions or equal distance in the same direction.
- See *Teacher's Resource Book* for additional remediation.

169

Mixed Problem Solving Review
The following skills and concepts are reviewed:

Translation of English sentences into algebraic equations. (Ex. 1, 2)
Operations with real numbers (Ex. 3, 4)

Project
The project will provide students with ample opportunity for constructing tables and drawings and will reinforce the skills learned in the lesson. You may wish to have students decide which mathematical model best suits each individual problem.

Lesson Quiz

1. Make a drawing to show that two cars have traveled in the same direction, but one car has traveled 25 mi. further than the other car.

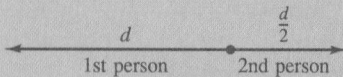

2. Make a drawing to show that two people have walked in opposite directions and one person has walked one-half the distance of the other person.

3. If d represents the distance a car has traveled, represent a car that has traveled 15 mi. less. $d - 15$
4. If t represents the time a jet plane has traveled, present a plane that has traveled twice as long. $2t$
5. Solve the equation $30t = 60$ $(t - 2)$ $t = 4$

PRACTICE EXERCISES

Use the table to write an equation. In each case, the distances are equal.

A 1.

	Rate	× Time	= Distance
Car 1	45	t	$45t$
Car 2	55	$t - 1$	$55(t - 1)$

$45t = 55(t - 1)$

2.

	Rate	× Time	= Distance
Train 1	65	$t + 1$	$65(t + 1)$
Train 2	70	t	$70t$

$65(t + 1) = 70t$

3.

	Rate	× Time	= Distance
Plane 1	550	$t + 2$	$550(t + 2)$
Plane 2	625	t	$625t$

$550(t + 2) = 625(t)$

Complete each table by writing an algebraic expression for each distance.

4.

	Rate	× Time	= Distance
1st Car	40	$t - 1$	?
2nd Car	30	t	?

$d = 40(t - 1)$
$d = 30(t)$

5.

	Rate	× Time	= Distance
Truck 1	$r + 20$	3	?
Truck 2	r	4	?

$d = 3(r + 20)$
$d = 4r$

6.

	Rate	× Time	= Distance
Going	20	t	?
Returning	35	$t - \frac{1}{2}$	?

$d = 20(t)$
$d = 35\left(t - \frac{1}{2}\right)$

Solve each equation.

7. $45t = 55(t - 1)$ $5\frac{1}{2}$ **8.** $65(t + 1) = 70t$ 13 **9.** $550(t + 2) = 625t$ $14\frac{2}{3}$

10. $4(r - 10) = 3r$ 40 **11.** $3(r + 30) = 4r$ 90 **12.** $20x = 35\left(x - \frac{1}{2}\right)$ $1\frac{1}{2}$

Organize the information in a table.   See below.

B 13. Two cars leave the same city. The first car is traveling at 40 mi/h. One hour later the second car leaves, traveling at 55 mi/h along the same road. In how many hours will the second car overtake the first car?

Additional Answers

13.

	rate	× time	= distance
car 1	40	$t + 1$	$40(t + 1)$
car 2	55	t	$55t$

14. Two hikers start walking in opposite directions from a camp at the same time. The average rate of the northbound hiker is 3 mi/h faster than the rate of the southbound hiker. If they are 22 mi apart after 2 h, what is the rate of each hiker? See below.

15. Gail and Bill drove to a beach at an average speed of 50 mi/h. They returned home over the same road at an average speed of 55/mi/h. The trip home took 30 min less time. How far is the beach from their home? See below.

16. Write three equations, using your tables from Exercises 13, 14, and 15. $40(t + 1) = 55t$; $2(r + 3) + 2r = 22$; $50\left(t + \frac{1}{2}\right) = 55t$

17. Solve the three equations you wrote in Exercise 16. $2\frac{2}{3}$ h; hiker 1: 7 mi/h, hiker 2: 4 mi/h; 275 mi

Solve the problem.

18. Two trains leave a city traveling at rates of 55 mi/h and 65 mi/h. The faster train leaves 30 min after the slower train. How long will it take for the faster train to pass the slower train? $2\frac{3}{4}$ h

Mixed Problem Solving Review

Write an equation for each sentence.

1. The product of a number squared and 4 is 64. $(x^2)(4) = 64$

2. A number less 5 is twice 6. $x - 5 = 2(6)$

Solve each problem.

3. Five times a number, decreased by 1, is -21. Find the number. -4

4. Ted bought a pair of sneakers at 25% off the price of $60. The sales tax was 5%. How much did he pay for the sneakers? $47.25

PROJECT

Working with a friend, review all the problem solving lessons in Chapters 1–4 and make a list of at least 10 problems that could have been solved by using a drawing, a table, or both. For example, on page 62, Exercise 33 could be solved using a table as follows:

Item	Quantity	Price	Total
Flour	3	$0.99	$2.97
Cereal	3	2.19	6.57
Juice	3	1.31	3.93

Answers may vary.

Additional Answers

14.

rate × time = distance

hiker 1	$r + 3$	2	$2(r + 3)$
hiker 2	r	2	$2r$

15.

rate × time = distance

going	50	$t + \frac{1}{2}$	$50\left(t + \frac{1}{2}\right)$
returning	55	t	$55t$

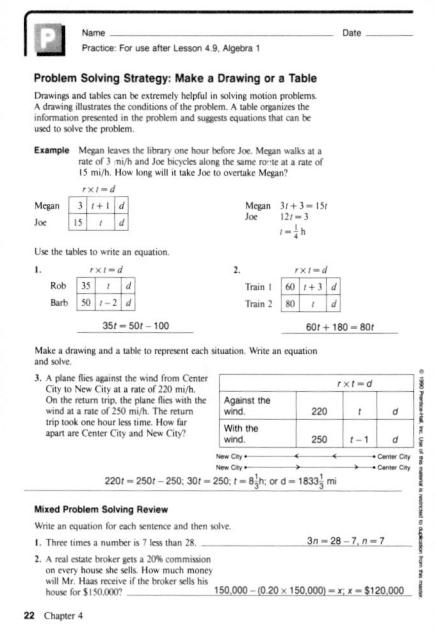
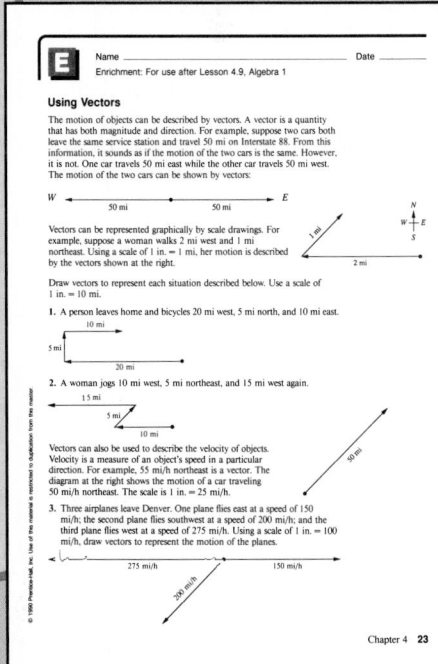

LESSON PLAN

Vocabulary
Uniform motion

Materials/Manipulatives
Teacher's Resource Book,
Transparency 4

BACKGROUND

A student's ability to organize information given in a problem, so that it can be used to solve the problem, is a key to success in this lesson. To determine a student's progress, analyze and classify specific errors in the student's work.

Error Analysis Classification
1. *Misunderstanding*
   Failed to understand the underlying concept of the problem
2. *Misapplied Strategy*
   Ignored some relevant information in the problem
   Wrote an incorrect equation
   Made error(s) in the solution process
   Stopped short in the process so that the answer given for the problem was incomplete

---

4.10 Problem Solving: Uniform Motion

Objective: To solve problems that involve uniform motion

An object that moves at a constant speed, or rate, is said to be in **uniform motion.** The formula $d = rt$ expresses the relationships among the distance d, the rate r, and the time t of a particular uniform motion.

Uniform motion problems may involve objects that move in the same direction, opposite directions, or round trips.

EXAMPLE 1 A car leaves a city traveling at a rate of 45 mi/h. One hour later, a second car leaves from the same place, along the same road at 54 mi/h. In how many hours will the second car overtake the first car?

Understand the Problem The two cars are traveling in the same direction. The first car, moving at 45 mi/h, travels 1 hour longer than the second car moving at 54 mi/h. Each car travels the same distance. You are asked to find the time of the second car.

Plan Your Approach Let t = the time (h) of the second car. Draw a sketch and organize the information in a table. Fill in rate and time for each car. Multiply the expressions for rate and time to obtain an algebraic expression for the distance traveled by each car.

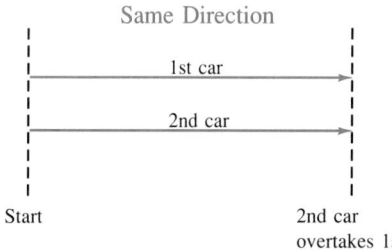

Same Direction

	Rate	× Time	= Distance
1st car	45	$t + 1$	$45(t + 1)$
2nd car	54	t	$54t$

Since each car travels the same distance,

$$45(t + 1) = 54t$$

Complete the Work

$$45(t + 1) = 54t$$
$$45t + 45 = 54t \qquad \textit{Multiply by 45.}$$
$$45 = 9t$$
$$5 = t$$

| | **Interpret the Results** | In 5 h, the second car travels 54 · 5, or 270 mi. In (5 + 1) h, the first car travels 45 · 6, or 270 mi. So, the second car overtakes the first in 5 h. |

EXAMPLE 2 Two hikers walking in opposite directions start from camp at the same time. The average rate of the westbound hiker is 2 km/h more than the rate of the eastbound hiker. If they are 15 km apart after 1.5 h, what is the rate of each hiker?

| | **Understand the Problem** | Let r = the rate (km/h) of the eastbound hiker. |

| | **Plan Your Approach** | Draw a sketch and make a table. The total of the two hiker's distances is 15 km. |

Opposite Directions

15 km apart after 1.5 h

West   Camp   East

	Rate	× Time =	Distance
Westbound hiker	$r + 2$	1.5	$1.5(r + 2)$
Eastbound hiker	r	1.5	$1.5r$

Since the total distance is 15 km, $1.5(r + 2) + 1.5r = 15$.

	Complete the Work	$1.5(r + 2) + 1.5r = 15$	
		$15(r + 2) + 15r = 150$	*Multiply each side by 10.*
		$15r + 30 + 15r = 150$	
		$30r + 30 = 150$	*Combine like terms.*
		$30r = 120$	
		$r = 4$	
		$r + 2 = 6$	

| | **Interpret the Results** | In 1.5 h the eastbound hiker walks 1.5(4), or 6 km. In 1.5 h the westbound hiker walks 1.5(6), or 9 km. 6 km + 9 km = 15 km.

So, the eastbound hiker walks at 4 km/h and the westbound hiker at 6 km/h. |

In Example 2, why were the two distances added to get the equation?

TEACHING SUGGESTIONS

- Review the distance formula before illustrating Example 1.
- Emphasize the importance of writing the correct unit of measure in solutions.
- Discuss why students should draw a sketch and make a table. A table helps one identify the unknown quantities, and a sketch helps to show the direction of the motion.
- Some students may find it helpful to write an informal word equation. In Example 1, students could write: First car's distance = Second car's distance, $45(t + 1) = 54t$, and then proceed to solve for t.

Critical Thinking

Comparing-Contrasting Discuss an alternate way of solving Example 2 by assigning the variable to the distance. Solve the problem using this method and discuss the merits of each approach.

	d	÷ t =	r
westbound	d	1.5	$\dfrac{d}{1.5}$
eastbound	$15 - d$	1.5	$\dfrac{15 - d}{1.5}$

$\dfrac{d}{1.5} = \dfrac{15 - d}{1.5} + 2$, so $d = 9$

Then the rate of the westbound hiker is $\dfrac{9}{1.5}$ or 6 km/h. The rate of the eastbound hiker is $\dfrac{15 - d}{1.5}$ or 4 km/h.

• For Example 1

1. Elois started out traveling at 60 km/h. Two hours later, Lisa left from the same point. She drove along the same road at 80 km/h. How many hours does Lisa have to drive to catch up to Elois? 6 h

2. Starting one hour later, Jeremy sets out riding his bicycle at 28 km/h to overtake his friend Greg, who is averaging 22 km/h. How long will it take Jeremy? $3\frac{2}{3}$ h

• For Example 2

3. Two planes, traveling in opposite directions leave an airport at the same time. If their average speeds are 550 mi/h and 600 mi/h respectively, in how many hours will they be 2875 mi apart? $2\frac{1}{2}$ h

4. Two cars on a highway passed one another going in opposite directions at 10:30 A.M. The southbound car was traveling 10 mi/h faster than the northbound car. At 1:00 P.M., they were 225 mi apart. At what speed was each car traveling? 50 mi/h; 40 mi/h

• For Example 3

5. Andre drove to visit his parents at an average speed of 75 km/h. He returned home in heavy traffic, along the same route at an average speed of 50 km/h. It took 45 min longer to return home than it did to get to his parents' house. How long did it take him to get home? $2\frac{1}{4}$ h

---

EXAMPLE 3 A family drives to the beach at an average speed of 45 mi/h and returns home on the same road at an average speed of 54 mi/h. If the trip home takes 20 min less than the trip to the beach, how far is the beach from the family's home? (*Hint:* First find the time for each part of the trip.)

Understand the Problem Let x = the time (h) of the trip to the beach. The return trip takes 20 min less time. However, the rates 45 and 54 are miles per hour, so you must changes 20 min to $\frac{1}{3}$ h.

Plan Your Approach Draw a sketch and make a table.

Round Trip

	Rate	× Time	= Distance
Going	45	x	$45x$
Returning	54	$x - \frac{1}{3}$	$54\left(x - \frac{1}{3}\right)$

Since this is a round trip, the distances are equal.

$$54\left(x - \frac{1}{3}\right) = 45x$$

Complete the Work

$$54x - 18 = 45x$$
$$9x = 18$$
$$x = 2 \qquad \textit{Time to the beach is 2 h.}$$

Interpret the Results If it takes 2 h to travel to the beach, the distance is 2 · 45, or 90 mi. This can be checked by finding the distance home from the beach, which must be the same.

The return trip time was $\left(2 - \frac{1}{3}\right)$ h which is $1\frac{2}{3}$, or $\frac{5}{3}$ h.

$$54 \cdot \frac{5}{3} = 90$$

So, the distance from the family's home to the beach is 90 mi.

CLASS EXERCISES

For each problem, describe the motion as *same direction; opposite direction;* or *round trip.* **Then draw a sketch, make a chart and write an equation for the problem.**

1. The Smiths left for vacation traveling south at an average rate of 50 km/h. Three hours after the Smiths depart, the Duprees set out to overtake them. If the Duprees travel at a rate of 70 km/h, how long will it take them to overtake the Smiths? Let t = time (h) Duprees travel. See below.

Additional Answers

1.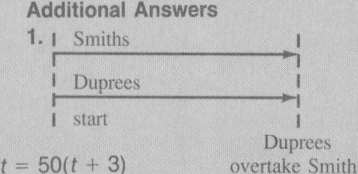

$70t = 50(t + 3)$

Duprees overtake Smiths

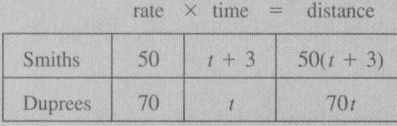

	rate	× time	= distance
Smiths	50	$t + 3$	$50(t + 3)$
Duprees	70	t	$70t$

2. Two planes leave Newark Airport at the same time. The rate of speed of the northbound plane is 100 mi/h faster than that of the southbound plane. At the end of 5 h, the planes are 2000 mi apart. Find the rate of each. Let r = rate (mi/h) of northbound plane. See side column.

3. Andre traveled from his home to the office at an average rate of 25 mi/h. By traveling 5 mi/h faster, he took 30 min less to return home. How far is his office from home? Let t = time (h) going to office. See side column.

4. Two trains leave Union Station at noon. One train travels north 5 mi/h faster than the train traveling south. After $3\frac{1}{2}$ h the two trains are 399 mi apart. Find how far the northbound train is from the station. Let r = rate (mi/h) of the southbound train. See side column.

PRACTICE EXERCISES

Solve each problem.

A 1. A ship leaves a dock moving at 24 mi/h. Three hours later, a second ship sets out from the same dock at 32 mi/h. How long will it take for the second ship to overtake the first? 9 h

2. Starting one hour later, Jonathan sets out walking at 8 km/h to overtake his little sister who averages 5 km/h. How long will it take Jonathan? $1\frac{2}{3}$ h

3. Robinsport and Titusville are 324 mi apart on a railroad line. Trains leave each of these depots at the same time headed for the other depot. One travels at 43 mi/h, the other at 38 mi/h. How long will it take for the two trains to pass one another? 4 h

4. Two trains leave from a station at the same time. They travel in opposite directions, one at 62 km/h, the other at 48 km/h. How long will it take before they are 550 km apart? 5 h

5. Two cyclists simultaneously start in opposite directions down a straight road, one at 22 km/h and the other at 28 km/h. How long will they have ridden by the time they are 175 km apart? $3\frac{1}{2}$ h

6. Two planes leave simultaneously from an airport, one flying east and the other west. They are 870 mi apart after $\frac{3}{4}$ h. If the eastbound plane averages 120 mi/h more than the westbound plane, at what rate is each plane flying? westbound 520 mi/h; eastbound 640 mi/h

7. At the same time, two buses leave a depot and travel in opposite directions on a straight road. The first bus averages 5 mi/h more than the second. If they are 142.5 mi apart after $1\frac{1}{2}$ h, how fast is each bus going? 1st bus 50 mi/h; 2nd bus 45 mi/h

4.10 Problem Solving: Uniform Motion **175**

LESSON FOLLOW-UP

Assignment Guide
- See p. 134B for assignments.
- In Class Exercise 3, you may wish to point out that time is given in minutes but the rates are in terms of mi/h. Caution students to watch for this in other exercises.

Test Yourself
See *Teacher's Resource Book*, Tests, pp. 35–36.

Additional Answers

2.

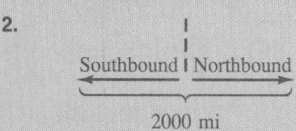

Southbound | Northbound
2000 mi

	rate	× time	= distance
North bound	r	5	$5r$
South bound	$r - 100$	5	$5(r - 100)$

$5(r - 100) + 5r = 2000$

3.

going
home ——————→ office
returning
home ←—————— office

	rate	× time	= distance
going	25	t	$25t$
returning	30	$t - \frac{1}{2}$	$30(t - \frac{1}{2})$

$30(t - \frac{1}{2}) = 25t$

4.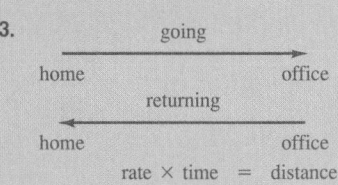

Southbound Northbound
399 mi
rate × time = distance

North bound	$r + 5$	$3\frac{1}{2}$	d
South bound	r	$3\frac{1}{2}$	d

$3\frac{1}{2}(r + 5) + 3\frac{1}{2}r = 399$

1. A cyclist leaves a town traveling at 9 mi/h faster than half the speed of a second cyclist. If the second cyclist starts out 2 h later and overtakes the first in 5 h, how fast is each going?   1st = 30 mi/h, 2nd = 42 mi/h

2. Two planes leave from cities 1925 mi apart at the same time and fly toward each other. One travels at 225 mi/h and the other at 325 mi/h. How long will it take for the two planes to meet? How far will each have traveled?   3.5 h; 1st plane, 787.5 mi; 2nd plane, 1137.5 mi

3. Derek paddled a canoe downriver at 4 mi/h. Twenty minutes later, from the same point, Jonathan traveled downriver in a sailboat at 12 mi/h. How long did it take Jonathan to pass Derek?   30 min

4. On a roundtrip to work, Jan traveled at an average speed of 35 mi/h going and 40 mi/h coming back over the same route. If the entire trip took $2\frac{1}{2}$ h, how far does Jan live from her job? $46\frac{2}{3}$ mi

8. On a round trip over the same roads, Sophia averaged 24 mi/h going and 30 mi/h coming back. If the whole trip took $13\frac{1}{2}$ h, what is the distance one way? (*Hint:* First find the time for each part of the round trip.)   180 mi

9. Enrique cycled to his grandmother's house at 15 km/h and returned home over the same route at 18 km/h. If the whole trip took 7 h and 20 min, how far does Enrique live from his grandmother's house? (*Hint:* First find the time for each part of the round trip.)   60 km

10. Two snails are 432 cm apart. If they travel toward each other at rates that differ by 2 cm/min and it takes them 27 min to meet, how fast is each snail going?   7 cm/min; 9 cm/min

11. On his way to visit Soren, Peter averaged 7 mi/h on his skateboard and 4 mi/h walking. If Soren lives 6 mi away and the whole trip took 1 h, how many miles did Peter travel by skateboard? (*Hint:* First find the two times.) $4\frac{2}{3}$ mi

12. After walking part of the way to a town 68 mi away at 4 mi/h, Erik was picked up by his friend Daniel who drove him the rest of the way. Daniel's car averaged 44 mi/h, and the whole trip took 2 h. How far did Daniel drive Erik? (*Hint:* First find the two times.)   66 mi

B 13. Twenty minutes after Maria left for work on the bus, Juan, noticing that she had left her purse at home, set out by car to overtake the bus. Juan averaged 12 mi/h more than the bus and he overtook it in 40 min. On the average, how fast was each vehicle traveling?   bus 24 mi/h; car 36 mi/h

14. On a recent 6-h bike trip of 70 mi, Lila spent 2 h on the first part of the trip where her average speed was half of her average speed on the second part. What was her speed on the first part?   7 mi/h

15. On their 1200-km trip to Texas, the Wallaces first took a train and later a plane. The train, traveling at 48 km/h, took 2 h longer than the plane, traveling at 240 km/h. How long did the whole trip take? $9\frac{2}{3}$ h

16. At 7:30 PM, a freight train leaves a station traveling east. At 10:30 PM, a passenger train leaves the same station going west at 10 mi/h faster than the freight train. At 3:30 AM the next day, they are 635 mi apart. What is the rate of each train?   freight: 45 mi/h; passenger: 55 mi/h

17. At 10:15 PM, a train left Petersburg, Virginia, traveling east at 40 mi/h. Two hours later, another train left the same station traveling west at 35 mi/h. At what time will the trains be 230 mi apart?   2:15 AM

18. Two buses leave the same station at the same time and travel in opposite directions. After 8 h, they are 360 km apart. The speed of the faster bus is 3 km/h less than twice that of the slower bus. Find the rate of each bus.   16 km/h; 29 km/h

19. At 6:00 AM, a freight train leaves a station at 40 mi/h, and at 7:30 AM a passenger train leaves at 64 mi/h, going in the same direction. At what time will the passenger train overtake the freight train? 10:00 AM

20. Two cyclists are traveling toward one another, one at 25 km/h, the other at 30 km/h. If they are 68.75 km apart at 7:45 AM, at what time will they meet? 9:00 AM

21. Benigno and Chris start at the same time from places 96 mi apart to cycle toward one another, Benigno at 16 mi/h and Chris at 12 mi/h. If Benigno rests for $\frac{1}{2}$ h on the way, after how many hours will they meet? $3\frac{5}{7}$ h

C **22.** Rosa drives to Barnesville at 50 mi/h and returns by a road 5 mi longer at 40 mi/h. The return trip takes 15 min longer. How long is each road?
going 25 mi; return 30 mi

23. Tina can run 2 m/s faster than her sister can. If she runs one lap of a track in 100 s, which is 25 s less than her sister's time, what is the length of one lap? 1000 m

24. Hendrik's average running speed is 375 m/min. This is 25 m/min faster than Esteban's running speed. If they want to finish at the same time, how much of a headstart, in time, should Esteban get for a 1500 m run?
approximately 17 sec

TEST YOURSELF

1. Find 2.5% of 30. 0.75   4.5

2. 15% of what number is 120? 800

3. 84 is what percent of 28? 300%

4. By how much will a $198 coat be reduced at a "30% off" sale? $59.40

5. A car originally cost $8400. It now costs $7980. What is the percent of decrease? 5%   4.6

6. The price of oil, currently $28 per barrel, is expected to rise by 20%. What will the new price be? $33.60

7. To 25 mL of 10% acid solution, 15 mL of water is added. What percent acid is the new solution? 6.25%   4.7

Solve each equation for the underlined variable.

$K = \dfrac{2j + M}{2}$

8. $x + \underline{y} = 0$ $y = -x$ **9.** $5\underline{a} - 10b = 15$ **10.** $M = -2(j - \underline{k})$ 4.8
                            $a = 2b + 3$

11. Two cyclists start from the same place at the same time. They travel in opposite directions. One averages 10 mi/h, and the other 12 mi/h. After how long will they be 66 mi apart? 3 h   4.9, 4.10

4.10 Problem Solving: Uniform Motion   **177**

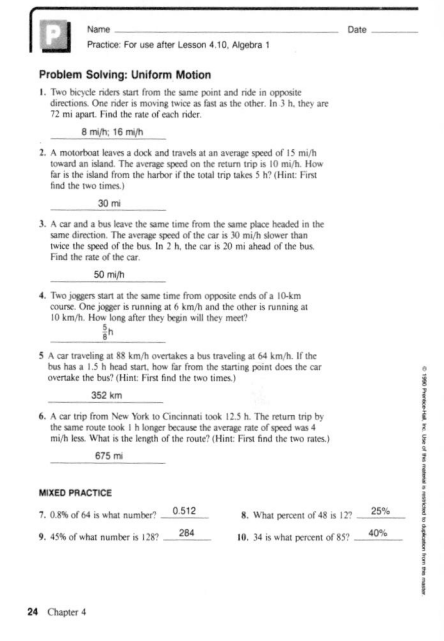

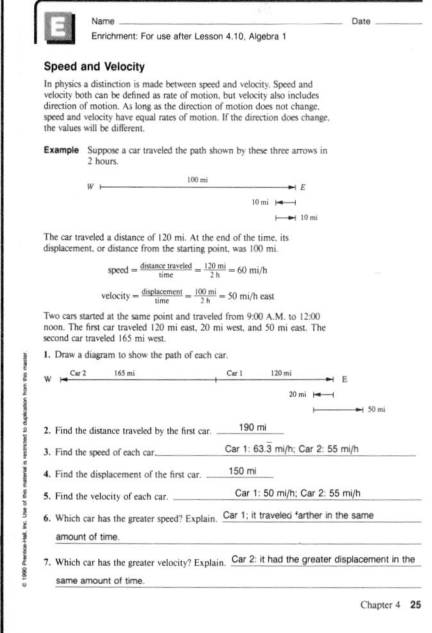

Vocabulary

consecutive integers (144)   percent (152)
even integers (144)   percent of decrease (156)
literal equation (164)   percent of increase (156)
odd integers (145)   uniform motion (172)

Steps for Solving Equations   4.1, 4.2, 4.4

- Use the distributive property to remove parentheses on each side.
- Combine like terms on each side.
- Use the addition or subtraction property for equations so that
  (a) all variable terms are on one side of the equation, and
  (b) all numerical terms are on the other side.
- Use the multiplication or division property for equations.

Note: You may be able to use shortcuts.

Solve and check.

1. $27 - d + 3d = 9$ -9
2. $5t - 4(2t - 3) = 0$ 4
3. $c - 9 = 3\frac{3}{4} + 2c$ $-12\frac{3}{4}$
4. $-3(4 - 2r) + r = 2r$ $\frac{12}{5}$
5. $0.5t + 0.5(t + 6) = 0.18$ -2.82
6. $-6(3p - 7) = 36$ $\frac{1}{3}$

Consecutive Integer Problems   If x is an integer, then three consecutive   4.3
integers that follow x are $x + 1$, $x + 2$, and $x + 3$. If y is an even integer or
an odd integer, then each consecutive even or odd integer that follows y will
be 2 greater than the one before: $y + 2$, $y + 4$, $y + 6$, and so on.

7. z is an even integer. Write four consecutive even integers that follow
   $z + 6$. $z + 8, z + 10, z + 12, z + 14$
8. Find three consecutive integers whose sum is -9. $-4, -3, -2$

Percent Problems   The three cases of percent can be expressed in the   4.5
general form: a is $b\%$ of c. To solve any percent problem, try to identify the
values of a, b, and c.

9. What is 5% of 57? 2.85
10. 4.5 is what percent of 150? 3%

11. For what investment, at an annual interest rate of 4.8%, would you receive an annual simple interest of $64.80? $1350

12. If 4 machines in a 128-machine shipment are defective, what percent are defective? $3\frac{1}{8}\%$

13. Last year 90 students took auto mechanics. This year the enrollment increased by 20%. How many students now take the course? 108 students

14. A calculator that cost $60 in 1980 now sells for $10. What was the percent of decrease? $83\frac{1}{3}\%$.

15. How many milliliters of water would you add to 75 mL of a 15% acid solution to make a 10% solution? 37.5 mL

Literal Equations   To solve a literal equation for one variable in terms of other variables, use the properties for equations to isolate the desired variable on one side of the equation.

4.8

Solve each literal equation for the underlined variable.

16. $3 = \underline{y} - 12x$ $y = 12x + 3$

17. $5(3m - \underline{n}) = p$ $n = \frac{15m - p}{5}$

18. $-5d + 4b\underline{x} = 7d + 5b\underline{x}$ $x = \frac{-12d}{b}$

Solve each literal equation for the underlined variable. Then find the value of this variable in terms of the other variables.

19. $p = 2\underline{a} + b$ Find a if $p = 15$ and $b = 4$. $a = \frac{p - b}{2}; \frac{11}{2}$

20. $C = 2\pi\underline{r}$ Find r if $C = 157$ and $\pi \approx 3.14$. $r = \frac{C}{2\pi}; 25$

Uniform Motion Problems   To solve problems that involve uniform motion, use the four problem-solving steps. Draw a sketch, and make a chart based on the formula $d = rt$.

4.9

21. Two planes left Kennedy Airport in New York City at 1:00 PM. One flew north at 250 mi/h and the other flew south at 300 mi/h. How many miles apart were the planes at 4:00 PM? 1650 mi

22. A truck and a car travel the same route, the truck at 72 km/h, and the car at 80 km/h. If the car leaves 1 h after the truck, how long does it take the car to overtake the truck? 9 h

23. John takes a bus from home to school. The bus averages 32 km/h. He walks home at 8 km/h. The bus ride takes 15 min less time than the walk home. How far is John's home from school? $2\frac{2}{3}$ km

Summary and Review   **179**

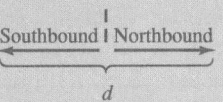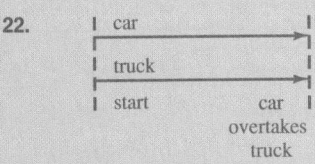

180

Solve and check.

1. $-8t - 7t + 9 = -31$ $2\frac{2}{3}$

2. $-5 - (6 + 3y) = 7$ -6

3. $d - 2 = 1\frac{3}{4} - 2d$ $\frac{5}{4}$

4. $2(p + 1) - 3(4p - 2) = 6p$ $\frac{1}{2}$

5. $\frac{1}{3}(2y - 9) = -18$ $-22\frac{1}{2}$

6. $0.05x - 0.02(8000 - x) = 85$ 3500

Solve each literal equation for the underlined variable. Assume that the literal coefficients are not zero.

7. $\underline{x} + 10c = c + 8$ $x = -9c + 8$

8. $A = \frac{1}{2}b\underline{h}$ $h = \frac{2A}{b}$

Solve this literal equation for the underlined variable. Then find the value of this variable in terms of the other variables.

9. $P = 2l + 2\underline{w}$ Then find the value of w if $P = 15.5$ and $l = 3.5$. $w = \frac{P - 2l}{2}$; 4.25

Write an equation and solve each problem.

10. What percent of 125 is 5? 4%

11. 5.6 is 25% of what number? 22.4

12. What is $33\frac{1}{3}\%$ of $6.90? $2.30

13. If the state sales tax rate is 7.5%, how much tax will be paid on an item that costs $24.98? $1.87

14. Find three consecutive even integers whose sum is -42. $-16, -14, -12$

15. The population of Los Angeles increased from 2.5 million in 1960 to 3 million in 1980. What was the percent of increase? 20%

16. To 150 g of a 5% sugar solution in water, 25 g of pure sugar was added. What was the percent of sugar in the new solution? 18.6%

17. A car leaves Washington, D.C., for New York City at the same time another car leaves New York City for Washington, D.C. The car from Washington, D.C., travels at an average rate of 45 mi/h; the other car averages 55 mi/h. If the two cities are 240 mi apart, how soon will the cars meet and how far will each have traveled? $2\frac{2}{5}$ h; 1st 108 mi, 2nd 132 mi

Challenge

An investment company invested one half its money at a 10% rate of simple interest, one third at 9%, and the remainder at 12%. If the company earned a total annual interest of $1110 from these investments, how much was invested at each rate? $5500 at 10%; $3700 at 9%; $1850 at 12%

The individual comments provided about each problem can be helpful in guiding students to solve these problems.

Select the best answer for each and write the appropriate letter.

1. Solve the equation
B
$$2x + 5 = x + 9.$$
A. 2　**B.** 4　**C.** 7　**D.** 8　**E.** 14

2. The equation representing the
D
sentence "The sum of two consecutive integers is 329." would be:

A. $x + 1 = 329$

B. $x + 2 = 329$

C. $x + x = 329$

D. $x + (x + 1) = 329$

E. $x + (x + 2) = 329$

3. Which of the following is *not*
D
equivalent to 0.025?

A. $\dfrac{25}{1000}$　**B.** $0.01(2.5)$

C. $\dfrac{1}{40}$　**D.** 0.25%　**E.** $\dfrac{5}{200}$

4. Solve the equation
A
$$5x + 5 = 3x - 13$$
A. -9　**B.** -1　**C.** 1　**D.** 4　**E.** 9

5. Find the value of the expression
B
below when $x = -1$ and $y = 3$.
$$3x(x + y) - 2xy^2$$
A. 6　**B.** 12　**C.** 15　**D.** 18　**E.** 24

6. Solve for x in the equation:
B
$$3x + 2b = 2x + a$$
A. $a + 2b$　　**B.** $a - 2b$

C. $a + b$　　**D.** $a - b$

E. $2a - 2b$

7. A train and a car are traveling at
E
different speeds. If the train travels 306 mi in 5 h, how many hours would it take the car to travel 153 mi?

A. 2　　**B.** $2\dfrac{1}{4}$　　**C.** $2\dfrac{1}{2}$　　**D.** 3

E. It cannot be determined from the information given.

8. Which of the following is(are) true?
E
I. If $x < y$ and $y < 4$, then $x < 4$.

II. 1% of 160 is 16

III. $\dfrac{3}{5} \times \dfrac{25}{6} \div \dfrac{5}{2} < \dfrac{3}{2}$

A. I only　　　　**B. II** only

C. III only　　　**D. II, III** only

E. I, III only

9. Mr. Miller bought a suit on sale at
C
30% off the original price of $150. If he also had to pay a sales tax of 6%, what was the total amount he paid?

A. $154.23　　**B.** $114

C. $111.30　　**D.** $106

E. $98.70

10. In a factory, Pete and Al make the
C
same machine part. On one day Al made 29 fewer than twice what Pete made and together they made 88 machine parts. How many did Pete make that day?

A. 29　**B.** 38　**C.** 39　**D.** 48　**E.** 49

3. This question could be useful when teaching techniques of taking multiple tests. By eliminating the obviously false choices of *A, C,* and *E,* only two choices remain to be considered.

8. It is important to stress that the students carefully read and evaluate I, II, and III as true or false before selecting an answer. Some students might be tempted to select *A,* since I is quickly seen to be true.

See *Teacher's Resource Book,* for Preparing for Standardized Tests.

See *Teacher's Resource Book, Cumulative Test*, pp. 41–44.

CUMULATIVE REVIEW (CHAPTERS 1–4)

Perform the indicated operation. 1.5–1.8

1. $-\frac{3}{4} \cdot \frac{2}{3}$ $-\frac{1}{2}$ 2. $\frac{5}{8} + \left(-\frac{1}{4}\right)$ $\frac{3}{8}$ 3. $-\frac{3}{10} \div \left(-\frac{2}{5}\right)$ $\frac{3}{4}$ 4. $-\frac{2}{3} - \left(-\frac{5}{6}\right)$ $\frac{1}{6}$

5. $\frac{1}{2} \div \left(-\frac{1}{4}\right)$ -2 6. $-\frac{3}{8} \cdot \left(-\frac{4}{5}\right)$ $\frac{3}{10}$ 7. $-\frac{2}{3} + \frac{3}{4}$ $\frac{1}{12}$ 8. $\frac{1}{3} \div \frac{3}{5}$ $\frac{5}{9}$

9. $-\frac{5}{6} + \left(-\frac{3}{8}\right)$ $-\frac{29}{24}$ 10. $-\frac{2}{3} \div \frac{4}{5}$ $-\frac{5}{6}$ 11. $-\frac{3}{4} - \frac{5}{12}$ $-\frac{7}{6}$ 12. $\frac{4}{9} \cdot -\frac{3}{8}$ $-\frac{1}{6}$

13. $\frac{2}{5} - \left(-\frac{3}{10}\right)$ $\frac{7}{10}$ 14. $-\frac{5}{6} + \frac{3}{4}$ $-\frac{1}{12}$ 15. $-\frac{4}{9} \div \left(-\frac{2}{3}\right)$ $\frac{2}{3}$ 16. $\frac{5}{6} \cdot \frac{4}{15}$ $\frac{2}{9}$

Simplify. 1.3, 2.1, 2.4, 2.5

17. $|8 - (-3)(-5)|$ 7 18. $24 - 8 \cdot 2$ 8 19. $-5[64 \div (8 - 12)^2]$
    -20
20. $7a^2 - 12a + 3a^2$ 21. $5x - 3(x + 2)$ $2x - 6$ 22. $-(-m^2 - 5)$ $m^2 + 5$
    $10a^2 - 12a$
23. $(5h + 4) - (3h - 5)$ $2h + 9$ 24. $5(a^2 + b) + 2(b - a^2)$ $3a^2 + 7b$

25. $7mn - 2(mn + 3) + 5$ $5mn - 1$ 26. $-3(x^2 - y^2) + 5(y^2 + x^2)$ $2x^2 + 8y^2$

Evaluate each expression if $x = 8$, $y = \frac{3}{4}$, and $z = -6$. 1.1, 2.1, and 2.2

27. $xy + z$ 0 28. $|z - 4y|$ 9 29. $\frac{5x + 2}{y}$ 56

30. $2(x^2 + 4z)$ 80 31. $\frac{(x + z)^2}{y - \frac{1}{2}}$ 16 32. $2x + 4(z + y)$ -5

33. $(|x| - |z|)^3$ 8 34. $x[2 + y(2 - z)]$ 64 35. $x(y \div z)$ -1

Answer each question or statement with an algebraic expression or equation. 2.6, 2.8

Let m be Marc's age now.

36. What was Marc's age 6 years ago? $m - 6$

37. Nancy is 2 years younger than Marc. What is Nancy's age now? $m - 2$

38. What will Nancy's age be 4 years from now? $m + 2$

39. The sum of their ages now is 30. $m + (m - 2) = 30$

40. 3 years ago the sum of their ages was 24. $(m - 3) + (m - 5) = 24$

Solve each equation and check your solution. 3.1, 3.2, 3.3, 4.1, 4.2, 4.4

41. $12 = 3(c - 1)$ 5

42. $20 = y + 20$ 0

43. $81 = -9x$ −9

44. $4p + 2 = 14$ 3

45. $1 - 9d = 0$ $\frac{1}{9}$

46. $32 = -16 + 14n$ $\frac{24}{7}$

47. $g + 6 = -8$ −14

48. $-\frac{1}{4} = \frac{t}{8}$ −2

49. $2a + \frac{3}{5} = \frac{2}{5}$ $-\frac{1}{10}$

50. $0.3r - 0.5 = 0.7$ 4

51. $-40b = 40$ −1

52. $5m + 30 - 3m = 42$ 6

53. $4h - 3 = 11 - 3h$ 2

54. $1 = 2\frac{1}{5} - \frac{2}{5}r$ 3

55. $9t - 4(t + 3) = 8$ 4

56. $8p - (2p - 5) = 23$ 3

57. Given the formula $S = \dfrac{a}{1 - r}$, find the value of a if $S = 8$ and   3.6
$r = -3$. 32

58. Evaluate $A = p + prt$ for t, if $A = \$840$, $p = \$600$, and $r = 0.08$. 5

59. In the formula $V = \pi r^2 h$, find the value of h if $V = 628$ and $r = 5$.
Use 3.14 for π. 8

60. Find the value of E in the formula $I = \dfrac{E}{R + r}$ if $I = 80$, $R = 12$, and
$r = 13$. 2000

61. Given the formula $P = 2l + 2w$, find the value of w if $P = 200$ and
$l = 75$. 25

Solve each problem by writing and solving an equation. 3.4, 4.3

62. 9 less than 4 times a number is 55. Find the number. $4n - 9 = 55$; 16

63. The perimeter of a rectangle is 42 cm. Find the length if the width is
6 cm. $42 = 2l + 2(6)$; 15 cm

64. Three more than twice Frank's age is 35. How old is Frank? $2a + 3 = 35$; 16

65. The sum of two consecutive integers is 49. Find the integers.
$n + (n + 1) = 49$; 24, 25

66. Sue's allowance is 3 times as much as Gloria's allowance. If the sum of
their allowances is \$48, how much is Gloria's allowance? $3q + q = 48$; \$12

For each exercise, translate the word equation into an algebraic equation and solve. See side column.

67. $a = ?$; $b = 15\%$; $c = 40$

68. $a = ?$; $b = 24\%$; $c = 68$

69. $a = 105$; $b = ?$; $c = 150$

70. $a = 125$; $b = ?$; $c = 2500$

71. $a = 48$; $b = 12\%$; $c = ?$

72. $a = 66$; $b = 15\%$; $c = ?$

73. $a = 91$; $b = 8\%$; $c = ?$

74. $a = 77$; $b = ?$; $c = 154$

75. $a = 4$; $b = 8\%$; $c = ?$

76. $a = 12$; $b = 12\%$; $c = ?$

77. What is 3% of 80?

78. What is 7% of 30?

79. What percent of 50 is 15?

80. What percent of 24 is 10?

81. 25% of $500 is what amount?

82. 45% of $650 is what amount?

83. 20% of what number is 5?

84. 80% of what number is 10?

85. 18 is what percent of 24?

86. 24 is what percent of 144?

87. Find $37\frac{1}{2}$% of 96.

88. Find $8\frac{1}{4}$% of 120.

89. 16 is 5% of what number?

90. 36 is 2% of what number?

91. 150% of what number is 30?

92. 250% of what number is 50?

93. What percent of 12 is 4?

94. What percent of 85 is 17?

95. What is $\frac{1}{2}$% of $200?

96. What is $\frac{1}{4}$% of $100?

Solve each literal equation for the underlined variable.

97. $x - \underline{y} = 9$ $y = x - 9$

98. $3\underline{m} - 5 = n$ $m = \frac{n+5}{3}$

99. $\frac{1}{2}\underline{g} + 3 = h$
$g = 2h - 6$

100. $a = 2(\underline{b} - 3c)$
$b = \frac{a+6c}{2}$

101. $\frac{2}{3}\underline{t} = 8s$ $t = 12s$

102. $\frac{1}{2}x + \underline{y} = 1\frac{1}{2}$
$y = 3 - 2y$

103. $2d = 5d - \underline{c}$ $c = 3d$

104. $j = \frac{1}{3}\underline{k} + 5$ $k = 3j - 15$

105. $0.2p - 0.3\underline{q} = 40$
$q = \frac{2p - 40}{3}$

Solve.   4.4, 4.6, 4.

106. The price of an $85 jacket was decreased 25%. What is the new price? $63.75

107. The population of Haverstown has increased from 835 to 1002. Find the percent of increase. 20%

108. If you have 200 mL of a 30% solution of acid in water, how much water would you add in order to make a 25% solution? 40 mL

109. A car leaves a city traveling at a rate of 40 mi/h. Two hours later a second car leaves from the same place, along the same road traveling 50 mi/h. In how many hours will the second car overtake the first car? 8 h

OVERVIEW • Chapter 5

SUMMARY

In Chapter 5, students are introduced to inequalities in one variable. Students learn how to use the addition, subtraction, multiplication, and division properties to solve inequalities. After they have solved an inequality, they learn how to graph the solution set. Their understanding of solving inequalities is then extended to solving combined inequalities. Students learn how to use the algebraic method and the number-line method to solve equations and inequalities involving absolute value. The problem solving lesson in this chapter introduces the inequality as a mathematical model that can be used to solve problems.

Toward the end of the chapter, students are given the opportunity to apply their skill in solving inequalities to real world situations.

CHAPTER OBJECTIVES

- To graph equations and inequalities on a number line
- To solve inequalities using the addition, subtraction, multiplication, and division properties
- To draw graphs of the solution sets of inequalities
- To solve inequalities using more than one inequality property
- To express answers in set-builder notation
- To solve combined inequalities
- To solve equations and inequalities involving absolute value

Problem Solving Strategy

To solve problems by writing an inequality as a mathematical model

CHAPTER HIGHLIGHTS

The *theme* of the chapter is sports competition. The chapter's *special features* show how algebra is applied to various sports activities.

PROBLEM SOLVING AND APPLICATIONS

Problem solving and applications form an integral part of each lesson. Students use inequalities to solve practical problems in many fields including sports, meteorology, mechanics, and other areas of mathematics. Problem Solving Lesson 5.8 affords students the opportunity to practice applying algebraic inequalities to concrete situations that arise in a variety of fields.

TECHNOLOGY

Calculator

Exercises in which a calculator may be used to facilitate computations are identified in the *Teacher's Edition.*

Computer

The computer features in Chapter 5 involve programs to graph inequalities involving decimals, and to solve inequalities. An explanation of how a computer solves an inequality is given. Students learn that a computer cannot directly solve an inequality. The computer actually solves an equation in calculation-ready form.

RESOURCES

Teacher's Resource Book

- Teaching Aids 1, 6, 17
- Transparency 2

Chapter Content	Basic	Average	Enriched	R	P	E
STUDENT TEXT				TEACHER'S RESOURCE BOOK		
5.1 Graphing Equations and Inequalities	D: 188/1-23 odd, 40 R: 188/4, 8, 18	D: 188/1-35 odd, 40 R: 188/2, 12, 20	D: 188/1-39 odd, 40, R: 188/12, 20	1	2	3
5.2 Solving Inequalities: Addition and Subtraction Properties	D: 192/1-15 odd, 36 R: 188/2, 12, 20	D: 192/1-31 odd, 36, 37 R: 188/22, 26, 34	D: 192/7-35 odd, 36-38 R: 189/28, 36, 38	4	5	6
5.3 Solving Inequalities: Multiplication and Division Properties	D: 197/1-15 odd, 37 R: 192/4, 8, 12	D: 197/1-29 odd, 37 R: 193/16, 26, 30	D: 197/9-35 odd, 37, 38 R: 192/20, 32, 34	7	8	9
5.4 Solving Inequalities; More Than One Property	D: 200/1-19 odd, 41 R: 197/6, 10, 14 Test Yourself	D: 200/1-33 odd, 41, 42 R: 197/12, 20, 24 Test Yourself	D: 200/5-39 odd, 41, 42 R: 197/22, 26, 28 Test Yourself	10	11	12
5.5 Combined Inequalities	D: 205/1-15 odd, 31 R: 200/2, 10, 20 205/2, 4, 6	D: 205/1-25 odd, 31, 32 R: 200/12, 24, 30	D: 205/7-29 odd, 31-33 R: 201/28, 36, 40	13	14	15
5.6 Absolute Value Equations	D: 208/1-23 odd, 39, 40 R: 205/4, 10, 16	D: 208/1-31 odd, 39-41 R: 205/14, 22, 26	D: 208/19-37 odd, 39-43 R: 205/18, 24, 32	16	17	18
5.7 Absolute Value Inequalities	D: 212/1-27 odd, 49 R: 208/12, 16, 20 212/2, 8, 12	D: 212/1-39 odd, 49 R: 208/22, 26, 28 212/4, 8, 12	D: 212/17-47 odd, 49, 50 R: 208/30, 34, 38	19	20	21
5.8 Problem Solving Strategy: Writing an Inequality	D: 216/1-7 odd MPSR: 1-3 R: Test Yourself	D: 216/1-9 odd MPSR: 1-3 R: Test Yourself	D: 216/3-11 odd MPSR: 1-3 R: Test Yourself		22	23

D = Daily   R = Review   MPSR = Mixed Problem Solving Review   R = Reteaching   P = Practice   E = Enrichment

	STUDENT TEXT				TEACHER'S RESOURCE BOOK	
Review And Testing	Test Yourself	201	Chapter Test	222	Spanish Chapter Summary and Review	9-10
	Test Yourself	217	Prep. for Stan. Tests	223	• Quizzes	49-52
	Chapter Sum. and Rev.	220	Maintaining Skills	224	• Chapter Test (Form A)	53-54
			Extra Practice	659	• Chapter Test (Form B)	55-56
					Calculator Test	9-10
Special Features	Logical Reasoning	189	Did You Know?	209	Applications—Chapter 5	24
	Math Club Activity	193	Algebra in Mechanics	213	Critical Thinking	5
	Extra	197	Project	217	Reading and Writing in Algebra	5
	Algebra in Geometry	205	Application	218	Technology	10-12

5 Inequalities in One Variable

BACKGROUND

Mathematics is integrated into a variety of competitive sports. Track and field activities use mathematical expressions and formulas to calculate a runner's distance, speed, or time. Algebraic computations are also used to design and measure tracks.

Knowing how to figure out distance, speed, and time is important in many sports activities and competitions. A good knowledge of mathematics can help produce solutions to otherwise complicated problems.

185

BACKGROUND

In the Capsule Review, students practice graphing points on a number line. These exercises prepare students for learning how to graph the solution sets of equations and inequalities.

Critical Thinking

Causal Explanation Does the comparison property hold true when the symbols $\geq$ and $\leq$ are used? Why or why not? The comparison property does hold true because the symbols are interpreted to read "greater/less than *or* equal to." Therefore both possibilities cannot be true at the same time.

Additional Answers

1.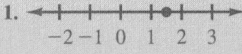
   −2 −1 0 1 2 3

2.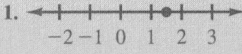
   −2 −1 0 1 2 3

3.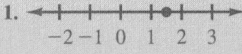
   −2 −1 0 1 2 3

4.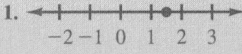
   −2 −1 0 1 2 3

5.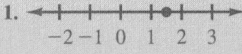
   −2 −1 0 1 2 3

5.1

Graphing Equations and Inequalities

Objective: To graph equations and inequalities on a number line

The graph of a real number is a *point* on a number line. You can graph equations and inequalities by locating their solutions on a number line.

Capsule Review

The arrows on a number line indicate direction. Choose a starting point, the origin, and label it "0." Then mark off equal units of distance on both sides of the origin. The graph of point B corresponds to what number on the number line?

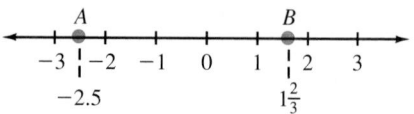

Point A is the graph of -2.5.

Graph these numbers on a number line. See side column.

1. 1.5   **2.** $-1\frac{2}{5}$ **3.** $\frac{1}{4}$ **4.** -1 **5.** -0.75

The solution set of $x = -2$ is $\{-2\}$. The graph of $x = -2$ is a point on the number line that corresponds to -2.

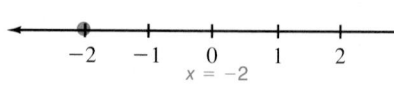

EXAMPLE 1 **Solve $3a + 6 = a - 5$. Then draw its graph by locating the solution on a number line.**

$$3a + 6 = a - 5$$
$$2a + 6 = -5 \qquad \textit{Subtract a from each side.}$$
$$2a = -11 \qquad \textit{Subtract 6 from each side.}$$
$$a = -5\frac{1}{2} \qquad \textit{Divide each side by 2.}$$

The solution is $-5\frac{1}{2}$.

You have used the symbols $=$, $<$, $>$, and $\neq$ to compare numbers. The following property is basic to the comparison of real numbers.

Comparison Property

For all real numbers a and b, one and only one of the following is true:

$$a = b \qquad a < b \qquad a > b$$

---

186   Chapter 5 Inequalities in One Variable

Using the set of real numbers as the replacement set, there are many values for x that make $x < 1$ true.

Replace x with 0.

$x < 1$

$0 < 1$ ✓ True

Replace x with $\frac{1}{2}$.

$x < 1$

$\frac{1}{2} < 1$ ✓ True

Replace x with -2.

$x < 1$

$-2 < 1$ ✓ True

The solution set of $x < 1$ is {all real numbers less than 1}. To graph such a solution set, recall that every point on the number line corresponds to a real number.

EXAMPLE 2   **Draw the graph of $x < 1$.**

The graph of $x < 1$ includes all points on the number line to the left of the graph of 1. An "open circle" shows that 1 is not a solution.

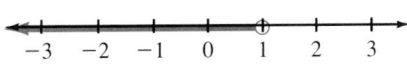

Sometimes comparisons are combined. For example:

Inequality	Read	Solution Set
$m \leq 5$	m is less than or equal to 5.	{5 and all real numbers less than 5}
$y \geq -\frac{1}{2}$	y is greater than or equal to $-\frac{1}{2}$.	$\left\{-\frac{1}{2}$ and all real numbers greater than $-\frac{1}{2}\right\}$

Unless stated otherwise, the replacement set for the variable in an inequality is the set of real numbers.

EXAMPLE 3   **Draw the graph of $y \geq -\frac{1}{2}$.**

A "closed circle" shows that $-\frac{1}{2}$ is a solution of $y \geq -\frac{1}{2}$.

From the graph of $y \geq -\frac{1}{2}$ in Example 3, identify other numbers that are solutions and numbers that are not solutions of the inequality.

EXAMPLE 4   **Draw the graph of $a \neq 1$.**

All real numbers except 1 are solutions of $a \neq 1$.

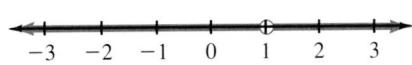

5.1 Graphing Equations and Inequalities   **187**

• For Examples 1 and 2, use a number line to point out the difference between graphing the solution of an equation and the solution of an inequality. Teaching Aid 1 and Transparency 2, in the *Teacher's Resource Book*, maybe helpful in distinguishing between graphs of equality and inequality.

• Point out that $\neq$ is an inequality symbol. Have students note the open circle on the graph and how it relates to the inequality.

CHALKBOARD EXAMPLES

• **For Example 1**

1. Solve $2c + c + 6 = 8.1$. Then draw its graph by locating the solution on a number line.

   $c = 0.7$

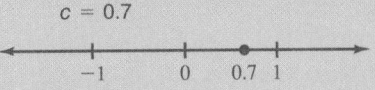

• **For Example 2**

2. Draw the graph of $z > 1\frac{1}{4}$.

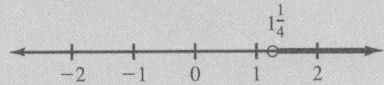

• **For Example 3**

3. Draw the graph of $x \leq 0$.

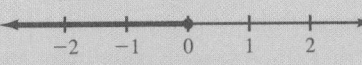

• **For Example 4**

4. Draw the graph of $c \neq -\frac{1}{2}$.

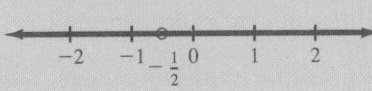

- **For Example 5**
  5. State the solution set of the in-
     equality whose graph is given.

$\left\{\text{all real numbers less than } -1\tfrac{1}{2}\right\}$

Common Error

- Students are likely to confuse the symbol $<$ with $>$. Have them note that the point of the symbol is towards the smaller number.
- See *Teacher's Resource Book* for additional remediation.

LESSON FOLLOW-UP

Discussion

Describe the difference between the two graphs $x \geq 1$ and $x > 1$. A "closed circle" shows that 1 is a solution of $x \geq 1$. An "open circle" shows that 1 is not a solution of $x > 1$.

Critical Thinking

Observation Draw a number line and label any two points, A and B. How many points are there between points A and B? Students should conclude that there is an infinite number.

Assignment Guide

- See p. 184B for assignments.
- See *Teacher's Resource Book, Technology,* pp. 10–12.

Lesson Quiz

Draw a graph of each equation or inequality.
1. $y \leq -2$

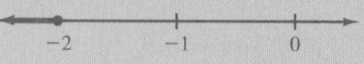

2. $z > \tfrac{1}{4}$

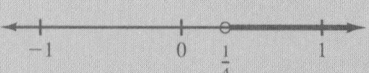

3. $2x - 1 \geq 10$

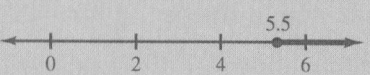

188

If you are given the graph of an equation or an inequality, you can determine its solution set.

EXAMPLE 5 State the solution set of the inequality whose graph is given.

The solution set is {all real numbers greater than 0}.

CLASS EXERCISES

Classify each statement as *true* or *false*.

1. $-16 > -15$ F
2. $-1\tfrac{1}{3} \neq -1\tfrac{1}{3}$ F
3. $-1.5 < 0.5$ T
4. $-\tfrac{1}{6} \geq -\tfrac{1}{6}$ T

Graph each equation or inequality. See below.

5. $x = -2.5$
6. $y < 2$
7. $c \geq -4$
8. $d \neq 0$

State the solution set of the equation or inequality whose graph is given.

9.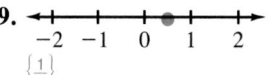
$\left\{\tfrac{1}{2}\right\}$

10.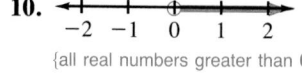
{all real numbers greater than 0}

11.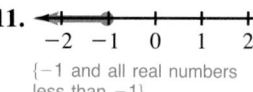
{−1 and all real numbers less than −1}

PRACTICE EXERCISES

Solve each equation. Then graph the solution on a number line. See p. 720.

A
1. $4a + 2 = a - 7$ −3
2. $6x + 3 = x - 12$ −3
3. $-7m + 4 = -m - 2$ 1
4. $-z + 8 = -7z + 2$ −1
5. $3y - y = 12 - y$ 4
6. $5n - n = 15 - n$ 3

Graph each equation or inequality. See p. 720.

7. $a < 2$
8. $c > 5$
9. $z < -\tfrac{1}{2}$
10. $x < -\tfrac{3}{4}$
11. $t > 0$
12. $m > 3$
13. $a \geq -\tfrac{1}{4}$
14. $y \geq -\tfrac{1}{2}$
15. $x = 0.50$
16. $y = 0.25$
17. $x \neq 2$
18. $y \neq 3$

State the solution set of the equation or inequality whose graph is given.

19.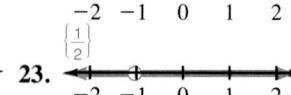
{0}

20.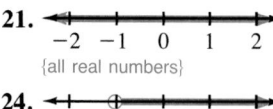
$\left\{\tfrac{1}{2}\right\}$

21.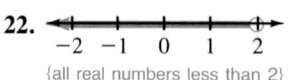
{all real numbers}

22.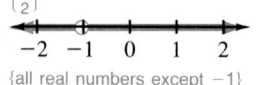
{all real numbers less than 2}

23.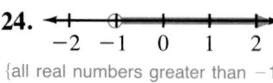
{all real numbers except −1}

24.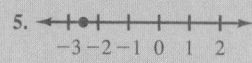
{all real numbers greater than −1}

188 Chapter 5 Inequalities in One Variable

 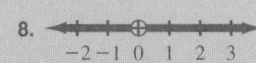

Solve each equation. Then graph the solution set. See below.

B **25.** $3x - 11 = -26$ {-5}

26. $-5y + 21 = 36$ {-3}

27. $7c - 9 = 6 + c$ $\left\{\frac{5}{2}\right\}$

28. $8r - 19 = -19 + 11r$ {0}

29. $6(2m + 3) = 4 - (m - 1)$ {-1}

30. $15 + (3z - 6) = (9 + z)2$ {9}

Graph the solution set of each inequality. Let the replacement set for the variable be the set of negative integers. See p. 720.

31. $a \leq 5$ **32.** $b \geq -5$ **33.** $z \neq -4$ **34.** $v \neq -1$

The **Transitive Property of Order** for $<$ and $>$ is as follows:
  For all real numbers x, y, and z,
  (a) if $x < y$ and $y < z$, then $x < z$; and (b) if $x > y$ and $y > z$, then $x > z$.

35. Use number lines to draw graphs to illustrate the transitive property of order in (a) and (b) above.

For which real numbers a and b is the statement true?

C **36.** If $a < b$, then $a^2 < b^2$.
  a, b non-neg. real numbers

37. If $a < b$, then $a^2 + b^2 > 2ab$.
  all real numbers

38. If $a < b$, then $\frac{1}{a} > \frac{1}{b}$.
  all non-zero real numbers except
Applications where $a < 0$ and $b > 0$

39. If $a < b$, then $a^2 = b^2$.
  all real numbers where a and b are additive inverses

40. Computer Computers can graph inequalities involving decimal numbers quickly and very accurately. This program graphs solutions in the -3.25 to 3 range. By changing the range and the increment in 10–20 you can use the program for larger numbers and/or smaller increments. What would you change in the program to graph: $x > 2.25$; $x < 1.75$?
line 10 and line 30; no change

```
10 INPUT "GRAPH OF X < ";N: PRINT : PRINT
20 FOR X =  - 3.25 TO 3 STEP .25
30 IF X < N THEN   PRINT "*";: GOTO 60
40 IF X = N THEN   PRINT "O";
50 PRINT "-";
60 NEXT X
70 PRINT : PRINT "-3..-2..-1...0...1..2...3"
80 END
```

LOGICAL REASONING

Lori has fifteen cubes that are identical except that one weighs less than each of the others. If she can compare these cubes on a balance scale, what is the fewest number of comparisons that will enable her to tell which cube weighs the least? 3 comparisons

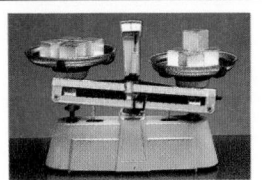

5.1 Graphing Equations and Inequalities **189**

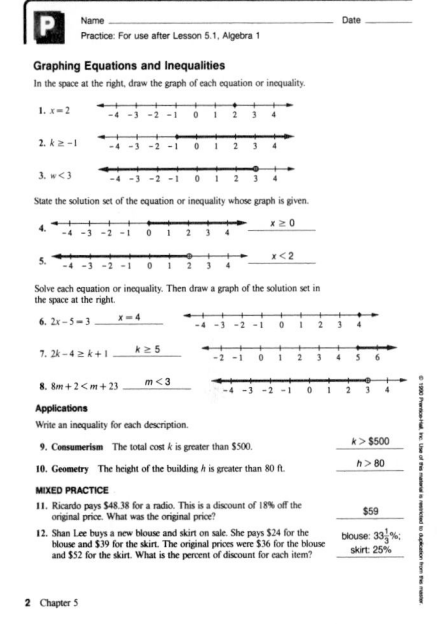
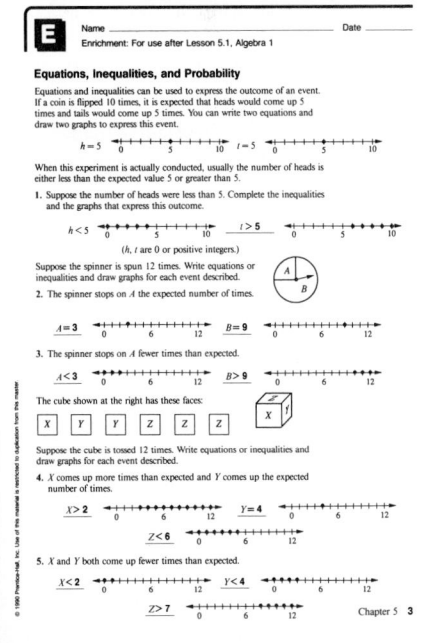
Additional Answers

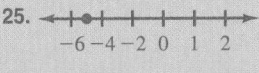

25.
  $-6 -4 -2\ 0\ 1\ 2$

26.
  $-3 -2 -1\ 0\ 1\ 2$

27.
  $-2 -1\ 0\ 1\ 2\ 3$

28.
  $-2 -1\ 0\ 1\ 2\ 3$

29.
  $-2 -1\ 0\ 1\ 2\ 3$

30.
  $-8 -4\ 0\ 4\ 8\ 12$

Materials/Manipulatives
Number lines
Overhead projector
*Teacher's Resource Book,
  Teaching Aid 1,
  Transparency 2*

BACKGROUND

- In the Capsule Review, students use a replacement set to find the solution set of each inequality. This review prepares students for their work in solving inequalities using the addition and subtraction properties.

- Before introducing the addition and subtraction properties for inequalities, students may benefit from reviewing Lesson 3.1, Solving Equations: Addition and Subtraction Properties. Point out that the addition and subtraction properties for inequalities are similar to the addition and subtraction properties for equations.

Critical Thinking

Observation Explain why the following inequality is true: For any two real numbers, *a* and *b*, if $a < b$, then $b > a$. Students should be able to conclude that if $a > b$ then $b < a$. An inequality may be read from either direction.

5.2 Solving Inequalities: Addition and Subtraction Properties

Objective: To solve inequalities using the addition and subtraction properties and to draw graphs of the solution sets

A solution of an inequality is any number from the replacement set that makes the inequality true. As with equations, some inequalities may be solved by using real number properties.

Capsule Review

The replacement set is the set of integers.

$2x < 9$	$x + 5 < 0$	$4 \geq x + 9$
Is 4 a solution?	Is -1 a solution?	Is -5 a solution?
$2 \cdot 4 < 9$	$-1 + 5 < 0$	$4 \geq -5 + 9$
$8 < 9$ ✓ True	$4 < 0$ False	$4 \geq 4$ ✓ True

Find the solution set of each inequality. Use $\{-2, -1, 0, 1, 2\}$ for the replacement set. If the solution set is the empty set, write Ø.

1. $3m > 0$ $\{1, 2\}$ **2.** $x + 2 < 0$ Ø   **3.** $n + 1 \leq 0$
$\{-2, -1\}$ **4.** $x - 4 \geq -4$
$\{0, 1, 2\}$

Consider the inequality $8 < 15$.

| Add 5 to each side. | Is $13 < 20$? | Yes |
| Subtract 9 from each side. | Is $-1 < 6$? | Yes |

Note that when the same real number is added to or subtracted from each side of $8 < 15$, the *order* (direction) of the inequality is unchanged.

Addition Property for Inequalities

For all real numbers a, b, and c: If $a > b$, then $a + c > b + c$
If $a < b$, then $a + c < b + c$

Subtraction Property for Inequalities

For all real numbers a, b, and c: If $a > b$, then $a - c > b - c$
If $a < b$, then $a - c < b - c$

To solve an inequality, you must express it as an equivalent inequality in which the variable term, with a coefficient of 1, is alone on one side.

EXAMPLE 1 Solve $n + 9 > 12$. **Graph the solution set.**

$$n + 9 > 12$$
$$n + 9 - 9 > 12 - 9 \qquad \textit{Subtract 9 from each side.}$$
$$n > 3 \qquad \textit{n > 3 is equivalent to n + 9 > 12.}$$

The solution set is
{all real numbers greater than 3}.

In Example 1, an open circle is drawn at 3 to show that 3 is *not* a solution. To check the solutions, replace the variable in the original inequality with the coordinates of some points on the graph and some points not on the graph.

Replace n with -1.	Replace n with 3.	Replace n with 10.
$n + 9 > 12$	$n + 9 > 12$	$n + 9 > 12$
$-1 + 9 > 12$	$3 + 9 > 12$	$10 + 9 > 12$
$8 > 12$ False	$12 > 12$ False	$19 > 12$ ✔ True
-1 is not a solution.	3 is not a solution.	10 is a solution.

EXAMPLE 2 Solve $1\frac{1}{2}y + 2 \le \frac{1}{2}y + 2$. **Graph the solution set.**

$$1\frac{1}{2}y + 2 \le \frac{1}{2}y + 2$$

$$1\frac{1}{2}y - \frac{1}{2}y + 2 \le \frac{1}{2}y - \frac{1}{2}y + 2 \qquad \textit{Subtract } \tfrac{1}{2}y \textit{ from each side.}$$

$$y + 2 \le 2$$
$$y + 2 - 2 \le 2 - 2 \qquad \textit{Subtract 2 from each side.}$$
$$y \le 0 \qquad \textit{y} \le 0 \textit{ is equivalent to } 1\tfrac{1}{2}y + 2 \le \tfrac{1}{2}y + 2.$$

The solution set is {all real numbers less than or equal to 0}.

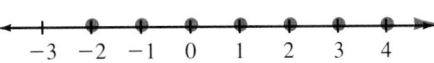

The closed circle at 0 shows that 0 *is* a solution.

EXAMPLE 3 Solve $5x - 4(x - 2) > 5$, **using the set of integers as the replacement set. Graph the solution set.**

$$5x - 4(x - 2) > 5$$
$$5x - 4x + 8 > 5 \qquad \textit{Use the distributive property.}$$
$$x + 8 > 5 \qquad \textit{Combine like terms.}$$
$$x > -3 \qquad \textit{Subtract 8 from each side.}$$

The solution set is {all integers greater than -3}, or $\{-2, -1, 0, 1, \ldots\}$.

On the number line in Example 3, the arrow in the positive direction is shaded. This shows that there is no last positive integer in the solution set. How would the graph differ if the replacement set is the set of real numbers?

5.2 Solving Inequalities: Addition and Subtraction Properties   **191**

 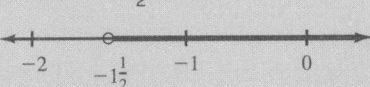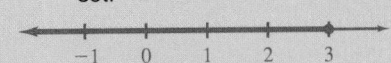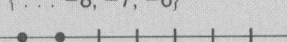

- **For Example 4**

4. Solve $1 - 4\frac{1}{2}y + 5\frac{1}{2}y \geq 2\frac{1}{2}$.

   The replacement set is the set of negative integers. $\emptyset$

Common Error

- In problems where the variable is on the right side of the inequality, students may graph $3 < d$ as all numbers less than 3. Emphasize that when an inequality is graphed, the variable should be written first, $d > 3$.
- See *Teacher's Resource Book* for additional remediation.

LESSON FOLLOW-UP

Assignment Guide

- See p. 184B for assignments.
- You may want students to work in pairs to solve Exercises 34–35.

Math Club Activity

Students practice translating English statements into algebraic expressions. These exercises help students maintain this problem solving skill.

Lesson Quiz

Solve each inequality. Draw a graph of the solution set.

1. $a + 6 \geq 5$ $a \geq -1$

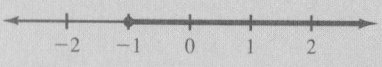

2. $1\frac{1}{2}c - 3 > 2\frac{1}{2}c + 1$ $c < -4$

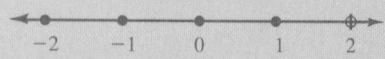

3. Solve $7c - 3(2c - 1) < 5$ using the set of integers as the replacement set. Draw a graph of the solution set. $c < 2$

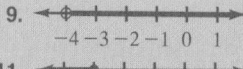

4. Solve $4 - 5\frac{1}{3}d + 6\frac{1}{3}d \geq 4$ using the set of negative integers as the replacement set. $\emptyset$

EXAMPLE 4 Solve $5x - 4x + 4 \geq 4$. The replacement set is the set of negative integers.

$$5x - 4x + 4 \geq 4$$
$$x + 4 \geq 4$$
$$x \geq 0$$

Using the replacement set of negative integers, there are no values of x that are greater than or equal to 0. The solution set is the empty set, $\emptyset$.

CLASS EXERCISES

Tell what must be done to the first inequality in order to get the second inequality.

1. $n - 4 \geq 6$; $n \geq 10$ add 4

2. $-2 < x - 4$; $2 < x$ add 4

3. $z + 1 < 5.5$; $z < 4.5$ subtract 1

4. $p + 4 > 4$; $p > 0$ subtract 4

5. $4x + 8 \geq 3x + 6$; $x \geq -2$
   subtract $3x$; subtract 8

6. $1\frac{1}{2}t - 1 < \frac{1}{2}t - 4$; $t < -3$
   add 1; subtract $\frac{1}{2}t$

7. $5y - 4y + 3 \leq 0$; $y \leq -3$
   combine like terms; subtract 3

8. $-\frac{1}{2}x + 8 + 1\frac{1}{2}x > 10$; $x > 2$
   combine like terms; subtract 8

Solve each inequality. Graph the solution set. See below.

9. $x + 4 > 0$ $x > -4$

10. $y - 5 \leq -5$ $y \leq 0$

11. $1\frac{1}{3}x - 3 \leq \frac{1}{3}x - 4$ $x \leq -1$

12. $3\frac{1}{4}x - 6 > 2\frac{1}{4}x + 1$ $x > 7$

13. $7(x - 1) - 6x < -8$ $x < -1$

14. $3(2x + 3) \geq 5x + 5$ $x \geq -4$

For Discussion

15. Find real numbers x, y, t and w where it is true that $x > y$ and $t > w$, but it is not true that $x - t > y - w$. Answers may vary. For example, $3 > 2$, $4 > -8$, but $3 - 4 > 2 - (-8)$ is false.

PRACTICE EXERCISES

Solve each inequality. Graph the solution set. See p. 720.

A
1. $m + 2 > 0$ $m > -2$

2. $c + 5 > 4$ $c > -1$

3. $3 + a < 4\frac{1}{2}$ $a < 1\frac{1}{2}$

4. $2 + x > 3\frac{1}{2}$ $x > 1\frac{1}{2}$

5. $x - 17 \geq -15$ $x \geq 2$

6. $m - 25 \geq -35$
   $m \geq -10$

7. $3\frac{1}{2}y + 2 \leq 2\frac{1}{2}y + 2$
   $y \leq 0$

8. $4\frac{2}{3}z - 1 \leq 3\frac{2}{3}z - 1$
   $z \leq 0$

9. $1\frac{1}{2}x + 6 > 2\frac{1}{2}x - 6$
   $x < 12$

10. $3x - 2(x - 4) > 7$
    $x > -1$

11. $4a - 3(a - 2) > 10$
    $a > 4$

12. $6c - 5(c - 3) > -18$
    $c > -3$

13. $8z - 7z + 7 \geq 7$ $z \geq 0$

14. $5x - 4x + 15 \geq 1$
    $x \geq -14$

15. $6x - 5x - 10 < 10$
    $x < 20$

192 Chapter 5 Inequalities in One Variable

 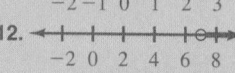

Solve each inequality using the replacement set of negative integers.

B **16.** $4z + 6 < 2z - 6$ {all integers less than -6}

17. $5x + 2 < x - 8$ {all integers less than $-\frac{5}{2}$}

18. $2t - 5 < t + 2$ {all integers less than 0}

19. $2x - 6 < -5 + x$ {all integers less than 0}

20. $3x + 6 < 2x + 6$ {all integers less than 0}

21. $6y + 5 < -5 + y$ {all integers less than -2}

22. $6x - 5(x - 1) > 2$ {$-2, -1$}

23. $6.5 < 2(t + 3) - t$ ∅

24. $7.2 < 3(x + 1) - x$ ∅

Solve each inequality. Graph the solution set.

25. $3t + 5.8 < 5.6 + 2t$ $t < -0.2$

26. $2m - 0.5 > m + 3.5$ $m > 4$

27. $5x + \frac{1}{4} > 4x + 10\frac{3}{4}$ $x > 10\frac{1}{2}$

28. $\frac{1}{2} + 3t + 1\frac{1}{2} \le 8\frac{1}{2} + 2t$ $t \le 6\frac{1}{2}$

Solve each inequality using the replacement set of positive integers.

29. $m - 5 > 1$ {7, 8, 9, ...}

30. $-3 + 10x \ge 9x + 7$ {10, 11, 12, ...}

31. $4z + 3 > z + 9$ {3, 4, 5, ...}

C **32.** Show by example that for all real numbers a, b, c, and d, if $a > b$ and $c < d$, then $a - c > b - d$. Answers may vary.

33. Show by example that for all real numbers a, b, c, and d, if $a > b$ and $c > d$, then it is not always true that $a - c > b - d$. Answers may vary.

34. *True or false:* $a + b \ge a - b$ for all real numbers a and b. False

35. *True or false:* $x(x - y) < x(x + y)$ for all real numbers x and y, $y \ne 0$. False

Applications

Write an inequality for the word sentence. Then solve the inequality.

36. Number Problem Seven more than some number y is greater than or equal to 0. $y + 7 \ge 0$; $y \ge -7$

37. Number Problem A number k decreased by 6 is less than -6. $k - 6 < -6$; $k < 0$

38. Number Problem The sum of x and $-\frac{1}{2}$ is greater than -5. $x + \left(-\frac{1}{2}\right) > -5$; $x > -4\frac{1}{2}$

MATH CLUB ACTIVITY

1. Let the number of points that you have in a game be represented by the variable s. There are three other players in the game. The first of these has two times as many points as you do. The second has 7 more points than the first. The third has half as many points as the second. Write an algebraic expression to represent the number of points that the third player has. $\frac{2s + 7}{2}$

2. During the first 6 plays of a football game, a team gained 6 yd, lost 3 yd, gained 8 yd, gained 9 yd, lost 7 yd, and then gained 2 yd. What is the total number of yd that the team lost and gained in all? How far from the starting point is the team now? lost 10 yd, gained 25 yd; 15 yd from the starting point

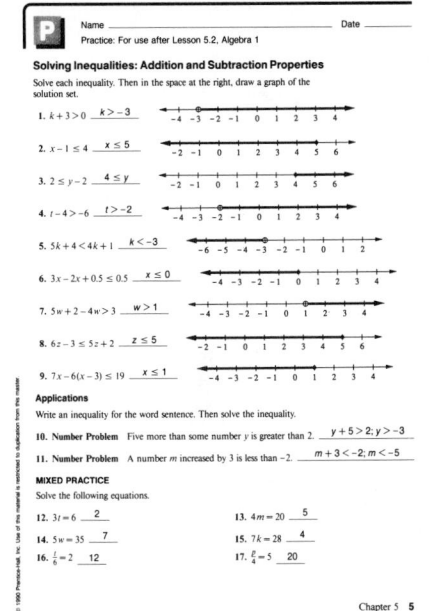

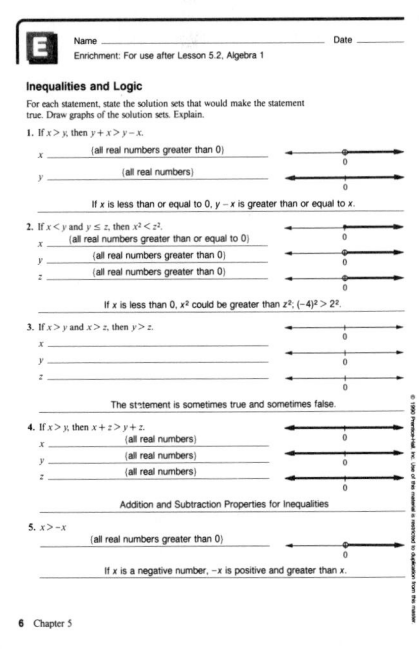

Additional Answers

25.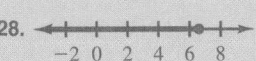

26.

27.

28.

BACKGROUND

In the Capsule Review, students review the multiplication and division properties for equations. This review prepares students for their work in solving inequalities using the multiplication and division properties.

Critical Thinking

Predicting Consequences Explain what would happen in the Multiplication Property for Inequalities if we allowed $c = 0$. Students should realize that the inequality would no longer exist. If $a > b$ and $c = 0$, then $ac = bc = 0$ and therefore the inequality would be false. Zero is not greater than zero.

5.3 Solving Inequalities: Multiplication and Division Properties

Objective: To solve inequalities using the Multiplication and Division Properties and to draw graphs of the solution sets

Kato wants to improve his school's rushing record of 1200 yd during the football season of 15 games. How many yards must he average per game in order to achieve his goal?

Let g represent the average number of yards Kato must gain in each of the 15 games.

$$15g > 1200$$

How can you solve the inequality $15g > 1200$?

Capsule Review

Multiplying or dividing each side of an equation by the same nonzero number results in an equivalent equation.

$14 = -2x$

$\dfrac{14}{-2} = \dfrac{-2x}{-2}$ *Divide by −2.*

$-7 = x$

$-\dfrac{1}{4}y = 6$

$(-4)\left(-\dfrac{1}{4}\right)y = (-4)(6)$ *Multiply by −4.*

$y = -24$

Tell what must be done to each side of the equation so that the variable y has a coefficient of 1 and is alone on one side of the equation.

1. $3y = -12$
  divide by 3

2. $25 = \dfrac{y}{-5}$
  multiply by −5

3. $-7y = 21$
  divide by −7

4. $6y = 9$
  divide by 6

If you multiply or divide each side of an inequality by a positive number, the resulting inequality is true.

When you multiply or divide each side of an inequality by a negative number, the *order* (direction) of the inequality is reversed. This leads to the following properties for inequalities.

194   Chapter 5 Inequalities in One Variable

> ### Multiplication Property for Inequalities
>
> For all real numbers a, b, and c: If $a > b$ and $c > 0$, then $ac > bc$.
> If $a > b$ and $c < 0$, then $ac < bc$.
>
> ### Division Property for Inequalities
>
> For all real numbers a, b, and c: If $a > b$ and $c > 0$, then $\dfrac{a}{c} > \dfrac{b}{c}$.
>
> If $a > b$ and $c < 0$, then $\dfrac{a}{c} < \dfrac{b}{c}$.

As a demonstration of the above properties, consider the inequality $15 > 10$.

Multiply by 2	$30 > 20$ ✔	True.
Multiply by -2	$-30 > -20$	False, unless the inequality sign is reversed.
	$-30 < -20$ ✔	True.

A similar demonstration can be shown using division.

The multiplication and division properties for inequalities are also true for "is less than" ($<$), "is less than or equal to" ($\le$), and "is greater than or equal to" ($\ge$).

EXAMPLE 1 **Solve $15g > 1200$. Graph the solution set.**

$15g > 1200$

$\dfrac{15g}{15} > \dfrac{1200}{15}$ *Divide each side by 15.*

$g > 80$ *The direction of the inequality is unchanged.*

Kato must average more than 80 yd per game.

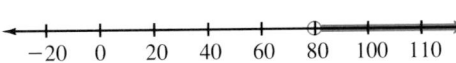

Substitute numbers such as 82, 90 and 100 in $15g > 1200$ to check the solution set.

EXAMPLE 2 **Solve $-7y > 21$. Graph the solution set.**

$-7y > 21$

$\dfrac{-7y}{-7} < \dfrac{21}{-7}$ *Divide each side by -7. Reverse the order of the inequality: change $>$ to $<$.*

$y < -3$

The solution set is {all real numbers less than -3}.

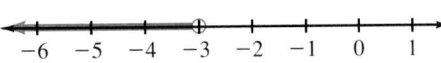

5.3 Solving Inequalities: Multiplication and Division Properties   **195**

 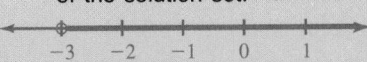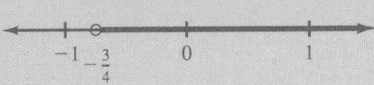

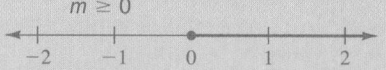

196

In Example 3, each side of the inequality is multiplied by the reciprocal of the coefficient of the variable.

EXAMPLE 3   **Solve $2 \leq 1\frac{2}{3}y - y$. Graph the solution set.**

$$2 \leq 1\frac{2}{3}y - y$$

$$2 \leq \frac{2}{3}y \qquad \textit{Combine like terms.}$$

$$\frac{3}{2} \cdot 2 \leq \frac{3}{2} \cdot \frac{2}{3}y \qquad \textit{Multiply each side by } \frac{3}{2}.$$

$$3 \leq y$$

$3 \leq y$ is the same as $y \geq 3$.

The solution set is {all real numbers greater than or equal to 3}.

CLASS EXERCISES

Tell what must be done to each side of the first inequality in order to get the second inequality.

1. $4n \geq -24$; $n \geq -6$
   divide by 4

2. $6 \leq -\frac{2}{3}y$; $-9 \geq y$
   multiply by $-\frac{3}{2}$

3. $-2t > 10$; $t < -5$
   divide by -2

4. $\frac{3}{4}m < -\frac{27}{40}$; $m < -\frac{9}{10}$
   multiply by $\frac{4}{3}$

5. $0.5y > -2.4$; $y > -4.8$
   divide by 0.5

6. $35 < -25k$; $1.4 > k$
   divide by -25

Solve each inequality. Graph the solution set.

7. $2x \geq 0$ {x: x ≥ 0}

8. $\frac{4}{5}y < -4$
   {y: y < −5}

9. $-3c > 9$
   {c: c < −3}

10. $-\frac{1}{2}d \leq 4$
    {d: d ≥ −8}

11. $-\frac{2}{3}m \geq 12$
    {m: m ≤ −18}

12. $-1.2t < -0.6$
    {t: t > 0.5}

13. $-4.6k > 1.38$
    {k: k < −0.3}

14. $1\frac{1}{5}y > -3\frac{1}{10}$
    $\left\{y: y > -\frac{31}{12}\right\}$

For Discussion

15. Why is zero (0) excluded in the statement of the Multiplication Property for Inequalities? *Hint:* What happens if you multiply both sides of $a > b$ by 0? If you multiply both sides by "0," the result is 0 > 0 which is a false statement. So, 0 is excluded.

16. Why is zero (0) excluded in the statement of the Division Property for Inequalities? If you divide by "0," the result is an undefined statement.

17. Why is zero (0) *not* excluded in the statements of the Addition and Subtraction Properties for Inequalities? "0" is included in the Addition and Subtraction Prop. because when you add or subtract zero from a number the result is that number.

 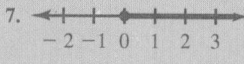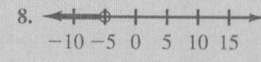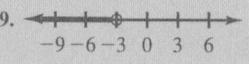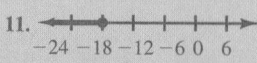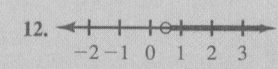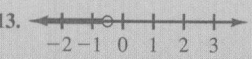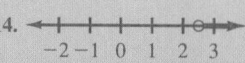

PRACTICE EXERCISES

Solve and check each inequality. Draw a graph of the solution set. See p. 721.

A **1.** $4x < 20$ $x < 5$ **2.** $7y < 28$ $y < 4$ **3.** $8a < 56$ $a < 7$

4. $5z < 55$ $z < 11$ **5.** $6b > 48$ $b > 8$ **6.** $9x > 63$ $x > 7$

7. $-7y > 42$ $y < -6$ **8.** $-3t > 36$ $t < -12$ **9.** $-4a < 28$ $a > -7$

10. $-9c < 54$ $c > -6$ **11.** $-2b > -64$ $b < 32$ **12.** $-5z > -40$ $z < 8$

13. $3x > -6$ $x > -2$ **14.** $4a > -16$ $a > -4$ **15.** $\frac{1}{2}y \le 3$ $y \le 6$

16. $\frac{4}{5}z \le 12$ $z \le 15$ **17.** $4 \le 1\frac{4}{5}x - x$ $x \ge 5$ **18.** $3 \le 1\frac{1}{3}y - y$ $y \ge 9$

B **19.** $5 \ge 1\frac{1}{2}z - z$ $z \le 10$ **20.** $2 \ge 1\frac{1}{6}b - b$ $b \le 12$ **21.** $6p - 9p < -21$ $p > 7$

22. $5x - 7x > 40$ $x < -20$ **23.** $6y > 2y - 1$ $y > -\frac{1}{4}$ **24.** $2c > 4c + 9$ $c < -4\frac{1}{2}$

25. $-\frac{5}{8}x \ge 25$ $x \le -40$ **26.** $-1.5t > -75$ $t < 50$ **27.** $-11z \le 1.21$ $z \ge -0.11$

28. $-\frac{3}{5}x \ge 15$ $x \le -25$ **29.** $-0.5m \le -1.5$ $m \ge 3$ **30.** $-0.6t > 1.08$ $t < -1.8$

C **31.** $-1.3t > 0.6$ $t < -0.462$ **32.** $-4h < 0.25$ $h > -0.0625$ **33.** $-\frac{1}{4}k > -2.4$ $k < 9.6$

34. $-2\frac{1}{2}m \ge -1\frac{3}{4}$ $m \le \frac{7}{10}$ **35.** $-15y - 7y \le 44$ $y \ge -2$ **36.** $-25 \ge 7w - 12w$ $w \ge 5$

Applications

Write an inequality for the word sentence. Then solve the inequality.

37. Number Problem Three-fourths of a number y is greater than -18. $\frac{3}{4}y > -18$; $y > -24$

38. Number Problem $-2x$ is less than or equal to $\frac{1}{2}$. $-2x \le \frac{1}{2}$; $x \ge -\frac{1}{4}$

EXTRA

A computer cannot directly solve an inequality. If you use an inequality such as $2x - 5 < 7$ in this program, you will get the correct solution. Note, however, the computer is really solving an equation in calculation ready form. It then decides whether it should print ''X <'' or ''X >'' as an answer by determining whether B and then A are positive or negative. Try using the program on some of the exercises.
Check students' work.

```
10 INPUT "FOR AN INEQUALITY IN THE FORM
     AX + B < C, ENTER A, B, C   ";A,B,C
20 PRINT : LET X = (C - B) / A
30 PRINT "THE SOLUTION OF ";A;"X + ";B;
     " < ";C;" IS "
40 IF B < 0 THEN 50
50 IF A < 0 THEN 70
60 PRINT "X < ";X: PRINT : PRINT : GOTO 80
70 PRINT "X > ";X: PRINT : PRINT
80 INPUT "ENTER Y IF YOU WANT ANOTHER
     INEQUALITY.  ";N$: PRINT
90 IF N$ = "Y" THEN 10
100 END
```

5.3 Solving Inequalities: Multiplication and Division Properties **197**

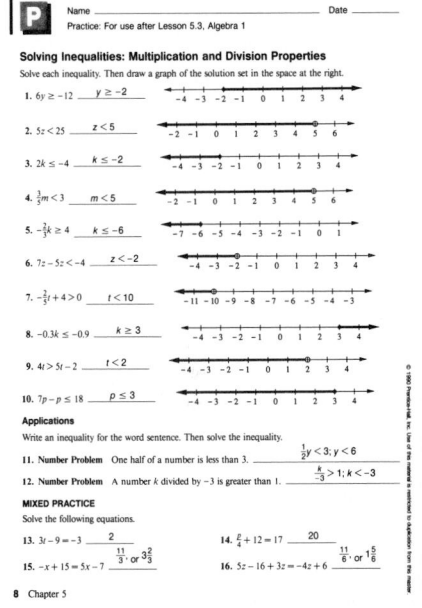
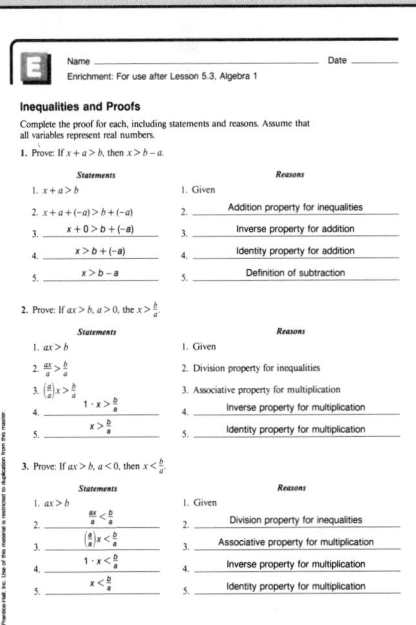

BACKGROUND

- In the Capsule Review, students solve equations using more than one property of equations. You may want to remind students that the addition or subtraction property for equations is used before the multiplication or division property. Students who are having difficulty should be referred to Lesson 3.3, Solving Equations: More Than One Property.
- Set-builder notation is introduced and used in this lesson to write the solution of an inequality. You may wish to point out that there are two forms of set-builder notation. For example, {all real numbers less than or equal to 6} can be written {$p: p \leq 6$} or {$p|p \leq 6$}.

Critical Thinking

Observation Write an inequality for which the resulting inequality is false, thus, the solution set is the empty set. Answers may vary. One example is $3x - 2(x - 3) > x + 6$. Students should observe that when the solution set of an inequality is the empty set, the two sides of the inequality may be equal.

5.4

Solving Inequalities: More Than One Property

Objective: To solve inequalities using more than one inequality property

To solve $9 + \frac{2}{3}x < 1$, you need to use more than one property of inequalities. The procedures are similar to those you used to solve equations.

Capsule Review

Solve: $-5z + 4 = -1$

$$-5z + 4 = -1$$
$$-5z + 4 - 4 = -1 - 4 \qquad \textit{Subtract 4 from each side.}$$
$$-5z = -5$$
$$\frac{-5z}{-5} = \frac{-5}{-5} \qquad \textit{Divide each side by } -5.$$
$$z = 1$$

The solution is 1.

Solve each equation.

1. $8x - 5 = 35$ 5   **2.** $6 - 7y = -36$ 6   **3.** $3(t - 4) + 14 = 16$ $\frac{14}{3}$

EXAMPLE 1   **Solve:** $9 + \frac{2}{3}x < 1$

$$9 + \frac{2}{3}x < 1$$
$$9 - 9 + \frac{2}{3}x < 1 - 9 \qquad \textit{Subtract 9 from each side.}$$
$$\frac{2}{3}x < -8$$
$$\frac{3}{2} \cdot \frac{2}{3}x < \frac{3}{2}(-8) \qquad \textit{Multiply each side by } \frac{3}{2}.$$
$$x < -12$$

The solution set is {all real numbers less than -12}.

The solution set in Example 1 can also be given using **set-builder** notation.
Read: {$x: x < -12$}, "the set of all real numbers x *such that* x is less than -12."

198   Chapter 5 Inequalities in One Variable

EXAMPLE 2   Solve $5p - 4 - 6p \geq -10$. State the solution set in set-builder notation.

$$5p - 4 - 6p \geq -10$$
$$-1p - 4 \geq -10 \qquad \text{\textit{Combine like terms.}}$$
$$-1p - 4 + 4 \geq -10 + 4 \qquad \text{\textit{Add 4 to each side.}}$$
$$-1p \geq -6$$
$$\frac{-1p}{-1} \leq \frac{-6}{-1} \qquad \text{\textit{Divide each side by} -1. \textit{Reverse the order of the inequality.}}$$
$$p \leq 6$$

The solution set is $\{p: p \leq 6\}$.

As you apply the properties to solve an inequality, the variable terms may ''drop out.'' If the numerical inequality is false, the solution set is the empty set. If the resulting numerical inequality is true, the solution set is the set of all real numbers.

EXAMPLE 3   Solve $2(4 - a) - 2 \leq -2a + 6$. Graph the solution set.

$$2(4 - a) - 2 \leq -2a + 6$$
$$8 - 2a - 2 \leq -2a + 6 \qquad \text{\textit{Use the distributive property.}}$$
$$-2a + 6 \leq -2a + 6 \qquad \text{\textit{Combine like terms.}}$$
$$2a + (-2a) + 6 \leq 2a + (-2a) + 6 \qquad \text{\textit{Add 2a to each side.}}$$
$$6 \leq 6 \quad \text{✓} \quad \text{True}$$

The solution set is $\{$all real numbers$\}$.
The graph is the entire number line.

EXAMPLE 4   Write and solve an inequality for the word sentence: **Seven decreased by 2 times a number x is greater than or equal to 19.**

$$\underbrace{\text{Seven decreased by } 2x}_{7 - 2x} \ \underbrace{\text{is greater than or equal to}}_{\geq} \ \underbrace{19.}_{19}$$

$$7 - 7 - 2x \geq 19 - 7$$
$$-2x \geq 12$$
$$\frac{-2x}{-2} \leq \frac{12}{-2}$$
$$x \leq -6$$

The solution set is $\{$all real numbers less than or equal to $-6\}$, or $\{x: x \leq -6\}$.

5.4 Solving Inequalities: More Than One Property   **199**

TEACHING SUGGESTIONS

• At this point, you may want to compare and contrast solving equations and solving inequalities. Have students solve equations and similar inequalities. Discuss the steps involved with both procedures.

• In Example 3, point out that sometimes the variable is eliminated. The resulting inequality is true, $6 \leq 6$, thus, the solution set is all real numbers, the replacement set. If the resulting inequality is false, the solution set is the empty set.

• Encourage students to check their solutions. You may want them to use a calculator where appropriate.

CHALKBOARD EXAMPLES

• **For Example 1**
Solve each inequality.
1. $3 - \frac{2}{5}y > 5$ $y < -5$
2. $\frac{3}{4} < 3c + \frac{1}{4}$ $c > \frac{1}{6}$

• **For Example 2**
Sove each inequality. State the solution set in set-builder notation.
3. $6b - 8b - 5 \leq 0$
   $\left\{b: b \geq \frac{-5}{2}\right\}$
4. $-8 \geq 3x + 4 - x$ $\{x: x \leq -6\}$

• **For Example 3**
Solve each inequality. Draw a graph of the solution set.
5. $3(5 - c) - 7 \geq -3c + 8$
   $\{$all real numbers$\}$

6. $2y - 3(y - 3) < -y + 9$ $\varnothing$

- **For Example 4**

  Write and solve an inequality for the word sentence.

  7. Two-fifths of a number c increased by 4 is less than or equal to -6.

  $\frac{2}{5}c + 4 \leq -6$; $\{c: c \leq -25\}$

Common Error

- Many students may become confused when applying the properties to solve an inequality and the variable terms "drop out." Explain to the students that if the variable terms "drop out" and the resulting numerical inequality is true, the solution set is the set of all real numbers. If the numerical inequality is false the solution set is the empty set.
- See *Teacher's Resource Book* for additional remediation.

LESSON FOLLOW-UP

Discussion

Show different ways of writing the solution set for $x \geq -2$. $\{x: x \geq -2\}$; {all real numbers greater than or equal to -2}

Assignment Guide

See p. 184B for assignments.

Test Yourself

See *Teacher's Resource Book, Tests*, pp. 49–50.

Lesson Quiz

Solve each inequality. State the solution set in set-builder notation.

1. $7 + \frac{3}{4}y > 1$ $\{y: y > -8\}$

2. $6a - 7 - 9a \leq -9$ $\left\{a: a \geq \frac{2}{3}\right\}$

3. $3(t - 2) - 4 \leq 3t - 4(2 - t)$
   $\left\{t: t \geq -\frac{1}{2}\right\}$

Enrichment

Solve $-2p - 6 \geq 12$ in two ways.

As a first step, you can add 6 to both sides or you can divide each term by -2. $\{p: p \leq -9\}$

200

CLASS EXERCISES

Tell what must be done to the first inequality to get the second inequality.

1. $2y - 10 > 18$; $y > 14$
   add 10; divide by 2

2. $1 - \frac{x}{4} \geq -8$; $x \leq 36$
   subtr. 1; mult. by -4

3. $\frac{2}{3}t + 15 \leq -1$; $t \leq -24$
   subtr. 15; mult. by $\frac{3}{2}$

4. $14 - 3(a + 4) < 0$; $a > \frac{2}{3}$
   distrib. -3; combine like terms; subtr. 2; divide by -3

Solve each inequality. Then draw its graph by locating the solution on a number line. See below.

5. $\frac{2}{3}t - 3 < 1$ $t < 6$

6. $-4x + 24 > -4$ $x < 7$

7. $-3 \leq \frac{a}{4} - 5$ $8 \leq a$

8. $12 - 3d < 1\frac{1}{2}$ $d > \frac{7}{2}$

9. $6p - 7p + 1 \geq 5$ $p \leq -4$

10. $2(x - 5) + 10 < -8$ $x < -4$

PRACTICE EXERCISES

Solve each inequality. Graph the solution set. See p. 721.

A   1. $5 + \frac{1}{3}y > 4$ $\{y: y > -3\}$

2. $5 + \frac{2}{3}d > 11$ $\{d: d > 9\}$

3. $4x + 5 - 6x \leq 9$
   $\{x: x \geq -2\}$

4. $5y + 7 - 7y \leq 13$
   $\{y: y \geq -3\}$

5. $3(c + 4) \geq 15$ $\{c: c \geq 1\}$

6. $2(y + 1) \geq 15$
   $\left\{y: y \geq \frac{13}{2}\right\}$

Solve each inequality. State the solution set in set-builder notation.

7. $6 - \frac{2}{3}x < 4$ $\{x: x > 3\}$

8. $2 - \frac{1}{4}c > 4$ $\{c: c < -8\}$

9. $0.8b - 7 \leq 0.2$
   $\{b: b \leq 9\}$

10. $0.4p - 4 > 3.6$
    $\{p: p > 19\}$

11. $y + 2 - 5y \geq 22$
    $\{y: y \leq -5\}$

12. $n + 5 - 7n \geq 13$
    $\left\{n: n \leq -\frac{4}{3}\right\}$

13. $1 + a < 3 - 2a$
    $\left\{a: a < \frac{2}{3}\right\}$

14. $1 + 4x < 5 - 6x$
    $\left\{x: x < \frac{2}{5}\right\}$

15. $9d - 4 \geq 12 + 5d$
    $\{d: d \geq 4\}$

16. $6a - 5 > 11 - 2a$
    $\{a: a > 2\}$

17. $5y - 2(y - 15) < 10$
    $\left\{y: y < -\frac{20}{3}\right\}$

18. $4t - 2(t - 1) < 4$
    $\{t: t < 1\}$

Write an inequality for each word sentence and then find the solution set.

19. A number y increased by 4 is greater than -11.
    $y + 4 > -11$; $\{y: y > -15\}$

20. The product of a number z and $-\frac{2}{3}$ is less than or equal to 16.
    $-\frac{2}{3}z \leq 16$; $\{z: z \geq -24\}$

B   21. One decreased by 7 times a number k is less than 5 times the number k increased by 3. $1 - 7k < 5k + 3$; $\left\{k: k > -\frac{1}{6}\right\}$

22. The product of 6 and the sum of d and 5 is greater than or equal to the sum of 3 and 6 times d. $6(d + 5) \geq 3 + 6d$; {all real numbers}

200   Chapter 5 Inequalities in One Variable

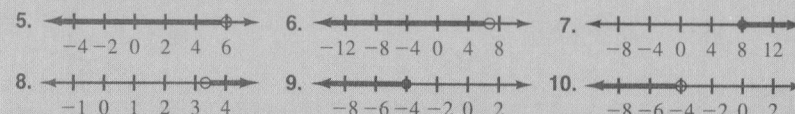

Give the solution set for each inequality.

23. $2n - 3(n + 3) \leq 14$ $\{n: n \geq -23\}$

24. $7x - (9x + 1) > -5$ $\{x: x < 2\}$

25. $4(3m - 1) \geq 2(m + 3)$ $\{m: m \geq 1\}$

26. $17 - (4y - 2) \geq 2(y + 3)$ $\left\{y: y \leq \frac{13}{6}\right\}$

27. $2(24 - w) - 11 \geq 17 - 2w$
$\{w: w \text{ is a real number}\}$

28. $5d - \frac{1}{2}(3d + 8) \leq -4 + \frac{7}{2}d$
$\{d: d \text{ is a real number}\}$

29. $\frac{1}{2} - t < -\frac{2}{3}$ $\left\{t: t > \frac{7}{6}\right\}$

30. $x + \frac{5}{12} \geq -\frac{3}{4}$ $\left\{x: x \geq -\frac{7}{6}\right\}$

31. $2 - 3x \neq 4 + 5x$ $\left\{x: x \neq -\frac{1}{4}\right\}$

32. $-1 + 2z \neq 5 - 2z$ $\left\{z: z \neq \frac{3}{2}\right\}$

33. $4 + 2(3 - 2w) \geq 4(3w - 5) - 6w$
$\{w: w \leq 3\}$

34. $5(1 - y) - 2(y + 7) \leq -10y$
$\{y: y \leq 3\}$

C **35.** $\frac{1}{2} - \frac{1}{3}y < \frac{3}{8} + \frac{1}{6}y$ $\left\{y: y > \frac{1}{4}\right\}$

36. $\frac{1}{2}n - \frac{1}{8} > \frac{3}{4} + \frac{6}{5}n$ $\left\{n: n < -\frac{5}{4}\right\}$

37. $6 - [2 - 5(7a + 9)] \geq a - (-a + 8)$ $\left\{a: a \geq -\frac{19}{11}\right\}$

38. $y - [y - (y - 4)] \leq 3 - [4 - (2y + 8)3]$ $\left\{y: y \geq -\frac{27}{5}\right\}$

39. $8m - (3 - m) \leq -\{-[-(3 - 9m)]\}$
$\{m: m \text{ is a real number}\}$

40. $-2\{-2[-2(2 - z)]\} > -16 + 8z$ $\varnothing$

Applications

Write an inequality for the word sentence. Then solve the inequality.

41. Number Problem Two-thirds of a number y, increased by 14, is greater than or equal to 8. $\frac{2}{3}y + 14 \geq 8$; {all real numbers ≥ -9}

42. Number Problem Six minus 3 times a number x is less than 30.
$6 - 3x < 30$; {all real numbers > -8}

TEST YOURSELF

Graph each inequality. See below.

1. $-2 < a$

2. $c \geq 3$

3. $b \neq 0$

5.1

State the solution set of the inequality whose graph is given.

4.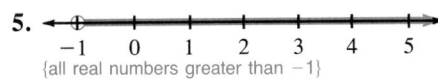
$-2 \quad -1 \quad 0 \quad 1 \quad 2 \quad 3$
{all real numbers equal to or less than 1}

5.
$-1 \quad 0 \quad 1 \quad 2 \quad 3 \quad 4 \quad 5$
{all real numbers greater than -1}

Solve each inequality. Graph the solution set. See p. 721.

6. $0 > d - 5$ $\{d: d < 5\}$

7. $p + 5.7 < 5.9$ $\{p: p < 0.2\}$

5.2

8. $-2.5y \leq 7.5$ $\{y: y \geq -3\}$

9. $\frac{2}{3}a < -8$ $\{a: a < -12\}$

5.3

10. $3t - 5t > -2$ $\{t: t < 1\}$

11. $3 - 4(x - 2) \geq 5$ $\left\{x: x \leq \frac{3}{2}\right\}$

5.4

12. $-\frac{1}{3}y + 5 < -2$ $\{y: y > 21\}$

13. $2(a - 6) > 2a - 2$ $\varnothing$

5.4 Solving Inequalities: More Than One Property **201**

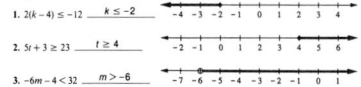

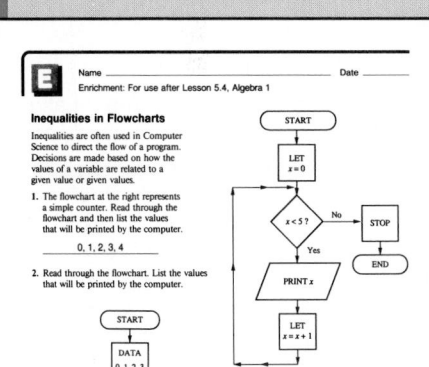

 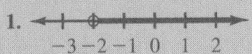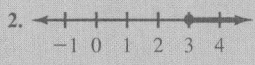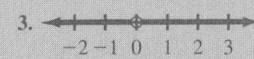

Vocabulary
Combined inequality
Conjunction
Disjunction
Intersection
Union

Materials/Manipulatives
Calculators
Number lines
Overhead projector
Teacher's Resource Book,
   Teaching Aid 17,
   Transparency 2

BACKGROUND

In the Capsule Review, students re-view classifying an inequality as true or false. Caution students to interpret the inequality symbol correctly. Re-view the meaning of the symbols $<$, $\leq$, $>$, and $\geq$.

Critical Thinking

Comparing-Contrasting The Latin language has two words meaning *or,* "aut" which means "one or the other but not both, " and "vel" which means "one or the other and possibly both." Determine which meaning of the word *or* can be used

Students should com-pare and contrast the meanings. The inclu-sive *or,* "vel," is used, "one or the other and possibly both."

5.5 Combined Inequalities

Objective: To solve combined inequalities and to draw graphs of the solution sets

In Olympic boxing competition, the mass of a welterweight must be at least 64 kg but no more than 67 kg. The mass of a welterweight can be expressed by a *combined inequality* with $>$, $<$, and $=$.

Capsule Review

Recall that $\leq$ means is less than or equal to, $\geq$ means is greater than or equal to, $<$ means is less than, and $>$ means is greater than.

Classify as *true* or *false*:
a. $13 > 5 \cdot 2 - (-3)$ **b.** $19 - 26 \leq 0 - 7$

a. $13 > 5 \cdot 2 - (-3)$ **b.** $19 - 26 \leq 0 - 7$
     $13 > 13$ False $-7 \leq -7$ ✔ True

Classify each inequality as *true* or *false*.

1. $18 - 9 < 5$ False   **2.** $6 \geq 4 + 2$ True   **3.** $-5 > -8 + 2$ True

Let m represent the mass of a welterweight boxer described above. "At least 64 kg" means that the mass can be exactly 64 kg but it cannot be less than 64 kg. That is, $m \geq 64$.

Also, the mass must be "no more than 67 kg." The mass can be exactly 67 kg but it cannot be greater than that: $m \leq 67$. A **combined inequality,** called a *conjunction,* expresses the mass:

$$m \geq 64 \text{ and } m \leq 67$$

> A **conjunction** is a sentence formed by joining two sentences with the word *and*.

A conjunction is true only if *both* of its sentences are true. To solve a conjunction of two open sentences for a given variable, you find the values of the variable for which both sentences are true.

202   Chapter 5 Inequalities in One Variable

EXAMPLE 1   **Graph the solution set for $m \geq 64$ and $m \leq 67$.**

The solution set is {64, 67, and all real numbers between 64 and 67}.

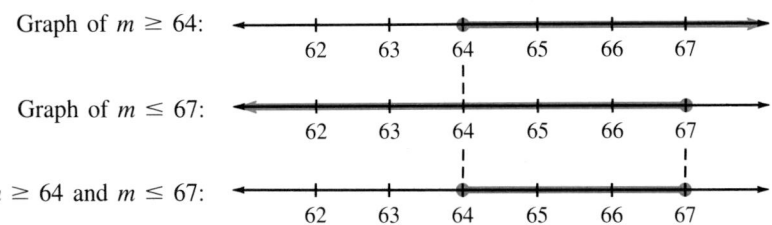

Graph of $m \geq 64$:

Graph of $m \leq 67$:

Graph of $m \geq 64$ and $m \leq 67$:

The graph of a combined inequality containing *and* is the **intersection** (overlap) of the graphs of the two inequalities. The conjunction $m \geq 64$ and $m \leq 67$ can be written in a more compact form as $64 \leq m \leq 67$.

EXAMPLE 2   **Graph the solution set for $-1 < x < 2$.**

Write the combined inequality with *and*: $x > -1$ and $x < 2$. Numbers greater than -1 and less than 2 make both inequalities true.

The solution set is {all real numbers between -1 and 2}.

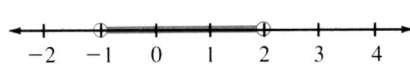

In Example 2, notice that $-1 < x$ is the same as $x > -1$.

EXAMPLE 3   **Graph: $4 < y$ and $y \leq 2$.**

Can this be written as the combined inequality $4 < y \leq 2$?

There are no values of y that are both greater than 4 and less than or equal to 2. The graph of $y > 4$ and the graph of $y \leq 2$ have no points in common. They do not intersect.

The solution set is { }.

Sometimes a combined inequality contains the word *or*.

> A **disjunction** is a sentence formed by joining two sentences with the word *or*.

A disjunction is true if either sentence is true or if both sentences are true.

5.5 Combined Inequalities   **203**

TEACHING SUGGESTIONS

- Emphasize the importance of the number line in solving a conjunction or disjunction. Using an overhead projector and Transparency 2, in the *Teacher's Resource Book,* may be helpful when discussing the examples.
- Tell students to use *and* for conjunctions and *or* for disjunctions.
- You may wish to point out the meaning of intersection and union using Venn Diagrams. Start the discussion of union and intersection by drawing a Venn diagram or using Teaching Aid 17, in the *Teacher's Resource Book,* for A: {0, 1, 2, 3, 4} and B: {−3, −2, −1, 0, 1}. Point out the union and the intersection.

CHALKBOARD EXAMPLES

- **For Example 1**
  1. Graph the solution set for $n \geq -2$ and $n \leq 5$.

  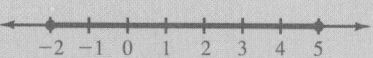

- **For Example 2**
  2. Graph the solution set for $-4 \leq x \leq 5$.

  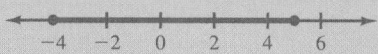

- **For Example 3**
  3. Graph: $2 < t$ and $t < 0$ Ø

- **For Example 4**
  4. Graph the solution set for $y < -1$ or $y \leq 1$.

  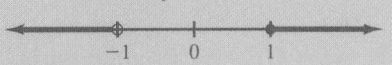

- **For Example 5**
  5. Solve: $n \leq 4$ or $n > -3$
  {all real numbers} or {n: n is a real number}

203

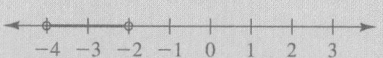
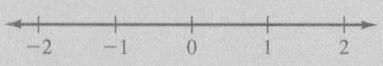
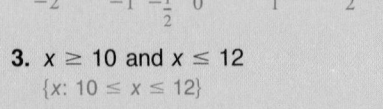
EXAMPLE 4 Graph the solution set for $x \leq 4$ or $x > 7$.

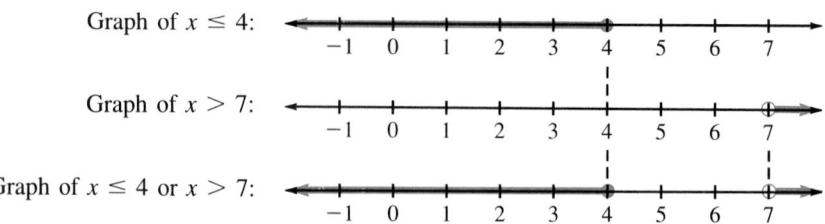

The solution set is {4, and all real numbers less than 4 or greater than 7}.

The graph of a combined inequality involving *or* is the **union** of the graphs of the two inequalities. The union contains both graphs.

EXAMPLE 5 Solve: $y < 2$ or $y \geq -2$

Numbers less than 2 are solutions of $y < 2$. Numbers greater than or equal to -2 are solutions of $y \geq -2$.

The solution set is {all real numbers}, or $\{y: y \text{ is a real number}\}$. The graph of $y < 2$ or $y \geq -2$ is the entire number line.

To solve some combined inequalities, you may have to use the properties of inequalities.

EXAMPLE 6 Solve $3 < 5 - 2x < 7$. Graph the solution set.

First write the combined inequality with *and*. Then solve each inequality separately.

$$
\begin{array}{ccc}
3 < 5 - 2x & \text{and} & 5 - 2x < 7 \\
3 - 5 < 5 - 5 - 2x & & 5 - 5 - 2x < 7 - 5 \\
\dfrac{-2}{-2} > \dfrac{-2x}{-2} & & \dfrac{-2x}{-2} > \dfrac{2}{-2} \\
1 > x & \text{and} & x > -1
\end{array}
$$

The solution set is {all real numbers between -1 and 1}, or $\{x: -1 < x < 1\}$.

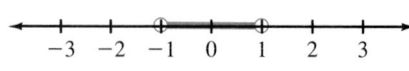

CLASS EXERCISES

Solve each inequality. Graph the solution set. See below.

1. $-1 < 2 + 3x < 5$

2. $y - 1 < -2$ or $y - 1 \geq 2$

Additional Answers

1.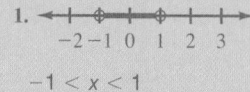

$-1 < x < 1$

2.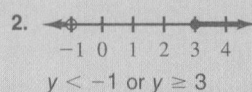

$y < -1$ or $y \geq 3$

PRACTICE EXERCISES

Graph the solution set for each inequality. See below.

A **1.** $m \geq 34$ and $m \leq 35$ **2.** $x \geq 21$ and $x \leq 22$ **3.** $y < 1$ and $y > -1$

4. $t < 5$ and $t > -5$ **5.** $-2 < r < 3$ **6.** $-4 < z < 5$

7. $3 \leq w < 9$ **8.** $8 \leq t < 15$ **9.** $a \leq -4$ or $a > 4$

10. $t \leq 0$ or $t > 3$ **11.** $y < 5$ or $y \geq 5$ **12.** $m < 3$ or $m \geq 3$

13. $4 < 3 - 2x < 8$ **14.** $3 < 5 - 3x < 9$ **15.** $5 < 2z + 1 < 7$

B **16.** $1 < 3a + 1 < 8$ **17.** $-1 \leq 2 - t < 3$ **18.** $-4 < 5 - p < 0$

19. $-3 \leq 8s + 5 \leq 21$ **20.** $-10 \leq 12r + 2 \leq 14$

21. $-4 \leq -4z - 8 \leq 8$ **22.** $-2 \leq -3m - 9 \leq 3$

23. $-6 < 2(w + 1) < 4$ **24.** $-6 < 3(x + 1) < 9$

25. $4a + 2a > 12$ and $3a - 9 < -2a$ **26.** $3(m - 3) > -3$ or $-8m > -24$

C **27.** $4 - 2w < 3w + 1 < 7$ **28.** $z - 2 \geq 2 - 3z \geq 1 - 4z$

29. $5y - 2 < 3$ or $-2 < 2(y - 3) < 4$ **30.** $2 - x < \frac{2}{3} - 2$ or $\frac{2}{3} - 2 \geq -1 + x$

Applications

31. Sports A baseball measures between 23 cm and 23.5 cm in circumference.
$23 < c < 23.5$

32. Sports The mass of a baseball is between 142 g and 148.8 g. $142 < M < 148.8$

33. Sports The length of a major league baseball bat may not be more than 107 cm. $l \leq 107$

ALGEBRA IN GEOMETRY

Graphs of inequalities may be lines, rays, segments, or points.

EXAMPLE 1 $x \leq -2$

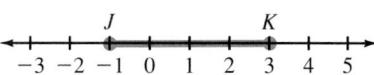

Ray *GH* starts at $G(-2)$ and goes forever in the direction of *H*.

EXAMPLE 2 $-1 \leq y \leq 3$

Segment *JK* has endpoints $J(-1)$ and $K(3)$.

Solve and graph each inequality. What part of a line does the graph represent?

1. $3r + 1 \leq -2$ or $\frac{1}{2}r + 4 \geq 6$
$\{r: r \leq -1$ or $r \geq 4\}$; 2 rays

2. $1 - 2y \geq 0$ and $2y + 7 \geq 11$
$\emptyset$; no part of the line

5.5 Combined Inequalities   **205**

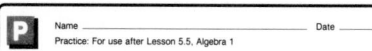
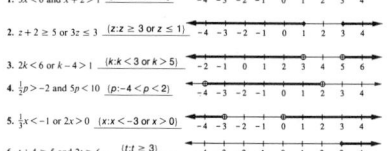
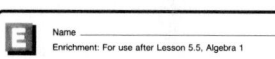
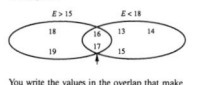
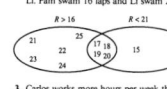
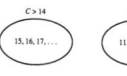

Additional Answers

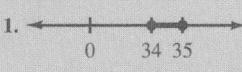

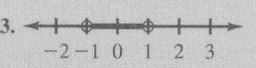

See Additional Answer section beginning p. 721.

205

5.6 Absolute Value Equations

Objective: To solve equations involving absolute value

The equation $|x| = 2$ is equivalent to a combined equation containing *or*, a
disjunction. The equation has two solutions. Can you find them?

Capsule Review

The absolute value of a number is the distance of its graph from the origin on
a number line. The absolute value of a number is always positive or zero.

Evaluate.

1. $|5|$ 5   **2.** $|-4|$ 4   **3.** $-|-6| - |-4|$ −10   **4.** $-|6 + (-6)|$ 0

In the equation $|x| = 2$, x is a number whose
graph is 2 units from the origin on a number
line. That is, $x = 2$ or $x = -2$.

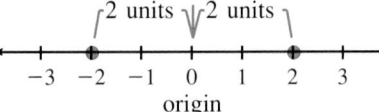

This suggests that to solve an equation that involves absolute value, first
write it as a disjunction, then solve the two resulting equations.

EXAMPLE 1   **Solve and check: $|2y + 1| = 6$**

$$2y + 1 = 6 \quad \text{or} \quad 2y + 1 = -6$$
$$2y = 5 \quad \quad \quad 2y = -7$$
$$y = \frac{5}{2} \quad \text{or} \quad y = -\frac{7}{2}$$

Check: $|2y + 1| = 6$ **Check:** $|2y + 1| = 6$

$\left|2\left(\frac{5}{2}\right) + 1\right| \stackrel{?}{=} 6$ $\left|2\left(-\frac{7}{2}\right) + 1\right| \stackrel{?}{=} 6$

$|5 + 1| \stackrel{?}{=} 6$ $|-7 + 1| \stackrel{?}{=} 6$

$6 = 6$ ✔ True $6 = 6$ ✔ True

The solution set is $\left\{\frac{5}{2}, -\frac{7}{2}\right\}$.

You can *count* to find the distance between points $A(-5)$ and $B(3)$.

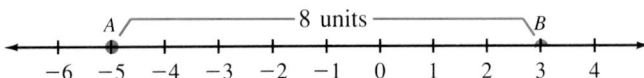

206   Chapter 5 Inequalities in One Variable

You can also *calculate* the distance between A and B, as follows:

$$|3 - (-5)| = |3 + 5| = 8 \text{ or } |-5 - 3| = |-8| = 8$$

Because of the absolute value signs, the coordinates -5 and 3 can be subtracted in either order. The equation $|3 - (-5)| = 8$ means that 3 is 8 units from -5. Similarly, the equation $|z - 5| = 6$ means that some number z is 6 units from 5. The equation can be solved by looking for appropriate values on the number line or by an algebraic method. Both methods are shown in Example 2.

EXAMPLE 2   Solve $|z - 5| = 6$ by two methods.

Solution by the number-line method:

$|z - 5| = 6$ Look for values of z that are 6 units from 5.

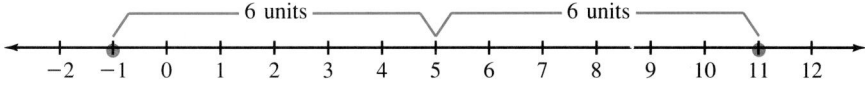

Since both 11 and -1 are 6 units from 5, $z = 11$ or $z = -1$.

Solution by the algebraic method:

$$
\begin{array}{lll}
z - 5 = 6 & \text{or} & z - 5 = -6 \\
z = 11 & \text{or} & z = -1
\end{array}
$$

So, the solution set is $\{11, -1\}$.

In $|t + 6| = 4$, you can change $|t + 6|$ to $|t - (-6)|$ to represent the distance between two points as the difference between their coordinates.

EXAMPLE 3   Solve: $|t + 6| = 4$

Change $|t + 6| = 4$ to $|t - (-6)| = 4$.
Use the number line. -10 and -2 are each 4 units from -6.

The solution set is $\{-10, -2\}$.

To solve an equation such as $|x| + 5 = 4 - 6$, you should isolate the term containing the absolute value.

EXAMPLE 4   Solve: $|x| + 5 = 4 - 6$

$$
\begin{array}{ll}
|x| + 5 = 4 - 6 & \\
|x| + 5 = -2 & \textit{Combine like terms.} \\
|x| + 5 - 5 = -2 - 5 & \textit{Subtract 5 from each side.} \\
|x| = -7 &
\end{array}
$$

What are the values of x that make this a true statement?

5.6 Absolute Value Equations   **207**

Discussion

Explain why it is necessary to first write an equation as a disjunction when solving an equation that involves absolute value. *Absolute value implies two distinct expressions, one positive and one negative.*

Assignment Guide

- See p. 184B for assignments.
- Calculators may be used to check solutions.

Did You Know?

Have students write combined inequalities for other phenomena in our universe; for example, how many days it takes for the earth to revolve around the sun. Remind students that our year is not exactly 365 days. $365 < d < 366$

Lesson Quiz

Solve and check each equation.

1. $|3x - 2| = 5$ $\left\{\frac{7}{3}, -1\right\}$
2. $|a| - 3 = 2 - 9$ $\emptyset$
3. $|m - 4| = 2$ $\{2, 6\}$
4. $\left|y + \frac{1}{5}\right| = 5$ $\left\{\frac{24}{5}, -\frac{26}{5}\right\}$

Enrichment

Explain how to solve $|2y - 1| = 6$ using the number-line method. Students may write $|2y - 1| = \left|2\left(y - \frac{1}{2}\right)\right|$ or $2\left|y - \frac{1}{2}\right|$. Therefore, $|2y - 1| = 6$ is equivalent to $2\left|y - \frac{1}{2}\right| = 6$ or $\left|y - \frac{1}{2}\right| = 3$; so, $\left\{-2\frac{1}{2}, 3\frac{1}{2}\right\}$.

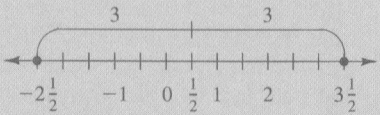

Students may also think of $|2y - 1| = 6$ as $2y - 1 = 6$ or $2y - 1 = -6$. So, $2y = 7$ or $2y = -5$. $\left\{-2\frac{1}{2}, 3\frac{1}{2}\right\}$

During a recent college bowl contest the following correct answer was given by one of the contestants:

The absolute value of a number represents the *distance* of its graph from the origin. This means that the absolute value of a number cannot be negative, so there are no values of x for which $|x| = -7$.

The solution set is the empty set, $\emptyset$.

CLASS EXERCISES

Translate each statement to an absolute value equation.

1. The distance from x to -9 is 5 units. $|x - (-9)| = 5; |x + 9| = 5$

2. m is 6 units away from -2. $|m - (-2)| = 6; |m + 2| = 6$

Change each absolute value equation to a disjunction. Then solve.

3. $|y + 4| = 11$ $\{7, -15\}$ $\quad y + 4 = 11$ or $y + 4 = -11$

4. $|12 - 2t| = 9$ $\quad 12 - 2t = 9$ or $12 - 2t = -9$ $\left\{\frac{3}{2}, \frac{21}{2}\right\}$

5. $|3z - 7| = 5$ $\quad 3z - 7 = 5$ or $3z - 7 = -5$ $\left\{4, \frac{2}{3}\right\}$

PRACTICE EXERCISES

Solve and check. Use the number line method for Exercises 1–4 and the method of your choice for Exercises 5–38.

A

1. $|x + 1| = 4$ $\{-5, 3\}$

2. $|z + 7| = 8$ $\{1, -15\}$

3. $|a + 3| = -2$ $\emptyset$

4. $|t + 2| = 0$ $\{-2\}$

5. $|x + 6| = -4 + 7$ $\{-9, -3\}$

6. $|4m + 1| = 3$ $\left\{-1, \frac{1}{2}\right\}$

7. $|2p + 7| = 9$ $\{1, -8\}$

8. $|3x + 8| = 11$ $\left\{-\frac{19}{3}, 1\right\}$

9. $|6z + 4| = 10$ $\left\{-\frac{7}{3}, 1\right\}$

10. $|3x - 1| = 5$ $\left\{-\frac{4}{3}, 2\right\}$

11. $|5y - 2| = 13$ $\left\{-\frac{11}{5}, 3\right\}$

12. $|4m - 3| = 9$ $\left\{-\frac{3}{2}, 3\right\}$

13. $|7h - 4| = 17$ $\left\{-\frac{13}{7}, 3\right\}$

14. $\left|\frac{1}{3}a - 2\right| = 4$ $\{18, -6\}$

15. $\left|\frac{3}{4}h - 5\right| = 1$ $\left\{\frac{16}{3}, 8\right\}$

16. $|g| + 4 = 7 - 12$ $\emptyset$

17. $|m| - 4 = 8 - 10$ $\{-2, 2\}$

18. $|p| - 3 = 7 - 12$ $\emptyset$

19. $|2(1 - 2m)| = 3$ $\left\{-\frac{1}{4}, \frac{5}{4}\right\}$

20. $|-3(2 - m)| = 6$ $\{0, 4\}$

21. $|3b + 5 + 2b| = 10$ $\{-3, 1\}$

B

22. $|3y - 2(y - 2) - 1| = 7$ $\{-10, 4\}$

23. $|4x - 3(x - 1) - 2| = 9$ $\{-10, 8\}$

24. $|13 - (k + 2)| = 1$ $\{10, 12\}$

25. $|y - (2y + 1)| = 3$ $\{-4, 2\}$

26. $|d + 3d| = 6$ $\left\{-\frac{3}{2}, \frac{3}{2}\right\}$

27. $\left|\frac{c - 1}{2}\right| = 5$ $\{-9, 11\}$

28. $\left|\frac{2 - d}{3}\right| = 21$ $\{-61, 65\}$

29. $\left|\frac{4 - m}{3}\right| + 2 = 7$ $\{-11, 19\}$

30. $\left|\frac{p + 1}{5}\right| + 1 = 6$ $\{24, -26\}$

31. $|4 - 2(n - 1)| = 3$ $\left\{\frac{3}{2}, \frac{9}{2}\right\}$

32. $|7x - (9x + 1)| = 5$ $\{-3, 2\}$

C

33. $|3c - 3| = 2c$ $\left\{\frac{3}{5}, 3\right\}$

34. $|2t - 1| = 3t$ $\left\{\frac{1}{5}\right\}$

35. $|4 - a| = 2a$ $\left\{\frac{4}{3}\right\}$

36. $|2 - 3s| = s$ $\left\{\frac{1}{2}, 1\right\}$

37. $|3y - 2| = 2y - 1$ $\left\{\frac{3}{5}, 1\right\}$

38. $|2z - 1| = 3z + 4$ $\left\{-\frac{3}{5}\right\}$

Applications

Translate each word statement into an absolute value equation. Then solve.

39. **Number Problem** The absolute value of the sum of 4 and some number is 16. $|4 + x| = 16; \{-20, 12\}$

40. **Number Problem** If 5 is subtracted from the absolute value of a number, the result is 27. $|x| - 5 = 27; \{-32, 32\}$

41. **Number Problem** The absolute value of the difference of twice a number and the number is 33. $|2x - x| = 33; \{-33, 33\}$

42. **Number Problem** The absolute value of the difference of four times a number and 4, multiplied by 5, is 20. $5|4x - 4| = 20; \{0, 2\}$

43. **Number Problem** If four is subtracted from the absolute value of the difference of twice a number and 2, multiplied by 2, the result is 24. $2|2x - 2| - 4 = 24; \{-6, 8\}$

DID YOU KNOW?

Throughout history people have feared and been fascinated by comets. When Halley's comet appeared in 1910, people bought "comet pills" to protect themselves from "comet fever" and disaster.

Most comets are named after their discoverers. Japanese amateur astronomers Kaoru Ikeya and Tsutomu Seki discovered the comet called Ikeya-Seki. As Ikeya-Seki came close to our sun in 1965, it accelerated to more than 1,000,000 mi/h and broke into three parts.

There are about 100,000 comets in the solar system. Most of them orbit the sun over long periods of time. These long-period comets may take many thousands of years to complete one trip around the sun.

The most famous short-period comet is Halley's comet, named for the English astronomer Edmund Halley. Halley's comet completes one trip every 76 to 79 years. Its most recent visit to the earth was in 1986.

Write a combined inequality to express the date of the next visit of Halley's comet to the earth. $2062 < d < 2065$

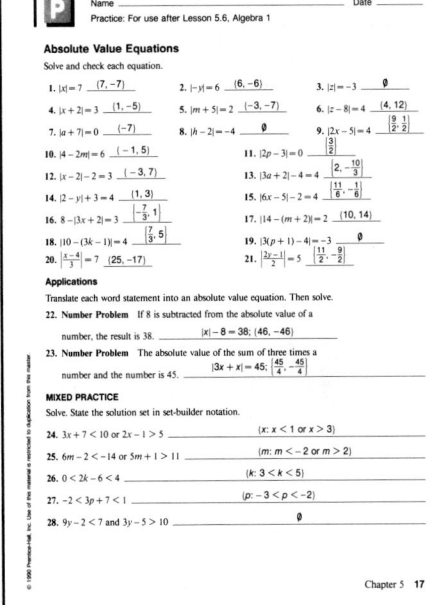

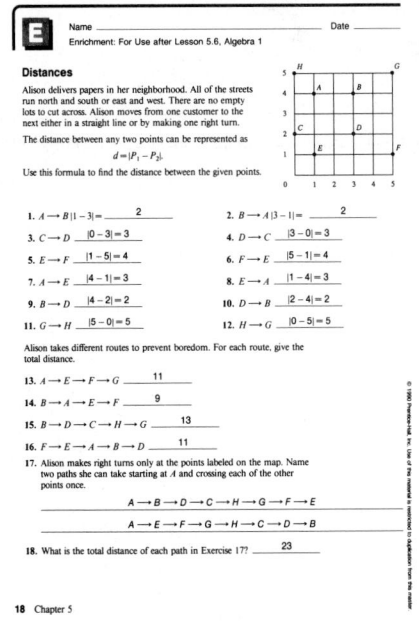

Materials/Manipulatives

Calculators
Number lines
Overhead projector
Teacher's Resource Book,
Teaching Aid 1,
Transparency 2

BACKGROUND

In the Capsule Review, students review conjunction and disjunction. Remind students to use *and* for conjunctions and *or* for disjunctions. For students who are having difficulty, you may want to review Lesson 5.5, Combined Inequalities.

Critical Thinking

Observation Find the solution set of $|z + 5| < 0$. Students should be able to conclude that the absolute value of any number is not less than 0. Therefore, the solution is ∅.

5.7 Absolute Value Inequalities

Objective: To solve and graph inequalities involving absolute value

An inequality involving absolute value can be written as a combined inequality containing either *and* or *or*.

Capsule Review

Conjunction: $r < 5$ *and* $r > -2$ can be written as $-2 < r < 5$.
Disjunction: $x > 0$ *or* $x = 0$ can be written as $x \geq 0$.

Write each combined inequality without *and* or without *or*.

1. $x > 0$ and $x < 5$
$\underset{0 < x < 5}{}$

2. $y > \frac{1}{4}$ or $y = \frac{1}{4}$ $\underset{y \geq \frac{1}{4}}{}$

3. $-3 < n$ and $n < 0$
$\underset{-3 < n < 0}{}$

The graph of $|x| = 3$ is found by locating points on a number line that are 3 units from the origin. The graph of $|x| > 3$, shown below, contains those points that are *more* than 3 units from the origin.

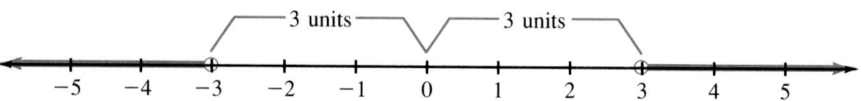

This suggests that $|x| > 3$ is equivalent to the disjunction $x < -3$ or $x > 3$.

EXAMPLE 1 Solve $|y - 2| > 4$. Graph the solution set.

Write $|y - 2| > 4$ as a disjunction.

$$y - 2 > 4 \quad \text{or} \quad y - 2 < -4$$
$$y > 6 \quad \text{or} \quad y < -2$$

The solution set is $\{y: y > 6 \text{ or } y < -2\}$.

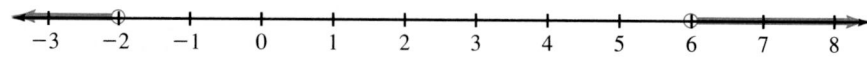

Since $|y - 2|$ represents the distance between y and 2 on a number line, $|y - 2| > 4$ means that y is more than 4 units from 2. This suggests that if the absolute value of an expression is *greater than* a given positive number, a disjunction results.

210   Chapter 5 Inequalities in One Variable

In $|w| < 3$, w represents numbers less than 3 units from the origin.

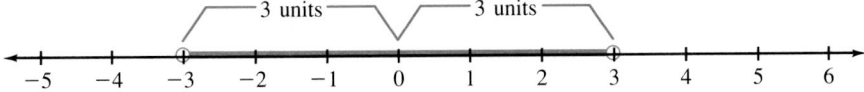

The graph shows that $w > -3$ and $w < 3$, which can be stated as $-3 < w < 3$. This suggests that if the absolute value of an expression is *less than* a given positive number, a conjunction results.

EXAMPLE 2 **Solve $|z + 5| < 2$ by two methods. Graph the solution set.**

Algebraic method:

$|z + 5| < 2$

$z + 5 < 2$	and	$z + 5 > -2$
$z < -3$	and	$z > -7$

Write the conjunction.

Number-line method:

$|z + 5| < 2$ must be written to show a *subtraction* of coordinates. $z + 5$ is equivalent to $z - (-5)$.

So, $|z + 5| < 2$ is equivalent to $|z - (-5)| < 2$. The values of z are less than 2 units from -5.

The solution set is
$\{z: z > -7 \text{ and } z < -3\}$,
or $\{z: -7 < z < -3\}$.

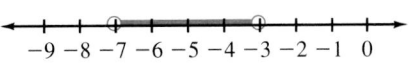

EXAMPLE 3 **Solve $|3t + 1| \leq 5$ by the algebraic method. Graph the solution set.**

$|3t + 1| \leq 5$ means $3t + 1 \leq 5$ and $3t + 1 \geq -5$.

$3t + 1 \leq 5$	and	$3t + 1 \geq -5$
$3t \leq 4$		$3t \geq -6$
$t \leq \dfrac{4}{3}$		$t \geq -2$

The solution set is
$\left\{t: -2 \leq t \leq \dfrac{4}{3}\right\}$.

The inequality in Example 3 cannot be solved as easily by the number-line method. Why?

The expression within the absolute-value symbol may need to be simplified. Also, isolate the absolute-value expression on one side of the inequality.

TEACHING SUGGESTIONS

- Emphasize that for real numbers a, b, and c, where $c > 0$, $|ax - b| > c$ is a disjunction and $|ax - b| < c$ is a conjunction.
- Stress the importance of both the algebraic and number-line methods in solving absolute value inequalities. Students should be encouraged to use both methods.
- You may wish to use Teaching Aid 1 and Transparency 2, in the *Teacher's Resource Book*, to demonstrate each example.

CHALKBOARD EXAMPLES

- **For Example 1**
  1. Solve $\left|t - \dfrac{1}{2}\right| > 2$. Draw a graph of the solution set.
  $\left\{t: t > \dfrac{5}{2} \text{ or } t < -\dfrac{3}{2}\right\}$

  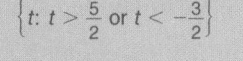

- **For Example 2**
  2. Solve $|n + 4| < 1$ by two methods. Draw a graph of the solution set. $\{n: n < -3 \text{ and } n > -5\}$

  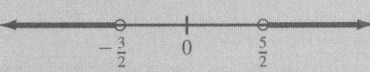

- **For Example 3**
  3. Solve $|1 - 2m| \leq 5$ by the algebraic method. Draw a graph of the solution set. $\{m: -2 \leq m \leq 3\}$

  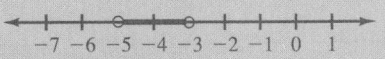

- **For Example 4**
  4. Solve $6 - |3(y - 1) - y| \leq 4$. Draw a graph of the solution set. $\left\{y: y \geq \dfrac{5}{2} \text{ or } y \leq \dfrac{1}{2}\right\}$

  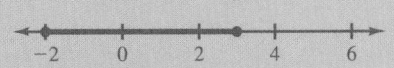

Common Error

- The most common error in solving absolute value inequalities is that students often do not know when an inequality is equivalent to a disjunction or a conjunction. Have students make a table of information using the examples illustrated in the textbook. Have them list each example, then classify it and the form of its solution. Discuss their tables and draw some conclusions about conjunctions and disjunctions.
- See *Teacher's Resource Book* for additional remediation.

LESSON FOLLOW-UP

Assignment Guide

- See p. 184B for assignments.
- Calculators may be used to check solutions.

Algebra in Mechanics

Ask students to consider what other aspects of mechanics probably have to allow for a *tolerance*, and why.

Lesson Quiz

Solve each inequality. Draw a graph of the solution set.

1. $|3x - 1| \leq 4$ $\left\{x: -1 \leq x \leq \frac{5}{3}\right\}$

Solve each inequality. Express your answer in set-builder notation.

2. $7 - |-b + 3(b - 1)| \geq 6$
  $\{b: 1 \leq b \leq 2\}$

3. $|t - 1| > 4$ $\{t: t > 5 \text{ or } t < -3\}$

4. $\left|\dfrac{x}{2} - 3\right| \leq 2$ $\{x: 2 \leq x \leq 10\}$

Enrichment

Explain the difference in the graphs of each open sentence, $|x - a| < 0$, $|x - a| > 0$, and $|x - a| = 0$, where a is a real number. $|x - a| < 0$ has no solution, and $|x - a| = 0$ has only one solution where $x = a$. $|x - a| > 0$ has the solution $\{x: x \neq a\}$.

212

EXAMPLE 4 Solve $8 - |-t + 2(t - 1)| \geq 6$. Graph the solution set.

$$8 - |-t + 2(t - 1)| \geq 6$$
$$8 - |-t + 2t - 2| \geq 6 \qquad \textit{Use the distributive property.}$$
$$8 - |t - 2| \geq 6 \qquad \textit{Combine like terms.}$$
$$-|t - 2| \geq -2 \qquad \textit{Subtract 8 from each side.}$$
$$|t - 2| \leq 2 \qquad \textit{Multiply each side by } -1.$$
$$\textit{Change} \geq \textit{to} \leq.$$

The values of t are 2 or less units from 2.

The solution set is
$\{t: 0 \leq t \leq 4\}$.

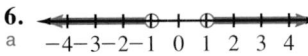

CLASS EXERCISES

Pair each inequality in Exercises 1–4 with one of the statements in a–d.

1. $|x| < 2$ b   **a.** Values of x are more than 0 units from 2.

2. $|x| \geq 2$ d   **b.** Values of x are less than 2 units from the origin.

3. $|x - 2| > 0$ a   **c.** Values of x are more than 0 units from -2.

4. $|x + 2| > 0$ c   **d.** The distance from x to the origin is 2 or more units.

Pair each graph in Exercises 5–8 with one of the inequalities in a–d.

5. c   **6.** a   **a.** $|y| > 1$

7. d   **8.** b   **b.** $|1 - y| \geq 0$

c. $|y| \leq 4$

d. $|y + 2| < 3$

PRACTICE EXERCISES

Solve and graph. Use the number line to solve Exercises 1–8. See below.

A **1.** $|y - 4| > 6$ **2.** $|x - 3| > 7$ **3.** $|z + 6| > 8$ **4.** $|a + 1| > 5$

5. $|c + 3| < 9$ **6.** $|b + 5| < 10$ **7.** $|t - 2| < 5$ **8.** $|w - 1| < 8$

9. $|x - 3| < 4$ **10.** $|a - 2| < 5$ **11.** $|2t - 3| < 0$ **12.** $|3t - 1| < 5$

13. $|2m - 9| > 1$ **14.** $|4q - 1| > 0$ **15.** $|2t + 3| \leq 6$ **16.** $|3x + 1| \leq 8$

17. $|5a - 2| \leq 9$ **18.** $|6b - 3| \leq 12$ **19.** $|a + 3| \geq 7$ **20.** $|b + 5| \geq 2$

21. $|4x - 8| \leq 2$ **22.** $|2q - 1| \leq 5$ **23.** $|2t| \geq 0$ **24.** $|3x| \geq 0$

B **25.** $7 - |-z + 3(z - 1)| \geq 5$ **26.** $14 - |-t + 2(t - 3)| \geq 9$

27. $8 - |-x + 2(x - 2)| \geq 2$ **28.** $9 - |-m + 3(m - 4)| \geq 7$

29. $3 + |2 - w| < 2$ **30.** $|m - 4| - 4 > -6$ **31.** $\left|\dfrac{2q - 4}{3}\right| \leq 1$

212 Chapter 5 Inequalities in One Variable

---

32. $\left|\dfrac{2 - 3b}{2}\right| \leq 1$ $\left\{0 \leq b \leq \frac{4}{3}\right\}$ **33.** $\left|\dfrac{2 - 2c}{3}\right| \geq 0$ **34.** $\left|\dfrac{3 - 4m}{4}\right| \geq 1$

{all real numbers} $\left\{m \leq -\frac{1}{4} \text{ or } m \geq \frac{7}{4}\right\}$

Solve each inequality. Express your answer in set-builder notation.

35. $|5 - (3d - 4)| > 6$ {d: d < 1 or d > 5} **36.** $|2 - (4 - 2f)| > 4$ {f: f < −1 or f > 3}

37. $-6 + |2t + 5(1 - t)| \leq -2$ **38.** $|3(1 - v) - 6| + 5 \leq 7$

$\left\{t: \frac{1}{3} \leq t \leq 3\right\}$ $\left\{v: -\frac{5}{3} \leq v \leq -\frac{1}{3}\right\}$

39. $\left|\dfrac{p + 1}{2}\right| + 3 \geq 3$ {p: p is a real number} **40.** $-2 + \left|\dfrac{1 - 2x}{3}\right| \geq -2$

{x: x is a real number}

C **41.** $|3z - 5| + 8 > 7$ {z: z is a real number} **42.** $-4 + |2 - 5m| \geq -6$

{m: m is a real number}

43. $|g - 1| < 3g$ $\left\{g: g > \frac{1}{4}\right\}$ **44.** $|4 - m| \geq 2m$ $\left\{m: m \leq \frac{4}{3}\right\}$

45. $|2 - y| > 2 - y$ {y: y > 2} **46.** $p + 6 \geq |p + 6|$ {p: p ≥ −6}

47. $|3k - 2| \leq 2k - 3$ ∅ **48.** $|2t - 1| > 3t + 5$ $\left\{t: t < -\frac{4}{5}\right\}$

Applications

Write an absolute value inequality for each situation.

49. Meteorology A meteorologist reported that the overnight temperature in the tri-state area was within 5 degrees of 0. |t − 0| < 5

50. Sports A poll shows that 85% of the sportscasters watched the Super Bowl. The poll has a plus or minus 3 percentage-point margin of error. (*Hint:* Let x = percentage who watched the Super Bowl.) |x − 85| ≤ 3

ALGEBRA IN MECHANICS

When you turn a faucet on and off, you expect water to flow and then to stop. A valve inside the faucet controls the flow of water. But what happens if the valve does not fit properly?

Manufactured parts may vary from the established standard by only a specified amount, called **tolerance.** For example, the standard diameter for a valve inside a faucet might be 2 cm, and a valve may not vary from this standard by more than 0.0001 cm; that is, the tolerance is ±0.0001.

The tolerance interval for any valve with a diameter x can be shown by writing $|x - 2| \leq 0.0001$. You can also use a combined inequality to show the interval: $1.9999 \leq x \leq 2.0001$.

Show the tolerance interval first using absolute value and then by using a combined inequality.

1. Standard: 6 mm **2.** Standard: 14 in. **3.** Standard: 2.75 in.
   Tolerance: ±0.001   Tolerance: ±0.5   Tolerance: ±0.001

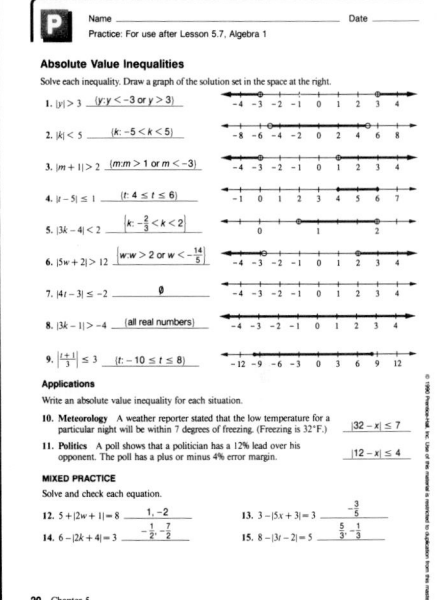

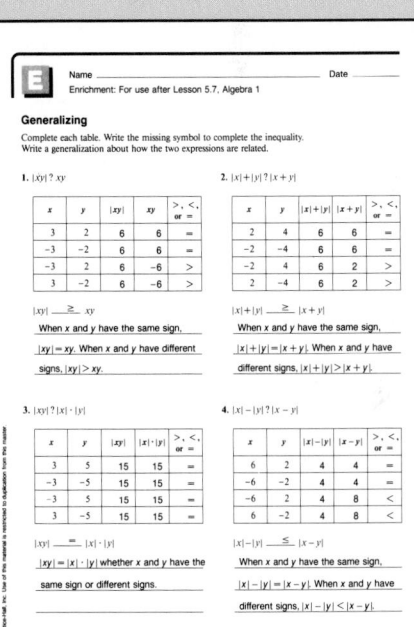

Additional Answers

32.
   −1 0 1 2 3 4

33.
   −2 −1 0 1 2 3

34.
   −2 −1 0 1 2 3

Algebra in Mechanics

1. |x − 6| ≤ 0.001; 5.999 ≤ x ≤ 6.001
2. |x − 14| ≤ 0.5; 13.5 ≤ x ≤ 14.5
3. |x − 2.75| ≤ 0.001; 2.749 ≤ x ≤ 2.751

BACKGROUND

A key to success in this lesson is the student's ability to correctly write phrases that translate into inequalities. To determine a student's progress, analyze errors in the student's work and then classify specific errors. Before introducing the lesson you may want to review the four problem solving steps using Teaching Aid 6, in the *Teacher's Resource Book.*

Error Analysis Classification

1. *Misunderstanding*
   Failed to understand the underlying concept of the problem
   May not have looked for the phrases that translate into inequalities
2. *Misapplied Strategy*
   Wrote an incorrect inequality
   Made error(s) in the solution process
   Stopped short in the process so that the answer given for the problem was incomplete

---

5.8

Problem Solving Strategy: Write an Inequality

In many problem solving situations, an inequality can be written to solve the problem. The inequality is one type of *mathematical model* of a real-world situation.

Oftentimes situations requiring the use of inequalities occur in financial planning, personal budget development, and other money making decisions that you may encounter.

EXAMPLE 1   Rates at a car rental agency are $160 a week plus $0.10 a mile. If Jane rents a car for a week, how far can she drive if she wants to spend no more than $250?

Understand the Problem   You are given the weekly rental ($160) and the mileage rate ($0.10 per mile). You must find the number of miles Jane can drive if she wants to spend *no more than* $250.

Plan Your Approach   Let y = the number of miles Jane can drive.
Total amount to spend ≤ 250, or $160 + 0.10y \leq 250$

Complete the Work
$$160 + 0.10y \leq 250$$
$$0.10y \leq 90 \qquad \text{\textit{Subtract 160 from each side.}}$$
$$y \leq 900 \qquad \text{\textit{Divide each side by 0.10.}}$$

Interpret the Results   Jane can drive 900 or fewer miles. Test 900 mi in the original statement: If she drives 900 mi, Jane will pay $160 plus ($0.10)(900). Will that cost no more than $250?

$$160 + (0.10)(900) \leq 250$$
$$160 + 90 \leq 250$$
$$250 \leq 250 \quad \checkmark \quad \text{True}$$

As shown in Example 1, *is less than, is less than or equal to, is greater than,* and *is greater than or equal to* are not the only phrases that are used in translating inequalities. For example, the symbols $\leq$ and $\geq$ are translated into the following equivalent phrases:

$\leq$
at most
no more than

$\geq$
at least
no less than

XAMPLE 2 There are four math tests in the first marking period. Sam's scores on three tests are 85, 91, and 76. What is the lowest score he can get on the fourth test to have an average greater than 85 for the marking period?

Understand the Problem You are given three test scores: 85, 91, and 76. You must find the lowest possible fourth test score for the average to be greater than 85.

Plan Your Approach Let x = the fourth test score.

The average of the four scores is: $\dfrac{85 + 91 + 76 + x}{4}$.

Translate the information into an inequality.

$$\underbrace{\text{The average}}_{\dfrac{85 + 91 + 76 + x}{4}} \qquad \underbrace{\text{is greater than}}_{>} \qquad \underbrace{85.}_{85}$$

Complete the Work
$85 + 91 + 76 + x > 340$ *Multiply each side by 4.*
$252 + x > 340$
$x > 88$ *Subtract 252 from each side.*

Interpret the Results The fourth test score must be greater than 88. Using whole numbers as the replacement set, the lowest possible fourth test score is 89.

CLASS EXERCISES

Write and solve an inequality that represents the given situation.

1. A freight elevator can safely hold no more than 2000 lb. What is the greatest number of 60-lb boxes the elevator can hold safely?
   $60x \leq 2000$; 33 boxes maximum
2. Sang-Ho received commissions of $150 and $225. How much must he receive from a third sale so his total commission will exceed $500?
   $150 + 225 + x > 500$; 3rd sale greater than $125

PRACTICE EXERCISES

1. A company's policy is to spend no more than $350,000 a year for salaries. The president's salary is $110,000. The salaries of the eight other employees are equal. How much can be spent on each salary? at most $30,000

2. Sally is paid $250 a week plus a commission equal to 3% of the sales. What must her sales be if she is to have a weekly income of no less than $460? at least $7000

5.8 Problem Solving Strategy: Write an Inequality   **215**

Discussion

Describe key words used in illustrating $\leq$ and $\geq$. is less than or equal to; is greater than or equal to; at most; at least; no more than; no less than

Assignment Guide

See p. 184B for assignments.

Test Yourself

See *Teacher's Resource Book,* Tests, pp. 51–52.

Mixed Problem Solving Review

- The following skills and concepts are reviewed:
  Writing an equation (Ex. 1, 2, 3)
  Solving uniform motion problems (Ex. 2)
  Solving inequalities (Ex. 3)
- The following problem solving strategies may be appropriate.
  Writing equations from word statements (Ex. 1)
  Making a drawing or table (Ex. 2)
  Writing an inequality (Ex. 3)

Project

Students learn how spreadsheets and mathematical computations can be applied to real-world situations.

Lesson Quiz

Solve.

1. Monica has scores of 75 and 89 on two English quizzes. What must she score on the next quiz in order to have an average greater than 83 for the three quizzes? 86
2. Ted has $10 to spend for the basketball game. He pays $5 for admission and $1.50 for popcorn. What is the maximum number of hot dogs he can buy if they cost $1.25 each? 2 hot dogs

Enrichment

Nine less than twice an integer is between -3 and 3. What integers are possible? $\{4, 5\}$ $(-3 < 2x - 9 < 3)$

3. Lisa's grades on four exams were 80, 92, 86, and 78. What is the lowest grade she can receive on the next exam to have an average greater than 85? 90

4. The amount of rainfall over a three-year period was 65 in., 72 in., and 59 in. How many inches of rain must fall during the fourth year for the average rainfall to be at least 68 in. for the four years? at least 76 in.

5. Freddie works two jobs. He earns $6 per hour doing one job and $100 a week doing the other job. How many hours must he work per week on the first job so that this combined weekly income is no less than $244? at least 24 h

6. The length of a rectangle is 2 ft more than the width. Find the minimum dimensions if the perimeter is more than 16 ft and the length and width are integers. width 4 ft, length 6 ft

7. The length of a rectangle is 4 m more than twice its width. Find the greatest possible value for the width if the perimeter is at most 38 m. 5 m

B   8. Manuel wishes to purchase 25¢ and 30¢ stamps. He decides to buy 10 fewer 30¢ stamps. How many of each can he buy for no more than $19.00? no more than 40 25¢ stamps; no more than 30 30¢ stamps

9. A taxi charges 75¢ for the first quarter mile and 35¢ for each additional quarter mile or part. How far did Jim ride if he paid less than $7.40 for his taxi? no more than 5 mi

10. A washing machine technician charges $27 for the first half hour and $18 for each half hour or part thereafter. How long did the technician work if the bill did not exceed $100? no more than $2\frac{1}{2}$ h

C   11. Mrs. Chavis will invest $10,000 in stock and bonds. She expects to receive $4\frac{1}{2}\%$ annual interest from the bonds and $2\frac{1}{2}\%$ annual interest from the stocks. She wants her annual income from the stocks and bonds to be at least $300. How much should Mrs. Chavis invest in each? bonds: at least $2500; stocks: at most $7500

12. If $450 is invested annually, part at 5% and the remainder at $4\frac{1}{2}\%$, how much must be invested at $4\frac{1}{2}\%$ to receive at least $21.50 in interest? no more than $200

Mixed Problem Solving Review

1. John bought some tapes on sale from a catalog for $5.69 each. The postage and handling charge was $2.50. If John paid a total of $70.78, how many tapes did he buy? 12 tapes

2. Two buses leave the terminal at the same time but go in opposite directions. One averages 10 mi/h more than the other. After 3 h, they are 270 mi apart. How fast is each bus traveling? 40 mi/h and 50 mi/h

3. Find the four smallest consecutive odd integers whose sum is greater than 48. 11, 13, 15, 17

PROJECT

A travel agent tries to get the best rate for clients when they rent a car. Use ads for different car rental companies and the spreadsheet to determine the cost of renting a car for 10 days. Check students' work.

```
======= A ===== B ===== C ===== D ===== E ===== F ===== G ===== H ===== I =====

1  RENTAL
2     WEEKLY RATE
3     DAILY RATE
4
5  INSURANCE
6     WEEKLY RATE
7     DAILY RATE
8
9  FUEL CHARGES
10
11 TRIP MILEAGE
12 DAILY FREE MILES
13 ADDITIONAL MILES CHARGE
14
15 TOTAL COST
```

TEST YOURSELF

Solve each inequality. Graph the solution set. See below.　　　　**5.5**

1. $3p + 1 > -2$ or $p + 5 < 2$
$\{p: p < -3 \text{ or } p > -1\}$

2. $-3 < 2m + 1 < 9$ $\{m: -2 < m < 4\}$

3. $1 - 2y > -9$ or $3y - 10 > 2$
$\{$all real numbers$\}$

4. $5 < -7k - 2$ and $\frac{3}{4}k + 6 < -3$
$\{k: k < -12\}$

Solve each equation.　　　　**5.6**

5. $|x - 3| = 4$ $\{-1, 7\}$

6. $|3t + 2| = 7$ $\left\{-3, \frac{5}{3}\right\}$

7. $1 + \left|m + \frac{2}{3}\right| = 2$ $\left\{-\frac{5}{3}, \frac{1}{3}\right\}$

8. $-5|6 - y| + 4 = -6$ $\{4, 8\}$

Solve each inequality. Graph the solution set. See below.　　　　**5.7**

9. $|y| > \frac{1}{2}$ $\left\{y: y < -\frac{1}{2} \text{ or } y > \frac{1}{2}\right\}$

10. $|x - 4| < 2$ $\{x: 2 < x < 6\}$

11. $|7 + f| > 13$ $\{f: f < -20 \text{ or } f > 6\}$

12. $|10 - 3g| + 4 > 3$ $\{$all real numbers$\}$

Write and solve an inequality that represents the given situation.　　　　**5.8**

13. Find any number n such that 11 decreased by $\frac{1}{3}$ of n is more than 5.
$11 - \frac{1}{3}n > 5$; number less than 18

14. Bill earns a 15% commission on his sales. If he hopes to earn at least $240 this week, what must his weekly sales be? $0.15s \geq 240$; at least $1600

15. In the past five races, Margot's times for the 100 m have been 13.1, 12.8, 13.0, 13.3, and 12.7 s. What time must Margot run in her next race, to have an average time less than 12.8 s? less than 11.9 s

5.8 Problem Solving Strategy: Write an Inequality　　　**217**

Additional Answers

1.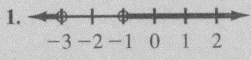
$-3 -2 -1\ 0\ 1\ 2$

2.
$-4 -2\ 0\ 2\ 4\ 6$

3.
$-2 -1\ 0\ 1\ 2\ 3$

4.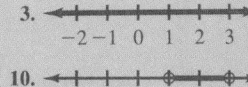
$-24 -18 -12 -6\ 0\ 6$

9.
$-2 -1\ 0\ 1\ 2\ 3$

10.
$-4 -2\ 0\ 2\ 4\ 6$

11.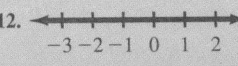
$-24 -18 -12 -6\ 0\ 6$

12.
$-3 -2 -1\ 0\ 1\ 2$

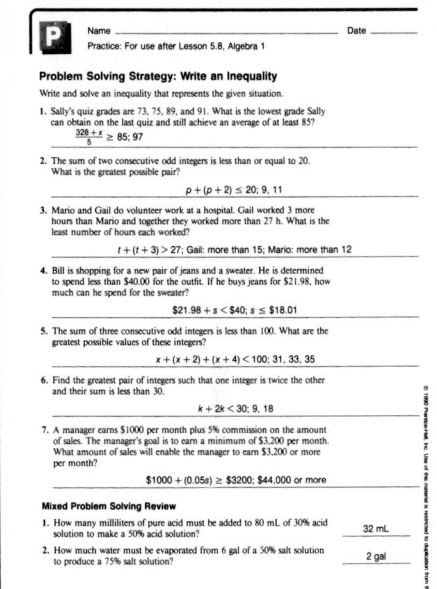

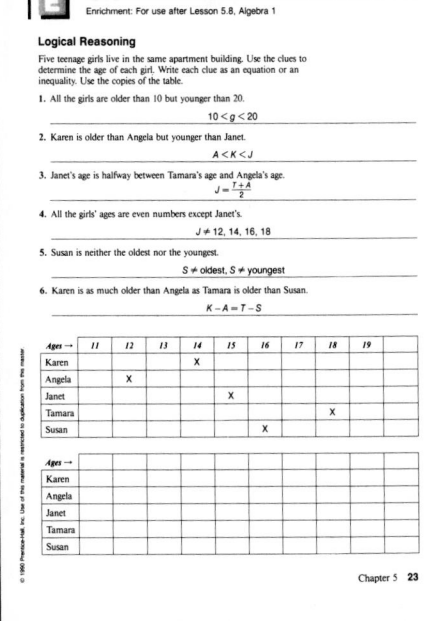

These problems involving marathon running afford students an opportunity to apply their skills and knowledge of inequalities to solve real world situations.

In Exercise 6, you may wish to remind students to watch the units of measure as they use the formula $r = \dfrac{d}{t}$.

See *Teacher's Resource Book*, Follow-up Application, p. 24.

APPLICATION:
Marathon Running

Did you know that the Olympic marathon race was originally run in the 1896 Olympics in Athens, Greece? This race commemorated an unknown messenger who ran 24 miles to announce a Greek victory. Preparing for a modern day marathon requires careful training and physical conditioning. In order to run a distance of 26 miles and 385 yards, marathon runners need to build up greater distances and faster times. Keeping careful track of their performances enables these long distance runners to structure a proper training schedule.

No official records are kept for marathon races due to varying course conditions and degrees of difficulty. The following table shows the men's and women's marathon gold medalists for the 1988 and 1984 Olympics.

Gelindo Bordin	Italy	1988	2 h 10 min 32 s
Rosa Mota	Portugal	1988	2 h 25 min 40 s
Carlos Lopes	Portugal	1984	2 h 9 min 55 s
Joan Benoit	U.S.A.	1984	2 h 24 min 52 s

EXAMPLE 1 While training for a marathon, Jane plans to run at least 40 mi each week. On Wednesday she is only able to run 4 mi. What is the least number of miles she must average daily by next Wednesday to meet her distance goal?

$$m = \text{number of miles run each day}$$
$$6m = \text{number of miles run for the 6 days}$$
$$6m + 4 \geq 40$$
$$6m \geq 36$$
$$m \geq 6$$

Therefore, Jane must average at least 6 mi each day for the next 6 days.

EXAMPLE 2 Dan wishes to run from 15 mi to 20 mi on weekdays. On Monday he ran 3 mi, on Tuesday $3\frac{1}{2}$ mi. Find the least and the greatest number of miles Dan needs to run over the next three days to maintain his training schedule.

$$m = \text{number miles run each day}$$
$$3m = \text{number of miles run for 3 days}$$

$$15 \le 3m + 6\frac{1}{2} \le 20$$

$$15 \le 3m + 6\frac{1}{2} \qquad \text{and} \qquad 3m + 6\frac{1}{2} \le 20$$

$$8\frac{1}{2} \le 3m \qquad\qquad\qquad\qquad 3m \le 13\frac{1}{2}$$

$$2\frac{5}{6} \le m \qquad\qquad\qquad\qquad\quad m \le 4\frac{1}{2}$$

So, Dan will need to run from $2\frac{5}{6}$ mi to $4\frac{1}{2}$ mi each day, or writing this as a combined inequality: $2\frac{5}{6} \le m \le 4\frac{1}{2}$.

Solve.

1. During a week of training Carlos wishes to run at least 27 mi. Due to bad weather he is only able to run 3 mi the first day. Find the least number of miles he must run each day to meet his goal. $m \ge 4 \text{ mi}$

2. During the third week of Carlos' training he wishes to increase his total distance to 35 mi from 27 mi. How much more must he average each day compared to the previous week? $1\frac{1}{7}\text{ mi}$

3. Christine ran for three consecutive days 10, 8.5, and 9 mi. What would be the fewest number of miles she should run over the next 3 days to reach her goal of 50 mi? $m \ge 7.5 \text{ mi}$

4. Katrina runs from 12 mi to 18 mi each week. Over a 2-day period she ran 2 mi and 3 mi, respectively. If she plans to run for only 4 more days, what is the least and greatest number of miles she must run to achieve her mileage goals? $1\frac{3}{4} \le m \le 3\frac{1}{4}\text{ mi}$

5. Adrienne ran $2\frac{1}{2}$ mi Monday and $2\frac{1}{4}$ mi Wednesday, and she plans to run again on Friday and Sunday. What would be the least and greatest number of miles she would need to run to average from 10 mi to 12 mi for that week? $2\frac{5}{8} \le m \le 3\frac{5}{8}\text{ mi}$

6. Using the table on page 218 find the average rate of each runner over the entire course of the marathon.
Bordin $\approx$12 mi/h, Mota $\approx$11 mi/h, Lopes $\approx$12 mi/h, Benoit $\approx$11 mi/h

- See *Teacher's Resource Book, Spanish Chapter Summary and Review*, pp. 9–10.
- See Extra Practice, p. 659.

Additional Answers

1.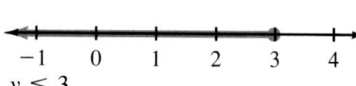
$-3\,{-}2\,{-}1\ 0\ \ 1\ \ 2$

2.
$-2\,{-}1\ 0\ \ 1\ \ 2\ \ 3$

3.
$-3\,{-}2\,{-}1\ 0\ \ 1\ \ 2$

4.
$-6\,{-}4\,{-}2\ 0\ \ 2\ \ 4$

5.
$-10\,{-}5\ 0\ \ 5\ \ 10\ \ 15$

6.
$-2\,{-}1\ 0\ \ 1\ \ 2\ \ 3$

7.
$-8\,{-}6\,{-}4\,{-}2\ 0\ \ 2$

8.
$-4\,{-}2\ 0\ \ 2\ \ 4\ \ 6$

9.
$-4\,{-}3\,{-}2\,{-}1\ 0\ \ 1$

CHAPTER 5   SUMMARY AND REVIEW

Vocabulary

combined inequality (202)   intersection (203)
conjunction (202)   set-builder notation (198)
disjunction (203)   union (204)

Graphing Simple Inequalities   The graphs of $x > -2$ and $y \le 3$ are shown.   **5.1**

$x > -2$

$-3\quad -2\quad -1\quad 0\quad 1$

$y \le 3$

$-1\quad 0\quad 1\quad 2\quad 3\quad 4$

Note the meaning of the "open circle" and the "closed circle."

Graph each equation or inequality. See side column.

1. $z = -3$ **2.** $v < 1$ **3.** $x \ge -2$ **4.** $t \ne -5.5$

Properties for Inequalities

5.2–5.4

Addition Property   For all real numbers a, b, and c,
if $a > b$, then $a + c > b + c$.

Subtraction Property   For all real number a, b, and c,
if $a > b$, then $a - c > b - c$.

Multiplication Property   For all real numbers a, b, and c,
(a) If $a > b$ and $c > 0$, then $ac > bc$.
(b) If $a > b$ and $c < 0$, then $ac < bc$.

Division Property   For all real numbers a, b, and c,
(a) If $a > b$ and $c > 0$, then $\dfrac{a}{c} > \dfrac{b}{c}$.

(b) If $a > b$ and $c < 0$, then $\dfrac{a}{c} < \dfrac{b}{c}$.

These properties are also true for $a < b$, $a \le b$, and $a \ge b$.

Solve each inequality. Graph the solution set. See side column.

5. $0 > x + 5$ $\{x < -5\}$ **6.** $y - \dfrac{1}{2} < 1$ $\left\{y < \dfrac{3}{2}\right\}$ **7.** $-1.5a > 3$ $\{a < -2\}$

8. $2(2 - x) + 3x \ge 0$ $\{x \ge -4\}$ **9.** $g - 2(3g + 1) > 5(4 + g) + 8$ $\{g < -3\}$

Combined Inequalities Combined inequalities containing "or" are disjunctions. Their graph is the *union* of the two graphs. Combined inequalities containing "and" are conjunctions. Their graph is the *intersection* of the two graphs.

Solve each inequality. Draw a graph of the solution set. See side column.

10. $3y + 7 < -8$ or $2(3 - y) < -4$ $\{y: y < -5$ or $y > 5\}$

11. $-(5 - 2x) + 3 \le 0$ and $2(7 - x) \le x + 17$ $\{x: -1 \le x \le 1\}$

12. $-3 < \frac{1}{2}(4 - 6v) < 6$ $\left\{v: -\frac{4}{3} < v < \frac{5}{3}\right\}$

Absolute Value Equations An absolute value equation can be treated as a disjunction (or) and the two resulting equations then solved. An absolute value equation can also be considered as a statement about the distance between two points on a number line.

Solve and check each equation.

13. $|m - 2| = 7$ $\{-5, 9\}$ 14. $|n + 3| = \frac{5}{3}$ $\left\{-\frac{14}{3}, -\frac{4}{3}\right\}$ 15. $|6x - (8x + 1)| = 9$ $\{-5, 4\}$

Absolute Value Inequalities To solve an absolute value inequality such as $|2r + 3| > 7$, change to the equivalent disjunction $2r + 3 > 7$ or $2r + 3 < -7$. When the absolute value inequality involves $<$, such as $|j + 4| < 6$, change to the equivalent conjunction $j + 4 < 6$ *and* $j + 4 > -6$.

Solve each inequality. Draw a graph of the solution set. See side column.

16. $|g - 3| > 5$
$\{g: -2 > g$ or $g > 8\}$

17. $5 - |4 - y| \le 3$
$\{y: y \le 2$ or $y \ge 6\}$

18. $\left|\dfrac{y - 8}{4}\right| \le 4$
$\{y: -8 \le y \le 24\}$

Write and solve an inequality that represents the given situation.

19. Half of a number x increased by 3 is greater than 2. Find x. $\frac{1}{2}x + 3 > 2; x > -2$

20. The sum of two consecutive even integers is less than 28. What are the largest possible consecutive integers whose sum is less than 28?
$i + i + 2 < 28$; 12, 14

21. Over a 5-week period, Wanda earned commissions of $17, $21, $19, $25, and $12. In order for her average for 6 weeks to be at least $20, how much must her commission for the sixth week be? $\frac{94 + x}{6} \ge 20$; at least $26

22. The length of a rectangle is 3 ft more than the width. If the perimeter is no more than 52 ft and the dimensions are integers, what are the largest possible dimensions? $4w + 6 < 52$; 14 ft × 11 ft

10.
$-10 -5 \ 0 \ 5 \ 10 \ 15$

11.
$-2 -1 \ 0 \ 1 \ 2 \ 3$

12.
$-2 -1 \ 0 \ 1 \ 2 \ 3$

16.
$-2 \ 0 \ 2 \ 4 \ 6 \ 8$

17.
$-2 \ 0 \ 2 \ 4 \ 6 \ 8$

18.
$0 \ 8 \ 16 \ 24 \ 32 \ 40$

See *Teacher's Resource Book*.
- Tests, pp. 53–56
- Calculator Test, pp. 9–10

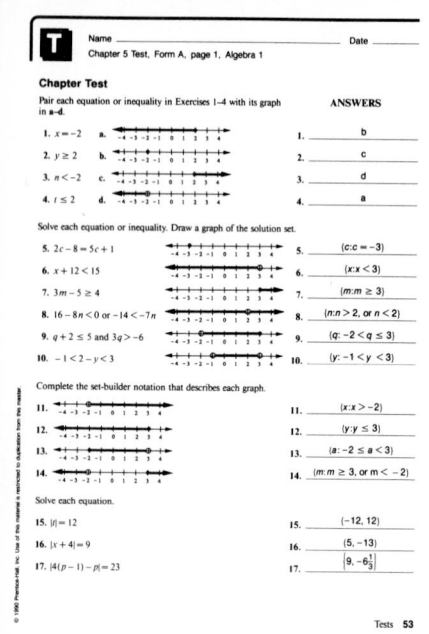

Draw a graph of each equation or inequality.

1. $y = 2$ 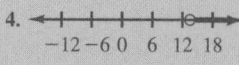 -2 -1 0 1 2 3   **2.** $x \le 0$ -2 -1 0 1 2 3   **3.** $m > -4$  -4 -2 0 2 4 6

Solve each inequality. Draw a graph of the solution set. See below.

4. $x - 5 > 8$ {x: x > 13}

5. $1 - 3y > 7$ {y: y < -2}

6. $18 - 3x > 0$ or $-16 > -8x$
{all real numbers}

7. $3y - 4 < 5$ and $2y > 1$ $\left\{ y: \frac{1}{2} < y < 3 \right\}$

Solve and check each equation.

8. $|b| = 3$ {-3, 3}

9. $|y - 3| = 7$ {-4, 10}

10. $|x - (3x + 2)| = 3$ $\left\{ -\frac{5}{2}, \frac{1}{2} \right\}$

Solve each inequality. Draw a graph of the solution set. See below.

11. $|a| > 4$ {a: a < -4 or a > 4}

12. $|3 - 2x| \ge 5$
{x: x ≤ -1 or x ≥ 4}

13. $|8 + a| < 2$
{a: -10 < a < -6}

Write and solve an inequality that represents the given situation.

14. Amy plans to spend at most $200 at a department store. If she purchases a dress that costs $75 and a pair of shoes for $45, how much can she spend on other items in the store? $x + 75 + 45 \le 200$; no more than $80

15. The sum of two consecutive odd integers is greater than -15. What are the smallest such integers? $x + x + 2 > -15$; -7, -5

16. If Seth increased the time he plans to spend cycling by 2 h, he would travel more than 3 times as far. If his average speed is 12 mi/h, how much time does he plan to spend cycling? $12(t + 2) > 3(12t)$; less than 1 h

17. Oscar had a certain amount of money in his savings account. After he withdrew $125, there was less than $500 in the account. How much money was originally in the account? $x - 125 < 500$; less than $625

18. If Lisa increased her rate by 15 mi/h, then in 2 h she would travel a greater distance than she does in 3 h at her present rate. What do you know about her present rate? $(r + 15)2 > 3r$; less than 30 mi/h

Challenge

Solve each inequality. Draw a graph of the solution set.

1. $|x - 1| < 0.5$ and $|x - 2| < 0.5$ no solution   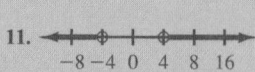 no solution

2. $|x + 1| < 1$ or $|x + 2| > 1$ {x: x < -3 or x > -2} 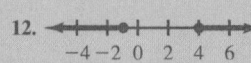 -4 -3 -2 -1 0 1

222   Chapter 5 Inequalities in One Variable

Additional Answers

4. -12 -6 0 6 12 18

5. -2 -1 0 1 2 3

6. -2 -1 0 1 2 3

7. 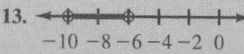 -2 -1 0 1 2 3

11. -8 -4 0 4 8 16

12. -4 -2 0 2 4 6

13. -10 -8 -6 -4 -2 0

Select the correct answer for each question.

1. Solve for x:

D
$$x + 3x + 4 = 2x - 6$$

A. 10 **B.** 5 **C.** -1
D. -5 **E.** -10

2. What is the sum of the following
E numbers?

8.03, 11.2, 7.863, 0.007

A. 8.785 **B.** 26.09 **C.** 26.90
D. 27.01 **E.** 27.10

3. Solve the inequality:

A
$$3x + 5 < x + 17$$

A. $x < 6$
B. $x > 6$
C. $x = 6$
D. $x < -6$
E. $x > -6$

4. The winner of a mile race crossed
C the finish line in 4 min and
38.42 s, while the second runner
took 4 min 39.8 s. By how many s
did the winner beat the second
place runner?
A. 4.44 **B.** 1.48 **C.** 1.38
D. 0.48 **E.** 0.38

5. Find the value of $|3a + 2b^2|$ when
D $a = -2$ and $b = -4$.
A. -22 **B.** 16 **C.** 22
D. 26 **E.** 38

6. Which sentence best describes the
A graph:

A. $x \geq -2$ **B.** $x > -2$
C. $x = -2$ **D.** $x \leq -2$
E. $x < -2$

7. Find the value of the expression
E $m^2n - n^3p^2$ when $m = 3$,
$n = -2$, and $p = -1$.
A. 26 **B.** 18 **C.** 10
D. -2 **E.** -10

8. Solve the equation:

A
$$3(x - 2) - 5(x + 4) = 4(2x + 11)$$

A. -7 **B.** -6 **C.** -3
D. 3 **E.** 6

9. A hardware store paid $299.95 for
C an order of 24 electric hedge
clippers, and marked a price of
$16.95 on each one. If all of the
clippers were eventually sold, how
much profit was made on the
order?
A. $16.85 **B.** $98.15
C. $106.85 **D.** $108.15
E. $109.65

10. Solve for b in the equation:
E
$$s = \frac{1}{2}(a + b + c)$$

A. $b = \dfrac{s - a - c}{2}$

B. $b = \dfrac{s - a + c}{2}$

C. $b = s - a - c$
D. $b = 2s - a + c$
E. $b = 2s - a - c$

11. How much sales tax would be
B charged on the total of $3.84,
$7.98, $14.95, and $9.95 in a city
which has a sales tax of $5\frac{1}{2}\%$?

A. $2.01 **B.** $2.02 **C.** $2.10
D. $2.19 **E.** $2.20

The individual comments provided
about the problems listed below can
be helpful in guiding students to solve
these problems.

2., 4. Aligning decimal points may
need some reinforcement.
9. The word *profit* used here does
not consider business overhead costs.
11. An extension of this problem
may be, "At what cent value of
one dollar does this sales tax
change from 1¢ to 2¢ to 3¢, and
so on?"

See *Teacher's Resource Book,* for
Preparing for Standardized Tests.

Maintaining Skills

The following skills and concepts are reviewed:

Applying properties of exponents
Reducing fractions
Combining like terms
Solving word problems involving percent

Simplify.

Example 1 $(-3)^3$

$$(-3)^3 = (-3)(-3)(-3) = (9)(-3) = -27$$

Example 2 $(2^3)^2$

$$(2^3)^2 = (2^3)(2^3) = (2 \cdot 2 \cdot 2)(2 \cdot 2 \cdot 2) = 8 \cdot 8 = 64$$

1. 10^5 100,000   **2.** 2^3 8   **3.** $(-1)^4$ 1   **4.** 5^2 25

5. $(-4)^3$ –64   **6.** $-(-3)^4$ –81   **7.** $(3^2)^3$ 729   **8.** $(2^3)^3$ 512

9. $[(-1)^3]^2$ 1   **10.** $[(-2)^2]^2$ 16   **11.** $(4^2)^2$ 256   **12.** $[(-3)^2]^3$ 729

Simplify.

Example 3 $\dfrac{18}{45}$

$$\frac{18}{45} = \frac{2 \cdot \overset{1}{\cancel{3}} \cdot \overset{1}{\cancel{3}}}{5 \cdot \underset{1}{\cancel{3}} \cdot \underset{1}{\cancel{3}}} = \frac{2}{5}$$

13. $\dfrac{7}{56}$ $\frac{1}{8}$ **14.** $\dfrac{9}{21}$ $\frac{3}{7}$ **15.** $\dfrac{15}{25}$ $\frac{3}{5}$ **16.** $\dfrac{12}{36}$ $\frac{1}{3}$ **17.** $\dfrac{20}{24}$ $\frac{5}{6}$ **18.** $\dfrac{14}{21}$ $\frac{2}{3}$

Simplify.

Example 4 $3a^2 + 5ab + 2a^2 - 7ab$ *Combine like terms.*

$$(3a^2 + 2a^2) + (5ab - 7ab) = 5a^2 + (-2ab) = 5a^2 - 2ab$$

19. $-2x^2 + 3xy - 3x^2 + 2xy$ –5x² + 5xy   **20.** $5m^2 - 2mn - 3m^2 + mn$ 2m² – mn

21. $2c^2 - (5cd + 3c^2) + c^2$ –5cd   **22.** $7s^2 - 3(s^2 - st) + st$ 4s² + 4st

23. $2p^2 + 4(q^2 - pq) + 2q^2$ 2p² – 4pq + 6q²   **24.** $-3(2ab - b^2) - (-2ab)$ 3b² – 4ab

Solve.

25. Bob took out a $3,500 loan for 1 year at 12% interest. What was the total cost of the loan? $3920

26. Kara bought a sweater for $24.98 and a pair of jeans for $25.89. How much did she spend if the sales tax is 8%? $54.94

27. Susan invested $1,800 for 3 years at 7% interest. How much simple interest did she earn? $378

OVERVIEW • Chapter 6

SUMMARY

In Chapter 6, students are introduced to monomials and polynomials. They learn how to utilize mathematical operations to simplify expressions, including exponents, in these forms. Students are then shown how to write numbers in scientific notation. This format leads logically to an understanding of polynomials. Students learn how to identify polynomials, binomials, and trinomials, and the degree of a monomial and polynomial. Students also simplify special polynomial cases, such as finding the square of a binomial, the product of two binomials, and the product of the sum and difference of two terms.

CHAPTER OBJECTIVES

- To identify and to multiply monomials
- To divide monomials and identify zero exponents
- To raise a monomial and quotient of two monomials to a power
- To write numbers in scientific notation and to multiply and divide numbers in this form
- To identify polynomials, binomials, trinomials, and the degree of a monomial and polynomial
- To simplify polynomials by combining like terms and writing them in ascending or descending order of exponents
- To add and subtract polynomials
- To multiply a polynomial by a monomial, and to simplify algebraic expressions that involve multiplication of a polynomial by a monomial
- To multiply two binomials using both vertical and horizontal formats and to multiply any two polynomials
- To find the square of a binomial and the product of the sum and the difference of two terms

Problem Solving Strategy

To recognize numbers arranged in a pattern as a sequence

To write an algebraic expression to represent the sequence

CHAPTER HIGHLIGHTS

The theme of the chapter is space. The chapter's special features demonstrate how mathematics can be applied to areas of space technology.

PROBLEM SOLVING AND APPLICATIONS

Problem solving and applications form an integral part of each lesson. Students learn how to perform calculations with monomials, polynomials, exponents, and scientific notation. They learn how these skills can be applied to many fields including astronomy, computer science, physics, and other areas of mathematics.

TECHNOLOGY

Calculator

A calculator can be used to facilitate computations. It is also used in the exercises in Lessons 6.1 and 6.3.

Computer

Computer usage involves a program for calculating the square of a number. Students are asked to find a pattern for the last digit of the squares of the numbers 1 through 20. When the students discover the pattern, they are asked to find the squares of the numbers 46 through 60 using the pattern.

RESOURCES

Teacher's Resource Book

- Teaching Aid 6
- Transparencies 8–12

STUDENT TEXT

**TEACHER'S
RESOURCE BOOK**

Chapter Content	Basic	Average	Enriched	R	P	E
6.1 Monomials and Multiplying Monomials	D: 228/1-20 odd, 44	D: 228/1-29 odd, 44	D: 228/13-43 odd, 44, 45	1	2	3
6.2 Dividing Monomials	D: 232/1-23 odd, 49 R: 228/6, 16, 28	D: 232/1-39 odd, 49 R: 228/10, 24, 32	D: 233/25-47 odd, 49, 50 R: 228/26, 34, 42	4	5	6
6.3 Monomials and Exponents	D: 236/1-13 odd, 37 R: 232/4, 12, 24	D: 236/1-27 odd, 37 R: 232/16, 26, 34	D: 236/15-35 odd, 37, 38 R: 233/18, 38, 44	7	8	9
6.4 Scientific Notation	D: 239/1-11 odd, 23 R: 236/2, 10, 12 Test Yourself	D: 239/1-17 odd, 23 R: 236/4, 12, 28 Test Yourself	D: 239/13-21 odd, 23 R: Test Yourself	10	11	12
6.5 Polynomials	D: 243/1-15 odd, 33 R: 239/2, 10, 12	D: 243/1-27 odd, 33, 34 R: 239/4, 8, 14	D: 244/21-31 odd, 33-35 R: 239/6, 14, 20	13	14	15
6.6 Adding and Subtracting Polynomials	D: 246/1-15 odd, 33 R: 243/4, 10, 12	D: 246/1-27 odd, 33 R: 2436, 10, 20	D: 247/17-31 odd, 33, 34 R: 244/8, 14, 26	16	17	18
6.7 Multiplying a Polynomial by a Monomial	D: 249/1-13 odd, 29, 30 R: 246/4, 12, 14	D: 249/1-23 odd, 29, 30, 31 R: 246/6, 22, 28	D: 249/15-27 odd, 29-33 R: 247/24, 26, 30	19	20	21
6.8 Multiplying Polynomials	D: 253/1-27 odd, 61, 62 R: 249/2, 4, 12 253/6, 12, 14	D: 253/1-47 odd, 61, 62, 63 R: 249/6, 18, 24 253/4, 6, 22	D: 253/29-59 odd, 61-65 R: 249/10, 26, 28	22	23	24
6.9 Multiplying Polynomials Special Cases	D: 258/1-17 odd, 37, 38 R: 254/4, 16, 22 Test Yourself	D: 258/1-29 odd, 37, 38, 39 R: 253/8, 18, 24 Test Yourself	D: 258/19-35 odd, 37-40 R: Test Yourself	25	26	27
6.10 Problem Solving Strategy: Look for a Pattern	D: 262/1-7 odd MPSR: 1-2 R: 258/4, 10, 18	D: 262/1-11 odd MPSR: 1-2 R: 258/8, 16, 20	D: 262/9-15 odd MPSR: 1-2 R: 258/22, 30, 36		28	29

D = Daily   R = Review   MPSR = Mixed Problem Solving Review   R = Reteaching   P = Practice   E = Enrichment

	STUDENT TEXT				**TEACHER'S RESOURCE BOOK**	
Reviewing	Test Yourself	239	Chapter Test	266	Spanish Chapter Summary and Review	11-12
And	Test Yourself	259	Prep. for Stan. Tests	267	• Quizzes	57-60
Testing	Chapter Sum. and Rev.	264	Cumulative Review	268	• Chapter Test (Form A)	61-62
			Extra Practice	660	• Chapter Test (Form B)	63-64
					Calculator Test	11-12
Special	Math Club Activity	229	Algebra in Health	247	Applications—Chapter 6	30
Features	Did You Know?	233	Extra	250	Critical Thinking	6
	Logical Reasoning	236	Algebra in Space Tech	255	Reading and Writing in Algebra	6
	Application	240	Project	263	Technology	13–14
	Critical Thinking	244				

6 Polynomials

Polynomial expressions are often used to represent very large or very small numbers. For example, the mass of the earth is approximately 5.9742×10^{24} kg, while the mass of a hydrogen atom is 1.6735×10^{-27} kg.

225

BACKGROUND

Astronomers use polynomial equations to perform various calculations. They are interested in finding the speed of the Earth in its orbit, $V = \dfrac{2\pi R}{T}$, or finding the acceleration of Earth towards the Sun, $a = \dfrac{V^2}{R}$.

BACKGROUND

In the Capsule Review, the exercises involve simplifying an expression given in exponent form. This review of factoring will help students understand how the term *monomial* is applied. Emphasize that a monomial is an expression that is either a numeral, a variable, or a *product* of a numeral and one or more variables.

Critical Thinking

Analyzing Whole-Part Relationships
Find the values of *y* that would make the following term classifiable as a monomial. Explain.

$$\frac{36x^2z^3}{y}$$

y could be any real number except zero. Division by zero is undefined. Since *y* is a numeral and not a variable, the term is a monomial.

6.1

Monomials and Multiplying Monomials

Objective: To identify and to multiply monomials

Recall that in a^n where a is any real number and n is any positive integer, a is called the *base* and n is called the *exponent*. The exponent indicates how many times the base is used as a factor.

Capsule Review

Expressions with exponents can be simplified by first rewriting the base in factored form.

EXAMPLE **Write in factored form. Then simplify:** **a.** 3^3 **b.** $-(-2)^4$

a. $3^3 = 3 \cdot 3 \cdot 3 = 27$ **b.** $-(-2)^4 = -[(-2)(-2)(-2)(-2)] = -[16] = -16$

Write in factored form. Then simplify.

1. 4^2 16 **2.** 5^3 125 **3.** -2^6 −64 **4.** $(-8)^2$ 64 **5.** $-(-10)^3$ 1000

In the expression $-2y^4$, -2 is the coefficient (numerical factor) and y^4 is the variable factor. In factored form:

$$-2y^4 = -2 \cdot y \cdot y \cdot y \cdot y \qquad y \text{ is the base.}$$

In an expression such as $(-x)^5$, the exponent 5 applies to the entire quantity within the parentheses, as shown below.

$$(-x)^5 = (-x)(-x)(-x)(-x)(-x) \qquad -x \text{ is the base.}$$

EXAMPLE 1 **Write in factored form:** **a.** 2^3x^2 **b.** $-5a^3b^4$

a. $2^3x^2 = 2 \cdot 2 \cdot 2 \cdot x \cdot x$ **b.** $-5a^3b^4 = -5 \cdot a \cdot a \cdot a \cdot b \cdot b \cdot b \cdot b$

The algebraic expression $-2y^4 + y^2 + \frac{1}{2}yx^3 - 7 + \frac{5}{y^2}$ consists of terms $-2y^4$, y^2, $\frac{1}{2}yx^3$, -7, and $\frac{5}{y^2}$. All these terms except $\frac{5}{y^2}$ are *monomials*.

A **monomial** is a real number, a variable, or a product of a real number and one or more variables.

$\frac{5}{y^2}$ is *not* a monomial because there is a variable in the denominator.

EXAMPLE 2 **Which of these terms are monomials?**

 a. $\frac{1}{2}x^2yz^2$ **b.** $\frac{-13}{2}$ **c.** $\sqrt{7}g^{23}$ **d.** $\frac{8a^2b^5}{c}$

 a. $\frac{1}{2}x^2yz^2$ *Yes*   **b.** $\frac{-13}{2}$ *Yes*

 c. $\sqrt{7}g^{23}$ *Yes; $\sqrt{7}$ is a real number.*

 d. $\frac{8a^2b^5}{c}$ *No; a variable cannot be in the denominator.*

To multiply two monomials with the same base, such as x^4 and x^3, add the exponents.

$$\overset{\text{4 factors}}{} \qquad \overset{\text{3 factors}}{}$$
$$x^4 \cdot x^3 = (x \cdot x \cdot x \cdot x) \cdot (x \cdot x \cdot x)$$
$$= x \cdot x \cdot x \cdot x \cdot x \cdot x \cdot x = x^7$$

Property of Exponents for Multiplication

For all real numbers a and all positive integers m and n:

$$a^m \cdot a^n = a^{m+n}$$

In order to use the above property, the monomials must have the same base.

$$m^3 \cdot m^5 = m^{3+5} = m^8 \qquad 3 \cdot 3^6 = 3^1 \cdot 3^6 = 3^{1+6} = 3^7$$

When you multiply two monomials, use the commutative and associative properties along with the property of exponents for multiplication.

EXAMPLE 3 **Simplify:** $(2x^2y)(3x^5y^2)$

$(2x^2y)(3x^5y^2)$
$= (2 \cdot 3)(x^2 \cdot x^5)(y \cdot y^2)$ *Commutative and associative properties for multiplication*
$= 6x^7y^3$ *Property of exponents for multiplication*

When some of the factors to be multiplied contain powers of 10, the product may be left in exponential form. Notice the form of the answer in Example 4.

EXAMPLE 4 **Multiply and write in exponential form:** $(3 \times 10^3)(7 \times 10^9)$

$(3 \times 10^3)(7 \times 10^9)$
$= (3 \times 7) \times (10^3 \times 10^9)$ *Commutative and associative properties for multiplication*
$= 21 \times 10^{12}$ $10^3 \times 10^9 = 10^{3+9} = 10^{12}$

6.1 Monomials and Multiplying Monomials   **227**

- In this lesson, students learn the property of exponents for multiplication by writing the product of monomials in factored form. In the beginning, you may want the students to multiply monomials using the property of exponents and then check their answers by using the factor form.
- You may want to discuss like and unlike terms at this time. Point out that in order to multiply monomials, although the terms can be unlike, the base of each term must be the same.
- Explain to students how the power key on a calculator is used. Have students check their answers for Exercises 19–24 using a calculator.

CHALKBOARD EXAMPLES

- **For Example 1**
 Write in factored form.
 1. 3^4a^3 $3 \cdot 3 \cdot 3 \cdot 3 \cdot a \cdot a \cdot a$
 2. $-11xy^3y^2$
    $-11 \cdot x \cdot y \cdot y \cdot y \cdot y \cdot y$

- **For Example 2**
 Which terms are monomials?
 3. $2ab^2c$ yes
 4. $\frac{3}{4}r^3$ yes
 5. -1.5 yes
 6. $-2.2ab^2$ yes
 7. $\frac{4x^2}{y}$ no

- **For Example 3**
 Simplify.
 8. $(3x^2y^2)(4xy^3)$ $12x^3y^5$
 9. $(6r^3s^4)(2r^2s^5)$ $12r^5s^9$
 10. $(3mn^4)(-4m^3n^2)$ $-12m^4n^6$

- **For Example 4**
 Multiply and write in exponential form.
 11. $(4 \times 10^5)(6 \times 10^8)$ 24×10^{13}
 12. $(5.3 \times 10^4)(1.2 \times 10)$
    6.36×10^5

227

228

Common Error

- When multiplying monomials, students often multiply the exponents instead of adding them. In $7^3 \cdot 7^2$, students may multiply exponents and get 7^6 instead of 7^5. Students also forget that x is actually x^1. In $x \cdot x^3$, they may get x^3 instead of the correct answer, x^4. Students who make these errors should write the monomials in factored form.
- See *Teacher's Resource Book* for additional remediation.

LESSON FOLLOW-UP

Discussion

Explain why rearranging the factors of $(3x^2y)(4xy^3)$ to $(3 \cdot 4)(x^2 \cdot x)(y \cdot y^3)$ is a valid step in solving the problem. The associative property is used to regroup the factors, and the commutative property is used to change the order of the factors.

Assignment Guide

See p. 224B for assignments.

Math Club Activity

Have students research some other games that are played in math competitions.

Lesson Quiz

Write in factored form.
1. -2^4 $-2 \cdot -2 \cdot -2 \cdot -2$
2. $(-r)^2$ $-r \cdot -r$

Which of these are monomials?
3. -7021 yes
4. $3z^2$ yes
5. $\dfrac{2k^3}{m^2}$ no
6. $5h^2i^4$ yes

Simplify.
7. $(3x^2)(2x)$ $6x^3$
8. $(r^3s)(2rs^5)$ $2r^4s^6$

Multiply and write in exponential form.
9. $(2 \times 10^3)(3 \times 10^8)$ 6×10^{11}
10. $(1.5 \times 10^4)(4 \times 10^6)$ 6×10^{10}

CLASS EXERCISES

Write in factored form.

1. $7y^3$ $7 \cdot y \cdot y \cdot y$

2. 3^2st^5 $3 \cdot 3 \cdot s \cdot t \cdot t \cdot t \cdot t \cdot t$

3. -4^2x^2z $-(4 \cdot 4 \cdot x \cdot x \cdot z)$

Which of these are monomials?

4. $2tu$ yes

5. $\dfrac{3z^2x}{y}$ no

6. $\dfrac{-2}{3}$ yes

7. $5ab^3$ yes

Simplify.

8. $a^4 \cdot a^3$ a^7

9. $3^3 \cdot 3^6$ 3^9, or 19,683

10. $(2x^3y)(2^3xy)$ $2^4x^4y^2$, or $16x^4y^2$

For Discussion

11. Explain how the associative property and the commutative property are used in multiplying $(a^2b)(ab^4)$. assoc. property is used to regroup the factors; commut. property is used to change their order; $(a^2b)(ab^4) = a^2(b \cdot a)b^4 = a^2(a \cdot b)b^4 = (a^2 \cdot a) \cdot (b \cdot b^4)$

12. Determine whether the property of exponents for multiplication can be used to find the product of x^6 and y^5. Explain your answer. How can you represent the product of x^6 and y^5? not possible; monomials must have the same base; $x^6 \cdot y^5$, or x^6y^5

PRACTICE EXERCISES

Write in factored form.

A
1. 3^3z^2 $3 \cdot 3 \cdot 3 \cdot z \cdot z$

2. 2^3y^2 $2 \cdot 2 \cdot 2 \cdot y \cdot y$

3. $-7a^3b^4$ $-7 \cdot a \cdot a \cdot a \cdot b \cdot b \cdot b \cdot b$

4. $-5c^3d^4$ $-5 \cdot c \cdot c \cdot c \cdot d \cdot d \cdot d \cdot d$

Which of these are monomials?

5. $\dfrac{1}{2}a^2bc^2$ yes

6. $\dfrac{2}{3}m^2np^2$ yes

7. $\dfrac{7x^2y^5}{z}$ no

8. $\dfrac{9c^2d^5}{e}$ no

9. $\sqrt{5}h^{25}$ yes

10. $\sqrt{3}l^{35}$ yes

11. $\dfrac{-15}{2}$ yes

12. $\dfrac{-17}{3}$ yes

Simplify.

13. $(3x^2y)(5x^5y^2)$ $15x^7y^3$

14. $(7m^2n)(2m^5n^2)$ $14m^7n^3$

15. $(6r^3s)(3r^4s^5)$ $18r^7s^6$

16. $(8a^3b)(2a^4b^5)$ $16a^7b^6$

17. $(4g^3)(5g^5)$ $20g^8$

18. $(7z^3)(3z^5)$ $21z^8$

Multiply and write in exponential form.

19. $(3 \times 10^2)(5 \times 10^7)$ 15×10^9

20. $(4 \times 10^5)(8 \times 10^8)$ 32×10^{13}

B
21. $(2 \times 10^5)(1.5 \times 10^4)$ 3×10^9

22. $(1.2 \times 10^4)(2 \times 10^6)$ 2.4×10^{10}

23. $(4.2 \times 10^6)(0.5 \times 10^2)$ 2.1×10^8

24. $(2.1 \times 10^3)(0.2 \times 10^3)$ 0.42×10^6

Simplify. All variable exponents represent positive integers.

25. $k^m \cdot k^4$ $_{k^{m+4}}$ **26.** $h \cdot h^b$ $_{h^{1+b}}$ **27.** $b^{x+1} \cdot b^2$ $_{b^{x+3}}$

28. $x^{a+4} \cdot x^3$ $_{x^{a+7}}$ **29.** $2 \cdot 2^{m-4} \cdot 2^3$ $_{2^m}$ **30.** $3 \cdot 3^{x-5} \cdot 3^2$ $_{3^{x-2}}$

Use the power key on your calculator to do the evaluations if $a = -19$ and $b = 171$.

C **31.** a^5 $_{-2,476,099}$ **32.** b^2 $_{29,241}$ **33.** a^4 $_{130,321}$ **34.** b^3 $_{5,000,211}$

Simplify. All variable exponents represent positive integers.

35. $(2r^{3x})(r^{2x}d^x)$ **36.** $(e^{3y}f^x)(3e^yf^x)$ **37.** $(9z^{3a}y^{2m})(-3z^{2a}y^{4m})$
$_{2r^{5x}d^x}$ $_{3e^{4y}f^{2x}}$ $_{-27z^{5a}y^{6m}}$

Evaluate each expression if $a = \frac{1}{2}$, $b = -3$, and $c = -1$.

38. $(6a^3)(2^{bc})$ $_6$ **39.** $(5b^2)(3^{2a})$ $_{135}$ **40.** $-5^{10a+b-c}$ $_{-125}$

41. $-3^{b+6a-3c}$ $_{-27}$ **42.** $-5^{6a}c^{-b}$ $_{125}$ **43.** $\dfrac{-3b^{-c}}{a^5}$ $_{288}$

Applications

Geometry Use the appropriate formula $A = lw$ for a rectangle to express the area.

44. The width of a rectangular mirror is $2a$. Its length is $4a$. Express the area in terms of a. $_{8a^2}$

45. A rectangular picture has a length of x and a width of $\frac{1}{2}x$. Express the area in terms of x. $_{\frac{1}{2}x^2}$

MATH CLUB ACTIVITY

In recent years, mathematicians have developed academic games that are both instructive and fun to play. Many cities have active math leagues in which competition is based on the ability to play a particular mathematical game.

Wff'n Proof is one such game used in many school competitions. Wff'n Proof is based on modern symbolic logic. It uses a form of reasoning called reverse Polish logic.

1. Find out what is meant by reverse Polish logic and give some examples.
   Enter numerals first then the operations. For example, $4 + 2$ is entered as 4 2 +.
2. Find out if your school has Wff'n Proof. If so, you may enjoy learning to play the game. If you belong to a Math Club, Wff'n Proof may provide an interesting stimulus to club activities.

3. Investigate other possible math club activities, such as written math test competitions sponsored by the Mathematics Association of America and the National Council of Teachers of Mathematics.

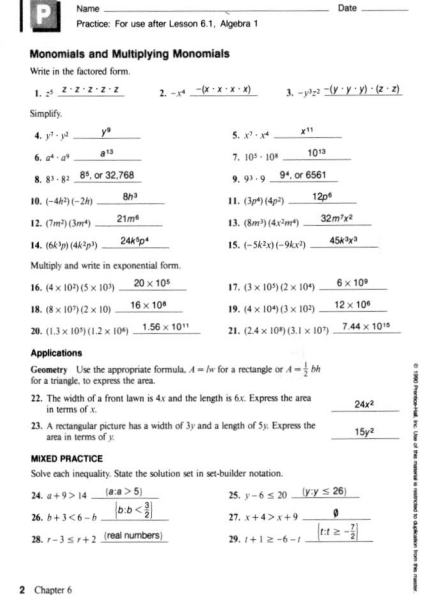

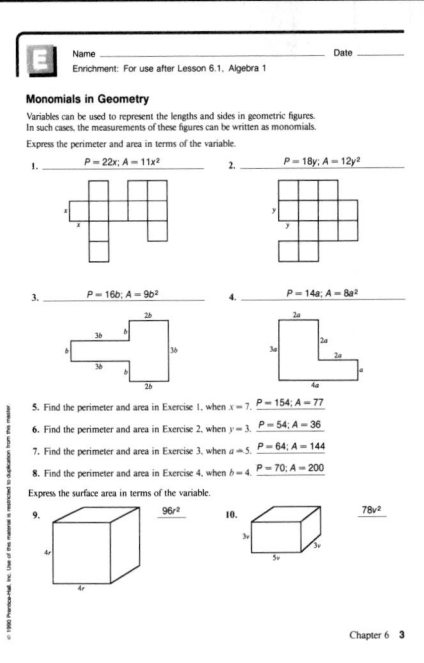

BACKGROUND

- In the Capsule Review, students simplify fractions by finding the prime factorization of the numerator and denominator and then dividing out common factors. Dividing out common factors will be used in the lesson to teach the property of exponents for division.
- Note that all answers are given in simplest form. A quotient of monomials is in simplest form when each base appears only once, when there are no powers of powers, and when all fractions are expressed in simplest form.

Critical Thinking

Causal Explanation Explain why, in the property of exponents for division, if m and n are positive integers, there are three separate cases for $\dfrac{a^m}{a^n}$.

The goal of the property is to get the exponent to be a positive integer, or 0.

6.2

Dividing Monomials

Objectives: To divide monomials
To identify zero exponents

You can simplify a fraction by dividing out common factors that occur in the numerator and the denominator. The same principle can be used to divide monomials.

Capsule Review

To simplify a fraction, write the numerator and denominator in factored form. Then divide out common factors.

$$\text{EXAMPLE} \qquad \frac{36}{48} = \frac{\overset{1}{2} \cdot \overset{1}{2} \cdot \overset{1}{3} \cdot 3}{\underset{1}{2} \cdot \underset{1}{2} \cdot 2 \cdot 2 \cdot \underset{1}{3}} = \frac{3}{2 \cdot 2} = \frac{3}{4}$$

Simplify.

1. $\dfrac{33}{55}$ $\dfrac{3}{5}$
2. $\dfrac{24}{18}$ $\dfrac{4}{3}$
3. $\dfrac{30}{75}$ $\dfrac{2}{5}$
4. $\dfrac{56}{42}$ $\dfrac{4}{3}$
5. $\dfrac{108}{144}$ $\dfrac{3}{4}$
6. $\dfrac{78}{52}$ $\dfrac{3}{2}$

To divide monomials, write each monomial in factored form. Then divide out common factors.

$$\frac{x^7}{x^5} = \frac{\overset{1}{\cancel{x}} \cdot \overset{1}{\cancel{x}} \cdot \overset{1}{\cancel{x}} \cdot \overset{1}{\cancel{x}} \cdot \overset{1}{\cancel{x}} \cdot x \cdot x}{\underset{1}{\cancel{x}} \cdot \underset{1}{\cancel{x}} \cdot \underset{1}{\cancel{x}} \cdot \underset{1}{\cancel{x}} \cdot \underset{1}{\cancel{x}}} = \frac{x^2}{1} = x^2$$

7 factors (numerator)   *5 factors* (denominator)

$$\frac{5^3}{5^6} = \frac{\overset{1}{\cancel{5}} \cdot \overset{1}{\cancel{5}} \cdot \overset{1}{\cancel{5}}}{\underset{1}{\cancel{5}} \cdot \underset{1}{\cancel{5}} \cdot \underset{1}{\cancel{5}} \cdot 5 \cdot 5 \cdot 5} = \frac{1}{5 \cdot 5 \cdot 5} = \frac{1}{5^3}$$

The examples above suggest the following property of exponents for division.

Property of Exponents for Division

For all real numbers a, $a \neq 0$, and for all positive integers m and n:

If $m > n$,
then $\dfrac{a^m}{a^n} = a^{m-n}$.

If $m < n$,
then $\dfrac{a^m}{a^n} = \dfrac{1}{a^{n-m}}$.

If $m = n$,
then $\dfrac{a^m}{a^n} = a^0 = 1$.

---

230   Chapter 6 Polynomials

EXAMPLE 1 Simplify: **a.** $\dfrac{y^6}{y^3}$ **b.** $\dfrac{y^2}{y^7}$ **c.** $\dfrac{y^{16}}{y^{16}}$ **Assume that $y \neq 0$.**

$$\textbf{a. } \frac{y^6}{y^3} = y^{6-3} \qquad \textbf{b. } \frac{y^2}{y^7} = \frac{1}{y^{7-2}} \qquad \textbf{c. } \frac{y^{16}}{y^{16}} = y^{16-16}$$

$$= y^3 \qquad\qquad\qquad = \frac{1}{y^5} \qquad\qquad = y^0$$

$$\qquad\qquad\qquad\qquad\qquad\qquad\qquad\qquad\qquad = 1$$

As with multiplication of monomials, this property of exponents is used only when the bases are the same. The property does not apply to a quotient such as $\dfrac{x^4}{y^4}$, which cannot be simplified further.

EXAMPLE 2 Simplify: $\dfrac{4a^2b^5}{2a^6b^2}$ **Assume that $a \neq 0$ and $b \neq 0$.**

Rewrite $\dfrac{4a^2b^5}{2a^6b^2}$ using the rules for multiplication of fractions.

$$\frac{4a^2b^5}{2a^6b^2} = \frac{4}{2} \cdot \frac{a^2}{a^6} \cdot \frac{b^5}{b^2} \qquad \textit{Use the property of exponents for division.}$$

$$= 2 \cdot \frac{1}{a^4} \cdot b^3 \qquad \textit{Multiply the remaining factors.}$$

$$= \frac{2b^3}{a^4}$$

You may want to use the commutative property for multiplication to align factors that have the same base.

EXAMPLE 3 Simplify: $\dfrac{12k^2m^3n}{-9m^3n^6k^5}$ **Assume that $k \neq 0$, $m \neq 0$, and $n \neq 0$.**

$$\frac{12k^2m^3n}{-9m^3n^6k^5} = \frac{12k^2m^3n}{-9k^5m^3n^6} \qquad \textit{Commutative property for multiplication}$$

$$= \frac{12}{-9} \cdot \frac{k^2}{k^5} \cdot \frac{m^3}{m^3} \cdot \frac{n^1}{n^6} \qquad \textit{n means n^1.}$$

$$= \frac{4}{-3} \cdot \frac{1}{k^3} \cdot 1 \cdot \frac{1}{n^5}$$

$$= \frac{4}{-3k^3n^5}, \text{ or } -\frac{4}{3k^3n^5}$$

In Example 4, there are powers of ten in both the numerator and the denominator. It is often convenient to keep the answer as a power of ten.

6.2 Dividing Monomials **231**

231

232

EXAMPLE 4   **Simplify:** $\dfrac{3 \times 10^{12}}{2 \times 10^6}$

$$\frac{3 \times 10^{12}}{2 \times 10^6} = \frac{3}{2} \times \frac{10^{12}}{10^6} = 1.5 \times 10^6$$

The third part of the property of exponents for division permits you to simplify an expression with a zero exponent.

EXAMPLE 5   **Simplify:**   **a.** 5^0 **b.** $(3x)^0$ **c.** $-x^0$ **Assume that $x \neq 0$.**

a. $5^0 = 1$ **b.** $(3x)^0 = 1$ **c.** $-x^0 = -1 \cdot x^0 = -1$

Use the power key on your calculator to verify that $5^0 = 1$.

CLASS EXERCISES

Simplify. Assume that no variable equals zero.

1. $\dfrac{x^6}{x^2}$ x^4 2. $\dfrac{a^3}{a^7}$ $\dfrac{1}{a^4}$ 3. $\dfrac{m^8}{m^8}$ 1 4. $\dfrac{3^3}{3^2}$ 3

5. $\dfrac{9}{9^3}$ $\dfrac{1}{81}$ 6. $\dfrac{10^2}{10}$ 10 7. $\dfrac{-2x^2y}{3x^2y}$ $-\dfrac{2}{3}$ 8. $\dfrac{3^3a^2b^3}{3ab^2c^4}$ $\dfrac{9ab}{c^4}$

9. In $\dfrac{12k^2m^3n}{-9k^5m^3n^6}$, why must it be assumed that $k \neq 0$, $m \neq 0$, and $n \neq 0$?
If any factor equals 0, then the denominator of the fraction equals 0. Division by zero is undefined.

10. In the definition $a^0 = 1$, why must it be stated that $a \neq 0$? (*Hint:* Is the following statement true or false: $\dfrac{0^3}{0^3} = 0^{3-3} = 0^0 = 1$? Why?)
False; division by 0 is undefined.

PRACTICE EXERCISES

Simplify. Assume that no variable equals zero.

A   1. $\dfrac{x^7}{x^4}$ x^3 2. $\dfrac{a^9}{a^2}$ a^7 3. $\dfrac{y}{y^9}$ $\dfrac{1}{y^8}$ 4. $\dfrac{i}{i^8}$ $\dfrac{1}{i^7}$

5. $\dfrac{b^2}{b^2}$ 1 6. $\dfrac{n^3}{n^3}$ 1 7. $\dfrac{8^2}{8}$ 8 8. $\dfrac{2^4}{2}$ 8

9. $\dfrac{10^3}{10^7}$ $\dfrac{1}{10^4}$ 10. $\dfrac{10^2}{10^5}$ $\dfrac{1}{10^3}$ 11. $\dfrac{6a^2b^5}{2a^6b^2}$ $\dfrac{3b^3}{a^4}$ 12. $\dfrac{9x^2y^5}{3x^6y^2}$ $\dfrac{3y^3}{x^4}$

13. $\dfrac{3ac^5}{7a^3}$ $\dfrac{3c^5}{7a^2}$ 14. $\dfrac{5mn^7}{9m^4}$ $\dfrac{5n^7}{9m^3}$ 15. $\dfrac{4th}{t^2}$ $\dfrac{4h}{t}$ 16. $\dfrac{8st}{s^2}$ $\dfrac{8t}{s}$

17. $\dfrac{20 \times 10^7}{5 \times 10^4}$ 4×10^3 18. $\dfrac{18 \times 10^6}{9 \times 10^5}$ 2×10 19. $\dfrac{6 \times 10^4}{2 \times 10^3}$ 3×10 20. $\dfrac{15 \times 10^7}{3 \times 10^2}$ 5×10^5

21. 8^0 1 22. $(5x)^0$ 1 23. $-t^0$ -1 24. -10^0 -1

B

25. $\dfrac{m^0}{2}$ $\tfrac{1}{2}$ 26. $-4b^0$ -4 27. $3(-x)^0$ 3 28. $-(-3x)^0$ -1

29. $\dfrac{-3a^5b^7}{6a^4b^8}$ $\dfrac{-a}{2b}$ 30. $\dfrac{-2c^6d^4}{4c^2d^5}$ $\dfrac{-c^4}{2d}$ 31. $\dfrac{5x^2y^4}{-3x^3y^2}$ $\dfrac{5y^2}{-3x}$ 32. $\dfrac{-4x^3y^5}{7x^4y}$ $\dfrac{-4y^4}{7x}$

33. $\dfrac{7x^2y^3z^7}{3x^4z^4}$ $\dfrac{7y^3z^3}{3x^2}$ 34. $\dfrac{9k^4m^5n}{-3k^3m}$ $-3km^4n$ 35. $\dfrac{-4p^2q^3r^4}{2qrp^2}$ $-2q^2r^3$ 36. $\dfrac{-6fde}{-4d^2ef^5}$ $\dfrac{3}{2df^4}$

Simplify. Write each answer in exponential form.

37. $\dfrac{4.2 \times 10^{14}}{3 \times 10^5}$ 1.4×10^9 38. $\dfrac{1.6 \times 10^{11}}{0.8 \times 10^3}$ 2×10^8 39. $\dfrac{-1.2 \times 10^4}{0.2 \times 10^5}$ $\frac{-6}{10}$, or $-\frac{3}{5}$ 40. $\dfrac{-4.6 \times 10^6}{2.3 \times 10^9}$ $\frac{-2}{10^3}$, or $\frac{-1}{500}$

Simplify. Assume that no variable equals zero. Exponents are positive integers.

C

41. $\dfrac{x^a}{x^2}$ $(a > 2)$ x^{a-2} 42. $\dfrac{z^c}{z^3}$ $(c < 3)$ $\frac{1}{z^{3-c}}$ 43. $\dfrac{y}{y^{2k}}$ $\frac{1}{y^{2k-1}}$ 44. $\dfrac{r^{m-1}}{r}$ $(m > 2)$ r^{m-2}

Find the value of x in each equation.

45. $\dfrac{3^x}{3^9} = \dfrac{1}{3^3}$ 6 46. $\dfrac{r}{r^x} = \dfrac{1}{r^5}$ 6 47. $\dfrac{t^{5-x}}{t^x} = t^3$ 1 48. $\dfrac{2^{3+x}}{2} = 2^7$ 5

Applications

Geometry The volume of a rectangular prism equals the product of the length, the width, and the height: $V = lwh$.

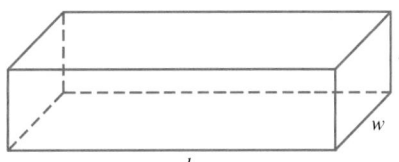

The volume and two dimensions of a rectangular prism are given. Find the third dimension.

49. volume $= x^6$, width $= x$, length $= x^3$ Find the height. x^2

50. volume $= 36x^8$, height $= 2x^2$, length $= 9x^4$ Find the width. $2x^2$

DID YOU KNOW?

In 1939 the physicist J. Robert Oppenheimer demonstrated mathematically that a star could implode. This means that under certain conditions a star could suddenly collapse into a superdense body. The diameter of this body might be only 10^1 miles, and a cubic inch might weigh 10^9 tons.

Suppose a star implodes into a spherical shape with a diameter of 10^1 miles. If a cubic inch weighs 10^9 tons, find the approximate weight of this superdense body. (*Hint:* Use $V = \frac{4}{3}\pi r^3$ to find the volume of the sphere in cubic inches. Then find its weight. There are 5280 ft in one mile.)
1.33181×10^{17} in.^{3}; 1.33181×10^{26} tons

6.2 Dividing Monomials **233**

Teacher's Resource Book
Reteaching—Chapter 6, p. 4.

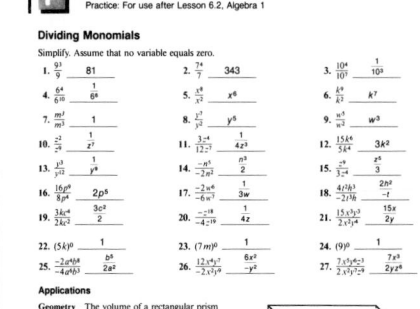

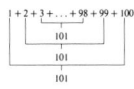

BACKGROUND

In the Capsule Review, students review the property of exponents for multiplication. Remind students to check whether or not their answers are reasonable. This review will prepare students to understand other rules for raising monomials to a power presented in this lesson.

TEACHING SUGGESTION

Assign a variety of examples that students may solve by factoring. Have students state the rule(s) used in solving these examples informally in their own words.

CHALKBOARD EXAMPLES

- **For Example 1**
  Simplify.
  1. $(r^3)^7$ r^{21} **2.** $(x^2)^2$ x^4

- **For Example 2**
  Simplify.
  3. $(-3^3)^2$ 729
  4. $[(-3)^2]^3$ 729

- **For Example 3**
  Simplify.
  5. $(-4 \times 10^3)^3$ -64×10^9
  6. $(2z^3)^3 \cdot 3z$ $24z^{10}$

| 6.3 | **Monomials and Exponents** |

Objectives: To raise a monomial to a power
To raise a quotient of monomials to a power

To simplify $(y^5)^3$, use the definition of exponents and the property of exponents for multiplication ($a^m \cdot a^n = a^{m+n}$).

$$(y^5)^3 = y^5 \cdot y^5 \cdot y^5 = y^{5+5+5} = y^{15}$$
$$\text{So, } (y^5)^3 = y^{15}$$

Capsule Review

Whenever you multiply expressions with the same base add the exponents.

EXAMPLE **Simplify:**   **a.** $x^3 \cdot x^4$ **b.** $3m \cdot 3^2 m^2$

a. $x^3 \cdot x^4 = x^{3+4} = x^7$ **b.** $3m \cdot 3^2 m^2 = 3 \cdot 3^2 \cdot m \cdot m^2 = 3^3 m^3 = 27m^3$

Simplify.

1. -6^2 -36 **2.** $(-1)^8$ 1   **3.** $ab \cdot a^2 b^3$ $a^3 b^4$ **4.** $(-3a)(-3a)$ $9a^2$

You can also simplify an expression such as $(y^5)^3$ by multiplying the exponents.

Property of Exponents

For all real numbers a and for all positive integers m and n:

$$(a^m)^n = a^{mn}$$

EXAMPLE 1 **Simplify:** $(x^6)^9$

$$(x^6)^9 = x^{6 \cdot 9} = x^{54} \qquad \textit{Multiply the exponents.}$$

Does $(x^6)^9$ mean the same as $x^6 \cdot x^9$?   Explain.

EXAMPLE 2 **Simplify:**   **a.** $-(2^2)^3$ **b.** $[(-2)^2]^3$ **c.** $(-2^2)^3$

   a. $-(2^2)^3 = -2^6 = -64$ 2 is the base.

   b. $[(-2)^2]^3 = (-2)^6 = 64$ -2 is the base.

   c. $(-2^2)^3 = (-4)^3 = -64$ 2 is the base first; then -4 is the base.

234   Chapter 6 Polynomials

To raise the product uv to the fourth power, write:

$$(uv)^4 = uv \cdot uv \cdot uv \cdot uv = u^4v^4$$

> For all real numbers a and b and for all positive integers m:
> $$(ab)^m = a^m b^m$$

This property of exponents is often used together with other exponent properties.

EXAMPLE 3 Simplify: **a.** $(-7 \times 10^5)^2$ **b.** $(3x^2)^3 \cdot 2x^4$

a. $(-7 \times 10^5)^2 = (-7)^2 \times (10^5)^2$ *Raise both factors, -7 and 10^5,*
$\qquad\qquad\qquad = 49 \times 10^{10}$ *to the 2nd power.*

b. $(3x^2)^3 \cdot 2x^4 = 3^3(x^2)^3 \cdot 2x^4$ *Raise 3 and x^2 to the 3rd power.*
$\qquad\qquad\qquad = 27x^6 \cdot 2x^4$
$\qquad\qquad\qquad = 54x^{10}$ *Multiply the two monomials,*
$\qquad\qquad\qquad\qquad$ *$27x^6$ and $2x^4$.*

Now consider raising a quotient to a power:

$$\left(\frac{u}{v}\right)^5 = \frac{u}{v} \cdot \frac{u}{v} \cdot \frac{u}{v} \cdot \frac{u}{v} \cdot \frac{u}{v} = \frac{u \cdot u \cdot u \cdot u \cdot u}{v \cdot v \cdot v \cdot v \cdot v} = \frac{u^5}{v^5}$$

> For all real numbers a and b, $b \neq 0$, and for all positive integers m:
> $$\left(\frac{a}{b}\right)^m = \frac{a^m}{b^m}$$

EXAMPLE 4 Simplify: $\left(\dfrac{-2c}{d^2}\right)^4; \ d \neq 0$

$\left(\dfrac{-2c}{d^2}\right)^4 = \dfrac{(-2c)^4}{(d^2)^4}$ *Raise the numerator and denominator to the 4th power.*

$\qquad\qquad = \dfrac{(-2)^4 c^4}{(d^2)^4} = \dfrac{16c^4}{d^8}$ *Raise the two factors of the numerator to the 4th power.*

CLASS EXERCISES

Simplify. Assume that no variable equals zero.

1. $(-d^2)^3$ $-d^6$ **2.** $[(-d)^2]^3$ d^6 **3.** $-(3^2)^3$ -3^6 or -729 **4.** $-(3^3)^2$ -3^6 or -729

5. $(3x^2y)^2$ $9x^4y^2$ **6.** $(-4y^2z^5)^3$ $-64y^6z^{15}$ **7.** $\left(\dfrac{-a}{b^2}\right)^5$ $\dfrac{-a^5}{b^{10}}$ **8.** $\left(\dfrac{-m}{b^3}\right)^8$ $\dfrac{m^8}{b^{24}}$

• **For Example 4**
Simplify.
7. $\left(-\dfrac{6x}{z^2}\right)^2$ $\dfrac{36x^2}{z^4}$

Common Error
• When working with monomials involving exponents, students often become confused when a negative sign is involved. In $(-5)^2$ the base is -5. In (-5^2) the base is 5. Students forget that the square in the second example is on the 5 not -5. Remind students that they should be aware of the positioning of the parentheses in polynomials like these. You may have students check their results using a calculator.
• See *Teacher's Resource Book* for additional remediation.

LESSON FOLLOW-UP

Critical Thinking
Predicting Consequences Predict whether any of the rules presented in this lesson could be applied to simplifying $(3ab^2 + 5a^2b)^2$? How does this example differ from the ones in the lesson? The lesson applies to powers of products and quotients. In a later lesson, some of the properties will be applied to simplifying this expression.

Assignment Guide
• See p. 224B for assignments.
• Have students run the computer program in Exercise 37 for a wide range of numbers.

Lesson Quiz
Simplify. No variable equals zero.
1. $(-3y^2)^4$ $81y^8$
2. $(-3p^3)(5p^3)^2$ $-75p^9$
3. $(2 \times 10^5)^2$ 4×10^{10}
4. $\left(\dfrac{12x^2}{6x^4}\right)^3$ $\dfrac{8}{x^6}$

235

PRACTICE EXERCISES

Simplify. Assume that no variable equals zero.

A
1. a. $(x^5)^6$ x^{30} b. $(z^3)^9$ z^{27}
2. a. $(3^2)^3$ 3^6, or 729   b. $(2^3)^4$ 2^{12}, or 4096
3. $-(10^2)^5$ -10^{10}
4. $-(10^3)^7$ -10^{21}
5. $[(-3)^2]^2$ $(-3)^4$, or 81
6. $[(-2)^3]^3$ $(-2)^9$, or -512
7. $\left(\dfrac{-a}{b^2}\right)^5$ $\dfrac{-a^5}{b^{10}}$
8. $\left(\dfrac{-m}{b^3}\right)^8$ $\dfrac{m^8}{b^{24}}$
9. $(-2 \times 10^3)^4$ 16×10^{12}
10. $(-5 \times 10^2)^3$ -125×10^6

11. $(2x^2)^3 \cdot 3x^4$ $24x^{10}$
12. $(3z^3)^2 \cdot 2z^5$ $18z^{11}$
13. $\left(\dfrac{-3a}{b^2}\right)^3$ $\dfrac{-27a^3}{b^6}$
14. $\left(\dfrac{-2c}{7d}\right)^2$ $\dfrac{4c^2}{49d^2}$

B
15. $\left(\dfrac{4y}{5x}\right)^2$ $\dfrac{16y^2}{25x^2}$
16. $\left(\dfrac{7w}{12y}\right)^2$ $\dfrac{49w^2}{144y^2}$
17. $\left(\dfrac{-2k^4}{3j^3}\right)^3$ $\dfrac{-8k^{12}}{27j^9}$
18. $\left(\dfrac{5x^3}{-2y^4}\right)^2$ $\dfrac{25x^6}{4y^8}$

19. $\left(\dfrac{2b}{18b^3}\right)^2$ $\dfrac{1}{81b^4}$
20. $\left(\dfrac{15d^5}{3d^2}\right)^2$ $25d^6$
21. $(2ab^3)^2$ $4a^2b^6$
22. $(3a^4b)^3$ $27a^{12}b^3$

23. $(-2m^3n)(5mn^2)^3$ $-250m^6n^7$
24. $(-3yz^4)(9yz^3)^2$ $-243y^3z^{10}$
25. $\dfrac{(3a^2)^3a^2}{-9}$ $-3a^8$

26. $\left(\dfrac{4a^2b}{-3a^5b^2}\right)^2$ $\dfrac{16}{9a^6b^2}$
27. $\left(\dfrac{-xy}{2x^2y^4}\right)^5$ $\dfrac{-1}{32x^5y^{15}}$
28. $\dfrac{(-2h^3)^5}{2h^4}$ $-16h^{11}$

Simplify. Assume that no variable equals zero. Exponents are positive integers.

29. $(-z^k)^4$ z^{4k}
30. $(-y^3)^{2j}$ y^{6j}
31. $(-2k^m)^5$ $-32k^{5m}$

C
32. $(-3j)^t(-3j^2)^{t+1}$ $-3^{2t+1}j^{3t+2}$
33. $\left(\dfrac{a^{2m+3}}{a^{m+1}}\right)^2$ a^{2m+4}
34. $\left(\dfrac{b^{2a+1}}{b^a}\right)^4$ b^{4a+4}

35. $[(-2a^2)^3(3b)^2]^2$ $5184a^{12}b^4$
36. $[(5c^3)^2(-2d^2)^3]^2$ $40{,}000c^{12}d^{12}$

Applications

Computer The squares of numbers present some very interesting number patterns. Use the program to print out the indicated squares. For $A = 1$ and $B = 20$, what pattern is true for the last digit of the square?

```
10 INPUT "ENTER THE SPAN, A TO B.  ";A,B
20 PRINT : PRINT : PRINT "NUMBER","SQUARE"
30 FOR X = A TO B
40 PRINT X,X * X
50 NEXT X
60 END
```

37. Use the pattern when $A = 46$ and $B = 60$ to write the squares of 46 to 60.
See below.
38. **Calculator** How would you solve Exercise 37 using a calculator?
Answers may vary.

LOGICAL REASONING

1. If 2^{27} is expanded (written without exponents), what will the last digit be? 8

2. Find a positive integer whose cube exceeds its square by 4624. 17

Additional Answers
37. The last digits of the squares form a pattern of 6, 9, 4, 1, 0, 1, 4, 9, 6, 5 and then the pattern repeats.

6.4

Scientific Notation

Objectives: To write numbers in scientific notation
To multiply and divide numbers written in scientific notation

Many numbers in science and engineering are very large or very small. Scientists use exponents to represent numbers:

diameter of Earth $= 420{,}000{,}000$ ft $= 4.2 \times 10^8$ ft
diameter of a cell $= 0.000025$ cm $= 2.5 \times 10^{-5}$ cm

Capsule Review

All the properties of exponents apply to monomials with base 10.

EXAMPLES **a.** $10^4 \times 10^2 = 10^6$ **b.** $\dfrac{10^3}{10^{10}} = \dfrac{1}{10^7}$
c. $(1.5 \times 10^5)^2 = 1.5^2 \times 10^{10}$

Simplify.

1. $10^3 \times 10^5$ **2.** $(13 \times 10^7)(3 \times 10^2)$ **3.** $(4 \times 10^2)^3$ **4.** $\dfrac{44 \times 10^8}{1.1 \times 10^4}$
10^8 39×10^9 64×10^6 40×10^4

Until now, you have used only nonnegative exponents. The following pattern suggests a definition for *negative exponents*.

$100 \div 10 = 10$	$10 \div 10 = 1$	$1 \div 10 = \dfrac{1}{10}$	$\dfrac{1}{10} \div 10 = \dfrac{1}{100}$
$\uparrow \qquad \uparrow$	$\uparrow \qquad \uparrow$	$\uparrow \qquad \uparrow$	$\uparrow \qquad \uparrow$
$10^2 \qquad 10^1$	$10^1 \qquad 10^0$	$10^0 \qquad 10^{-1}$	$10^{-1} \qquad 10^{-2}$

Notice that $10^{-1} = \dfrac{1}{10^1}$, $10^{-2} = \dfrac{1}{10^2}$, and so on.

> For all real numbers a, $a \neq 0$, and for all positive integers n:
>
> $$a^{-n} = \frac{1}{a^n}$$

Using this definition, you need only one rule for dividing powers.

$$\frac{y^4}{y^6} = y^{4-6} = y^{-2}, \text{ or } \frac{1}{y^2}$$

LESSON PLAN

Vocabulary
Scientific notation

Materials/Manipulatives
Calculators

BACKGROUND

In the Capsule Review, students review the properties of exponents in preparation for learning about scientific notation. You may wish to point out that 10 is used as a base in all these exercises.

Critical Thinking

Observation One reason for using scientific notation is to represent very large or very small numbers in a convenient, concise form. Identify at least two other reasons for writing numbers in scientific notation. Answers may vary. Through discussion, students should recognize the following: ease in computation, standardized form, convenience of storing numbers in the memory of calculators, computers, and so on.

TEACHING SUGGESTION

You may want students to continue the chart for negative and positive exponents. Have students continue the pattern established for 10^3, 10^{-3}, 10^4, 10^{-4}, and so on.

CHALKBOARD EXAMPLES

- **For Example 1**

  Is the number written in scientific notation? If not, explain.

  1. 3.5×7^3

  No; 7^3 is not a power of 10.

  2. 2.8179×10^{-7} Yes.

- **For Example 2**

  Write in scientific notation.

  3. 236,700 2.367×10^5

- **For Example 3**

  Write in scientific notation.

  4. 0.0432 4.32×10^{-2}

- **For Example 4**

  5. Simplify: $(1 \times 10^{-12})(3.26 \times 10^5)$. Write the answer in scientific notation. 3.26×10^{-7}

- **For Example 5**

  6. Simplify: $\dfrac{3.2 \times 10^7}{4 \times 10^2}$. Write the answer in scientific notation.
  8×10^4

LESSON FOLLOW-UP

Assignment Guide

- See p. 224B for assignments.
- You may have students use a calculator for Exercises 19–22.
- See *Teacher's Resource Book, Technology*, pp. 13–14.

Test Yourself

See *Teacher's Resource Book*, Tests, pp. 57–58.

Lesson Quiz

1. Is 0.6×10^3 written in scientific notation? If not, explain.

No; $0.6 < 1$.

2. Write 0.0678 in scientific notation.

6.78×10^{-2}

Simplify. Write the answer in scientific notation.

3. $(5 \times 10^3)(3 \times 10^4)$ 1.5×10^8

4. $\dfrac{15 \times 10^{13}}{2 \times 10^6}$ 7.5×10^7

A number is written in **scientific notation** when it is expressed in the form $n \times 10^m$, where n is a real number such that $1 \le n < 10$ and m is an integer.

EXAMPLE 1   **Is the number written in scientific notation? If not, explain.**
a. 3.459×10^{-3} **b.** 4×2^4 **c.** 18.7×10^3

a. Yes   **b.** No; 2^4 is not a power of ten.   **c.** No; 18.7 is greater than ten.

EXAMPLE 2   **Write 18,459 in scientific notation.**

$$18,459$$
$$= 1.8459 \times 10^4$$

Move the decimal point 4 places to the left. Then multiply by 10^4, or 10,000.

So, $18,459 = 1.8459 \times 10^4$. To check, multiply $1.8459 \times 10,000$.

EXAMPLE 3   **Write 0.00987 in scientific notation.**

$$0.00987$$
$$= 0.009\,87 \times 10^{-3}$$

Move the decimal point 3 places to the right. Then multiply by 10^{-3} or $\frac{1}{10^3}$.

So, $0.00987 = 9.87 \times 10^{-3}$. How would you check?

EXAMPLE 4   **Simplify by mental computation: $(5.87 \times 10^{12})(1 \times 10^6)$. Give your answer in scientific notation.**

$$(5.87 \times 10^{12})(1 \times 10^6) = (5.87 \times 1)(10^{12} \times 10^6) = 5.87 \times 10^{18}$$

EXAMPLE 5   **Simplify by mental computation: $\dfrac{2.4 \times 10^8}{6 \times 10^4}$. Give your answer in scientific notation.**

$$\frac{2.4 \times 10^8}{6 \times 10^4} = \frac{2.4}{6} \times \frac{10^8}{10^4} = 0.4 \times 10^4 = 4 \times 10^{-1} \times 10^4 = 4 \times 10^3$$

CLASS EXERCISES

Write each number in scientific notation.

1. 100,000 1×10^5

2. 0.00105 1.05×10^{-3}

3. 72834.5 7.28345×10^4

4. 6.2 6.2×10^0

238   Chapter 6 Polynomials

PRACTICE EXERCISES

Is the number written in scientific notation? If not, explain.

A **1.** 27×10^{36}
no; 27 is greater than 10

2. 4×10^{-17} yes

3. 0.009×10^3
no; 0.009 is less than 1

4. 0.7×10^{83}
no; 0.7 is less than 1

Write each number in scientific notation.

5. 2,000,000
2×10^6

6. 8,000,000
8×10^6

7. 0.00765
7.65×10^{-3}

8. 0.00438
4.38×10^{-3}

Simplify. Write the answer in scientific notation.

9. $(3.98 \times 10^2)(1 \times 10^7)$ 3.98×10^9

10. $(4.34 \times 10^5)(2 \times 10^8)$ 8.68×10^{13}

11. $(5.23 \times 10^4)(4 \times 10^6)$ 2.092×10^{11}

12. $(7.12 \times 10^3)(3 \times 10^2)$ 2.136×10^6

B **13.** $\dfrac{1.8 \times 10^{12}}{2 \times 10^5}$
9×10^6

14. $\dfrac{4.5 \times 10^{13}}{5 \times 10^6}$
9×10^6

15. $\dfrac{3.6 \times 10^{15}}{6 \times 10^5}$
6×10^9

16. $\dfrac{4.9 \times 10^9}{7 \times 10^3}$
7×10^5

17. $\dfrac{(2 \times 10^3)(4 \times 10^8)}{6 \times 10^2}$ $1.\overline{3} \times 10^9$

18. $\dfrac{(1.5 \times 10^{11})(2 \times 10^{15})}{3 \times 10^9}$ 1×10^{17}

C **19.** $(-1.5 \times 10^3)^2(1.6 \times 10^2)^3$
9.216×10^{12}

20. $(1.2 \times 10^2)^3(-2.4 \times 10^3)^2$
9.95328×10^{12}

21. $\left(\dfrac{6.4 \times 10^3}{8 \times 10}\right)^2(0.5 \times 10^2)$ 3.2×10^5

22. $\left(\dfrac{4.8 \times 10^{12}}{1.6 \times 10^3}\right)^3(9 \times 10^3)$ 2.43×10^{32}

Applications

23. Computer A computer can perform 8×10^8 arithmetic operations per second. How many operations is that per minute? per day? per year? 4.8×10^{10}; 6.912×10^{13}; 2.52288×10^{16}

TEST YOURSELF

Is the expression a monomial? If not, tell why not.   6.1

1. $3x^2 + y^2$
no; expression has 2 terms

2. $-\dfrac{3}{4}a^4$ yes

3. m^2n yes

4. $\dfrac{-5r^2}{s^3}$
no; variable is in the denominator

Simplify. Assume that no variable equals zero.   6.2, 6.3

5. $-4x(3x^3)$ $-12x^4$

6. $2^4a^3b^2 \cdot 2a^2b$
$2^5a^5b^3$, or $32a^5b^3$

7. -3^4 -81

8. $\dfrac{a^{11}}{a^7}$ a^4

9. $\dfrac{3xy^4}{-1.5x^4y^5}$ $\dfrac{-2}{x^3y}$

10. $4s^0$ 4

Simplify if necessary. Then write each answer in scientific notation.   6.4

11. 0.000312 3.12×10^{-4}

12. 1,938,500 1.9385×10^6

13. $\dfrac{23}{100,000}$ 2.3×10^{-4}

Teacher's Resource Book
Reteaching—Chapter 6, p. 10.

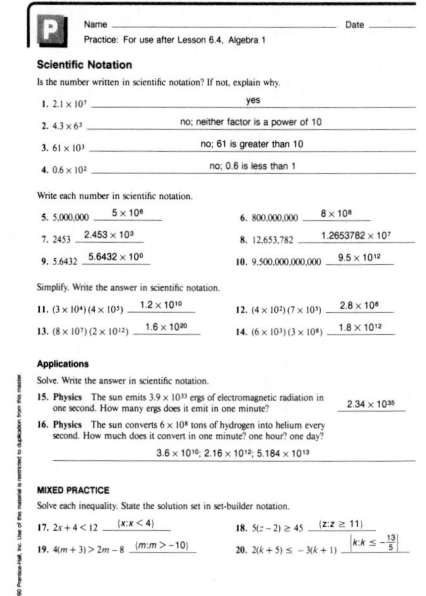

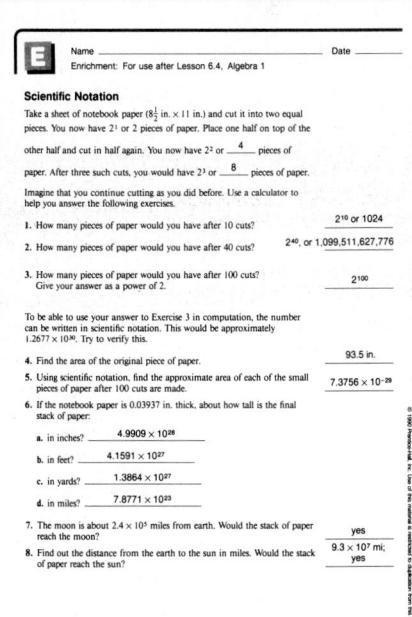

APPLICATION:
Fluid Motion

The mathematician John von Neumann played an important role in the development of the computer as we know it today. His special interest in fluid dynamics was a key factor in his work in developing a computer. Due to the complexity of the equations used to represent fluid motion, the calculations were extremely tedious and time consuming. This led to von Neumann's design and construction of a machine that served as a model for today's computers. He built the machine in the late 1940s.

Second-generation computers measured calculations in milliseconds.

$$1 \text{ millisecond} = \frac{1}{1000} \text{ second} = 10^{-3} \text{ of a second}$$

Third-generation computers measured calculations in nanoseconds. One nanosecond is the time that electricity takes to travel 1 foot.

$$1 \text{ nanosecond} = \frac{1}{1,000,000,000} \text{ second} = 10^{-9} \text{ of a second}$$

Today's fastest computers measure calculations in picoseconds.

$$1 \text{ picosecond} = \frac{1}{1,000,000,000,000} \text{ second} = 10^{-12} \text{ of a second}$$

Computers print these numbers in their own form of scientific notation called exponential notation. For example, 6.84273×10^7 would appear on the computer as 6.84273E+7 and 9.51×10^{-6} as 9.51E−6. The number after the E corresponds to the exponent when a number is in scientific notation.

This program allows you to utilize the speed of the computer to calculate about how many molecules of water flow over Niagara Falls in a given time.

```
10 LET D = 840000000000
20 LET M = 1700000000000000000000
30 PRINT "M = MOLECULES PER DROP   D = DROPS
     PER MINUTE": PRINT : PRINT
40 INPUT "HOW MANY MINUTES? ";X: PRINT : PRINT
50 PRINT "IN ";X;" MINUTES, ABOUT ";M * D * X;
     " MOLECULES OF WATER FLOW OVER NIAGARA
     FALLS." : END
```

Solve.

Run the program to determine the molecules that flow in:

1. 1 minute
   1.428×10^{33}
2. 15 minutes
   2.142×10^{34}
3. 30 minutes
   4.284×10^{34}
4. 60 minutes
   8.568×10^{34}
5. If the weight of water in a lake is 1.58×10^{18} tons, after how much time would the number of molecules flowing over the falls be approximately equal to the number of tons? 1.1064×10^{-15} min

6.5 Polynomials

6.5

Objectives: To identify polynomials, binomials, and trinomials, and the degree of a monomial and polynomial
To simplify polynomials by combining like terms and writing them in ascending or descending order of exponents

Each of the following is an example of a monomial or term:

y variable $5x^2$ product of a constant and a variable
-16 numeral or constant $9ab^2c^3$ product of a constant and several variables

Capsule Review

You have been shown how to combine like terms using the distributive property:

a. $x + 3x$
$= 1 \cdot x + 3 \cdot x$
$= (1 + 3)x$
$= 4x$

b. $\frac{1}{2}mn^2 - 6mn^2 + mn = \left(\frac{1}{2} - 6\right)mn^2 + mn$
$= \left(\frac{1}{2} - \frac{12}{2}\right)mn^2 + mn = -\frac{11}{2}mn^2 + mn$

Simplify, if possible, by combining like terms.

1. $a + 4a$ 5a   **2.** $-2x^3 - \frac{7x^3}{3}$ $-\frac{13}{3}x^3$ **3.** $x^2y - 7x^2y^2$ not possible   **4.** $6s^3t^2 - 6s^3t^2$ 0

The **degree of a monomial** is the sum of the exponents of its variables. If the monomial is a nonzero constant, the degree is 0. The constant 0 has no degree.

monomial	x	$4ab^2$	m^3n^5	$-\frac{7}{8}$	gh	0
degree	1	3	8	0	2	no degree

EXAMPLE 1   **State the degree:**   **a.** $\frac{1}{2}x$ **b.** $8a^2b^5$ **c.** 6

Monomial	**Degree**	**Reason**
a. $\frac{1}{2}x$	1	$\frac{1}{2}x = \frac{1}{2}x^1$. Exponent is 1.
b. $8a^2b^5$	7	Sum of exponents $(2 + 5)$ is 7.
c. 6	0	The degree of a nonzero constant is 0.

6.5 Polynomials   **241**

Vocabulary
Ascending order
Binomial
Degree of a monomial
Degree of a polynomial
Descending order
Monomial
Polynomial
Trinomial

BACKGROUND

In the Capsule Review, students practice combining like terms of algebraic expressions. You may want to review the meaning of like terms and unlike terms. Students should give examples of each. This exercise leads logically to an understanding of the definition of a polynomial.

TEACHING SUGGESTIONS

- Students should learn and use the special names for polynomials with one, two, and three terms; namely, monomial, binomial, and trinomial. Point out the meaning of the prefixes *mono-*, *bi-*, and *tri-*, and have students name and define other words with these prefixes.
- Point out that unless otherwise noted, answers are usually given in descending order with respect to one variable in a polynomial.

Critical Thinking

Causal Explanation Explain why the terms of a polynomial can be arranged in ascending or descending order. The commutative and/or associative properties for addition allow reordering of the terms.

CHALKBOARD EXAMPLES

- **For Example 1**

State the degree.
1. -4 0   **2.** $7r$ 1
3. $-c^3d^4$ 7

- **For Example 2**

State the degree.
4. $4x^2y^2 - 2xy^5 - 3$ 6
5. $3a^3b^2 - \frac{1}{3}a^2b + 5ab^2 -$
$2b + 3$ 5

- **For Example 3**

Simplify. Write the result in descending order of the exponents of *s*.
6. $3r^2s^2 + 5rs^3 - 9r^2s^2 + 4s$
$5rs^3 - 6r^2s^2 + 4s$
7. $3s^2t - 6s^2t + 5s^3$
$5s^3 - 3s^2t$

- **For Example 4**

Simplify. Write the result in ascending order of exponents.
8. $3(m^3 + 4) - 2(4m^3 - m^2 + 3m + 1) + 4m$
$10 - 2m + 2m^2 - 5m^3$

A **polynomial** is a monomial or a sum or difference of monomials. The following are examples of polynomials.

$$-3x^2 \qquad \frac{7}{8}a + 2b^3 \qquad -y^4 + 5y - 11 \qquad 5x^3y + x^2 + 2y^4 - 19$$

The monomials that make up a polynomial are called its terms. Polynomials of two or three terms are used so often they have special names.

monomial	one term	$0.006t$	mn	$-5x^3y^4z^2$
binomial	two terms	$3x + 2$	$3m + 5n$	$x + y$
trinomial	three terms	$3x^2 + 2x - 1$	$a^2 + 2ab + b^2$	$x + y + z$

The **degree of a polynomial** is the *highest* degree of any of its terms after it has been simplified.

The degree of $6x^3 + 4x^2 + 7$ is 3.

EXAMPLE 2   **State the degree of $2x^2y^2 + \frac{2}{3}x^2y + 8xy^2 - 5$.**

$$2x^2y^2 + \frac{2}{3}x^2y + 8xy^2 - 5$$

$$\downarrow \qquad \downarrow \qquad \downarrow \qquad \downarrow$$
$$4 \qquad 3 \qquad 3 \qquad 0$$

Add the exponents in each monomial. The highest degree is 4.

So, the degree of the polynomial $2x^2y^2 + \frac{2}{3}x^2y + 8xy^2 - 5$ is 4.

The polynomial $x^5 + 2x^3 - 7x^2 + 6x - 11$ is said to be arranged in **descending order,** since the degree of each term is lower than that of the preceding terms. In **ascending order,** the polynomial is written as $-11 + 6x - 7x^2 + 2x^3 + x^5$.

If a polynomial has more than one variable, it can be written in descending or ascending order of the exponents with respect to one variable. For example, $6ab^4 + 10a^2b^2 - 2a^3b + 3a^4$ is in descending order with respect to *b*.

To simplify a polynomial, combine like terms. Remember that like terms contain the same variables with the same exponents.

EXAMPLE 3   **Simplify: $-2x^2y^2 - 3x^3y + 8x^2y^2 + 5xy^3$. Write the result in descending order of the exponents with respect to *y*.**

$$-2x^2y^2 - 3x^3y + 8x^2y^2 + 5xy^3$$
$$= (-2x^2y^2 + 8x^2y^2) - 3x^3y + 5xy^3 \qquad \text{Group like terms.}$$
$$= 6x^2y^2 - 3x^3y + 5xy^3 \qquad \text{Combine like terms.}$$
$$= 5xy^3 + 6x^2y^2 - 3x^3y \qquad \text{Write in descending order.}$$

242   Chapter 6 Polynomials

EXAMPLE 4 Simplify: $6(x^3 - 3) - 5(3x^3 + 2x^2 + 1) + 25$. **Write the result in ascending order of the exponents.**

$$6(x^3 - 3) - 5(3x^3 + 2x^2 + 1) + 25$$
$$= 6x^3 + 6(-3) - 5(3x^3) - 5(2x^2) - 5(1) + 25 \quad \textit{Distributive property}$$
$$= 6x^3 - 18 - 15x^3 - 10x^2 - 5 + 25$$
$$= -9x^3 - 10x^2 + 2 \quad \textit{Combine like terms.}$$
$$= 2 - 10x^2 - 9x^3 \quad \textit{Ascending order}$$

Note that the degree of the polynomial is 3.

CLASS EXERCISES

State the degree.

1. $3x$ 1   **2.** $-12xy^3z^5$ 9   **3.** $\dfrac{-7}{8}$ 0   **4.** $wxyz$ 4   **5.** $0.1h$ 1

6. $\dfrac{3y}{4} - 7$ 1   **7.** $2a^2 + \dfrac{4a}{5} - 8$ 2   **8.** $4c^3 + 3c^2d^2 - 8cd + \dfrac{1}{2}d^3$
                                                         4

9. $3x^3 - 2x^2y^2 + 18x^2y + 3x^3$ 4   **10.** $-2x^2y^3 - xy^4 + x^2y^2 + xy^4 + x^3y^2$ 5

Simplify. Write the result in descending order of the exponents with respect to a.

11. $2a + 8a - a^2$ $-a^2 + 10a$ **12.** $2ab^2 + (-5ab^2)$ $-3ab^2$

13. $\dfrac{1}{3}a^3c - 3a^3c + a$ $-\dfrac{8}{3}a^3c + a$ **14.** $\dfrac{1}{2}a^4 - 2(a^5 - 2a^3 + 1) + a^2$
                                                 $-2a^5 + \dfrac{1}{2}a^4 + 4a^3 + a^2 - 2$

PRACTICE EXERCISES

State the degree.

A   **1.** $\dfrac{3}{4}x$ 1   **2.** $\dfrac{7}{8}z$ 1   **3.** $7m^2n^5$ 7   **4.** $12r^3s^6$ 9   **5.** 9 0   **6.** 18 0

7. $5x^2y^2 + \dfrac{1}{2}x^2y^2 + 6xy - 3$ 4   **8.** $4r^2s^2 + \dfrac{5}{7}r^2s^2 + 10rs - 5$ 4

9. $xy + 3x^2y^2 - \dfrac{4}{5}x^2y - 9x^3y^2$ 5   **10.** $ab + 4a^2b^2 - \dfrac{1}{9}a^2b - 3a^3b^2$ 5

Simplify. Write the result in descending order of the exponents with respect to x.

11. $-3x^2y^2 - 4x^3y + 9x^2y^2 + 2xy^3$ **12.** $-7x^2y^2 - 5x^3y + 10x^2y^2 + 9xy^3$
     $-4x^3y + 6x^2y^2 + 2xy^3$ $-5x^3y + 3x^2y^2 + 9xy^3$

13. $5x^2y^2 + 2xy^3 - 4xy^3$ **14.** $-2x^3y + 6x^3y - 2xy^3$
     $5x^2y^2 - 2xy^3$ $4x^3y - 2xy^3$

15. $3(x^3 - 5) - 5(4x^3 + 5x^2 + 1) + 30$ **16.** $5(x^3 - 6) - 7(3x^3 + 3x^2 + 1) + 15$
     $-17x^3 - 25x^2 + 10$ $-16x^3 - 21x^2 - 22$

B   **17.** $4x^2z + \dfrac{9}{8}xz^2 - 3xz^2$ $4x^2z - \dfrac{15}{8}xz^2$ **18.** $0.5xy^2 - 0.7x^2y + 0.4xy^2 + 0.7x^2y$
                                                                    $0.9xy^2$

19. $-5x^2z + \dfrac{2}{5}x^2z + 2xz^2$ $-\dfrac{23}{5}x^2z + 2xz^2$ **20.** $0.2xy^2 - 0.6x^2y - 0.3xy^2 + 0.1xy^2$
                                                                    $-0.6x^2y$

6.5 Polynomials   **243**

Common Error

- When determining the degree of a monomial, many students forget that if a variable has no exponent, the exponent is 1; for example, the degree of ab^2 is 3 because $ab^2 = a^1b^2$. Students who make this error should be required to write all variables in a polynomial with an exponent as a first step before determining the degree of a monomial.
- See *Teacher's Resource Book* for additional remediation.

LESSON FOLLOW-UP

Discussion

Why is 6 the degree of the monomial, $3^3a^2b^4$, and not $3 + 2 + 4 = 9$? Explain.   The degree of a monomial is the sum of the exponents of its *variables*.

Critical Thinking

Classifying The prefix "poly," as in polynomial, is a combining form meaning much or many. We define a polynomial as "a monomial or a sum of monomials." How can a monomial (one term) be a polynomial?   The motivation is to provide a classification scheme for expressions with any (counting) number of terms.

See *Teacher's Resource Book,* for Critical Thinking Activity, p. 6.

Assignment Guide

See p. 224B for assignments.

Lesson Quiz

State the degree.
   1. $3x^3y$ 4   **2.** 31.6   0
   3. $gh^2 + 11g^2h^2 - \dfrac{2}{3}gh + \dfrac{5}{7}$ 4

Simplify. Write the result in descending order of the exponents of x.
   4. $4x^8 + 3x^8 - 2x$ $7x^8 - 2x$
   5. $11 + x - 8 + 4(3x - 1)$
     $13x - 1$
   6. $4x^3z^2 - 2x^3z^2 + \dfrac{4}{7}xz^3$
     $2x^3z^2 + \dfrac{4}{7}xz^3$
   7. $0.3xy^2 + 0.9x^3y - 0.3xy^2 + 0.6x^3y$ $1.5x^3y$

243

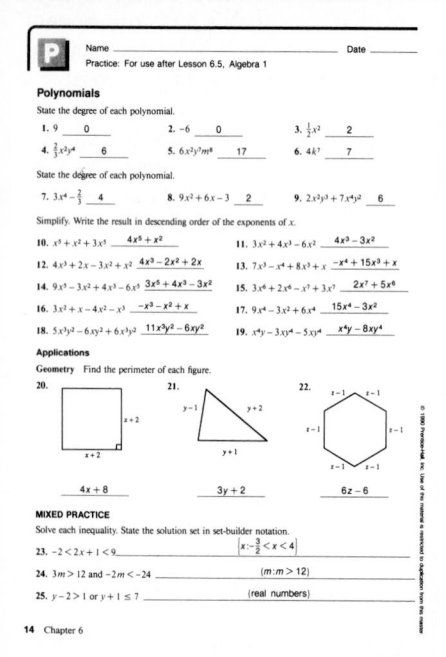

Simplify. Write the result in descending order of the exponents of the underlined variable.

21. $\frac{1}{2}c\underline{d}e - \frac{1}{2}(c\underline{d}^2 + c\underline{d}e)$ $-\frac{1}{2}cd^2$

22. $f\underline{g} + \frac{1}{3}(\underline{g}^2 - 3f\underline{g}) + \frac{1}{3}\underline{g}^2$ $\frac{2}{3}g^2$

23. $4\underline{x}^2 + 3(\underline{x}^2 - 3) - 2(4 - 7\underline{x}^2)$ $21x^2 - 17$

24. $a\underline{b}^2 - 4(a + \underline{b}) + 2(a\underline{b}^2 - \underline{b})$ $3ab^2 - 6b - 4a$

25. $4(2x\underline{y}^2 + 3x^2\underline{y}) - 2(2\underline{y}x^2 + 5\underline{y}^2x)$ $-2xy^2 + 8x^2y$

26. $6(x\underline{z}^3 + x^2\underline{z}) - 7(\underline{z}^2x - 2x^3\underline{z})$ $6xz^3 - 7xz^2 + 14x^3z + 6x^2z$

Simplify. Write the result in descending order of the exponents with respect to x. Assume that a is a positive integer.

C

27. $x^a - x^{3a} + x^a + x^{2a}$ $-x^{3a} + x^{2a} + 2x^a$

28. $x^{2a} + x^a - x^{4a} - x^{2a}$ $-x^{4a} + x^a$

29. $-2x^a + 3x^{2a} + x^a - 2x^{2a}$ $x^{2a} - x^a$

30. $x^{2a} - 2x^a + 3x^a + x^a$ $x^{2a} + 2x^a$

Simplify. Then evaluate if $x = -2$, $y = \frac{1}{2}$, and $a = 2$.

31. $3xy^a + 2x^ay - 3x^ay + y^a$ $-\frac{13}{4}$

32. $x^ay^a - 2y^a + x^ay^a - 6y$ $-\frac{3}{2}$

Applications

Geometry Find the perimeter of each figure.

33.

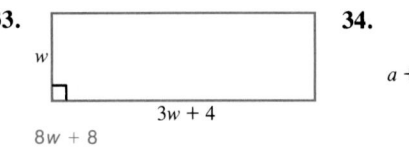

w

$3w + 4$

$8w + 8$

34.

$a + 1$

$a + 1$

$4a + 4$

35.

$x + 3$ $2x - 1$

$3x - 5$

$6x - 3$

CRITICAL THINKING: Classifying

Your first task in classifying items is to decide on a characteristic or characteristics of interest. Then you must decide which item(s) contain the given characteristic.

Polynomials can be classified by these characteristics: (a) number of terms, (b) degree, and (c) number of variables.

$$x^2 + y^2 \qquad 3a^2 + 2ab + b^2 \qquad 5xy^2 + 3 \qquad 0 \qquad y^3 - m^3 \qquad r^3$$

Classify the polynomials above by listing the ones that belong to each of the following categories.

1. polynomials with two terms
$x^2 + y^2$; $5xy^2 + 3$; $y^3 - m^3$

2. second-degree polynomials
$x^2 + y^2$; $3a^2 + 2ab + b^2$

3. polynomials in two variables
$x^2 + y^2$; $3a^2 + 2ab + b^2$; $5xy^2 + 3$; $y^3 - m^3$

4. third-degree binomials in two variables
$5xy^2 + 3$; $y^3 - m^3$

5. List two other ways that polynomials may be classified.
by coefficients; ascending (descending) order

6.6 Adding and Subtracting Polynomials

Objectives: To add polynomials
To subtract polynomials

You have used the distributive property to combine the like terms (monomials) of a polynomial. To *combine* like terms means to *add* or *subtract* like terms.

$$4x + 6y + 3x - 3y$$
$$= (4x + 3x) + (6y - 3y)$$
$$= (4 + 3)x + (6 - 3)y$$
$$= 7x + 3y$$

Capsule Review

When combining terms express the result in descending order of the exponents of one of the variables.

EXAMPLE
$$7m - 3m^2 - 2m^4 - 5 - 4m^4 + 3m^3 - 7m^2 + 1$$
$$= (-2m^4 - 4m^4) + 3m^3 + (-3m^2 - 7m^2) + 7m + (-5 + 1)$$
$$= -6m^4 + 3m^3 - 10m^2 + 7m - 4$$

Simplify.

1. $a^2 + 4a + 3a^2$ $\quad 4a^2 + 4a$ 2. $2m - 18m$ $\quad -16m$ 3. $-2x^3 - 7x^2$ $\quad -2x^3 - 7x^2$

4. $m^3n - 7m^2n^2 + 5m^2n^2 - 3m$ $\quad m^3n - 2m^2n^2 - 3m$ 5. $\frac{1}{2}s - \frac{1}{3}s^2 + s - s^2$ $\quad -\frac{4}{3}s^2 + \frac{3}{2}s$

To add polynomials, add the like terms of the polynomials. The addition can be shown horizontally or vertically.

EXAMPLE 1   Add $3x^3 + x^2 - 2x - 5$ and $x^2 - 5x + 7$.

Add horizontally

$$(3x^3 + x^2 - 2x - 5) + (x^2 - 5x + 7)$$
$$= 3x^3 + (x^2 + x^2) + (-2x - 5x) + (-5 + 7) \quad \text{Group like terms.}$$
$$= 3x^3 + (1 + 1)x^2 + (-2 - 5)x + (-5 + 7) \quad \text{Use the distributive}$$
$$= 3x^3 + 2x^2 - 7x + 2 \qquad\qquad\qquad\qquad \text{property.}$$

Add vertically

$$3x^3 + x^2 - 2x - 5$$
$$\underline{x^2 - 5x + 7} \quad \text{Align like terms vertically.}$$
$$3x^3 + 2x^2 - 7x + 2 \quad \text{Add like terms in each column.}$$

6.6 Adding and Subtracting Polynomials   **245**

LESSON PLAN

BACKGROUND

In the Capsule Review, students simplify polynomials by combining like terms. This activity provides a logical introduction to the addition and subtraction of polynomials.

TEACHING SUGGESTION

Point out that when you subtract polynomials you are actually adding the opposite of each term. In both formats, the opposite of each term in the second polynomial is added to the first polynomial.

CHALKBOARD EXAMPLES

- **For Example 1**
  1. Add $4x^3 + x^2 - 3x - 5$ and $x^2 - 4x + 6$.
  $4x^3 + 2x^2 - 7x + 1$

- **For Example 2**
  2. Subtract $a^2 - 2a + 7$ from $4a^3 + 3a^2 - 3a + 5$.
  $4a^3 + 2a^2 - a - 2$

- **For Example 3**
  3. Subtract. $(8n^3 - 7n + 4) - (3n^3 - 2n^2 + 7)$
  $5n^3 + 2n^2 - 7n - 3$

Common Error

- When adding polynomials, students often add the exponents of the terms as well as the coefficients: $5x^2 + 3x^2 = 8x^4$, instead of $8x^2$. These students should think of the variables in like terms as units.

- See *Teacher's Resource Book* for additional remediation.

245

Explain how adding 234 and 59 is like adding polynomials. *They are alike in that like terms (powers of ten) are added "term by term." If 234 and 59 are written as $2 \times 10^2 + 3 \times 10 + 4$ and $5 \times 10 + 9$, respectively, the numbers take on the appearance of polynomials.*

Critical Thinking

Causal Explanation Show students the directive: Subtract the first polynomial from the second. Ask them to explain whether or not it matters which one is subtracted from the other. *It does matter: subtraction of real numbers is not commutative.*

Assignment Guide

See p. 224B for assignments.

Lesson Quiz

Add.

1. $2a - b + 4c$
$a + 2b - 2c$
$\overline{3a + b + 2c}$

Subtract.

2. $9r - 4s + 7t$
$\underline{-4r - 2t}$
$13r - 4s + 9t$

Add or subtract, as indicated.

3. $(5c^2 + 2c) + (c^2 - 3c)$
$6c^2 - c$

4. $(3x^2 + 2x + 1) - (2x^2 + 5x - 3)$
$x^2 - 3x + 4$

To subtract a polynomial, add the opposite of each term of the polynomial being subtracted and then simplify.

EXAMPLE 2 Subtract $x^2 - 5x + 7$ from $3x^3 + x^2 - 2x - 5$.

$(3x^3 + x^2 - 2x - 5) - (x^2 - 5x + 7)$
$= 3x^3 + x^2 - 2x - 5 + (-x^2) + 5x + (-7)$ *Add the opposite of each term.*
$= 3x^3 + 3x - 12$ *Combine like terms.*

EXAMPLE 3 Subtract: $(5a^3 - a^2 - 6) - (4a^3 - a - 9)$

Align like terms.   Add the opposite of each term subtracted.

$5a^3 - a^2 - 6$ $5a^3 - a^2 - 6$
$\underline{4a^3 - a - 9}$ ← opposites → $\underline{-4a^3 + a + 9}$
 $a^3 - a^2 + a + 3$

CLASS EXERCISES

Add.

1. $11r + 3s + 2t$ $\qquad$ **2.** $5a + 4b$ $\qquad$ **3.** $3d - 6e + 7f$
$\underline{r + 2s - t}$ $\qquad\qquad$ $\underline{-3a + b}$ $\qquad\qquad$ $\underline{d + 4e - 4f}$
$12r + 5s + t$ $\qquad\qquad$ $2a + 5b$ $\qquad\qquad$ $4d - 2e + 3f$

Add or subtract, as indicated.

4. $(2x + 5) + (3x - 2)$ $5x + 3$ $\qquad$ **5.** $(4c^2 + 3c) + (c^2 + 6c)$ $5c^2 + 9c$

6. $(3h + 2k + 4) + (7h - k + 3)$ $\qquad$ **7.** $(9m^2 + 16m - 3) + (2m^2 + 3m - 1)$
$10h + k + 7$ $\qquad\qquad\qquad\qquad\qquad\qquad$ $11m^2 + 19m - 4$
8. $(4c^2 + 7c) - (3c^2 + 5c)$ $c^2 + 2c$ $\qquad$ **9.** $(3k - d) - (2k - 3d)$ $k + 2d$

10. $(-11a^2 + 2a - 1) - (7a^2 + 4a - 1)$ $-18a^2 - 2a$

11. $(6r^3 - 3r + 7) - (6r^3 - 3r + 7)$ 0

PRACTICE EXERCISES

Add.

A $\qquad$ **1.** $5x^3 + x^2 - 3x - 7$ $\qquad\qquad$ **2.** $8x^3 + x^2 - 5x - 9$
$\underline{\phantom{5x^3 + {}} x^2 - 6x + 9}$ $\qquad\qquad\qquad$ $\underline{\phantom{8x^3 + {}} x^2 - 8x + 11}$
$5x^3 + 2x^2 - 9x + 2$ $\qquad\qquad\qquad$ $8x^3 + 2x^2 - 13x + 2$

3. $7r + 2s - 2t$ $\qquad\qquad\qquad$ **4.** $8j - 3k + 6m$
$\underline{\phantom{7r + {}} 4s - 3t}$ $\qquad\qquad\qquad\qquad$ $\underline{-2j + 3m}$
$7r + 6s - 5t$ $\qquad\qquad\qquad\qquad$ $6j - 3k + 9m$

5. $2x^3 + 6x^2 + x$ and $3x^2 - 2x + 2$ $\qquad$ **6.** $3x^3 + 7x^2 + 6x$ and $2x^3 + 3x$
$2x^3 + 9x^2 - x + 2$ $\qquad\qquad\qquad\qquad\qquad$ $5x^3 + 7x^2 + 9x$
7–12. For Exercises 1–6, subtract the second polynomial from the first polynomial.
See below.

246 $\quad$ Chapter 6 Polynomials

Add or subtract, as indicated.

13. $(5x^3 + x^2 - 3x - 8) - (x^2 - 7x + 9)$ $5x^3 + 4x - 17$

14. $(6x^3 + 3x^2 - x - 6) - (x^2 - 8x + 9)$ $6x^3 + 2x^2 + 7x - 15$

15. $(3m^3 - m^7 - 6) - (2m^3 - m^7 - 9)$ $m^3 + 3$

16. $(7n^3 - n^2 - 8) - (6n^3 - n^2 - 10)$ $n^3 + 2$

B 17. $(3c^3 - 3c) + (2c^3 - c)$ $5c^3 - 4c$

18. $(8x^2 + 3) + (7x^2 + 10)$ $15x^2 + 13$

19. $(7a + 3b - c) + (6a - 2b + 3c)$ $13a + b + 2c$

20. $(x^2 + 2x + 1) + (2x^2 - 3x + 4)$ $3x^2 - x + 5$

21. $(9r + 3s + 8) + (3s + 2)$ $9r + 6s + 10$

22. $(4x + 10y + 7) + (x + 2y)$ $5x + 12y + 7$

Subtract the first polynomial from the second polynomial.

23. $(2j + k - 2m); (3j + 2k + 4m)$ $j + k + 6m$

24. $(4a - 3b + 2c); (6a + 5b - 3c)$ $2a + 8b - 5c$

25. $(2x^2 - 2x + 5); (3x^2 + 3x + 5)$ $x^2 + 5x$

26. $(5a^2 - 11a - 3); (7a^2 - 11a + 7)$ $2a^2 + 10$

27. $(6x^3 + 4x^2 + 3x); (3x^4 - 7x^3 - 3x^2)$ $3x^4 - 13x^3 - 7x^2 - 3x$

28. $(4z^3 + 3z^2 + 4); (-7z^3 + 11z^2 + 12z)$ $-11z^3 + 8z^2 + 12z - 4$

Add or subtract, as indicated.

C 29. $(11a^2 + 3a + 8) + (6a^2 - 2a + 4) - (3a^2 + 5)$ $14a^2 + a + 7$

30. $(3y^2 - 7y + 9) + (2y^2 + 8y - 4) - (2y - 3)$ $5y^2 - y + 8$

31. $(17x^3 + 3x^2 + 4x) - (7x^3 - 2x + 4) - (4x^2 - 3)$ $10x^3 - x^2 + 6x - 1$

32. $(4z^3 + 7z^2 + 8z) - (2z^3 - 11z + 3) - (2z^2 + 4)$ $2z^3 + 5z^2 + 19z - 7$

Applications

33. **Number Problem** If n is an integer, write an expression to represent the sum of n and the next three consecutive integers. Simplify. $4n + 6$

34. **Geometry** The length of a rectangle is 4 cm greater than its width w. Write an expression to represent the perimeter. Simplify. $4w + 8$

ALGEBRA IN HEALTH

A scientist observed that the growth of a bacteria over t hours could be approximated by the polynomial $0.0035t^3 - 0.15t^2 + 1.5t + 10$. Use this program to print out a chart for times of 0 h to 40 h.

```
10 PRINT "TIME","BACTERIA GROWTH"
20 FOR T = 0 TO 40
30 PRINT T,0.0035 * T ^ 3 - 0.15 *
   T ^ 2 + 1.5 * T + 10
40 NEXT T
```

At what times does the bacteria start to decay? To grow?

6 h;   22 h

6.6 Adding and Subtracting Polynomials   **247**

Teacher's Resource Book
Reteaching—Chapter 6, p. 16.

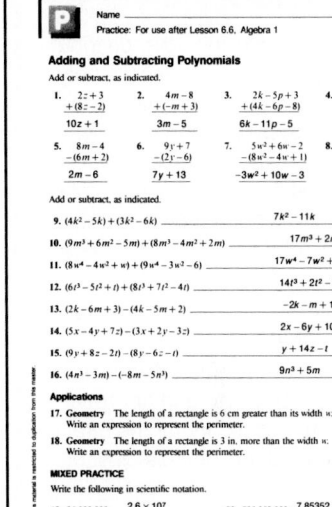

BACKGROUND

In the Capsule Review, the distributive property is used to multiply a polynomial by a constant. The same property must be applied when multiplying a polynomial by a monomial. Remind students to watch the signs in a polynomial when distributed by a negative constant or a monomial that is negative.

Critical Thinking

Observation Scan the lesson and list the concepts, skills, and/or properties which are necessary for the effective understanding of this lesson. Answers may vary. Students may list some of the following examples.
Concepts: polynomial, monomial
Skills: multiplying monomials, combining like terms
Properties: property of exponents for multiplication, distributive property

TEACHING SUGGESTIONS

- Students learn to multiply a polynomial by a monomial using two formats, vertical or horizontal. Students may use either format. However, exercises similar to Example 2 are better suited to using a horizontal format.
- Point out that in all the examples and exercises, the answers are given in descending order in terms of one variable.

6.7

Multiplying a Polynomial by a Monomial

Objectives: To multiply a polynomial by a monomial
To simplify algebraic expressions that involve multiplication of a polynomial by a monomial

The distributive property provides you with a method for multiplying a polynomial by any monomial. The monomial may be a constant or it may have variable factors. The polynomial may have any number of terms.

Capsule Review

$$\text{EXAMPLE} \quad 3(m^3 - 7m^2 + m - 1) = 3(m^3) + 3(-7m^2) + 3(m) + 3(-1)$$
$$= 3m^3 - 21m^2 + 3m - 3$$

Simplify. Use the distributive property.

1. $3(m^2 - 7m + 3)$ $3m^2 - 21m + 9$

2. $-3(4n^2 + 5p^2)$ $-12n^2 - 15p^2$

3. $\frac{1}{2}(a + 2b)$ $\frac{1}{2}a + b$

4. $0.2(x^2 + 4x - 6)$ $0.2x^2 + 0.8x - 1.2$

5. $2(-6x^3 + x^2 - 0.3x + 0.1)$
$-12x^3 + 2x^2 - 0.6x + 0.2$

6. $-\frac{2}{3}(12y^2 - 9y + 18)$ $-8y^2 + 6y - 12$

To multiply a polynomial by a monomial, you will often use the property of exponents for multiplication: $a^m \cdot a^n = a^{m+n}$.

EXAMPLE 1 **Simplify:** $-3x^2(x^3 - 5x^2 + 7x - 1)$

Horizontal format

$$-3x^2(x^3 - 5x^2 + 7x - 1)$$
$$= (-3x^2)(x^3) + (-3x^2)(-5x^2) + (-3x^2)(7x) + (-3x^2)(-1)$$
$$= -3x^5 + 15x^4 - 21x^3 + 3x^2$$

Vertical format

$$\begin{array}{r} x^3 - 5x^2 + 7x - 1 \\ -3x^2 \\ \hline -3x^5 + 15x^4 - 21x^3 + 3x^2 \end{array}$$
Multiply each term in the top row by $-3x^2$.

In Example 2, the parentheses are removed by multiplying each term of each polynomial by a monomial factor. Then the like terms are combined.

248   Chapter 6 Polynomials

EXAMPLE 2 Simplify: $-5xy^2(3xy - 2x^2) + 4x^2y(y^2 - 2xy + 7)$

$$-5xy^2(3xy - 2x^2) + 4x^2y(y^2 - 2xy + 7)$$
$$= [(-5xy^2)(3xy) + (-5xy^2)(-2x^2)] + [(4x^2y)(y^2) + (4x^2y)(-2xy) + (4x^2y)(7)]$$
$$= -15x^2y^3 + 10x^3y^2 + 4x^2y^3 - 8x^3y^2 + 28x^2y$$
$$= (-15x^2y^3 + 4x^2y^3) + (10x^3y^2 - 8x^3y^2) + 28x^2y \qquad \text{Group like terms.}$$
$$= -11x^2y^3 + 2x^3y^2 + 28x^2y \qquad\qquad\qquad\quad \text{Combine like terms.}$$

CLASS EXERCISES

Multiply.

1. $3x - 2y$
$\underline{4y}$
$12xy - 8y^2$

2. $9r + 3s + 2t$
$\underline{2rst}$
$18r^2st + 6rs^2t + 4rst^2$

3. $-3ab(2a - 4b)$ $\; -6a^2b + 12ab^2$

4. $-3d^2f(2d - 4e + 6f)$
$-6d^3f + 12d^2ef - 18d^2f^2$

5. $2x(3x - 2)$ $\; 6x^2 - 4x$

6. $-3c(2c + 6)$ $\; -6c^2 - 18c$

7. $(3c - 5)(-5c)$ $\; -15c^2 + 25c$

8. $(-2k - 3)(-3k)$ $\; 6k^2 + 9k$

9. $-11a^2b^3(7a^2 + 3b + c)$
$-77a^4b^3 - 33a^2b^4 - 11a^2b^3c$

10. $-8rs^4(-6r^3 - 2s^2 + rs)$
$48r^4s^4 + 16rs^6 - 8r^2s^5$

PRACTICE EXERCISES

Multiply and simplify, where possible.

A **1.** $-5x^2(x^3 - 6x^2 + 8x - 5)$
$-5x^5 + 30x^4 - 40x^3 + 25x^2$
3. $2p^3(-3p^4 + 2p^2 - 5)$
$-6p^7 + 4p^5 - 10p^3$
5. $3p^2q(4p + 2q - r)$
$12p^3q + 6p^2q^2 - 3p^2qr$
7. $-2x^2(-x^3 + x - 3)$ $\; 2x^5 - 2x^3 + 6x^2$
9. $5mn^2(3m^3 - 2n^2 - mn + p)$
$15m^4n^2 - 5m^2n^3 - 10mn^4 + 5mn^2p$
11. $7hk(7h - k + 8)$
$49h^2k - 7hk^2 + 56hk$
13. $-2ab^2(3ab - 2a^2) + 5a^2b(b^2 - 3ab + 8)$ $\; -a^2b^3 - 11a^3b^2 + 40a^2b$
14. $-4xy^2(5xy - 3x^2) + 3x^2y(y^2 - 5xy + 9)$ $\; -17x^2y^3 - 3x^3y^2 + 27x^2y$

B **15.** $2y(-y + 1) + 5(y - 2)$ $\; -2y^2 + 7y - 10$
16. $3x(2 - 3x) + 4(3x - 1)$
$-9x^2 + 18x - 4$
17. $2m(1 - 3m^2) + 3m^2(4m - 2)$
$6m^3 - 6m^2 + 2m$
18. $5g^2(3 - 2g) + g(g + 3g^2)$
$-7g^3 + 16g^2$
19. $(-3ab^2 + 2a^2b)(-2ab)$
$6a^2b^3 - 4a^3b^2$
20. $(-6d^2e^2 + 7de)(-d^2e^2)$
$6d^4e^4 - 7d^3e^3$
21. $5rs^4(3r^3 - 2s^2r + s)$
$15r^4s^4 - 10r^2s^6 + 5rs^5$
22. $6a^2b(7a^2 + 3ab - b)$
$42a^4b + 18a^3b^2 - 6a^2b^2$
23. $3abc^3(-4a^2c + 2b^2c^3 - ab)$
$-12a^3bc^4 - 3a^2b^2c^3 + 6ab^3c^6$
24. $8x^2yz(3x^2y + 7xz^2 - yz)$
$24x^4y^2z + 56x^3yz^3 - 8x^2y^2z^2$

C **25.** $-7m(m^2 - m) + 2m^2(n + m)$
$-5m^3 + 7m^2 + 2m^2n$
26. $-9t^2(r^3 - s) + 3t(tr^3 + 5ts)$
$-6r^3t^2 + 24st^2$

6.7 Multiplying a Polynomial by a Monomial **249**

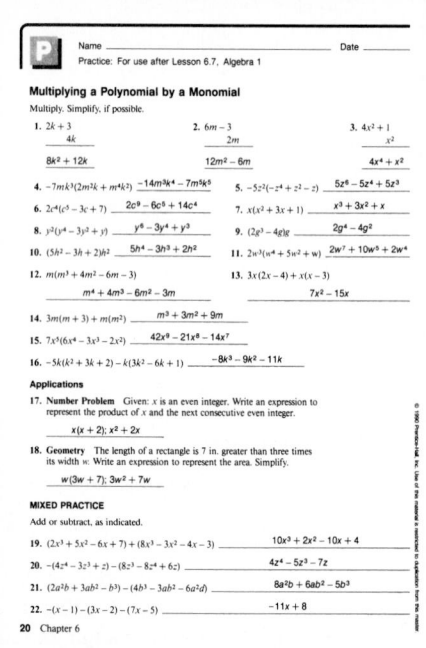

Simplify. All variable exponents represent nonnegative integers.

27. $4a^x(6a^x - 2a^2 + 4)$
$24a^{2x} - 8a^{x+2} + 16a^x$

28. $2y^b(7y^b + 3y^3 - 8)$
$14y^{2b} + 6y^{b+3} - 16y^b$

Applications

29. Number Problem If j is an odd integer, write an expression to represent the product of j and the next consecutive odd integer. Simplify. $j^2 + 2j$

30. Number Problem If e is an even integer, write an expression to represent the product of e and the *preceding* consecutive even integer. Simplify. $e^2 - 2e$

31. Geometry The length of a rectangle is 2 cm greater than its width w. Write an expression to represent the area. Simplify. $w^2 + 2w$

32. Geometry The length of a rectangle is 5 in. greater than twice its width w. Write an expression to represent the area. Simplify. $2w^2 + 5w$

33. Geometry The width of a rectangle is 10 cm less than three times its length l. Write an expression to represent the area. $3l^2 - 10l$

EXTRA

The 4-digit base 10 numeral 3134_{10} can be represented as a polynomial in x with $x = 10$, as shown below.

$$3134_{10} = 3 \cdot 10^3 + 1 \cdot 10^2 + 3 \cdot 10 + 4$$

The polynomial is $3x^3 + x^2 + 3x + 4$.

The 4-digit base 5 numeral 3134_5 can also be represented as a polynomial in x with $x = 10$.

$$\begin{aligned} 3134_5 &= 3 \cdot 5^3 + 1 \cdot 5^2 + 3 \cdot 5 + 4 \\ &= 3 \cdot 125 + 1 \cdot 25 + 3 \cdot 5 + 4 \\ &= 375 + 25 + 15 + 4 \\ &= 419 \end{aligned}$$

The polynomial is $4x^2 + x + 9$.

Express these numerals as polynomials in x with $x = 10$.

1. 301_{10} $3x^2 + 1$

2. 1092_{10} $x^3 + 9x + 2$

3. 4123_5 $5x^2 + 3x + 8$

4. 100101_2 $3x + 7$

5. 5482_9 $4x^3 + 4x + 3$

6. 11111_2 $3x + 1$

Multiplying Polynomials

Objectives: To multiply two binomials
To multiply any two polynomials using both vertical and horizontal formats

The distributive property can be used to multiply two binomials such as $(x + y)(a + b)$.

Capsule Review

EXAMPLE $3a(a + 2) + 4a(2a - 5) = 3a^2 + 6a + 8a^2 - 20a = 11a^2 - 14a$

Simplify by using the distributive property and combining like terms.

1. $5z(z + 7) - 2(z + 7)$ $5z^2 + 33z - 14$ **2.** $6y(y^2 - y) + 4(y + y^2)$ $6y^3 - 2y^2 + 4y$

3. $2ab(a - b) + b(ab + a)$ $2a^2b - ab^2 + ab$ **4.** $(2x - 3)4x + (2x - 3)9$ $8x^2 + 6x - 27$

To multiply two binomials such as $(x + y)(a + b)$, think of $(x + y)$ as one factor. Distribute $(x + y)$ over both terms of $(a + b)$. Then use the distributive property a second time.

$$(x + y)(a + b) = (x + y) \quad (x + y)b$$
$$= xa + ya + xb + yb$$

The four terms of the product are xa, ya, xb, and yb. Each term is the product of one term from the first factor, $(x + y)$, and one term from the second factor, $(a + b)$. Try to relate these terms to the steps in the **FOIL method** for multiplying two binomials, shown below.

FOIL Method for Multiplying Two Binomials

To multiply two binomials, find:

F   The product of the two **FIRST** terms

O   The product of the two **OUTSIDE** terms

I   The product of the two **INSIDE** terms

L   The product of the two **LAST** terms

$$(x + y)(a + b)$$

$$xa + xb + ya + yb$$
$$\text{F} \quad \text{O} \quad \text{I} \quad \text{L}$$

If the outer and inner products (O and I) are like terms, they can be combined.

Vocabulary
FOIL method

Materials/Manipulatives
Calculators
*Teacher's Resource Book,
Transparencies 8, 8a, 11, 12*

BACKGROUND

- In the Capsule Review, students must multiply a binomial by a monomial using the distributive property. You may want to remind students to watch their signs when they distribute a negative number, as in Exercise 1.
- The FOIL method is a memory technique used for multiplying two binomials. Students may find that when the first terms are similar and the last terms are similar in each binomial, then the outer and inner products will be similar, and may be combined.

- You may want to use a model or Transparencies 8, 8a, and 11, to show the product of two binomials. Ask students to think of each binomial as a side of a rectangle. The product of the binomials is the area of the rectangle. The diagram below is a model of

$(x + y)(a + b) = xa + ya + xb + yb$

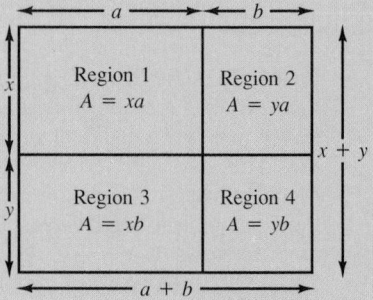

Area (of overall rectangle)
$= (a + b)(x + y)$
Area = A(region 1) + A(region 2) + A (region 3) + A (region 4)
Area = $xa + ya + xb + yb$
Therefore, $(a + b)(x + y)$
$= xa + xb + ya + yb$

Students may make models as a method of checking their answers.
- In Example 2, some students may want to skip the second step, writing the binomial as a sum. Students should be encouraged to rewrite all subtraction as addition of the opposite until they are comfortable with using the FOIL method. You may want to use Transparency 12, in the *Teacher's Resource Book*, to help with any misunderstanding students may have on the FOIL method.
- In Example 3, point out that the terms of one of the factors are rewritten in descending order. Students should be encouraged to do this so that their answer is in the proper form.

EXAMPLE 1 **Use the FOIL method to multiply $(x + 3)(x + 7)$.**

$$\begin{array}{cccc} \text{F} & \text{O} & \text{I} & \text{L} \\ \downarrow & \downarrow & \downarrow & \downarrow \end{array}$$
$$(x + 3)(x + 7) = x \cdot x + x \cdot 7 + 3 \cdot x + 3 \cdot 7$$
$$= x^2 + 7x + 3x + 21$$
$$= x^2 + 10x + 21$$

Multiplying polynomials that involve subtraction may be easier if you think of subtracting as adding the opposite.

EXAMPLE 2 **Multiply: $(3a + b)(a - 2b)$**

$$(3a + b)(a - 2b)$$
$$= (3a + b)[a + (-2b)] \quad a - 2b \text{ means } a + (-2b).$$
$$\begin{array}{cccc} \text{F} & \text{O} & \text{I} & \text{L} \\ \downarrow & \downarrow & \downarrow & \downarrow \end{array}$$
$$= 3a \cdot a + 3a \cdot (-2b) + b \cdot a + b \cdot (-2b)$$
$$= 3a^2 + (-6ab) + ab + (-2b^2)$$
$$= 3a^2 - 5ab - 2b^2$$

When one or both of the polynomials have more than two terms, arrange the terms in descending order with respect to the degree of a variable. Then multiply.

Compare the horizontal and the vertical formats in the next example.

EXAMPLE 3 **Multiply: $(-2y + y^2 - 3y^3)(4y - 5)$**

$$(-2y + y^2 - 3y^3)(4y - 5)$$
$$= (-3y^3 + y^2 - 2y)(4y - 5) \quad \textit{Arrange in descending order.}$$
$$= [-3y^3 + y^2 + (-2y)][4y + (-5)] \quad \textit{Rewrite the subtractions as additions.}$$

Horizontal format

$$[-3y^3 + y^2 + (-2y)][4y + (-5)]$$
$$= [-3y^3 + y^2 + (-2y)] \cdot 4y + [-3y^3 + y^2 + (-2y)] \cdot (-5) \quad \textit{Distributive property}$$
$$= [-3y^3 \cdot 4y + y^2 \cdot 4y + (-2y) \cdot 4y] + [-3y^3 \cdot (-5) + y^2 \cdot (-5) + (-2y) \cdot (-5)]$$
$$= [-12y^4 + 4y^3 - 8y^2] + [15y^3 - 5y^2 + 10y]$$
$$= -12y^4 + 19y^3 - 13y^2 + 10y \quad \textit{Combine like terms. Arrange in descending order.}$$

Vertical format

$$-3y^3 + y^2 + (-2y)$$
$$4y + (-5)$$
$$\overline{15y^3 - 5y^2 + 10y} \quad \textit{Multiply by } -5.$$
$$-12y^4 + 4y^3 - 8y^2 \quad \quad \textit{Multiply by 4y. Align like terms.}$$
$$\overline{-12y^4 + 19y^3 - 13y^2 + 10y} \quad \textit{Add.}$$

In Example 3, does one format seem more convenient? Does one format make you more aware of the sign of each term?

CLASS EXERCISES

Multiply.

1. $(x + 1)(x - 5)$ $x^2 - 4x - 5$

2. $(y + 2)(y - 4)$ $y^2 - 2y - 8$

3. $(c + d)(e + f)$ $ce + cf + de + df$

4. $(a - b)(c - d)$ $ac - ad - bc + bd$

5. $(3c + 4)(2c - 5)$ $6c^2 - 7c - 20$

6. $(g - 5)(3g + 7)$ $3g^2 - 8g - 35$

7. $(x + 3)(-2x + x^2 - 3)$ $x^3 + x^2 - 9x - 9$ **8.** $(z + 2)(-7z + z^2 - 6)$ $z^3 - 5z^2 - 20z - 12$

9. $(2h - 3)^2$ means $(2h - 3)(2h - 3)$. Write $(2h - 3)^2$ as a polynomial with three terms. $4h^2 - 12h + 9$

10. Write $(3x - 2)(x + 3)$ as a polynomial with three terms. $3x^2 + 7x - 6$

11. Write $(2x - 4)(2x + 4)$ as a polynomial with two terms. $4x^2 - 16$

For Discussion

12. Use the vertical format to multiply $(x + y)(a + b)$. Are your results equivalent to those of the FOIL method? Explain. $xa + ya + xb + yb$; yes; with both methods each term of one binomial is multiplied by each term of the other binomial.

13. Without changing the order of terms in the first factor, use FOIL to multiply $(1 - 2y)(3y + 4)$. Why would it have been better to rewrite the first factor in descending order of the exponents before multiplying? $-6y^2 - 5y + 4$; product would be in descending order of the exponents, which makes it easier to combine like terms.

14. When multiplying two binomials, when will the product be a trinomial? when like terms can be combined *and* when it's not in the form $(a + b)(a - b)$ which yields $a^2 - b^2$

PRACTICE EXERCISES

Multiply.

A **1.** $(a + 5)(a - 8)$ $a^2 - 3a - 40$

2. $(x + 5)(x - 6)$ $x^2 - x - 30$

3. $(h + 1)(h - 7)$ $h^2 - 6h - 7$

4. $(m + 4)(m - 2)$ $m^2 + 2m - 8$

5. $(a + 5)(3a - 4)$ $3a^2 + 11a - 20$

6. $(p + 6)(4p - 3)$ $4p^2 + 21p - 18$

7. $(2m - 9)(6 + 5m)$ $10m^2 - 33m - 54$

8. $(3n - 2)(5 + 6n)$ $18n^2 + 3n - 10$

9. $(7r - 3)(r - 5)$ $7r^2 - 38r + 15$

10. $(3j - 7)(j - 2)$ $3j^2 - 13j + 14$

11. $(5x - 8)(2x - 3)$ $10x^2 - 31x + 24$

12. $(2y - 5)(7y - 3)$ $14y^2 - 41y + 15$

13. $(4y + z)(y - 2z)$ $4y^2 - 7yz - 2z^2$

14. $(5b + d)(b - 2d)$ $5b^2 - 9bd - 2d^2$

15. $(2j - 3k)(4j + k)$ $8j^2 - 10jk - 3k^2$

16. $(p - q)(2p + 3q)$ $2p^2 + pq - 3q^2$

17. $(3b + 7)(3 - 2b)$ $-6b^2 - 5b + 21$

18. $(4a + 5)(2 - 4a)$ $-16a^2 - 12a + 10$

6.8 Multiplying Polynomials **253**

Lesson Quiz

Multiply.

1. $(x + 3)(x + 2)$ $x^2 + 5x + 6$
2. $(2g + h)(g + 3h)$
   $2g^2 + 7gh + 3h^2$
3. $(2a - 5)(a + 4)$ $2a^2 + 3a - 20$
4. $(3k - 7)(5 + 3k)$
   $9k^2 - 6k - 35$
5. $(8j - 3)(j + 3)$ $8j^2 + 21j - 9$
6. $(5r - 7)(3r + 4)$ $15r^2 - r - 28$
7. $(2b + 5)^2$ $4b^2 + 20b + 25$
8. $(x + 4)(x^2 - 2x + 5)$
   $x^3 + 2x^2 - 3x + 20$
9. $(c - 5)(2c - c^2 + c^3)$
   $c^4 - 6c^3 + 7c^2 - 10c$
10. $(-3a^2 + 2a^3 - a)(3a - 1)$
    $6a^4 - 11a^3 + a$

Enrichment

Use the distributive property to multiply $(x^2 + 5)(x^2 - 3)$.
$(x^2 + 5)(x^2) - (x^2 + 5)(3)$
$= (x^4 + 5x^2) - (3x^2 + 15)$
$= x^4 + 5x^2 - 3x^2 - 15$
$= x^4 + 2x^2 - 15$

19. $(-2y + y^2 - 4y^3)(6y - 3)$
    $-24y^4 + 18y^3 - 15y^2 + 6y$
20. $(-5x + x^2 - 3x^3)(4x - 6)$
    $-12x^4 + 22x^3 - 26x^2 + 30x$
21. $(4z + z^2 - 5z^3)(2z + 3)$
    $-10z^4 - 13z^3 + 11z^2 + 12z$
22. $(8m + 3m^2 - 2m^3)(m + 5)$
    $-2m^4 - 7m^3 + 23m^2 + 40m$
23. $(x^2 + 3x - 5)(x + 2)$
    $x^3 + 5x^2 + x - 10$
24. $(y^2 + 11y - 12)(y + 5)$
    $y^3 + 16y^2 + 43y - 60$
25. $(z - 3)(z^2 - 5z - 12)$
    $z^3 - 8z^2 + 3z + 36$
26. $(w - 4)(w^2 - 5w + 1)$
    $w^3 - 9w^2 + 21w - 4$
27. $(c^2 + 2c + 1)(c - 5)$ $c^3 - 3c^2 - 9c - 5$
28. $(d^2 - 2d + 3)(d + 2)$ $d^3 - d + 6$

B

29. $(3 + k)(7k - k^2 + 8)$
    $-k^3 + 4k^2 + 29k + 24$
30. $(5 + n)(3n + 2 - n^2)$
    $-n^3 - 2n^2 + 17n + 10$
31. $(y - 3)(-2y + 1 + y^2)$
    $y^3 - 5y^2 + 7y - 3$
32. $(x + 2)(-1 + x^2 + 3x)$
    $x^3 + 5x^2 + 5x - 2$
33. $(3x - 4)^2$ $9x^2 - 24x + 16$
34. $(2y - 7)^2$ $4y^2 - 28y + 49$

35. $(2a - 3b)^2$ $4a^2 - 12ab + 9b^2$
36. $(3p - 4q)^2$ $9p^2 - 24pq + 16q^2$

37. $(2a^2 - a + 5)(3a + 2)$
    $6a^3 + a^2 + 13a + 10$
38. $(4b^2 + b - 2)(5b + 3)$
    $20b^3 + 17b^2 - 7b - 6$
39. $(2c + 1)(-c^2 + 5c - 2)$
    $-2c^3 + 9c^2 + c - 2$
40. $(3d + 2)(-d^2 - 3d + 1)$
    $-3d^3 - 11d^2 - 3d + 2$
41. $(5g^2 + 3 - 2g)(2g - 1)$
    $10g^3 - 9g^2 + 8g - 3$
42. $(4 + 2h^2 - 5h)(3h - 1)$
    $6h^3 - 17h^2 + 17h - 4$
43. $(x - 5)(3x - x^2 + x^3)$
    $x^4 - 6x^3 + 8x^2 - 15x$
44. $(y - 3)(2y^2 - y^3 + y)$
    $-y^4 + 5y^3 - 5y^2 - 3y$
45. $(2y^3 + 2y - y^2)(2y - 3)$
    $4y^4 - 8y^3 + 7y^2 - 6y$
46. $(-2x^2 + 3x^3 - x)(3x - 4)$
    $9x^4 - 18x^3 + 5x^2 + 4x$
47. $(t^2 + 2t)(5t^2 - 6t - 2)$
    $5t^4 + 4t^3 - 14t^2 - 4t$
48. $(2v^2 + v)(3v^2 - 2v - 3)$
    $6v^4 - v^3 - 8v^2 - 3v$

C

49. $(a + b)(a^2 - ab + b^2)$ $a^3 + b^3$
50. $(c - d)(c^2 + cd + d^2)$ $c^3 - d^3$
51. $(y + 3)(y^3 - 2y^2 + 3)$
    $y^4 + y^3 - 6y^2 + 3y + 9$
52. $-4(x - 3)(x + 2)$ $-4x^2 + 4x + 24$
53. $(x + 3)(x + 3)(x + 3)$
    $x^3 + 9x^2 + 27x + 27$
54. $(x - 2)(x - 2)(x - 2)$
    $x^3 - 6x^2 + 12x - 8$
55. $(4b - 1)^3$ $64b^3 - 48b^2 + 12b - 1$
56. $(3d - 1)^3$ $27d^3 - 27d^2 + 9d - 1$

Hint: In Exercises 57–60, some powers of the variable do not appear in the polynomials. In $x^3 - x + 2$, there is no x^2 term. In $3x^2 - 1$, there is no x-term. When you multiply such polynomials vertically, be sure that like terms are aligned in the columns.

57. $(x^3 - x + 2)(3x^2 - 1)$
    $3x^5 - 4x^3 + 6x^2 + x - 2$
58. $(5y^3 - y)(y^4 + y^2 - 1)$
    $5y^7 + 4y^5 - 6y^3 + y$
59. $(2a^3 - a^2 + 3)(5a^2 - 2a + 1)$
    $10a^5 - 9a^4 + 4a^3 + 14a^2 - 6a + 3$
60. $(3b^2 + b - 2)(4b^3 - 2b^2 - 6)$
    $12b^5 - 2b^4 - 10b^3 - 14b^2 - 6b + 12$

Applications

61. **Number Problem**   If n is an integer, write an expression to represent the product of the next two consecutive integers. Simplify. $n^2 + 3n + 2$

62. **Geometry**   The width of a rectangle is $(x + 2)$ cm. Its length is 3 cm greater than its width. Write an expression to represent the area. Simplify.
    $x^2 + 7x + 10$

63. **Geometry**   The length of a rectangle is 5 in. greater than twice its width, $(x + 1)$ in. Write an expression to represent the area. Simplify.
    $2x^2 + 9x + 7$

64. Geometry One rectangle is $(2x + 1)$ units wide and $(x + 4)$ units long. A second rectangle has a width of $(2x - 9)$ units and length of $(x + 9)$ units. Which has the greater area? How much greater?
first rectangle; 85 sq. units greater

65. Number Problem If e is an even integer, write an expression to represent the product of the next two consecutive even integers. Simplify.
$e^2 + 6e + 8$

ALGEBRA IN SPACE TECHNOLOGY

Radio signals travel so rapidly, approximately 1.86×10^5 mi/s, that on Earth the signals seem to be received the instant they are sent. You have to wait, however, before hearing any message from space. For example, sunspot activity causes radio signals to be emitted. How many seconds does it take one such signal to reach Earth when Earth is at its nearest point to the Sun?

Distance from Sun (mi)

Planet	Maximum	Minimum
Mercury	4.34×10^7	2.86×10^7
Venus	6.77×10^7	6.68×10^7
Earth	9.46×10^7	9.14×10^7
Mars	1.55×10^8	1.29×10^8
Jupiter	5.07×10^8	4.61×10^8
Saturn	9.37×10^8	8.38×10^8
Uranus	1.86×10^9	1.67×10^9
Neptune	2.82×10^9	2.76×10^9
Pluto	4.55×10^9	2.76×10^9

Distance = rate × time, or $d = rt$.

Solving for t, you have $t = \dfrac{d}{r}$.

$d = 9.14 \times 10^7$ mi and $r = 1.86 \times 10^5$ mi/s

$$t = \frac{9.14 \times 10^7}{1.86 \times 10^5}$$

$$= 4.91 \times 10^2, \text{ or } 491 \text{ seconds}$$

Find the number of seconds it takes for a radio signal to travel from the Sun to each of the planets when the planet is (a) at its maximum distance from the Sun, and (b) at its minimum distance from the Sun. Use a calculator.

6.8 Multiplying Polynomials **255**

Teacher's Resource Book
Reteaching—Chapter 6, p. 22.

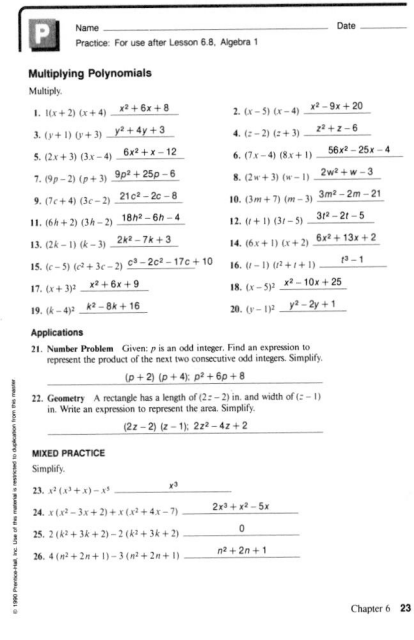

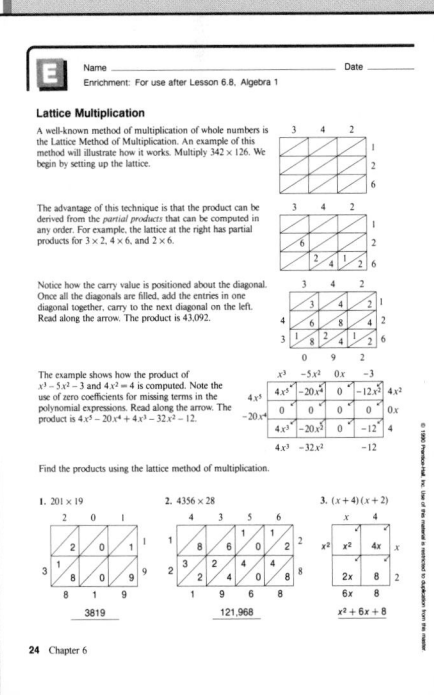

Additional Answers

Planet	Maximum	Minimum
Mercury	2.33×10^2	1.54×10^2
Venus	3.64×10^2	3.59×10^2
Earth	5.09×10^2	4.91×10^2
Mars	8.33×10^3	6.94×10^3
Jupiter	2.726×10^3	2.478×10^3

Planet	Maximum	Minimum
Saturn	5.038×10^3	4.505×10^3
Uranus	1.00×10^4	8.978×10^3
Neptune	1.5161×10^4	1.4839×10^4
Pluto	2.4462×10^4	1.4839×10^4

BACKGROUND

In the Capsule Review, students find the square of each number or expression. You may wish to point out that when squaring an expression with exponents, you apply the property of exponents, and the rule: For all real numbers a and for all positive integers m and n, $(a^m)^n = a^{mn}$. This review leads logically to a discussion of squaring a binomial that is the sum or the difference of two terms.

6.9

Multiplying Polynomials: Special Cases

Objectives: To find the square of a binomial
To find the product of the sum and the difference of two terms

To square a number or an algebraic expression means to use it as a factor two times. Suppose the number is positive or the algebraic expression represents a positive quantity. Then the number or expression could represent the length of a side of a square, as shown below.

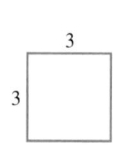

Area = $3 \cdot 3$,
or 3^2

Area = $x \cdot x$,
or x^2

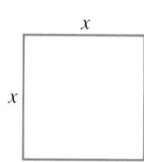

Area = $(x + y)(x + y)$,
or $(x + y)^2$

Capsule Review

EXAMPLE   **a.** $(b^3)^2 = b^6$ **b.** $(-3x^2y)^2 = (-3)^2(x^2)^2y^2$
$= 9x^4y^2$

Find the square of each number or expression.

1. -12 144 **2.** $3r$ $9r^2$ **3.** $-5m$ $25m^2$ **4.** $7p^2$ $49p^4$

5. $\frac{a}{2}$ $\frac{a^2}{4}$ **6.** $\frac{2x^4}{3}$ $\frac{4x^8}{9}$ **7.** $\frac{1}{3}s^4t$ $\frac{1}{9}s^8t^2$ **8.** $6st^2u$ $36s^2t^4u^2$

9. $0.2xy$ $0.04x^2y^2$ **10.** $-1.2gh^5$ $1.44g^2h^{10}$ **11.** $\frac{2}{5}d^2e^2$ $\frac{4}{25}d^4e^4$ **12.** $0.1a^5b^3c^2$ $0.01a^{10}b^6c^4$

Notice what happens when you square a binomial that is a sum of two terms.

$(x + y)^2 = (x + y)(x + y) = x \cdot x + x \cdot y + y \cdot x + y \cdot y$ *FOIL*
$= x^2 + xy + yx + y^2$
$= x^2 + 2xy + y^2$

There is a change when the binomial is a difference of two terms. Use FOIL.

$(x - y)^2 = (x - y)(x - y) = x \cdot x + x \cdot (-y) + (-y) \cdot x + (-y) \cdot (-y)$
$= x^2 + (-xy) + (-yx) + y^2$
$= x^2 - 2xy + y^2$

256   Chapter 6 Polynomials

Square of a Binomial: $(m + n)^2$ or $(m - n)^2$

- Square the first term: m^2
- Double the product of the two terms: $+ 2mn$ for $(m + n)^2$
  $- 2mn$ for $(m - n)^2$
- Square the last term: n^2
- Write the sum of the three terms: $(m + n)^2 = m^2 + 2mn + n^2$
  $(m - n)^2 = m^2 - 2mn + n^2$

EXAMPLE 1 **Simplify:** $(2a + 3b)^2$

$$(2a + 3b)^2 = (2a)^2 + 2(2a \cdot 3b) + (3b)^2$$
$$= 4a^2 + 12ab + 9b^2$$

EXAMPLE 2 **Simplify:** $(3m^2 - 11)^2$

$$(3m^2 - 11)^2 = (3m^2)^2 + 2[3m^2 \cdot (-11)] + (-11)^2$$
$$= 9m^4 - 66m^2 + 121$$

If you forget the rule for squaring a binomial, you can rewrite the square as a product of two binomials and apply the FOIL method.

Example 3 shows how squaring a binomial can apply to *mental arithmetic*.

EXAMPLE 3 **Simplify:** 39^2

$$39^2 = (40 - 1)^2$$
$$= 40^2 - 2(40 \cdot 1) + 1^2$$
$$= 1600 - 80 + 1 = 1521$$

Another special case of binomial multiplication is a product of the form $(x + y)(x - y)$.

$$(x + y)(x - y) = x \cdot x + x \cdot (-y) + yx + y \cdot (-y)$$
$$= x^2 + (-xy) + yx + (-y^2)$$
$$= x^2 - y^2$$

Product of the Sum and Difference of the Same Two Terms:
$(m + n)(m - n)$

- Square the first term: m^2
- Square the last term: n^2
- Write the difference of the two squares: $(m + n)(m - n) = m^2 - n^2$

6.9 Multiplying Polynomials: Special Cases **257**

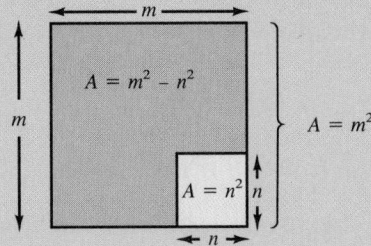
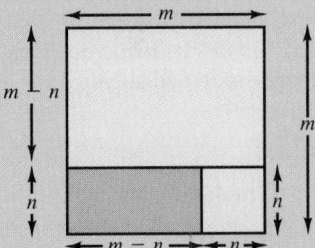
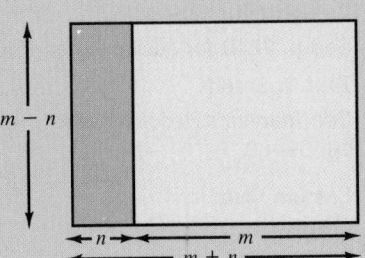

- **For Example 1**

  Simplify:
  1. $(4m + 2n)^2$
     $16m^2 + 16mn + 4n^2$
  2. $(3a + 4b)^2$
     $9a^2 + 24ab + 16b^2$

- **For Example 2**

  Simplify:
  3. $(2x^2 - 3)^2$ $4x^4 - 12x^2 + 9$
  4. $(5x^2 - 2)^2$ $25x^4 - 20x^2 + 4$

- **For Example 3**

  Simplify:
  5. 23^2 529   6. 41^2 1681

- **For Example 4**

  Simplify:
  7. $(2x^2 + y^2)(2x^2 - y^2)$
     $4x^4 - y^4$
  8. $(3x^2 + y)(3x^2 - y)$ $9x^4 - y^2$

Common Error

- Many students may write the square of a binomial as $(m + n)^2 = m^2 + n^2$ and $(m - n)^2 = m^2 - n^2$. Have these students check their answers using the FOIL method.
- See *Teacher's Resource Book* for additional remediation.

LESSON FOLLOW-UP

Critical Thinking

Analyzing Whole-Part Relationships
Use the special methods in this lesson to find a shortcut for multiplying 67 × 73. $67 \times 73 = (70 - 3)(70 + 3) = 70^2 - 3^2 = 4900 - 9 = 4891$.

Assignment Guide

See p. 224B for assignments.

Test Yourself

See *Teacher's Resource Book*, Tests, pp. 59–60.

Lesson Quiz

Simplify.
1. $(3r + 2)^2$ $9r^2 + 12r + 4$
2. $(2z - 9)^2$ $4z^2 - 36z + 81$
3. $(3m - 8)(3m + 8)$ $9m^2 - 64$

EXAMPLE 4 **Simplify:** **a.** $(z + 3)(z - 3)$ **b.** $(2r^3 + 5)(2r^3 - 5)$

a. $(z + 3)(z - 3) = (z)^2 - (3)^2$
$$= z^2 - 9$$

b. $(2r^3 + 5)(2r^3 - 5) = (2r^3)^2 - (5)^2$
$$= 4r^6 - 25$$

CLASS EXERCISES

Simplify.

1. $(c + d)^2$ $c^2 + 2cd + d^2$
2. $(r + 3s)^2$ $r^2 + 6rs + 9s^2$
3. $(m - n)^2$ $m^2 - 2mn + n^2$
4. $(2r - s)^2$ $4r^2 - 4rs + s^2$
5. $(u + v)(u - v)$ $u^2 - v^2$
6. $(7m + 1)(7m - 1)$ $49m^2 - 1$
7. $(62)^2$ 3844
8. 89^2 7921
9. $(30 + 3)^2$ 1089
10. $(70 - 1)(70 + 1)$ 4899
11. $(3x^3 - 4y^2)(3x^3 + 4y^2)$ $9x^6 - 16y^4$
12. $(5x^3 - 2y^2)(5x^3 + 2y^2)$ $25x^6 - 4y^4$
13. $(3m^2 + 16m)(3m^2 - 16m)$
    $9m^4 - 256m^2$
14. $(10x^4 - 15x^2)(10x^4 + 15x^2)$
    $100x^8 - 225x^4$
15. $(4y^5 + 3y^4)(4y^5 - 3y^4)$ $16y^{10} - 9y^8$
16. $(16a^2b^2 - 4ab)(16a^2b^2 + 4ab)$
    $256a^4b^4 - 16a^2b^2$

For Discussion

17. How would you use the procedure shown in Example 3, on the previous page, to simplify 102^2? Write 102^2 as $(100 + 2)^2$ then square the binomial.

18. Would it be useful to use $(47 - 2)^2$ to simplify 45^2? Explain. no; use $(50 - 5)^2$

19. True or false? The square of a binomial is always a trinomial. true

PRACTICE EXERCISES

Simplify.

A
1. $(3x + 2y)^2$
   $9x^2 + 12xy + 4y^2$
2. $(5a + 3b)^2$
   $25a^2 + 30ab + 9b^2$
3. $(8m + 2n)^2$
   $64m^2 + 32mn + 4n^2$
4. $(4j + 6k)^2$
   $16j^2 + 48jk + 36k^2$
5. $(4m^2 - 6)^2$
   $16m^4 - 48m^2 + 36$
6. $(6r^2 - 4)^2$
   $36r^4 - 48r^2 + 16$
7. $(7s^2 - 3)^2$
   $49s^4 - 42s^2 + 9$
8. $(3j^2 - 7)^2$
   $9j^4 - 42j^2 + 49$
9. $(24)^2$ 576
10. $(45)^2$ 2025
11. $(12)^2$ 144
12. $(52)^2$ 2704
13. $(x + 4)(x - 4)$ $x^2 - 16$
14. $(h + 9)(h - 9)$ $h^2 - 81$
15. $(y + 5)(y - 5)$
    $y^2 - 25$
16. $(m + 2)(m - 2)$ $m^2 - 4$
17. $(4x^3 - 3)(4x^3 + 3)$
    $16x^6 - 9$
18. $(5b^3 - 8)(5b^3 + 8)$
    $25b^6 - 64$

B
19. $(2t - u)^2$ $4t^2 - 4tu + u^2$
20. $(3j - h)^2$ $9j^2 - 6jh + h^2$
21. $(d^2 + e^2)^2$
    $d^4 + 2d^2e^2 + e^4$
22. $(f^2 + g^2)^2$ $f^4 + 2f^2g^2 + g^4$
23. $(h^2 - j^2)(h^2 + j^2)$
    $h^4 - j^4$
24. $(k^2 - m^2)(k^2 + m^2)$
    $k^4 - m^4$
25. $(1 - 12g^3h^2)^2$
    $1 - 24g^3h^2 + 144g^6h^4$
26. $(2 - 6x^3y^2)^2$
    $4 - 24x^3y^2 + 36x^6y^4$
27. $(5ab^3 + 6c^2d^4)^2$
    $25a^2b^6 + 60ab^3c^2d^4 + 36c^4d^8$
28. $(3ef^3 + 4g^2h^4)^2$
    $9e^2f^6 + 24ef^3g^2h^4 + 16g^4h^8$
29. $(61x^3y^2z)^2$ $3721x^6y^4z^2$
30. $(82a^4b^0c^5)^2$ $6724a^8c^{10}$

Simplify and express as a polynomial. All variable exponents represent nonnegative integers.

C **31.** $(4 - a^x)(4 + a^x)$ $16 - a^{2x}$

32. $(y^b + 2)(y^b - 2)$ $y^{2b} - 4$

33. $(x^{a+1} + x)^2$ $x^{2a+2} + 2x^{a+2} + x^2$

34. $(a^{x+2} + 2a)^2$ $a^{2x+4} + 4a^{x+3} + 4a^2$

35. $(3^{2y+1} - 2)^2$ $3^{4y+2} - 4(3^{2y+1}) + 4$

36. $(5^{1-3x} - 4)^2$ $5^{2-6x} - 8(5^{1-3x}) + 16$

Applications

Geometry   Find the area.

37.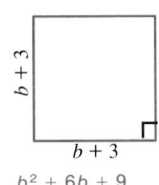
$a + 1$
$a^2 + 2a + 1$

38.
$b + 3$
$b^2 + 6b + 9$

39.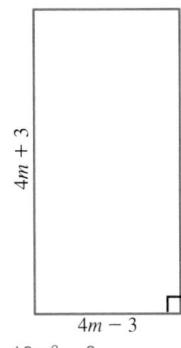
$2x + 3$
$2x - 3$
$4x^2 - 9$

40.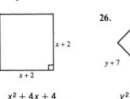
$4m + 3$
$4m - 3$
$16m^2 - 9$

TEST YOURSELF

Simplify. Write the result in descending order of the exponents with respect to x.   6.5

1. $4x^3 + x - x^3 - 5x$ $3x^3 - 4x$

2. $-5x^2y + x^3y^3 + 9x + 3x^2y$
$x^3y^3 - 2x^2y + 9x$

Add or subtract, as indicated.   6.6

3. $(5y^2 + 6) + (-3y^2 - 10)$ $2y^2 - 4$

4. $(a^3 + 5a^2 - 6) - (-4a^2 - a + 9)$ $a^3 + 9a^2 + a - 15$

Multiply. The multiplication may be done in horizontal or in vertical form.   6.7

5. $(-2y)(-3y^2 + y)$ $6y^3 - 2y^2$

6. $(4x^3 + 2x^2 - 1)(-3x^4)$
$-12x^7 - 6x^6 + 3x^4$

7. $(11a^2b)(5a^3b^2 - 3a^2b^3 + 7ab^4)$
$55a^5b^3 - 33a^4b^4 + 77a^3b^5$

8. $-3t(1 - 2t^2) + 8(5t - 4)$
$6t^3 + 37t - 32$

Simplify.   6.8, 6.9

9. $(3r + 7)(r + 11)$ $3r^2 + 40r + 77$

10. $(1 - 5j)(3 + 4j)$ $3 - 11j - 20j^2$

11. $(8n - 15)(3n + 5)$ $24n^2 - 5n - 75$

12. $(z - 6)(-2z + 3z^2 + 9)$
$3z^3 - 20z^2 + 21z - 54$

13. $(9y + 3)^2$ $81y^2 + 54y + 9$

14. $(2x + 3)(2x - 3)$ $4x^2 - 9$

15. $(5a - 9b)^2$ $25a^2 - 90ab + 81b^2$

16. $(b^4 - 11a)(b^4 + 11a)$ $b^8 - 121a^2$

6.9 Multiplying Polynomials: Special Cases   **259**

Problem Solving Strategy:
Look for a Pattern

Vocabulary
Fibonacci sequence
Sequence

Materials/Manipulatives
*Teacher's Resource Book,
Teaching Aid 6,
Transparency 10*

BACKGROUND

- Patterns are very important problem solving tools. Students will need to have practice in identifying patterns before they can effectively employ this strategy.
- A student's ability to organize information given in a problem, so that it can be used to solve the problem, is a key to success in this lesson. To determine a student's progress, analyze errors in the student's work and then classify specific errors.

Error Analysis Classification

1. *Misunderstanding*
   Failed to understand that a pattern existed and could be used to solve the problem
2. *Missapplied Strategy*
   Used the wrong pattern
   Applied the pattern incorrectly

The numbers 1, 1, 2, 3, 5, 8, 13, 21, . . . are arranged in a definite pattern. Each number is the sum of the two preceding numbers. When numbers are arranged in a pattern, they form a **sequence.** Finding a pattern is a problem solving strategy. If a pattern exists and is identified, then the pattern can be used to solve the problem.

EXAMPLE 1   Write an algebraic expression that represents the sum of the first n odd positive integers.

Understand the Problem

Read the problem.

What are the given facts?
The odd positive integers 1, 3, 5, 7, 9, ...

What are you asked to find?
An algebraic expression that represents the sum of any number n of odd positive integers.

Plan Your Approach

Choose a strategy.

Positive Odd Integers	Sums
1	$1 = 1$
1, 3	$1 + 3 = 4$
1, 3, 5	$1 + 3 + 5 = 9$
1, 3, 5, 7	$1 + 3 + 5 + 7 = 16$
1, 3, 5, 7, 9	$1 + 3 + 5 + 7 + 9 = 25$
1, 3, 5, 7, 9, 11	$1 + 3 + 5 + 7 + 9 + 11 = 36$
1, 3, 5, 7, 9, 11, 13	$1 + 3 + 5 + 7 + 9 + 11 + 13 = 49$

Complete the Work

Find the pattern.

Number of Odd Integers	Sums
1 (1)	$1 = 1^2$
2 (1, 3)	$4 = 2^2$
3 (1, 3, 5)	$9 = 3^2$
4 (1, 3, 5, 7)	$16 = 4^2$
5 (1, 3, 5, 7, 9)	$25 = 5^2$
6 (1, 3, 5, 7, 9, 11)	$36 = 6^2$
7 (1, 3, 5, 7, 9, 11, 13)	$49 = 7^2$

Interpret the Results	**State your conclusion.**

A pattern does exist. For any number, n, of positive odd integers, the pattern suggests that the sum is n^2.

Check your conclusion.

Suppose there are eight positive odd integers. According to the pattern, the sum of the first eight positive odd integers should be 8^2, or 64.

$$1 + 3 + 5 + 7 + 9 + 11 + 13 + 15 = 64 \ \text{✓}$$

Recall the sequence; 1, 1, 2, 3, 5, 8, 13, 21, . . . which was presented at the beginning of the lesson. This sequence is known as the **Fibonacci Sequence.**

The following numbers follow the same pattern as the Fibonacci sequence. They are called a *Fibonacci-like* sequence.

5, 9, 14, 23, 37, 60, 97, 157, 254, 411, 665, 1076, 1741, 2817, 4558

EXAMPLE 2 Given fifteen consecutive numbers of any Fibonacci-like sequence, show that the sum of the first thirteen of them is equal to the fifteenth number minus the second number.

Understand the Problem You are asked to show that the sum of the first thirteen numbers of the given sequence is equal to the fifteenth number minus the second number.

Plan Your Approach

In this problem, the pattern is given: any number in the sequence is the sum of the two preceding numbers.

Let a represent the first number in the sequence.

Let b represent the second number in the sequence.

Write the first fifteen numbers in the sequence using a and b.

a
b
$a + b$
$a + 2b$
$2a + 3b$
$3a + 5b$
$5a + 8b$
$8a + 13b$
$13a + 21b$
$21a + 34b$
$34a + 55b$
$55a + 89b$
$89a + 144b$
$144a + 233b$
$233a + 377b$

Complete the Work

Sum of First Thirteen Numbers	Difference of Fifteenth and Second Numbers
$233a + 376b$	$(233a + 377b) - b$

Interpret the Results

Is $233a + 376b$ equal to $(233a + 377b) - b$?

$(233a + 376b) \stackrel{?}{=} (233a + 377b) - b$

$233a + 376b = 233a + 376b$ ✓

- Before introducing this lesson, you may want to review the problem solving steps. Teaching Aid 6, in the *Teacher's Resource Book,* may be helpful.
- Develop the idea of numbers forming a pattern, using the following example: 2, 5, 8, 11, 14, 17, ... Point out that each term is 3 more than the preceeding term. Ask students to suggest examples of patterns in the real world.
- Demonstrate many "Fibonacci-like" sequences and have students construct some sequences of their own. You may want to use Transparency 10, in the *Teacher's Resource Book,* to review Pascal's triangle.
- Review the process of adding like terms of algebraic expressions in preparation for discussing Example 2.
- Emphasize that patterns can be used to form conjectures. A conjecture is an intelligent guess at a solution, but it is *not* a solution until proven to be one.

CHALKBOARD EXAMPLES

- **For Example 1**
  1. Discover the pattern. 2, 3, 5, 8, 12, . . .   The pattern is add 1, add 2, add 3, add 4, ...

- **For Example 2**
  2. For the given sequence, find the sum of the first thirteen numbers and show that it is equal to the fifteenth number minus the second number. 1, 1, 2, 3, 5, 8, 13, 21, . . .

  $a = 1; b = 1$
  $233a + 376b = (233a + 377b) - b$
  $233(1) + 376(1) = [(233)(1) + (377)(1)] - 1$
  $233 + 376 = (233 + 377) - 1$
  $609 = 610 - 1$
  $609 = 609$

Critical Thinking

Generalization Examine the following sequence of numbers:

$$2, 4, 8, 16, \ldots$$

The pattern is ×2. Write an algebraic expression for the next term in the sequence, if the first term is called n.

If $n = 2$ $(n^1 = 2)$
$n^2 = 4$
$n^3 = 8$
$n^4 = 16$
$n^5 = 32$
the fifth term is n^5.

Assignment Guide

See p. 224B for assignments.

Mixed Problem Solving Review

- The following skills and concepts are reviewed:
  Solving uniform motion problems (Ex. 1)
  Solving inequalities (Ex. 2)
- The following problem solving strategies may be appropriate:
  Using a formula (Ex. 1)
  Making a drawing or table (Ex. 1)
  Writing an inequality to solve the problem (Ex. 2)

Project

Students should observe that even numbers greater than 2 can be expressed as the sum of prime numbers. They learn the difference between a conjecture and a theorem. Have the students present their conjecture to the class and support it with examples.

Lesson Quiz

Find the next three numbers in each sequence.
1. 2, 4, 7, 11, . . .   16, 22, 29
2. 3, 6, 12, 24, . . .   48, 96, 192
3. 9, 6, 3, 0, . . .   −3, −6, −9
4. 10, 100, 1000, . . .
    10,000, 100,000, 1,000,000
5. 0, 1, 8, 27, . . .   64, 125, 216

262

CLASS EXERCISES

Look for a pattern to find the next three numbers in each sequence.

1. 1, 1, 2, 3, 5, 8, 13, 21, $\underline{?}$, $\underline{?}$, $\underline{?}$ 34, 55, 89

2. 2, 4, 6, 8, 10, 12, 14, $\underline{?}$, $\underline{?}$, $\underline{?}$ 16, 18, 20

3. 3, 7, 10, 17, 27, 44, 71, $\underline{?}$, $\underline{?}$, $\underline{?}$ 115, 186, 301

4. 1, 2, 3, 5, 8, 13, 21, 34, $\underline{?}$, $\underline{?}$, $\underline{?}$ 55, 89, 144

PRACTICE EXERCISES

Look for a pattern to find the next three numbers in each sequence.

A **1.** 10, 100, 1000, 10,000, $\underline{?}$, $\underline{?}$, $\underline{?}$ 100,000, 1,000,000, 10,000,000

2. 2, 6, 18, 54, 162, $\underline{?}$, $\underline{?}$, $\underline{?}$ 486, 1458, 4374

3. 0, 3, 8, 15, 24, $\underline{?}$, $\underline{?}$, $\underline{?}$ 35, 48, 63

4. Find the sum of these thirteen Fibonacci-like numbers: 5, 9, 14, 23, 37, 60, 97, 157, 254, 411, 665, 1076, 1741. 4549

5. Find the fifteenth number in the sequence given in Exercise 4. 4558

6. In Exercise 4, is the fifteenth number in the sequence minus the second number equal to the sum of the first thirteen numbers? yes

7. Write a Fibonacci-like sequence that starts with the numbers 6, 12.
6, 12, 18, 30, 48, 78, 126, . . .
8. Find the sum of the first thirteen numbers in your sequence for Exercise 7. Is the fifteenth number minus the second number equal to the sum of the first thirteen numbers? 5910; yes

B **9.** Use a pattern to find an algebraic expression that can be used to find the sum of the first n positive integers. *Hint:* Use the product of n and $n + 1$.
$1 + 2 = 3$
$1 + 2 + 3 = 6$
$1 + 2 + 3 + 4 = 10$
$1 + 2 + 3 + 4 + 5 = 15$
$1 + 2 + 3 + 4 + 5 + 6 = 21 \ldots$ and so on. $\frac{n(n + 1)}{2}$

10. Starting with two 2's, construct a sequence using the same rule used in the Fibonacci sequence. 2, 2, 4, 6, 10, 16, 26, 42, . . .

11. In Exercise 10, how does the eighth number in the sequence compare with the eighth number in the Fibonacci sequence? It is twice as large.

12. Use a pattern and algebraic notation to show that the sum of the first ten consecutive numbers in a Fibonacci-like sequence is 11 times the seventh number in the sequence. $55a + 88b = 11(5a + 8b)$

262   Chapter 6 Polynomials

13. Use your calculator to determine which ten consecutive terms of the Fibonacci sequence have a sum of 45,991. 233, 377, 610, 987, 1597, 2584, 4181, 6765, 10,946, 17,711

14. The figure below is called Pascal's triangle. The first seven rows and diagonals are shown. Look for patterns to find numbers in the eighth row. 1, 7, 21, 35, 35, 21, 7, 1

```
                1
             1     1
          1     2     1
       1     3     3     1
    1     4     6     4     1
 1     5    10    10     5     1
1     6    15    20    15     6     1
```

15. Can you discover the Fibonacci sequence using Pascal's triangle? It is hard to spot, but it is there. *Hint:* Draw a series of parallel sloping diagonals so that the first just starts at the top 1 and so on.

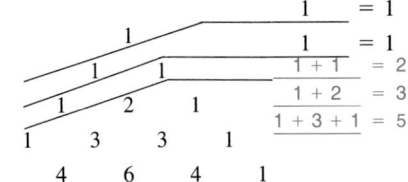

$$1 = 1$$
$$1 = 1$$
$$1 + 1 = 2$$
$$1 + 2 = 3$$
$$1 + 3 + 1 = 5$$

Mixed Problem Solving Review

1. Two jet planes leave Chicago at 2 PM. One travels north at 850 km/h and the other south at 750 km/h. At what time will they be 4000 km apart? 4:30 PM

2. There are three tests given during the school term. Lauren received grades of 83 and 74 on the first two tests. What grade must Lauren get on the last test in order to have an average for the term of no less than 80? at least an 83

PROJECT

A **prime number** is divisible only by itself and 1. For example, the first ten prime numbers are 2, 3, 5, 7, 11, 13, 17, 19, 23, and 29. Observe a pattern in the following numbers and write a *conjecture* about them. A **conjecture** is a guess that something is true. Try a few more examples of your own. Do you think your conjecture is true? See below.

4 = 2 + 2	16 = 3 + 13	6 = 3 + 3	18 = 7 + 11
8 = 3 + 5	20 = 7 + 13	10 = 5 + 5	22 = 11 + 11
12 = 5 + 7	24 = 5 + 19	14 = 7 + 7	26 = 3 + 23

6.10 Problem Solving Strategy: Look for a Pattern   **263**

- See *Teacher's Resource Book, Spanish Chapter Summary and Review,* pp. 11–12.
- See Extra Practice, p. 660.

CHAPTER 6 SUMMARY AND REVIEW

Vocabulary

ascending order of a polynomial (242)	FOIL method (251)
binomial (242)	monomial (226)
degree of a monomial (241)	polynomial (242)
degree of a polynomial (242)	scientific notation (238)
descending order of a polynomial (242)	sequence (260)
Fibonacci Sequence (261)	trinomial (242)

Properties of Exponents For all real numbers a and b, $a \neq 0$, and all positive integers m and n: **6.1–6.3**

$$a^m \cdot a^n = a^{m+n} \qquad (a^m)^n = a^{mn} \qquad (ab)^m = a^m b^m$$

$$\frac{a^m}{a^n} = a^{m-n}, \text{ if } m > n \qquad \frac{a^m}{a^n} = \frac{1}{a^{n-m}}, \text{ if } m < n \qquad \frac{a^m}{a^n} = a^0 = 1, \text{ if } m = n$$

Simplify.

1. $a^3 \cdot a^4$ a^7

2. $3 \cdot 3^2$ 3^3, or 27

3. $(-3ac^2)(5a^3c^3)$ $-15a^4c^5$

4. Multiply and write in exponential form: $(-3 \times 10^2)(2.5 \times 10^5)$ -7.5×10^7

Simplify. Assume that no variable equals zero.

5. $\dfrac{x^5}{x^3}$ x^2

6. $\dfrac{y^2}{y^8}$ $\dfrac{1}{y^6}$

7. $\dfrac{x^{12}}{x^{12}}$ 1

8. $\dfrac{12x^3y^4}{-9x^2y^9}$ $\dfrac{4x}{-3y^5}$

Simplify. Write each answer in exponential form.

9. $\dfrac{3.9 \times 10^5}{1.3 \times 10}$ 3×10^4

10. $\dfrac{7.5 \times 10^5}{2.5 \times 10^6}$ 3×10^{-1}

Simplify. Assume that no variable equals zero.

11. y^0 1

12. $(-3)^0$ 1

13. $\left(\dfrac{5a}{c^4}\right)^2$ $\dfrac{25a^2}{c^8}$

14. $\dfrac{-3x^2yz^7}{9yx^3z^4}$ $\dfrac{-z^3}{3x}$

Scientific Notation A number is in scientific notation when it is expressed in the form $n \times 10^m$ where n is a real number such that $1 \leq n < 10$ and m is an integer. **6.4**

Simplify. Write the answer in scientific notation.

15. $289{,}000$ 2.89×10^5

16. 0.041 4.1×10^{-2}

17. $(3.2 \times 10^3)(5 \times 10^2)$ 1.6×10^6

18. $(4.2 \times 10^4)(3 \times 10^2)$ 1.26×10^7

19. $\dfrac{8.1 \times 10^8}{9 \times 10^4}$ 9.0×10^3

20. $\dfrac{2.4 \times 10^9}{8 \times 10^6}$ 3.0×10^2

State the degree of each monomial term and the degree of the polynomial.   **6.5**

21. $3x$ 1; 1

22. $-8a^3b^5 + 2a^2b + 4$ 8, 3, 0; 8

Simplify. Write the result in descending order of the exponent with respect to x.

23. $5 + x^2 + 3x^3 - 2x^2$
$3x^3 - x^2 + 5$

24. $-2x^3y^2 + 3x^4y - xy - x^3y^2 + y^3 - 4y^3$
$3x^4y - 3x^3y^2 - xy - 3y^3$

Adding and Subtracting Polynomials   To find the sum of polynomials,   **6.6**
add their like terms. To subtract one polynomial from another, add the
opposite of each term of the polynomial you are subtracting.

Add or subtract, as indicated.

25. $3x - 2y$
   $\underline{+ \; 6x + 4y}$
    $9x + 2y$

26. $10r - 3s + 2t$
   $\underline{- \quad r + 2s - \; t}$
    $9r - 5s + 3t$

27. $(2y + 3) - (3y - 2)$
   $-y + 5$

28. $(-9a^3 + 6a^2 - 3) - (5a^2 + a - 3)$ $-9a^3 + a^2 - a$

Multiply. Simplify if possible.   **6.7**

29. $3x(x^2 + 2y - 1)$
  $3x^3 + 6xy - 3x$

30. $-2a^5(a^2 - 3a + 5)$
  $-2a^7 + 6a^6 - 10a^5$

31. $(-7xy + y^2)5x^2y$
  $-35x^3y^2 + 5x^2y^3$

The FOIL Method of Multiplying Two Binomials   **6.8**

$$(x + y)(a + b) = xa + xb + ya + yb$$
$$ \;\; \text{F} \quad\;\; \text{O} \quad\;\; \text{I} \quad\;\; \text{L}$$

Multiply.

32. $(2a + 4)(a + 7)$
  $2a^2 + 18a + 28$

33. $(b - 3)(3b - 8)$
  $3b^2 - 17b + 24$

34. $(c + 4d)(5c - 2d)$
  $5c^2 + 18cd - 8d^2$

Special Cases
of Polynomial
Multiplication
  $(m + n)^2 = (m + n)(m + n) = m^2 + 2mn + n^2$ **6.9**
  $(m - n)^2 = (m - n)(m - n) = m^2 - 2mn + n^2$
  $(m + n)(m - n) = m^2 - n^2$

Simplify.

35. $(d - 9)^2$
  $d^2 - 18d + 81$

36. $(3z^2 + 7)^2$
  $9z^4 + 42z^2 + 49$

37. $(5x - 4)(5x + 4)$
  $25x^2 - 16$

Look for a pattern to find the next three numbers in each sequence.   **6.10**

38. 2, 8, 32, 128, $\underline{\;512\;}$, $\underline{\;2048\;}$, $\underline{\;8192\;}$

39. 0, 4, 9, 15, 22, $\underline{\;30\;}$, $\underline{\;39\;}$, $\underline{\;49\;}$

See *Teacher's Resource Book.*
- *Tests,* pp. 61–64
- *Calculator Tests,* pp. 11–12

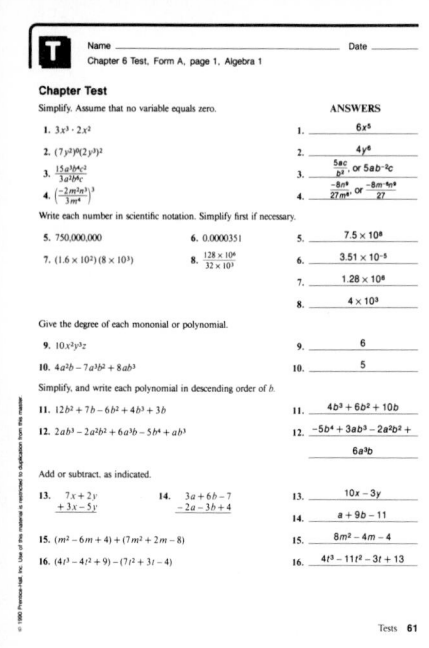

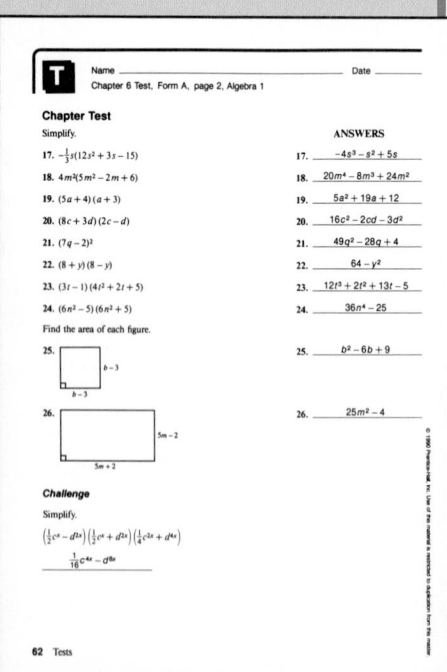

Simplify. Assume that no variable equals zero.

1. $3^3 \cdot 3^2$ 3^5, or 243

2. $\dfrac{c}{c^7}$ $\dfrac{1}{c^6}$

3. $(8m)^0$ 1

4. $-9b^0$ -9

5. $(2^3)^2$ 2^6, or 64

6. $(-4xy^2)(-6x^3y^5)$ $24x^4y^7$

7. $\dfrac{14c^4d^3e^2}{7c^5de^2}$ $\dfrac{2d^2}{c}$

8. $\dfrac{(-3a)^3}{2}$ $\dfrac{-27a^3}{2}$

9. $\left(\dfrac{5b^2c^3}{10b^4}\right)^4$ $\dfrac{c^{12}}{16b^8}$

Rewrite in scientific notation any number that is not already in scientific notation. Simplify first if necessary.

10. 9.9×10^{-5}
scientific notation

11. 5100 5.1×10^3

12. $\dfrac{125 \times 10^5}{25 \times 10^2}$ 5×10^3

13. 1.034 1.034×10^0

14. $(2.4 \times 10)(5 \times 10^3)$ 1.2×10^5

15. $(0.2 \times 10^2)^3$ 8×10^3

State the degree of each monomial and the degree of the polynomial.

16. $-\dfrac{5}{8}$ 0; 0

17. $4t^3 + 7t^2v^2 - tv^3 - 6v^5$ 3, 4, 4, 5; 5

Simplify. Write the result in descending order of the exponent of *y*.

18. $-3y^2 + 2y - 9 + y^2 - y^3$
$-y^3 - 2y^2 + 2y - 9$

19. $5x^2y - 3(xy^2 + y^3 - 2x^2y) + x^3$
$-3y^3 - 3xy^2 + 11x^2y + x^3$

Add or subtract, as indicated.

20.
$\begin{aligned} x - 9y \\ + \;3x + 6y \\ \hline 4x - 3y \end{aligned}$

21.
$\begin{aligned} 4a - 3b + 2c \\ -\;\;a - 7b + 5c \\ \hline 3a + 4b - 3c \end{aligned}$

22. $(2x^2 - x + 7) + (x^2 + 2x - 3)$
$3x^2 + x + 4$

23. $(2c^4 + c^2 - c) - (c^2 + 2c)$
$2c^4 - 3c$

Simplify.

24. $2x(x - 3y + z)$ $2x^2 - 6xy + 2xz$

25. $(2b^2 + 3b - 1)(-3b^3)$
$-6b^5 - 9b^4 + 3b^3$

26. $(k + 3)(2k + 5)$ $2k^2 + 11k + 15$

27. $(4y - 3)^2$ $16y^2 - 24y + 9$

28. $(5r^2 - 1)(5r^2 + 1)$ $25r^4 - 1$

29. $(7c^2 - 2c + 3)(c^2 + 6)$
$7c^4 - 2c^3 + 45c^2 - 12c + 18$

Challenge

Simplify: $(3x^3 - 2y^2)^3$ $27x^9 - 54x^6y^2 + 36x^3y^4 - 8y^6$

Select the best choice for each question.

1. Which fraction is exactly halfway
B between $\frac{1}{6}$ and $\frac{3}{2}$?

   A. $\frac{4}{5}$ **B.** $\frac{5}{6}$ **C.** $\frac{4}{7}$

   D. $\frac{5}{7}$ **E.** $\frac{5}{9}$

2. When $n = -3$ and $s = -1$, which
D of the following would be largest?
   A. $13s^2$ **B.** $5ns$
   C. $n^2 + s^2$ **D.** $2n^2$
   E. $-4(n + s)$

3. Find the value of $\frac{2}{3}$ of the quantity
A (60% of 150).
   A. 60   **B.** 75   **C.** 90
   D. 120 **E.** 190

4. When $3xy - 2xz + 5yz$ is
C subtracted from $5xy + 3yz$, the
  result is:
   A. $-2xy - 2xz + 2yz$
   B. $2xy - 2xz - 2yz$
   C. $2xy + 2xz - 2yz$
   D. $2xy - 2xz + 2yz$
   E. $2xy + 2xz + 2yz$

5. The number 7,130,000, when
A written in scientific notation,
  becomes:
   A. 7.13×10^6
   B. 71.3×10^6
   C. 7.13×10^5
   D. 71.3×10^5
   E. 7.13×10^4

6. When a $20 bill is used to pay for
B items costing $4.50, $7.95, $1.98,
  79¢, and 5¢, what is the change?
   A. $4.18 **B.** $4.73 **C.** $5.18
   D. $5.73 **E.** $5.63

7. The solution set for
D $2(x + 3) > x + 4$ is:
   A. $\{x | x > 10\}$
   B. $\{x | x > 2\}$
   C. $\{x | x > 0\}$
   D. $\{x | x > -2\}$
   E. $\{x | x > -10\}$

8. What percent of 480 is 2.4?
D **A.** 50% **B.** 5% **C.** 1%
   D. $\frac{1}{2}\%$ **E.** $\frac{1}{4}\%$

9. Solve the equation:
C $2(x - 1) = 3(x + 2) - 8$
   A. 4   **B.** 2   **C.** 0
   D. -2 **E.** -4

10. $(2x + 5y)(x - 3y)$ equals:
E **A.** $2x^2 + xy + 15y^2$
   B. $2x^2 - xy + 15y^2$
   C. $2x^2 - 15y^2$
   D. $2x^2 + xy - 15y^2$
   E. $2x^2 - xy - 15y^2$

11. $(-2a^2b^3c)(7ab^2c^4) =$
B **A.** $-14a^2b^5c^4$
   B. $-14a^3b^5c^5$
   C. $-14a^2b^6c^4$
   D. $-14a^3b^5c^4$
   E. None of the above

12. One day Mr. Prompt left home at
A 7:47 AM and drove to his office. If
  he arrived there at 8:39 AM, how
  long did it take for the drive to
  work?
   A. 52 min
   B. 58 min
   C. 62 min
   D. 68 min
   E. 1 h 32 min

The individual comments provided about some problems can be helpful in guiding students to solve these problems.

1. An alternate method of solution is to find the difference between $\frac{1}{6}$ and $\frac{3}{2}$. Then, add half of this difference to $\frac{1}{6}$.

3. This could also be done in one step: $\frac{2}{3} \cdot \frac{3}{5} \cdot 150 = 60$.

8. Students should be encouraged to use estimation. For example, using the fact that 1% of 480 equals 4.8 quickly narrows the choices to D or E.

See *Teacher's Resource Book* for Preparing for Standardized Tests.

See *Teacher's Resource Book, Cumulative Test*, pp. 65–68.

CUMULATIVE REVIEW (CHAPTERS 1–6)

Perform the indicated operation. 1.5–1.8, 6.6–6.8

1. $0.1 \times (-5)$ –0.5

2. $8.6 - (0.6)$ 8.0

3. $-2.1 \div (-0.3)$ 7

4. $-5.2 + 3.1$ –2.1

5. $(2x - 3) - (7x - 4)$ –5x + 1

6. $(8h^2 - 6) + (7 - 5h^2)$ 3h² + 1

7. $(9m^2 + 8) - (m + 6)$ 9m² – m + 2

8. $3y(y^2 - 2y + 4)$ 3y³ – 6y² + 12y

9. $-2b^2(-2b + 3a - 1)$ 4b³ – 6ab² + 2b²

10. $(g + 2)(g - 3)$ g² – g – 6

11. $(2n - 1)(3n - 4)$ 6n² – 11n + 4

12. $(p + 1)(p^2 + 3p - 2)$
p³ + 4p² + p – 2

Simplify. Assume that no variable equals zero. 6.1–6.3, 2.1–2.4

13. $3 + 2 \cdot 6$ 15

14. $[2 - (-2)^3]^2$ 100

15. $|6 - 9| + 5$ 8

16. $3a^2 + 5a - 7a^2$
–4a² + 5a

17. $-(3xy) - (xy)$ –4xy

18. $d^5 \cdot d^3$ d⁸

19. $(3n^2)(2n^3)$ 6n⁵

20. $(s^2)(st^2)$ s³t²

21. $(2p^2)^3$ 8p⁶

22. $\dfrac{b^2}{b^3}$ $\frac{1}{b}$

23. $\dfrac{3m^4}{12m^2}$ $\frac{m^2}{4}$

24. $\dfrac{(-9k^5)^2}{18k^3}$ $\frac{9k^7}{2}$

Solve each equation or inequality. 4.3–4.5, 5.2–5.6, 5.8

25. $-5 = r + 9$ –14

26. $c - 8 > 1$
{all real numbers greater than 9}

27. $-3m = 24$ –8

28. $-2p < 12$
{all real numbers greater than –6}

29. $\dfrac{x}{2} + 1 = 11$ 20

30. $|3a - 5| = 7$ $\left\{4, -\frac{2}{3}\right\}$

31. $3(t - 2) = 9$ 5

32. $5d + 7 \geq 2$
{all real numbers greater than or equal to –1}

33. $0.5n - 1 = 4.5$ 11

34. $3y + 8 = 7y - 4$ 3

35. $b - (2b - 3) + (5b - 2) = 17$ 4

36. $f \geq 1$ and $f < 3$
{1 and all real numbers between 1 and 3}

37. $z < -2$ or $z \geq 0$
{all real numbers less than –2 or greater than or equal to 0}

Solve. 4.3, 4.9, 5.8

38. Find three consecutive integers. The sum of the second number and the third number is 23. 10, 11, 12

39. Two cyclists simultaneously start in opposite directions down a straight road. The average rate of one cyclist is 5 km/h more than the average rate of the other cyclist. If they are 90 km apart after 2 h, what is the rate of each cyclist? 20 km/h, 25 km/h

40. The length of a rectangle is 2 more than 3 times its width. Find the least possible value for the width if the perimeter is at least 24 m. 2.5 m

OVERVIEW • Chapter 7

SUMMARY

In Chapter 7, students are introduced to factoring polynomials. They learn various procedures for factoring, simplifying, and evaluating polynomials of several types. Identifying and classifying numbers as either prime or composite are presented in the early lessons. This will provide a better understanding when the students find the prime factorization of a number. Students are then taught how to use the prime factorization of a number(s) to find the greatest common factor (GCF) of two or more integers. In the final lessons of the chapter, students will learn how to factor perfect square trinomials and the difference of two squares.

After this chapter is completed, students will be able to use these factoring procedures to solve polynomial equations.

CHAPTER OBJECTIVES

- To identify numbers as prime or composite
- To identify the positive integral factors of a number, and to find its prime factorization
- To find the greatest common factor (GCF) of two or more integers and to factor the greatest common monomial factor from a polynomial
- To factor a trinomial of the form $x^2 + bx + c, c > 0$
- To factor a trinomial of the form $x^2 + bx + c, c < 0$
- To factor a trinomial of the form $ax^2 + bx + c$
- To factor perfect square trinomials
- To factor a polynomial by removing a common binomial factor and by grouping the terms
- To factor a polynomial completely
- To solve polynomial equations by factoring

Problem Solving Strategy

To set up and solve problems by using polynomial equations

CHAPTER HIGHLIGHTS

The *theme* of the chapter is gardening. Students learn how factoring polynomials can be applied to real-world situations, such as gardening.

PROBLEM SOLVING AND APPLICATIONS

Problem solving and applications form an integral part of each lesson. Students learn that many practical problems are solved by setting up and solving a polynomial equation by factoring. Lesson 7.10, the strategy of *Using Polynomial Equations,* affords students the opportunity to review mathematical operations involving polynomials. This skill will facilitate all subsequent work with polynomials.

TECHNOLOGY

Computer

In Chapter 7, students are introduced to a computer program that will determine what length and width dimensions will enclose the greatest area, given a length of fencing. The program illustrates how two unknowns, length and width, can be determined by one given dimension.

RESOURCES

Teacher's Resource Book

- Teaching Aids 6, 7, 8

- Transparencies 11, 12

STUDENT TEXT				TEACHER'S RESOURCE BOOK		
Chapter Content	Basic	Average	Enriched	R	P	E
7.1 Factors and Powers	D: 272/1-15 odd, 37, 39	D: 272/1-31 odd, 37, 39, 41	D: 272/17-35 odd, 37-41	1	2	3
7.2 Monomial Factors of Polynomials	D: 276/1-19 odd, 41 R: 272/4, 6, 12	D: 276/1-33 odd, 41, 43 R: 272/10, 14, 30	D: 276/21-39 odd, 41-43 R: 272/18, 22, 34	4	5	6
7.3 Factoring $x^2 + bx + c, c > 0$	D: 280/1-29 odd, 59, 61 R: 276/4, 6, 16	D: 280/1-49 odd, 59, 61, 63 R: 276/8, 12, 32	D: 280/31-57 odd, 59-64 R: 276/30, 34, 38	7	8	9
7.4 Factoring $x^2 + bx + c, c < 0$	D: 284/1-23 odd, 43 R: 280/4, 6, 14	D: 284/1-37 odd, 43 R: 280/10, 14, 18	D: 284/25-41 odd, 43 R: 280/36, 38, 40	10	11	12
7.5 Factoring $ax^2 + bx + c$	D: 287/1-23 odd, 51, 53 R: Test Yourself	D: 287/1-41 odd, 51, 53 R: Test Yourself	D: 287/25-49 odd, 51-54 R: Test Yourself	13	14	15
7.6 Factoring: Special Cases	D: 290/1-27 odd, 52 R: 287/2, 8, 10	D: 290/1-47 odd, 52, 53 R: 287/14, 16, 18	D: 290/29-51 odd, 52, 53 R: 287/32, 34, 38	16	17	18
7.7 Factoring by Grouping	D: 294/1-25 odd, 45 R: 290/4, 14, 16 294/2, 8, 14	D: 294/1-37 odd, 45, 46 R: 290/18, 24, 28	D: 294/27-43 odd, 45, 46 R: 290/36, 40, 44	19	20	21
7.8 Factoring Completely	D: 298/1-35 odd, 53 R: 294/10, 18, 20 298/4, 12, 18	D: 298/1-43 odd, 53, 55 R: 294/18, 20, 24 298/4, 12, 18	D: 298/37-51 odd, 53-56 R: 294/28, 40, 42	22	23	24
7.9 Solving Polynomial Equations by Factoring	D: 302/1-23 odd, 49 R: Test Yourself	D: 302/1-41 odd, 49, 51 R: Test Yourself	D: 302/25-47 odd, 49-51 R: Test Yourself	25	26	27
7.10 Problem Solving Strategy: Using Polynomial Equations	D: 306/1-9 odd MPSR 1-4 R: 302/4, 6, 12	D: 306/1-13 odd MPSR 1-4 R: 302/22, 24, 26	D: 306/11-19 MPSR 1-4 R: 302/26, 28, 44		28	29

D = Daily   R = Review   MPSR = Mixed Problem Solving Review   R = Remediation   P = Practice   E = Enrichment

	STUDENT TEXT				TEACHER'S RESOURCE BOOK	
Reviewing And Testing	Test Yourself	288	Chapter Test	312	Spanish Chapter Summary and Review	13-14
	Test Yourself	303	Prep. for Stan. Test	313	• Quizzes	69-72
	Chapter Sum. and Rev.	310	Maintaining Skills	314	• Chapter Test (Form A)	73-74
			Extra Practice	661	• Chapter Test (Form B)	75-76
					Calculator Test	13-14
Special Features	Biography	273	Logical Reasoning	291	Applications—Chapter 7	30
	Extra	277	Historical Note	295	Critical Thinking	7
	Did You Know?	281	Algebra in Geometry	299	Reading and Writing in Algebra	7
	Algebra in Recreation	284	Project	307	Technology	15-16
			Application	308		

7 Factoring Polynomials

A gardener must visualize how a garden will be landscaped before it is tilled and planted. Very often mathematics can be helpful in determining the structure of the topsoil and the sizes of different plots.

269

BACKGROUND

For gardeners to design a landscape, they have to take into account the dimensions of the land. This would involve mathematical formulas such as those for area and perimeter. This chapter will show how polynomials are integrated into problems involving real-world situations.

Vocabulary
Composite number
Prime factorization
Prime number

Materials/Manipulatives
Calculators
Teacher's Resource Book,
*   Teaching Aid 7*

BACKGROUND

In the Capsule Review, students review writing a product of factors by using exponents. Students will use this skill in the lesson when writing the prime factorization of a number.

7.1

Factors and Exponents

Objectives: To identify numbers as prime or composite
To identify the positive integral factors of a number and
to find its prime factorization

Steven is designing a rectangular vegetable garden that has an area of 20 yd^2. If the dimensions in yards are to be whole numbers, how many choices are there for the length and the width? Steven set up the table below.

$l \cdot w = A$
$l \cdot w = 20$

l	1	2	4	5	10	20
w	20	10	5	4	2	1

When two or more numbers are multiplied, each number is called a *factor*. That is, 2 and 10 are factors of 20 because $2 \cdot 10 = 20$. Also, 20 is *divisible by* 2 and 10, since the remainder is 0 when 20 is divided by 2 or by 10 in both cases. Notice that 1, 2, 4, 5, 10, and 20 are all factors of 20. Unless stated otherwise, the term *factors* will mean positive integers in this lesson.

Capsule Review

An exponent tells how many times the base is used as a factor.

EXAMPLES $2 \cdot 2 \cdot 2 \cdot 3 \cdot 3 = 2^3 \cdot 3^2$ $3 \cdot 5 \cdot 5 \cdot 7 \cdot 5 \cdot 3 = 3^2 \cdot 5^3 \cdot 7$

Write each as the product of its factors by using exponents.

1. $2 \cdot 2 \cdot 2 \cdot 2$ 2^4 **2.** $5 \cdot 5 \cdot 5$ 5^3 **3.** $2 \cdot 3 \cdot 5 \cdot 5$ $2 \cdot 3 \cdot 5^2$

4. $3 \cdot 5 \cdot 7 \cdot 7 \cdot 7$ $3 \cdot 5 \cdot 7^3$ **5.** $1 \cdot 1 \cdot 1 \cdot 1 \cdot 1$ 1^5 **6.** $3 \cdot 3 \cdot 3 \cdot 3 \cdot 3$ 3^5

7. $5 \cdot 3 \cdot 5$ $3 \cdot 5^2$ **8.** $2 \cdot 7 \cdot 2 \cdot 7$ $2^2 \cdot 7^2$ **9.** $10 \cdot 10 \cdot 10 \cdot 11 \cdot 11$ $10^3 \cdot 11^2$

Integers greater than 1 are classified as *prime* or *composite,* depending on their factors. The integer 1 is neither prime nor composite.

A **prime number** is a positive integer with exactly two positive integral factors, itself and 1.

A **composite number** is a positive integer that has more than two positive integral factors.

The prime and composite numbers that are less than 20 are given below.

Prime: 2, 3, 5, 7, 11, 13, 17, 19
Composite: 4, 6, 8, 9, 10, 12, 14, 15, 16, 18

Every composite number can be written as the product of prime numbers. This is called its **prime factorization.** The prime factorization of 30 is $2 \cdot 3 \cdot 5$, since the factors 2, 3, and 5 are all prime numbers.

If a prime number appears as a factor more than once, you may use an exponent to express the power of the factor.

EXAMPLE 1   **Find the prime factorization of 198.**

$$198 = 2 \cdot 99 \qquad \textit{Divide by 2, the first prime number.}$$
$$= 2 \cdot 3 \cdot 33 \qquad \textit{99 is not divisible by 2, so try division by 3.}$$
$$= 2 \cdot 3 \cdot 3 \cdot 11 \qquad \textit{33 is divisible by 3.}$$
$$= 2 \cdot 3^2 \cdot 11 \qquad \textit{11 is a prime number.}$$

So, the prime factorization of 198 is $2 \cdot 3^2 \cdot 11$.

A prime factorization is not complete until all the factors are prime.

EXAMPLE 2   **Find the prime factorization of 4675.**

$$4675 = 5 \cdot 935 \qquad \textit{4675 is not divisible by 2 or 3. Divide by 5.}$$
$$= 5 \cdot 5 \cdot 187 \qquad \textit{Divide by 5 again.}$$
$$= 5 \cdot 5 \cdot 11 \cdot 17 \qquad \textit{187 is not divisible by 7. Divide by 11.}$$
$$= 5^2 \cdot 11 \cdot 17 \qquad \textit{17 is a prime number.}$$

So, the prime factorization of 4675 is $5^2 \cdot 11 \cdot 17$.

CLASS EXERCISES

List all positive integers that are factors of the number.

1. 15 1, 3, 5, 15   **2.** 6 1, 2, 3, 6   **3.** 16 1, 2, 4, 8, 16   **4.** 24
1, 2, 3, 4, 6, 8, 12, 24

State whether the number is *prime* or *composite*.

5. 23 prime   **6.** 21 composite   **7.** 1 neither   **8.** 51 composite

Find the prime factorization of the number.

9. 14 $2 \cdot 7$ **10.** 18 $2 \cdot 3^2$ **11.** 13 prime   **12.** 60 $2^2 \cdot 3 \cdot 5$

TEACHING SUGGESTIONS

- Students review prime numbers, composite numbers, and the prime factorization of a number. This lesson lays the foundation for work in this chapter on the greatest common factor (GCF) of two or more numbers and factoring polynomials.
- You may want students to find all prime numbers less than 100 by using the Sieve of Eratosthenes. Teaching Aid 7, in the *Teacher's Resource Book* may be useful. The Sieve of Eratosthenes is the process of determining all prime numbers from 2 to *n*. The process starts by writing down all the numbers from 2 to *n* and removing those numbers after 2 which are multiples of 2, then removing those numbers after 3 which are multiples of 3, and so on. Continue until all multiples of primes not greater than $\sqrt{n}$, except the primes themselves, have been removed. Only prime numbers will remain.
- When writing the prime factorization of a number, use the exponent form where feasible.

Critical Thinking

Analyzing Whole-Part Relationships
Explain why divisibility by 2, 3, and 5 was tested, but divisibility by 4 was omitted in Example 2. Students, through reasoning, should conclude that since 4675 was not divisible by 2, it is not divisible by 4 and 4 is not a prime factor.

CHALKBOARD EXAMPLES

- **For Example 1**
  Find the prime factorization.
  1. 100 $2^2 \cdot 5^2$
  2. 156 $2^2 \cdot 3 \cdot 13$

- **For Example 2**
  Find the prime factorization.
  3. 2695 $5 \cdot 7^2 \cdot 11$
  4. 3750 $2 \cdot 3 \cdot 5^4$

Common Error

- Students often make errors by thinking that all odd numbers, such as 57, 91, and 119, are prime. These students should list the first ten prime numbers, 2, 3, 5, 7, 11, 13, 17, 19, 23, and 29, and use each as a divisor of the given number.
- See *Teacher's Resource Book* for additional remediation.

LESSON FOLLOW-UP

Discussion

Are all real numbers either prime or composite? No; for example, -2.75 and $\sqrt{2}$ are neither prime nor composite. Only the positive integers greater than 1 can be classified prime or composite (by definition).

Assignment Guide

- See p. 268B for assignments.
- You may want students to use calculators to complete the exercises.
- See *Teacher's Resource Book*, Technology, pp. 15–16.

Biography

Have students work in pairs to complete the exercises and the research.

Lesson Quiz

Find the prime factorization.

1. 12 $2^2 \cdot 3$ 2. 21 $3 \cdot 7$
3. 78 $2 \cdot 3 \cdot 13$ 4. 34 $2 \cdot 17$
5. 138 $2 \cdot 3 \cdot 23$ 6. 507 $3 \cdot 13^2$
7. 3388 $2^2 \cdot 7 \cdot 11^2$

Enrichment

Christian Goldbach's conjecture states that every even number greater than four could be written as the sum of two odd primes. Is this true for the even numbers >4 and <100. yes

---

For Discussion

13. Is there more than one prime factorization of any composite number? (The order of the factors does not count.) Explain.
No; prime factorization is unique.

14. Explain why 1 is neither prime nor composite. 1 does not have exactly two positive integral factors, so it is not prime; 1 does not have exactly two different positive integral factors so it is not composite.

PRACTICE EXERCISES

Find the prime factorization of the number.

A
1. 26 $2 \cdot 13$
2. 33 $3 \cdot 11$
3. 52 $2^2 \cdot 13$
4. 70 $2 \cdot 5 \cdot 7$
5. 154 $2 \cdot 7 \cdot 11$
6. 135 $3^3 \cdot 5$
7. 195 $3 \cdot 5 \cdot 13$
8. 315 $3^2 \cdot 5 \cdot 7$
9. 105 $3 \cdot 5 \cdot 7$
10. 165 $3 \cdot 5 \cdot 11$
11. 143 $11 \cdot 13$
12. 273 $3 \cdot 7 \cdot 13$
13. 3575 $5^2 \cdot 11 \cdot 13$
14. 1925 $5^2 \cdot 7 \cdot 11$
15. 9625 $5^3 \cdot 7 \cdot 11$
16. 7425 $3^3 \cdot 5^2 \cdot 11$

B
17. 2205 $3^2 \cdot 5 \cdot 7^2$
18. 1155 $3 \cdot 5 \cdot 7 \cdot 11$
19. 1760 $2^5 \cdot 5 \cdot 11$
20. 1716 $2^2 \cdot 3 \cdot 11 \cdot 13$
21. 242 $2 \cdot 11^2$
22. 338 $2 \cdot 13^2$
23. 288 $2^5 \cdot 3^2$
24. 455 $5 \cdot 7 \cdot 13$
25. 101 prime
26. 107 prime
27. 1000 $2^3 \cdot 5^3$
28. 1875 $3 \cdot 5^4$

Find the next prime number after the given prime number.

29. 53 59
30. 71 73
31. 107 109
32. 127 131

If x is a prime number, must the expression represent a composite number? Justify your answer.

C
33. $3x$ yes
$3x$ is the product of two primes

34. $x + x$ yes
$x + x = 2x$. $2x$ is the product of two primes.

35. x^2 yes
$x \cdot x = x^2$ is a product of two primes.

36. $x + 4$ no
If $x = 3$, $x + 4 = 7$ and 7 is a prime number.

Applications

Computer Suppose you have a given length of fencing. You need to determine what length and width dimensions will enable you to enclose the greatest area. This program considers the length of the fencing as the perimeter and then checks each combination of length and width dimensions.

```
10 INPUT "ENTER THE FENCING LENGTH.
   ";P: PRINT
20 PRINT "LENGTH","WIDTH","AREA"
30 FOR W = 1 TO P / 2 - 1
40 LET L = (P - 2 * W) / 2
50 LET A = L * W: PRINT L,W,A
60 NEXT W
70 END
```

Run the program for the following lengths. See below.

37. 12
38. 79
39. 250
40. 86.4

41. Run the program for a variety of fencing lengths. Does any pattern emerge for the maximum dimensions?

272   Chapter 7 Factoring Polynomials

Additional Answers
37. length 3, width 3, area 9
38. length 19.5, width 20, area 390
39. length 62, width 63, area 3906
40. length 21.2, width 22, area 466.4
41. As the length increases the area increases, as the length decreases the area decreases.

BIOGRAPHY: Hypatia

Hypatia was born in Alexandria, Egypt, in 370 A.D. Her father, Theon, was a mathematician and philosopher, which probably stimulated her interest in these fields. Historians today identify Hypatia as the first notable mathematician who was a woman.

Hypatia devoted most of her scholarly attention to mathematics and astronomy, and wrote several commentaries on the works of scholars such as Diophantus and Ptolemy.

The philosophy of Hypatia was more scholarly and scientific and less mystical and pagan than that of the Athenian school then in existence. Because her school symbolized learning and science, however, it was identified with paganism by early religious fanatics. Around 412 A.D., a group of these fanatics brutally murdered Hypatia. Her death signaled the beginning of the decline of Alexandria as an important center of learning.

1. Diophantine problems (or equations) are a particular type of problem named after Diophantus, a contemporary of Hypatia. Diophantine problems are indeterminate algebraic problems with restriction of the solutions to integers. One possible integral solution of $x^2 + y^2 = z^2$ is $8^2 + 6^2 = 10^2$, with $x = 8$, $y = 6$, and $z = 10$. Find three other integral solutions.

2. A student's transcript shows x 5-hour courses, and y 3-hour courses. The total number of course hours is 64. Study the graph and find the number of each type of course taken. Possible solutions are $x = 2$ and $y = 18$, or $x = 5$ and $y = 13$. How many other integer solutions are there? How would you check your answers?

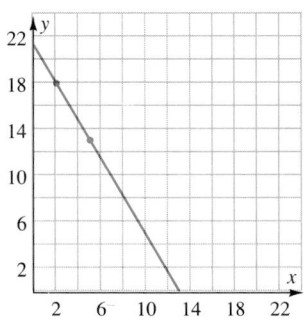

3. Research the life of one or more contemporaries of Hypatia who were associated with the remarkable scholarship in Egypt and Greece at that time.

7.1 Factors and Exponents   **273**

Teacher's Resource Book
Reteaching—Chapter 7, p. 1.

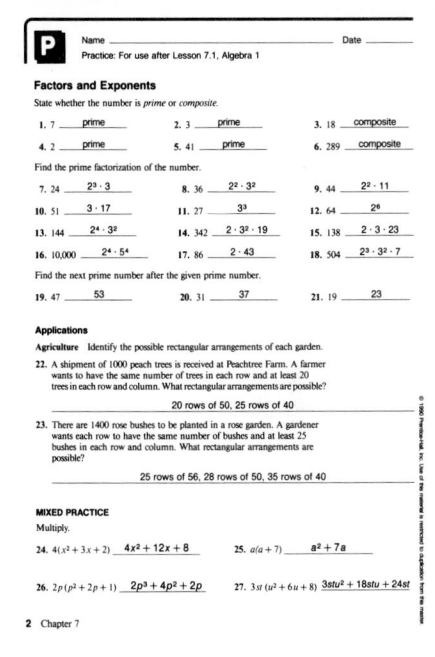

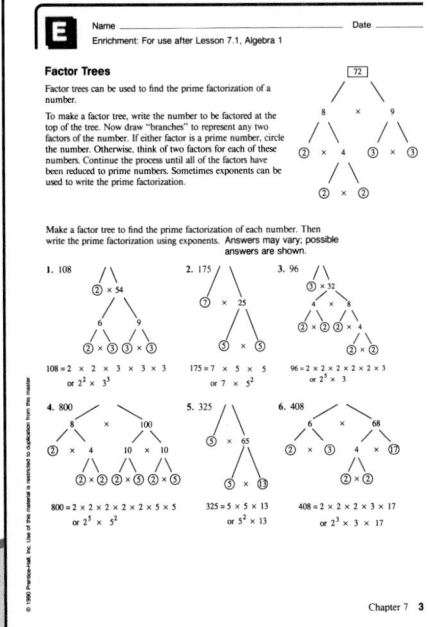

BACKGROUND

In the Capsule Review, students find missing factors by using the property of exponents for division. Students having difficulty should check their answers by using the property of exponents for multiplication. This review will help them factor polynomials in this lesson.

7.2

Monomial Factors of Polynomials

Objectives: To find the greatest common factor (GCF) of two or more integers
To factor the greatest common monomial factor from a polynomial

Jenny raises golden retriever puppies. She wants to place a rectangular pen for the dogs along a wall. The area of the pen should be 112 yd². If the length of the pen is 16 yd, what is the width?

$$\text{Area} = \text{length} \times \text{width}$$

$$112 = 16 \cdot \underline{?} \qquad \textit{Missing factor}$$

$$\frac{112}{16} = 7 \qquad \textit{Divide 112 by 16 to find the missing factor.}$$

So, $112 = 16 \cdot 7$, and the width of the pen is 7 yd.

Capsule Review

EXAMPLES $12a^7 = 4a^3 \cdot \underline{?}$ $\qquad 18a^5b^4 = -3ab \cdot \underline{?}$

$\dfrac{12a^7}{4a^3} = 3a^{7-3}$, or $3a^4$ $\qquad \dfrac{18a^5b^4}{-3ab} = -6a^{5-1}b^{4-1}$, or $-6a^4b^3$

So, the missing factor is $3a^4$: $\quad$ So, the missing factor is $-6a^4b^3$:
$12a^7 = 4a^3 \cdot 3a^4$ $\qquad\qquad 18a^5b^4 = -3ab(-6a^4b^3)$

Divide to find the missing factor.

1. $x^5 = x^2 \cdot \underline{?}$ x^3 $\qquad$ **2.** $4y^4 = y \cdot \underline{?}$ $4y^3$ $\qquad$ **3.** $-9m^3 = 3m \cdot \underline{?}$
$\qquad\qquad\qquad\qquad\qquad\qquad\qquad\qquad\qquad\qquad\qquad\qquad\qquad\qquad -3m^2$

4. $a^4b^3 = b \cdot \underline{?}$ a^4b^2 $\qquad$ **5.** $20x^5y^4 = -4xy^3 \cdot \underline{?}$ $\qquad$ **6.** $56rs = 7r \cdot \underline{?}$ $8s$
$\qquad\qquad\qquad\qquad\qquad\qquad\qquad -5x^4y$

7. $32m^3n^3 = 4mn^2 \cdot \underline{?}$ $\qquad$ **8.** $-15x^3 = 3x \cdot \underline{?}$ $-5x^2$ $\qquad$ **9.** $-52mn^3 = -m \cdot \underline{?}$
$\quad 8m^2n$ $\qquad\qquad\qquad\qquad\qquad\qquad\qquad\qquad\qquad\qquad\qquad\qquad\qquad\qquad 52n^3$

A **common factor** of two or more integers is a factor of each integer. For example, 5 is a common factor of 15 and 25. The **greatest common factor (GCF)** of two or more integers is the greatest integer that is a factor of each.

EXAMPLE 1 **Find the GCF of 45 and 63.**

First, find the prime factorization of each number.
$45 = 3 \cdot 3 \cdot 5$, or $3^2 \cdot 5$
$63 = 3 \cdot 3 \cdot 7$, or $3^2 \cdot 7$ $\qquad 3^2$ *appears in both factorizations.*

So, the greatest common factor of 45 and 63 is 3^2, or 9.

274 Chapter 7 Factoring Polynomials

The concept of greatest common factor applies to monomials and polynomials. Write the monomials $21x^2$ and $-28xy^3$ in factored form:

$$21x^2 = 3 \cdot 7 \cdot x \cdot x$$
$$-28xy^3 = -1 \cdot 2 \cdot 2 \cdot 7 \cdot x \cdot y \cdot y \cdot y$$

The greatest common factor of these two monomials is $7x$, the product of their common factors. The GCF of two or more monomials is the product of the common factors of both the coefficients and all the common variables. For example,

$$4x^3y = 2 \cdot 2 \cdot x \cdot x \cdot x \cdot y$$
$$12x^2y^3 = 2 \cdot 2 \cdot 3 \cdot x \cdot x \cdot y \cdot y \cdot y$$

To find the GCF multiply the common factors: $2 \cdot 2 \cdot x \cdot x \cdot y = 4x^2y$. The monomials contain powers of x and powers of y. x^2 and y are the greatest powers of the variables that occur in both monomials.

To factor a polynomial means to write the polynomial as a product of other polynomials. First find the greatest common factor of its terms. Then use the distributive property to write the polynomial in factored form.

Polynomial	Find the GCF of the terms	Use the distributive property
$21x^2 - 28xy^3 \longrightarrow$	$7x(3x) - 7x(4y^3) \longrightarrow$	$7x(3x - 4y^3)$

In this example, $7x$ is the GCF of the terms $21x^2$ and $-28xy^3$. It is a *common monomial factor* of the terms. A *binomial factor* of $21x^2 - 28xy^3$ is $(3x - 4y^3)$.

EXAMPLE 2 **Factor: $3x^3y - 15x^2y^4$**

$3x^3y - 15x^2y^4$ *The GCF of the terms is $3x^2y$.*
$3x^2y(x) - 3x^2y(5y^3)$ *Factor out the GCF from each term.*
$3x^2y(x - 5y^3)$ *Write the polynomial in factored form.*

Check by multiplying $3x^2y$ and $x - 5y^3$. The product should be the original polynomial.

EXAMPLE 3 **Factor: $8m^4n^2 + 18m^3n^2 - 6m^2n$**

$8m^4n^2 + 18m^3n^2 - 6m^2n$ *The GCF is $2m^2n$.*
$2m^2n(4m^2n) + 2m^2n(9mn) - 2m^2n(3)$ *Factor out the GCF from each term.*
$2m^2n(4m^2n + 9mn - 3)$ *Factored form of the polynomial*

Check by multiplying: Is $2m^2n(4m^2n + 9mn - 3) = 8m^4n^2 + 18m^3n^2 - 6m^2n$?

When a measure is given as a polynomial, consider whether it can be expressed in factored form.

EXAMPLE 4 **Find the area of the shaded region.**

7.2 Monomial Factors of Polynomials **275**

- Students use the concept of prime factorization to find the greatest common factor (GCF) of two or more integers. The concept is then extended to include the greatest common monomial factor of a polynomial.
- After discussing Example 1, you may want to introduce numbers that are relatively prime, that is, numbers that have no factors in common other than 1. For example, 12 and 55 are relatively prime.
- You may wish to use an overhead projector to illustrate Example 4.

CHALKBOARD EXAMPLES

- **For Example 1**
  Find the GCF of each group of numbers.
  1. 54, 81 27   **2.** 24, 72, 96 24

- **For Example 2**
  Factor.
  3. $18x^3y^2 - 6xy^4$ $6xy^2(3x^2 - y^2)$
  4. $4x^6y^4 + 6xy^3$ $2xy^3(2x^5y + 3)$

- **For Example 3**
  Factor.
  5. $12m^3n^5 - 9mn^2 + 24m^4n$
  $3mn(4m^2n^4 - 3n + 8m^3)$
  6. $46x^3y^4 - 23x^2y^3 - 69xy^2$
  $23xy^2(2x^2y^2 - xy - 3)$

- **For Example 4**
  7. Find the area of the shaded region. $2r^2(5 - \pi)$

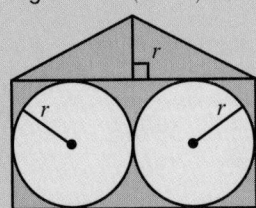

A side of the square measures $2r$. Why?

$$\text{Area}_{\text{shaded}} = A_{\text{square}} + A_{\text{triangle}} - A_{\text{circle}}$$
$$= (2r)^2 + \frac{1}{2}(2r \cdot r) - (\pi r^2)$$
$$= 4r^2 + r^2 - \pi r^2$$
$$= 5r^2 - \pi r^2$$
$$= r^2(5 - \pi) \quad \textit{Factored form of the polynomial}$$

The area of the shaded region is $r^2(5 - \pi)$.

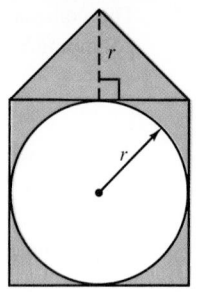

CLASS EXERCISES

Find the GCF of each group of numbers.

1. $14, 24$ 2
2. $15, 19$ 1
3. $24, 36, 42$ 6
4. $7, 35, 105$ 7

Factor.

5. $3p + 6$
$3(p + 2)$
6. $10z + 15$
$5(2z + 3)$
7. $8k - 4$
$4(2k - 1)$
8. $27r + 9t$
$9(3r + t)$
9. $2x + 7x^2$
$x(2 + 7x)$
10. $14y - y^4$
$y(14 - y^3)$
11. $8a^2 + 12a$
$4a(2a + 3)$
12. $12 - 12a$
$12(1 - a)$

For each of the following, first find the GCF, then factor.

13. $3pq^2 + 18p^2q$ $3pq$; $3pq(q + 6p)$
14. $11j^4k^5 - 13j^3k^2$ j^3k^2; $j^3k^2(11jk^3 - 13)$

PRACTICE EXERCISES

Find the GCF of each group of numbers.

A
1. $35, 49$ 7
2. $39, 52$ 13
3. $144, 126$ 18
4. $154, 198$ 22
5. $25, 75, 100$ 25
6. $32, 40, 56$ 8
7. $112, 224, 104$ 8
8. $174, 216, 162$ 6

Factor.

9. $2x^3y - 12x^2y^4$
$2x^2y(x - 6y^3)$
10. $5a^2b - 15a^3b^3$
$5a^2b(1 - 3ab^2)$
11. $7cd^3 + 14c^3d^5$
$7cd^3(1 + 2c^2d^2)$
12. $6mn^4 + 18m^5n^2$
$6mn^2(n^2 + 3m^4)$
13. $13x^2y^3 + 26x^2y^2$
$13x^2y^2(y + 2)$
14. $33w^3y^2 + 11w^2y^2$
$11w^2y^2(3w + 1)$
15. $12m^4n^5 - 18mn^3$
$6mn^3(2m^3n^2 - 3)$
16. $7a^2b^3 - 9a^4b^3$
$a^2b^3(7 - 9a^2)$
17. $4j^3k - 6jk^2 + 8jk$
$2jk(2j^2 - 3k + 4)$
18. $5m^3n - 15mn^2 + 10mn$
$5mn(m - 3n + 2)$
19. $4a^2b + 8a^2b^2 + 12ab$
$4ab(a + 2ab + 3)$
20. $9cd^2 + 6c^2d + 3cd$
$3cd(3d + 2c + 1)$

B
21. $12x^3y^4 + 36x^4y^4 - 60x^3y^5$
$12x^3y^4(1 + 3x - 5y)$
22. $10x^4y^4 + 15x^4y^7 - 25x^5y^6$
$5x^4y^4(2 + 3y^3 - 5xy^2)$
23. $24m^3n^2 + 21m^2n^3 - 39m^2n^4$
$3m^2n^2(8m + 7n - 13n^2)$
24. $49jk^2 - 21j^2k^3 + 84j^3k^4$
$7jk^2(7 - 3jk + 12j^2k^2)$
25. $13x^5y^4 - 11x^3y^4 + 17x^4y^3$
$x^3y^3(13x^2y - 11y + 17x)$
26. $23s^3t^4 - 19s^2t^5 + 29s^4t^3$
$s^2t^3(23st - 19t^2 + 29s^2)$
27. $42l^3m^2 - 36l^2m^5 - 54l^4m$
$6l^2m(7lm - 6m^4 - 9l^2)$
28. $72c^2d^5 - 64c^3d - 28c^2d^4$
$4c^2d(18d^4 - 16c - 7d^3)$
29. $33x^5y^7 - 99x^6y^9 - 66x^5y^8$
$33x^5y^7(1 - 3xy^2 - 2y)$
30. $76a^4b^5 - 38a^5b^5 - 114ab$
$38ab(2a^3b^4 - a^4b^4 - 3)$
31. $89r^2s^9 + 113r^3s^7 + 73r^4s^3$
$r^2s^3(89s^6 + 113rs^4 + 73r^2)$
32. $71x^8y^9 + 119x^7y^6 + 97x^4y^8$
$x^4y^6(71x^4y^3 + 119x^3 + 97y^2)$

33. $-15a^3b^4 - 35a^4b^5 - 55a^2b^4$
$\ -5a^2b^4(3a^2 + 7a^2b + 11)$

34. $-22w^3z^4 - 28w^2z^5 - 34wz^4$
$\ -2wz^4(11w^2 + 14wz + 17)$

C **35.** $-115x^4y^4 - 225x^5y^5 - 285x^6y^6$
$\ -5x^4y^4(23 + 45xy + 57x^2y^2)$

36. $-145m^4n^7 - 280m^5n^6 - 310m^6n^9$
$\ -5m^4n^6(29n + 56m + 62m^2n^3)$

37. $77c^4d^6e^3 + 28c^5d^2e^4$
$\ 7c^4d^2e^3(11d^4 + 4ce)$

38. $56j^3k^2l^4 + 72j^2kl^3$
$\ 8j^2kl^3(7jkl + 9)$

39. $54x^2y^5z^3 - 36x^3y^2z^2$
$\ 18x^2y^2z^2(3y^3z - 2x)$

40. $42s^2t^3u^4 + 35s^3t^2u^3$
$\ 7s^2t^2u^3(6tu + 5s)$

Applications

Geometry Find the area of the shaded region. Give the answer in factored form.

41.

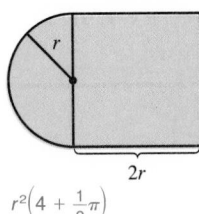

$2r$

$r^2\left(4 + \frac{1}{2}\pi\right)$

42.

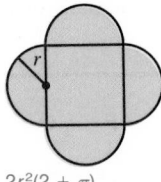

$2r^2(2 + \pi)$

43.

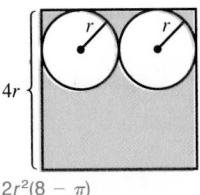

$4r$

$2r^2(8 - \pi)$

EXTRA

For some numbers, it is difficult to determine if there is a GCF greater than 1, and if so, what it is. You can use Euclid's Algorithm to find the GCF. This program will do it for you or you can use a calculator and follow the steps in the example below.

```
10 INPUT "ENTER TWO NUMBERS.  ";X,Y
20 IF X > Y THEN   GOTO 40
30 R = Y -  INT (Y / X) * X:A = X:Y = R: GOTO 50
40 R = X -  INT (X / Y) * Y:A = Y:Y = R
50 IF R = 0 THEN   PRINT "GCF = ";A: GOTO 70
60 GOTO 20
70 END
```

EXAMPLE Factor $368x + 805$ by finding the GCF of 368 and 805.

Solution 1. Divide the larger number (805) by the smaller number (368).

$368\overline{)805}\ \ 2r69$

2. Divide the previous divisor (368) by the remainder (69).

$69\overline{)368}\ \ 5r23$

3. Repeat step 2 until the remainder is 0.

$23\overline{)69}\ \ 3r0$

4. When the remainder is 0, the GCF is the divisor in that step.

GCF = 23

Answer $368x + 805 = 23(16x + 35)$

Use Euclid's Algorithm to factor each expression.

1. $765x + 187$
$17(45x + 11)$

2. $136x + 255$
$17(8x + 15)$

3. $460x + 161$
$23(20x + 7)$

4. $1276x + 435$
$29(44x + 15)$

5. $264x + 605$
$11(24x + 55)$

6. $286x + 385$
$11(26x + 35)$

7. $736x + 483$
$23(32x + 21)$

8. $351x + 455$
$13(27x + 35)$

Teacher's Resource Book

Reteaching—Chapter 7, p. 4.

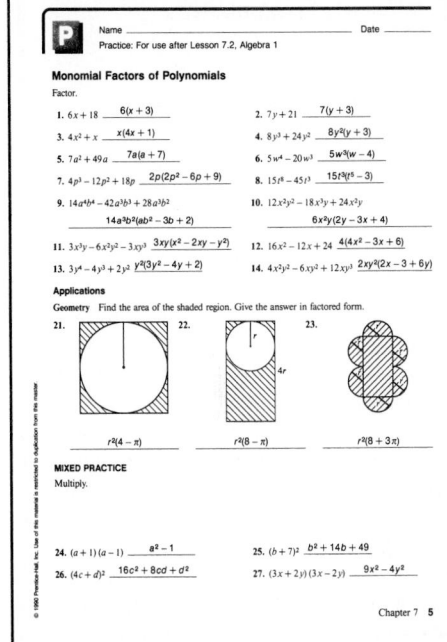

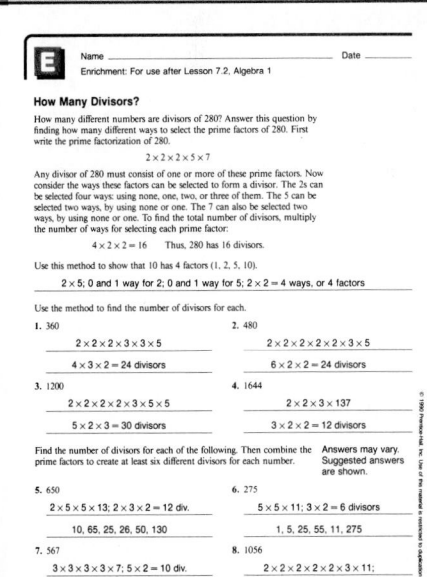

Materials/Manipulatives
Graph paper
Overhead projector
Teacher's Resource Book,
Teaching Aid 8,
Transparencies 8, 8a, 12

BACKGROUND

In the Capsule Review, students multiply two binomials using the FOIL method. You may want the students to discover that, in each exercise, the coefficient of each variable is 1 and the operation sign in each pair of binomials is the same. It is important that students understand the FOIL method before learning to factor the trinomials in this lesson. You may want to review Transparency 12, in the *Teacher's Resource Book,* for students having difficulty in factoring. You may also want to review how to find all numerical factors of an integer.

Critical Thinking

Causal Explanation Examine Exercise 6 in the Capsule Review and explain why $(11 - a)(10 - a)$ has the same product as $(a - 11)(a - 10)$.
Students should explain that $a - 11 = -1(11 - a)$ and $a - 10 = -1(10 - a)$; so, $(a - 11)(a -.10) = -1(11 - a)$ $[-1(10 - a)] = (-1)(-1)(11 - a)$ $(10 - a) = (11 - a)(10 - a)$.

7.3 Factoring $x^2 + bx + c, c > 0$

Objective: To factor a trinomial of the form $x^2 + bx + c, c > 0$

Factoring a trinomial of the form $x^2 + bx + c$ means to express the trinomial as the product of two binomials of the form $(x + r)(x + s)$.

Capsule Review

$$\begin{array}{cccc} \text{F} & \text{O} & \text{I} & \text{L} \\ | & | & | & | \end{array}$$

EXAMPLES $(x + 2)(x + 7) = x^2 + 7x + 2x + 14 = x^2 + 9x + 14$
$(1 - y)(12 - y) = 12 - y - 12y + y^2 = 12 - 13y + y^2$

Multiply.

1. $(x + 1)(x + 2)$
$x^2 + 3x + 2$
2. $(t - 2)(t - 5)$
$t^2 - 7t + 10$
3. $(y + 3)(y + 4)$
$y^2 + 7y + 12$
4. $(m - 10)(m - 50)$
$m^2 - 60m + 500$
5. $(100 + z)(8 + z)$
$800 + 108z + z^2$
6. $(11 - a)(10 - a)$
$110 - 21a + a^2$

Factoring a trinomial involves recognizing patterns, estimating, looking for clues, and multiplying to check.

Consider how FOIL can be used in factoring trinomials into two binomial factors $(x + r)(x + s)$ in which the coefficient of the first term is 1.

EXAMPLE 1 **Factor:** $x^2 + 7x + 10$

The product of the second terms, r and s of the binomials, must be 10, the last term of the trinomial. The sum of the outer and inner products must be $7x$. The table below shows how to test pairs of factors of 10.

Factors of 10	Possible Binomial Factors	Sum of Outer and Inner Products	
1, 10	$(x + 1)(x + 10)$	$10x + 1x = 11x$	
$-1, -10$	$(x - 1)(x - 10)$	$-10x + (-1x) = -11x$	
2, 5	$(x + 2)(x + 5)$	$5x + 2x = 7x$	←Correct middle term
$-2, -5$	$(x - 2)(x - 5)$	$-5x + (-2x) = -7x$	

So, $x^2 + 7x + 10 = (x + 2)(x + 5)$.
Check by multiplying: $(x + 2)(x + 5) = x^2 + 5x + 2x + 10 = x^2 + 7x + 10$

Example 1 suggests a *factoring clue:* When the first term of a trinomial has a coefficient of 1 and the middle and the last terms are positive, you need to test only the positive factors of the last term.

EXAMPLE 2   Factor: $m^2 - 5m + 6$

Factors of 6	Possible Binomial Factors	Sum of Outer and Inner Products
1, 6	$(m + 1)(m + 6)$	$6m + 1m = 7m$
$-1, -6$	$(m - 1)(m - 6)$	$-6m + (-1m) = -7m$
2, 3	$(m + 2)(m + 3)$	$3m + 2m = 5m$
$-2, -3$	$(m - 2)(m - 3)$	$-3m + (-2m) = -5m \leftarrow$ *Correct middle term*

So, $m^2 - 5m + 6 = (m - 2)(m - 3)$. Check by multiplying.

Example 2 leads to another *factoring clue:* When the first term of a trinomial has a coefficient of 1 and the middle term is negative and the last term is positive, you need to test only the negative factors of the last term.

EXAMPLE 3   Factor: $12 - 8a + a^2$

$$12 - 8a + a^2$$
$$= a^2 - 8a + 12 \qquad \textit{Write the terms in descending order.}$$
$$= (a - \underline{\ ?\ })(a - \underline{\ ?\ }) \qquad \textit{Both second terms are negative.}$$

Factors of 12	Possible Binomial Factors	Sum of Outer and Inner Products
$-1, -12$	$(a - 1)(a - 12)$	$-12a + (-1a) = -13a$
$-4, -3$	$(a - 4)(a - 3)$	$-3a + (-4a) = -7a$
$-6, -2$	$(a - 6)(a - 2)$	$-2a + (-6a) = -8a \leftarrow$ *Correct middle term*

So, $12 - 8a + a^2 = (a - 6)(a - 2)$. Check by multiplying.
If you so desire, exercises of this type can also be factored without rearranging the terms of the polynomial: $12 - 8a + a^2 = (6 - a)(2 - a)$.

You may use the factoring process to factor a trinomial that contains more than one variable.

EXAMPLE 4   Factor: $a^2 + 7ab + 12b^2$

$$a^2 + 7ab + 12b^2 = (a + \underline{\ ?\ })(a + \underline{\ ?\ }) \qquad \text{Both factors of } 12b^2 \text{ must be positive.}$$

Factors of $12b^2$	Possible Binomial Factors	Sum of Outer and Inner Products
$1b, 12b$	$(a + 1b)(a + 12b)$	$12ab + 1ab = 13ab$
$2b, 6b$	$(a + 2b)(a + 6b)$	$6ab + 2ab = 8ab$
$3b, 4b$	$(a + 3b)(a + 4b)$	$4ab + 3ab = 7ab \leftarrow$ *Correct middle term*

So, $a^2 + 7ab + 12b^2 = (a + 3b)(a + 4b)$. Check by multiplying.

7.3 Factoring $x^2 + bx + c$, $c > 0$ **279**

- **For Example 3**

    3. Factor: $24 + 14x + x^2$

    $(x + 2)(x + 12)$

- **For Example 4**

    4. Factor: $r^2 + 16rs + 63s^2$

    $(r + 7s)(r + 9s)$

Common Error

- Students often make errors by incorrectly placing the signs in the binomial factors. For students who make this type of error, have them use Teaching Aid 8, in the *Teacher's Resource Book,* to avoid any sign errors.

Factor 1 (F₁)	Factor 2 (F₂)	Product	Sum
$+$	$+$	$+$	$+$
$-$	$-$	$+$	$-$

By referring to this chart, some factors can immediately be eliminated. Also, remind students to check their answers by multiplying.

- See *Teacher's Resource Book* for additional remediation.

LESSON FOLLOW-UP

Assignment Guide

See p. 268B for assignments.

Did You Know?

Students learn how the distributive property can be used in multiplying two binomials. The feature allows the students to visualize the distributive property geometrically.

Lesson Quiz

Factor. Check by multiplying.
1. $y^2 + 16y + 15$ $(y + 1)(y + 15)$
2. $r^2 - 34r + 64$ $(r - 32)(r - 2)$
3. $z^2 + 25z + 100$ $(z + 20)(z + 5)$
4. $k^2 - 30k + 125$ $(k - 5)(k - 25)$
5. $18 + 9d + d^2$ $(d + 6)(d + 3)$
6. $-10r + r^2 + 24$ $(r - 4)(r - 6)$
7. $j^2 - 16jk + 48k^2$ $(j - 4k)(j - 12k)$

280

CLASS EXERCISES

Find the missing factors. Check by multiplying.

1. $x^2 + 5x + 6 = (x + 2)(x + \underline{?})$ 3
2. $b^2 - 13b + 12 = (b - 1)(b - \underline{?})$ 12
3. $u^2 - 8u + 7 = (u - \underline{?})(u - \underline{?})$ 1; 7
4. $z^2 - 18z + 17 = (z - \underline{?})(z - \underline{?})$ 1; 17

Factor. Check by multiplying.

5. $x^2 + 4x + 3$
$(x + 1)(x + 3)$
6. $m^2 + 3m + 2$
$(m + 1)(m + 2)$
7. $y^2 - 6y + 5$
$(y - 1)(y - 5)$
8. $p^2 - 2p + 1$
$(p - 1)(p - 1)$
9. $7 + 8m + m^2$
$(1 + m)(7 + m)$
10. $11 - 12d + d^2$
$(1 - d)(11 - d)$

PRACTICE EXERCISES

Factor. Check by multiplying.

A
1. $x^2 + 10x + 9$
$(x + 1)(x + 9)$
2. $y^2 + 14y + 13$
$(y + 1)(y + 13)$
3. $a^2 + 12a + 11$
$(a + 1)(a + 11)$
4. $r^2 + 6r + 8$
$(r + 2)(r + 4)$
5. $z^2 + 30z + 29$
$(z + 1)(z + 29)$
6. $t^2 + 16t + 39$
$(t + 3)(t + 13)$
7. $y^2 + 14y + 33$
$(y + 3)(y + 11)$
8. $x^2 + 20x + 91$
$(x + 7)(x + 13)$
9. $s^2 - 7s + 6$
$(s - 1)(s - 6)$
10. $k^2 - 5k + 4$
$(k - 1)(k - 4)$
11. $m^2 - 42m + 41$
$(m - 1)(m - 41)$
12. $b^2 - 20b + 19$
$(b - 1)(b - 19)$
13. $y^2 - 13y + 22$
$(y - 2)(y - 11)$
14. $n^2 - 9n + 14$
$(n - 2)(n - 7)$
15. $z^2 - 20z + 51$
$(z - 3)(z - 17)$
16. $g^2 - 12g + 35$
$(g - 5)(g - 7)$
17. $65 - 18b + b^2$
$(13 - b)(5 - b)$
18. $26 - 15n + n^2$
$(13 - n)(2 - n)$
19. $36 - 15z + z^2$
$(12 - z)(3 - z)$
20. $54 - 21a + a^2$
$(18 - a)(3 - a)$
21. $48 + 19y + y^2$
$(3 + y)(16 + y)$
22. $12 + 7d + d^2$
$(3 + d)(4 + d)$
23. $72 - 17f + f^2$
$(8 - f)(9 - f)$
24. $54 - 15r + r^2$
$(6 - r)(9 - r)$
25. $a^2 + 12ab + 27b^2$
$(a + 3b)(a + 9b)$
26. $n^2 + 12np + 35p^2$
$(n + 5p)(n + 7p)$
27. $x^2 - 8xy + 7y^2$
$(x - y)(x - 7y)$
28. $s^2 - 14st + 13t^2$
$(s - t)(s - 13t)$
29. $r^2 + 5rt + 6t^2$
$(r + 2t)(r + 3t)$
30. $z^2 + 8xz + 12x^2$
$(z + 6x)(z + 2x)$

B
31. $m^2 - 26mn + 25n^2$
$(m - n)(m - 25n)$
32. $r^2 + 33rs + 32s^2$
$(r + s)(r + 32s)$
33. $s^2 + 11st + 18t^2$
$(s + 2t)(s + 9t)$
34. $j^2 - 7jk + 12k^2$
$(j - 3k)(j - 4k)$
35. $y^2 - 10yz + 16z^2$
$(y - 2z)(y - 8z)$
36. $m^2 + 9mn + 20n^2$
$(m + 4n)(m + 5n)$
37. $x^2 - 27xy + 50y^2$
$(x - 2y)(x - 25y)$
38. $s^2 - 16st + 48t^2$
$(s - 4t)(s - 12t)$
39. $r^2 + 20rt + 64t^2$
$(r + 4t)(r + 16t)$
40. $a^2 + 32ab + 60b^2$
$(a + 2b)(a + 30b)$
41. $m^2 - 27mn + 72n^2$
$(m - 3n)(m - 24n)$
42. $n^2 - 29nq + 100q^2$
$(n - 4q)(n - 25q)$
43. $m^2 - 6mn - 16n^2$
$(m + 2n)(m - 8n)$
44. $s^2 - 9st + 18t^2$
$(s - 3t)(s - 6t)$
45. $c^4 + 8c^2 + 12$
$(c^2 + 2)(c^2 + 6)$
46. $u^4 - 16u^2 + 28$
$(u^2 - 2)(u^2 - 14)$
47. $y^4 - 11y^2 + 24$
$(y^2 - 3)(y^2 - 8)$
48. $n^4 - 18n^2 + 32$
$(n^2 - 2)(n^2 - 16)$

C
49. $(a + 1)^2 + 8(a + 1) + 7$
$(a + 2)(a + 8)$
50. $(x + 2)^2 + 4(x + 2) + 3$
$(x + 3)(x + 5)$
51. $(x - 1)^2 + 2(x - 1) + 1$
x^2
52. $(a + 2)^2 + 2(a + 2) + 1$
$(a + 3)^2$
53. $36 - 15(z + 1) + (z + 1)^2$
$(2 - z)(11 - z)$
54. $44 - 15(x + 2) + (x + 2)^2$
$(2 - x)(9 - x)$
55. $a^{2x} + 3a^x + 2$
$(a^x + 1)(a^x + 2)$
56. $b^{2y} + 5b^y + 6$
$(b^y + 2)(b^y + 3)$
57. $x^{4n} - 7x^{2n} + 12$
$(x^{2n} - 3)(x^{2n} - 4)$
58. $y^{4m} - 13y^{2m} + 12$
$(y^{2m} - 1)(y^{2m} - 12)$

280 Chapter 7 Factoring Polynomials

Applications

Geometry The area of each rectangle is given. Find the binomials to represent the length and the width.

59.

$l = x + 4; w = x + 1$

60.

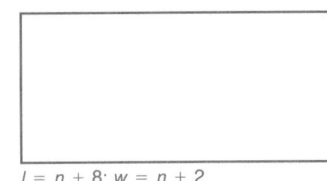

$l = y + 3; w = y + 2$

61. Area $= m^2 + 4m + 3$

$l = m + 3; w = m + 1$

62. Area $= n^2 + 10n + 16$

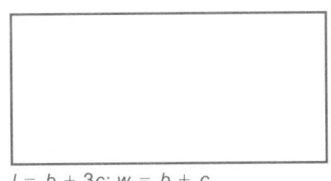

$l = n + 8; w = n + 2$

63. Area $= x^2 + 3xa + 2a^2$

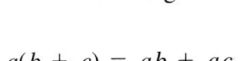

$l = x + 2a; w = x + a$

64. Area $= b^2 + 4bc + 3c^2$

$l = b + 3c; w = b + c$

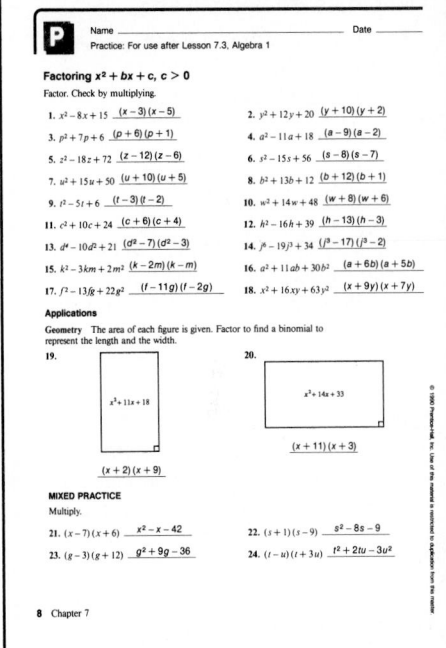
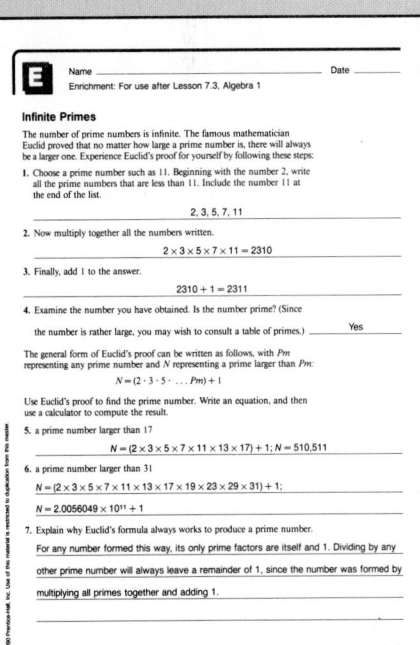

DID YOU KNOW?

The distributive property can be illustrated geometrically. Think of a rectangle divided into two smaller rectangles as illustrated. The area of the largest rectangle is $a(b + c)$. The area of the right rectangle is ab. The area of the left rectangle is ac. The sum of the areas of the two smaller rectangles is equal to the area of the large rectangle. Therefore,

$$a(b + c) = ab + ac$$

Can you find a way to illustrate geometrically the multiplication of two binomials: $(a + b)(c + d)$?

BACKGROUND

In the Capsule Review, the exercises involve multiplying two binomials using the FOIL method. Review Transparency 12, in the *Teacher's Resource Book,* for students having difficulty in factoring binomials. In each exercise, the coefficient of the quadratic term (x^2) is 1, and the numerical terms in each binomial pair have opposite signs. These exercises prepare the students for factoring by reversing the multiplication process.

Critical Thinking

Comparing-Contrasting Compare and contrast the lesson objectives of Lessons 7.3 and 7.4. Students should discover that both lessons factor trinomials of the form $x^2 + bx + c$. In these trinomials, the coefficient of the quadratic term (x^2) is 1; however, in Lesson 7.3, the constant term c is positive. In Lesson 7.4, the constant term c is negative.

7.4

Factoring $x^2 + bx + c$, $c < 0$

Objective: To factor a trinomial of the form $x^2 + bx + c$, $c < 0$

Susan made up this riddle for Rebecca: "I'm thinking of two numbers. The product of the numbers is -24, and the sum of the numbers is -2." Rebecca tried a few combinations in her head before coming up with the answer: "The numbers must be -6 and $+4$." Is any other combination possible?

Capsule Review

EXAMPLES $(x - 3)(x + 1) = x^2 + 1x - 3x - 3 = x^2 - 2x - 3$
  $(x + 6)(x - 2) = x^2 - 2x + 6x - 12 = x^2 + 4x - 12$

Multiply.

1. $(x + 4)(x - 2)$
  $x^2 + 2x - 8$
2. $(x - 5)(x + 7)$
  $x^2 + 2x - 35$
3. $(x - 4)(x + 5)$
  $x^2 + x - 20$
4. $(x - 7)(x + 6)$
  $x^2 - x - 42$
5. $(y - 9)(y + 11)$
  $y^2 + 2y - 99$
6. $(s + 3)(s - 12)$
  $s^2 - 9s - 36$

Many factoring problems are like the riddle described above. You look for two numbers whose sum and product you know. Consider how to factor trinomials in which the coefficient of the first term is 1 and the sign of the last term is negative.

EXAMPLE 1 **Factor:** $x^2 + 3x - 10$

Factors of -10	Possible Binomial Factors	Sum of Outer and Inner Products
$-1, 10$	$(x - 1)(x + 10)$	$10x + (-1x) = 9x$
$1, -10$	$(x + 1)(x - 10)$	$-10x + 1x = -9x$
$2, -5$	$(x + 2)(x - 5)$	$-5x + 2x = -3x$
$-2, 5$	$(x - 2)(x + 5)$	$5x + (-2x) = 3x$ ←*Correct middle term*

So, $x^2 + 3x - 10 = (x - 2)(x + 5)$. Check by multiplying.

Notice that the placement of signs in the binomial factors is important. In Example 1, the factors are incorrect if we change the signs:

$$(x + 2)(x - 5) = x^2 - 5x + 2x - 10 = x^2 - 3x - 10$$

└incorrect sign

282 Chapter 7 Factoring Polynomials

EXAMPLE 2 Factor: $a^2 - 5a - 24$

Factors of -24 (not all listed)	Possible Binomial Factors	Sum of Outer and Inner Products
8, -3	$(a + 8)(a - 3)$	$-3a + 8a = 5a$
-8, 3	$(a - 8)(a + 3)$	$3a + (-8a) = -5a \leftarrow$ *Correct middle term*

So, $a^2 - 5a - 24 = (a - 8)(a + 3)$. Check by multiplying.

EXAMPLE 3 Factor: $m^2 - 5mn - 14n^2$

Factors of $-14n^2$	Possible Binomial Factors	Sum of Outer and Inner Products
$-1n$, $14n$	$(m - 1n)(m + 14n)$	$14mn + (-1mn) = 13mn$
$1n$, $-14n$	$(m + 1n)(m - 14n)$	$-14mn + 1mn = -13mn$
$-2n$, $7n$	$(m - 2n)(m + 7n)$	$7mn + (-2mn) = 5mn$
$2n$, $-7n$	$(m + 2n)(m - 7n)$	$-7mn + 2mn = -5mn \leftarrow$ *Correct middle term*

So, $m^2 - 5mn - 14n^2 = (m + 2n)(m - 7n)$. Check by multiplying.

Examples 1, 2, and 3 lead to a *factoring clue:* When the first term of a trinomial has a coefficient of 1 and the last term is negative, one factor of the last term is positive and the other is negative.

CLASS EXERCISES

Find the missing signs.

1. $x^2 + 2x - 3 = (x \overset{+}{\underline{?}} 3)(x \overset{-}{\underline{?}} 1)$

2. $b^2 - 11b - 12 = (b \overset{+}{\underline{?}} 1)(b \overset{-}{\underline{?}} 12)$

3. $m^2 - 6m - 7 = (m \overset{+}{\underline{?}} 1)(m \overset{-}{\underline{?}} 7)$

4. $z^2 + z - 6 = (z \overset{-}{\underline{?}} 2)(z \overset{+}{\underline{?}} 3)$

Find the missing factors.

5. $x^2 + x - 6 = (x + \overset{3}{\underline{?}})(x - \overset{2}{\underline{?}})$

6. $b^2 - 15b - 16 = (b + \overset{1}{\underline{?}})(b - \overset{16}{\underline{?}})$

7. $u^2 - 8u - 9 = (u - \overset{9}{\underline{?}})(u + \overset{1}{\underline{?}})$

8. $z^2 + 3z - 18 = (z - \overset{3}{\underline{?}})(z + \overset{6}{\underline{?}})$

Factor. Check by multiplying.

9. $x^2 + 4x - 5$
$(x - 1)(x + 5)$

10. $m^2 - 3m - 10$
$(m + 2)(m - 5)$

11. $y^2 - 6y - 16$
$(y + 2)(y - 8)$

For Discussion

12. The coefficient of the third term of the trinomials in this lesson is negative. What clue does this give about the signs of the second terms in the binomial factors? See below.

7.4 Factoring $x^2 + bx + c$, $c < 0$ **283**

Additional Answers

12. If the middle term is positive, then the larger second term in the binomial factors will be positive. If the middle term is negative, then the larger second term in the binomial factors will be negative.

283

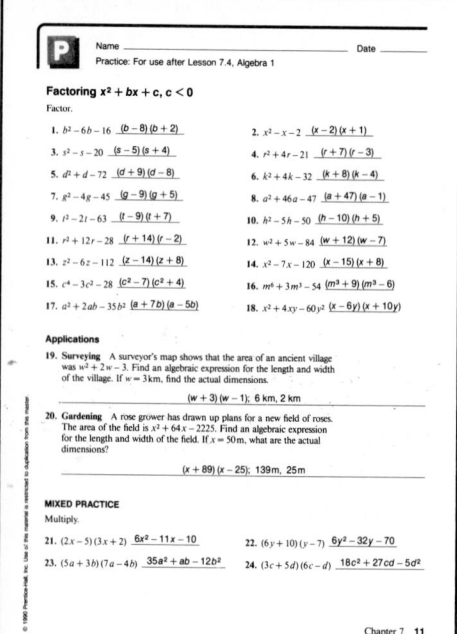

Name _____ **Date** _____

Practice: For use after Lesson 7.4, Algebra 1

Factoring $x^2 + bx + c$, $c < 0$

Factor.

1. $b^2 - 6b - 16$ $(b-8)(b+2)$
2. $x^2 - x - 2$ $(x-2)(x+1)$
3. $s^2 - s - 20$ $(s-5)(s+4)$
4. $r^2 + 4r - 21$ $(r+7)(r-3)$
5. $d^2 + d - 72$ $(d+9)(d-8)$
6. $k^2 + 4k - 32$ $(k+8)(k-4)$
7. $g^2 - 4g - 45$ $(g-9)(g+5)$
8. $a^2 + 46a - 47$ $(a+47)(a-1)$
9. $t^2 - 2t - 63$ $(t-9)(t+7)$
10. $h^2 - 5h - 50$ $(h-10)(h+5)$
11. $r^2 + 12r - 28$ $(r+14)(r-2)$
12. $w^2 + 5w - 84$ $(w+12)(w-7)$
13. $z^2 - 6z - 112$ $(z-14)(z+8)$
14. $x^2 - 7x - 120$ $(x-15)(x+8)$
15. $c^4 - 3c^2 - 28$ $(c^2-7)(c^2+4)$
16. $m^6 + 3m^3 - 54$ $(m^3+9)(m^3-6)$
17. $a^2 + 2ab - 35b^2$ $(a+7b)(a-5b)$
18. $x^2 + 4xy - 60y^2$ $(x-6y)(x+10y)$

Applications

19. **Surveying** A surveyor's map shows that the area of an ancient village was $w^2 + 2w - 3$. Find an algebraic expression for the length and width of the village. If $w = 3$ km, find the actual dimensions.
$(w+3)(w-1)$; 6 km, 2 km

20. **Gardening** A rose grower has drawn up plans for a new field of roses. The area of the field is $x^2 + 64x - 2225$. Find an algebraic expression for the length and width of the field. If $x = 50$ m, what are the actual dimensions?
$(x+89)(x-25)$; 139 m, 25 m

MIXED PRACTICE

Multiply.

21. $(2x-5)(3x+2)$ $6x^2 - 11x - 10$
22. $(6y+10)(y-7)$ $6y^2 - 32y - 70$
23. $(5a+3b)(7a-4b)$ $35a^2 + ab - 12b^2$
24. $(3c+5d)(6c-d)$ $18c^2 + 27cd - 5d^2$

Chapter 7 **11**

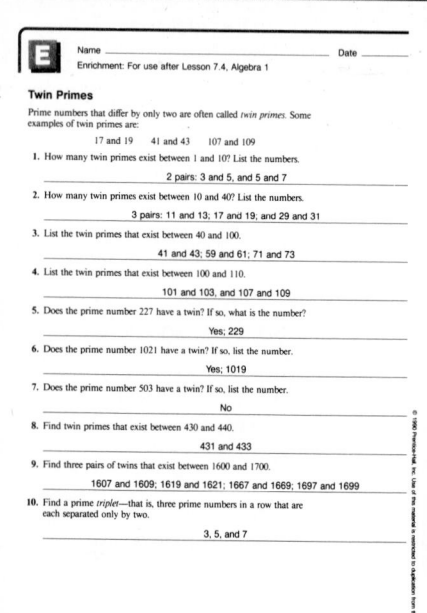

Name _____ **Date** _____

Enrichment: For use after Lesson 7.4, Algebra 1

Twin Primes

Prime numbers that differ by only two are often called *twin primes*. Some examples of twin primes are:

17 and 19   41 and 43   107 and 109

1. How many twin primes exist between 1 and 10? List the numbers.
2 pairs: 3 and 5, and 5 and 7

2. How many twin primes exist between 10 and 40? List the numbers.
3 pairs: 11 and 13; 17 and 19; and 29 and 31

3. List the twin primes that exist between 40 and 100.
41 and 43; 59 and 61; 71 and 73

4. List the twin primes that exist between 100 and 110.
101 and 103, and 107 and 109

5. Does the prime number 227 have a twin? If so, what is the number?
Yes; 229

6. Does the prime number 1021 have a twin? If so, list the number.
Yes; 1019

7. Does the prime number 503 have a twin? If so, list the number.
No

8. Find twin primes that exist between 430 and 440.
431 and 433

9. Find three pairs of twins that exist between 1600 and 1700.
1607 and 1609; 1619 and 1621; 1667 and 1669; 1697 and 1699

10. Find a prime *triplet*—that is, three prime numbers in a row that are each separated only by two.
3, 5, and 7

12 Chapter 7

PRACTICE EXERCISES

Factor. Check by multiplying.

A

1. $x^2 + 4x - 5$
$(x+5)(x-1)$
2. $a^2 + 6a - 7$
$(a+7)(a-1)$
3. $m^2 - 9m - 10$
$(m-10)(m+1)$
4. $z^2 - 23z - 24$
$(z-24)(z+1)$
5. $x^2 + 2x - 8$
$(x+4)(x-2)$
6. $a^2 + 7a - 18$
$(a+9)(a-2)$
7. $m^2 - 4m - 12$
$(m-6)(m+2)$
8. $z^2 - 8z - 20$
$(z-10)(z+2)$
9. $x^2 + 2x - 3$
$(x+3)(x-1)$
10. $y^2 + 12y - 13$
$(y+13)(y-1)$
11. $a^2 + 5a - 6$
$(a+6)(a-1)$
12. $z^2 + 8z - 9$
$(z+9)(z-1)$
13. $m^2 - m - 12$
$(m-4)(m+3)$
14. $b^2 - b - 56$
$(b-8)(b+7)$
15. $k^2 - 13k - 30$
$(k-15)(k+2)$
16. $s^2 - 2s - 24$
$(s-6)(s+4)$
17. $x^2 - xy - 6y^2$
$(x-3y)(x+2y)$
18. $m^2 - 2mn - 15n^2$
$(m-5n)(m+3n)$
19. $r^2 - 4rs - 21s^2$
$(r+3s)(r-7s)$
20. $n^2 - 11np - 42p^2$
$(n-14p)(n+3p)$
21. $x^2 - 6xy - 40y^2$
$(x-10y)(x+4y)$

B

22. $a^2 - 6ab - 27b^2$
$(a-9b)(a+3b)$
23. $k^2 - 5kj - 36j^2$
$(k-9j)(k+4j)$
24. $w^2 - 8wz - 48z^2$
$(w-12z)(w+4z)$
25. $x^2 - xy - 2y^2$
$(x-2y)(x+y)$
26. $s^2 - 4st - 5t^2$
$(s-5t)(s+t)$
27. $r^2 + 5rt - 14t^2$
$(r+7t)(r-2t)$
28. $a^2 - 6ab - 27b^2$
$(a-9b)(a+3b)$
29. $y^2 - 14yz - 32z^2$
$(y-16z)(y+2z)$
30. $n^2 - 2np - 48p^2$
$(n-8p)(n+6p)$
31. $x^2 - 8xy - 20y^2$
$(x-10y)(x+2y)$
32. $s^2 - st - 42t^2$
$(s-7t)(s+6t)$
33. $r^2 + 3rt - 54t^2$
$(r+9t)(r-6t)$
34. $a^2 - 9ab - 52b^2$
$(a-13b)(a+4b)$
35. $y^2 - 15yz - 100z^2$
$(y-20z)(y+5z)$
36. $n^2 - 11np - 80p^2$
$(n-16p)(n+5p)$

C

37. $y^4 + 23y^2 - 50$
$(y^2+25)(y^2-2)$
38. $z^6 - 10z^3 - 75$
$(z^3-15)(z^3+5)$
39. $(a-1)^2 - 4(a-1) - 32$
$(a-9)(a+3)$
40. $(b+2)^2 + 15(b+2) - 54$
$(b+20)(b-1)$

Applications

41. **Gardening** A surveyor's map shows a plan for a rectangular rose garden whose area is $a^2 + 25ab - 350b^2$. Find an algebraic expression for the length and the width. If $a = 200$ ft and $b = 10$ ft, find the actual dimensions of the garden. $(a+35b)(a-10b)$; 550 ft × 100 ft

ALGEBRA IN RECREATION

A large target for skydivers is marked out on a field. The target is made up of concentric circles with radii of lengths 2 m, 4 m, 6 m, 8 m, and 10 m. The skydivers score points by landing within the target—the closer to the center, the greater the number of points.

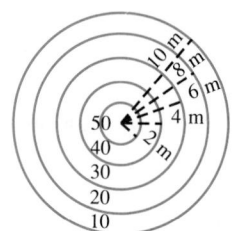

Find the area of the bull's-eye or ring that gives each number of points.

1. 50 4π
2. 40 12π
3. 30 20π
4. 20 28π
5. 10 36π

Factoring $ax^2 + bx + c$

Objective: To factor a trinomial of the form $ax^2 + bx + c$

When the coefficient of the first term of a trinomial is *not* 1, the number of possible binomial factors increases. A partial list of possible factors of $2y^2 - 11y + 12$ is given below.

$(2y - 4)(y - 3)$ $(y - 6)(2y - 2)$ $(2y - 3)(y - 4)$ $(2y - 12)(y - 1)$

What are some of the other possible binomial factors? Which are correct? You can check your answer by multiplication.

Capsule Review

EXAMPLES
$$(2x + 1)(x - 2)$$
$$= 2x^2 - 4x + x - 2$$
$$= 2x^2 - 3x - 2$$

$$(3a - 4)(2a - 3)$$
$$= 6a^2 - 9a - 8a + 12$$
$$= 6a^2 - 17a + 12$$

Multiply.

1. $(2m + 1)(m + 1)$
   $2m^2 + 3m + 1$
2. $(t + 3)(3t + 1)$
   $3t^2 + 10t + 3$
3. $(3y + 2)(y - 2)$
   $3y^2 - 4y - 4$
4. $(5y - 2)(y + 4)$
   $5y^2 + 18y - 8$
5. $(3h - 1)(h - 7)$
   $3h^2 - 22h + 7$
6. $(2x + 3)(3x + 1)$
   $6x^2 + 11x + 3$
7. $(3a + b)(a - b)$
   $3a^2 - 2ab - b^2$
8. $(2s - t)(3s + 2t)$
   $6s^2 + st - 2t^2$
9. $(4u - 3v)(3u - 4v)$
   $12u^2 - 25uv + 12v^2$

The technique for factoring trinomials like $2x^2 - 3x - 5$ is much the same as for trinomials in which the coefficient of x^2 is 1. However, there is no straightforward way in which to find the factors other than by simply listing all the possibilities. You must test various factors of *both* the first term and the last term of the trinomial, then look for combinations that will make the middle term work out.

EXAMPLE 1   Factor: $2x^2 - 3x - 5$

Factors of $2x^2$	Factors of -5	Possible Binomial Factors	Sum of Outer and Inner Products
$2x, x$	$-1, 5$	$(2x - 1)(x + 5)$	$10x + (-1x) = 9x$
		$(x - 1)(2x + 5)$	$5x + (-2x) = 3x$
	$1, -5$	$(2x + 1)(x - 5)$	$-10x + 1x = -9x$
		$(x + 1)(2x - 5)$	$-5x + 2x = -3x$ ←Correct middle term

So, $2x^2 - 3x - 5 = (x + 1)(2x - 5)$. Check by multiplying.

Vocabulary
Prime polynomial

Materials/Manipulatives
Teacher's Resource Book, Teaching Aid 8, Transparency 12

BACKGROUND

In the Capsule Review, students multiply two binomials by using the FOIL method. You may wish to review Transparency 12, in the *Teacher's Resource Book*, on the FOIL method. In each exercise, the coefficient of the quadratic term is not 1. In this lesson, students learn to reverse this multiplication process by factoring trinomials in which the coefficient of the first term is not 1.

EXAMPLE 2 **Factor:** $6x^2 + 19x + 3$

There are two possible ways to factor $6x^2$.

Factors of $6x^2$	Factors of 3	Possible Binomial Factors	Sum of Outer and Inner Products
$3x, 2x$	3, 1	$(3x + 3)(2x + 1)$	$3x + 6x = 9x$
		$(3x + 1)(2x + 3)$	$9x + 2x = 11x$
$6x, x$	3, 1	$(6x + 3)(x + 1)$	$6x + 3x = 9x$
		$(6x + 1)(x + 3)$	$18x + 1x = 19x$ ←*Correct middle term*

So, $6x^2 + 19x + 3 = (6x + 1)(x + 3)$.

Again, you should check all factorizations by multiplying the resulting factors. The check for this example is left for you.

To factor a given trinomial, there may be many binomial factors to check. Practice and experience will help you make better estimates. It is not efficient to list and check every possible combination.

EXAMPLE 3 **Factor:** $6x^2 - x - 12$

There are two possible ways to factor $6x^2$.

Factors of $6x^2$	Factors of -12	Possible Binomial Factors	Sum of Outer and Inner Products
$3x, 2x$	12, -1	$(3x + 12)(2x - 1)$	$-3x + 24x = 21x$
	$-12, 1$	$(3x - 12)(2x + 1)$	$3x + (-24x) = -21x$
	4, -3	$(3x + 4)(2x - 3)$	$-9x + 8x = -1x$ ←*Correct middle term*

Note that there are many other possible pairs of binomial factors, but you do not need to list all of them. Once you find the correct pair of factors, you can stop.

So, $6x^2 - x - 12 = (3x + 4)(2x - 3)$. Check by multiplying.

Not all trinomials have binomial factors in which the coefficients are integers. For example:

$$3x^2 - 2x + 6 \neq (3x - 2)(x - 3)$$
$$\neq (3x - 3)(x - 2)$$
$$\neq (3x - 1)(x - 6)$$
$$\neq (3x - 6)(x - 1)$$

When a polynomial has no polynomial factors with integral coefficients except itself and 1, it is a **prime polynomial** *with respect to the integers.* $3x^2 - 2x + 6$ is a prime polynomial.

286   Chapter 7 Factoring Polynomials

EXAMPLE 4 Factor: $4x^2 + 59x - 15$

There are two possible ways to factor $4x^2$.

In the product of the binomial factors $(2x + \underline{\ ?\ })(2x - \underline{\ ?\ })$, the coefficient of the middle term is an even number since 2 is a factor of both the inner and outer products. In this case, you can immediately eliminate all such combinations, since the coefficient of the middle term, $59x$, is an odd number.

Factors of $4x^2$	Factors of -15	Possible Binomial Factors	Sum of Outer and Inner Products
$4x, x$	$3, -5$	$(4x + 3)(x - 5)$	$-20x + 3x = -17x$
	$-3, 5$	$(4x - 3)(x + 5)$	$20x + (-3x) = 17x$
	$1, -15$	$(4x + 1)(x - 15)$	$-60x + 1x = -59x$
	$-1, 15$	$(4x - 1)(x + 15)$	$60x + (-1x) = 59x$ ←*Correct middle term*

So, $4x^2 + 59x - 15 = (4x - 1)(x + 15)$. Check by multiplying.

CLASS EXERCISES

Find the missing signs or factors.

1. $2x^2 + x - 3 = (2x \overset{+}{\underline{\ ?\ }} 3)(x \overset{-}{\underline{\ ?\ }} 1)$ 2. $2x^2 + 3x - 5 = (2x + \overset{5}{\underline{\ ?\ }})(x - \overset{1}{\underline{\ ?\ }})$

3. $3b^2 - 20b - 7 = (3b \overset{+}{\underline{\ ?\ }} 1)(b \overset{-}{\underline{\ ?\ }} 7)$ 4. $5b^2 - 34b - 7 = (5b + \overset{1}{\underline{\ ?\ }})(b - \overset{7}{\underline{\ ?\ }})$

Factor. Check by multiplying.

5. $3x^2 + 20x - 7$ $(3x - 1)(x + 7)$ 6. $2m^2 - 3m - 14$ $(2m - 7)(m + 2)$

7. $6y^2 + 25y + 21$ $(6y + 7)(y + 3)$ 8. $4x^2 - 4x - 3$ $(2x - 3)(2x + 1)$

PRACTICE EXERCISES

Factor. Check by multiplying.

A
1. $3x^2 - 22x - 16$ $(3x + 2)(x - 8)$
2. $2m^2 - 11m - 21$ $(2m + 3)(m - 7)$
3. $5z^2 - 13z - 6$ $(5z + 2)(z - 3)$
4. $7r^2 - 23r - 20$ $(7r + 5)(r - 4)$
5. $2m^2 + 7m + 5$ $(2m + 5)(m + 1)$
6. $3s^2 + 17s + 20$ $(3s + 5)(s + 4)$
7. $15r^2 + 44r + 21$ $(5r + 3)(3r + 7)$
8. $14k^2 + 29k + 12$ $(7k + 4)(2k + 3)$
9. $81l^2 + 72l + 15$ $(9l + 3)(9l + 5)$
10. $9q^2 + 27q + 20$ $(3q + 5)(3q + 4)$
11. $6z^2 - z - 5$ $(z - 1)(6z + 5)$
12. $12c^2 - 7c - 10$ $(4c - 5)(3c + 2)$
13. $4m^2 - 16m - 9$ $(2m - 9)(2m + 1)$
14. $16x^2 - 8x - 15$ $(4x + 3)(4x - 5)$
15. $2x^2 + 9x - 11$ $(2x + 11)(x - 1)$
16. $5a^2 + 2a - 7$ $(5a + 7)(a - 1)$
17. $14d^2 + 11d - 15$ $(2d + 3)(7d - 5)$
18. $10k^2 + 3k - 4$ $(2k - 1)(5k + 4)$
19. $24x^2 - 47x + 20$ $(8x - 5)(3x - 4)$
20. $34d^2 - 41d + 15$ $(17d - 5)(2d - 3)$
21. $20z^2 + 49z + 30$ $(5z + 6)(4z + 5)$
22. $22n^2 + 47n + 6$ $(22n + 3)(n + 2)$
23. $26c^2 + 29c - 15$ $(13c - 5)(2c + 3)$
24. $18n^2 + 11n - 24$ $(9n - 8)(2n + 3)$
B
25. $3x^2 - xy - 2y^2$ $(3x + 2y)(x - y)$
26. $7s^2 - 20st - 3t^2$ $(7s + t)(s - 3t)$
27. $2r^2 + 15rt + 7t^2$ $(2r + t)(r + 7t)$
28. $4y^2 + 8yz + 3z^2$ $(2y + 3z)(2y + z)$
29. $3a^2 - 16ab + 5b^2$ $(3a - b)(a - 5b)$
30. $7s^2 - 19st + 10t^2$ $(7s - 5t)(s - 2t)$

• **For Example 4**
Factor.
7. $4x^2 - 9x + 2$ $(x - 2)(4x - 1)$

Common Error

• Students often make errors by incorrectly placing the signs in the binomial factors. For example, when factoring $7z^2 - 17z - 12$, students may think that because the middle and the last term are negative, both factors are negative. Students who make this kind of error should be encouraged to check their answer by multiplying.
• See *Teacher's Resource Book* for additional remediation.

LESSON FOLLOW-UP

Assignment Guide

• See p. 268B for assignments.
• In Exercises 25–42, there are two variables in each trinomial. Students should be encouraged to place the variables in the factors first.

Test Yourself

See *Teacher's Resource Book*, Tests, pp. 69–70.

Lesson Quiz

Factor and check by multiplying. If the polynomial cannot be factored, write prime.
1. $2y^2 + 15y + 7$ $(2y + 1)(y + 7)$
2. $3u^2 + 8u + 5$ $(3u + 5)(u + 1)$
3. $5t^2 + 7t - 6$ $(5t - 3)(t + 2)$
4. $6s^2 - 25s + 11$ $(2s - 1)(3s - 11)$
5. $15r^2 - 8r - 16$ $(5r + 4)(3r - 4)$
6. $42q^2 + 31q + 4$ $(6q + 1)(7q + 4)$
7. $2p^2 + 11pn + 5n^2$ $(2p + n)(p + 5n)$
8. $3m^2 - 4mk - 7k^2$ $(3m - 7k)(m + k)$
9. $3r^2 + 15rt - 3t^2$ $3(r^2 + 5rt - t^2)$

Enrichment

Factor: $-4v^2 + 30v - 14$
$-2(2v - 1)(v - 7)$

287

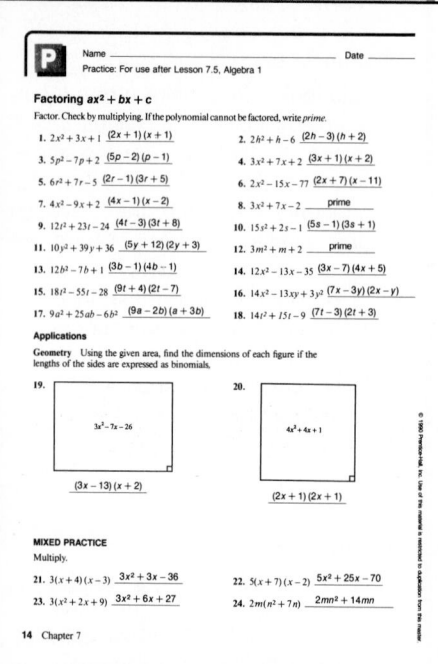

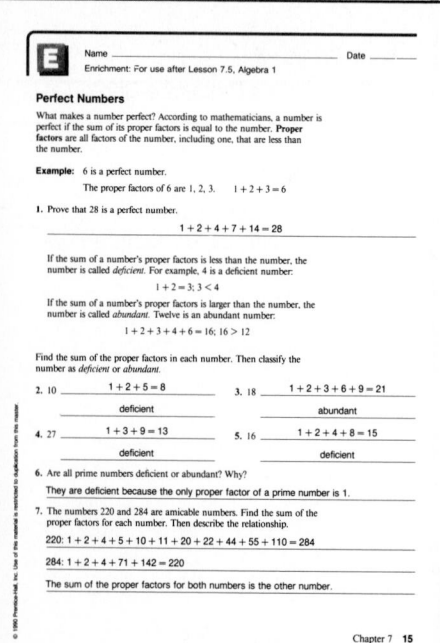

31. $6n^2 - np - 2p^2$
$(3n - 2p)(2n + p)$

32. $8n^2 - 9np - 14p^2$
$(8n + 7p)(n - 2p)$

33. $5x^2 + 18xy - 8y^2$
$(5x - 2y)(x + 4y)$

34. $5r^2 + 29rt - 5t^2$
prime

35. $3a^2 + 15ab - 7b^2$
prime

36. $10c^2 + 99cd - 10d^2$
$(10c - d)(c + 10d)$

37. $12x^2 + 35xy + 18y^2$
$(4x + 9y)(3x + 2y)$

38. $24g^2 + 50gh + 21h^2$
$(12g + 7h)(2g + 3h)$

39. $14k^2 - 83km + 33m^2$
$(7k - 3m)(2k - 11m)$

40. $20r^2 - 53rt - 21t^2$
$(20r + 7t)(r - 3t)$

41. $27a^2 - 12ab - 32b^2$
$(9a + 8b)(3a - 4b)$

42. $36m^2 + 12mn - 35n^2$
$(6m + 7n)(6m - 5n)$

C

43. $4(x + 2)^2 + 11(x + 2) + 6$
$(4x + 11)(x + 4)$

44. $6(y + 5)^2 + 11(y + 5) - 10$
$(3y + 13)(2y + 15)$

45. $12(a - 3)^2 - 19(a - 3) - 21$
$(4a - 9)(3a - 16)$

46. $15(b - 2)^2 - 37(b - 2) + 18$
$(5b - 19)(3b - 8)$

47. $6x^{2k} + 25x^k + 14$
$(3x^k + 2)(2x^k + 7)$

48. $15c^{4r} + 14c^{2r} - 16$
$(5c^{2r} + 8)(3c^{2r} - 2)$

49. $10x^{4k+6} - 7x^{2k+3} - 12$
$(5x^{2k+3} + 4)(2x^{2k+3} - 3)$

50. $20d^{2r+16} - 23d^{r+8} + 6$
$(5d^{r+8} - 2)(4d^{r+8} - 3)$

Applications

Geometry Using the given area, find the dimensions of each figure if the length of each side is expressed as a binomial.

51.

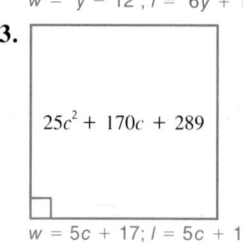

$6y^2 - 71y - 12$

$w = y - 12$; $l = 6y + 1$

52.

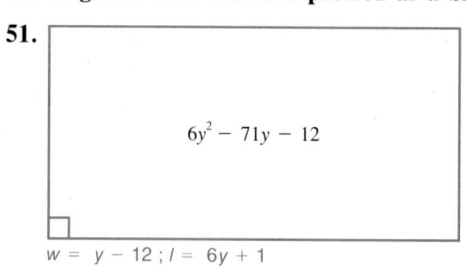

$16b^2 - 289b + 18$

$w = b - 18$; $l = 16b - 1$

53.

$25c^2 + 170c + 289$

$w = 5c + 17$; $l = 5c + 17$

54.

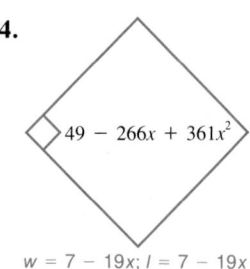

$49 - 266x + 361x^2$

$w = 7 - 19x$; $l = 7 - 19x$

TEST YOURSELF

Find the prime factorization of the number.   7.1

1. 110 $2 \cdot 5 \cdot 11$ **2.** 105 $3 \cdot 5 \cdot 7$ **3.** 180 $2^2 \cdot 3^2 \cdot 5$ **4.** 250 $2 \cdot 5^3$ **5.** 147 $3 \cdot 7^2$

Factor. Check by multiplying.   7.2–7.5

6. $9a + 18$ $9(a + 2)$ **7.** $42x - 14x^3$ $14x(3 - x^2)$ **8.** $51p^2q + 3pq$
$3pq(17p + 1)$

9. $a^2 + 12a + 35$
$(a + 7)(a + 5)$ **10.** $t^2 + 20t + 36$
$(t + 18)(t + 2)$ **11.** $m^2 - 16m + 60$
$(m - 10)(m - 6)$

12. $x^2 + 5x - 50$
$(x - 5)(x + 10)$ **13.** $y^2 - 11y - 60$
$(y - 15)(y + 4)$ **14.** $m^2 - mn - 6n^2$
$(m - 3n)(m + 2n)$

15. $2x^2 + 25x + 12$
$(2x + 1)(x + 12)$ **16.** $8y^2 - 2y - 3$
$(2y + 1)(4y - 3)$ **17.** $3x^2 + 4x - 4$
$(3x - 2)(x + 2)$

288   Chapter 7 Factoring Polynomials

7.6 Factoring: Special Cases

Objectives: To factor perfect square trinomials
To factor a difference of two squares

When you square a binomial, the product is called a **perfect square trinomial.**

$(x + 4)^2 = (x + 4)(x + 4) = x^2 + 8x + 16$

| square of the first term | twice the product of the two terms | square of the last term |

$x^2 + 8x + 16$ is a perfect square trinomial.

Capsule Review

Squaring a binomial results in a trinomial.

EXAMPLE $(x + 3)^2 = (x + 3)(x + 3) = x^2 + (2)(3)x + (3)^2$
$= x^2 + 6x + 9$

Multiply.

1. $(x + 2)(x + 2)$ **2.** $(m - 5)(m - 5)$ **3.** $(2 - 3x)^2$
   $x^2 + 4x + 4$ $m^2 - 10m + 25$ $4 - 12x + 9x^2$

EXAMPLE 1   **Is the polynomial a perfect square trinomial?**
         a. $x^2 - 8x + 16$ **b.** $36m^4 + 36m^2n + 9n^2$

a. Yes; x^2 and 16 are the squares of x and 4, respectively, and $8x$ is twice the product of x and 4:

$$x^2 - 8x + 16 = (x)^2 - 2(4 \cdot x) + (4)^2$$

b. Yes; $36m^4$ and $9n^2$ are the squares of $6m^2$ and $3n$, and $36m^2n$ is twice the product of $6m^2$ and $3n$:

$$36m^4 + 36m^2n + 9n^2 = (6m^2)^2 + 2(6m^2 \cdot 3n) + (3n)^2$$

After you identify a polynomial as a perfect square trinomial, its factors are relatively easy to find, as shown in Example 2.

EXAMPLE 2   **Factor:** $64m^{12} + 16m^6 + 1$

$64m^{12} + 16m^6 + 1$
$= (8m^6)^2 + 2(8m^6 \cdot 1) + 1^2$ *The polynomial is a perfect square trinomial.*
$= (8m^6 + 1)(8m^6 + 1)$, or $(8m^6 + 1)^2$

CHALKBOARD EXAMPLES

- **For Example 1**
  1. Is the polynomial $m^2 + 6m + 9$ a perfect square trinomial? yes

- **For Example 2**
  2. Factor: $16x^{20} + 8x^{10} + 1$
  $(4x^{10} + 1)(4x^{10} + 1)$ or $(4x^{10} + 1)^2$

- **For Example 3**
  3. Is the binomial $36x^3 - 4$ a difference of two squares? no

- **For Example 4**
  4. Factor: $25a^6b^{10} - 144$
  $(5a^3b^5 + 12)(5a^3b^5 - 12)$

Common Error

- Students often make errors in finding the difference of two squares. For example, when factoring $25^5 - 9$, students may think that, because the two numbers are perfect squares, the binomial is a difference of two squares. In fact, it is not, because the exponent of 25 is 5, and 5 is not a square. Students should check their answer by multiplying.
- See *Teacher's Resource Book* for additional remediation.

LESSON FOLLOW-UP

Assignment Guide
See p. 268B for assignments.

Lesson Quiz
Factor.
1. $k^2 - 25$ $(k + 5)(k - 5)$
2. $196m^6 - 25r^8$
  $(14m^3 + 5r^4)(14m^3 - 5r^4)$
3. $z^2 + 22z + 121$
  $(z + 11)(z + 11)$ or $(z + 11)^2$
4. $9u^2 - 6u + 1$
  $(3u - 1)(3u - 1)$ or $(3u - 1)^2$
5. $9a^2b^2 + 24ab + 16$
  $(3ab + 4)(3ab + 4)$ or $(3ab + 4)^2$

When you multiply binomials that are the sum and difference of the same two numbers, the product is a **difference of two squares.**

$$(x + 7)(x - 7) = (x)^2 - (7)^2 = x^2 - 49$$

square of the first term   square of the last term

$x^2 - 49$ is a difference of two squares.

EXAMPLE 3 **Is the binomial a difference of two squares?**

  a. $25x^2 - 1$ **b.** $x^4y - 9$ **c.** $144m^6n^2 - 625$

a. Yes; $25x^2 - 1 = (5x)^2 - (1)^2$. **b.** No; the exponent of y is 1, and y^1 is not a square.

c. Yes; $144m^6n^2 - 625 = (12m^3n)^2 - (25)^2$.

After you identify a polynomial as a difference of two squares, its factors are relatively easy to find.

EXAMPLE 4 **Factor:** $m^{10}n^8 - 49$

$m^{10}n^8 - 49 = (m^5n^4)^2 - (7)^2$ *The polynomial is a difference of two squares.*
$\qquad\qquad\quad = (m^5n^4 - 7)(m^5n^4 + 7)$

CLASS EXERCISES

Factor the polynomial.

1. $4x^2 - 9y^2$
   $(2x + 3y)(2x - 3y)$
2. $100a^2 - 16b^4z^8$
   $(10a + 4b^2z^4)(10a - 4b^2z^4)$
3. $16r^2s^2 - 81t^{10}$
   $(4rs + 9t^5)(4rs - 9t^5)$
4. $x^2 + 2xy + y^2$
   $(x + y)^2$
5. $25m^2 + 20m + 4$
   $(5m + 2)^2$
6. $81m^4 + 72m^2n + 16n^2$
   $(9m^2 + 4n)^2$

PRACTICE EXERCISES

Is the polynomial a perfect square trinomial?

A
1. $x^2 + 2x + 1$ yes
2. $y^2 + 8y + 16$ yes
3. $3a^2 + 18ab + 6b^2$ no
4. $25z^2 + 5xz + x^2$ no
5. $36m^2 - 36m + 9$ yes
6. $16b^2 - 24b + 9$ yes

Factor the polynomial.

7. $x^2 - 12x + 36$
   $(x - 6)(x - 6)$
8. $x^2 + 14x + 49$
   $(x + 7)(x + 7)$
9. $4d^2 + 36d + 81$
   $(2d + 9)(2d + 9)$
10. $9h^2 + 24h + 16$
   $(3h + 4)^2$
11. $k^2 + 20k + 100$
   $(k + 10)^2$
12. $s^2 + 26s + 169$
   $(s + 13)^2$
13. $81y^2 - 36y + 4$
   $(9y - 2)^2$
14. $16n^2 - 56n + 49$
   $(4n - 7)^2$
15. $25t^2 + 10t + 1$
   $(5t + 1)^2$
16. $49r^2 + 14r + 1$
   $(7r + 1)^2$
17. $100k^{10} + 20k^5 + 1$
   $(10k^5 + 1)^2$
18. $36y^{10} + 12y^5 + 1$
   $(6y^5 + 1)^2$

19. $25y^8 + 10y^4 + 1$ $(5y^4 + 1)^2$ **20.** $9x^{12} + 6x^6 + 1$ $(3x^6 + 1)^2$ **21.** $a^{10}b^4 - 16$ $(a^5b^2 - 4)(a^5b^2 + 4)$

22. $m^{16}n^8 - 25$ $(m^8n^4 - 5)(m^8n^4 + 5)$ **23.** $x^{18}y^{10} - 36$ $(x^9y^5 - 6)(x^9y^5 + 6)$ **24.** $c^{12}d^6 - 64$ $(c^6d^3 - 8)(c^6d^3 + 8)$

Is the binomial a difference of two squares?

25. $x^2 - 9$ yes   **26.** $a^2 - 121$ yes   **27.** $4a^2 - 100$ yes   **28.** $16z^2 - 49$ yes

B   **29.** $49k^3 - 25$ no   **30.** $81z^2 - 16z$ no   **31.** $225a^2 - 100$ yes   **32.** $144m^2 - 81$ yes

Factor the polynomial.

33. $144x^4y^2 - 625$ $(12x^2y + 25)(12x^2y - 25)$ **34.** $121m^6n^2 - 81$ $(11m^3n + 9)(11m^3n - 9)$ **35.** $a^6b^2c^4 - d^2$ $(a^3bc^2 + d)(a^3bc^2 - d)$

36. $e^6f^4g^6 - h^2$ $(e^3f^2g^3 + h)(e^3f^2g^3 - h)$ **37.** $4p^4q^4r^8 - 81$ $(2p^2q^2r^4 + 9)(2p^2q^2r^4 - 9)$ **38.** $9x^8y^4z^2 - 64$ $(3x^4y^2z + 8)(3x^4y^2z - 8)$

39. $49r^2s^2 + 14rs + 1$ $(7rs + 1)^2$ **40.** $25a^2b^2 + 20ab + 4$ $(5ab + 2)^2$

41. $36x^6y^4 - 36x^3y^2 + 9$ $9(2x^3y^2 - 1)^2$ **42.** $64c^6d^8 - 32c^3d^4 + 4$ $4(4c^3d^4 - 1)^2$

43. $e^{64}f^{100} - g^{144}h^{36}$ $(e^{32}f^{50} + g^{72}h^{18})(e^{32}f^{50} - g^{72}h^{18})$ **44.** $25x^{50} - 49y^{200}$ $(5x^{25} + 7y^{100})(5x^{25} - 7y^{100})$

45. $(a + 1)^2 - a^2$ $2a + 1$ **46.** $(x - 2)^2 - x^2$ $-4(x - 1)$

C   **47.** $(x - 1)^2 + 2(x - 1) + 1$ x^2 **48.** $(a + 2)^2 + 2(a + 2) + 1$ $(a + 3)^2$

49. $(a^2 + 2ab + b^2) - c^2$ $(a + b - c)(a + b + c)$ **50.** $m^2 - (n^2 + 2np + p^2)$ $(m + n + p)(m - n - p)$

51. $(x + 1)^2 + 2(x + 1)(2x + 3) + (2x + 3)^2$ $(3x + 4)^2$

Applications

Geometry   Find the area of the shaded region. Factor, if possible.

52.

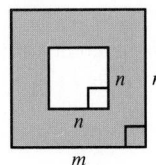

$m^2 - n^2 = (m + n)(m - n)$

53.

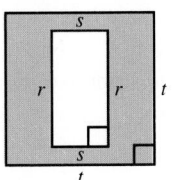

$t^2 - rs$

54. Calculator   Factor $x^2 - 187x - 4368$. $(x - 208)(x + 21)$

LOGICAL REASONING

Find the fallacy in the following argument.

Suppose that for all real numbers,	$x = y$.
Since $x^2 = y^2$, then	$x^2 - y^2 = 0$.
Multiply each side of the equation by 2.	$2(x^2 - y^2) = 0$.
Factor the difference of two squares.	$2(x + y)(x - y) = 0$.
Divide each side of the equation by $(x - y)$.	$2(x + y) = 0$.
Divide each side of the equation by $(x + y)$, and	$2 = 0$.

Since $x = y$, $(x - y) = 0$. You cannot divide each side of the equation by 0.

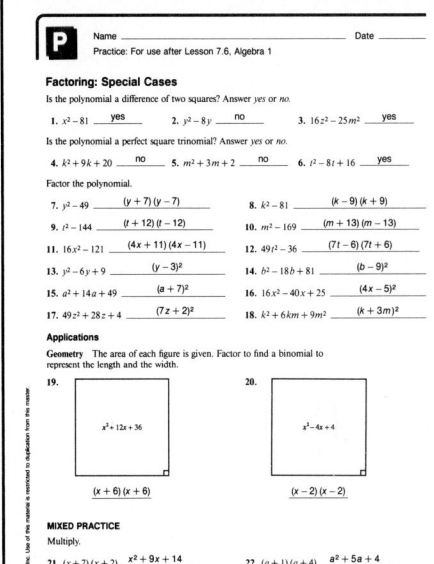

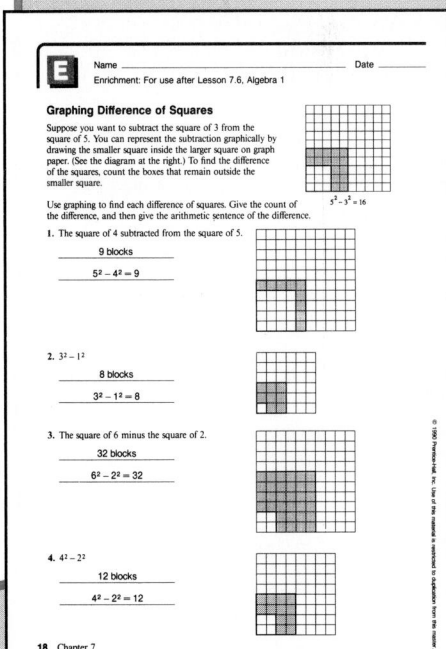

In the Capsule Review, students identify which two binomials are inverses. You may want to review the concept of inverses and state that if two polynomials are inverses, their sum is zero. In this lesson, if inverse polynomials are present, students must rewrite one as the product of −1 and its additive inverse.

Factoring by Grouping

7.7

Objectives: To factor a polynomial by removing a common binomial factor

To factor a polynomial by grouping the terms

Some polynomials may contain common binomial factors. Sometimes these binomial factors are opposites, or additive inverses.

Capsule Review

The inverse of a is $-a$. To find the inverse of a polynomial, use this property.

EXAMPLES
  a. $x - y, y - x$
$-1(x - y) = -x + y$
$\qquad\qquad\quad = y - x$
So, $x - y$ and $y - x$ are inverses.

  b. $2x + 1, 2x - 1$
$-1(2x + 1) = -2x - 1$
$\qquad\qquad -2x - 1 \neq 2x - 1$
So, $2x + 1$ and $2x - 1$ are *not* inverses.

Are these polynomials inverses of each other?

1. $1 - m, m - 1$ inverses
2. $3t - 4, 4 - 3t$ inverses
3. $3y - 2, -2 - 3y$
                                                 not inverses
4. $5y - 2, 5y + 2$
    not inverses
5. $4h^2 + 5, 5 - 4h^2$
    not inverses
6. $-2x - 3, 2x + 3$
    inverses

In the polynomial $6(a + b) + 3(a + b)$, the binomial $(a + b)$ is common to both terms. The distributive property can be used to factor out $(a + b)$.

$$6(a + b) + 3(a + b) = (6 + 3)(a + b)$$
$$= 9(a + b)$$

EXAMPLE 1 **Factor:** $8(x + y) - 5(x + y) + (x + y)$

$$8(x + y) - 5(x + y) + (x + y) = [8 - 5 + 1](x + y)$$
$$= 4(x + y)$$

Another method of using the distributive property to factor is as follows:

$\quad 8x + 8y - 5x - 5y + x + y$ *Multiply.*
$= 8x - 5x + x + 8y - 5y + y$ *Group like terms.*
$= 4x + 4y = 4(x + y)$ *Combine and use distributive property.*

If opposite polynomials (additive inverses) are present, rewrite one of them as the product of -1 and its additive inverse, then examine the polynomial for common factors. In Example 2, $b - a$ is rewritten as $-1(a - b)$.

292   Chapter 7 Factoring Polynomials

EXAMPLE 2 **Factor:** $16(a - b) - 19(b - a)$

$$16(a - b) - 19(b - a) = 16(a - b) - 19[-1(a - b)]$$
$$= 16(a - b) + 19(a - b)$$
$$= (16 + 19)(a - b)$$
$$= 35(a - b)$$

When a polynomial has four terms, it may help to group pairs of terms. This method of factoring is called *factoring by grouping*.

EXAMPLE 3 **Factor:** $16a - 16b + 19b - 19a$

$$16a - 16b + 19b - 19a = [16a - 16b] + [19b - 19a]$$
$$= [16(a - b)] + [19(b - a)]$$
$$= [16(a - b)] + [-19(a - b)]$$
$$= [16 + (-19)](a - b)$$
$$= (16 - 19)(a - b)$$
$$= -3(a - b)$$

Quite often a polynomial can be factored by employing more than one of the techniques already discussed. At times the basic approach to be used can be recognized after rearranging and regrouping of terms. Sometimes you must factor more than once.

EXAMPLE 4 **Factor:** $4h - 4k - h^3 + h^2k$

$$4h - 4k - h^3 + h^2k$$
$$= 4(h - k) - h^2(h - k)$$ *Factor out $-h^2$ from the last two terms.*
$$= (h - k)(4 - h^2)$$ *$4 - h^2$ is a difference of two squares.*
$$= (h - k)(2 - h)(2 + h)$$

In the next example, the first two terms are a difference of two squares. However, this arrangement does not result in a complete factoring.

EXAMPLE 5 **Factor:** $25y^2 - 4x^2 + 12x - 9$

$$25y^2 - 4x^2 + 12x - 9 = (25y^2 - 4x^2) + (12x - 9)$$
$$= (5y - 2x)(5y + 2x) + 3(4x - 3)$$

There is no common factor. Look for a different grouping of the terms.

$$25y^2 - 4x^2 + 12x - 9$$
$$= [25y^2] - [4x^2 - 12x + 9]$$ *$4x^2 - 12x + 9$ is a perfect square trinomial.*
$$= (5y)^2 - (2x - 3)^2$$ *$(5y)^2 - (2x - 3)^2$ is a difference of two squares.*
$$= [5y - (2x - 3)][5y + (2x - 3)]$$
$$= (5y - 2x + 3)(5y + 2x - 3)$$

7.7 Factoring by Grouping   **293**

TEACHING SUGGESTIONS

- This is sometimes a difficult lesson for students, because many times it is necessary to group a polynomial in several different ways before finding the arrangement which will work. Encourage students to take their time and to work carefully.
- Emphasize that in each example, it helps to look for a common factor first.
- Some students may benefit from underlining or circling common factors.

Critical Thinking

Observation Example 5 illustrates that some groupings are not effective and that many times a different grouping structure is necessary so that the polynomial can be factored. Examine Example 4 to find other groupings which will allow the polynomial to be factored.   Answers may vary. One possible solution is $(4h - h^3) + (-4k + h^2k) = h(4 - h^2) - k(4 - h^2) = (h - k)(4 - h^2) = (h - k)(2 - h)(2 + h)$

CHALKBOARD EXAMPLES

- **For Example 1**
  1. Factor: $7(a + 2b) + (a + 2b) - 3(a + 2b)$ $5(a + 2b)$

- **For Example 2**
  2. Factor: $11(x - 3) + 7(3 - x)$ $4(x - 3)$

- **For Example 3**
  3. Factor: $4d - 4g + 9g - 9d$ $5(g - d)$

- **For Example 4**
  4. Factor: $25r - r^3 - r^2s + 25s$ $(r + s)(5 - r)(5 + r)$

- **For Example 5**
  5. Factor: $49n^2 - 9m^2 + 24m - 16$ $(7n - 3m + 4)(7n + 3m - 4)$

293

Common Error

- Students often make errors when factoring out binomials. For example, students may correctly group and factor $ay + ab + cy + cb$ as $a(y + b) + c(y + b)$, and then incorrectly write this as $ac(y + b)$. Again, encourage students to check all answers by multiplying.
- See *Teacher's Resource Book* for additional remediation.

LESSON FOLLOW-UP

Assignment Guide

- See p. 268B for assignments.
- Since many exercises require trials of different groupings, these exercises may require more time.

Historical Note

Have students work in pairs to complete the research. News magazines or scientific journals may be used to find the most up-to-date information on prime numbers.

Lesson Quiz

Factor.
1. $5(a + 2) - 2(a + 2) + 7(a + 2)$
   $10(a + 2)$
2. $3a(x - 2) - 2(2 - x)$
   $(x - 2)(3a + 2)$
3. $xw + yw + 7x + 7y$
   $(x + y)(w + 7)$
4. $rt + st - 5r - 5s$ $(r + s)(t - 5)$
5. $g^3 - g^2 + 4 - 4g$
   $(g - 1)(g - 2)(g + 2)$

Enrichment

As a follow-up to the Historical Note, have students find a function $f(n)$ that yields primes for all positive integers less than n.   Answers may vary. A sample answer is: $f(n) = n^2 - n + 41$ for $n < 41$.

294

CLASS EXERCISES

Is there a common factor for the polynomial? If so, what is it?

1. $2x^2 + 4x$ yes; $2x$

2. $15x^2 + 12x + 6x^3$ yes; $3x$

3. $8(j + k) + 3(j + k)$ yes; $j + k$

4. $2a(c - d) + 3(-c - d)$ no

5. $3(a - b) + c(a + b)$ no

6. $2k(m - n) + 4(m - n)$ yes; $2(m - n)$

Factor.

7. $8(x + y) - 3(x + y)$ $(x + y)5$

8. $7(x - 3) + 2(3 - x)$ $5(x - 3)$

9. $11(j - 2) + 17(2 - j)$ $-6(j - 2)$

10. $ab + b^2 + ca + cb$ $(a + b)(b + c)$

11. $[r - rt] + [st - s]$ $(1 - t)(r - s)$

12. $[9 + 9c] - [d^2 + cd^2]$
    $(1 + c)(3 + d)(3 - d)$

For Discussion

13. How can factoring be used to simplify: $(4^2)(5)^2(3^2) - (16)(25)(5^2)$?
    $4^2 5^2(3^2 - 5^2) = 4^2 5^2(3 - 5)(3 + 5)$

PRACTICE EXERCISES

Factor.

A

1. $7(a + 3) - 5(a + 3) + 3(a + 3)$
   $5(a + 3)$

2. $13(g + 2) - 2(g + 2) + 8(g + 2)$
   $19(g + 2)$

3. $5(x - 3) + 2(x - 3) - 3(x - 3)$
   $4(x - 3)$

4. $7(r - 4) + 5(r - 4) - 4(r - 4)$
   $8(r - 4)$

5. $3x(x - 2) + 2x(x - 2) - 4(x - 2)$
   $(5x - 4)(x - 2)$

6. $2m(n - 2p) + (4mn - 8mp) + (-2n$
   $2(3m - 1)(n - 2p)$

7. $11(j - 2) - 6(2 - j) + 2(j - 2)$
   $19(j - 2)$

8. $9(x - 5) - 4(5 - x) + 5(x - 5)$
   $18(x - 5)$

9. $9a(b - c) + 2(c - b) + 3a(b - c)$
   $2(6a - 1)(b - c)$

10. $4x(y - z) + 5(z - y) + 7x(y - z)$
    $(11x - 5)(y - z)$

11. $4(3 - j) + 2j(j - 3) + 8(j - 3)$
    $2(j + 2)(j - 3)$

12. $5(2 - m) + 3m(m - 2) + 7(m - 2)$
    $(3m + 2)(m - 2)$

13. $10a - 10b + 12b - 12a$
    $-2(a - b)$

14. $21x - 21y + 15x - 15y$
    $36(x - y)$

15. $13r - 13s - 8s + 8r$
    $21(r - s)$

16. $11m - 11n + 10n - 10m$
    $m - n$

17. $6h - 6k - h^4 + h^3 k$
    $(6 - h^3)(h - k)$

18. $5m - 5n - m^5 + m^4 n$
    $(5 - m^4)(m - n)$

19. $rs + rt - 3s - 3t$
    $(s + t)(r - 3)$

20. $mn + np + 2m + 2p$
    $(m + p)(n + 2)$

21. $3rt + st + 3rw + sw$
    $(3r + s)(t + w)$

22. $2ab - b + 14a - 7$
    $(2a - 1)(b + 7)$

23. $ac - 2a + 3bc - 6b$
    $(c - 2)(a + 3b)$

24. $4wx - 6wy + 6xz - 9yz$
    $(2x - 3y)(2w + 3z)$

25. $36y^2 - 9x^2 - 24x - 16$
    $(6y - 3x - 4)(6y + 3x + 4)$

26. $49w^2 - 16x^2 - 24x - 9$
    $(7w - 4x - 3)(7w + 4x + 3)$

B

27. $x^2 + zy + xy + zx$
    $(x + y)(x + z)$

28. $3ab + 12c + 9a + 4bc$
    $(b + 3)(3a + 4c)$

29. $15ab - 9bc + 20ac - 12c^2$
    $(3b + 4c)(5a - 3c)$

30. $6mn + 12mp - 5np - 10p^2$
    $(n + 2p)(6m - 5p)$

31. $6rt - 5s + 2t - 15rs$
    $(3r + 1)(2t - 5s)$

32. $2pq - 5qr - 4p + 10r$
    $(q - 2)(2p - 5r)$

294   Chapter 7 Factoring Polynomials

33. $r^2 - (4s + t)^2$
$(r + 4s + t)(r - 4s - t)$

34. $m^2 - (2n - 3p)^2$
$(m + 2n - 3p)(m - 2n + 3p)$

35. $a^2 + 6a + 9 - c^2$
$(a + 3 + c)(a + 3 - c)$

36. $x^2 - 4x + 4 - y^2$
$(x - 2 + y)(x - 2 - y)$

37. $25y^2 - 4x^2 + 12x - 9$
$(5y + 2x - 3)(5y - 2x + 3)$

38. $121m^2 - 4n^2 - 52n - 169$
$(11m + 2n + 13)(11m - 2n - 13)$

C **39.** $x^{2r+1} + xy + 3x^{2r}z^{3r} + 3z^{3r}y$ $(x^{2r} + y)(x + 3z^{3r})$

40. $2a^{k+3} + 2a^2b^k + a^{k+1}c^{2k+3} + b^kc^{2k+3}$ $(a^{k+1} + b^k)(2a^2 + c^{2k+3})$

41. $m^rp + np + m^rn^{2r} + n^{2r+1}$
$(m^r + n)(p + n^{2r})$

42. $2a^{n+2} + 2a^2b^2 + a^nc^{2n} + b^2c^{2n}$
$(a^n + b^2)(2a^2 + c^{2n})$

43. $x^{2a} + 2x^ay^b + y^{2b} - 1$
$(x^a + y^b + 1)(x^a + y^b - 1)$

44. $m^{2x} - 2m^xn^y + n^{2y} - 4$
$(m^x - n^y + 2)(m^x - n^y - 2)$

Applications

Geometry Write a polynomial in factored form for each.

45. A square is circumscribed about a circle. The area of the circle is $49y^2$ and the area of the square is $9x^2 - 6xy + y^2$. Write a polynomial in factored form to represent the difference of the two areas. $3(x + 2y)(3x - 8y)$

46. A square is enclosed in a circle. The area of the square is $(4r^2 - 32r + 64)$ and the area of the circle is $484r^2$. Write a polynomial in factored form to represent the difference of the two areas. $32(5r + 2)(3r - 1)$

HISTORICAL NOTE

Throughout the history of mathematics, many of the very best scholars have been fascinated by the study of prime numbers. Sometime between 300 and 200 B.C., Euclid developed his proof that there is an infinite number of primes, and Eratosthenes developed his "sieve" for determining the primes less than a given number. An unwieldy formula was derived from the Sieve of Eratosthenes for determining the number of primes less than a given number when the primes less than the square root of the given number are known. In 1870, Ernst Meissel improved on the formula derived from the work of Eratosthenes by which he was able to show that the number of primes below 10^8 is 5,761,455. Twenty-three years later, the Danish mathematician Bertelsen proclaimed that the number of primes less than 10^9 is 50,847,478.

Mathematicians also have long been challenged by finding some method to test whether a large number is prime. In 1876, the French mathematician Anatole Lucas verified the 39-digit number $2^{127} - 1$ as a prime, and for more than 75 years this was the greatest verified prime. Since the advent of modern computer techniques, greater primes have been verified.

Research: Find out what the largest verified prime number is today.

Mersenne primes are expressed in the form $2^n - 1$. The largest prime yet found, has 65,050 digits when $n = 216,091$.

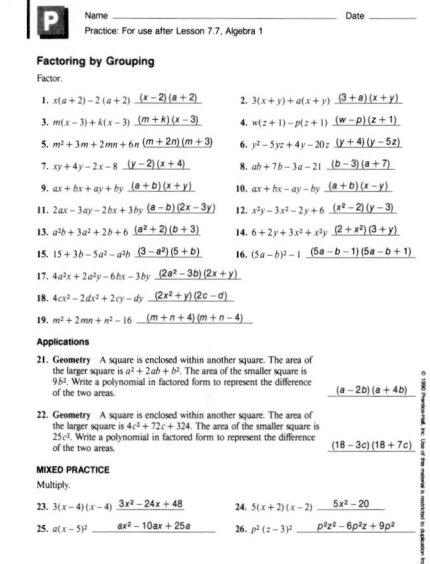

Name _____ Date _____
Practice: For use after Lesson 7.7, Algebra 1

Factoring by Grouping
Factor.

1. $x(a + 2) - 2(a + 2)$ $(x - 2)(a + 2)$
2. $3(x + y) + a(x + y)$ $(3 + a)(x + y)$
3. $m(x - 3) + k(x - 3)$ $(m + k)(x - 3)$
4. $w(z + 1) - p(z + 1)$ $(w - p)(z + 1)$
5. $m^2 + 3m + 2mn + 6n$ $(m + 2n)(m + 3)$
6. $y^2 - 5yz + 4y - 20z$ $(y + 4)(y - 5z)$
7. $xy + 4y - 2x - 8$ $(y - 2)(x + 4)$
8. $ab + 7b - 3a - 21$ $(b - 3)(a + 7)$
9. $ax + bx + ay + by$ $(a + b)(x + y)$
10. $ax + bx - ay - by$ $(a + b)(x - y)$
11. $2ax - 3ay - 2bx + 3by$ $(a - b)(2x - 3y)$
12. $x^2y - 3x^2 - 2y + 6$ $(x^2 - 2)(y - 3)$
13. $a^2b + 3a^2 + 2b + 6$ $(a^2 + 2)(b + 3)$
14. $6 + 2y + 3x^2 + x^2y$ $(2 + x^2)(3 + y)$
15. $15 + 3b - 5a^2 - a^2b$ $(3 - a^2)(5 + b)$
16. $(5a - b)^2 - 1$ $(5a - b - 1)(5a - b + 1)$
17. $4a^2x + 2a^2y - 6bx - 3by$ $(2a^2 - 3b)(2x + y)$
18. $4cx^2 - 2dx^2 + 2cy - dy$ $(2x^2 + y)(2c - d)$
19. $m^2 + 2mn + n^2 - 16$ $(m + n + 4)(m + n - 4)$

Applications

21. **Geometry** A square is enclosed within another square. The area of the larger square is $a^2 + 2ab + b^2$. The area of the smaller square is $9b^2$. Write a polynomial in factored form to represent the difference of the two areas. $(a - 2b)(a + 4b)$

22. **Geometry** A square is enclosed within another square. The area of the larger square is $4c^2 + 72c + 324$. The area of the smaller square is $25c^2$. Write a polynomial in factored form to represent the difference of the two areas. $(18 - 3c)(18 + 7c)$

MIXED PRACTICE
Multiply.

23. $3(x - 4)(x - 4)$ $3x^2 - 24x + 48$
24. $5(x + 2)(x - 2)$ $5x^2 - 20$
25. $a(x - 5)^2$ $ax^2 - 10ax + 25a$
26. $p^2(z - 3)^2$ $p^2z^2 - 6p^2z + 9p^2$

20 Chapter 7

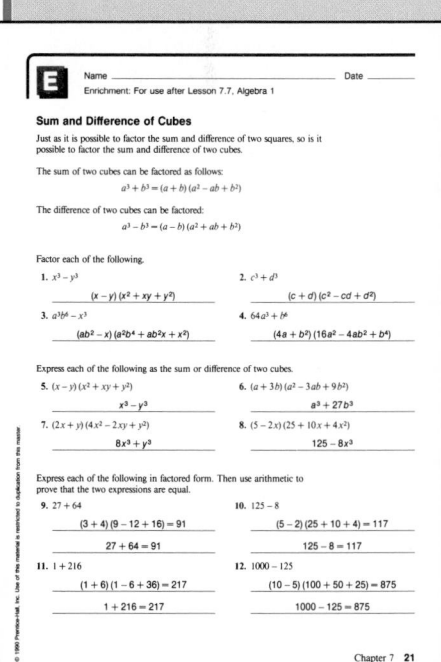

Name _____ Date _____
Enrichment: For use after Lesson 7.7, Algebra 1

Sum and Difference of Cubes

Just as it is possible to factor the sum and difference of two squares, so is it possible to factor the sum and difference of two cubes.

The sum of two cubes can be factored as follows:
$a^3 + b^3 = (a + b)(a^2 - ab + b^2)$

The difference of two cubes can be factored:
$a^3 - b^3 = (a - b)(a^2 + ab + b^2)$

Factor each of the following.

1. $x^3 - y^3$
$(x - y)(x^2 + xy + y^2)$
2. $c^3 + d^3$
$(c + d)(c^2 - cd + d^2)$
3. $a^3b^6 - x^3$
$(ab^2 - x)(a^2b^4 + ab^2x + x^2)$
4. $64a^3 + b^6$
$(4a + b^2)(16a^2 - 4ab^2 + b^4)$

Express each of the following as the sum or difference of two cubes.

5. $(x - y)(x^2 + xy + y^2)$
$x^3 - y^3$
6. $(a + 3b)(a^2 - 3ab + 9b^2)$
$a^3 + 27b^3$
7. $(2x + y)(4x^2 - 2xy + y^2)$
$8x^3 + y^3$
8. $(5 - 2x)(25 + 10x + 4x^2)$
$125 - 8x^3$

Express each of the following in factored form. Then use arithmetic to prove that the two expressions are equal.

9. $27 + 64$
$(3 + 4)(9 - 12 + 16) = 91$
$27 + 64 = 91$
10. $125 - 8$
$(5 - 2)(25 + 10 + 4) = 117$
$125 - 8 = 117$
11. $1 + 216$
$(1 + 6)(1 - 6 + 36) = 217$
$1 + 216 = 217$
12. $1000 - 125$
$(10 - 5)(100 + 50 + 25) = 875$
$1000 - 125 = 875$

Chapter 7 **21**

Vocabulary
Factor completely

Materials/Manipulatives
Overhead projector
Teacher's Resource Book,
  Transparencies 8, 8a, 11, 12

BACKGROUND

- In the Capsule Review, students factor polynomials by factoring out the greatest common factor (GCF). Point out that in this lesson, factoring out the greatest common monomial factor will be the first step in factoring each polynomial.
- This lesson pulls together all the factoring skills learned in the previous lessons in this chapter. Before you start the lesson, you may want to review Transparencies 8, 8a, 11, and 12, in the *Teacher's Resource Book*. In particular, review factoring a perfect square trinomial and the difference of two squares.

Critical Thinking
Classifying   Identify a basic property which allows students to factor a common monomial factor from a polynomial.   distributive property

---

7.8

Factoring Completely

Objective: To factor a polynomial completely

Factoring is an important skill in algebra. The techniques for factoring polynomials that have been developed in previous lessons will enable you to factor a polynomial completely. A polynomial is **factored completely** when it is written as a product of prime polynomials. Recall that a prime polynomial is one that cannot be factored.

Capsule Review

When you factor a polynomial of any number of terms, the first step is to factor out the greatest common monomial factor, if any.

EXAMPLE $4x^2y^3 - 6x^2y^2 + 2xy^2 = 2xy^2(2xy - 3x + 1)$

Factor out the greatest common factor (GCF).

1. $5x + 10y$ $5(x + 2y)$ **2.** $2h^4 + 4h^3$ $2h^3(h + 2)$ **3.** $9c^2 - 3c$ $3c(3c - 1)$

4. $6ab^2 + 8a^3b^2$ **5.** $2m^3n - 8m^5n^2$ **6.** $5s^2t - 15st^4$
$2ab^2(3 + 4a^2)$ $2m^3n(1 - 4m^2n)$ $5st(s - 3t^3)$

7. $9x^2y^3 - 12xy^4 + 8xy^2$ **8.** $15a^4b^4 - 10a^4b^2 - 5b^4$
$xy^2(9xy - 12y^2 + 8)$ $5b^2(3a^4b^2 - 2a^4 - b^2)$

After you have factored out the greatest common monomial factor, if any, factor the remaining polynomial as before.

To factor a polynomial completely:

1. Factor out the greatest monomial factor (GCF).

2. If the polynomial has two or three terms, look for:
   - a perfect square trinomial,
   - a difference of two squares, or
   - a pair of binomial factors.

3. If there are four or more terms, group terms, if possible, in ways that can be factored. Then factor out any common polynomials.

4. Check that each factor is prime.

5. Check your answer by multiplying all the factors.

EXAMPLE 1   Factor: $5a^3 - 20ab^2$

$$5a^3 - 20ab^2$$
$$= 5a(a^2 - 4b^2) \qquad \text{\textit{5a is the GCF.}}$$
$$= 5a(a - 2b)(a + 2b) \qquad \text{\textit{$a^2 - 4b^2$ is a difference of two squares: $(a)^2 - (2b)^2$.}}$$

Check: $5a(a - 2b)(a + 2b) = 5a(a^2 + 2ab - 2ab - 4b^2)$
$$= 5a(a^2 - 4b^2) = 5a^3 - 20ab^2$$

EXAMPLE 2   Factor: $32x^3 - 16x^2 + 2x$

$$32x^3 - 16x^2 + 2x$$
$$= 2x(16x^2 - 8x + 1) \qquad \text{\textit{Factor out 2x.}}$$
$$= 2x(4x - 1)(4x - 1) \qquad \text{\textit{$16x^2 - 8x + 1$ is a perfect square trinomial.}}$$
$$= 2x(4x - 1)^2$$

Check: $2x(4x - 1)(4x - 1) = 2x(16x^2 - 8x + 1)$
$$= 32x^3 - 16x^2 + 2x$$

EXAMPLE 3   Factor: $18x^4y + 15x^3y - 12x^2y$

$$18x^4y + 15x^3y - 12x^2y = 3x^2y(6x^2 + 5x - 4)$$
$$= 3x^2y(3x + 4)(2x - 1)$$

Check: $3x^2y(3x + 4)(2x - 1) = 3x^2y(6x^2 + 5x - 4)$
$$= 18x^4y + 15x^3y - 12x^2y$$

Sometimes a pattern for factoring is not immediately obvious. After you have factored out the GCF, the pattern for further factoring may be easier to see.

EXAMPLE 4   Factor: $3x^9 - 48x$

$$3x^9 - 48x$$
$$= 3x(x^8 - 16) \qquad \text{\textit{Factor out 3x.}}$$
$$= 3x(x^4 + 4)(x^4 - 4) \qquad \text{\textit{$x^8 - 16$ is a difference of squares:}}$$
$$= 3x(x^4 + 4)(x^2 - 2)(x^2 + 2) \qquad \text{\textit{$(x^4)^2 - (4)^2$.}}$$

Why is $x^2 + 2$ not factored? Why is $x^4 + 4$ not factored?

CLASS EXERCISES

Find the GCF.

1. $2x^2 + 4x + 6$ 2

2. $2r^3 + 4r^2$ $2r^2$

3. $3xy^2 + 9x^3y$ $3xy$

4. $12a^2b^3 + 14ab^4$ $2ab^3$

5. $9r^2s^3 + 12rs^4 + 8r^3s^2$ rs^2

6. $128x^3yz^3 + 16xy^5z^4 + 48x^4y^3z$ $16xyz$

TEACHING SUGGESTIONS

- Review the five steps for factoring, presented before Example 1. Make sure students understand each step by defining the terms used. Give examples of rules, where appropriate.
- Emphasize the importance of checking answers by multiplying.
- In Example 2, point out that when students factor out $2x$, 1 becomes the constant in the trinomial.
- You may wish to use an overhead projector and a transparency to show students how to factor out the greatest common monomial factor. Emphasize the importance of checking that there are no more common factors.

CHALKBOARD EXAMPLES

For Exercises 1–5, factor:

- **For Example 1**
  1. $27x^3 - 3xy^2$
     $3x(3x + y)(3x - y)$

- **For Example 2**
  2. $4m^3 - 48m^2 + 144m$
     $4m(m - 6)(m - 6)$
  3. $18x^2 - 12x + 2$
     $2(3x - 1)(3x - 1)$

- **For Example 3**
  4. $8x^2y^3 + 4x^2y^2 - 12x^2y$
     $4x^2y (2y + 3)(y - 1)$

- **For Example 4**
  5. $2d^5 - 162d$
     $2d(d^2 + 9)(d + 3)(d - 3)$

Common Error

- Some students forget to factor out the greatest common monomial factor first. Point out that this is an important step because, many times, it makes it easier to factor further. For students who make this error, suggest that they check each coefficient and each variable, one at a time.
- See *Teacher's Resource Book* for additional remediation.

Assignment Guide

- See p. 268B for assignments.
- Emphasize that students should factor each polynomial completely. Some students may be tempted to factor out the greatest common monomial factor and then not continue the factoring process.
- See *Teacher's Resource Book,* for Reading and Writing in Algebra activity, p. 7.

Algebra in Geometry

Too often, students are so anxious to get an answer that they fail to see a shortcut or fail to do it mentally. This feature brings this skill to the attention of students. It also encourages them to improve their number sense. In the introduction, point out that the factored form is easier when $x = 16$ and $y = 14$.

Lesson Quiz

Factor.

1. $3z^2 - 6z - 72$ $3(z - 6)(z + 4)$
2. $6x^2 + 3x - 45$
   $3(2x - 5)(x + 3)$
3. $4w^2 - 196$ $4(w + 7)(w - 7)$
4. $3v^3 - 75v$ $3v(v + 5)(v - 5)$
5. $4v^3 - 16v^2 + 16v$ $4v(v - 2)^2$
6. $63t^3 + 69t^2 - 60t$
   $3t(7t - 4)(3t + 5)$
7. $8x^3 - 8x^2 + 2x$ $2x(2x - 1)^2$
8. $30s^3 - 65s^2 - 140s$
   $5s(3s + 4)(2s - 7)$
9. $4p^2 + 8pq - 12q^2$
   $4(p + 3q)(p - q)$
10. $14m^2t - 35mt^2 - 21t^3$
    $7t(2m + t)(m - 3t)$

Enrichment

In Exercise 53, the volume of the rectangular prism is $x^3 + 3x^2 + 2x$. Could this prism have dimensions that are different than the factors that you found? Why or why not? No, the factors are unique, i.e., there is only one set of 3 factors for the polynomial. These factors are prime in the set of polynomials with integer coefficients.

298

Factor.

7. $3x^2 + 21x^4$
   $3x^2(1 + 7x^2)$
8. $3b^2 + 6b + 3$
   $3(b + 1)^2$
9. $4z^2 - 4$
   $4(z - 1)(z + 1)$
10. $2w^2 + 8w - 24$
    $2(w + 6)(w - 2)$
11. $t^3 + 7t^2 + 12t$
    $t(t + 4)(t + 3)$
12. $4h^3 + 12h^2 + 8h$
    $4h(h + 2)(h + 1)$

PRACTICE EXERCISES

Factor completely.

A 1. $5x^2 - 20$ $5(x + 2)(x - 2)$
2. $6a^2 - 6$ $6(a + 1)(a - 1)$

3. $3k^2 - 147$ $3(k + 7)(k - 7)$
4. $5m^2 - 125$ $5(m + 5)(m - 5)$

5. $4y^3 - 36yz^2$ $4y(y - 3z)(y + 3z)$
6. $27p^3 - 108pq^2$ $27p(p - 2q)(p + 2q)$

7. $6x^3 - 24xy^2$ $6x(x + 2y)(x - 2y)$
8. $3r^3 - 48rs^2$ $3r(r - 4s)(r + 4s)$

9. $2x^2 + 6x - 20$ $2(x + 5)(x - 2)$
10. $3x^2 - 6x - 24$ $3(x - 4)(x + 2)$

11. $6k^2 + 12k + 6$ $6(k + 1)^2$
12. $8c^2 - 24c + 16$ $8(c - 2)(c - 1)$

13. $10k^2 + 35k + 15$ $5(2k + 1)(k + 3)$
14. $12r^2 - 45r - 12$ $3(4r + 1)(r - 4)$

15. $-4x^2 - 4x + 24$ $-4(x + 3)(x - 2)$
16. $-3d^2 - 6d + 24$ $-3(d - 2)(d + 4)$

17. $-10m^2 + 40m + 210$ $-10(m + 3)(m - 7)$
18. $-6x^2 + 36x + 96$ $-6(x + 2)(x - 8)$

19. $75x^3 - 30x^2 + 3x$ $3x(5x - 1)^2$
20. $48y^3 - 24y^2 + 3y$ $3y(4y - 1)^2$

21. $12x^3 + 24x^2 + 12x$ $12x(x + 1)^2$
22. $27m^3 + 36m^2 + 12m$
    $3m(3m + 2)^2$

23. $8x^4y + 4x^3y - 12x^2y$
    $4x^2y(2x + 3)(x - 1)$
24. $24m^4n - 12m^3n - 12m^2n$
    $12m^2n(2m + 1)(m - 1)$

25. $12r^4s^2 + 6r^3s^2 - 6r^2s^2$
    $6r^2s^2(r + 1)(2r - 1)$
26. $45j^4k^2 + 45j^3k^2 - 20j^2k^2$
    $5j^2k^2(3j + 4)(3j - 1)$

27. $18x^5y^3 - 15x^4y^4 - 18x^3y^5$
    $3x^3y^3(3x + 2y)(2x - 3y)$
28. $32x^5y^2 - 48x^4y^3 - 32x^3y^4$
    $16x^3y^2(2x + y)(x - 2y)$

29. $16x^6y^4 - 48x^5y^5 + 36x^4y^6$
    $4x^4y^4(2x - 3y)^2$
30. $18a^5b^3 - 60a^4b^4 + 50a^3b^5$
    $2a^3b^3(3a - 5b)^2$

B 31. $-12m^7p^2 - 60m^6p^3 - 75m^5p^4$
    $-3m^5p^2(2m + 5p)^2$
32. $-36d^5f^5 - 96d^4f^6 - 64d^3f^7$
    $-4d^3f^5(3d + 4f)^2$

33. $2x^9 - 50x$ $2x(x^4 - 5)(x^4 + 5)$
34. $3r^9 - 27r$ $3r(r^4 - 3)(r^4 + 3)$

35. $2x^7 - 32x$ $2x(x^3 - 4)(x^3 + 4)$
36. $3x^7 - 75x$ $3x(x^3 - 5)(x^3 + 5)$

37. $3m^5 - 60m^3 + 192m$
    $3m(m + 4)(m - 4)(m + 2)(m - 2)$
38. $2m^5 - 68m^3 + 450m$
    $2m(m + 3)(m - 3)(m + 5)(m - 5)$

39. $18r^6 - 170r^4 + 72r^2$
    $2r^2(3r + 2)(3r - 2)(r + 3)(r - 3)$
40. $8r^6 - 50r^4 + 72r^2$
    $2r^2(2r - 3)(2r + 3)(r - 2)(r + 2)$

41. $192x^6y^5 - 144x^5y^5 + 27x^4y^5$
    $3x^4y^5(8x - 3)^2$
42. $75x^6y^5 - 60x^5y^5 + 12x^4y^5$
    $3x^4y^5(5x - 2)^2$

43. $6(a - 1)^2 - 15(a - 1) - 9$
    $3(2a - 1)(a - 4)$
44. $4(b + 2)^2 + 20(b + 2) - 24$
    $4(b + 8)(b + 1)$

C 45. $5(a + 1)^2 - 5(a - 1) - 20$
    $5(a + 2)(a - 1)$
46. $3(a + 2)^2 - 3(a - 1) - 27$
    $3(a - 1)(a + 4)$

47. $a^4 + 4a^3 - 5a^2 - 36a - 36$
    $(a + 3)(a - 3)(a + 2)^2$
48. $a^4 + 4a^3 - 12a^2 - 64a - 64$
    $(a + 4)(a - 4)(a + 2)^2$

49. $3a^{17} + 30a^9 + 75a$
    $3a(a^8 + 5)^2$
50. $4a^{19} + 24a^{10} + 36a$
    $4a(a^9 + 3)^2$

51. $x^{3k+21} + 2x^{2k+14} + x^{k+7}$
    $x^{k+7}(x^{k+7} + 1)^2$
52. $3a^{9z-27} - 13a^{6z-18} - 10a^{3z-9}$
    $a^{3z-9}(3a^{3z-9} + 2)(a^{3z-9} - 5)$

Applications

Geometry The volume (*lwh*) of each rectangular prism below is expressed as a polynomial. Factor each polynomial into three factors corresponding to the length, width, and height of the prism.

53.

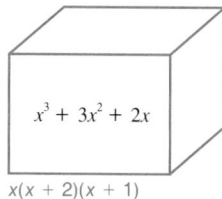

$x^3 + 3x^2 + 2x$

$x(x + 2)(x + 1)$

54.

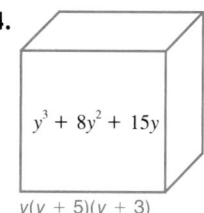

$y^3 + 8y^2 + 15y$

$y(y + 5)(y + 3)$

55.

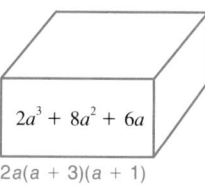

$2a^3 + 8a^2 + 6a$

$2a(a + 3)(a + 1)$

56.

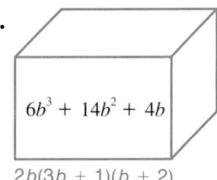

$6b^3 + 14b^2 + 4b$

$2b(3b + 1)(b + 2)$

ALGEBRA IN GEOMETRY

Applying what you know about factoring can often make computations easier to perform. Suppose, for example, that you must find the area of the shaded region in the figure below for different values of *x* and *y*. One way is to find the area of each square and then find the difference.

$$x^2 - y^2$$

Another way is to use the factored form.

$$(x - y)(x + y)$$

Suppose $x = 16$ and $y = 14$. Which of these two ways is easier to use?

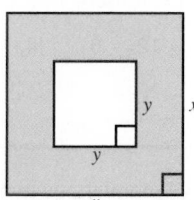

For each figure below, write and factor an expression that makes the computation for finding the area of the shaded region easy to perform.

1.

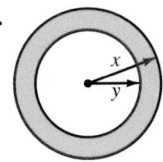

$\pi x^2 - \pi y^2;\ \pi(x - y)(x + y)$

2.

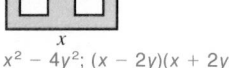

$x^2 - 4y^2;\ (x - 2y)(x + 2y)$

3.

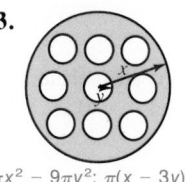

$\pi x^2 - 9\pi y^2;\ \pi(x - 3y)(x + 3y)$

7.8 Factoring Completely   **299**

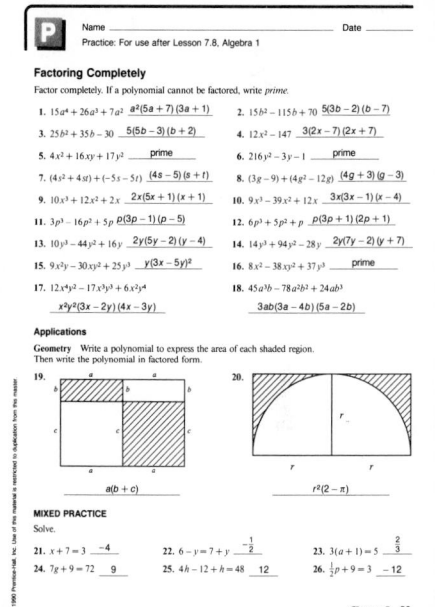
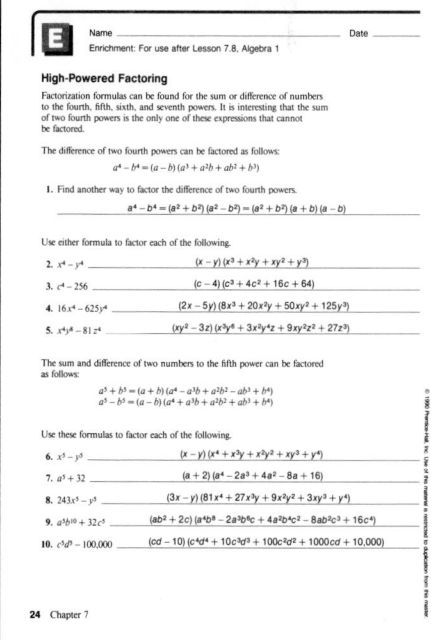

Vocabulary
Zero-product property

Materials/Manipulatives
Overhead projector
*Teacher's Resource Book,
   Teaching Aid 8,
Transparencies 8, 8a, 11, 12*

BACKGROUND

In the Capsule Review, students are given a replacement set and asked to see which numbers are solutions. This Capsule Review stresses the importance of factoring in finding solutions of polynomial equations.

7.9

Solving Polynomial Equations by Factoring

Objective: To solve polynomial equations by factoring

One important use of factoring is in finding the solutions of *polynomial equations*. A **polynomial equation** is an equation whose sides are both polynomials. Some polynomial equations are given special names.

For all real numbers a, b, and c and $a \neq 0$:

$$ax + b = 0 \text{ is called a } linear \ equation$$
$$ax^2 + bx + c = 0 \text{ is called a } quadratic \ equation$$

Capsule Review

A number that gives a true sentence is a solution of the equation. The set of all solutions is the solution set of the equation. You can check solutions by substituting in the original equation.

EXAMPLE $x^2 = x + 6$ Replacement set: {0, 3}

Try 0. $0^2 \overset{?}{=} 0 + 6$
              $0 \neq 6$
Try 3. $3^2 \overset{?}{=} 3 + 6$
              $9 = 9$ ✔   True

So, 3 is a solution of $x^2 = x + 6$ and 0 is *not* a solution.

Test the numbers in the replacement set to see which are solutions.

1. $3x^2 - 12 = 0$ {4, −2} 4 not; −2 solution **2.** $y^2 - 7y = -12$ {3, 4} 3, 4 solutions

3. $9m^2 = 3m$ $\left\{0, -\dfrac{1}{3}\right\}$ 0 solution; $-\dfrac{1}{3}$ not **4.** $a^2 = \dfrac{1}{4}$ $\left\{\dfrac{1}{2}, -\dfrac{1}{2}\right\}$ $\dfrac{1}{2}, -\dfrac{1}{2}$ solutions

Some polynomial equations can be solved by first factoring and then applying the *zero-product property*. This property states that if the product of two factors is zero, then one or both of the factors must be zero.

> **Zero-Product Property**
>
> For all real numbers a and b, if $ab = 0$, then $a = 0$ or $b = 0$ or both a and $b = 0$.

The zero-product property is true for any number of factors.

300   Chapter 7 Factoring Polynomials

EXAMPLE 1   Solve: $(2x - 1)(x + 6) = 0$

By the zero-product property, at least one of the factors must equal zero.

$(2x - 1)(x + 6) = 0$

$2x - 1 = 0$	$x + 6 = 0$	*Set each factor equal to 0.*
$2x = 1$	$x = -6$	*Solve for x.*
$x = \frac{1}{2}$		

Check: Replace x with $\frac{1}{2}$.

$(2x - 1)(x + 6) = 0$

$\left(2 \cdot \frac{1}{2} - 1\right)\left(\frac{1}{2} + 6\right) \stackrel{?}{=} 0$

$(0)\left(6\frac{1}{2}\right) \stackrel{?}{=} 0$

$0 = 0 \; \checkmark$

Replace x with -6.

$(2x - 1)(x + 6) = 0$

$[2(-6) - 1](-6 + 6) \stackrel{?}{=} 0$

$(-12 - 1)(0) \stackrel{?}{=} 0$

$(-13)(0) \stackrel{?}{=} 0$

$0 = 0 \; \checkmark$

So, the solutions are $\frac{1}{2}$ and -6.

EXAMPLE 2   Solve: $a^2 - 7a = 0$

$a^2 - 7a = 0$

$a(a - 7) = 0$ *Factor.*

$a = 0$	$a - 7 = 0$	*Set each factor equal to 0.*
	$a = 7$	

The solutions are 0 and 7. The check is left for you.

Always begin with the equation in the form $ax^2 + bx + c = 0$.

EXAMPLE 3   Solve: $x^2 - x = 6$

$x^2 - x = 6$

$x^2 - x - 6 = 6 - 6$ *Subtract 6 from each side.*

$x^2 - x - 6 = 0$

$(x - 3)(x + 2) = 0$ *Factor.*

$x - 3 = 0$	$x + 2 = 0$	*Set each factor equal to 0.*
$x = 3$	$x = -2$	

Check the solutions by substituting in the original equation.

Check: $x^2 - x = 6$

$3^2 - 3 \stackrel{?}{=} 6$ *Replace x with 3.*

$6 = 6 \; \checkmark$

$x^2 - x = 6$

$(-2)^2 - (-2) \stackrel{?}{=} 6$ *Replace x with -2.*

$6 = 6 \; \checkmark$

The solutions are 3 and -2.

7.9 Solving Polynomial Equations by Factoring   **301**

TEACHING SUGGESTION

This lesson combines all the factoring skills previously learned in this Chapter. Learning to factor is important in finding solutions for polynomial equations. You may wish to review several cases of factoring using Teaching Aid 7, and Transparencies 8, 8a, 11, and 12 in the *Teacher's Resource Book,* before introducing this lesson. Be sure to encourage students to check their solutions by substituting in the original equations.

Critical Thinking

Causal Explanation   Explain the significance of the Zero-product property to our number system. The Zero-product property is an important property in our number system since it allows us to solve polynomial equations that can be expressed in the form $ab = 0$.

CHALKBOARD EXAMPLES

- **For Example 1**
  Solve.
  1. $(3x - 1)(x + 5) = 0$ $\frac{1}{3}, -5$

  2. $(2x - 3)(x + 4) = 0$ $\frac{3}{2}, -4$

- **For Example 2**
  Solve.
  3. $x^2 - 4x = 0$ $0, 4$
  4. $x^2 + 7x = 0$ $0, -7$

- **For Example 3**
  Solve.
  5. $x^2 - x = 12$ $-3, 4$
  6. $x^2 + 3x = 10$ $-5, 2$

- **For Example 4**
  Solve.
  7. $36x^2 - 12x + 1 = 0$ $\frac{1}{6}$

  8. $16x^2 - 16x + 4 = 0$ $\frac{1}{2}$

A polynomial equation may have more than one *solution*, or *root*. Sometimes, however, the roots may be the same number.

EXAMPLE 4   Solve: $25x^2 - 10x + 1 = 0$

$$25x^2 - 10x + 1 = 0$$
$$(5x - 1)(5x - 1) = 0$$
$$5x = 1 \quad \vert \quad 5x = 1$$
$$x = \frac{1}{5} \quad \vert \quad x = \frac{1}{5}$$

The solution is $\frac{1}{5}$. Check by substituting $\frac{1}{5}$ for x in the original equation.

CLASS EXERCISES

Solve. Check your solutions.

1. $2r(r - 3) = 0$ $0, 3$
2. $(x - 4)(3x + 2) = 0$ $4, -\frac{2}{3}$
3. $3m^2 - m = 0$ $0, \frac{1}{3}$
4. $2z^2 + 3z = 0$ $0, -\frac{3}{2}$
5. $y^2 + 7y + 6 = 0$ $-6, -1$
6. $2x^2 + 13x - 7 = 0$ $\frac{1}{2}, -7$
7. $2m^2 + m - 1 = 0$ $\frac{1}{2}, -1$
8. $c^2 + 8c + 16 = 0$ -4
9. $x^2 - 4x = 12$ $6, -2$
10. $3w^2 + 5w = 12$ $\frac{4}{3}, -3$

PRACTICE EXERCISES

Solve. Check your solutions.

A   1. $(3x - 2)(x + 4) = 0$ $\frac{2}{3}, -4$
2. $(4z - 3)(z + 5) = 0$ $\frac{3}{4}, -5$
3. $(2x - 6)(x + 6) = 0$ $3, -6$
4. $(5x - 8)(x + 9) = 0$ $\frac{8}{5}, -9$
5. $(5x + 3)(x - 2) = 0$ $-\frac{3}{5}, 2$
6. $(7x + 5)(x - 3) = 0$ $-\frac{5}{7}, 3$
7. $m^2 + 4m = 0$ $0, -4$
8. $n^2 + 5n = 0$ $0, -5$
9. $2w^2 - 8w = 0$ $0, 4$
10. $3z^2 - 6z = 0$ $0, 2$
11. $5x^2 + 15x = 0$ $0, -3$
12. $4r^2 + 16r = 0$ $0, -4$
13. $x^2 + 2x = 8$ $-4, 2$
14. $z^2 - 4z = 21$ $7, -3$
15. $3m^2 + 4m = -1$ $-\frac{1}{3}, -1$
16. $2z^2 + 4z = 16$ $-4, 2$
17. $4m^2 - 11m = 3$ $-\frac{1}{4}, 3$
18. $5m^2 - 7m = 6$ $-\frac{3}{5}, 2$
19. $r^2 - r - 90 = 0$ $10, -9$
20. $t^2 - 3t - 18 = 0$ $6, -3$
21. $x^2 - 8x + 15 = 0$ $5, 3$
22. $3k^2 + 17k + 10 = 0$ $-\frac{2}{3}, -5$
23. $3m^2 - 7m - 20 = 0$ $4, -\frac{5}{3}$
24. $2n^2 + 13n - 24 = 0$ $-8, \frac{3}{2}$

302   Chapter 7 Factoring Polynomials

B

25. $3r^2 + 4r = 15$ $\frac{5}{3}, -3$

26. $2x^2 - 11x = 21$ $-\frac{3}{2}, 7$

27. $6y^2 - 10 = -11y$ $-\frac{5}{2}, \frac{2}{3}$

28. $15s^2 - 28 = s$ $-\frac{4}{3}, \frac{7}{5}$

29. $14a^2 = 29a + 15$ $-\frac{3}{7}, \frac{5}{2}$

30. $6b^2 = -b + 35$ $-\frac{5}{2}, \frac{7}{3}$

31. $24d^2 + 18d = -4d + 2$ $-1, \frac{1}{12}$

32. $2t^2 + 12t = 18t + 108$ $-6, 9$

33. $n^3 + 4n^2 - 21n = 0$ $0, -7, 3$

34. $m^3 - m^2 - 20m = 0$ $0, 5, -4$

35. $6x^3 - 7x^2 - 20x = 0$ $0, -\frac{4}{3}, \frac{5}{2}$

36. $10n^3 - 29n^2 - 21n = 0$ $0, -\frac{3}{5}, \frac{7}{2}$

37. $16j^3 + 44j^2 = 126j$ $0, -\frac{9}{2}, \frac{7}{4}$

38. $15k^3 - 114k^2 = 189k$ $0, -\frac{7}{5}, 9$

39. $30x^3 = 21x^2 + 135x$ $0, -\frac{9}{5}, \frac{5}{2}$

40. $12b^3 = 86b^2 + 80b$ $0, -\frac{5}{6}, 8$

41. $72a^3 - 132a^2 = -108a^2 + 198a$
$0, -\frac{3}{2}, \frac{11}{6}$

42. $120y^3 + 72y^2 = 140y^2 + 84y$
$0, -\frac{3}{5}, \frac{7}{6}$

C

43. $(t - 2)^2 + 7(t - 2) + 12 = 0$ $-2, -1$

44. $(y + 4)^2 + 3(y + 4) - 10 = 0$ $-9, -2$

45. $(x + 3)^3 + 2(x + 3)^2 - 8(x + 3) = 0$ $-7, -3, -1$

46. $(z - 3)^3 + 9(z - 3)^2 + 14(z - 3) = 0$ $-4, 1, 3$

47. $a^5 - 10a^3 + 9a = 0$ $0, -3, 3, -1, 1$

48. $2b^5 - 100b^3 + 98b = 0$ $0, -7, 7, -1, 1$

Applications

Number Problems For each problem, let n represent the missing number. Write a quadratic equation to solve the problem.

49. A number squared added to five times the number equals 24. $n^2 + 5n = 24$

50. Three times a number, subtracted from the number squared, equals 18.
$n^2 - 3n = 18$

51. Twice the square of a number equals the difference of the number and 10.
$2n^2 = n - 10$

TEST YOURSELF

Factor. If a polynomial cannot be factored write *prime*. 7.6–7.8

1. $2y^2 - 98$ $2(y - 7)(y + 7)$

2. $5y + 25y^3$ $5y(1 + 5y^2)$

3. $4a^3 - 12a^2 + 8a$ $4a(a - 2)(a - 1)$

4. $7(m + n) - w(m - n)$ prime

5. $x(1 - y) - 2x(y - 1)$ $3x(1 - y)$

6. $9y^2 - 4x^2 + 12x - 9$
$(3y - 2x + 3)(3y + 2x - 3)$

7. $16x^2 + 64$ $16(x^2 + 4)$

Solve. Check your answers. 7.9

8. $m(m - 4) = 0$ $0, 4$

9. $a^2 - 9a - 10 = 0$ $-1, 10$

10. $24b^2 - 32b + 12 = 9b$ $\frac{4}{3}, \frac{3}{8}$

11. $2x^2 - 5x - 12 = 0$ $-\frac{3}{2}, 4$

7.9 Solving Polynomial Equations by Factoring **303**

Teacher's Resource Book
Reteaching—Chapter 7, p. 25.

P

Name _____ Date _____
Practice: For use after Lesson 7.9, Algebra 1

Solving Polynomial Equations by Factoring

Solve. Check your answers.

1. $x^2 - 4x = 0$ 0, 4
2. $y^2 + 6y = 0$ 0, -6
3. $k(k + 1) = 0$ 0, -1
4. $w(w + 2) = 0$ 0, -2
5. $n(n - 3) = 0$ 0, 3
6. $p(p - 7) = 0$ 0, 7
7. $(k + 2)(k + 1) = 0$ -2, -1
8. $(w + 5)(w - 2) = 0$ -5, 2
9. $y^2 - 6y + 9 = 0$ 3
10. $4y^2 + 20y = 0$ 0, -5
11. $9z^2 - 18z = 0$ 0, 2
12. $x^2 + 10x + 25 = 0$ -5
13. $r^2 - 3r - 10 = 0$ 5, -2
14. $p^2 + 5p - 6 = 0$ -6, 1
15. $z^2 - 7z + 10 = 0$ 5, 2
16. $t^2 - 15t - 16 = 0$ 16, -1
17. $3y^2 - 4y - 4 = 0$ 2, $\frac{2}{3}$
18. $4z^2 - 9z + 2 = 0$ $\frac{1}{4}$, 2
19. $3w^2 + 11w - 4 = 0$ $\frac{1}{3}$, -4
20. $2r^2 + r - 6 = 0$ $\frac{3}{2}$, -2

Applications

Number Problems For each problem, let n represent the missing number. Write a quadratic equation that can be used to solve the problem.

21. The sum of the squares of two consecutive even integers is 20.
$x^2 + (x + 2)^2 = 20$

22. The sum of five times an integer and the product of three and the square of the integer is two.
$5n + 3n^2 = 2$

MIXED PRACTICE

23. The sum of three consecutive even integers is 84. What are the integers? 26, 28, 30

24. The sum of 18 and a number is equal to the product of the number and 3. What is the number? 9

26 Chapter 7

E

Name _____ Date _____
Enrichment: For use after Lesson 7.9, Algebra 1

More High-Powered Factoring

The sum and difference of two numbers to the sixth power can be factored as follows:
$$a^6 + b^6 = (a^2 + b^2)(a^4 - a^2b^2 + b^4)$$
$$a^6 - b^6 = (a - b)(a^5 + a^4b + a^3b^2 + a^2b^3 + ab^4 + b^5)$$

Use the above formulas to factor each of the following.

1. $x^6 - y^6$ $(x - y)(x^5 + x^4y + x^3y^2 + x^2y^3 + xy^4 + y^5)$
2. $c^6 + d^6$ $(c^2 + d^2)(c^4 - c^2d^2 + d^4)$
3. $a^6 + 64$ $(a^2 + 4)(a^4 - 4a^2 + 16)$
4. $64x^6 - y^6z^6$ $(2x - yz)(32x^5 + 16x^4yz + 8x^3y^2z^2 + 4x^2y^3z^3 + 2xy^4z^4 + y^5z^5)$

The sum and difference of two numbers to the seventh power can be factored as shown below:
$$a^7 + b^7 = (a + b)(a^6 - a^5b + a^4b^2 - a^3b^3 + a^2b^4 - ab^5 + b^6)$$
$$a^7 - b^7 = (a - b)(a^6 + a^5b + a^4b^2 + a^3b^3 + a^2b^4 + ab^5 + b^6)$$

Use the formulas to factor each of the following.

5. $x^7 + y^7$ $(x + y)(x^6 - x^5y + x^4y^2 - x^3y^3 + x^2y^4 - xy^5 + y^6)$
6. $128 - a^7$ $(2 - a)(64 + 32a + 16a^2 + 8a^3 + 4a^4 + 2a^5 + a^6)$
7. Based on what you have learned in this and the last lesson, derive a factorization formula for the difference of two numbers to the eighth power. Show your formula below.
$a^8 - b^8 = (a - b)(a^7 + a^6b + a^5b^2 + a^4b^3 + a^3b^4 + a^2b^5 + ab^6 + b^7)$, or
$(a^4 + b^4)(a^4 - b^4) = (a^4 + b^4)(a + b)(a - b)(a^2 + b^2)$

Use your formula to factor each of the following.

8. $x^8 - 256$ $(x - 2)(x^7 + 2x^6 + 4x^5 + 8x^4 + 16x^3 + 32x^2 + 64x + 128)$
9. $a^8b^8 - c^8$ $(ab - c)(a^7b^7 + a^6b^6c + a^5b^5c^2 + a^4b^4c^3 + a^3b^3c^4 + a^2b^2c^5 + abc^6 + c^7)$

Chapter 7 27

BACKGROUND

To completely understand a problem in this lesson, the student must have the ability to organize and use the information given in the problem. Analyze errors in the student's work and then classify specific errors.

Error Analysis Classification

1. *Misunderstanding*
   Failed to understand the underlying concept of the problem
   May not have looked for the phrases that translate into equations
2. *Misapplied Strategy*
   Wrote an incorrect equation
   Made errors in the solution process
   Stopped short on the process so that the answer given for the problem was incomplete

---

7.10

Problem Solving Strategy:
Use Polynomial Equations

Many practical problems are solved by setting up and solving a polynomial equation. The polynomial equations in this lesson can be solved by factoring.

EXAMPLE 1 A gardener is planning to make a rectangular garden with an area of 80 ft^2. She has 12 yd of fencing to put around the perimeter of the garden. What should the dimensions of the garden be?

▫ **Understand the Problem**

What are the given facts?
The problem involves a rectangular garden with area 80 ft^2 and perimeter 12 yd.

What are you asked to find?
You are asked to find the length and width of the rectangular garden.

▫ **Plan Your Approach**

Choose a strategy.
1. Draw a diagram.

2. Units of measure must be the same. Change 12 yd to 36 ft.
$$36 = 2l + 2w$$
$$18 = l + w$$
$$18 - w = l$$

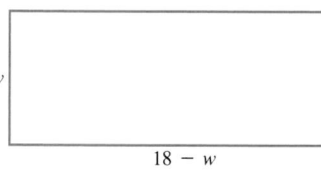

▫ **Complete the Work**

Write a word equation.
Area of a rectangle equals length times width.

$$A = (18 - w)w$$

$$80 = (18 - w)w \qquad \textit{Replace A with 80.}$$
$$80 = 18w - w^2$$
$$w^2 - 18w + 80 = 0 \qquad \textit{Solve the equation.}$$
$$(w - 10)(w - 8) = 0$$

$w - 10 = 0$	$w - 8 = 0$ *Set each factor equal to 0*
$w = 10$	$w = 8$
$l = 18 - 10 = 8$	$l = 18 - 8 = 10$

▫ **Interpret the Results**

State your answer.
The dimensions of the garden are 8 ft and 10 ft.

Check the conclusion: A rectangle 8 ft by 10 ft has an area of 8×10, or 80 ft^2. The perimeter is $2(10) + 2(8)$, or 36 ft, which is also 12 yd.

EXAMPLE 2 **Find three consecutive even integers such that the second times the third is 12 times the first.**

Understand **What are the given facts?**
the Problem The second number times the third is 12 times first.
Let n = first even integer.
Then $n + 2$ = second even integer and
$\quad n + 4$ = third even integer.

Plan Your **Write an equation.**
Approach $$(n + 2) \cdot (n + 4) = 12 \cdot (n)$$

Complete $(n + 2)(n + 4) = 12n$
the Work $n^2 + 6n + 8 = 12n$ *Multiply $(n + 2)(n + 4)$.*
$\quad n^2 - 6n + 8 = 0$ *Subtract 12n from each side.*
$(n - 4)(n - 2) = 0$

$n - 4 = 0 \quad | \quad n - 2 = 0$ *Set each factor equal to 0.*
$\quad n = 4 \quad | \quad \quad n = 2$

$n + 2 = 6 \quad | \quad n + 2 = 4$
$n + 4 = 8 \quad | \quad n + 4 = 6$

Interpret There are two sets of answers.
the Results The three integers are 4, 6, and 8 or 2, 4, and 6.
Check: $6 \times 8 \overset{?}{=} 12 \times 4 \qquad 4 \times 6 \overset{?}{=} 12 \times 2$
$\quad \quad \quad 48 = 48 \; \checkmark \qquad \quad \quad 24 = 24 \; \checkmark$

CLASS EXERCISES

The length of a rectangular piece of cloth is 3 in. more than its width. If the area of the cloth is 130 in.^{2}, find the width.

1. What information is given? What are you asked to find? given: length of rectangular cloth is 3 in. more than width and area is 130 in.^{2}; find: width
2. What mathematical idea is important in this problem? area of rectangle = length $\times$ width
3. Draw a diagram to represent the piece of cloth. Label the dimensions in terms of one variable. Check students' diagrams.
4. What equation could you use to solve this problem? $w(w + 3) = 130$
5. Solve the equation and check the answer(s). $w = 10$ in.; $l = 13$ in.
6. If the solution set includes a negative number, what does this mean? A negative number cannot be a solution to the problem; width cannot be negative.

7.10 Problem Solving Strategy: Use Polynomial Equations **305**

TEACHING SUGGESTION

Stress the key words and phrases that are used in solving word problems presented in this lesson. Students should be familiar with such words or phrases as *area, perimeter, consecutive even,* and *consecutive odd.* Use Teaching Aid 6, in the *Teacher's Resource Book,* to review the four problem solving steps before introducing the lesson.

Critical Thinking
Analyzing Whole-Part Relationships
In Example 1, the first step in solving the problem is to change 12 yd to 36 ft. Explain why this conversion of units was made. The area of the garden is given in square feet, so the dimensions of the garden should be in feet. An alternative would be to convert the area to square yards, so that the dimensions (and perimeter) would be in yards.

CHALKBOARD EXAMPLES

• **For Example 1**
 A gardener is planning to make a rectangular garden with area 80 ft^2. She has 14 yd of fencing to put around the perimeter of the garden. What should the dimensions of the garden be? 16 ft $\times$ 5 ft

• **For Example 2**
 Find three consecutive even integers such that the second times the third is 15 times the first.
 8, 10, 12

LESSON FOLLOW-UP

Assignment Guide

See p. 268B for assignments.

Mixed Problem Solving Review

- The following skills and concepts are reviewed:
  Writing an equation (Ex. 1)
  Working with percents (Ex. 2)
  Solving inequalities (Ex. 4)
  Solving uniform motion problems (Ex. 3)
- The following problem solving strategies may be appropriate:
  Writing an equation from word statements (Ex. 1)
  Making a drawing or table (Ex. 2 and 3)

Project

Students learn how to use the formula, $h = vt - 5t^2$ and what each variable represents. Have students work in groups to complete the exercises.

Lesson Quiz

Solve.
1. The area of a rectangular garden is 90 ft². If the length is 9 ft more than the width, find the dimensions.
   15 ft × 6 ft
2. Find two consecutive odd integers whose product is 143.
   11, 13 or −13, −11

PRACTICE EXERCISES

Solve. Check your solutions.

A 1. The area of a rectangular garden is 140 ft². If its length is 4 ft more than its width, find the dimensions. 14 ft × 10 ft

2. The length of a rectangular rug is 3 ft more than the width. If the area of the rug is 180 ft², find the dimensions. 15 ft × 12 ft

3. The perimeter of a rectangular piece of tin is 40 cm. If the area is 84 cm², what are its dimensions? 14 cm × 6 cm

4. A rectangular patio has an area of 96 m² and its perimeter is 44 m. Find the dimensions of the patio. 16 m × 6 m

5. Find two consecutive even integers whose product is 48. −8, −6 or 6, 8

6. Find two consecutive even integers whose product is 120. −12, −10 or 10, 12

7. The product of two consecutive odd integers is 63. Find the numbers. −9, −7 or 7

8. The product of two consecutive odd integers is 143. Find the numbers.
   −13, −11 or 11, 13
9. Find the least of three consecutive even integers if the first times the third is 4 greater than seven times the second integer. 6

B 10. Find the greatest of three consecutive odd integers if the product of the second and third is 8 more than 13 times the first. 11

11. Last year Rosa's garden measured 10 m by 25 m. This year she increased the length and decreased the width by the same amount. If her garden has an area of 216 m², find its dimensions. 27 m × 8 m

12. Iris has a square garden and wants to make it larger. If she extended one side 5 ft and the adjacent side 2 ft, the resulting garden would be rectangular with an area of 130 ft². What would its dimensions be? 13 ft × 10 ft

13. When Seth draped a rectangular tablecloth over a square table, 5 in. of cloth hung over each of two opposite sides and 6 in. hung over the other two sides. Find the dimensions of the table if the area of the tablecloth is 1680 in.². 30 in. × 30 in.

14. A rectangular tablecloth has an area of 1085 in.². When it is draped over a square table, it hangs 5 in. over two opposite sides and 3 in. over the other two sides. Find the dimensions of the table. 25 in. × 25 in.

C 15. A rectangular photograph is mounted in a frame which is 1 in. wide. If the photograph is twice as long as it is wide and the area of the photograph and frame together is 60 in.², what are the dimensions of the photograph?
   8 in. × 4 in.
16. A rectangular swimming pool, 10 ft by 25 ft, is surrounded by a deck that is the same width all around the pool. If the pool and deck together have an area of 594 ft², how wide is the deck? 4 ft

306   Chapter 7 Factoring Polynomials

Mixed Problem Solving Review

1. The length of a rectangle is 6 times its width. The perimeter of the rectangle is 70 cm. Find the length and width. length = 30 cm; width = 5 cm

2. Ms. Wayne, a chemist, needs to make a 12% alcohol solution. How many milliliters of an 8% alcohol solution must be added to 10 mL of a 20% alcohol solution to get a 12% solution? 20 mL

3. Lauren and Erik are 228 km apart. To meet, Lauren drives 64 km/h and Erik drives 56 km/h. Lauren is delayed by traffic for 45 minutes. How soon will they meet? 2.3 h

4. David is 10 kg heavier than Joanne. Together they weigh less than 100 kg. How much do they each weigh?
David weighs less than 55 kg; Joanne weighs less than 45 kg

PROJECT

Work together in small groups. Let your group be a club that studies, builds, and launches model rockets. It is important to know the formula $h = vt - 5t^2$. It tells you the height h in meters of a rocket t seconds after launch at an initial velocity of v meters per second.

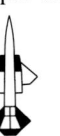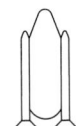

EXAMPLE Suppose you launch a rocket with an initial velocity of 30 m/s. How high will the rocket be 4 s after launch?

Write the formula.
$$h = vt - 5t^2$$
$$h = 30(4) - 5(4^2) = 120 - 80 = 40$$
So, the rocket will be 40 m high.

1. You launch your rocket with an initial velocity of 45 m/s. How high will it be after 6 s? 90 m

2. What initial velocity is necessary for a rocket if you want it to have an altitude of 50 m, 10 s after launch? 55 m/s

3. If you launch a rocket at an initial velocity of 50 m/s, how many seconds after launch will it strike the ground? 10 s

4. Suppose the record flight in your state is 32 seconds. Your club wants to beat this record. This means you must design and build a rocket that can be launched at a velocity that will keep it in the air for longer than 32 seconds. What velocity is that? greater than 160 m/s

7.10 Problem Solving Strategy: Use Polynomial Equations **307**

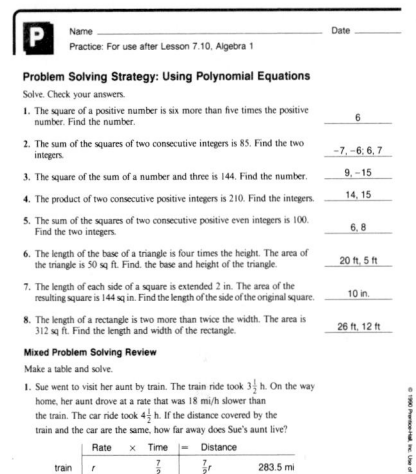

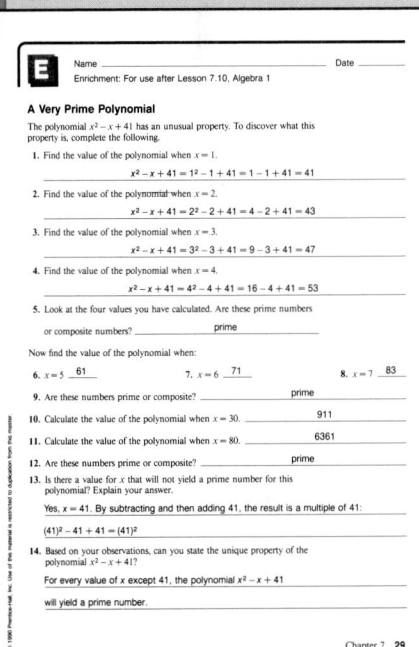

Application

The problems provided on agriculture afford students an opportunity to apply their factoring skills to solve polynomial equations pertaining to real world situations.

See *Teacher's Resource Book,* Follow-up Application, p. 30.

APPLICATION:
Agriculture

Did you know that $\frac{1}{5}$ of the total number of farms in the United States account for 80% of the produce sold in this country? Farmland covers about $\frac{1}{2}$ of the area of the United States, that is more than one billion acres. There are about 2,300,000 farms with an average size of about 440 acres. This intensive agriculture makes the best use of the land.

Most farmers grow their produce in fields and store it in a building or bin. Rectangular and round bins are commonly used on farms for storing small grains. To determine their storage needs farmers take into consideration the capacity of a bin. The capacity of a bin is represented in units, usually **bushels.** A bushel is a unit of dry measure for grain, fruit, and so on, equal to 4 pecks or 32 qt.

To compute the number of bushels of grain in a bin use the following formulas, in which the dimensions are in feet.

Rectangular Bins

Length $\times$ width $\times$ height $\times 0.8 = lwh(0.8) =$ number of bushels

Round Bins

Diameter squared $\times$ height $\times 0.625 = d^2(h)(0.625) =$ number of bushels

EXAMPLE 1   A farmer has a rectangular bin with the following dimensions: $l = 20$ ft, $w = 18$ ft and $h = 12$ ft. How much grain can be stored in two bins?

$lwh(0.8) =$ number of bushels
$(20)(18)(12)(0.8) = 3456$ bushels
$3456 \times 2 = 6912$ bushels

The farmer can store 6912 bushels in two bins. Farmers must also use other formulas in their work. Often they must estimate the amount of fencing needed to enclose their land.

EXAMPLE 2 A farmer has 2 mi of fencing to enclose 100 acres for a wheat field. Estimate the dimensions of the field.

Hint: 1 mi = 5280 ft   1 acre = 43,530 ft^2

Estimate: 2 mi is about 10,000 ft   100 acres is about 4,000,000 ft^2

$2l + 2w = 10,000$

$l = 5000 - w$

$l \cdot w = 4,000,000$

$(5000 - w)w = 4,000,000$

$w^2 - 5000w + 4,000,000 = 0$

$(w - 4000)(w - 1000) = 0$

$l = 4000 \qquad w = 1000$

The wheat field is about 4000 ft by 1000 ft.

A farmer can intensify his efforts by using the same amount of fencing to enclose a greater area. With the same 2 mi of fencing, find the approximate dimensions of the field with the greatest area. about 2500 ft × 2500 ft

Explain the problem solving strategy you would use to solve this problem.
Answers may vary.
You could use the computer program on page 272 to solve the problem.

How are the problem solving strategy and the computer program similar? How do they differ?

Solve. Use the computer program on page 272 for Exercises 4 and 6, if you wish.

1. What is the capacity in bushels of a rectangular bin that has 5040 ft^3 of space? 4032 bushels

2. What is the capacity in bushels of a round bin that has a diameter of 16 ft and a height of 12 ft? 1920 bushels

3. The length of a rectangular bin is twice its width. The height of the bin is 14 ft and the area of the floor of the bin is 450 ft^2. Find the length, width, and the capacity of bushels of the bin. l = 30 ft; w = 15 ft; 5040 bushels

4. A farmer has 2 mi of fencing to enclose 150 acres for a corn field. Estimate the dimensions of the field. 3000 ft × 2000 ft

5. The length of a corn field is 4 times its width. The perimeter is 3 mi. Estimate how many plants can be grown in the field if you grow 28,000 plants per acre. 6,400,000 plants

6. A corn field is bounded on one side by a stone wall 1 mi long. Estimate how many acres a farmer can enclose with 2 mi of fencing. 320 acres

- See *Teacher's Resource Book, Spanish Chapter Summary and Review*, pp. 13–14.
- See Extra Practice, p. 661.

CHAPTER 7 SUMMARY AND REVIEW

Vocabulary

common factor (274)

composite number (270)

difference of two squares (290)

factor completely (296)

greatest common factor (GCF) (274)

perfect square trinomial (289)

polynomial equation (300)

prime number (270)

prime factorization (270)

quadratic equation (300)

zero-product property (300)

Factors and Powers   A prime number has exactly two factors—itself   7.1
and 1. A composite number can be written as a product of prime numbers.

State whether the number is *prime* or *composite*.

1. 23 prime   **2.** 33 composite   **3.** 45 composite   **4.** 89 prime

Find the prime factorization.

5. 48 $2^4 \cdot 3$ **6.** 300 $2^2 \cdot 3 \cdot 5^2$ **7.** 120 $2^3 \cdot 3 \cdot 5$ **8.** 64 2^6

Factoring a Polynomial   The greatest common factor (GCF) of two or   7.2
more integers is the greatest integer that is a factor of each.

Find the GCF of each group of numbers.

9. 35 and 200 5   **10.** $12x^2$ and $16x^3y$ $4x^2$

Factor.

11. $3ab^2 - 9a^2b^2$ $3ab^2(1 - 3a)$ **12.** $6m^3n^2 + 12m^2n^2 - 18m^2n$ $6m^2n(mn + 2n - 3)$

Factoring a Trinomial $x^2 + bx + c$ Factoring a trinomial means   7.3, 7.4
to express the trinomial as the product of two binomials of the form
$(x + r)(x + s)$.

Factor. Check by multiplying.

13. $x^2 + 5x + 6$ $(x + 3)(x + 2)$ **14.** $y^2 - 14y + 33$ $(y - 11)(y - 3)$ **15.** $a^2 + 12ab + 11b^2$ $(a + 11b)(a + b)$

16. $c^2 + c - 56$ $(c + 8)(c - 7)$ **17.** $y^2 - 10y - 24$ $(y - 12)(y + 2)$ **18.** $x^2 + 2xy - 15y^2$ $(x - 3y)(x + 5y)$

Factoring a Trinomial $ax^2 + bx + c$ To factor trinomials when the   7.5
coefficient of the first term is not 1, you must test various factors of both the
first term of the trinomial and the last term.

Factor. Check by multiplying.

19. $2m^2 + 15m + 7$

$(2m + 1)(m + 7)$

20. $3x^2 + 5x - 12$

$(3x - 4)(x + 3)$

21. $6x^2 - x - 15$

$(3x - 5)(2x + 3)$

Special Cases of Polynomial Factoring   7.6

$$a^2 + 2ab + b^2 = (a + b)(a + b) = (a + b)^2$$
$$a^2 - 2ab + b^2 = (a - b)(a - b) = (a - b)^2$$
$$a^2 - b^2 = (a + b)(a - b)$$

Factor.

22. $w^2 - 49$ $(w + 7)(w - 7)$

23. $100m^2 - 16n^2$

$4(5m - 2n)(5m + 2n)$

24. $y^2 + 2y + 1$ $(y + 1)^2$

Factoring a Polynomial Completely   To factor a polynomial   7.7, 7.8
completely, look for:

- greatest common monomial factor, GCF
- a perfect square trinomial
- a difference of two squares
- a pair of binomial factors
- a grouping of terms

Check that each factor is prime.

Check your answer by multiplying all the factors.

Factor.

25. $7m^2 - 28$

$7(m - 2)(m + 2)$

26. $x^3y - 9xy$

$xy(x - 3)(x + 3)$

27. $6a^3 + 12a^2 + 9a$

$3a(2a^2 + 4a + 3)$

28. $3w(z + 3) - 2(z + 3)$ $(z + 3)(3w - 2)$

29. $9(x - y) + 4(y - x)$ $5(x - y)$

30. $cx - cd + dy - xy$ $(x - d)(c - y)$

31. $36x^3 - 24x^2 + 4x$ $4x(3x - 1)^2$

32. $75x^2 - 3$ $3(5x - 1)(5x + 1)$

33. $18x^2 - 45$ $9(2x^2 - 5)$

Solving Polynomial Equations   Factoring can be used to find solutions   7.9
of polynomial equations.

Solve. Check your solutions.

34. $m^2 + 6m = 0$

$0, -6$

35. $r^2 - 2r - 80 = 0$

$-8, 10$

36. $t^2 - 3t = 18$

$-3, 6$

Using Polynomial Equations   Practical problems can be solved by   7.10
setting up and solving a polynomial equation.

37. Find two consecutive even integers whose product is 728. $-28, -26$ or $26, 28$

38. The length of a rectangular rug is 3 ft more than the width. If the area of
the rug is 270 ft^2, find its dimensions. 18 ft $\times$ 15 ft

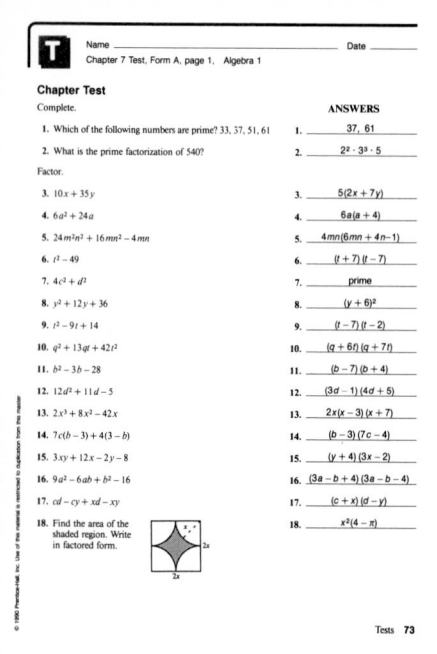

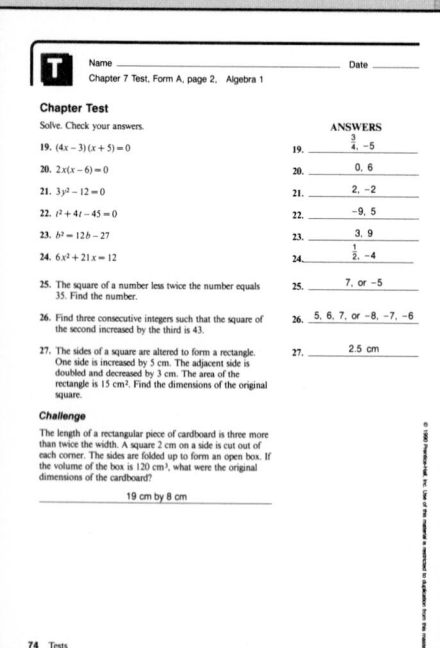

State whether the number is *prime* or *composite*.

1. 25 composite   **2.** 29 prime   **3.** 17 prime   **4.** 63 composite

Find the prime factorization.

5. 24 $2^3 \cdot 3$ **6.** 200 $2^3 \cdot 5^2$ **7.** 34 $2 \cdot 17$ **8.** 75 $3 \cdot 5^2$

Factor. Check by multiplying. Write *prime* if the polynomial is prime.

9. $9a + 6b$ $3(3a + 2b)$ **10.** $25 - 5y^2$ $5(5 - y^2)$ **11.** $8a^2b^3 - 6ab^2$
$2ab^2(4ab - 3)$

12. $a^2 - 16$ $(a - 4)(a + 4)$ **13.** $x^2 - 25y^2$ $(x - 5y)(x + 5y)$ **14.** $y^2 + 4y + 4$ $(y + 2)^2$

15. $x^2 + 6x + 5$ **16.** $n^2 - 16n + 55$ **17.** $p^2 + p + 20$ prime
$(x + 5)(x + 1)$ $(n - 5)(n - 11)$
18. $x^2 + 4xy - 21y^2$ **19.** $2m^2 + 7m + 3$ **20.** $6x^3 - 2x^2 - 20x$
$(x + 7y)(x - 3y)$ $(2m + 1)(m + 3)$ $2x(3x + 5)(x - 2)$
21. $2d(f + 2) - (f + 2)$ $(f + 2)(2d - 1)$ **22.** $5(a - b) - 2(b - a)$ $7(a - b)$

23. $dy - de + ez - yz$ $(y - e)(d - z)$ **24.** $16x^2 - 8xy + y^2 - 9$
$(4x - y + 3)(4x - y - 3)$

Solve. Check your solutions.

25. $(x - 2)(3x + 1) = 0$ $2, -\frac{1}{3}$ **26.** $b^2 + 5b = 0$ $-5, 0$

27. $s^2 - 6s + 8 = 0$ $2, 4$ **28.** $z^2 - 14z = -49$ 7

29. The sum of a negative number and its square is 72. Find the number. -9

30. Find two consecutive odd integers whose product is 255. $15, 17$ or $-17, -15$

31. The length of a rectangular garden is three times it width. Increasing its width by 1 ft and its length by 3 ft results in a garden with an area of 75 ft^2. Find the new dimensions. $15 \text{ ft} \times 5 \text{ ft}$

Challenge

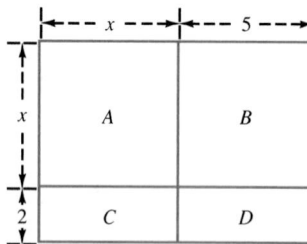

a. Find the area of the smaller rectangles A, B, C, and D. A: x^2; B: $5x$; C: $2x$; D: 10

b. Write the total area of the large rectangle as the sum of the areas of the smaller rectangles. $x^2 + 5x + 2x + 10$

c. Simplify the expression in (b).
$x^2 + 7x + 10$
d. Write the total area in factored form.
$(x + 5)(x + 2)$

Directions: In each item you are to compare a quantity in column 1 with a quantity in column 2. Write the letter of the correct answer from these choices:

A. The quantity in column 1 is greater than the quantity in column 2.
B. The quantity in column 2 is greater than the quantity in column 1.
C. The quantity in column 1 is equal to the quantity in column 2.
D. The relationship cannot be determined from the given information.

Notes: Information centered over both columns refers to one or both of the quantities being compared. A symbol that appears in both columns has the same meaning in each column. All variables represent real numbers.

Column 1	Column 2
1. $\dfrac{3}{2} + \dfrac{4}{5}$ A	$\dfrac{2}{3} + \dfrac{5}{4}$
2. $\dfrac{1}{3}$ of 276 A	$\dfrac{3}{5}$ of 150

$$12 < n \text{ and } n < 42$$

Column 1	Column 2
3. Average of D 12, n, and 42	27

$$a = -2, b = 3$$

Column 1	Column 2
4. $a^2 b - ab$ B	$1 - ab^2$
5. 0.0064 A	$\dfrac{2}{625}$

$$n > 5$$
$$n < t$$

Column 1	Column 2
6. 5 B	t
7. 30% profit on \$650 A	25% profit on \$765
8. 3.4×10^3 C	3400
9. $|3(2 - 6) + 4|$ B	$|6 - 4(-2)|$

$$x < 0$$

Column 1	Column 2
10. x D	$\dfrac{1}{x}$
11. $(a + b)(a - b)$ C	$a^2 - b^2$

Use this circle graph to answer questions 12–14.

History test grades given to 35 9th graders

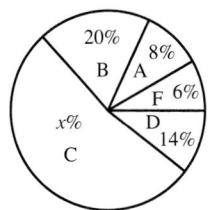

20% B 8% A F 6% D 14% C $x\%$

(*Note:* All numbers rounded to the nearest whole number and figure not drawn to scale.)

Column 1	Column 2
12. x A	48
13. Total number B of A's given.	4
14. Total receiving A a C or better	25

The individual comments provided about some problems can be helpful in guiding students to solve these problems.

3. This can be a good example of the guess–and–check method of solving problems. Have students guess a number less than 27 and another number greater than 27. Students should see that D is the only choice.

5. An alternate method of solution is to change $\dfrac{2}{625} = \dfrac{4}{1250} = \dfrac{8}{2500} = \dfrac{32}{10,000}$;   therefore, $\dfrac{2}{625} = 0.0032$.

10. Students should be encouraged to try several values such that $x < 0$, including values between -1 and 0.

See *Teacher's Resource Book,* for Preparing for Standardized Tests.

Maintaining Skills

The following skills and concepts are reviewed:

Addition, subtraction, multiplication and division of fractions

Rewriting fractions using the least common denominator (LCD)

Solving problems involving geometry

Multiply.

Example 1 $\dfrac{3}{4} \times \dfrac{4}{15}$ $\quad \dfrac{\overset{1}{\cancel{3}}}{\underset{1}{\cancel{4}}} \times \dfrac{\overset{1}{\cancel{4}}}{\underset{5}{\cancel{15}}} = \dfrac{1 \times 1}{1 \times 5} = \dfrac{1}{5}$

Divide.

Example 2 $\dfrac{2}{3} \div \dfrac{8}{9}$ $\quad \dfrac{2}{3} \div \dfrac{8}{9} = \dfrac{\overset{1}{\cancel{2}}}{\underset{1}{\cancel{3}}} \times \dfrac{\overset{3}{\cancel{9}}}{\underset{4}{\cancel{8}}} = \dfrac{1 \times 3}{1 \times 4} = \dfrac{3}{4}$

Perform the indicated operation.

1. $\dfrac{3}{4} \times \dfrac{2}{3}$ $\;\frac{1}{2}$
2. $\dfrac{2}{7} \times \dfrac{5}{10}$ $\;\frac{1}{7}$
3. $\dfrac{5}{8} \times \dfrac{4}{25}$ $\;\frac{1}{10}$
4. $\dfrac{3}{4} \times \dfrac{3}{7}$ $\;\frac{9}{28}$

5. $\dfrac{4}{5} \div \dfrac{14}{15}$ $\;\frac{6}{7}$
6. $\dfrac{3}{8} \div \dfrac{9}{10}$ $\;\frac{5}{12}$
7. $\dfrac{5}{7} \div \dfrac{2}{5}$ $\;\frac{25}{14}$
8. $\dfrac{5}{6} \div \dfrac{5}{8}$ $\;\frac{4}{3}$

Rewrite each pair of fractions using the least common denominator (LCD).

Example 3 $\dfrac{5}{12}$ and $\dfrac{7}{8}$ $\quad \dfrac{5}{12} = \dfrac{5}{12} \cdot \dfrac{2}{2} = \dfrac{10}{24}$ and $\dfrac{7}{8} = \dfrac{7}{8} \cdot \dfrac{3}{3} = \dfrac{21}{24}$

9. $\dfrac{5}{9}$ and $\dfrac{2}{3}$ $\;\frac{5}{9}, \frac{6}{9}$
10. $\dfrac{6}{11}$ and $\dfrac{1}{3}$ $\;\frac{18}{33}, \frac{11}{33}$
11. $\dfrac{5}{18}$ and $\dfrac{7}{12}$ $\;\frac{10}{36}, \frac{21}{36}$
12. $\dfrac{3}{8}$ and $\dfrac{5}{6}$ $\;\frac{9}{24}, \frac{20}{24}$

Example 4 $\dfrac{5}{12} + \dfrac{7}{8}$ $\quad \dfrac{5}{12} + \dfrac{7}{8} = \dfrac{5}{12} \cdot \dfrac{2}{2} + \dfrac{7}{8} \cdot \dfrac{3}{3} = \dfrac{10}{24} + \dfrac{21}{24} = \dfrac{31}{24}$

Perform the indicated operation.

13. $\dfrac{2}{3} + \dfrac{3}{8}$ $\;\frac{25}{24}$
14. $\dfrac{7}{12} - \dfrac{3}{18}$ $\;\frac{5}{12}$
15. $\dfrac{3}{10} + \dfrac{5}{12}$ $\;\frac{43}{60}$
16. $\dfrac{3}{4} - \dfrac{7}{12}$ $\;\frac{1}{6}$

Example 5

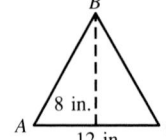

Area $= \dfrac{1}{2}$ base $\times$ height

$\qquad = \dfrac{1}{2}(8)(12) = (4)(12) = 48$

Area $= 48$ in.^{2}

Find the area.

17. rectangle: 4 in. wide, 10 in. long
40 in.^{2}

18. triangle: 9 in. base, 5 in. height
$22\frac{1}{2}$ in.^{2}

OVERVIEW • Chapter 8

SUMMARY

In Chapter 8, students use their factoring skills to simplify and perform algebraic operations on rational expressions. Students learn to check for restrictions in the denominator of rational expressions by identifying values of the variables which make the expression undefined. The importance of checking solutions for rational equations is to find possible extraneous roots. Students learn how to express ratios in simplest form and to solve equations using proportions. They use this knowledge to solve real-life problems involving rates and proportions.

After this chapter is completed, students should be able to simplify and perform operations involving rational expressions. They will be able to solve equations of real world situations involving percent, measurement, and work problems.

CHAPTER OBJECTIVES

- To identify values for variables that make a rational expression undefined and to simplify rational expressions
- To multiply and divide rational expressions
- To find the LCD of two or more rational expressions and to express a fraction as an equivalent fraction with a given denominator
- To add and subtract rational expressions
- To add or subtract a polynomial and a rational expression and to simplify complex rational expressions
- To divide polynomials
- To express ratios in simplest form and to solve equations involving proportions
- To solve rational equations, including some with extraneous solutions
- To solve work and motion problems involving rational equations

Problem Solving Strategy

To solve problems by breaking the problem into simpler parts, and putting these parts back together to represent the original problem

CHAPTER HIGHLIGHTS

The *theme* of the chapter is food. The chapter's special features and applications demonstrate how rational expressions are integrated into real world situations.

PROBLEM SOLVING AND APPLICATIONS

Problem solving and applications form an integral part of each lesson. Students use rational expressions and equations to solve problems and arrive at solutions. The problem solving Lesson 8.10 affords students the opportunity to solve work and motion problems involving rational equations in a variety of situations.

TECHNOLOGY

Calculator

The emphasis of calculators in this chapter is on manipulating rational equations into calculator-ready form. Students learn that an equation must be expressed in calculator-ready form before substituting values into the equation. Once this is done, they input the sequence into the calculator.

RESOURCES

Teacher's Resource Book

- Teaching Aids 6, 9
- Transparencies 13, 24

Chapter Content	Basic	Average	Enriched	R	P	E
8.1 Simplifying Rational Expressions	D: 318/1-25 odd, 47 R: 318/4, 12, 14	D: 319/1-39 odd, 47, 48	D: 319/27-45 odd, 47, 48	1	2	3
8.2 Multiplying Rational Expressions	D: 322/1-20 odd, 43, 45 R: 318/2, 6, 8	D: 322/1-35 odd, 43, 45, 47 R: 319/22, 24, 26	D: 322/23-41 odd, 45, 47, 49 R: 319/32, 34, 36	4	5	6
8.3 Dividing Rational Expressions	D: 326/1-17 odd, 41 R: 322/6, 8, 10	D: 326/1-33 odd, 41, 42 R: 322/8, 18, 28	D: 326/19-39 odd, 40-42 R: 322/24, 26, 38	7	8	9
8.4 Least Common Denominator (LCD)	D: 331/1-19 odd, 41 R: 326/6, 8, 14 331/2, 8, 14	D: 331/1-33 odd, 41, 42 R: 326/16, 24, 28 331/4, 8, 18	D: 331/21-39, 41, 42 R: 326/24, 30, 36	10	11	12
8.5 Adding and Subtracting Rational Expressions	D: 335/1-21 odd, 41 R: 331/6, 10, 12	D: 335/1-31 odd, 41 R: 331/10, 22, 30	D: 335/23-39, 41 R: 331/22, 24, 26	13	14	15
8.6 Mixed Expressions and Complex Rational Expressions	D: 339/1-23 odd, 46 R: 335/6, 10, 12 Test Yourself	D: 339/1-37 odd, 46, 47 R: 335/24, 26, 28 Test Yourself	D: 339/25-45 odd, 46, 47 R: Test Yourself	16	17	18
8.7 Dividing Polynomials	D: 344/1-19 odd, 39 R: 339/12, 20, 22	D: 344/1-31 odd, 39 R: 339/18, 24, 30	D: 344/21-37 odd, 39 R: 339/26, 28, 40	19	20	21
8.8 Ratios and Proportions	D: 348/1-21 odd, 39, 41 R: 344/6, 12, 14	D: 348/1-31 odd, 39, 41, 43 R: 344/18, 22, 24	D: 348/23-37 odd, 39-43 R: 344/24, 26, 28	22	23	24
8.9 Solving Rational Equations	D: 352/1-19 odd, 38 R: 348/4, 10, 16 352/2, 4, 8	D: 352/1-31 odd, 38, 39 R: 348/22, 24, 28 352/2, 10, 16	D: 352/21-37 odd, 38, 39 R: 348/24, 26, 28	25	26	27
8.10 Problem Solving: Work and Motion	D: 357/1-6 odd R: 352/10, 12, 14	D: 357/1-9 odd R: 352/10, 14, 18	D: 357/7-11 odd R: 352/22, 26, 28		28	29
8.11 Problem Solving Strategy: Solve a Simpler Problem	D: 360/1-5 odd MPSR: 1-3 R: Test Yourself	D: 360/1-9 odd MPSR: 1-3 R: Test Yourself	D: 360/7-11 odd MPSR: 1-3 R: Test Yourself		30	31

D = Daily   R = Review   MPSR = Mixed Problem Solving Review   R = Reteaching   P = Practice   E = Enrichment

STUDENT TEXT   TEACHER'S RESOURCE BOOK

	STUDENT TEXT				TEACHER'S RESOURCE BOOK	
Review And Testing	Test Yourself	340	Chapter Test	364	Spanish Chapter Summary and Review	15-16
	Test Yourself	361	Prep. for Stan. Tests	365	• Quizzes	77-80
	Chapter Sum. and Rev.	362	Cumulative Review	366	• Chapter Test (Form A)	81-82
			Extra Practice	662	• Chapter Test (Form B)	83-84
					Calculator Test	15-16
Special Features	Extra	319	Application	341	Applications—Chapter 8	32
	Writing in Algebra	323	Algebra in Health	344	Critical Thinking	8
	Logical Reasoning	327	Biography	349	Reading and Writing in Algebra	8
	Logical Reasoning	332	Critical Thinking	353	Technology	17
	Algebra in Physics	336	Math Club Activity	357		
			Project	361		

8 Rational Expressions

Food packaging and labels contain nutritional information that is important to a healthy diet. Calculating the calories per serving and the recommended daily percentages of nutrients involves the use of rational expressions.

315

BACKGROUND

Mathematical expressions and equations are sometimes used in cooking. Many algebraic formulas are used in measuring ingredients. Cooks may use rational expressions in converting measurements such as cups to pints or ounces to pounds.

BACKGROUND

In the Capsule Review, students practice reducing rational expressions by dividing by common factors. This review prepares students for this lesson on factoring when multiplying rational expressions.

Critical Thinking

Prediction Predict what would happen if you always multiplied the factors first, and then simplified the product. Students should discuss that in exercises similar to Example 2, you would get the same answer and it would probably take the same amount of time as the method shown in the book. However, in exercises like Examples 4 and 5, multiplying before simplifying would be impractical.

8.2

Multiplying Rational Expressions

Objective: To multiply rational expressions

When you multiply rational numbers, you look for common factors to simplify the product or to simplify the multiplication.

$$\frac{2}{3} \cdot \frac{9}{10} = \frac{2 \cdot 9}{3 \cdot 10} = \frac{\overset{3}{\cancel{18}}}{\underset{5}{\cancel{30}}} = \frac{3}{5} \qquad \text{or} \qquad \frac{2}{3} \cdot \frac{9}{10} = \frac{2}{\underset{1}{\cancel{3}}} \cdot \frac{\overset{3}{\cancel{9}}}{\underset{5}{\cancel{10}}} = \frac{3}{5}$$

This same skill may also be used when you multiply rational expressions.

Capsule Review

EXAMPLE   Simplify: $\dfrac{15a^2b}{3a^3}$

$$\frac{15a^2b}{3a^3} = \frac{\overset{5}{\cancel{15a^2}}b}{\underset{a}{\cancel{3a^3}}} = \frac{5b}{a} \qquad \textit{Divide by common factors.}$$

Simplify.

1. $\dfrac{10m^2}{2m^3}$ $\frac{5}{m}$ 2. $\dfrac{12x^2y^3}{4x^3y^2}$ $\frac{3y}{x}$ 3. $\dfrac{3m+6}{2m+4}$ $\frac{3}{2}$ 4. $\dfrac{2x^2+x-6}{4-x^2}$ $\frac{2x-3}{2-x}$

The rule for multiplying rational expressions is similar to the rule for multiplying rational numbers.

Multiplication of Rational Expressions

If $\dfrac{P}{Q}$ and $\dfrac{R}{S}$ are rational expressions with $Q \neq 0$ and $S \neq 0$,

then $\dfrac{P}{Q} \cdot \dfrac{R}{S} = \dfrac{P \cdot R}{Q \cdot S}$.

From now on, to make your work simpler, you will not be asked to state the restrictions upon the variables. You may assume that all denominators do not equal zero.

EXAMPLE 1   **Multiply:** $\dfrac{2}{g} \cdot \dfrac{5}{3gh}$

$$\frac{2}{g} \cdot \frac{5}{3gh} = \frac{2 \cdot 5}{g \cdot 3gh} = \frac{10}{3g^2h} \qquad \text{Can the product be simplified? Why?}$$

320   Chapter 8 Rational Expressions

EXAMPLE 2 **Multiply:** $\dfrac{4b}{3a^3} \cdot \dfrac{15ab^2}{2b}$

$$\dfrac{4b}{3a^3} \cdot \dfrac{15ab^2}{2b} = \dfrac{\overset{2}{\cancel{4b}}}{\underset{a^2}{\cancel{3a^3}}} \cdot \dfrac{\overset{5}{\cancel{15}}ab^2}{\underset{1}{\cancel{2b}}}$$ *Divide by common factors.*

$$\dfrac{2}{a^2} \cdot \dfrac{5b^2}{1} = \dfrac{10b^2}{a^2}$$ *Multiply.*

When multiplying rational expressions that have polynomials in the numerator and in the denominator, factor the polynomials and then look for common factors.

EXAMPLE 3 **Multiply:** $\dfrac{m-1}{2m+4} \cdot \dfrac{3m+6}{4m-1}$

$$\dfrac{m-1}{2m+4} \cdot \dfrac{3m+6}{4m-1} = \dfrac{m-1}{2\cancel{(m+2)}} \cdot \dfrac{3\cancel{(m+2)}}{4m-1}$$ *Factor, and then divide by common factors.*

$$= \dfrac{3(m-1)}{2(4m-1)} = \dfrac{3m-3}{8m-2}$$ *Multiply the remaining factors.*

EXAMPLE 4 **Multiply:** $\dfrac{2x^2-5x-12}{6x} \cdot \dfrac{-3x-12}{x^2-16}$

$$\dfrac{2x^2-5x-12}{6x} \cdot \dfrac{-3x-12}{x^2-16} = \dfrac{(2x+3)\cancel{(x-4)}}{\underset{2}{\cancel{6x}}} \cdot \dfrac{\overset{-1}{\cancel{-3}}\cancel{(x+4)}}{\cancel{(x+4)}\cancel{(x-4)}}$$ *Factor. Divide.*

$$= \dfrac{-1(2x+3)}{2x} = -\dfrac{2x+3}{2x}$$ *Multiply.*

EXAMPLE 5 **Multiply:** $\dfrac{2x^2-2x-4}{4-x^2} \cdot \dfrac{2x^2+x-6}{4x^2-2x-6}$

$$\dfrac{2x^2-2x-4}{4-x^2} \cdot \dfrac{2x^2+x-6}{4x^2-2x-6}$$

$$= \dfrac{2(x+1)(x-2)}{(2-x)(2+x)} \cdot \dfrac{(2x-3)(x+2)}{2(x+1)(2x-3)}$$ *Factor.*

$$= \dfrac{\cancel{2}\cancel{(x+1)}\cancel{(x-2)}}{-1\cancel{(x-2)}\cancel{(2+x)}} \cdot \dfrac{\cancel{(2x-3)}\cancel{(x+2)}}{\cancel{2}\cancel{(x+1)}\cancel{(2x-3)}}$$ *Rewrite opposites. Divide.*

$$= \dfrac{1}{-1} = -1$$ *Multiply.*

8.2 Multiplying Rational Expressions **321**

321

Common Error

- Students often do not simplify a problem before and after multiplying. Emphasize that factoring the numerator and denominator of each expression before multiplying will facilitate computations.
- See *Teacher's Resource Book* for additional remediation.

LESSON FOLLOW-UP

Assignment Guide

See p. 314B for assignments.

Writing in Algebra

Students make up their own rational expressions for Exercises 2, 3, and 4, that satisfy the condition in the exercise.

See *Teacher's Resource Book* for Reading and Writing in Algebra Activity p. 8.

Lesson Quiz

Multiply. Express each product in simplest form.

1. $\dfrac{10}{18} \cdot \dfrac{27}{5}$ 3

2. $\dfrac{8}{21} \cdot \dfrac{7}{4}$ $\dfrac{2}{3}$

3. $\dfrac{5x}{3x^2} \cdot \dfrac{4}{x^2y}$ $\dfrac{20}{3x^3y}$

4. $\dfrac{10b^2}{c^3} \cdot \dfrac{a^2}{2b^3}$ $\dfrac{5a^2}{bc^3}$

5. $\dfrac{12ab^2}{5b^3c^2} \cdot \dfrac{5ac}{3a}$ $\dfrac{4a}{bc}$

6. $\dfrac{5k^2}{12} \cdot \dfrac{3k^2 - 15k}{k - 5}$ $\dfrac{5k^3}{4}$

7. $\dfrac{17}{a - 7} \cdot \dfrac{6a^2 - 42a}{12ab^2}$ $\dfrac{17}{2b^2}$

8. $\dfrac{2h + 4}{3h - 9} \cdot \dfrac{6h - 18}{4h + 20}$ $\dfrac{h + 2}{h + 5}$

9. $\dfrac{3k^2 - 15k}{4k + 6} \cdot \dfrac{2}{3k}$ $\dfrac{k - 5}{2k + 3}$

10. $\dfrac{r^2 + 3r - 10}{2r + 1} \cdot \dfrac{2r^2 + 7r + 3}{r + 5}$

    $(r - 2)(r + 3)$

CLASS EXERCISES

Multiply. Express the product in simplest form.

1. $\dfrac{1}{2} \cdot \dfrac{5}{9}$ $\dfrac{5}{18}$

2. $\dfrac{4}{7} \cdot \dfrac{21}{6}$ 2

3. $\dfrac{m}{6} \cdot \dfrac{m}{2}$ $\dfrac{m^2}{12}$

4. $\dfrac{a}{b} \cdot \dfrac{b}{-a}$ -1

5. $\dfrac{uv}{u^2} \cdot \dfrac{uv^2}{v}$ v^2

6. $\dfrac{3b^2}{a} \cdot \dfrac{2a^2}{b}$ $6ab$

7. $\dfrac{5ab^2}{c^2} \cdot \dfrac{3ac^3}{10b^3}$ $\dfrac{3a^2c}{2b}$

8. $\dfrac{xy + y}{xy} \cdot \dfrac{x}{y}$ $\dfrac{x + 1}{y}$

9. $\dfrac{s^2 + 3s}{6s + 12} \cdot \dfrac{2s + 4}{s + 3}$ $\dfrac{s}{3}$

10. $\dfrac{t^2 + 5t + 6}{t - 3} \cdot \dfrac{t^2 - 2t - 3}{t^2 + 3t + 2}$ $t + 3$

PRACTICE EXERCISES

Multiply. Express the product in simplest form.

A

1. $\dfrac{3}{x} \cdot \dfrac{2}{5xy}$ $\dfrac{6}{5x^2y}$

2. $\dfrac{4}{a} \cdot \dfrac{3}{7ab}$ $\dfrac{12}{7a^2b}$

3. $\dfrac{3}{xy} \cdot \dfrac{4}{5x}$ $\dfrac{12}{5x^2y}$

4. $\dfrac{7}{2ab} \cdot \dfrac{3}{2b}$ $\dfrac{21}{4ab^2}$

5. $\dfrac{3x}{2y^3} \cdot \dfrac{10yx^2}{3x}$ $\dfrac{5x^2}{y^2}$

6. $\dfrac{2b}{5a^3} \cdot \dfrac{20ab^2}{4b}$ $\dfrac{2b^2}{a^2}$

7. $\dfrac{3rs}{2t^2} \cdot \dfrac{4rt}{5s^2}$ $\dfrac{6r^2}{5st}$

8. $\dfrac{10xy}{3z^2} \cdot \dfrac{9yz}{5x^2}$ $\dfrac{6y^2}{xz}$

9. $\dfrac{12pq}{7r^3} \cdot \dfrac{49qr}{14p^2}$ $\dfrac{6q^2}{pr^2}$

10. $\dfrac{24ab}{3c^3} \cdot \dfrac{5bc}{15a^2}$ $\dfrac{8b^2}{3ac^2}$

11. $\dfrac{28m^3n^2}{3p} \cdot \dfrac{18n^2p^2}{7mn}$ $24m^2n^3p$

12. $\dfrac{m - 2}{3m + 9} \cdot \dfrac{2m + 6}{2m - 4}$ $\dfrac{1}{3}$

13. $\dfrac{x - 5}{4x + 6} \cdot \dfrac{6x + 9}{3x - 15}$ $\dfrac{1}{2}$

14. $\dfrac{n + 3}{2n - 8} \cdot \dfrac{6n - 24}{2n + 1}$ $\dfrac{3(n + 3)}{2n + 1}$

15. $\dfrac{2c + 4}{6c - 8} \cdot \dfrac{c - 5}{c + 2}$ $\dfrac{c - 5}{3c - 4}$

16. $\dfrac{r + 4}{2r + 18} \cdot \dfrac{3r + 27}{r - 7}$ $\dfrac{3(r + 4)}{2(r - 7)}$

17. $\dfrac{b + 2}{3b + 36} \cdot \dfrac{b + 12}{2b - 3}$ $\dfrac{b + 2}{3(2b - 3)}$

18. $\dfrac{2x^2 - 2x - 4}{8x} \cdot \dfrac{-8x - 16}{x^2 - 4}$ $-\dfrac{2(x + 1)}{x}$

19. $\dfrac{3r^2 - 10r - 8}{2r} \cdot \dfrac{-2r - 8}{r^2 - 16}$ $-\dfrac{3r + 2}{r}$

20. $\dfrac{x^2 - 4x - 5}{25 - x^2} \cdot \dfrac{x^2 + 2x - 15}{x^2 - 2x - 3}$ -1

21. $\dfrac{2z^2 + z - 6}{4 - z^2} \cdot \dfrac{z^2 + 3z - 10}{2z^2 + 7z - 15}$ -1

B

22. $\dfrac{32a^5b^3}{7c^2d^3} \cdot \dfrac{28c^3d^2}{24a^2b^5}$ $\dfrac{16a^3c}{3b^2d}$

23. $\dfrac{45q^2r^3}{8s^3t^5} \cdot \dfrac{24s^5t^2}{18q^4r}$ $\dfrac{15r^2s^2}{2q^2t^3}$

24. $\dfrac{7t^2 - 28t}{2t^2 - 5t - 12} \cdot \dfrac{6t^2 - t - 15}{49t^3}$ $\dfrac{3t - 5}{7t^2}$

25. $\dfrac{18i^2 - 6i}{3i^4} \cdot \dfrac{10i^2 - 7i - 12}{15i^2 + 7i - 4}$ $\dfrac{2(2i - 3)}{i^3}$

26. $\dfrac{2\theta^2 + 7\theta + 3}{3\theta^2 + 14\theta + 15} \cdot \dfrac{6\theta^2 + 19\theta + 15}{4\theta^2 + 8\theta + 3}$ 1

27. $\dfrac{15n^2 + 16n + 4}{20n^2 + 43n + 14} \cdot \dfrac{8n^2 + 50n + 63}{6n^2 + 31n + 18}$ 1

28. $\dfrac{9a^2 + 43a - 10}{27a^2 + 12a - 4} \cdot \dfrac{6a^2 - 11a - 10}{5a^2 + 29a + 20}$ $\dfrac{2a - 5}{5a + 4}$

29. $\dfrac{10l^2 - 67l - 21}{20l^2 - 84l - 27} \cdot \dfrac{3l^2 + 8l - 35}{3l^2 - 28l + 49}$ $\dfrac{l + 5}{2l - 9}$

30. $\dfrac{10a^2 - 7a - 12}{9 - 4a^2} \cdot \dfrac{2a^2 - a - 6}{7a^2 - 10a - 8}$ $-\dfrac{5a + 4}{7a + 4}$

31. $\dfrac{7l^2 + 33l - 10}{15 - 17l - 4l^2} \cdot \dfrac{28l^2 - 9l - 9}{49l^2 + 7l - 6}$ -1

322   Chapter 8 Rational Expressions

32. $\dfrac{6w^2 - 19w - 7}{2w^2 + 3w - 35} \cdot \dfrac{15 - 37w - 8w^2}{24w^2 - w - 3}$ -1 **33.** $\dfrac{2a^2 + 5a + 2}{10 + 29a - 21a^2} \cdot \dfrac{3a^2 + 7a - 20}{a^2 + 6a + 8}$ $-\dfrac{2a + 1}{7a + 2}$

34. $\dfrac{4y^2 + 14y + 6}{18y^2 + 69y + 21} \cdot \dfrac{12y^2 + 102y + 210}{y^2 + 4y + 3}$ **35.** $\dfrac{4s^2 - 2s - 2}{3s^2 + s - 10} \cdot \dfrac{3s^2 - 17s + 20}{8s^2 + 28s + 12}$
See below.   See below.

C **36.** $\dfrac{f^2 - r^2}{f^2 + fr - 2r^2} \cdot \dfrac{f^2 + 3fr + 2r^2}{f^2 + 2fr + r^2}$ 1 **37.** $\dfrac{a^2 + 5ae + 6e^2}{2a^2 + 7ae + 3e^2} \cdot \dfrac{2a^2 + 11ae + 5e^2}{a^2 + 7ae + 10e^2}$ 1

38. $\dfrac{2c^2 + cd - 3d^2}{2c^2 - 9cd - 35d^2} \cdot \dfrac{2c^2 + 7cd + 5d^2}{2c^2 + 5cd + 3d^2}$ **39.** $\dfrac{6t^2 + 5tu + u^2}{2t^2 + 3tu + u^2} \cdot \dfrac{7t^2 + 4tu - 3u^2}{6t^2 + 29tu + 9u^2}$
See below.   See below.

40. $\dfrac{2\theta^2 + 90c + 7c^2}{3\theta^2 + 2\theta c - c^2} \cdot \dfrac{3\theta^2 + 13\theta c + 4c^2}{2\theta^2 + 13\theta c + 21c^2}$ **41.** $\dfrac{3r^2 - 4re - 4e^2}{4r^2 - 4re - 3e^2} \cdot \dfrac{2r^2 + re - 6e^2}{6r^2 + re - 2e^2}$
$\dfrac{(3\theta + c)(\theta + 4c)}{(3\theta - c)(\theta + 3c)}$ $\dfrac{(r - 2e)(r + 2e)}{(2r - e)(2r + e)}$

Applications

Calculator   Can the following expressions be entered directly into your calculator? Write the input sequence for each using $a = -2$, $b = 3$, and $c = 8$ and evaluate.

42. $5a^3 + c$ -32 **43.** $\dfrac{-6ab^2c}{bc}$ 36 **44.** $\dfrac{a^4 + 2b}{a + b}$ 22

45. $\dfrac{(a - b)^3}{(a + b)^2}$ -125 **46.** $\dfrac{2(b + c)}{2c}$ 1.375 **47.** $\dfrac{3b + 8c}{4bc}$ 0.7604

Geometry   Find the volume of each rectangular solid with the given dimensions. ($V = lwh$)

48. length: $\dfrac{x - 2}{x^2 + 2x - 35}$; width: $\dfrac{3x + 2}{4}$; height: $\dfrac{x - 5}{3x + 2}$ $\dfrac{x - 2}{4(x + 7)}$

49. length: $\dfrac{3x^2 + 8x - 3}{2x^2 + 5x - 3}$; width: $\dfrac{4x - 6}{3x - 1}$; height: $\dfrac{2x - 1}{2x^2 + 7x - 15}$ $\dfrac{2}{x + 5}$

WRITING IN ALGEBRA

Use the expression $x^2 + 5x + 6$ as part of your answer for each of the following. Answers 2–4 may vary.

1. Write an equation that shows the factored form of the expression. $(x + 3)(x + 2)$

2. Write a rational expression that can be simplified. Example: $\dfrac{x^2 + 5x + 6}{x + 2}$

3. Write a rational expression that cannot be simplified. Example: $\dfrac{x^2 + 5x + 6}{x - 1}$

4. Write a rational expression that is undefined when $x = -3$. Example: $\dfrac{x^2 + 5x + 6}{x + 3}$

Additional Answers

34. $\dfrac{4(2y + 1)(y + 5)}{(3y + 1)(y + 1)}$ **38.** $\dfrac{c - d}{c - 7d}$

35. $\dfrac{(s - 1)(s - 4)}{2(s + 2)(s + 3)}$ **39.** $\dfrac{7t - 3u}{2t + 9u}$

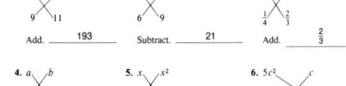

- In the Capsule Review, students practice dividing rational numbers. This review will help to show students that multiplying rational expressions can be used in simplifying division problems involving rational expressions.
- A review of reciprocals may be helpful before starting the lesson. Use both rational numbers and rational expressions in your examples.

Critical Thinking

Comparing-Contrasting How is division of rational numbers like multiplication? Multiplication and division are inverse operations, so division by a given number (not 0) is the same as multiplying by the reciprocal of that number.

8.3

Dividing Rational Expressions

Objective: To divide rational expressions

Multiplication and division are opposite (inverse) operations. Recall that the rules for dividing involve *reciprocals* or *multiplicative inverses*. Reciprocals are two numbers whose product is 1. For example, $\frac{3}{4} \cdot \frac{4}{3} = 1$. Thus $\frac{3}{4}$ and $\frac{4}{3}$ are reciprocals. Are $2\frac{1}{2}$ and $\frac{2}{5}$ reciprocals? Why?

Capsule Review

To divide by a fraction, multiply by the reciprocal of the fraction.

EXAMPLE Divide: $\frac{5}{8} \div \frac{3}{4}$

$$\overset{\text{reciprocals}}{\frac{5}{8} \div \frac{3}{4}} = \frac{5}{8} \cdot \frac{4}{3} = \frac{5}{\underset{2}{\cancel{8}}} \cdot \frac{\overset{1}{\cancel{4}}}{3} = \frac{5}{6}$$

Divide. Simplify if possible.

1. $\frac{2}{3} \div \frac{4}{5}$ $\frac{5}{6}$ **2.** $6 \div \frac{3}{8}$ 16   **3.** $\frac{3}{4} \div 2$ $\frac{3}{8}$ **4.** $3\frac{1}{2} \div 4$ $\frac{7}{8}$

The rule for dividing rational expressions is similar to the rule for dividing fractions.

Division of Rational Expressions

If $\frac{P}{Q}$ and $\frac{R}{S}$ are rational expressions and $Q \neq 0$, $R \neq 0$, and $S \neq 0$,

then $\dfrac{P}{Q} \div \dfrac{R}{S} = \dfrac{P}{Q} \cdot \dfrac{S}{R} = \dfrac{P \cdot S}{Q \cdot R}$

EXAMPLE 1 **Divide:** $\dfrac{3}{a} \div \dfrac{6b}{5a}$

$$\frac{3}{a} \div \frac{6b}{5a} = \frac{3}{a} \cdot \frac{5a}{6b} \qquad \textit{Multiply by } \tfrac{5a}{6b}, \textit{ the reciprocal of } \tfrac{6b}{5a}.$$

$$= \frac{\cancel{3}}{\cancel{a}} \cdot \frac{5\cancel{a}}{\underset{2}{\cancel{6}b}} = \frac{5}{2b}$$

324   Chapter 8 Rational Expressions

EXAMPLE 2 **Divide:** $\dfrac{x^2 + x - 2}{3x^2 + 9x + 6} \div (x - 1)$

$$\frac{x^2 + x - 2}{3x^2 + 9x + 6} \div (x - 1)$$

$$= \frac{x^2 + x - 2}{3x^2 + 9x + 6} \cdot \frac{1}{(x - 1)}$$ *Multiply by the reciprocal of $\frac{(x - 1)}{1}$.*

$$= \frac{(x - 1)(x + 2)}{3(x + 2)(x + 1)} \cdot \frac{1}{(x - 1)}$$ *Factor.*

$$= \frac{\cancel{(x - 1)}\cancel{(x + 2)}}{3\cancel{(x + 2)}} \cdot \frac{1}{\cancel{(x - 1)}}$$ *Divide by common factors.*

$$= \frac{1}{3(x + 1)}$$ *The answer may be left in factored form.*

Rational expressions involving both multiplication and division should be simplified by performing operations from left to right unless parentheses indicate a different order.

EXAMPLE 3 **Simplify:** $\dfrac{2m^2 - 5m - 3}{9 - m^2} \div \dfrac{4m + 2}{2m^2 + 2m - 12} \cdot \dfrac{2}{m - 2}$

$$\frac{2m^2 - 5m - 3}{9 - m^2} \div \frac{4m + 2}{2m^2 + 2m - 12} \cdot \frac{2}{m - 2}$$

$$= \frac{2m^2 - 5m - 3}{9 - m^2} \cdot \frac{2m^2 + 2m - 12}{4m + 2} \cdot \frac{2}{m - 2}$$

$$= \frac{(2m + 1)\cancel{(m - 3)}}{-1\cancel{(m - 3)}(m + 3)} \cdot \frac{\cancel{2}(m + 3)\cancel{(m - 2)}}{\cancel{2}\cancel{(2m + 1)}} \cdot \frac{2}{\cancel{(m - 2)}}$$

$$= \frac{2}{-1} = -2$$

CLASS EXERCISES

Simplify.

1. $\dfrac{3}{4} \div \dfrac{9}{8}$ $\dfrac{2}{3}$

2. $\dfrac{3}{7} m \div \dfrac{2m^3}{21m}$ $\dfrac{9}{2m}$

3. $\dfrac{d}{e} \div \dfrac{e^2}{d^3}$ $\dfrac{d^4}{e^3}$

4. $\dfrac{a^2 b}{2a} \div ab^2$ $\dfrac{1}{2b}$

5. $\dfrac{a - 2}{ab} \div \dfrac{a - 2}{a}$ $\dfrac{1}{b}$

6. $\dfrac{x - 3}{6} \div \dfrac{3 - x}{2}$ $-\dfrac{1}{3}$

7. $\dfrac{y + 3}{y + 2} \div (y + 2)$ $\dfrac{y + 3}{y^2 + 4y + 4}$

8. $\dfrac{x^2 + 3x + 2}{x^2 - 4x + 3} \div \dfrac{x + 2}{x - 3}$ $\dfrac{x + 1}{x - 1}$

9. $\dfrac{p}{q} \div \dfrac{r}{q} \cdot \dfrac{p}{q}$ $\dfrac{p^2}{qr}$

8.3 Dividing Rational Expressions   **325**

Common Error

- Students often make errors when solving problems involving multiplication and/or division of three or more fractions. To emphasize the importance of performing the operations from left to right, have them do some simple fraction problems first.
- See *Teacher's Resource Book* for additional remediation.

LESSON FOLLOW-UP

Discussion

Are $3\frac{2}{5}$ and $\frac{5}{17}$ reciprocals? Explain.

yes; $3\frac{2}{5} \cdot \frac{5}{17} = \frac{17}{5} \cdot \frac{5}{17} = 1.$

Assignment Guide

See p. 314B for assignments.

Logical Reasoning

Discuss that although Steps 2–4 can be interchanged, in most cases it is easier to simplify before you multiply.

Lesson Quiz

Express each in simplest form.

1. $\frac{5i}{2k} \div \frac{15i}{k^2}$ $\frac{k}{6}$

2. $\frac{2a^2}{b^2} \div \frac{14a}{3b}$ $\frac{3a}{7b}$

3. $\frac{z+2}{4} \div \frac{z+2}{48}$ 12

4. $\frac{3r-2}{12} \div \frac{2-3r}{4}$ $-\frac{1}{3}$

5. $\frac{n+5}{n+14} \div (n+5)$ $\frac{1}{n+14}$

6. $\frac{7z-21}{3z+5} \div (z-3)$ $\frac{7}{3z+5}$

7. $\frac{3a+6}{7a-28} \div \frac{6a+12}{6a-8}$ $\frac{3a-4}{7(a-4)}$

8. $\frac{r^2+9r+20}{r^2-64} \div \frac{r+5}{r+8}$ $\frac{r+4}{r-8}$

9. $\frac{b-a}{3b+2a} \div \frac{a-b}{2a-b} \cdot$ $\frac{2a-5b}{2a-b}$ $\frac{2a-5b}{3b+2a}$

10. $\frac{k-5}{8k+12} \cdot \frac{2k+3}{3k+1} \div \frac{5-k}{12k+4}$ -1

326

PRACTICE EXERCISES

Divide.

A

1. $\frac{15}{a} \div \frac{3b}{2a}$ $\frac{10}{b}$

2. $\frac{9}{x} \div \frac{3y}{4x}$ $\frac{12}{y}$

3. $\frac{6}{2c} \div \frac{3d}{4c}$ $\frac{4}{d}$

4. $\frac{r^2}{7s^2} \div \frac{3r}{28s}$ $\frac{4r}{3s}$

5. $\frac{d^2}{3e^2} \div \frac{4d}{2e}$ $\frac{d}{6e}$

6. $\frac{15a^2}{4b^2} \div \frac{5a}{2b}$ $\frac{3a}{2b}$

7. $\frac{3z-51}{2z+5} \div (z-17)$ $\frac{3}{2z+5}$

8. $\frac{11k+121}{7k-15} \div (k+11)$ $\frac{11}{7k-15}$

9. $\frac{x^2+10x-11}{x^2+12x+11} \div (x-1)$ $\frac{1}{x+1}$

10. $\frac{z^2+2z-15}{z^2+9z+20} \div (z-3)$ $\frac{1}{z+4}$

11. $\frac{3r-21}{5r+15} \div \frac{3r+6}{7r+21}$ $\frac{7(r-7)}{5(r+2)}$

12. $\frac{5a+10}{2a-20} \div \frac{7a+14}{14a-20}$ $\frac{5(7a-10)}{7(a-10)}$

13. $\frac{x^2+7x+10}{x^2-36} \div \frac{x+5}{x-6}$ $\frac{x+2}{x+6}$

14. $\frac{a^2-9}{a^2-2a-24} \div \frac{a-3}{a-6}$ $\frac{a+3}{a+4}$

15. $\frac{2a^2}{3b} \div \frac{a}{b} \div \frac{5b^2}{2a}$ $\frac{4a^2}{15b^2}$

16. $\frac{r^4s}{3} \div \frac{r^3}{s^2} \div \frac{3s}{4}$ $\frac{4rs^2}{9}$

17. $\frac{b-a}{2b+a} \cdot \frac{a+2b}{b+a} \div \frac{b-a}{b+a}$ 1

18. $\frac{2r+s}{3s-1} \div \frac{s-3}{1-3s} \cdot \frac{s-3}{s+2r}$ -1

B

19. $\frac{18a^3c^2}{25b^2} \div \frac{12a^2c}{5b}$ $\frac{3ac}{10b}$

20. $\frac{24x^5y^3}{18z^2} \div \frac{15x^2y}{12z}$ $\frac{16x^3y^2}{15z}$

21. $\frac{5x^2}{y^2-36} \div \frac{25xy-25x}{y^2-7y+6}$ $\frac{x}{5(y+6)}$

22. $\frac{4a^3}{b^2-4} \div \frac{6ab-18a}{b^2-b-6}$ $\frac{2a^2}{3(b-2)}$

23. $(16-c^2) \div \frac{2c^2-c-36}{12c-54}$ $6(4-c)$

24. $(27-3r^2) \div \frac{5r^2-9r-18}{45r+54}$ $-27(3+r)$

25. $\frac{10h^2+21h-10}{12h^2-7h-12} \div \frac{2h^2+9h+10}{4h^2+11h+6}$ $\frac{5h-2}{3h+4}$

26. $\frac{6n^2+7n-24}{2n^2+3n-9} \div \frac{-9n^2+64}{8n^2+21n-9}$ $\frac{8n-3}{2-3n}$

27. $\frac{8t^2+2t-15}{6t^2-2t-4} \div \frac{15-22t+8t^2}{6t^2-5t-6}$ $\frac{2t+3}{2t-2}$

28. $\frac{3a^2+7a-6}{4a^2+8a-5} \div \frac{6-7a-3a^2}{2a^2+a-1}$ $-\frac{a+1}{2a+5}$

29. $\frac{5x^2+10x-15}{5-6x+x^2} \div \frac{2x^2+7x+3}{4x^2-8x-5}$ $\frac{5(2x-5)}{x-5}$

30. $\frac{12x^2+19x+5}{2x^2-7x+3} \div \frac{10x+5}{3x-2} \cdot \frac{2x^2-5x-3}{12x^2-5x-3}$ $\frac{(4x+5)(3x-2)}{5(2x-1)(4x-3)}$

31. $\frac{14y^2+13y+3}{30y^2-27y-21} \div \frac{6y^2+11y-10}{25y^2-50y+21} \cdot \frac{2y+5}{5y-3}$ $\frac{7y+3}{3(3y-2)}$

32. $\frac{x^2+6x+8}{x^2+x-2} \div \frac{x+4}{2x+4} \div \frac{x+3}{x-1}$ $\frac{2(x+2)}{x+3}$

33. $\frac{2y^2-5y-3}{4y^2-12y-7} \div \frac{4y+5}{2y-7} \div \frac{y-3}{3y-1}$ $\frac{3y-1}{4y+5}$

326 Chapter 8 Rational Expressions

C 34. $\dfrac{3a^2}{b^2-16} \div \dfrac{3ab+6a}{b^2+6b+8}$ $\dfrac{a}{b-4}$ 35. $\dfrac{5x^2}{y^2-25} \div \dfrac{5xy-25x}{y^2-10y+25}$ $\dfrac{x}{y+5}$

36. $\dfrac{2a^2-ab-6b^2}{2b^2+9ab-5a^2} \div \dfrac{2a^2+7ab+6b^2}{a^2-4b^2}$ $-\dfrac{a-2b}{b+5a}$

37. $\dfrac{4g^2-8gh-12h^2}{8h^2+10gh+2g^2} \div \dfrac{12h^2+18gh+6g^2}{g^2-16h^2}$ $\dfrac{(g-3h)(g-4h)}{3(h+g)(2h+g)}$

38. $\dfrac{m^2+5mn-6n^2}{6m^2-mn} \div \dfrac{m^2-n^2}{2m^2-5mn-3n^2} \div \dfrac{m^2+3mn-18n^2}{3m^2+mn-2n^2}$ $\dfrac{(2m+n)(3m-2n)}{m(6m-n)}$

39. $\dfrac{3c^2-7cd-6d^2}{c^2+6cd+9d^2} \div \dfrac{3c^2-17cd+24d^2}{c^2-9d^2} \div \dfrac{6c^2+7cd-3d^2}{3c^2+cd-24d^2}$ $\dfrac{(3c+2d)(c-3d)}{(3c-d)(2c+3d)}$

Applications

Solve.

40. **Physics** June conducted an experiment to determine the stress on a copper bar. She used the formula stress $= \dfrac{\text{force}}{\text{area}}$. The force she applied was $4x - 6$ lb. She found the area of the bar to be $2x^2 + 5x - 12$ ft^2. Calculate the stress. $\dfrac{2}{x+4}$ lb/ft^2

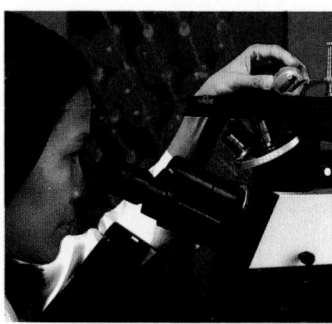

41. **Manufacturing** The efficiency of a machine is defined as the work output divided by the work input. Crystal had to calculate the efficiency of an industrial lathe. She found the work output to be $3x^2 + 5x - 2$ J (joules) and the work input to be $x + 2$ J. What is the efficiency? $3x - 1$

42. **Transportation** A train travels $x^2 - 9$ mi in $x + 3$ h. Find the rate. Use the formula distance $=$ rate $\times$ time. $x - 3$ mi/h

LOGICAL REASONING

Identifying and ordering a series of steps is helpful in understanding a computational skill. A series of steps is needed to divide rational expressions.

1. What are the steps?
   1. Take reciprocal of the divisor. 2. Factor, if possible. 3. Divide by common factors. 4. Multiply.

2. If you change the order of any of the steps, would it make a difference? Why? Yes, step 1 must be done before step 4.

3. Which steps can be interchanged? Step 4 can be done before steps 2 and 3.

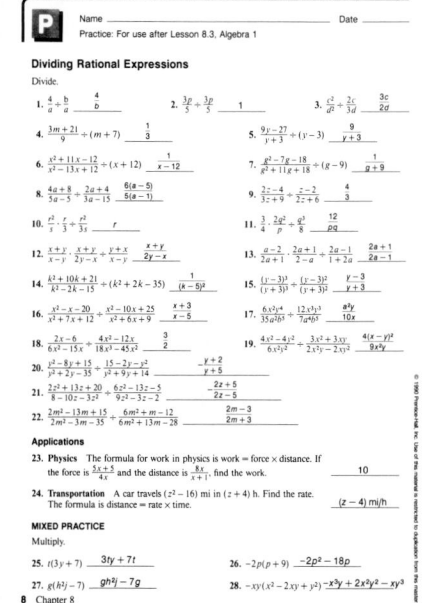

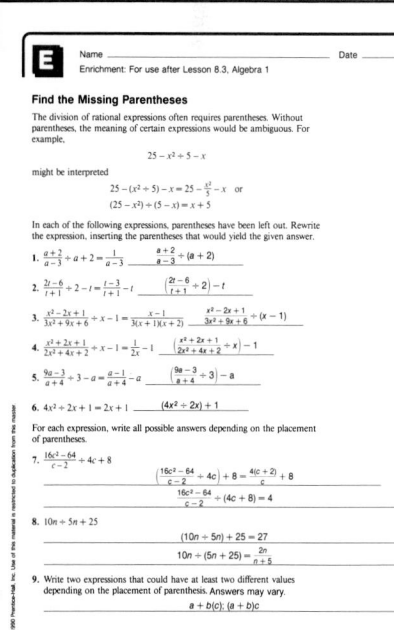

BACKGROUND

- In the Capsule Review, students practice finding the prime factorization of algebraic expressions. This review prepares students to factor denominators when trying to find the LCD for two or more rational expressions.
- You may wish to review prime and composite numbers before introducing this lesson. Have students list the first ten prime numbers and factors for various numbers less than 100.

  2, 3, 5, 7, 11, 13, 17, 19, 23, 29...

8.4

Least Common Denominator (LCD)

Objectives: To find the LCD of two or more rational expressions
To express a fraction as an equivalent fraction with a given denominator

Fractions that have the same denominator can easily be added or subtracted. Fractions that have different denominators must first be expressed as equivalent fractions with a common denominator before they can be added or subtracted. The **least common denominator (LCD)** is the smallest possible common denominator of the fractions.

$$\frac{1}{2a} + \frac{1}{3a} \qquad\qquad \frac{6}{12a} + \frac{4}{12a} \qquad\qquad \frac{3}{6a} + \frac{2}{6a}$$

common denominator $\qquad$ least common denominator

You can use prime factorization to find the LCD of fractions or rational expressions.

Capsule Review

EXAMPLE **Find the prime factorization of $3575m^3n$.**

$$3575 = \underline{\quad ? \quad} \qquad \longleftarrow \text{Not divisible by 2 or 3, try 5.}$$
$$= 5 \times 715 \qquad \longleftarrow \text{Try 5 again.}$$
$$= 5 \times 5 \times 143 \qquad \longleftarrow \text{143 is not divisible by 7; try 11.}$$
$$= 5 \times 5 \times 11 \times 13 \longleftarrow \text{13 is a prime number.}$$

Prime factorization of $3575m^3n$: $\quad 5 \cdot 5 \cdot 11 \cdot 13 \cdot m \cdot m \cdot m \cdot n$

Find the prime factorization of the following.

1. 36 $2 \cdot 2 \cdot 3 \cdot 3$ **2.** $12g^2h$ **3.** $140x^3$ **4.** $825abc$

$\qquad\qquad\qquad\qquad 2 \cdot 2 \cdot 3 \cdot g \cdot g \cdot h \quad 2 \cdot 2 \cdot 5 \cdot 7 \cdot x \cdot x \cdot x \quad 3 \cdot 5 \cdot 5 \cdot 11 \cdot a \cdot b \cdot c$

5. $23m^3np^2$ **6.** $1875e^2f$ **7.** $1000x^2y^3z$ **8.** $100,000n^5$

$23 \cdot m \cdot m \cdot m \cdot n \cdot p \cdot p \quad 3 \cdot 5 \cdot 5 \cdot 5 \cdot 5 \cdot e \cdot e \cdot f \quad 2 \cdot 2 \cdot 2 \cdot 5 \cdot 5 \cdot 5 \cdot x \cdot x \cdot y \cdot y \cdot y \cdot z$

8. $2 \cdot 2 \cdot 2 \cdot 2 \cdot 2 \cdot 5 \cdot 5 \cdot 5 \cdot 5 \cdot 5 \cdot n \cdot n \cdot n \cdot n \cdot n$

Sometimes you can find the LCD by looking for common factors.

EXAMPLE 1 **Find the least common denominator (LCD):** $\dfrac{1}{12ab}$ and $\dfrac{2b}{3a}$

Factor: $12ab = 3a \cdot 4b$ *3a is a factor of 12ab.*

So, $12ab$ is the LCD of $\dfrac{1}{12ab}$ and $\dfrac{2b}{3a}$.

328   Chapter 8 Rational Expressions

Sometimes it is difficult to recognize common factors.

> To find the least common denominator (LCD):
>
> - Factor each denominator into primes.
> - Write the greatest power of each prime factor that appears in any denominator. Use exponents.
> - Multiply these factors.

EXAMPLE 2   **Find the LCD:** $\dfrac{5}{12a^3b}$ and $\dfrac{-3}{10ab^2}$

Factor denominators: $12a^3b = 2 \cdot 2 \cdot 3 \cdot a \cdot a \cdot a \cdot b$
$10ab^2 = 2 \cdot 5 \cdot a \cdot b \cdot b$

Greatest Powers: $2^2, 3, 5, a^3, b^2$
Multiply: $2^2 \cdot 3 \cdot 5 \cdot a^3 \cdot b^2 = 60a^3b^2$

The LCD of $\dfrac{5}{12a^3b}$ and $\dfrac{-3}{10ab^2}$ is $60a^3b^2$.

To obtain equivalent expressions that have a given LCD, compare each denominator with the LCD to find the missing factors. The LCD from Example 2 is used in Example 3.

EXAMPLE 3   **Change** $\dfrac{5}{12a^3b}$ **to an equivalent expression with denominator** $60a^3b^2$**.**

$\dfrac{5}{12a^3b} = \dfrac{?}{60a^3b^2}$ *Look for missing factors.*
$12a^3b \cdot 5b = 60a^3b^2$

$\dfrac{5}{12a^3b} \cdot \dfrac{5b}{5b} = \dfrac{25b}{60a^3b^2}$ *Multiply numerator and denominator by 5b.*
$\dfrac{5b}{5b} = 1$; the expressions are equivalent.

How would you change $\dfrac{-3}{10ab^2}$ to an equivalent expression that has the denominator $60a^3b^2$?

You can use prime factorization to find the LCD when the denominators are polynomials.

EXAMPLE 4   **Find the LCD:** $\dfrac{3}{5n + 5}$ and $\dfrac{n + 2}{n^2 + 5n + 4}$

Factor denominators: $5n + 5 = 5(n + 1)$
$n^2 + 5n + 4 = (n + 1)(n + 4)$

Greatest powers: $5, (n + 1), (n + 4)$

The LCD is $5(n + 1)(n + 4)$. You may leave the LCD in factored form.

8.4 Least Common Denominator (LCD)   **329**

- **For Example 1**

Find the LCD.

1. $\dfrac{1}{6fg}$ and $\dfrac{3f}{2g}$ $6fg$

2. $\dfrac{3}{8a^2b}$ and $\dfrac{5}{6ab}$ $24a^2b$

- **For Example 2**

3. Change $\dfrac{3}{16wz^2}$ to an equivalent expression that has the denominator $48wz^5$. $\dfrac{9z^3}{48wz^5}$

- **For Example 3**

4. Find the LCD:

$\dfrac{3x}{x^2 - 4}$ and $\dfrac{x + 4}{x^2 + x - 2}$

$(x - 2)(x + 2)(x - 1)$

- **For Example 4**

5. Change $\dfrac{c + 3}{4c + 6}$ to an equivalent expression that has the denominator $2(2c + 3)(c - 3)$.

$\dfrac{(c + 3)(c - 3)}{2(2c + 3)(c - 3)}$

- **For Example 5**

6. Change $\dfrac{4k}{2 - k}$ to an equivalent expression that has the denominator $k^2 - 4$. $\dfrac{-4k(k + 2)}{k^2 - 4}$

Common Error

- Some students may find the least common denominator of two or more fractions by finding the product of the denominators. Point out that, though this is a common denominator, it is not the least common denominator. You may want to illustrate an example using integers as denominators.
- See *Teacher's Resource Book* for additional remediation.

EXAMPLE 5 Change $\dfrac{3}{5n + 5}$ to an equivalent expression that has the denominator $5(n + 1)(n + 4)$.

$$\dfrac{3}{5n + 5} = \dfrac{3}{5(n + 1)}$$ *Factor the denominator. Notice that $(n + 4)$ is missing.*

$$= \dfrac{3}{5(n + 1)} \cdot \dfrac{n + 4}{n + 4}$$ *Multiply by 1 in the form $\dfrac{n + 4}{n + 4}$.*

$$= \dfrac{3(n + 4)}{5(n + 1)(n + 4)}$$

How would you change $\dfrac{n + 2}{n^2 + 5n + 4}$ to an equivalent expression that has the denominator $5(n + 1)(n + 4)$?

Be on the alert for binomial factors that are the same or that are opposites.

EXAMPLE 6 Change $\dfrac{2a}{3 - a}$ to an equivalent expression that has the denominator $a^2 - 9$.

$$a^2 - 9 = (a + 3)(a - 3)$$ *Factor.*

$$\dfrac{2a}{3 - a} = \dfrac{2a}{-1(a - 3)} = \dfrac{-2a}{a - 3}$$ *Look for common factors. The opposite of $3 - a$ is a factor of $a^2 - 9$.*

$$\dfrac{-2a}{a - 3} \cdot \dfrac{a + 3}{a + 3} = \dfrac{-2a(a + 3)}{(a - 3)(a + 3)}$$ *Multiply by the missing factor, $a + 3$.*

CLASS EXERCISES

Find the LCD.

1. $\dfrac{3}{8}; \dfrac{9}{24}$ 24

2. $\dfrac{5}{12}; \dfrac{7}{18}$ 36

3. $\dfrac{1}{5x}; \dfrac{3}{20x^2}$ $20x^2$

4. $\dfrac{7b}{3a^2}; \dfrac{2a}{5b^2}$ $15a^2b^2$

5. $\dfrac{5}{18m^2n}; \dfrac{7}{24n^2}$ $72m^2n^2$

6. $\dfrac{3}{2a}; \dfrac{5}{2a + 4}$ $2a(a + 2)$

7. $\dfrac{1}{x - 3}; \dfrac{1}{x + 5}$ $(x - 3)(x + 5)$

8. $\dfrac{1}{3m + 9}; \dfrac{1}{m^2 + 4m + 3}$ $3(m + 3)(m + 1)$

Write equivalent expressions. Use the least common denominator.

9. $\dfrac{4}{3xy}; \dfrac{7}{12x^2}$ $\dfrac{16x}{12x^2y}; \dfrac{7y}{12x^2y}$

10. $\dfrac{3}{a^2 - 16}; \dfrac{5}{12 + a - a^2}$

$\dfrac{3(a + 3)}{(a - 4)(a + 4)(a + 3)}; \dfrac{-5(a + 4)}{(a - 4)(a + 4)(a + 3)}$

PRACTICE EXERCISES

Find the LCD.

A

1. $\dfrac{1}{5ab}; \dfrac{3b}{2a}$ $10ab$ **2.** $\dfrac{1}{10rs}; \dfrac{2s}{12r}$ $60rs$ **3.** $\dfrac{1}{6x}; \dfrac{3}{14y}$ $42xy$ **4.** $\dfrac{7}{6c}; \dfrac{c^2}{9d}$ $18cd$

5. $\dfrac{11}{14a^3b}; \dfrac{-15}{21ab^2}$ $42a^3b^2$ **6.** $\dfrac{5}{24s^3t}; \dfrac{-13}{6st^2}$ $24s^3t^2$ **7.** $\dfrac{-4}{18xy^3}; \dfrac{2}{6x^2y}$ $18x^2y^3$ **8.** $\dfrac{-7}{13cd^3}; \dfrac{5}{3c^2d}$ $39c^2d^3$

9. $\dfrac{2}{3n+3}; \dfrac{n+4}{n^2+6n+5}$ $3(n+1)(n+5)$ **10.** $\dfrac{7}{6x+6}; \dfrac{x+3}{x^2+9x+8}$ $6(x+1)(x+8)$ **11.** $\dfrac{4}{3r-27}; \dfrac{5}{4r+10}$ $6(r-9)(2r+5)$

12. $\dfrac{15}{8y-36}; \dfrac{17}{5y+15}$ $20(2y-9)(y+3)$ **13.** $\dfrac{3}{t^2-36}; \dfrac{7}{t-6}$ $(t+6)(t-6)$ **14.** $\dfrac{7}{x^2-4}; \dfrac{3}{x-2}$ $(x+2)(x-2)$

Find the LCD and write the equivalent expressions with the LCD as the denominator.

15. $\dfrac{5}{12mn^2}; \dfrac{3m}{4n}$ $\dfrac{5}{12mn^2}; \dfrac{9m^2n}{12mn^2}$ **16.** $\dfrac{1}{45ab^2}; \dfrac{5a}{18b}$ $\dfrac{2}{90ab^2}; \dfrac{25a^2b}{90ab^2}$ **17.** $\dfrac{5}{7y+7}; \dfrac{3}{y^2+4y+3}$ $\dfrac{5(y+3)}{7(y+1)(y+3)}; \dfrac{21}{7(y+1)(y+3)}$

18. $\dfrac{5}{2h+2}; \dfrac{2}{h^2+4h+3}$ $\dfrac{5(h+3)}{2(h+1)(h+3)}; \dfrac{4}{2(h+1)(h+3)}$ **19.** $\dfrac{3y}{y^2-9}; \dfrac{2}{y-3}$ $\dfrac{3y}{y^2-9}; \dfrac{2(y+3)}{y^2-9}$ **20.** $\dfrac{3a}{a^2-25}; \dfrac{1}{5-a}$ $\dfrac{3a}{(a^2-25)}; \dfrac{-(a+5)}{(a^2-25)}$

Find the LCD.

B

21. $\dfrac{1}{x^2+5x+6}; \dfrac{x}{x^2+7x+10}$ $(x+3)(x+2)(x+5)$ **22.** $\dfrac{3r}{r^2-r-12}; \dfrac{5}{r^2-4r-21}$ $(r-4)(r+3)(r-7)$

23. $\dfrac{6}{12c^2+13c-35}; \dfrac{10c}{3c^2-11c-42}$ $(3c+7)(4c-5)(c-6)$ **24.** $\dfrac{13}{6h^2-17h+12}; \dfrac{6h}{8h^2+2h-21}$ $(2h-3)(3h-4)(4h+7)$

25. $\dfrac{1}{16x^2-43x-15}; \dfrac{3}{2x^2+7x+3}$ $(x-3)(16x+5)(2x+1)(x+3)$ **26.** $\dfrac{17x}{12x^2-7x-12}; \dfrac{3}{6x^2-5x-6}$ $(3x-4)(4x+3)(2x-3)(3x+2)$

Write equivalent expressions having the same denominator. Use the LCD.

27. $\dfrac{3}{2a^2}; \dfrac{9}{3b}; \dfrac{a+b}{6ab^2}$ $\dfrac{9b^2}{6a^2b^2}; \dfrac{18a^2b}{6a^2b^2}; \dfrac{a(a+b)}{6a^2b^2}$ **28.** $\dfrac{m}{3n^2}; \dfrac{n+1}{15m^2n}; \dfrac{3}{4mn}$ $\dfrac{20m^3}{60m^2n^2}; \dfrac{4n(n+1)}{60m^2n^2}; \dfrac{45mn}{60m^2n^2}$

29. $\dfrac{8n}{5-3n}; \dfrac{5n^2}{9n^2-25}$ See below. **30.** $\dfrac{5r}{3-2r}; \dfrac{3r}{4r^2-9}$ $\dfrac{-5r(2r+3)}{260m^2n^2}; \dfrac{3r^2}{60m^2n^2}$

31. $\dfrac{3d}{2d^2-4d}; \dfrac{d+3}{d^2-d-2}$ See below. **32.** $\dfrac{5x+1}{x^2+3x-4}; \dfrac{x}{3x^2+12x}$ $\dfrac{-5f(2r+3)}{(2r-3)(2r+3)}; \dfrac{3r^2}{(2r-3)(2r+3)}$ See below.

33. $\dfrac{c}{3c+3}; \dfrac{c^2}{c^2+3c+2}; \dfrac{3c}{c+2}$ $\dfrac{c(c+2)}{3(c+1)(c+2)}; \dfrac{3c^2}{3(c+1)(c+2)}; \dfrac{9c(c+1)}{3(c+1)(c+2)}$ **34.** $\dfrac{y+1}{5y+15}; \dfrac{4}{y^2+5y+6}; \dfrac{2y}{y+2}$ $\dfrac{(y+1)(y+2)}{5(y+3)(y+2)}; \dfrac{20}{5(y+3)(y+2)}; \dfrac{10y(y+3)}{5(y+3)(y+2)}$

Find the LCD.

C

35. $\dfrac{1}{15x^2-xy-28y^2}; \dfrac{x+11}{12x^2+7xy-12y^2}$ $(5x-7y)(3x+4y)(4x-3y)$ **36.** $\dfrac{6}{8x^2-14xy-15y^2}; \dfrac{y-4}{4x^2-25y^2}$ $(2x-5y)(4x+3y)(2x+5y)$

Additional Answers

29. $\dfrac{-8n(3n+5)}{(3n-5)(3n+5)}; \dfrac{5n^2}{(3n-5)(3n+5)}$

31. $\dfrac{3d(d+1)}{2d(d-2)(d+1)}; \dfrac{2d(d+3)}{2d(d-2)(d+1)}$

32. $\dfrac{3x(5x+1)}{3x(x+4)(x-1)}; \dfrac{x(x-1)}{3x(x+4)(x-1)}$

LESSON FOLLOW-UP

Critical Thinking

Causal Explanation Why is it desirable to use the least common denominator for a given set of fractions? Fractions with the same (common) denominator can easily be added or subtracted. The smaller the numbers involved, the more easily the addition or subtraction can be accomplished; thus, the least common denominator is used.

Assignment Guide

See p. 314B for assignments.

Logical Reasoning

Emphasize that when the hypothesis is not true, the conclusion may or may not be true.

Lesson Quiz

Find the LCD.

1. $\dfrac{3}{7k^3}; \dfrac{19}{7k}$ $7k^3$

2. $\dfrac{1}{6a^2b}; \dfrac{8}{9b^2}$ $18a^2b^2$

3. $\dfrac{2}{3j^2-j}; \dfrac{1}{4j}$ $4j(3j-1)$

4. $\dfrac{6}{2z+18}; \dfrac{7}{6z+3}$ $6(z+9)(2z+1)$

5. $\dfrac{8}{2k^2+3k-20}; \dfrac{1}{3k+12}$ $3(k+4)(2k-5)$

Find the LCD and write the equivalent expressions with the LCD as the denominator.

6. $\dfrac{5}{9s^2t}; \dfrac{2s}{3t^2}$ $\dfrac{5t}{9s^2t^2}; \dfrac{6s^3}{9s^2t^2}$

7. $\dfrac{3}{8m^3}; \dfrac{m+1}{m^3-m^2}$ $\dfrac{3(m-1)}{8m^3(m-1)}; \dfrac{8m(m+1)}{8m^3(m-1)}$

Enrichment

Find the LCD:

$$\dfrac{3x}{x^3+3x^2-4x}; \dfrac{5}{5x+20};$$

$$\dfrac{3x}{3x^2-12x+9}; \dfrac{x+2}{x^4-16x^2}$$

$15x^2(x+4)(x-4)(x-3)(x-1)$

331

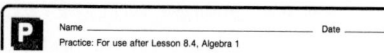

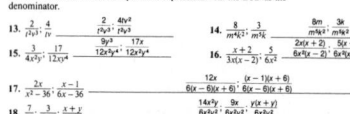

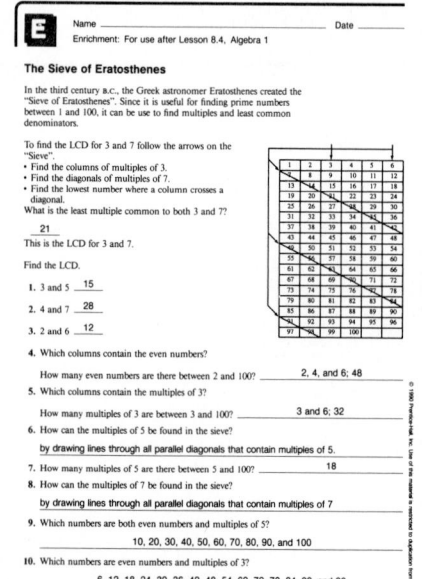

37. $\dfrac{1}{8a^4 - 8b^4}$; $\dfrac{b-7}{(3a-3b)^2}$
$72(a-b)^2(a-b)(a^2+b^2)$

38. $\dfrac{7}{3a^4 + 6a^2b^2 + 3b^4}$; $\dfrac{3}{2a^4 - 2b^4}$
$6(a^2+b^2)^2(a^2-b^2)$

39. $\dfrac{1}{15m^2 - 2m - 8}$; $\dfrac{3}{3m^2 - 10m - 8}$; $\dfrac{5}{6m - 24}$ $6(5m-4)(3m+2)(m-4)$

40. $\dfrac{7}{2t^2 - 2t - 12}$; $\dfrac{13}{4t^2 + 10t + 4}$; $\dfrac{17}{6t + 3}$ $6(t+2)(t-3)(2t+1)$

Applications

41. Photography When a camera is in focus it satisfies the equation $\dfrac{1}{p} + \dfrac{1}{q} = \dfrac{1}{f}$. Find the LCD if $p = x^2$, $q = 2x$ and $f = 3x^3$. $6x^3$

42. Construction The forces acting on a concrete slab can be found using the rational expression $1 - \dfrac{4c}{\pi l} + \dfrac{c^3}{3l^3}$. Write the expression using the least common denominator. $\dfrac{3\pi l^3}{3\pi l^3} - \dfrac{12cl^2}{3\pi l^3} + \dfrac{\pi c^3}{3\pi l^3}$

LOGICAL REASONING

A statement written in if-then form is called a conditional.

EXAMPLES   **a.** If $\underset{\uparrow}{\text{it rains on Monday}}$, then $\underset{\uparrow}{\text{Carlos will stay home}}$.

hypothesis   conclusion

When the hypothesis is true, ⟶ It rains on Monday.
the conclusion is true. ⟶ Carlos stays home.
When the hypothesis is not true, ⟶ It does not rain on Monday.
the conclusion may or may not be true. ⟶ Carlos may or may not stay home.

b. If a and b are both even numbers, then $a + b$ is even.

When the hypothesis is true, ⟶ a and b both even
the conclusion is true. ⟶ $a + b$ even
When the hypothesis is not true, ⟶ a and b not both even
the conclusion may or may not be true. ⟶ $a + b$ even or odd

The sentences in the exercise are true. What can you conclude?

1. If x is divisible by 10, then x is divisible by 2. x is not divisible by 10.
x may or may not be divisible by 2

2. If a polygon has 4 sides, then it has 4 angles. $ABCD$ is a polygon with 4 sides.
figure $ABCD$ has 4 angles

3. All integers are rational numbers. x is an integer.
x is a rational number

4. All factors of x are factors of y. n is not a factor of x.
n may or may not be a factor of y

8.5 Adding and Subtracting Rational Expressions

Objective: To add and subtract rational expressions

Rational expressions are added or subtracted in the same way as fractions. As with fractions, you may need to find the LCD of the rational expressions before you add or subtract.

Capsule Review

EXAMPLE **Find the LCD:** $\dfrac{3}{5x^2y}$; $\dfrac{x}{5x^2 + 10x}$

Factor the denominators.
$$5x^2y = 5 \cdot x \cdot x \cdot y$$
$$5x^2 + 10x = 5 \cdot x \cdot (x + 2)$$

Multiply the greatest powers of the prime factors.
$$5x^2y(x + 2)$$

Find the LCD.

1. $\dfrac{2}{x}$; $\dfrac{3}{6x}$ $6x$ **2.** $\dfrac{2}{ab^3}$; $\dfrac{6}{a^2b}$ a^2b^3 **3.** $\dfrac{-1}{2xy}$; $\dfrac{x}{2x^2 + 6x}$ **4.** $\dfrac{3}{d - 3}$; $\dfrac{d}{d^2 - 9}$

$2xy(x + 3)$ $(d - 3)(d + 3)$

The method for adding or subtracting rational expressions may be generalized as follows.

Addition and Subtraction of Rational Expressions

If $\dfrac{P}{Q}$ and $\dfrac{R}{Q}$ are rational expressions with $Q \neq 0$, then

$$\frac{P}{Q} + \frac{R}{Q} = \frac{P + R}{Q} \quad \text{and} \quad \frac{P}{Q} - \frac{R}{Q} = \frac{P - R}{Q}.$$

EXAMPLE 1 **Add:** $\dfrac{4}{3m} + \dfrac{2}{3m}$

$$\frac{4}{3m} + \frac{2}{3m} = \frac{4 + 2}{3m} = \frac{\overset{2}{\cancel{6}}}{\cancel{3}m} = \frac{2}{m}$$

BACKGROUND

In the Capsule Review, students practice finding the least common denominator for a pair of rational expressions. This review will be essential in adding and subtracting rational expressions.

When subtracting it is often helpful to use parentheses when you rewrite polynomial numerators to clearly indicate the expression(s) being subtracted.

EXAMPLE 2 **Subtract:** $\dfrac{5n}{n+2} - \dfrac{n-8}{n+2}$

$$\dfrac{5n}{n+2} - \dfrac{n-8}{n+2} = \dfrac{5n-(n-8)}{n+2} \quad \longleftarrow \textit{Parentheses are necessary.}$$

$$= \dfrac{5n-n+8}{n+2}$$

$$= \dfrac{4n+8}{n+2} = \dfrac{4(n+2)}{(n+2)} = 4$$

To add or subtract rational expressions with unlike denominators, first write them as equivalent expressions with a least common denominator.

EXAMPLE 3 **Combine:** $\dfrac{3}{4a} + \dfrac{5}{6a^2} - \dfrac{1}{a}$

$$\dfrac{3}{4a} + \dfrac{5}{6a^2} - \dfrac{1}{a} \qquad \textit{The LCD is } 2^2 \cdot 3 \cdot a^2, \textit{ or } 12a^2.$$

$$= \dfrac{3}{4a} \cdot \dfrac{3a}{3a} + \dfrac{5}{6a^2} \cdot \dfrac{2}{2} - \dfrac{1}{a} \cdot \dfrac{12a}{12a} \qquad \textit{Write equivalent expressions that have the LCD.}$$

$$= \dfrac{9a}{12a^2} + \dfrac{10}{12a^2} - \dfrac{12a}{12a^2}$$

$$= \dfrac{9a+10-12a}{12a^2} = \dfrac{10-3a}{12a^2} \qquad \textit{Combine like terms in the numerator and simplify.}$$

It is important to notice binomial factors that are the same or opposites.

EXAMPLE 4 **Add:** $\dfrac{2y+1}{9-y^2} + \dfrac{2}{y-3} - \dfrac{1}{y+3}$

$$\dfrac{2y+1}{9-y^2} + \dfrac{2}{y-3} - \dfrac{1}{y+3} = \dfrac{2y+1}{(3-y)(3+y)} + \dfrac{2}{y-3} - \dfrac{1}{y+3}$$

$$= \dfrac{2y+1}{-(y-3)(y+3)} + \dfrac{2}{y-3} - \dfrac{1}{y+3}$$

$$= \dfrac{-(2y+1)}{(y-3)(y+3)} + \dfrac{2}{y-3} \cdot \dfrac{y+3}{y+3} - \dfrac{1}{y+3} \cdot \dfrac{y-3}{y-3}$$

$$= \dfrac{-(2y+1)+2(y+3)-1(y-3)}{(y-3)(y+3)}$$

$$= \dfrac{-2y-1+2y+6-y+3}{(y-3)(y+3)}$$

$$= \dfrac{8-y}{(y-3)(y+3)}$$

- In this lesson, students will add and subtract rational expressions with like and unlike denominators. In Examples 3 and 4, they use skills learned in the previous lesson for finding the LCD of rational expressions. They use the LCD to write equivalent expressions. You may wish to stress that finding *any* common denominator is correct; however, it facilitates computations if the least common denominator is used.
- You may want to use Teaching Aid 8 and Transparency 13, in the *Teacher's Resource Book,* to review several examples of adding and subtracting rational expressions.
- For Example 4, when factoring $9 - y^2$, emphasize that one of the factors is the same and one is the opposite of the other denominators.

Critical Thinking

Observation When adding or subtracting rational expressions, does using the LCD guarantee that the answer (sum or difference) is in simplest form? Hint: Look at Example 2.
No. Example 2 had to be simplified.

CHALKBOARD EXAMPLES

- **For Example 1**
  Add.

  1. $\dfrac{2}{3c} + \dfrac{2}{3c}$ $\quad \dfrac{4}{3c}$

  2. $\dfrac{3}{4x} + \dfrac{4}{4x}$ $\quad \dfrac{7}{4x}$

- **For Example 2**
  Subtract.

  3. $\dfrac{3}{h-3} - \dfrac{h}{h-3}$ $\quad -1$

  4. $\dfrac{3n}{n+4} - \dfrac{n-8}{n+4}$ $\quad 2$

CLASS EXERCISES

Combine. Simplify if possible.

1. $\dfrac{9}{11} - \dfrac{3}{11}$ $\frac{6}{11}$

2. $\dfrac{x}{4} + \dfrac{3x}{4}$ x

3. $\dfrac{3}{2ab} - \dfrac{5}{2ab}$ $-\frac{1}{ab}$

4. $\dfrac{m}{m-3} + \dfrac{2}{m-3}$ $\frac{m+2}{m-3}$

5. $\dfrac{2c}{3d^2} + \dfrac{3}{2cd}$ $\frac{4c^2+9d}{6cd^2}$

6. $\dfrac{3r}{r^2-9} - \dfrac{5r}{r+3}$ $\frac{18r-5r^2}{(r-3)(r+3)}$

PRACTICE EXERCISES

Combine. Simplify if possible.

A

1. $\dfrac{5}{2m} + \dfrac{3}{2m}$ $\frac{4}{m}$

2. $\dfrac{5}{6n} + \dfrac{7}{6n}$ $\frac{2}{n}$

3. $\dfrac{5}{4x} - \dfrac{3}{4x}$ $\frac{1}{2x}$

4. $\dfrac{6}{5z} - \dfrac{1}{5z}$ $\frac{1}{z}$

5. $\dfrac{3z}{z+2} - \dfrac{z-4}{z+2}$ 2

6. $\dfrac{5c}{c+7} - \dfrac{c-28}{c+7}$ 4

7. $\dfrac{2}{a-2} - \dfrac{a}{a-2}$ -1

8. $\dfrac{3}{b-3} - \dfrac{b}{b-3}$ -1

9. $\dfrac{3}{2a} + \dfrac{2}{4a^2} - \dfrac{1}{a}$ $\frac{a+1}{2a^2}$

10. $\dfrac{3}{3x} + \dfrac{6}{9x^2} - \dfrac{1}{x}$ $\frac{2}{3x^2}$

11. $\dfrac{1}{3m^2} - \dfrac{4}{6m} - \dfrac{1}{m}$ $\frac{1-5m}{3m^2}$

12. $\dfrac{8}{16r^2} - \dfrac{3}{8r} - \dfrac{1}{r}$ $\frac{-11r+4}{8r^2}$

13. $\dfrac{4}{2a+8} - \dfrac{a}{5a+20}$ $\frac{10-a}{5(a+4)}$

14. $\dfrac{a}{a+3} - \dfrac{3}{a+5}$ $\frac{a^2+2a-9}{(a+3)(a+5)}$

15. $\dfrac{5}{l+4} + \dfrac{3}{l-1}$ $\frac{8l+7}{(l+4)(l-1)}$

16. $\dfrac{i}{7i+14} + \dfrac{6}{3i+6}$ $\frac{i+14}{7(i-2)}$

17. $\dfrac{5x+1}{25-x^2} + \dfrac{5}{x-5}$ $\frac{24}{(x-5)(x+5)}$

18. $\dfrac{3z+2}{16-z^2} + \dfrac{3}{z-4}$ $\frac{10}{(z-4)(z+4)}$

19. $\dfrac{4r+1}{9-r^2} + \dfrac{4}{r-3}$ $\frac{11}{(r+3)(r-3)}$

20. $\dfrac{y+3}{4-y^2} + \dfrac{1}{y-2}$ $\frac{-1}{(y+2)(y-2)}$

21. $\dfrac{2}{y-1} + \dfrac{6y-2}{y^2+2y-3}$ $\frac{8y+4}{(y-1)(y+3)}$

22. $\dfrac{5}{d-3} - \dfrac{d-4}{d^2-d-6}$ $\frac{4d+14}{(d-3)(d+2)}$

B

23. $\dfrac{2a^2-a}{2a^2+a-3} - \dfrac{6}{2a^2+a-3}$ $\frac{a-2}{a-1}$

24. $\dfrac{l^2}{2l^2-l-6} + \dfrac{l-6}{2l^2-l-6}$ $\frac{l+3}{2l+3}$

25. $\dfrac{g^3+3g}{g^2+2g} + \dfrac{g^2-g}{g^2+2g} - \dfrac{4\,g(g+2)}{g^2+2g}$ $\frac{g^3+g^2+2g-4}{g^2+2g}$

26. $\dfrac{e^3+e^2}{2e^2+6e} + \dfrac{e^3+2e^2}{2e^2+6e} - \dfrac{e^2+12}{2e^2+6e}$ $\frac{e^3+e^2-6}{e(e+3)}$

27. $\dfrac{b-2}{2b} + \dfrac{b+3}{3b} - \dfrac{b-2}{6b^2}$ $\frac{5b^2-b+2}{6b^2}$

28. $\dfrac{r+3}{4r} - \dfrac{r+2}{3r^2} + \dfrac{r-4}{12r^2}$ $\frac{r^2+2r-4}{4r^2}$

29. $\dfrac{u-5}{2u+4} + \dfrac{u+3}{3u-6}$ $\frac{5u^2-11u+42}{6(u+2)(u-2)}$

30. $\dfrac{n+5}{4n+16} + \dfrac{n-1}{3n-9}$ $\frac{7n^2+18n-61}{12(n+4)(n-3)}$

31. $\dfrac{3a-2}{a^2-a-12} + \dfrac{a+3}{a-4}$ $\frac{a^2+9a+7}{(a-4)(a+3)}$

32. $\dfrac{n^2+1}{n^2-2n-15} + \dfrac{n-1}{n+3}$ $\frac{2n^2-6n+6}{(n-5)(n+3)}$

8.5 Adding and Subtracting Rational Expressions   **335**

- **For Example 3**
  Combine.

5. $\dfrac{3}{16a} + \dfrac{9}{8a^3} - \dfrac{3a}{16a^2}$ $\frac{9}{8a^3}$

6. $\dfrac{3}{4x} + \dfrac{5}{8x^2} - \dfrac{1}{x}$ $\frac{5-2x}{8x^2}$

- **For Example 4**
  Add.

7. $\dfrac{k+5}{25-k^2} - \dfrac{2}{k+5} + \dfrac{3}{k-5}$ $\frac{20}{(k+5)(k-5)}$

LESSON FOLLOW-UP

Discussion

Explain how the LCD is used in adding or subtracting rational expressions. Rational expressions are added/subtracted in the same manner as fractions. The LCD of rational expressions is the smallest possible common denominator of the expressions. Using the LCD facilitates computations.

Assignment Guide

See p. 314B for assignments.

Lesson Quiz

Combine. Simplify if possible.

1. $\dfrac{5z}{12} + \dfrac{5z}{12}$ $\frac{5z}{6}$

2. $\dfrac{8}{a^2b} - \dfrac{3}{a^2b}$ $\frac{5}{a^2b}$

3. $\dfrac{5}{r-5} - \dfrac{r}{r-5}$ -1

4. $\dfrac{5k}{k+5} - \dfrac{k-3}{k+5}$ $\frac{4k+3}{k+5}$

5. $\dfrac{5t+9}{3t-7} + \dfrac{4t-30}{3t-7}$ 3

6. $\dfrac{3m-2}{m+7} - \dfrac{2m+5}{m+7}$ $\frac{m-7}{m+7}$

7. $\dfrac{12}{k} - \dfrac{5}{k^2}$ $\frac{12k-5}{k^2}$

8. $\dfrac{2}{4p^2} - \dfrac{2p+3}{6p^3}$ $\frac{p-3}{6p^3}$

9. $\dfrac{r}{r+2} + \dfrac{5}{r-6}$ $\frac{r^2-r+10}{(r+2)(r-6)}$

10. $\dfrac{t}{3t+6} - \dfrac{2}{5t+10}$ $\frac{5t-6}{15(t+2)}$

11. $\dfrac{5x-2}{x^2+x-20} - \dfrac{3}{x+5} + \dfrac{x}{x-4}$ $\frac{x+2}{x-4}$

335

C 33. $\dfrac{7d - 2}{d^2 + 2d - 8} - \dfrac{4}{d + 4} - \dfrac{d}{d - 2}$ $\dfrac{d + 3}{d + 4}$

34. $\dfrac{i - 24}{i^2 - 3i - 18} - \dfrac{3}{i + 3} + \dfrac{i}{i - 6}$ $\dfrac{i - 2}{i - 6}$

35. $\dfrac{t}{8t^2 + 10t - 3} - \dfrac{3}{4t^2 + 19t - 5}$
See below.

36. $\dfrac{a}{6a^2 - 7a - 20} - \dfrac{2}{3a^2 - 2a - 8}$
See below.

37. $\dfrac{n + 2}{n^2 + n - 6} + \dfrac{n - 5}{3n^2 + 13n + 12}$
See below.

38. $\dfrac{2t + 1}{3t^2 - 31t - 22} + \dfrac{t - 7}{12t^2 - 19t - 18}$
See below.

39. $\dfrac{6}{k^2 + 2k - 15} + \dfrac{3}{k^2 - 3k} + \dfrac{5}{k^2 - 9}$
See below.

40. $\dfrac{b}{2b^2 + b - 6} - \dfrac{2}{2b^2 - 3b} + \dfrac{b + 1}{b^2 - 4}$
See below.

Applications

41. Physics Kinetic energy (E_K) is the energy of motion. The work of an external force is equal to the change in kinetic energy:

$$w = E_{K_2} - E_{K_1}$$

The data from an experiment on kinetic energy is at the right. Find the work for each time the experiment was run.

$\dfrac{-8}{a(a + 4)}$; $\dfrac{6}{(h + 1)(h - 1)}$; $\dfrac{-3d - 15}{(d - 3)(d + 3)}$

Work and Kinetic Energy

Work	E_{K_1}	E_{K_2}
a. ?	$\dfrac{2}{a}$	$\dfrac{2}{a + 4}$
b. ?	$\dfrac{3}{h + 1}$	$\dfrac{3}{h - 1}$
c. ?	$\dfrac{5}{d - 3}$	$\dfrac{2d}{d^2 - 9}$

ALGEBRA IN PHYSICS

An electric circuit is the path followed by an electric current. A simple circuit consists of a switch, a battery, and a light bulb. The amount of current (I) is related to the voltage (V) in the battery and the resistance (R) in the light bulb. What happens if more light bulbs are added to the circuit? How does the resistance change? Light bulbs can be added in series or parallel.

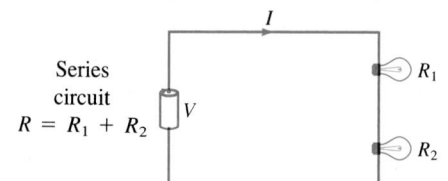

Series circuit
$R = R_1 + R_2$

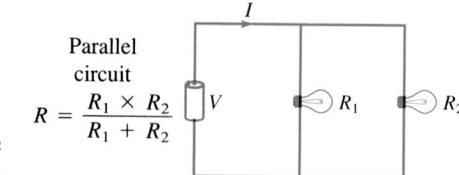

Parallel circuit
$R = \dfrac{R_1 \times R_2}{R_1 + R_2}$

Solve for R if $R_1 = 0.5$ ohms and $R_2 = 3.0$ ohms.

1. Find the total resistance if two light bulbs are placed in series.
$R = 0.5 + 3.0$; 3.5 ohms

2. Find the total resistance if they are parallel. $R = \dfrac{(0.5)(3.0)}{0.5 + 3.0}$; 0.429 ohm

3. Which circuit provides the least amount of total resistance? parallel

336   Chapter 8 Rational Expressions

Additional Answers

35. $\dfrac{t^2 - t - 9}{(4t - 1)(t + 5)(2t + 3)}$

36. $\dfrac{a^2 - 6a + 10}{(3a + 4)(2a - 5)(a - 2)}$

37. $\dfrac{4n^2 + 3n + 18}{(3n + 4)(n + 3)(n - 2)}$

38. $\dfrac{9t^2 - 32t + 68}{(3t + 2)(t - 11)(4t + 9)}$

39. $\dfrac{14k^2 + 67k + 45}{k(k - 3)(k + 3)(k + 5)}$

40. $\dfrac{3b^3 - 5b^2 - 3b + 8}{b(2b - 3)(b + 2)(b - 2)}$

Mixed Expressions and Complex Rational Expressions

Objectives: To add or subtract a polynomial and a rational expression
To simplify complex rational expressions

Recall that a mixed number such as $2\frac{3}{4}$ is the sum of an integer and a fraction $\left(2 + \frac{3}{4}\right)$. You can express a mixed number as a fraction.

Capsule Review

EXAMPLE Express $2\frac{3}{4}$ as a fraction.

$$2\frac{3}{4} = 2 + \frac{3}{4}$$

$$= \frac{2}{1} \cdot \frac{4}{4} + \frac{3}{4} \qquad \textit{Express the whole number 2 as a fraction with the LCD 4. Combine.}$$

$$= \frac{8}{4} + \frac{3}{4} = \frac{11}{4}$$

Express each mixed number as a fraction.

1. $2\frac{2}{3}$ $\frac{8}{3}$ 2. $3\frac{1}{4}$ $\frac{13}{4}$ 3. $1\frac{3}{8}$ $\frac{11}{8}$ 4. $11\frac{14}{15}$ $\frac{179}{15}$ 5. $2\frac{1}{100}$ $\frac{201}{100}$ 6. $99\frac{99}{100}$ $\frac{9999}{100}$

A **mixed expression** is the sum or difference of a polynomial and a rational expression. Examples are: $2 + \frac{1}{x}$ and $m + 2 - \frac{5}{m - 1}$. The procedure for combining a polynomial and a rational expression is similar to expressing a mixed number as a fraction.

EXAMPLE 1 Combine: $2 + \frac{1}{x}$

$$2 + \frac{1}{x} = \frac{2}{1} \cdot \frac{x}{x} + \frac{1}{x} \qquad \textit{Express 2 as a fraction with a denominator of x.}$$

$$= \frac{2x}{x} + \frac{1}{x} = \frac{2x + 1}{x}$$

A **complex rational expression** is a rational expression whose numerator or denominator contains one or more rational expressions.

$$\frac{\dfrac{3}{x}}{\dfrac{5}{x^2}}; \quad \frac{\dfrac{1}{m} + \dfrac{1}{n}}{\dfrac{2}{3m} + \dfrac{2}{3n}}; \quad \frac{a - \dfrac{2}{2a - 3}}{2a - 1 - \dfrac{8}{2a - 3}}$$

8.6 Mixed Expressions and Complex Rational Expressions   **337**

LESSON PLAN

Vocabulary
Complex rational expression
Mixed expression

Materials/Manipulatives
*Teacher's Resource Book,
Teaching Aid 9,
Transparency 13*

BACKGROUND

- In the Capsule Review, students practice changing a mixed number to an improper fraction. This review will be beneficial later in this lesson when working with rational expressions.

- Many students may change a mixed number to an improper fraction by multiplying the denominator by the whole number and adding the product to the numerator. Try to discourage this method, and emphasize the method described in the Capsule Review. Knowing this new method will help the students later when manipulating rational expressions.

- For Example 1, students write a mixed expression as a rational expression.
- For Examples 2 and 3, have students make a list of the denominators of each rational expression. After they find the LCD from this list, multiply the numerator and the denominator of each term of the rational expression by the LCD.
- For students still having difficulty in adding and subtracting rational expressions, review Teaching Aid 9 and Transparency 13, in the *Teacher's Resource Book*.

CHALKBOARD EXAMPLES

- **For Example 1**
  Combine.

  1. $5 + \dfrac{1}{c}$ $\dfrac{5c + 1}{c}$

  2. $m + 1 - \dfrac{2}{m + 1}$
  $\dfrac{m^2 + 2m - 1}{m + 1}$

- **For Example 2**

  3. Simplify: $\dfrac{\dfrac{3}{g^2} - \dfrac{3}{e^2}}{\dfrac{1}{g} + \dfrac{1}{e}}$ $\dfrac{3(e - g)}{ge}$

- **For Example 3**

  4. Simplify: $\dfrac{x + 4 + \dfrac{5}{x - 2}}{x + 6 + \dfrac{15}{x - 2}}$

  $\dfrac{x - 1}{x + 1}$

Common Error

- Sometimes students forget to multiply each term of the numerator and denominator of a complex rational expression by the LCD. Encourage students to recall the distributive property and to use arrows if necessary.
- See *Teacher's Resource Book* for additional remediation.

One way to simplify $\dfrac{\dfrac{3}{x}}{\dfrac{5}{x^2}}$ is to rewrite it as $\dfrac{3}{x} \div \dfrac{5}{x^2}$ and divide. Another way to simplify a rational expression is to multiply the numerator and denominator by the LCD.

EXAMPLE 2   **Simplify:** $\dfrac{\dfrac{1}{m} + \dfrac{1}{n}}{\dfrac{2}{3m} + \dfrac{2}{3n}}$

$$\dfrac{\dfrac{1}{m} + \dfrac{1}{n}}{\dfrac{2}{3m} + \dfrac{2}{3n}} = \dfrac{\left(\dfrac{1}{m} + \dfrac{1}{n}\right) \cdot 3mn}{\left(\dfrac{2}{3m} + \dfrac{2}{3n}\right) \cdot 3mn} \qquad \begin{array}{l} \textit{Multiply numerator and} \\ \textit{denominator by } 3mn, \textit{ the} \\ \textit{LCD of } \dfrac{1}{m}, \dfrac{1}{n}, \dfrac{2}{3m}, \dfrac{2}{3n}. \end{array}$$

$$= \dfrac{\dfrac{1}{m} \cdot 3mn + \dfrac{1}{n} \cdot 3mn}{\dfrac{2}{3m} \cdot 3mn + \dfrac{2}{3n} \cdot 3mn} = \dfrac{3n + 3m}{2n + 2m} = \dfrac{3(n + m)}{2(n + m)} = \dfrac{3}{2}$$

EXAMPLE 3   **Simplify:** $\dfrac{a - \dfrac{2}{2a - 3}}{2a - 1 - \dfrac{8}{2a - 3}}$

$$\dfrac{a - \dfrac{2}{2a - 3}}{2a - 1 - \dfrac{8}{2a - 3}} = \dfrac{\left(a - \dfrac{2}{(2a - 3)}\right) \cdot (2a - 3)}{\left((2a - 1) - \dfrac{8}{(2a - 3)}\right) \cdot (2a - 3)}$$

$$= \dfrac{a(2a - 3) - \dfrac{2}{(2a - 3)} \cdot (2a - 3)}{(2a - 1)(2a - 3) - \dfrac{8}{(2a - 3)} \cdot (2a - 3)}$$

$$= \dfrac{2a^2 - 3a - 2}{4a^2 - 8a + 3 - 8}$$

$$= \dfrac{2a^2 - 3a - 2}{4a^2 - 8a - 5} = \dfrac{(2a + 1)(a - 2)}{(2a + 1)(2a - 5)} = \dfrac{a - 2}{2a - 5}$$

CLASS EXERCISES

Combine.

1. $4 + \dfrac{1}{3}$ $\dfrac{13}{3}$
2. $a + \dfrac{b}{c}$ $\dfrac{ac + b}{c}$
3. $x + 3 - \dfrac{4}{x - 2}$ $\dfrac{x^2 + x - 10}{x - 2}$
4. $\dfrac{t}{t + 1} + 5t$ $\dfrac{5t^2 + 6t}{t + 1}$

Simplify.

5. $\dfrac{\frac{2}{3}}{\frac{5}{6}}$ $\frac{4}{5}$

6. $\dfrac{\frac{3s}{8}}{\frac{s}{4}}$ $\frac{3}{2}$

7. $\dfrac{\frac{2n}{m^2} - \frac{1}{m}}{1 + \frac{2n}{m^2}}$ $\frac{2n-m}{m^2+2n}$

8. $\dfrac{h + \frac{3}{2h+5}}{h - \frac{4h+3}{2h+5}}$ $\frac{h+1}{h-1}$

PRACTICE EXERCISES

Combine. Simplify if possible.

A

1. $2 + \dfrac{3}{x}$ $\frac{2x+3}{x}$

2. $4 - \dfrac{8}{a}$ $\frac{4a-8}{a}$

3. $3 - \dfrac{10}{x}$ $\frac{3x-10}{x}$

4. $4 - \dfrac{5}{b}$ $\frac{4b-5}{b}$

5. $2z - \dfrac{z+1}{z}$ $\frac{2z^2-z-1}{z}$

6. $3c - \dfrac{c+1}{c}$ $\frac{3c^2-c-1}{c}$

7. $\dfrac{2y+3}{4y} + y - 3$ $\frac{4y^2-10y+3}{4y}$

8. $\dfrac{3r+5}{3r} + 2 - r$ $\frac{-3r^2+9r+5}{3r}$

9. $d + \dfrac{d-3}{2d+1}$ $\frac{2d^2+2d-3}{2d+1}$

10. $c + \dfrac{c-2}{3c-1}$ $\frac{3c^2-2}{3c-1}$

11. $\dfrac{2u-1}{u+2} + u$ $\frac{u^2+4u-1}{u+2}$

12. $\dfrac{3v-1}{v+3} - v$ $\frac{-v^2-1}{v+3}$

13. $\dfrac{\frac{1}{x}+\frac{1}{z}}{\frac{1}{2x}+\frac{1}{2z}}$ 2

14. $\dfrac{\frac{1}{r}+\frac{1}{s}}{\frac{3}{5r}+\frac{3}{5s}}$ $\frac{5}{3}$

15. $\dfrac{\frac{1}{u}-\frac{1}{v}}{\frac{5}{2u}-\frac{5}{2v}}$ $\frac{2}{5}$

16. $\dfrac{\frac{1}{a}-\frac{1}{b}}{\frac{3}{4a}-\frac{3}{4b}}$ $\frac{4}{3}$

17. $\dfrac{\frac{m}{n}+\frac{2}{n^2}}{2-\frac{m}{n^2}}$ $\frac{mn+2}{2n^2-m}$

18. $\dfrac{\frac{5}{v^2}+\frac{u}{v}}{\frac{u}{v}-3}$ $\frac{5+uv}{uv-3v^2}$

19. $\dfrac{1+\frac{4}{a}}{1-\frac{16}{a^2}}$ $\frac{a}{a-4}$

20. $\dfrac{1+\frac{5}{b}}{1-\frac{25}{b^2}}$ $\frac{b}{b-5}$

21. $\dfrac{3-\frac{12}{d+4}}{2-\frac{8}{d+4}}$ $\frac{3}{2}$

22. $\dfrac{5-\frac{25}{c+5}}{3-\frac{15}{c+5}}$ $\frac{5}{3}$

23. $\dfrac{u-\frac{4}{u+3}}{1+\frac{1}{u+3}}$ $u-1$

24. $\dfrac{v-\frac{3}{v+2}}{1+\frac{1}{v+2}}$ $v-1$

B

25. $\dfrac{x-\frac{3}{3x-4}}{3x-1-\frac{9}{3x-4}}$ $\frac{3x^2-4x-3}{9x^2-15x-5}$

26. $\dfrac{b-\frac{6}{2b-4}}{2b-1-\frac{10}{2b-4}}$ $\frac{b+1}{2b+1}$

27. $\dfrac{z-\frac{20z+10}{3z+7}}{z-\frac{7z+5}{3z+7}}$ $\frac{3z^2-13z-10}{3z^2-5}$

28. $\dfrac{a-\frac{36a+6}{5a+11}}{a-\frac{3a-3}{5a+11}}$ $\frac{5a^2-25a-6}{5a^2+8a+3}$

29. $x + 1 - \dfrac{4}{x+1}$ $\frac{x^2+2x-3}{x+1}$

30. $y + 3 - \dfrac{1}{y+3}$ $\frac{y^2+6y+8}{y+3}$

31. $a - 2 + \dfrac{3}{a+1}$ $\frac{a^2-a+1}{a+1}$

32. $b - 4 - \dfrac{2}{b+3}$ $\frac{b^2-b-14}{b+3}$

33. $\dfrac{m-3}{2m+5} + m - 4$ $\frac{2m^2-2m-23}{2m+5}$

34. $\dfrac{n+2}{5n-3} + n - 6$ $\frac{5n^2-32n+20}{5n-3}$

LESSON FOLLOW-UP

Assignment Guide

See p. 314B for assignments.

Test Yourself

See *Teacher's Resource Book,* Tests, pp. 77–78.

Critical Thinking

Predicting Consequences Can complex rational expressions be simplified by this method?

Step 1   Simplify the numerator into a single rational expression.

Step 2   Simplify the denominator into a single rational expression.

Step 3   Multiply the numerator by the reciprocal of the denominator.   Yes

Lesson Quiz

Combine. Simplify if possible.

1. $5 - \dfrac{7}{e}$ $\frac{5e-7}{e}$

2. $2 + \dfrac{3}{x-3}$ $\frac{2x-3}{x-3}$

3. $2p - \dfrac{p+4}{p}$ $\frac{2p^2-p-4}{p}$

4. $\dfrac{5r+3}{3r} + r - 4$ $\frac{3r^2-7r+3}{3r}$

5. $\dfrac{\frac{s}{2}}{\frac{3s}{7}}$ $\frac{7}{6}$

6. $\dfrac{\frac{x}{2}-\frac{x}{3}}{\frac{x}{6}+\frac{2}{3}}$ $\frac{x}{x+4}$

7. $\dfrac{1-\frac{9}{t}}{1-\frac{81}{t^2}}$ $\frac{t}{t+9}$

8. $\dfrac{a-\frac{2}{a+1}}{1+\frac{1}{a+1}}$ $a-1$

Enrichment

Combine and simplify:

$\dfrac{1}{x + \dfrac{1}{1+\frac{x+1}{3-x}}}$ $\frac{4}{3x+3}$

339

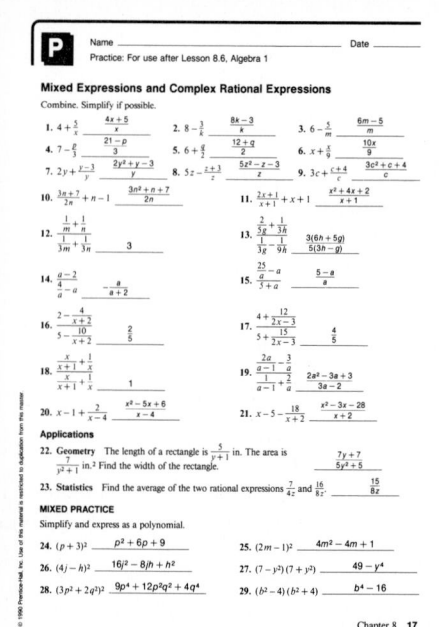

35. $\dfrac{1 + \dfrac{1}{c} - \dfrac{6}{c^2}}{\dfrac{1}{c} - \dfrac{2}{c^2}}$ $c + 3$

36. $\dfrac{1 - \dfrac{2}{z} - \dfrac{8}{z^2}}{\dfrac{1}{z} + \dfrac{2}{z^2}}$ $z - 4$

37. $\dfrac{a - 1 - \dfrac{3}{a + 1}}{a + 5 + \dfrac{3}{a + 1}}$ $\dfrac{a - 2}{a + 4}$

C 38. $\dfrac{b - 2 - \dfrac{25}{b - 2}}{b + 2 - \dfrac{5}{b - 2}}$ $\dfrac{b - 7}{b - 3}$

39. $\dfrac{\dfrac{2n + 6}{n + 3} - \dfrac{n - 2}{n + 2}}{\dfrac{n^2 - 9}{n^2 + 5n + 6}}$ $\dfrac{n + 6}{n - 3}$

40. $\dfrac{\dfrac{2t + 2}{t} - \dfrac{t - 5}{t - 3}}{\dfrac{t^2 - 4}{t^2 - 3t}}$ $\dfrac{t + 3}{t + 2}$

41. $\dfrac{\dfrac{u - 1}{u + 1} - \dfrac{u + 1}{u - 1}}{\dfrac{u - 1}{u + 1} + \dfrac{u + 1}{u - 1}}$ $-\dfrac{2u}{u^2 + 1}$

42. $\dfrac{\dfrac{v + 2}{v - 2} + \dfrac{v - 2}{v + 2}}{\dfrac{v + 2}{v - 2} - \dfrac{v - 2}{v + 2}}$ $\dfrac{v^2 + 4}{4v}$

43. $\dfrac{\dfrac{x + 2}{x} - \dfrac{3}{x + 1}}{\dfrac{x - 1}{x^2 + x} + \dfrac{3}{x + 1}}$ $\dfrac{x^2 + 2}{4x - 1}$

44. $\dfrac{\dfrac{r + 3}{r^2 + 4r} + \dfrac{r - 1}{r + 4}}{\dfrac{r - 2}{r + 4} - \dfrac{3}{r}}$ $\dfrac{r^2 + 3}{r^2 - 5r - 12}$

45. $\dfrac{\dfrac{2}{a^2 - 4} + \dfrac{2}{a^2 + a - 2}}{\dfrac{6}{a^2 - 1} - \dfrac{3}{a^2 - a - 2}}$ $\dfrac{4a^2 - 2a - 6}{3a^2 - 3a - 18}$

Applications

46. **Statistics**   Find the mean for the two rational expressions $\dfrac{2}{3x}$ and $\dfrac{1}{x^2}$. $\dfrac{2x + 3}{6x^2}$

47. **Electricity**   The total resistance in a parallel circuit is $R = \dfrac{R_1 \times R_2}{R_1 + R_2}$.

Simplify the expression for R if $R_1 = \dfrac{3}{a}$ and $R_2 = \dfrac{a + 3}{a^3}$. $\dfrac{3a + 9}{a(3a^2 + a + 3)}$

TEST YOURSELF

Simplify.   8.1–8.3

1. $\dfrac{m^2 + 2m - 24}{6m} \cdot \dfrac{2m + 6}{m^2 - m - 12}$ $\dfrac{m + 6}{3m}$

2. $\dfrac{y - x}{2y + 3x} \cdot \dfrac{3x + 2y}{x + y} \div \dfrac{x - y}{x + y}$ -1

Write equivalent expressions having the same denominator. Use the LCD.   8.4

3. $\dfrac{3}{10ab^2} ; \dfrac{2a}{5b}$ $\dfrac{3}{10ab^2} ; \dfrac{4a^2b}{10ab^2}$

4. $\dfrac{4}{p - 2} ; \dfrac{p}{p^2 - 5p + 6}$ $\dfrac{4(p - 3)}{(p - 2)(p - 3)} ; \dfrac{p}{(p - 2)(p - 3)}$

Combine. Simplify if possible.   8.5–8.6

5. $\dfrac{m - 1}{3m^2} + \dfrac{m + 3}{2m} - \dfrac{m - 2}{6m^2}$ $\dfrac{3m + 10}{6m}$

6. $\dfrac{5x}{x + 4} - \dfrac{(x - 3)}{(x + 4)}$ $\dfrac{4x + 3}{x + 4}$

7. $y - \dfrac{1}{3}$ $\dfrac{3y - 1}{3}$

8. $\dfrac{\dfrac{r + 1}{r^2 - 4}}{\dfrac{r^2 - 1}{r + 2}}$ $\dfrac{1}{(r - 2)(r - 1)}$

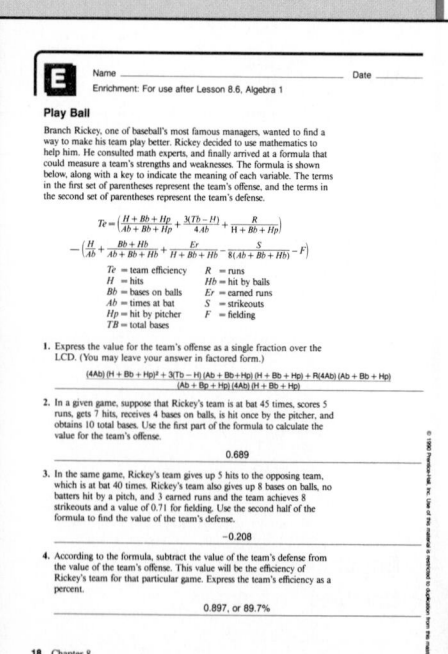

APPLICATION:
Interest

Did you know that you can use a formula to find the monthly payment required when you borrow to make a purchase? You will need a calculator to use the formula.

Suppose you borrow $100,000 to buy a health food franchise. The annual interest rate is 18%. The loan is to be repaid over a 10-year period. What will be your monthly payment?

$$m = \frac{A\left(\frac{r}{12}\right)\left(1 + \frac{r}{12}\right)^n}{\left(1 + \frac{r}{12}\right)^n - 1}$$

m = monthly payment
A = amount borrowed
r = annual rate of interest
n = number of months of the loan

Calculation-Ready Form

$$m = \frac{100{,}000\left(\frac{0.18}{12}\right)\left(1 + \frac{0.18}{12}\right)^{120}}{\left(1 + \frac{0.18}{12}\right)^{120} - 1}$$

$$= 1801.85$$

The monthly payment is $1801.85.

Solve these problems.

1. What is the monthly payment on a loan of $1500 at 12% interest for 18 months? $91.47

2. What is the monthly payment on a loan of $3000 at 9.5% interest for 24 months? $137.74

3. Sue has $1000 for the down payment on a used car. She has budgeted a monthly car payment of $150, and would like to pay off a car loan in two years. Which of these cars should she consider? car A or car B

Car	Price	Annual Interest
A	$4200	8%
B	3800	9.5%
C	5200	6%

4. Harvey borrows $40,000 to buy a bookstore. The annual rate of interest is 18%, and he will repay the loan in 36 monthly payments. Find his monthly payment and how much interest he will pay in all. $1446.10; $12,059.45

5. The Jacksons are buying a health food franchise. The purchase price is $145,000. They will make a down payment of 20%, and will finance the remaining amount over a period of 20 years at an annual rate of 11.4% interest. What will their monthly payments be? $1229.08

BACKGROUND

In the Capsule Review, students practice long division. Point out that the process is important here, and not the actual answer. This process is similar to the process used in the lesson to divide polynomials.

TEACHING SUGGESTIONS

- For Examples 3 and 4, students divide polynomials that do not have common factors, and therefore a remainder will result. Most students have an easier time when they see the parallel between long division with numbers and long division with polynomials.
- For Example 4, emphasize the importance of writing the terms in the dividend in descending order, and putting a zero in as a placeholder if one of the terms is missing. Point out that in long division with numbers containing a zero, the zero is acting as a placeholder.

CHALKBOARD EXAMPLES

- **For Example 1**
  Divide and check.
  1. $(2x^3 + 4x^2 - 2x + 3) \div 2x$
     $x^2 + 2x - 1 + \dfrac{3}{2x}$
  2. $(6w^4 + 4w^3 - w^2) \div 2w^3$
     $3w + 2 - \dfrac{1}{2w}$

- **For Example 2**
  Divide.
  3. $(a^2 - 2a - 8) \div (a - 4)$
     $a + 2$
  4. $(x^2 + x - 12) \div (x - 3)$
     $x + 4$

8.7 Dividing Polynomials

Objective: To divide polynomials

Division of one polynomial by another when there are no common factors is similar to long division in arithmetic.

Capsule Review

EXAMPLE   **Divide and check: 13,680 ÷ 325**

$$
\begin{array}{r}
42 \leftarrow \text{quotient} \\
325\overline{)13,680} \\
-13\ 00 \\
\hline
680 \\
-650 \\
\hline
30 \leftarrow \text{remainder}
\end{array}
$$

Check:

Quotient × divisor + remainder = dividend
42   ×   325   +   30   = 13,680

Divide and check.

1. $19,663 \div 612$ 32 R:79
2. $13,820 \div 488$ 28 R:156
3. $38,040 \div 421$ 90 R:150
4. $97,979 \div 126$ 777 R:77
5. $50,505 \div 500$ 101 R:5
6. $37,925 \div 350$ 108 R:125

To divide a polynomial by a monomial, divide *each* term of the polynomial by the monomial. Check the results.

EXAMPLE 1   **Divide and check: $(9w^4 + 3w^3 - w^2) \div 3w^3$**

$$\frac{9w^4 + 3w^3 - w^2}{3w^3} = \frac{9w^4}{3w^3} + \frac{3w^3}{3w^3} - \frac{w^2}{3w^3} \qquad \textit{Divide each term by the monomial.}$$

$$= 3w + 1 - \frac{1}{3w} \qquad \textit{Simplify.}$$

Check: $\left(3w + 1 - \dfrac{1}{3w}\right)3w^3 = 9w^4 + 3w^3 - w^2$ ✔

When you divide one polynomial by another, factor if possible and then divide by any common factors.

EXAMPLE 2   **Divide: $(a^2 + 3a - 4) \div (a + 4)$**

$$\frac{a^2 + 3a - 4}{a + 4} = \frac{(a - 1)(a + 4)}{(a + 4)} = a - 1$$

342   Chapter 8 Rational Expressions

If the polynomials cannot be factored or if there are no common factors, follow a procedure similar to long division.

EXAMPLE 3 **Divide and check:** $(2y^2 + 3y - 11) \div (y - 3)$

$$
\begin{array}{r}
2y + 9 \\
y - 3{\overline{\smash{\big)}\,2y^2 + 3y - 11}} \\
\underline{-(2y^2 - 6y)} \downarrow \\
9y - 11 \\
\underline{-(9y - 27)} \\
16
\end{array}
$$

Divide.   *Think:* $2y^2 \div y = 2y$
Multiply. $(y - 3)2y = 2y^2 - 6y$
Subtract. $2y^2 + 3y - (2y^2 - 6y) = 9y$

Divide.   *Think:* $9y \div y = 9$
Multiply. $(y - 3)9 = 9y - 27$
Subtract. $9y - 11 - (9y - 27) = 16$

So, $\dfrac{2y^2 + 3y - 11}{y - 3} = 2y + 9 + \dfrac{16}{y - 3}$ *Write the remainder as a fraction.*

Check: Quotient $\times$ divisor $+$ remainder $=$ dividend
$(2y + 9) \cdot (y - 3) + \quad 16 \quad = (2y^2 + 3y - 27) + 16$
$\qquad\qquad\qquad\qquad\qquad\qquad = 2y^2 + 3y - 11$ ✔

When you divide polynomials, write the terms of the dividend in descending order of the exponents of a variable. If a term is missing, insert a zero or a zero coefficient, as a placeholder.

EXAMPLE 4 **Divide:** $(7b + 4b^3) \div (2b - 1)$

$$
\begin{array}{r}
2b^2 + b + 4 \\
2b - 1{\overline{\smash{\big)}\,4b^3 + 0b^2 + 7b + 0}} \\
\underline{-(4b^3 - 2b^2)} \\
2b^2 + 7b \\
\underline{-(2b^2 - b)} \\
8b + 0 \\
\underline{-(8b - 4)} \\
4
\end{array}
$$

Terms in descending order, with zeros as place holders.

So, $(7b + 4b^3) \div (2b - 1) = 2b^2 + b + 4 + \dfrac{4}{2b - 1}$

Check: Does $(2b^2 + b + 4)(2b - 1) + 4 = 4b^3 + 7b$?

CLASS EXERCISES

Divide and check.

1. $(8q^2 - 32q^3) \div 2q$ $4q - 16q^2$

2. $(14t^4 - 28t^3 + 35t^2 - 7t) \div 7t^2$ $2t^2 - 4t + 5 - \dfrac{1}{t}$

3. $(n^2 - 5n + 4) \div (n - 4)$ $n - 1$

4. $(6s^2 - 7s + 5) \div (2s - 3)$ $3s + 1 + \dfrac{8}{2s - 3}$

5. $(2x^3 - 3x^2 - 10x + 3) \div (x - 3)$ $2x^2 + 3x - 1$

6. $(3a^3 - 16) \div (a - 2)$ $3a^2 + 6a + 12 + \dfrac{8}{a - 2}$

8.7 Dividing Polynomials   **343**

• **For Example 3**
Divide and check.
5. $(2x^2 + x - 11) \div (x + 2)$
$2x - 3 - \dfrac{5}{x + 2}$
6. $(a^2 - 6a + 8) \div (a - 4)$
$(a - 2)$

• **For Example 4**
Divide.
7. $(6y^3 + y^2 - 7) \div (2y - 1)$
$3y^2 + 2y + 1 - \dfrac{6}{2y - 1}$
8. $(6w^2 - 9w - 12) \div (2w - 5)$
$3w + 3 + \dfrac{3}{2w - 5}$

Common Error

• Students often forget to write the terms of the dividend in descending order of exponents and to insert a zero or a zero coefficient as a placeholder if a term is missing. Have students practice writing polynomials in descending order of exponents.
• See *Teacher's Resource Book* for additional remediation.

LESSON FOLLOW-UP

Critical Thinking
Causal Explanation What does it mean if the remainder is zero when you divide polynomials using the long division method? The denominator is a factor of the numerator.

Assignment Guide
See p. 314B for assignments.

Lesson Quiz
Divide and check.
1. $(28a^2 - 42a^4) \div 7a^2$ $4 - 6a^2$
2. $(r^3 - 3r^2 + 20r - 6) \div r$
$r^2 - 3r + 20 - \dfrac{6}{r}$
3. $(8f^2 + 26f + 15) \div (2f + 5)$
$4f + 3$
4. $(d^2 + 3d - 7) \div (d - 2)$
$d + 5 + \dfrac{3}{d - 2}$
5. $(t^3 + 2t^2 - 5t + 3) \div (t + 3)$
$t^2 - t - 2 + \dfrac{9}{t + 3}$

343

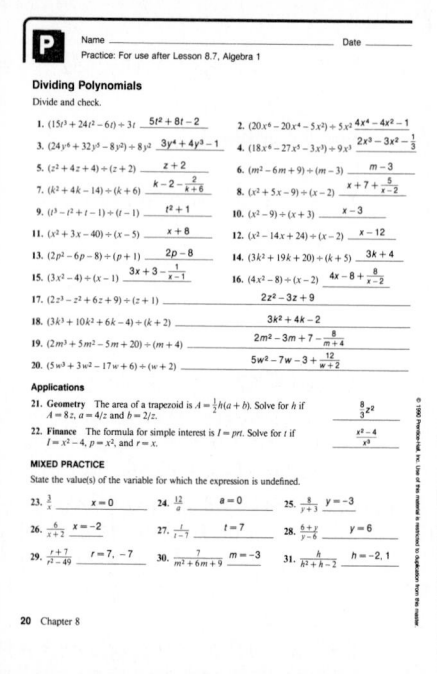

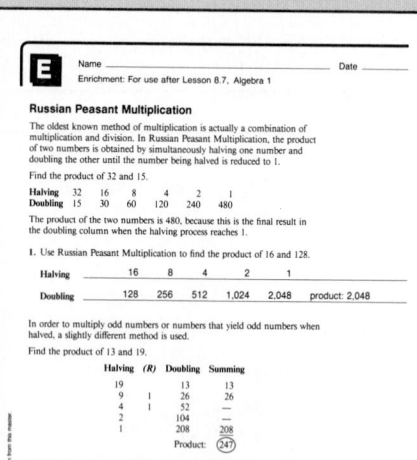

PRACTICE EXERCISES

A   **Divide and check.**

1. $(6x^4 + 3x^3 - x^2) \div 3x^3$ $2x + 1 - \frac{1}{3x}$ **2.** $(10z^4 + 5z^3 - z^2) \div 5z^3$ $2z + 1 - \frac{1}{5z}$

3. $(x^3 - 18x^2 + 3x - 7) \div x$ $x^2 - 18x + 3 - \frac{7}{x}$ **4.** $(c^3 + 11c^2 - 15c + 8) \div c$ $c^2 + 11c - 15 + \frac{8}{c}$

5. $(3y^4 - 15y^3 + 21y^2 + 6y - 9) \div 3y$ $y^3 - 5y^2 + 7y + 2 - \frac{3}{y}$

6. $(4m^4 + 6m^3 - 20m^2 + 8m - 12) \div 2m$ $2m^3 + 3m^2 - 10m + 4 - \frac{6}{m}$

7. $(n^2 + n - 30) \div (n + 6)$ $n - 5$ **8.** $(a^2 - 2a - 24) \div (a + 4)$ $a - 6$

9. $(k^2 + 11k + 18) \div (k + 6)$ $k + 5 - \frac{12}{k+6}$ **10.** $(r^2 + 3r + 5) \div (r + 2)$ $r + 1 + \frac{3}{r+2}$

11. $(3j^2 + 7j - 5) \div (j - 3)$ $3j + 16 + \frac{43}{j-3}$ **12.** $(s^2 + 2s - 24) \div (s - 8)$ $s + 10 + \frac{56}{s-8}$

13. $(10m^2 + 9m - 36) \div (2m - 3)$ $5m + 12$ **14.** $(15h^2 - 62h + 40) \div (5h - 4)$ $3h - 10$

15. $(d^2 - 7d + 4) \div (d - 3)$ $d - 4 - \frac{8}{d-3}$ **16.** $(2m^2 - 3m + 5) \div (m - 2)$ $2m + 1 + \frac{7}{m+2}$

17. $(8b + 2b^3) \div (b - 1)$ $2b^2 + 2b + 10 + \frac{10}{b-1}$ **18.** $(9a + 3a^3) \div (a - 1)$ $3a^2 + 3a + 12 + \frac{12}{a-1}$

19. $(3x^3 - 3) \div (x + 1)$ $3x^2 - 3x + 3 - \frac{6}{x+1}$ **20.** $(6 + 3q^3) \div (q - 2)$ $3q^2 + 6q + 12 + \frac{30}{q-2}$

B   **21.** $(18s^2 - 51s) \div 3s$ $6s - 17$ **22.** $(108a^3 - 72a^4) \div 9a^3$ $-8a + 12$

23. $(18p^5q^4 - 54p^3q^3 + 27p^2q^5 - 9pq^2) \div 9pq^2$ $2p^4q^2 - 6p^2q + 3pq^3 - 1$

24. $(21a^3b^2 + 56a^5b - 28a^2b + 63a^5b^2) \div 7a^2b$ $3ab + 8a^3 - 4 + 9a^3b$

25. $(p^3 + 3p^2 - 5p - 4) \div (p + 2)$ **26.** $(a^3 + 2a^2 + 4a - 5) \div (a + 3)$

27. $(6h^3 + 5h^2 - 9h - 7) \div (2h + 1)$ **28.** $(9t^3 - 3t^2 - 9t + 5) \div (3t + 2)$

29. $(x^3 - 3x + 5) \div (x - 4)$ $x^2 + 4x + 13 + \frac{57}{x-4}$ **30.** $(y^3 + 4y - 7) \div (y - 3)$ $y^2 + 3y + 13 + \frac{32}{y-3}$

31. $(9h^3 - 4h + 2) \div (3h - 1)$ $3h^2 + h - 1 + \frac{1}{3h-1}$ **32.** $(4j^3 - 5j - 3) \div (2j + 3)$ $2j^2 - 3j + 2 - \frac{9}{2j+3}$

C   **33.** $(27t^3 - 343) \div (3t - 7)$ $9t^2 + 21t + 49$ **34.** $(64h^3 - 125) \div (4h - 5)$ $16h^2 + 20h + 25$

35. $(15x^2 + 7xy - 2y^2) \div (5x - y)$ $3x + 2y$ **36.** $(10m^2 - 11mn + 3n^2) \div (2m - n)$ $5m - 3n$

37. $(6p^2 + 10pq + 6q^2) \div (3p + 2q)$ $2p + 2q + \frac{2q^2}{3p + 2q}$ **38.** $(12c^2 + 25cd + 12d^2) \div (3c + 4d)$ $4c + 3d$

Applications

39. **Finance**   The amount (A) in a savings account is $A = p + prt$. Solve for
p if $A = x^2 - 1$, $r = \frac{1}{x}$, and $t = x^2$. Find the principal (p) if $x = \$101$.
$p = x - 1;\ \$100$

ALGEBRA IN HEALTH

An almanac provides a table of the Recommended Daily Allowances from
infancy to 51+ years. The nutritive value of various foods is also given. Use
this information to plan three nutritious meals for each member of your family.
Check students' work.

Additional Answers

25. $p^2 + p - 7 + \frac{10}{p + 2}$

26. $a^2 - a + 7 - \frac{26}{a + 3}$

27. $3h^2 + h - 5 - \frac{2}{2h + 1}$

28. $3t^2 - 3t - 1 + \frac{7}{3t + 2}$

<table>
<tr><td>8.8</td><td></td></tr>
</table>

Ratios and Proportions

Objectives: To express ratios in simplest form
To solve equations involving proportions

One bag of fruit labeled A has 3 lb of apples and 4 lb of oranges. Another bag labeled B has 6 lb of apples and 8 lb of oranges. In bag A, you can say that the assortment has a 3 to 4 mixture of apples to oranges. This relationship is called a *ratio.*

A **ratio** is the comparison of two quantities by division.

What is the ratio of apples to oranges in bag B? Are the ratios found for each bag equal? How do you know?

A statement that ratios are equal is called a **proportion.** The proportion of apples to oranges can be written in several ways.

$$3 \text{ is to } 4 \text{ as } 6 \text{ is to } 8 \qquad 3{:}4 = 6{:}8 \qquad \frac{3}{4} = \frac{6}{8}$$

Capsule Review

To simplify ratios you will need to express fractions in simplest form, and to solve proportions, you will need to use the properties of equations.

Divide and express as a fraction in simplest form.

1. $\frac{225}{400}$ $\frac{9}{16}$ **2.** $3 \div 126$ $\frac{1}{42}$ **3.** $1\frac{1}{4} \div 2\frac{5}{8}$ **4.** $3\frac{1}{2} \div 7\frac{1}{2}$

Solve.

5. $6d = -20$ $-\frac{10}{3}$ **6.** $12y = 72$ 6   **7.** $\frac{3}{4}a = 3$ 4   **8.** $\frac{-x}{3} = \frac{1}{4}$ $-\frac{3}{4}$

A ratio can be expressed in a variety of ways as shown in the example below.

EXAMPLE 1   **Express in simplest form:**

     a. \$2.40 per \$6   **b.** $1\frac{1}{2}$ out of 5   **c.** 2.4 cm to 40 mm

8.8 Ratios and Proportions   **345**

LESSON PLAN

Vocabulary
Extremes
Means
Proportion
Ratio

Materials/Manipulatives
Overhead projector

BACKGROUND

In the Capsule Review, students practice dividing and expressing fractions in simplest form. Solving proportions by using properties of equations provides practice for comparing ratios and solving proportions presented in this lesson.

Critical Thinking

Observation What real-world experiences have you had where ratios are involved?
Answers may vary. Examples:
Sports–Batting average
Financial–Price to earnings ratio
School–Percent correct on a test

- For Example 1, students compare two quantities by expressing ratios in simplest form. For Example 1C, stress that the units must be the same in order to compare and express the ratio in simplest form.
- For Examples 2 and 3, students use the property of proportions. You may wish to call this the "cross-multiply" property.
- For Example 4, emphasize that the map distance is in the numerators of the fractions and the real distance is in the denominators of the fractions. You may also rewrite the proportion as follows:

$$\frac{1.5 \text{ cm}}{4.25 \text{ cm}} = \frac{24 \text{ km}}{x \text{ km}}$$

- Use an overhead projector to illustrate several examples involving the concept of dimensional analysis.

a. $\dfrac{\$2.40}{\$6} = \dfrac{240}{600}$

$= \dfrac{4}{10}$, or $\dfrac{2}{5}$

b. $1\dfrac{1}{2} \div 5 = \dfrac{3}{2} \cdot \dfrac{1}{5}$

$= \dfrac{3}{10}$

c. $\dfrac{2.4 \text{ cm}}{40 \text{ mm}} = \dfrac{24 \text{ mm}}{40 \text{ mm}}$

$= \dfrac{24}{40}$ or $\dfrac{3}{5}$

Notice that in Example 1c, 2.4 cm was changed to 24 mm. When simplifying ratios with different units within the same kind of measure, begin by expressing the measure using the same units.

In the proportion $3:4 = 6:8$ in the opening problem, 4 and 6 are called the **means**; and 3 and 8 are called the **extremes**.

In general, $\dfrac{a}{b} = \dfrac{c}{d}$ or $a:b = c:d$ b and c are the means and a and d are the extremes

means / extremes

Property of Proportions

In a proportion, the product of the means equals the product of the extremes. For all real numbers a, b, c, and d; $b \neq 0$ and $d \neq 0$:

If $\dfrac{a}{b} = \dfrac{c}{d}$, then $a \cdot d = b \cdot c$.

If $\dfrac{a}{b} = \dfrac{c}{d}$, how would you show that $a \cdot d = b \cdot c$?

This property is useful when you check to see whether two ratios are equal.

EXAMPLE 2   **True or false?**   **a.** $15:24 = 100:160$ **b.** $\dfrac{3 \text{ lb}}{7 \text{ in.}^2} = \dfrac{10 \text{ lb}}{24 \text{ in.}^2}$

a. $15:24 \overset{?}{=} 100:160$

$\dfrac{15}{24} \times \dfrac{100}{160}$

$24 \times 100 \overset{?}{=} 15 \times 160$

$2400 = 2400$ ✓

true

b. $\dfrac{3 \text{ lb}}{7 \text{ in.}^2} = \dfrac{10 \text{ lb}}{24 \text{ in.}^2}$

$\dfrac{3 \text{ lb}}{7 \text{ in.}^2} \times \dfrac{10 \text{ lb}}{24 \text{ in.}^2}$

$7 \times 10 \overset{?}{=} 3 \times 24$

$70 \neq 72$

false

The property of proportions is used to solve for an unknown quantity in a proportion.

EXAMPLE 3 Solve: **a.** $\dfrac{3}{7} = \dfrac{10}{x}$ **b.** $\dfrac{2s - 21}{3} = \dfrac{s}{5}$

$\qquad\qquad$ **a.** $\dfrac{3}{7} = \dfrac{10}{x}$ **b.** $\dfrac{2s - 21}{3} = \dfrac{s}{5}$

$\qquad\qquad\qquad 3x = 7(10) \qquad\qquad 3s = 5(2s - 21)$

$\qquad\qquad\qquad\qquad x = \dfrac{70}{3} \qquad\qquad\quad 3s = 10s - 105$

$\qquad\qquad\qquad\qquad\qquad\qquad\qquad\qquad -7s = -105$

$\qquad\qquad\qquad\qquad\qquad\qquad\qquad\qquad\quad s = 15$

Many real-world problems are solved by using proportions.

EXAMPLE 4 **The scale on a map states: 1.5 cm represents 24 km. What distance does 4.25 cm on the map represent?**

$\dfrac{1.5 \text{ cm}}{24 \text{ km}} = \dfrac{4.25 \text{ cm}}{x} \longrightarrow \text{map distance} \atop \longrightarrow \text{real distance in km}$ Write the ratios in the same order.

$(1.5 \text{ cm})(x \text{ km}) = (4.25 \text{ cm})(24 \text{ km})$

$\qquad\qquad x = \dfrac{(4.25 \text{ cm})(24 \text{ km})}{1.5 \text{ cm}}$ *Units common to both numerator and denominator can be divided out.*

$\qquad\qquad x = \dfrac{102 \text{ km}}{1.5} = 68 \text{ km}$

So, on the map 4.25 cm represents 68 km.

CLASS EXERCISES

Express as a ratio in simplest form.

1. 0.2 to 3 $\frac{1}{15}$

2. $2\frac{1}{2}$ out of 3 $\frac{5}{6}$

3. $4a^2 : 2ab$ $\frac{2a}{b}$

4. 1.5 cm to 45 mm $\frac{1}{3}$

True or false?

5. $\dfrac{2}{5} = \dfrac{6}{15}$ true

6. $\dfrac{2}{7} = \dfrac{9}{31}$ false

7. $\dfrac{1\frac{1}{2}}{1} = \dfrac{3}{2}$ true

8. $2:9 = 3:18$ false

Solve.

9. $\dfrac{8}{x} = \dfrac{2}{5}$ 20

10. $\dfrac{3n}{2} = \dfrac{-9}{10}$ $-\frac{3}{5}$

11. $\dfrac{a + 1}{9} = \dfrac{2}{3}$ 5

12. $8 = \dfrac{40}{m - 3}$ 8

13. If $\frac{1}{2}$ in. represents 20 mi, what distance does 4 in. represent? 160 mi

8.8 Ratios and Proportions **347**

PRACTICE EXERCISES

Express as a ratio, in simplest form.

A
1. 6 to 8 $\frac{3}{4}$
2. 48 to 32 $\frac{3}{2}$
3. $\frac{1}{2}$ to 3 $\frac{1}{6}$
4. 4 to $2\frac{2}{3}$ $\frac{3}{2}$
5. 0.5 to 2.5 $\frac{1}{5}$
6. 7.5 to 6 $\frac{5}{4}$
7. 2 to $4x$ $\frac{1}{2x}$
8. $3y$ to y^2 $\frac{3}{y}$
9. 5 ft to 2 yd $\frac{5}{6}$
10. 2.4 cm to 36 mm $\frac{2}{3}$
11. $3.20 to $0.80 $\frac{4}{1}$
12. 0.72 to 0.6 $\frac{6}{5}$

True or False?

13. $\frac{5}{12} = \frac{3}{7}$ false
14. $\frac{4}{9} = \frac{7}{16}$ false
15. $\frac{6}{15} = \frac{16}{40}$ true
16. $\frac{9}{30} = \frac{16}{55}$ false

17. If 3 cans of Miller's Chunky Vegetable Soup cost $0.93, then 5 cans cost $1.55.   true

18. A supermarket sells 5 lemons at a cost of $0.95, then 8 lemons will cost $1.52.   true

Solve.

19. $\frac{5}{6} = \frac{30}{s}$ 36
20. $\frac{28}{r} = \frac{4}{7}$ 49
21. $\frac{s+4}{12} = \frac{7}{4}$ 17
22. $\frac{9}{5} = \frac{18}{t+2}$ 8

B
23. $\frac{8}{a} = \frac{16}{3}$ $\frac{3}{2}$
24. $\frac{5}{24} = \frac{x}{12}$ $\frac{5}{2}$
25. $\frac{18p}{54} = \frac{12}{9}$ 4
26. $\frac{12c}{28} = \frac{15}{7}$ 5
27. $\frac{5}{3n+5} = \frac{5}{5n-2}$ $\frac{7}{2}$
28. $\frac{5}{3+b} = \frac{3}{7b+1}$ $\frac{1}{8}$
29. $\frac{4}{x+3} = \frac{2}{2x+1}$ $\frac{1}{3}$
30. $\frac{4}{y+4} = \frac{2}{3y+2}$ 0
31. $\frac{s-2}{5} = \frac{2s+3}{3}$ -3
32. $\frac{t+3}{2} = \frac{2t-5}{6}$ -14

C
33. $\frac{2}{2m+3} = \frac{3m-2}{4}$ $-2, \frac{7}{6}$
34. $\frac{a}{a+3} = \frac{4}{5a}$ $-\frac{6}{5}, 2$
35. $\frac{q}{3} = \frac{4}{q+4}$ $-6, 2$
36. $\frac{5}{p+2} = \frac{p}{7}$ $5, -7$
37. $\frac{w-3}{3} = \frac{3}{w+5}$ $4, -6$
38. $\frac{11}{u-2} = \frac{u+7}{2}$ $-9, 4$

Applications

39. **Entertainment** A party punch contained 2 qt of pineapple juice, 3 pt of orange juice, $2\frac{1}{2}$ c of cranberry juice, and $1\frac{3}{4}$ c of ice. Find the following ratios.
   a. pineapple juice to ice $\frac{32}{7}$
   b. cranberry juice to orange juice $\frac{5}{12}$
   c. orange juice to pineapple juice $\frac{3}{4}$

40. **Cartography** According to a map's scale, 1.5 cm represents 6 km. What distance does 3.25 cm represent? 13 km

41. **Cartography** If 2.5 cm represents 10 km, what distance does 4.25 cm represent? 17 km

42. **Travel** A car traveled 66 mi in $1\frac{1}{2}$ h. At the same speed, how many miles will the car travel in 2 h? 88 mi

43. **Travel** If a cyclist traveled 45 mi in $2\frac{1}{2}$ h, how long would it take her to travel 153 mi? 8.5 h

BIOGRAPHY

Jean-Victor Poncelet (1788–1867), an officer in the French army, was captured during Napoleon's Russian campaign. While he was in prison, Poncelet created the area of mathematics known as *projective geometry*.

Investigation

One of the important ideas in projective geometry is cross-ratio.

- Draw four lines, *a*, *b*, *c*, and *d* through a point *O*.
- Draw a line *l* that intersects these lines at points *A*, *B*, *C*, and *D*.
- Consider the ratios $\frac{AC}{AD}$ and $\frac{BC}{BD}$.

  Form the cross-ratio: $\frac{(AC)(BD)}{(AD)(BC)}$

  An extraordinary fact is that this ratio has the same numerical value for all positions of the line *l*. Make several drawings, and measure to verify this fact.
  Answers may vary.

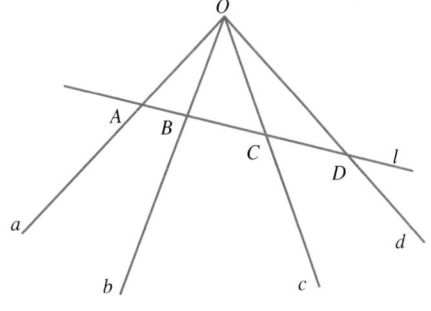

8.8 Ratios and Proportions **349**

Teacher's Resource Book
Reteaching—Chapter 8, p. 22.

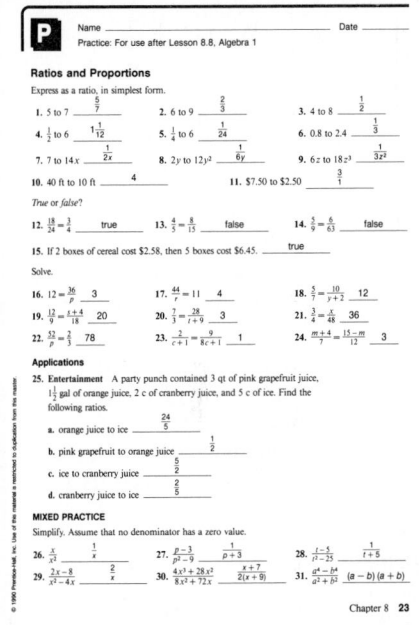

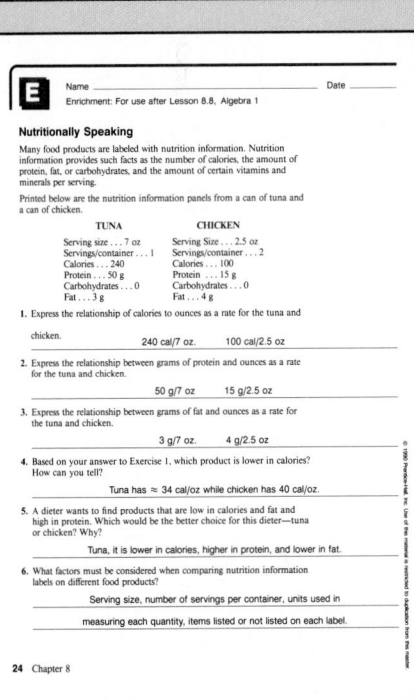

BACKGROUND

- In the Capsule Review, students practice finding the least common denominator of three rational expressions. This review will aid students in solving equations containing rational expressions.
- Remind students to look for factors which are opposites, such as $x - y$ and $y - x$.

Critical Thinking

Classifying Use a dictionary to find the origin and meaning of the word *extraneous*. (Hint: Look up the word strange, too.) *Extraneous* means "not essential" or "strange." *Strange* comes from the French *éstrange* and Latin *extraneus,* meaning "external" or "foreign." Also, from the French, *extra* means "on the outside." Thus, an extraneous solution is one that is "external" or "extra." It is a "strange" solution in the sense that it satisfies the resulting equation, but not the original equation.

8.9

Solving Rational Equations

Objective: To solve rational equations, including some with extraneous solutions

In an earlier lesson you used the least common denominator (LCD) to help you add and subtract rational expressions. In this lesson the LCD will help you simplify and then solve equations.

Capsule Review

EXAMPLE Find the LCD: $\dfrac{5}{6xy}, \dfrac{x}{2x - 4}$, and $\dfrac{10x}{4 - 2x}$

Factor the denominators:
$$6xy = 2 \cdot 3 \cdot x \cdot y$$
$$2x - 4 = 2(x - 2)$$
$$4 - 2x = (-1)(2)(x - 2)$$

The LCD is the product of the prime factors, each raised to the greatest power that appears in any one denominator. The negative one from the last denominator need not be included.

$$2 \cdot 3xy(x - 2), \text{ or } 6xy(x - 2)$$

Find the LCD.

1. $\dfrac{2}{x}; \dfrac{3}{5x}; \dfrac{x}{5}$ $5x$

2. $\dfrac{1}{ab}; \dfrac{2}{ab^3}; \dfrac{7}{a^2b}$ a^2b^3

3. $\dfrac{9}{11m}; \dfrac{13}{44m^2}; \dfrac{m}{2}$ $44m^2$

4. $\dfrac{4}{y}; \dfrac{3}{2 + y}; \dfrac{x}{2y^2 + 4y}$ $2y(y + 2)$

5. $\dfrac{s}{4}; \dfrac{3}{r + s}; \dfrac{r}{2r + 2s}$ $4(r + s)$

6. $\dfrac{d}{3 - d}; \dfrac{3}{d - 3}; \dfrac{d}{d^2 - 9}$ $(d + 3)(d - 3)$

An equation that contains rational expressions is easier to solve if you first eliminate all denominators other than 1.

> **To solve an equation that contains rational expressions:**
> - Multiply each term of the equation by the least common denominator.
> - Solve the resulting equation.

When checking a solution, you need to replace each variable in the original equation, not in the resulting equation, to make sure that the denominator does not equal zero.

EXAMPLE 1 Solve and check: $2m - \dfrac{4}{5} = \dfrac{-2m}{15}$

$$2m - \frac{4}{5} = \frac{-2m}{15} \qquad \textit{The LCD is 15.}$$

$$(15)2m - (15)\frac{4}{5} = (15)\frac{-2m}{15} \qquad \textit{Multiply each term by the LCD.}$$

$$30m - 12 = -2m \qquad \textit{Solve the transformed equation.}$$
$$32m = 12$$

$$m = \frac{12}{32}, \text{ or } \frac{3}{8}$$

Check: $\underset{4}{2}\left(\dfrac{3}{\underset{}{8}}\right) - \dfrac{4}{5} \overset{?}{=} \underset{5}{\dfrac{\cancel{-2}}{\cancel{15}}}\underset{-4}{\left(\dfrac{3}{8}\right)}$ *In the original equation, replace m with $\frac{3}{8}$.*

$$\frac{3}{4} - \frac{4}{5} \overset{?}{=} -\frac{1}{20}$$

$$-\frac{1}{20} = -\frac{1}{20} \checkmark$$

Since division by zero is undefined, -4 cannot be used as a solution in the next example. This is called an *extraneous solution*. An **extraneous solution** is an apparent solution which does not satisfy the original equation.

EXAMPLE 2 Solve and check: $\dfrac{a}{a + 4} = 3 - \dfrac{4}{a + 4}$

$$\frac{a}{a + 4} = 3 - \frac{4}{a + 4} \qquad \textit{The LCD is (a + 4).}$$

$$\frac{a}{\cancel{a+4}}\cancel{(a+4)} = 3(a + 4) - \frac{4}{\cancel{a+4}}\cancel{(a+4)} \qquad \textit{Multiply by the LCD.}$$

$$a = 3(a + 4) - 4 \qquad \textit{Solve.}$$
$$a = 3a + 12 - 4$$
$$-2a = 8$$
$$a = -4$$

Check: $\dfrac{-4}{-4 + 4} \overset{?}{=} 3 - \dfrac{4}{-4 + 4}$ Replace a with -4 in the original equation. The denominator is 0, and so -4 is an extraneous solution. The equation is said to have no solution.

EXAMPLE 3 Solve and check: $\dfrac{d}{d + 2} - \dfrac{2}{2 - d} = \dfrac{d + 6}{d^2 - 4}$

$$\frac{d}{d + 2} - \frac{2}{2 - d} = \frac{d + 6}{d^2 - 4}$$

$$\frac{d}{d + 2} + \frac{2}{d - 2} = \frac{d + 6}{(d + 2)(d - 2)} \qquad \textit{Factor. Rewrite } \frac{-2}{2 - d} \textit{ as } \frac{2}{d - 2}.$$

Discussion

Why is it necessary to check solutions in the original equation? Checking solutions into the original equation will help determine whether the solution is an extraneous solution.

Assignment Guide

- See p. 314B for assignments.
- See *Teacher's Resource Book* for Critical Thinking Activity p. 8.

Lesson Quiz

Solve and check. If the equation has no solution, write "no solution."

1. $\dfrac{n}{5} + \dfrac{n}{6} = 11$ 30

2. $\dfrac{3e}{2} - \dfrac{5e}{6} = 8$ 12

3. $\dfrac{5x}{5} - \dfrac{11x}{5} = -9$ $\dfrac{15}{2}$

4. $3 - \dfrac{8}{t} = 5$ -4

5. $\dfrac{a}{a+3} = 2 - \dfrac{1}{a+3}$ -5

6. $\dfrac{3}{n} + \dfrac{5}{3} = \dfrac{7}{n}$ $\dfrac{12}{5}$

7. $\dfrac{6}{5q} + \dfrac{2}{3} = \dfrac{16}{15q}$ $-\dfrac{1}{5}$

8. $\dfrac{u-1}{u} + \dfrac{9}{4u} = 6$ $\dfrac{1}{4}$

9. $\dfrac{3i}{i-5} + 7 = \dfrac{5i}{i-5}$ 7

10. $\dfrac{z}{z+6} = 4 - \dfrac{6}{z+6}$ no solution

Enrichment

Solve:

$$\dfrac{4}{y^2 + 2y - 15} + \dfrac{2}{y^2 - y - 6}$$
$$= \dfrac{y+3}{y^2 + 7y + 10}$$ 9, -3

Multiply by the LCD: $(d+2)(d-2)$

$$\dfrac{d}{d+2}\cancel{(d+2)}(d-2) + \dfrac{2}{d-2}(d+2)\cancel{(d-2)} = \dfrac{d+6}{\cancel{(d+2)}\cancel{(d-2)}}(d+2)(d-2)$$

$$d(d-2) + 2(d+2) = d+6 \qquad \text{Solve.}$$
$$d^2 - 2d + 2d + 4 = d+6$$
$$d^2 - d - 2 = 0$$
$$(d+1)(d-2) = 0 \qquad \text{Factor.}$$

$d + 1 = 0 \quad | \quad d - 2 = 0$ Zero Product Rule
$\quad d = -1 \quad | \qquad d = 2$

Check: In the original equation, replace d with -1 and then with 2. Which of these is an extraneous solution?

CLASS EXERCISES

Solve and check. If the equation has no solution, write "no solution."

1. $\dfrac{y}{3} + \dfrac{2}{3} = 1$ 1

2. $\dfrac{1}{3} + \dfrac{5z}{6} = 2$ 2

3. $\dfrac{3}{a} - \dfrac{5}{a} = 2$ -1

4. $\dfrac{2}{3} - \dfrac{5}{m} = \dfrac{1}{3m}$ 8

5. $x + \dfrac{2}{3} = \dfrac{5x}{6}$ -4

6. $5 + \dfrac{2}{p} = \dfrac{17}{p}$ 3

7. $\dfrac{b}{b+3} = 2 - \dfrac{3}{b+3}$ no solution

8. $\dfrac{5}{f} + \dfrac{3}{f+1} = \dfrac{7}{f}$ 2

9. $\dfrac{1}{g-3} + 1 = \dfrac{3}{g^2 - 3g}$ -1

PRACTICE EXERCISES

Solve and check. If the equation has no solution, write "no solution."

A   **1.** $3m - \dfrac{3}{4} = \dfrac{2m}{3}$ $\dfrac{9}{28}$

2. $2y - \dfrac{3}{4} = \dfrac{3y}{8}$ $\dfrac{6}{13}$

3. $5x - \dfrac{2}{3} = \dfrac{-5x}{6}$ $\dfrac{4}{35}$

4. $4t - \dfrac{3}{5} = \dfrac{-2t}{3}$ $\dfrac{9}{70}$

5. $\dfrac{5e}{3} - \dfrac{7e}{6} = 2$ 4

6. $\dfrac{7f}{3} - \dfrac{8f}{15} = 9$ 5

7. $\dfrac{b}{b+3} = 5 - \dfrac{3}{b+3}$ no solution

8. $\dfrac{x}{x+5} = 3 - \dfrac{5}{x+5}$ no solution

9. $\dfrac{2t}{t-4} = 5 - \dfrac{1}{t-4}$ 7

10. $\dfrac{3s}{s-5} = 7 - \dfrac{1}{s-5}$ 9

11. $\dfrac{2}{i} - \dfrac{8}{i} = -15$ $\dfrac{2}{5}$

12. $\dfrac{7}{j} - \dfrac{9}{j} = -14$ $\dfrac{1}{7}$

13. $2 - \dfrac{8}{m} = 6$ -2

14. $1 - \dfrac{9}{k} = 4$ -3

15. $\dfrac{5}{2s} + \dfrac{3}{4} = \dfrac{9}{4s}$ $-\dfrac{1}{3}$

16. $\dfrac{2}{3t} + \dfrac{1}{2} = \dfrac{3}{4t}$ $\dfrac{1}{6}$

17. $\dfrac{u+1}{u} + \dfrac{1}{2u} = 4$ $\dfrac{1}{2}$

18. $\dfrac{v+2}{v} + \dfrac{4}{3v} = 11$ $\dfrac{1}{3}$

19. $\dfrac{4w+5}{w-4} = \dfrac{5w}{w-4}$ 5

20. $\dfrac{2x+4}{x-3} = \dfrac{3x}{x-3}$ 4

B
21. $\dfrac{y}{y-3} = \dfrac{3}{y-3} - 1$ no solution   **22.** $\dfrac{z}{z+2} = 3 - \dfrac{2}{z+2}$ no solution

23. $\dfrac{c}{c+6} = \dfrac{1}{c+2}$ 2, –3   **24.** $\dfrac{h}{h+5} = \dfrac{2}{h+5}$ –5, 2   **25.** $\dfrac{3}{e-1} = \dfrac{2e}{e+4}$ $-\dfrac{3}{2}$, 4

26. $\dfrac{4}{c-4} = \dfrac{3c}{c+3}$ $-\dfrac{2}{3}$, 6   **27.** $\dfrac{4}{k} + \dfrac{2}{3} = 10k$ $\dfrac{2}{3}$, $-\dfrac{3}{5}$ **28.** $5f = \dfrac{7}{2} + \dfrac{6}{f}$ $-\dfrac{4}{5}$, $\dfrac{3}{2}$

29. $\dfrac{2}{e-2} = 2 - \dfrac{4}{e}$ 1, 4   **30.** $6 - \dfrac{2}{r} = \dfrac{-5}{r-3}$ $\dfrac{1}{2}$, 2   **31.** $\dfrac{2e}{e-4} - 2 = \dfrac{4}{e+5}$ –14

C **32.** $\dfrac{r+1}{r-1} = \dfrac{r}{3} + \dfrac{2}{r-1}$ 3   **33.** $\dfrac{2}{a+2} = \dfrac{a}{a-2} + \dfrac{13}{4-a^2}$ 3, –3

34. $\dfrac{e+1}{e+2} = \dfrac{-1}{e-3} + \dfrac{e-1}{e^2-e-6}$ 0, 2   **35.** $\dfrac{f-2}{f-4} = \dfrac{1}{f+2} + \dfrac{f+3}{f^2-2f-8}$ 3, –1

36. $\dfrac{u}{2u-2} + \dfrac{u+1}{2u+1} = \dfrac{-3u}{2u^2-u-1}$ $\dfrac{1}{4}$, –2   **37.** $\dfrac{s}{3s+2} + \dfrac{s+3}{2s-4} = \dfrac{-2s}{3s^2-4s-4}$ $-\dfrac{6}{5}$, –1

Applications

38. Geometry The perimeter of a triangle is 24 cm. Side c of the triangle is 2 cm longer than side a. Side b is $\dfrac{3}{5}$ as long as side c. What are the lengths of the three sides of the triangle? $a = 8$, $b = 6$, $c = 10$

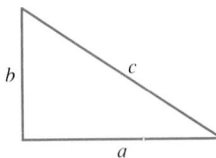

39. Accounting The librarian reports that $940 of the total book allowance for the three classes in the school has been spent. Class A spent $\dfrac{1}{3}$ of the total allowance; Class B spent $\dfrac{1}{4}$; Class C spent $\dfrac{1}{5}$. How much of the book allowance is left? $260

CRITICAL THINKING: Generalizing

Shown below are three different rectangles that have one thing in common: The number of units in the perimeter is equal to the number of units in the area. Give the dimensions for another rectangle in which this is true.
Answers may vary. For example, width: 4; length: 4

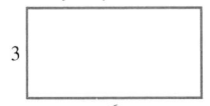
3 ... 6

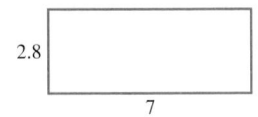
2.8 ... 7

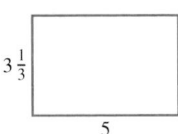
$3\frac{1}{3}$ ... 5

State a generalization to give the dimensions for an infinite number of rectangles that satisfy the given conditions. There is a limit for one of the dimensions. What is it? rectangles with the relationship: $l = \dfrac{2w}{w-2}$, $w > 2$

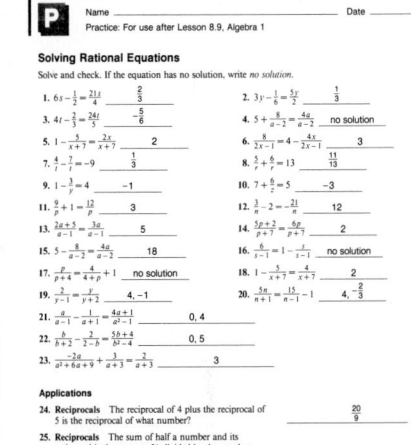

Materials/Manipulatives
*Teacher's Resource Book,
Transparency 24*

BACKGROUND

- For work problems, the formula to be used is:

  [work RATE] · [TIME worked] = [part of JOB DONE]

  To find the work rate, both sides of the equation are divided by the time worked.
- For motion problems, the formula to be used is:

  [RATE of speed] · [TIME] = [DISTANCE]

  To find the rate or the time, divide both sides of the equation by the other factor.

Error Analysis Classification

1. *Misunderstanding*
   Failed to understand the underlying concept of the problem
   May not have looked for key phrases to translate into equations
2. *Misapplied Strategy*
   Wrote an incorrect equation
   Made an error in the solution process
   Stopped short on the process so that the answer given for the problem was incomplete

---

8.10

Problem Solving: Work and Motion

Objective: To solve work and motion problems involving rational equations

Work, like motion, is related to rate and time.

[work RATE] · [TIME worked]
= [part of JOB DONE]

Manuel can word process a monthly report in 4 h. What is his rate per hour?

$$r \cdot 4 = 1 \text{ monthly report}$$

$$r = \frac{1}{4} \text{ of the monthly report per hour}$$

What part of the report can be typed in 3 h?

$$\frac{1}{4} \cdot 3 = \frac{3}{4} \text{ of the report}$$

What part of the report can be typed in 15 min? 15 min = $\frac{1}{4}$ h

$$\frac{1}{4} \cdot \frac{1}{4} = \frac{1}{16} \text{ of the report}$$

The solution to all work problems is based on the amount of work done per unit of time. To solve problems where two or more people work together at different rates, find that part of the job each person completes and set up an appropriate equation.

EXAMPLE 1 **Eric can wash the family van in 1 h. Stephanie can wash it in 45 min. How long will it take them if they work together?**

Understand the Problem

What are the given facts?
The job can be completed by Eric in 1 h and by Stephanie in 45 min.

What are you asked to find?
The time needed to complete the job if they work together.

Plan Your Approach

Measurement units must be the same. Change 1 h to 60 min.
Find each person's rate of work.
Let n = the number of minutes working together.

	Work rate ·	time worked =	part of job done
Eric	$\frac{1}{60}$	n	$\frac{n}{60}$
Stephanie	$\frac{1}{45}$	n	$\frac{n}{45}$

> The sum of the parts of the job done must be equal to 1, the complete job.

Write an equation.

$$\underset{\text{of job done.}}{\text{Eric's part}} + \underset{\text{of job done.}}{\text{Stephanie's part}} = \text{complete job}$$

$$\frac{n}{60} \quad + \quad \frac{n}{45} \quad = 1$$

☐ **Complete the Work**

$$\frac{n}{60} + \frac{n}{45} = 1 \qquad \textit{Multiply by the LCD, 180.}$$

$$3n + 4n = 180$$
$$7n = 180$$
$$n = \frac{180}{7}, \text{ or } 25\frac{5}{7} \text{ min}$$

☐ **Interpret the Results**

State your conclusion.

In $25\frac{5}{7}$ min the job is completed.

Check your conclusion.

Notice that $25\frac{5}{7}$ min is less time than it would take either to do the job alone.

Eric did $\frac{180}{7} \cdot \frac{1}{60}$, or $\frac{3}{7}$ of the job.

Stephanie did $\frac{180}{7} \cdot \frac{1}{45}$, or $\frac{4}{7}$.

$\frac{3}{7} + \frac{4}{7} = 1$ complete job

EXAMPLE 2 Phillip left his home at 2:15 PM and had driven 60 mi when he ran out of gas. He had to walk 2 mi to a gas station, where he arrived at 4:15 PM. If he drives 10 times faster than he walks, how fast does he walk?

☐ **Understand the Problem**

Let r = rate walking and $10r$ = rate driving

☐ **Plan Your Approach**

$\dfrac{d}{r} = t$

	Distance	Rate	Time
Driving	60	$10r$	$\dfrac{60}{10r}$
Walking	2	r	$\dfrac{2}{r}$

8.10 Problem Solving: Work and Motion **355**

TEACHING SUGGESTIONS

- In this lesson, students will see how real life situations can be expressed as a fractional equation. Encourage students to use the four-step method for solving problems, and in this case, the second and third steps will involve setting up and then solving a fractional equation which represents the problem situation.

- Emphasize the importance of reading each question carefully, and then thinking about what it means. Students should identify what they are looking for and choose a variable to represent it. After finding and solving an equation, it is important to check the solution against the facts in the problem. (Remind students that sometimes an answer cannot be used as the solution because it does not fit the restrictions of the problem.)

- This lesson lends itself well to students working in cooperative groups. Many times when several students "talk" about the problem which needs to be solved, they are able to understand it better.

- When discussing Example 2 use Transparency 24, in the *Teacher's Resource Book*.

CHALKBOARD EXAMPLES

- **For Example 1**
  1. Carla can wash the family truck in 2 hr and her brother Van can wash it in 1 hr and 20 min. How long will it take them if they work together? 48 min

- For Example 2

2. A businesswoman traveled 1200 mi on an airplane which left at 9:45 AM. She then traveled an additional 120 mi by helicopter and arrived at her destination at 1:15 PM. If the rate of the plane was four times the rate of the helicopter, what was the rate of each? helicopter: 120 mi/h; airplane: 480 mi/h

Common Error

- Students often make errors when solving work problems involving minutes and hours. Stress to students that the units must be the same when solving an equation in minutes and hours. Students must change the hours to minutes or vice versa.
- See *Teacher's Resource Book* for additional remediation.

LESSON FOLLOW-UP

Assignment Guide

See p. 314B for assignments.

Lesson Quiz

Solve. Check your answers.

1. George can trim a cherry tree in 25 min and Martha can do it in 30 min. How long will it take them if they do it together? $13\frac{7}{11}$ min

2. Jose can repair a car in 4 hr 10 min. Mark can do it in 5 h 50 min. How long would it take them to do it together? 2 h $25\frac{5}{6}$ min

3. An automobile and a small plane left at the same time traveling in the same direction to an airport 450 mi away. If the rate of the plane is three times the rate of the automobile, and the plane arrived 6 hr ahead of the automobile, what was the rate of each? automobile: 50 mi/h; airplane: 150 mi/h

---

Time driving + time walking = 2 h (2:15 to 4:15)

$$\frac{60}{10r} + \frac{2}{r} = 2$$

Complete the Work

$$(10r) \cdot \frac{60}{10r} + (10r) \cdot \frac{2}{r} = (10r)2$$

$$60 + 20 = 20r$$

$$r = 4 \text{ mi/h}$$

Phillip walked at the rate of 4 mi/h.

Interpret the Results

Check: Driving time is $\frac{60}{40}$, or $1\frac{1}{2}$ h.

Walking time is $\frac{2}{4}$, or $\frac{1}{2}$ h.

Total time is $1\frac{1}{2} + \frac{1}{2} = 2$ h. ✔

CLASS EXERCISES

Barry can paint a room in 12 h, Carrie can paint it in 10 h, and Harry takes only 9 h. If Barry and Carrie work together for 2 h, how long will it take Harry to finish the job?

1. What information is given? What are you asked to find? Each person's time working alone, and that Barry and Carrie work for 2 h. Time needed by Harry to finish

2. What is each person's rate? Barry: $\frac{1}{12}$; Carrie: $\frac{1}{10}$; Harry: $\frac{1}{9}$

3. After 2 h, what part of the job has Barry done? Has Carrie done? Have they done together? Barry: $\frac{1}{6}$; Carrie: $\frac{1}{5}$; together: $\frac{11}{30}$

4. What equation could you use to solve this problem? Solve it. $\frac{x}{9} + \frac{11}{30} = 1$; 5 h 42 min

PRACTICE EXERCISES

Solve. Check your answers.

A

1. Marian can weed a garden in 3 h, and Robin can do it in 4 h. How long will it take them if they work together? $\frac{12}{7}$ h

2. David can unload a delivery truck in 20 min, and Allie can do it in 35 min. If they work together, how long will it take? $12\frac{8}{11}$ min

3. Art can paint a set of kitchen cabinets in 5 h. His mother can do it in 4 h. How long will it take them if they work together? $2\frac{2}{9}$ h

4. Peggy can gather a bushel of apples in 45 min. Peter can gather a bushel in 75 min. How long will it take Peggy and Peter to gather a bushel of apples if they work together? $28\frac{1}{8}$ min

5. It took Rhoda the same time to drive 275 mi as it took Van to drive 240 mi. If Rhoda's rate was 7 mi/h faster than Van's rate, how fast did each person drive? Rhoda: 55 mi/h; Van: 48 mi/h

6. On Saturday, Earl rode his bike for 3 h longer than Alice. Earl traveled 135 km and Alice traveled 90 km. If they both averaged the same rate of speed, how long did Earl ride? 9 h

B **7.** It took Maggie a total of 4 h to drive 75 mi to the airport and then fly 2100 mi to a city in Mexico. If the plane rate is 12 times faster than her car, how fast did she drive? $62\frac{1}{2}$ mi/h

8. To get to his grandmother's house, Fred must drive 135 mi on a freeway and then 45 mi along a country road. If the trip takes 5 h, and he can travel three times faster on the freeway than on the country road, how fast does he travel on the freeway? 54 mi/h

9. Two pipes fill a storage tank in 9 hours. If the larger pipe fills the tank three times as fast as the smaller one, how long would it take the larger pipe to fill the tank alone? 12 h

10. A bathtub can be filled in 20 min with both faucets running. If the cold water faucet runs twice as fast as the hot water, how long would it take the cold water faucet to fill the tub by itself? 30 min

C **11.** Sumi can wash the windows of an office building in $\frac{3}{4}$ the time it takes her apprentice. One day they worked on the building together for 2 h 16 min, and then Sumi continued alone. It took her 4 h 32 min more to complete the job. How long would it take her apprentice to wash all the windows? 11 h 20 min

12. Tim can trim 10 trees in $\frac{2}{3}$ the time it takes Tom. They trim trees together for 1 h 11 min. Then Tom continues alone until a total of 10 trees are trimmed (it took him 35 min 30 s). Working alone, how long would it take Tim to trim 10 trees? 2 h 22 min

MATH CLUB ACTIVITY

This problem is similar to one used in a high school mathematics examination sponsored by the Mathematical Association of America. Find the solution.

A town's population increased by 1500 people, and then the new population decreased by 6%. The town now had 510 more people than it did before the 1500 increase. What was the original population? x + 1500 − [(0.06)(x + 1500)] = x + 510; 15,000

8.10 Problem Solving: Work and Motion **357**

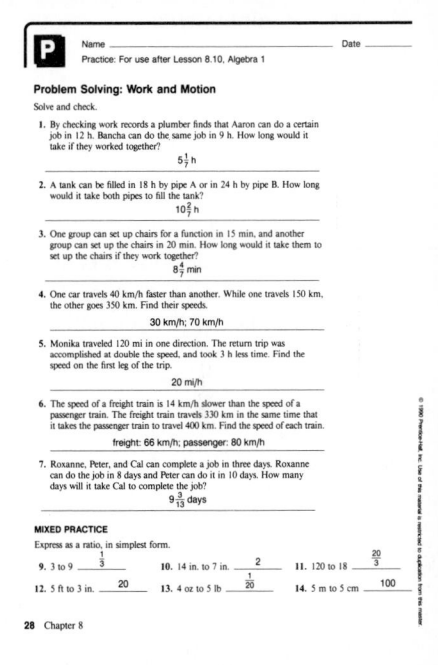
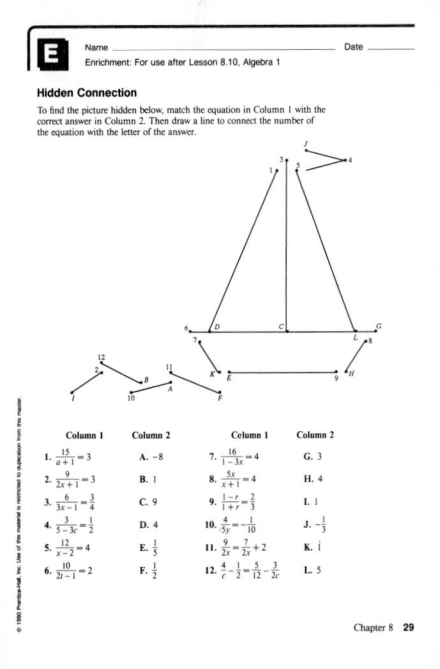

BACKGROUND

A key to success in this lesson is the students' ability to organize and use information given in a problem, and to then solve the problem. Analyze errors in the students' work and then classify specific errors.

Error Analysis Classification

1. *Misunderstanding*
   Failed to understand the underlying concept of the problem
   May have overlooked key phrases that translate into an equation
2. *Misapplied Strategy*
   Wrote an incorrect equation
   Made error(s) in the solution process
   Stopped short in the process so that the answer given for the problem was incomplete

---

8.11

Problem Solving Strategy: Solve a Simpler Problem

Sometimes a difficult problem can be solved by breaking it up into simpler parts, and then putting these parts back together to represent the original problem.

EXAMPLE Sawyer Automotive Co. often buys large shipments of surplus tires for a given amount of money. Adding $15 to their cost per tire, they then sell as many of each shipment as they can. They need a formula for their profit on each shipment in terms of the total shipment cost t, the original number of tires in the shipment, n, and the number of tires unsold, u.

Understand the Problem **What are the given facts?**
Sawyer bought n tires for t dollars. They sold all but u tires. Each tire sold was sold for $15 more than it cost.

What are you asked to find?
Find a formula which gives the profit on each shipment.

Plan Your Approach **Choose a strategy.**
Write a word equation which expresses the profit in terms of total sales and total cost. Total cost is t. Consider the parts which make up total sales.

Complete the Work **Write a word equation.**

Profit = *total sales* − *total cost*
     = *total sales* − t

Total sales = (*number sold*)(*price per tire*)
       = $(n - u)$(*price per tire*)

Price per tire = *original cost per tire* + 15

$$\text{Original cost per tire} = \frac{total\ cost}{original\ number\ of\ tires} = \frac{t}{n}$$

Putting this all together from the opposite direction:

$$\text{Original cost per tire} = \frac{t}{n}$$

$$\text{Price per tire} = \frac{t}{n} + 15$$

$$\text{Total sales} = (n - u)\left(\frac{t}{n} + 15\right)$$

358 Chapter 8 Rational Expressions

$$\text{Profit} = (n - u)\left(\frac{t}{n} + 15\right) - t$$

Simplify the rational expression.

$$(n - u)\left(\frac{t}{n} + 15\right) - t = n\left(\frac{t}{n} + 15\right) - u\left(\frac{t}{n} + 15\right) - t$$

$$= t + 15n - \frac{ut}{n} - 15u - t$$

$$= 15n - 15u - \frac{ut}{n}$$

Interpret the Results

State your answer.

For a shipment costing t dollars, the profit, p, for n tires, of which u are unsold, is given by:

$$p = 15n - 15u - \frac{ut}{n}$$

Check your answer.

Choose convenient numbers for t, n, and u. Find the profit, p, first without the formula, then with the formula.

Assume there was a shipment of 100 tires with a total cost of $5000, with 10 tires unsold.

Without the formula:

Each tire cost $\frac{5000}{100}$ or $50.

The selling price was $50 + 15$ or $65 per tire.

$100 - 10$ or 90 tires were sold.

So, total sales were $90(65)$ or $5850.

Profit was $5850 - 5000$ or $850.

With the formula:

$t = 5000$, $n = 100$, and $u = 10$. Find p.

$$p = 15n - 15u - \frac{ut}{n}$$

$$p = 15(100) - 15(10) - \frac{10(5000)}{100} \quad \textit{Calculation-ready form}$$

$$p = 850$$

The two methods confirm one another.

CLASS EXERCISES

Solve.

1. In the Example, if the company wishes to raise its profit by adding $18 to the original price per tire, what will be its new formula? $p = 18n - 18u - \frac{tu}{n}$

359

2. If the company always succeeds in selling the whole shipment of tires when they add $15 to the cost of each tire, how should its profit formula be changed? $p = 15n$

PRACTICE EXERCISES

Solve.

A 1. What profit will be made if all but 14 of a shipment of 650 tires, purchased for $12,225, are sold? $9276.69

2. What profit will be made if all but 23 of a shipment of 545 tires, purchased for $11,500, are sold? $7344.68

3. If the shipments purchased by the company always consist of 500 tires, change the profit formula. Use the new formula to determine the profit if such a shipment costs $11,000 and 45 tires are not sold? $p = \dfrac{15 \times (500)^2 - 7500u - u!}{500}$ $5835.00

4. If the cost of the shipments purchased by the company is always $10,000, regardless of the number of tires obtained, change the profit formula to correspond to this fact. Use the new formula to determine what profit will be made if such a shipment contains 475 tires and 45 tires are not sold. $p = \dfrac{15n^2 - 15un - 10,000u}{n}$, $5502.63

5. If Andres works r h/wk at the deli for $5.50 per h and s h/wk at the service station for $4.50 per h, find a formula for t, his total weekly income in dollars before deductions. $t = r(5.50) + s(4.50)$

6. Unleaded premium gasoline costs c cents/gal at the full service pump and z cents/gal at the self service pump. Write a formula for finding the amount saved, s, using the self service pump, rather than the full service pump, to fill a 12.5 gal gasoline tank. $s = 12.5(c - z)$

B 7. If Camilo averages u mi/h over the first 10 mi of his commute to work and v mi/h over the next 7 mi, write a formula for his commuting time, t. $t = \dfrac{10v + 7}{uv}$

8. If Juana can do a job alone in j hours and Kate can do it alone in k hours, write a formula for the time, t, it takes them working together. $t = \dfrac{jk}{j + k}$

9. Sue bought n dress patterns for $200. She sold all but 3 of them for $2 more per pattern than she paid for them. In terms of n, write a formula for r, the amount she received for the patterns sold. $r = (n - 3)\left(\dfrac{200}{n} + 2\right)$

10. For $125 Zhian bought h hot dogs to sell at the football game. He sold all but 11 of them for $0.25 more per hot dog than he paid. In terms of h, write a formula for a, the amount of his sales. $a = (h - 11)\left(\dfrac{125}{h} + 0.25\right)$

C 11. If the company in the Example on page 358 is concerned not with the total cost of a tire shipment, t, but with its cost per tire, c, revise the profit formula to use the variable c instead of t. $p = 15n - 15u - uc$

360 Chapter 8 Rational Expressions

12. If the company in the Example on page 358 later finds that the unsold tires may be disposed of by selling them for $5 more than the original cost per tire, revise the profit formula to take account of this. $p = 15n - 10u$

Mixed Problem Solving Review

1. An express train traveling at 0.75 km/min passes a subway platform 5 min after a local train traveling at 0.50 km/min. In how many minutes should the express overtake the local? 10 min

2. If 25 oz of a 15% alcohol solution in water is to have the alcohol concentration doubled, how much alcohol must be added? 5.357 oz

3. A floor 36 ft × 24 ft is partially covered by a rug so that a uniform border of bare floor is left. If the area of the rug is 540 ft², how wide is the border? 3 ft

PROJECT

Form a team with two classmates to solve the following problem: Suppose that your team has some sort of small business. Considering your costs, mark-up, sales, and at least two other factors, devise a profit formula for your business. Show that your formula will give reasonable results.
Check students' work.

TEST YOURSELF

Divide these polynomials. 8.7

1. $(18y^3 - 3y^2 + 15y) \div 3y^3$
$6 - \frac{1}{y} + \frac{5}{y^2}$

2. $(3m^3 - 5m^2 - 9) \div (m + 3)$
$3m^2 - 14m + 42 - \frac{135}{m + 3}$

Express as a ratio in simplest form. 8.8–8.9

3. 7.2 mm to 18 cm $\frac{1}{25}$

4. 3 gal to 4 pt 6:1

5. If 2.5 cm on a map represents 100 m, what distance is represented by 32.5 cm? 1300 m

Solve these equations. 8.10–8.11

6. $\frac{5}{2y} - \frac{12}{y} = -19\frac{1}{2}$

7. $\frac{3z}{z + 4} - 2 = \frac{3}{z - 5}$ 14, 2

8. If Said can clean a room in 2 h while his little sister requires 3 h, how long should it take them working together? 1 h 12 min

9. If you buy posters for a total of $25 and sell each of them for $1.50 more per poster than the cost, write a profit formula. n = number sold, b = number bought, $p = n\left(\frac{25}{b} + 1.50\right) - 25$

8.11 Problem Solving Strategy: Solve a Simpler Problem **361**

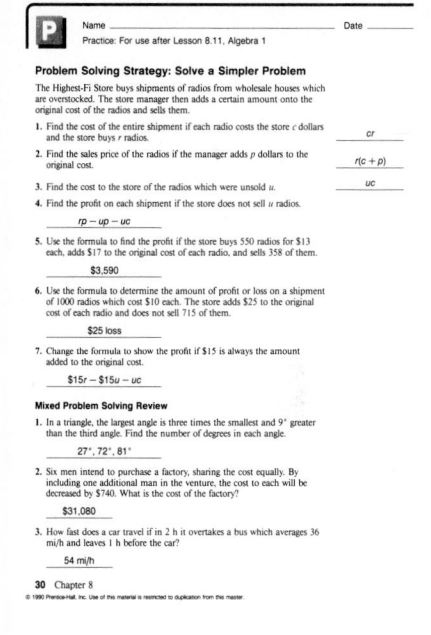

- See *Teacher's Resource Book, Spanish Chapter Summary and Review,* pp. 15–16.
- See *Extra Practice,* p. 662.

Vocabulary

complex rational expression (337)	mixed expression (337)
extraneous solution (351)	proportion (345)
extremes (346)	ratio (345)
least common denominator (328)	rational expression (316)
means (346)	simplest form (317)

Simplifying Rational Expressions To simplify a rational expression, factor the numerator and denominator. Divide both by the common factors. Restrictions on the denominator include values that make the denominator equal to zero.   **8.1**

Simplify and state the restrictions, if any.

1. $\dfrac{3b^3}{9b^2}$ $\frac{b}{3}; b \neq 0$

2. $\dfrac{4}{2x + 6}$ $\frac{2}{x+3}; x \neq -3$

3. $\dfrac{m - 1}{(m - 1)(m + 2)}$ $\frac{1}{m+2}; m \neq 1, -2$

4. $\dfrac{4 - y}{y^2 - 16}$ $\frac{-1}{y+4}; y \neq -4, 4$

Multiplying and Dividing Rational Expressions To multiply rational expressions, factor the numerators and the denominators, divide common factors, then multiply remaining factors. To divide rational expressions, multiply by the reciprocal of the divisor.   **8.2–8.3**

Multiply or divide. Simplify if possible.

5. $\dfrac{32x^2y}{25z^2} \cdot \dfrac{20z}{8xy}$ $\frac{16x}{5z}$

6. $\dfrac{2w}{3} \div \dfrac{4w}{9}$ $\frac{3}{2}$

7. $\dfrac{2 + a}{1 + a} \cdot \dfrac{a^2 - 1}{a^2 - 4}$ $\frac{a-1}{a-2}$

8. $\dfrac{2r^2 + 9r - 5}{r - 3} \div \dfrac{r^2 + 2r - 15}{r}$ $\frac{r(2r - 1)}{(r - 3)^2}$

Adding and Subtracting Rational Expressions To add or subtract rational expressions, you need common denominators. Write the rational expressions with a common denominator and combine.   **8.4–8.5**

Find the LCD. Write equivalent expressions, use the LCD.

9. $\dfrac{1}{8m^3n}; \dfrac{5}{12mn^2}$ $\frac{3n}{24m^3n^2}; \frac{10m^2}{24m^3n^2}$

10. $\dfrac{5}{c + 1}; \dfrac{3}{c - 2}$ $\frac{5(c - 2)}{(c + 1)(c - 2)}; \frac{3(c + 1)}{(c + 1)(c - 2)}$

11. $\dfrac{2x}{x^2 - 9}; \dfrac{3}{x + 3}$ $\frac{2x}{(x + 3)(x - 3)}; \frac{3(x - 3)}{(x + 3)(x - 3)}$

Add or subtract.

12. $\dfrac{1}{8m^3n} + \dfrac{5}{12mn^3}$ $\frac{3n^2 + 10m^2}{24m^3n^3}$

13. $\dfrac{5}{c + 1} - \dfrac{3}{c - 2}$ $\frac{2c - 13}{(c + 1)(c - 2)}$

14. $\dfrac{3}{x + 3} - \dfrac{2x}{x^2 - 9}$ $\frac{x - 9}{(x + 3)(x - 3)}$

Simplifying a Complex Rational Expression To simplify a complex rational expression, multiply the numerator and denominator by the LCD of all the rational expressions in the complex rational expression.   8.6

Simplify.

15. $u + 2 - \dfrac{1}{u + 2}$

$\dfrac{u^2 + 4u + 3}{(u + 2)}$

16. $\dfrac{1 - \dfrac{1}{r}}{\dfrac{1}{r^2}}$ $r(r - 1)$

17. $\dfrac{\dfrac{y}{x^2} - \dfrac{1}{y}}{\dfrac{1}{xy} + \dfrac{1}{x^2}}$ $y - x$

Dividing Polynomials To divide polynomials, divide by common factors. If the polynomial cannot be factored, divide as in long division.   8.7

Divide.

18. $\dfrac{12z^2 + 42z}{6z}$ $2z + 7$

19. $\dfrac{2r^3 + 19r^2 + 40r - 25}{r + 5}$ $2r^2 + 9r - 5$

Solving a Proportion To solve for an unknown quantity in a proportion, use the property of proportions. In a proportion, the product of the means equals the product of the extremes.   8.8

Solve.

20. $\dfrac{10}{y} = \dfrac{15}{3}$ 2

21. $\dfrac{5}{12} = \dfrac{n}{6}$ $\dfrac{5}{2}$

22. $\dfrac{7}{9} = \dfrac{28}{x + 3}$ 33

Solving Rational Equations To solve a rational equation, multiply each term of the equation by the least common denominator, then solve. Check for any extraneous solutions.   8.9

Solve and check. If the equation has no solution, write *no solution*.

23. $\dfrac{d}{5} + \dfrac{3d}{2} = 17$ 10

24. $\dfrac{5}{x + 3} - \dfrac{2}{x} = \dfrac{9}{2}$ $\dfrac{4}{3}, 1$

Solving Work and Motion Problems To solve work and motion problems involving different rates, use rational equations.   8.10

Solve.

25. James can wash a car in 45 min, and Bertha can do it in 30 min. How long will it take them if they work together? 18 min

26. It took a plane the same time to fly 1125 mi as it took a car to go 125 mi. If the plane's rate is 400 mi/h faster than the car's rate, how fast did the car go? 50 mi/h

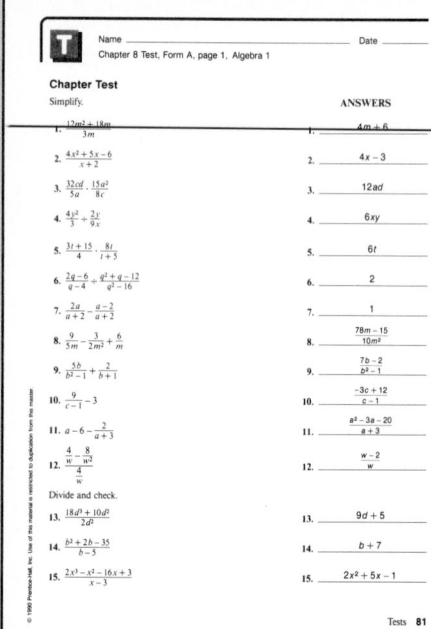

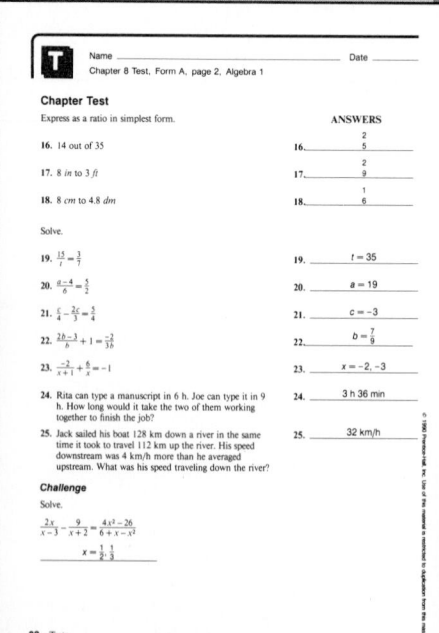

CHAPTER 8 TEST

Simplify.

1. $\dfrac{9m - 15}{3}$ $3m - 5$

2. $\dfrac{3x^2 + 8x - 3}{x^2 - x - 12}$ $\dfrac{3x - 1}{x - 4}$

3. $\dfrac{25ab}{3c} \cdot \dfrac{12}{5a}$ $\dfrac{20b}{c}$

4. $\dfrac{2d}{5} \div \dfrac{4d}{15}$ $\dfrac{3}{2}$

5. $\dfrac{5}{x + 1} \cdot \dfrac{2x + 2}{6}$ $\dfrac{5}{3}$

6. $\dfrac{a^2 + a - 2}{a^2 - 9} \div \dfrac{a + 2}{a + 3}$ $\dfrac{a - 1}{a - 3}$

7. $\dfrac{4}{y - 4} - \dfrac{y}{y - 4}$ -1

8. $\dfrac{5}{6k} + \dfrac{3}{4k^2} - \dfrac{2}{3k}$ $\dfrac{2k + 9}{12k^2}$

9. $\dfrac{1}{a + 1} - \dfrac{2}{a - 3}$ $\dfrac{-a - 5}{(a + 1)(a - 3)}$

10. $\dfrac{3}{u} - 6$ $\dfrac{3 - 6u}{u}$

11. $g + 5 - \dfrac{1}{g + 5}$ $\dfrac{g^2 + 10g + 24}{g + 5}$

12. $\dfrac{\dfrac{1}{x^2} - 4}{\dfrac{1}{x}}$ $\dfrac{1 - 4x^2}{x}$

Divide and check.

13. $\dfrac{14p^2 + 21p}{7p}$ $2p + 3$

14. $\dfrac{c^2 - c - 4}{c - 2}$ $c + 1 + \dfrac{-2}{c - 2}$

15. $\dfrac{3x^3 + 2x^2 - 6x + 4}{x + 2}$ $3x^2 - 4x + 2$

Express as a ratio or rate in simplest form.

16. 8 out of 20 $\dfrac{2}{5}$

17. 3 pt to 2 qt $\dfrac{3}{4}$

18. 1.5 cm to 30 mm $\dfrac{1}{2}$

Solve.

19. $\dfrac{b}{5} + \dfrac{5b}{3} = 2$ $\dfrac{15}{14}$

20. $\dfrac{x + 1}{x} - 7 = \dfrac{9}{2x} - \dfrac{7}{12}$

21. $\dfrac{1}{r} + \dfrac{2}{r - 1} = -2$ $-1, \dfrac{1}{2}$

22. Sadie can make a pizza in 40 min, and Alvin can make one in 30 min. How long will it take them if they work together? $17\dfrac{1}{7}$ min

Challenge

1. Solve for r: $\dfrac{-2}{r - 2} - \dfrac{r}{r + 2} = \dfrac{r + 6}{4 - r^2}$ -1

2. A tub can be filled in 15 min by a hot-water faucet and in 12 min by the cold-water faucet. The drain can empty the tub in 20 min. How long will it take the tub to fill if both faucets and the drain are open? 10 min

The individual comments provided about some problems can be helpful in guiding students to solve these problems.

Select the best choice for each question.

1. $\frac{5}{6} + \frac{2}{5} - \frac{7}{10} = \underline{?}$
B
A. $\frac{1}{2}$ B. $\frac{8}{15}$ C. $\frac{17}{30}$ D. $\frac{19}{30}$ E. $\frac{13}{15}$

2. $\left(\frac{6a^2b^3}{2ab}\right)^2$ equals
D
A. $3a^2b^2$ B. $9a^2b^2$ C. $3a^2b^4$
D. $9a^2b^4$ E. $9a^3b^5$

3. $\frac{8 \times 10^8}{4 \times 10^6} = \underline{?}$
A
A. 200 B. 20 C. 2
D. 0.2 E. 0.02

4. Solve for x if $\frac{16}{7} = \frac{x}{28}$.
A
A. 64 B. 32 C. 28 D. 14 E. 4

5. A $450 stereo is on sale at a $33\frac{1}{3}\%$
C
discount. If there is a 6% sales tax, what is the total cost of the stereo while it is on sale?
A. $480 B. $327 C. $318
D. $301.80 E. $300.18

6. $\frac{4}{3y} + \frac{1}{2x}$ equals
C
A. $\frac{5}{6xy}$ B. $\frac{8x + 3y}{5xy}$

C. $\frac{8x + 3y}{6xy}$ D. $\frac{5}{3y + 2x}$

E. $\frac{4x + y}{5xy}$

7. If light travels 1.86×10^5 mi in
A
one second, how many miles does it travel in two seconds?
A. 3.72×10^5 B. 3.72×10^7
C. 3.72×10^{10} D. 1.86×10^7
E. 1.86×10^{10}

8. Solve the equation: $3(2x - 1) + 4(x + 1) = 2(3x + 4) - 9$
E
A. 2 B. $\frac{1}{2}$ C. $-\frac{23}{4}$ D. -2 E. $-\frac{1}{2}$

Use this bar graph to answer questions 9–11.

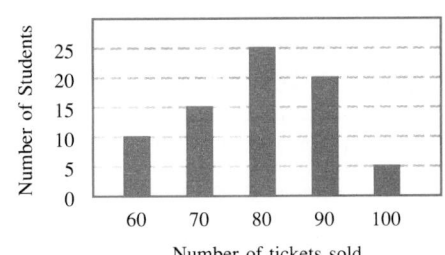

Number of Students (y-axis), values 0, 5, 10, 15, 20, 25

Number of tickets sold (x-axis): 60, 70, 80, 90, 100

9. How many students sold 70 tickets?
C
A. 5 B. 10 C. 15 D. 20 E. 25

10. How many students sold 80 or
B
more tickets?
A. 40 B. 50 C. 60 D. 65
E. It cannot be determined from the information given.

11. What was the total number of
E
tickets sold?
A. 75 B. 400 C. 4050
D. 5450 E. 5950

12. If x is subtracted from y and this
C
difference is divided by the sum of x and $2y$, the result is:
A. $\frac{x - y}{x + 2y}$ B. $\frac{2y - x}{x + y}$ C. $\frac{y - x}{x + 2y}$

D. $\frac{x + 2y}{y - x}$ E. $\frac{y + x}{2y - x}$

2. Although the problem could be worked by squaring the quantities first, then reducing, students should be encouraged to simplify when possible as they work through a problem.

7. A review of the associative property for multiplication might be helpful here, if students choose incorrect answers for this problem.

See *Teacher's Resource Book* for Preparing for Standardized Tests.

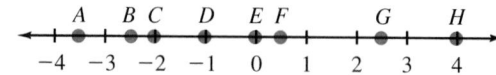

CUMULATIVE REVIEW (CHAPTERS 1–8)

For Exercises 1–8 refer to the number line below. 1.2

A B C D E F G H

−4 −3 −2 −1 0 1 2 3 4

Give the coordinate of each point.

1. D −1 **2.** E 0 **3.** C −2 **4.** F $\frac{1}{2}$

5. G $2\frac{1}{2}$ **6.** H 4 **7.** A $-3\frac{1}{2}$ **8.** B $-2\frac{1}{2}$

State the solution set of the equation or inequality whose graph is given. 5.1

9. −4−3−2−1 0 1 2 3 4
$x \geq 1$

10. −4−3−2−1 0 1 2 3 4
$x < 0$

11. −4−3−2−1 0 1 2 3 4
$x \neq -2$

12. −4−3−2−1 0 1 2 3 4
$-2 < x < 1$

13. −4−3−2−1 0 1 2 3 4
$x \leq -1$ or $x > 0$

14. −4−3−2−1 0 1 2 3 4
$-1 \leq x \leq 1$

Solve each equation or inequality. 3.1–3.3, 4.1–4.3, 5.2–5.6

15. $5x + 8 = -7$ −3 **16.** $\frac{a}{3} - 6 = 2$ 24 **17.** $t - (-3) \geq 9$ $t \geq 6$

18. $-8m < 32$ $m > -4$ **19.** $|y| + 7 = 3$ no solution **20.** $3b - 4 = b + 1$ $\frac{5}{2}$

21. $\frac{2n}{3} - 5 = \frac{1}{3}$ 8 **22.** $2c - 3 > 20$ $x > \frac{23}{2}$ **23.** $5 - \frac{4}{r} = 3$ 2

24. $z^2 + 2z = 0$ −2, 0 **25.** $-2 \leq 3p + 4 \leq 13$ $-2 \leq p \leq 3$ **26.** $|4d - 7| = 29$ 9, $-\frac{11}{2}$

27. $8n - 2(3n - 1) = 26$ 12 **28.** $g^2 + 2g - 24 = 0$ −6, 4

29. $2.7 - 0.2k = 0.7k$ 3 **30.** $2y + 3 > 3$ or $3y - 4 \leq -7$ $y > 0$ or $y \leq -1$

31. $\frac{5}{m + 3} = \frac{3}{m - 1}$ 7 **32.** $\frac{1}{p + 1} - \frac{1}{p - 2} = 0$ no solution

Write each number in scientific notation. 6.4

33. 6,000,000 6×10^6 **34.** 450 4.5×10^2 **35.** 12,800 1.28×10^4 **36.** 790,000,000 7.9×10^8

Evaluate each expression if $x = \frac{1}{2}$, $y = \frac{2}{3}$ and $z = -6$. 1.7, 2.2

37. $y \cdot z - 1$ −5 **38.** $\frac{2}{x} - z$ 10 **39.** $2(x - 1) + z^2$ 35

40. $y\left(\dfrac{x+3}{z-1}\right)$ $-\frac{1}{3}$　　**41.** $x^2 y z$ -1　　**42.** $\dfrac{y-z}{y+1} - x^2$ $\frac{15}{4}$

43. $[z(x+y)+5]^3$ -8　　**44.** $\left(\dfrac{x}{y}+\dfrac{y}{x}\right)\dfrac{z}{5}$ $-\frac{5}{2}$　　**45.** $|(2+z)^2 - 20|$ 4

46. $x^2 - y^2$ $-\frac{7}{36}$　　**47.** $(z)(x^2)(y^2)$ $-\frac{2}{3}$　　**48.** $\dfrac{|x-y||x+y|}{z}$ $-\frac{7}{216}$

Simplify. Assume that no denominator equals zero.　　2.1, 6.1–6.3, 8.1, 8.4–8.7

49. $4 + 12 \div (-3+1)$ -2　　**50.** $[(-2)^3 + 3^2]^5$ 1　　**51.** $|2-7| - (-3)^2$ -4

52. $(3m^2 n)(2m^3 n^2)$ $6m^5 n^3$　　**53.** $(-2b^3)^2$ $4b^6$　　**54.** $(2p+3)^2$ $4p^2 + 12p + 9$

55. $\dfrac{3x^2 y}{9y^2 x}$ $\frac{x}{3y}$　　**56.** $\dfrac{3c+9}{15}$ $\frac{c+3}{5}$　　**57.** $\dfrac{a-b}{b-a}$ -1

58. $\dfrac{5g^2 - 5}{g+1}$ $5(g-1)$　　**59.** $\dfrac{z+2}{z^2 - 4}$ $\frac{1}{z-2}$　　**60.** $\dfrac{d^2 - 9}{3-d}$ $-(d+3)$

61. $5a^2 + 3a - 2(a^2 - a)$ $3a^2 + 5a$　　**62.** $2t(3t-4) - (t-1)^2$ $5t^2 - 6t - 1$

63. $\dfrac{r^2 - 25}{r+5} + 2(r-5)$ $3r - 15$　　**64.** $\dfrac{f-2}{f^2 - 4} + \dfrac{f+1}{f+2}$ 1

65. $\dfrac{h^2 - 9}{h+1} \cdot \dfrac{h^2 + 2h + 1}{h-3}$ $(h+3)(h+1)$　　**66.** $\dfrac{h^2 + 2h - 15}{h^2 + h - 12} \cdot \dfrac{h^2 + 2h - 8}{h^2 + 3h - 10}$ 1

67. $\dfrac{k^2 - 25}{k^2 + 4k + 4} \div \dfrac{k^2 + 10k + 25}{k^2 - 4}$ $\frac{(k-5)(k-2)}{(k+5)(k+2)}$　　**68.** $\dfrac{m^2 - 3m - 10}{m^2 - 25} \div \dfrac{m^2 - m - 6}{m^2 + 2m - 15}$ 1

Write the missing reasons in the proof.　　3.5

69. Prove: For all real numbers x, y, and z, if $x = y$, then $x + z = z + y$.

Proof:

Statement	Reason
$x = y$	Given
$x + z = x + z$	**a.** _?_ reflexive property
$x + z = y + z$	**b.** _?_ substitution
$x + z = z + y$	**c.** _?_ commutative property

Solve.　　4.7

70. If you have 70 mL of a 35% solution of acid in water, how much water would you add in order to make a 25% acid solution? 28 mL

71. How many ounces of pure salt must be added to 40 oz of a 20% solution of salt in water to produce a 50% salt solution? 24 oz

72. Adding 30 mL of water to 70 mL of a 20% sugar solution in water will result in a new solution of what concentration? 14%

Factor completely. 7.7–7.8

73. $4a - 8b$ $4(a - 2b)$　　**74.** $12x + 15y$ $3(4x + 5y)$　　**75.** $6c^2 - 9c$ $3c(2c - 3)$

76. $10m^2 + 5m$ $5m(2m + 1)$　　**77.** $21p^3 + 14p^2 - 28p$　　**78.** $k^2 - 9$ $(k + 3)(k - 3)$
$7p(3p^2 + 2p - 4)$

79. $d^2 + 8d + 16$ $(d + 4)^2$　　**80.** $5t^2 - 20$ $5(t + 2)(t - 2)$　　**81.** $g^2 + 2g - 15$
$(g + 5)(g - 3)$

82. $9a^2 - 25$　　**83.** $r^2 - 10r + 24$　　**84.** $6y^2 + 5y - 6$
$(3a - 5)(3a + 5)$　　$(r - 6)(r - 4)$　　$(3y - 2)(2y + 3)$

Find the LCD of each group of fractions. 8.4

85. $\dfrac{3}{2a^3}; \dfrac{2}{3a^2}$ $6a^3$　　**86.** $\dfrac{1}{a^2b}; \dfrac{5}{ab^2}$ a^2b^2　　**87.** $\dfrac{1}{3x}; \dfrac{x}{x + 1}$ $3x(x + 1)$

Perform the indicated operation. 6.6, 8.1–8.5

88. $\left(-\dfrac{3}{2}\right) + \dfrac{3}{4} - \left(-\dfrac{1}{2}\right)$ $-\dfrac{1}{4}$　　**89.** $\dfrac{2}{3}\left[\dfrac{1}{2} + \left(-\dfrac{5}{6}\right)\right]$ $-\dfrac{2}{9}$　　**90.** $\dfrac{3}{5}\left(-\dfrac{1}{3} \div \dfrac{1}{6}\right)$ $-\dfrac{6}{5}$

91. $\dfrac{5}{4b} + \dfrac{3}{2b^2}$ $\dfrac{5b + 6}{4b^2}$　　**92.** $\dfrac{t}{t^2 - 9} - \dfrac{3}{3 - t}$ $\dfrac{4t + 9}{t^2 - 9}$　　**93.** $5h + \dfrac{h + 3}{h + 2}$
$\dfrac{5h^2 + 11h + 3}{h + 2}$

94. $\dfrac{m - 2}{m + 2} - \dfrac{2m^2 + 6}{m^2 - 4} - \dfrac{m + 2}{2 - m}$ $\dfrac{2}{m^2 - 4}$　　**95.** $\dfrac{(a - 2)^2 - (a - 2)}{a^2 - 5a + 6}$ 1

96. $(2m + 5)(5m - 2)$　　**97.** $4x^2y(x - 2y^2 + 1)$　　**98.** $3d(d + 2)^2$
$10m^2 + 21m - 10$　　$4x^3y - 8x^2y^3 + 4x^2y$　　$3d^3 + 12d^2 + 12d$

99. $(3a^2 + 5a - 3) - (2a^2 - 2a + 1)$　　**100.** $(4p^5 + 6p^3 - 2p^2) \div 2p^2$
$a^2 + 7a - 4$　　$2p^3 + 3p - 1$

Solve. 4.3, 4.6, 4.9, 8.8, 8.10

101. The price of a $65 jacket is decreased by 15%. Find the new price. $55.25

102. Rates at a car rental agency are $128 a week plus $0.12 a mile. Frank rents a care for a week. How far can he drive if he wants to spend no more than $200? 600 mi or less

103. Find three consecutive odd integers such that the first times the third is 1 more than 4 times the second. 3, 5, 7 or −3, −1, 1

104. If a map scale is $\frac{1}{4}$ inch = 15 miles, what distance does $2\frac{1}{2}$ inches represent? 150 mi

105. Allison can cut her parents lawn in 2 h, while her brother Jason does it in 2.5 h. Working together how long will it take them? $66\frac{2}{3}$ min

106. A train left San Mateo Station and traveled east at 75 mi/h. A second train left the same station 1.5 h later and traveled east at 85 mi/h. How many hours will it take for the second train to catch the first one. $11\frac{1}{4}$ h

107. The Ward family drove to the beach in $3\frac{1}{2}$ h at an average speed of 50 mi/h. The return trip took $4\frac{1}{5}$ h. What was the average speed for the trip home? $41\frac{2}{3}$ mi/h

OVERVIEW • Chapter 9

SUMMARY

In Chapter 9, students are introduced to linear equations. They learn how to determine an equation of a line by using two points, one point and the slope, or by examining a graph. In addition, students are shown how to write linear equations in standard and slope intercept form. This will provide a better understanding in determining the graph of each equation. Students graph equations by calculating the slope and/or y-intercept of each equation.

In the final lessons of the chapter, students will learn how to graph linear inequalities in two variables. They learn to distinguish between open and closed half-planes and to determine which part of the graph to shade.

CHAPTER OBJECTIVES

- To graph ordered pairs of numbers
- To identify a solution of an equation in two variables
- To graph linear equations from their x- and y-intercepts
- To find the slope of a line from its graph or from the coordinates of two points of the line
- To draw a line with a given slope through a given point
- To use the slope-intercept form to graph a linear equation
- To use slope to determine if two lines are parallel
- To determine an equation of a line, given the slope of the line and the coordinates of one point
- To determine an equation of a line, given the coordinates of two points of the line
  To graph linear inequalities in two variables

Problem Solving Strategy

To show relationships between two variables and make predictions or estimates of graphs in a coordinate plane

CHAPTER HIGHLIGHTS

The *theme* of the chapter is physical science. The basic concepts of this chapter show students how linear equations can be applied to real world situations.

PROBLEM SOLVING AND APPLICATIONS

Problem solving and applications form an integral part of each lesson. Lesson 9.3, the strategy of *Estimating from Graphs,* affords students the opportunity to make predictions and estimates from graphs.

TECHNOLOGY

Computer

In Chapter 9, students are introduced to various computer programs for finding intercepts to be used in graphing, which enables the student to make predictions or estimates.

Calculator

A graphing calculator may be used as an aid to graphing linear equations. It can also be used to verify solutions and to check if an ordered pair satisfies an equation.

RESOURCES

Teacher's Resource Book

- Teaching Aids 10, 11, 12
- Transparencies 14, 15, 16, 17, 18, 19, 20

STUDENT TEXT				TEACHER'S RESOURCE BOOK		
Chapter Content	Basic	Average	Enriched	R	P	E
9.1 Graphing Ordered Pairs	D: 372/1-23 odd, 43	D: 372/1-33 odd, 43-44	D: 373/25-41, 42-44	1	2	3
9.2 Graphs of Linear Equations	D: 379/1-23 odd, 41 R: 372/6, 14, 20	D: 379/1-31 odd, 39 R: 372/8, 22, 28	D: 379/25-41, 42 odd, 40-42 R: 372/28, 34, 36	4	5	6
9.3 Problem Solving Strategy: Estimating from Graphs	D: 381/1-7 odd MPSR: 1-5 R: 379/6, 10, 12	D: 381/1-11 odd MPSR: 1-5 R: 379/10, 14, 16	D: 382/9-15 odd MPSR: 1-5 R: 379/26, 30, 34		7	8
9.4 Slope	D: 387/1-23 odd R: 381/2, 4, 6 Test Yourself	D: 387/1-35 odd R: 381/2, 4, 6 Test Yourself	D: 388/25-41 odd R: 382/10, 12 Test Yourself		9	10
9.5 Slope-Intercept Form of a Linear Equation	D: 394/1-27 odd R: 387/6, 10, 12	D: 394/1-45 odd R: 387/18, 24, 30	D: 394/29-51 odd R: 387/26, 30, 34	11	12	13
9.6 Equation of a Line	D: 398/1-19 odd R: 394/10, 14, 18	D: 398/1-31 odd R: 394/26, 30, 38	D: 399/21-37 odd R: 394/36, 44, 48	14	15	16
9.7 Linear Inequalities in Two Variables	D: 403/1-21 odd R: 398/6, 10, 14 Test Yourself	D: 403/1-33 odd R: 398/10, 14, 18 Test Yourself	D: 404/23-43 odd R: Test Yourself	17	18	19

D = Daily   R = Review   MPSR = Mixed Problem Solving Review   R = Reteaching   P = Practice   E = Enrichment

STUDENT TEXT				TEACHER'S RESOURCE BOOK	
Reviewing	Test Yourself	388	Chapter Test	408	Spanish Chapter Summary and Review	17-18
And	Test Yourself	405	Prep. for Stan. Tests	409	• Quizzes	93-96
Testing	Chapter Sum. and Rev.	406	Maintaining Skills	410	• Chapter Test (Form A)	97-98
			Extra Practice	663	• Chapter Test (Form B)	99-100
					Calculator Test	17-18
Special	Math Club Activity	374	Application	389	Applications—Chapter 9	20
Features	Did You Know?	379	Extra	395	Critical Thinking	9
	Project	383	Critical Thinking	400	Reading and Writing in Algebra	9
					Technology	18-19

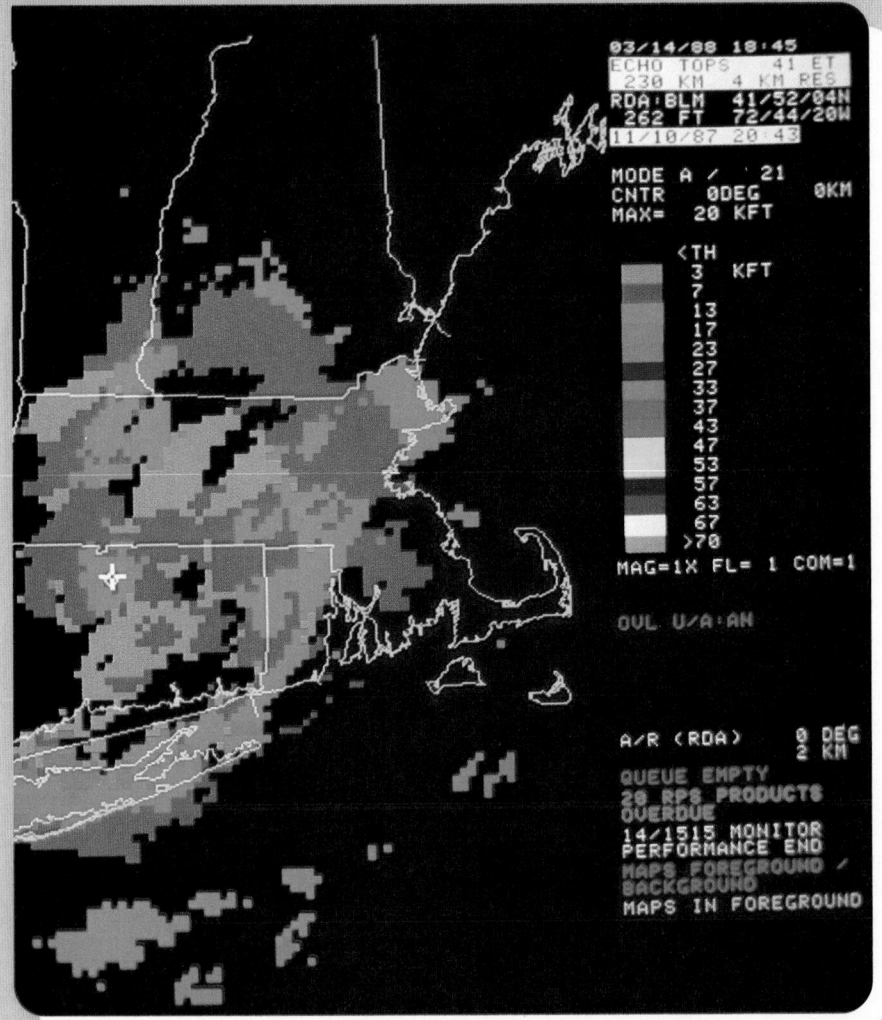

BACKGROUND

Meteorologists impose linear graphs on area maps to assist them in tracking storms. The use of tables and computer programs allows meteorologists to make predictions and estimates from graphs.

Physical scientists use graphs to represent numerical data. These graphs provide an easily interpreted method for analyzing trends, patterns, or direction of the numerical data.

369

Vocabulary

Abscissa
Coordinate system
Coordinates
Graph
Ordered pair
Ordinate
Origin
Plot
Quadrant
x-axis
y-axis

Materials/Manipulatives

Graph paper
Straightedge
Teacher's Resource Book,
  Teaching Aids 10, 11
  Transparencies 14, 15

BACKGROUND

- In the Capsule Review, the exercises provide students with practice in locating points, using coordinates on a number line. In this lesson, this concept is extended to the coordinate system in a plane.
- You may want to discuss how students graphed Exercise 4. Refer students who are having difficulty with these exercises to Lesson 1.2.

Additional Answers

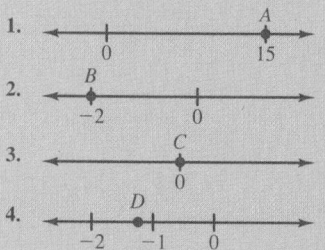

9.1

Graphing Ordered Pairs

Objectives: To graph ordered pairs of numbers
To identify a solution of an equation in two variables

Many maps use a grid system to help you locate a street or town. You are directed to a particular section of the map by finding the intersection of a vertical column with a horizontal row. On the map at the right, Eaton is in the intersection of column C and row 2.

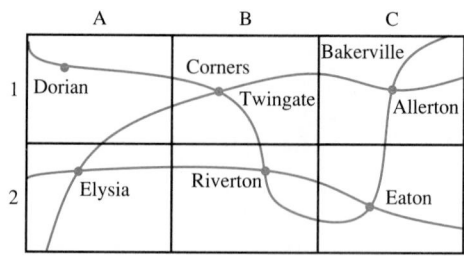

Capsule Review

The graph of a real number is a point on a number line. The number is called the *coordinate* of the point.

Use the coordinates to locate these points on a number line. See side column.

1. $A(15)$ **2.** $B(-2)$ **3.** $C(0)$ **4.** $D\left(-1\frac{1}{4}\right)$

A **coordinate system** in a plane is determined when two number lines are drawn in the plane so that they intersect at right angles. The zero point of each line is common to both lines and is called the **origin.** The horizontal number line is called the **x-axis.** The vertical number line is called the **y-axis.** The negative directions are to the left of the origin on the *x*-axis and down from the origin on the *y*-axis.

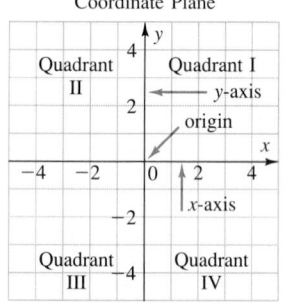

Coordinate Plane

The axes separate the coordinate plane into four **quadrants,** as shown at the right. Points on the axes are not in any quadrant.

Each point in a coordinate plane is assigned a unique **ordered pair** of real numbers, (x, y). The two numbers paired with a given point are called the *coordinates* of that point.

$$P(5, -3)$$

x-coordinate   *y*-coordinate
Read: Point *P*, with coordinates 5 and -3.

370   Chapter 9 Linear Equations

The x- and y-coordinates are known, respectively, as the **abscissa** and the **ordinate**.

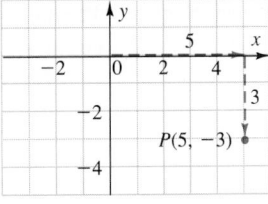

To locate or *plot* a point in a coordinate plane, always start at the origin. For $P(5, -3)$ move 5 units to the right from the origin and then move down 3 units. A point at that location is the *graph* of the ordered pair $(5, -3)$.

The order is important: $(5, -3)$ and $(-3, 5)$ are two different ordered pairs. How would you graph the point $Q(-3, 5)$?

EXAMPLE 1 **Graph the points $A(4, 1)$, $B(-1, 3)$, $C(-2, 0)$, and $D(-2, -4)$ in a coordinate plane.**

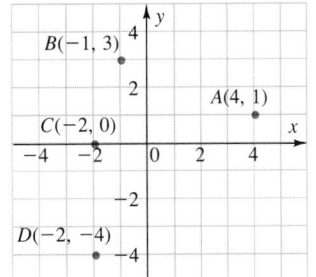

$A(4, 1)$
right 4 up 1

$B(-1, 3)$
left 1 up 3

$C(-2, 0)$
left 2 stay on axis

$D(-2, -4)$
left 2 down 4

Any ordered pair of real numbers names a unique point in the plane. Conversely, every point in the plane has a unique pair of coordinates. The coordinates of the origin are $(0, 0)$.

A solution of an equation containing two variables consists of two real numbers, one for each variable. For example:

$$x - y = 10 \qquad \text{A solution is } x = 12 \text{ and } y = 2.$$

You can write this solution as the ordered pair $(12, 2)$. Of course, there are other ordered pairs of numbers whose difference is 10: $(10, 0)$, $(15, 5)$, $(5, -5)$, and so on.

You can use substitution to decide whether a given ordered pair is a solution of an equation. The first number in the ordered pair is the value for x, and the second number is the value for y.

EXAMPLE 2 **Determine whether $(-2, -4)$, $(4, 16)$, and $(-3, 9)$ are solutions of the equation $2x - y = 0$.**

$(-2, -4)$	$(4, 16)$	$(-3, 9)$
$2x - y = 0$	$2x - y = 0$	$2x - y = 0$
$2(-2) - (-4) \overset{?}{=} 0$	$2(4) - 16 \overset{?}{=} 0$	$2(-3) - 9 \overset{?}{=} 0$
$-4 + 4 \overset{?}{=} 0$	$8 - 16 \overset{?}{=} 0$	$-6 - 9 \overset{?}{=} 0$
$0 = 0 \ ✔$	$-8 \neq 0$	$-15 \neq 0$

$(-2, -4)$ is a solution. $(4, 16)$ and $(-3, 9)$ are not solutions.

9.1 Graphing Ordered Pairs **371**

TEACHING SUGGESTIONS

- It is important for students to understand and use the graphing terminology presented in this lesson. The formal language is intended to prepare students for their geometry course.
- Emphasize that the abscissa x is the first number in the ordered pair, and the ordinate y is the second number. Some students may find it easier to make a table of the ordered pairs so that the substitutions in the equations for x and y are made correctly.
- For Example 3, stress that all of the solutions of the equation lie on the same line. Have students confirm this by finding an ordered pair on the line and checking to see if it is a solution of the equation.
- Teaching Aids 10, 11 and Transparencies 14, 15, in the *Teacher's Resource Book,* may be helpful when introducing the Examples and reviewing the Class Exercises.

Critical Thinking

Observation Suppose the horizontal axis in a graph was changed so that the unit distance was twice the unit distance of the vertical axis. Describe the effect of this on any graph. Students should discover that the graphs would be distorted. This technique is commonly used when people want to distort the interpretation of data.

- **For Example 1**

  1. Plot $E(3, 2)$, $F(-4, -2)$, $G(-2, 2)$, $H(6, -1)$, $I(1.5, 2)$, and $J(-3, -2.5)$ in a coordinate plane.

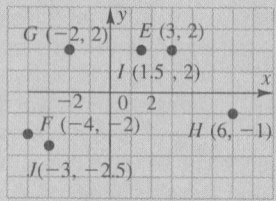

- **For Example 2**

  2. Determine whether $(8, 4)$, $(10, 2)$, and $(20, 7)$ are solutions of the equation $x - 2y = 6$.
  no; yes; yes

- **For Example 3**

  3. The ordered pairs $(5, 2)$, $(8, 4)$, and $(-1, -2)$ are solutions of the equation $2x = 3y + 4$. Plot the corresponding points in a coordinate plane, and then connect them.

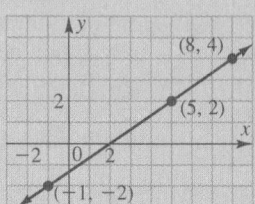

Common Error

- Some students interchange the role of the abscissa and the ordinate in an ordered pair. Have these students plot pairs of points, such as (4, 1) and (1, 4), and have them explain how they plotted each point.
- See *Teacher's Resource Book* for additional remediation.

EXAMPLE 3 The ordered pairs **(0, 6)**, **(4, 9)**, and **(−4, 3)** are solutions of the equation $3x = 4y - 24$. Graph the corresponding points in a coordinate plane and then connect them.

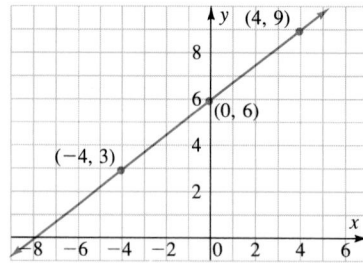

These points appear to lie on a line. $(-8, 0)$ is another solution of the equation. Does the point that corresponds to this ordered pair lie on the same line as the other points? yes

CLASS EXERCISES

Graph the points in a coordinate plane. See below.

1. $T(4, 1)$ **2.** $R(-3, -6)$ **3.** $U(-2, 5)$ **4.** $V(2, -5)$

State the coordinates and the quadrant (or axis) for each point.

5. D **6.** A **7.** K **8.** J
(3, 5), I   (0, −3), y-axis   (6, −5), IV   (−1, 4), II
9. C **10.** F **11.** H **12.** I
(−3, 0), x-axis   (−5, −2), III   (0, 6), y-axis   (5, 0), x-axis

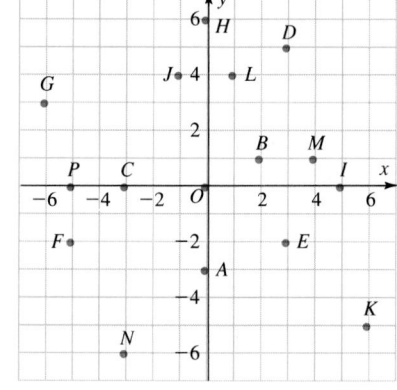

Name the point that is the graph of each ordered pair.

13. $(2, 1)$ B   **14.** $(3, -2)$ E

15. $(0, 0)$ O   **16.** $(-6, 3)$ G

17. $(-5, 0)$ P   **18.** $(1, 4)$ L

19. $(4, 1)$ M   **20.** $(-3, -6)$ N

State whether (0, 1) is a solution for each equation.

21. $x + 2y = 2$ solution   **22.** $3x - y = -1$ solution   **23.** $x = y + 1$ not a solution

24. $-x + y = -1$ not a solution   **25.** $4x + y = 3$ not a solution   **26.** $xy = 0$ solution

PRACTICE EXERCISES

Graph the points in a coordinate plane. See Additional Answer section beginning p. 719.

A   **1.** $A(1, 2)$ **2.** $B(3, 4)$ **3.** $C(0, 4)$ **4.** $D(3, 0)$

     5. $E(5, 9)$ **6.** $F(3, 2)$ **7.** $G(-1, 5)$ **8.** $H(-3, 1)$

372   Chapter 9 Linear Equations

Additional Answers   **Class Exercises**

1-4.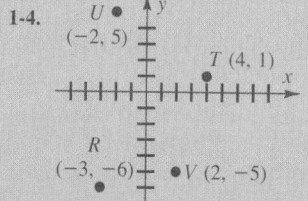

9. $I(-11, 10)$ **10.** $J(-7, 4)$ **11.** $K(-4, 2)$ **12.** $L(-6, -6)$

13. $M(-3, -5)$ **14.** $S(-1, -7)$ **15.** $P\left(-1, 1\frac{1}{2}\right)$ **16.** $Q\left(-4, \frac{1}{2}\right)$

Determine which of the ordered pairs listed are solutions of the equation.

17. $3x - y = -2$
  $(-3, -7), (3, 5)$
  $(-3, -7)$
19. $x + 3y = 6$
  $(3, 1), (4, 2)$
  $(3, 1)$

18. $5x - y = -7$
  $(2, 5), (0, 7)$
  $(0, 7)$
20. $x + 5y = 1$
  $\left(0, \frac{1}{5}\right), (3, 2)$ $\left(0, \frac{1}{5}\right)$

Graph the ordered pairs in a coordinate plane, and then connect them.
See Additional Answer section beginning p. 719.

21. $(0, 1), (2, 4), (-1, 6)$ **22.** $(1, 0), (3, 2), (-2, 3)$

23. $(2, 5), (-3, 2), (0, 5)$ **24.** $(1, 6), (-5, 0), (1, 4)$

B **25.** $(-3, -2), (-5, 0), (6, -1)$ **26.** $(-4, -3), (-2, 1), (4, -3)$

27. $(-5, 0), (0, -5), (5, 0)$ **28.** $(-8, -1), (4, 0), (3, 5)$

Identify the axis on which each point lies.

29. $P(x, y)$, if $x = 0$ and y is any real number. y-axis

30. $T(x, y)$, if x is any real number and $y = 0$. x-axis

Give two equations for which the ordered pair is a solution.
Answers may vary. Possible solutions are given.

31. $(1, -3)$
  $y = \frac{1}{2}x - \frac{7}{2}$
  $y = 3x - 6$
32. $\left(\frac{1}{2}, -2\right)$
  $y = 4x - 4$
  $y = 8x - 6$
33. $(-16, -3)$
  $y = \frac{1}{8}x - 1; y = \frac{1}{4}x + 1$
34. $(7, 49)$
  $y = 2x + 35$
  $y = 6x + 7$

The coordinates of three vertices of a rectangle are given. Graph the three vertices and determine the coordinates of the fourth vertex. See below.

C **35.** $(-1, -4), (4, -4), (4, 4)$ $(-1, 4)$ **36.** $(1, 3), (1, -2), (-2, -2)$ $(-2, 3)$

Complete each statement.

37. A line through points that have the same ordinate is __?__ (parallel) to the x-axis and __?__ (perpendicular) to the y-axis.

38. A line through points that have the same abscissa is __?__ (perpendicular) to the x-axis and __?__ (parallel) to the y-axis.

39. A line through points where $x = -2$ and a line through points where $y = 4$ have __one ?__ point(s) in common. Give the coordinates of the point(s), if any. $(-2, 4)$

9.1 Graphing Ordered Pairs **373**

LESSON FOLLOW-UP

Assignment Guide
- See p. 368B for assignments.

- See *Teacher's Resource Book, Technology,* p. 18.

Lesson Quiz

Plot these points in the same coordinate plane.
  1. $A(3, 2)$ **2.** $B(-4, 1)$
  3. $C(6, -5)$ **4.** $D(-1, -6)$
  5. $E\left(\frac{1}{2}, -2\right)$ **6.** $F(-3.5, -2.5)$

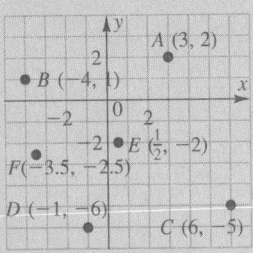

Determine which of the ordered pairs listed are solutions of the equation.
  7. $x + y = -3$ $(0, -3), (-1, 4)$
  $(0, -3)$

  8. $x - 2y = 4$ $(10, -3), \left(5, \frac{1}{2}\right)$
  $\left(5, \frac{1}{2}\right)$

Plot the ordered pairs in a coordinate plane, and then connect them.
  9. $(1, 2), (-3, 4), (3, 1)$
  10. $(1, 4), (-1, 0), (-2, -2)$

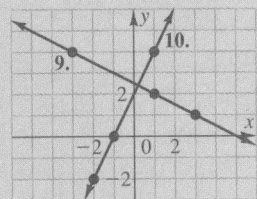

Additional Answers

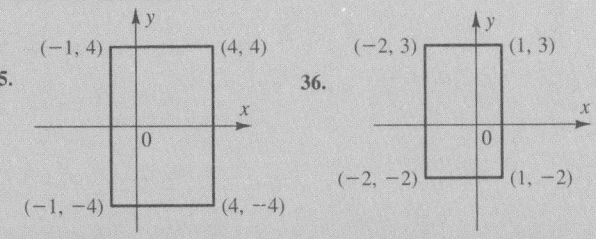

35.

36.

373

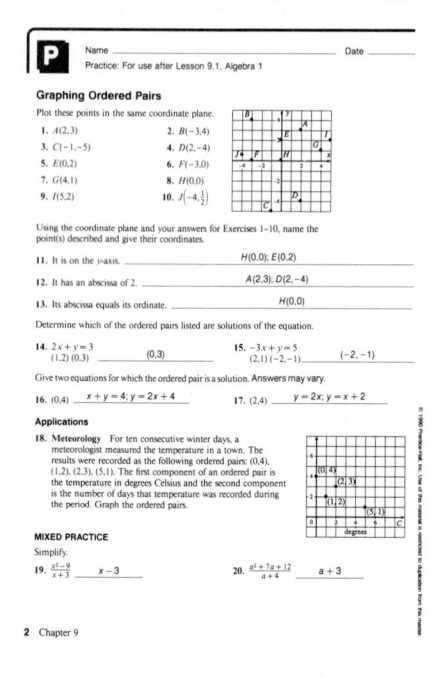

Graph the six ordered pairs in the same coordinate plane. Make a statement about the relationship between x and y. Then write an equation in terms of x and y that states the relationship.

40. $(-3, -3), (-2, -2), (-1, -1), (0, 0), (1, 1), (2, 2)$
x and y coordinates are equal; $y = x$; see below.

41. $(-2, -1), (-1, 0), (0, 1), (1, 2), (2, 3), (3, 4)$
y-coordinate is one more than the x-coordinate; $y = x + 1$; see below.

Applications

Draw and label the axes. Then graph the data to answer the question.
See Additional Answer section beginning p. 719 for graphs.

42. Chemistry A chemistry student measured the temperature c (in degrees Celsius) of a chemical reaction after m minutes and recorded the ordered pairs (c, m): $(2.5, 7.5), (5, 10), (10, 15), (20, 25)$. Find the temperature after 25 min. At what time will the temperature be 100°C? 30°C, 95 min

43. Transportation In the equation $d = 24t$, d represents the number of miles traveled by a truck moving at an average speed of 24 mi/h and t represents the time in hours.
    ordered pairs of (time, distance) with first coordinate t
a. For this situation, what do the pairs (t, d) represent? and second coordinate d
b. Are the following pairs (t, d) members of the solution set of this equation: $(2.5, 60)$? $(1.75, 42)$? $(0.5, 14)$? $(3.5, 84)$? $(0, 0)$?
$(1.75, 42), (2.5, 60), (3.5, 84),$ and $(0, 0)$ are solutions.

44. Economics A computer programmer's salary s is represented by the equation $s = 50h + 100$, where h represents the number of hours needed to complete a program.
a. Which of the following pairs of numbers (h, s) are members of the solution set for the equation? $(0.5, 125)$? $(1.25, 162)$? $(2.5, 225)$? $(3.0, 300)$? $(5.5, 375)$? $(0.5, 125), (2.5, 225), (5.5, 375)$
b. Use the graph to determine the minimum amount the programmer earns. $100

MATH CLUB ACTIVITY

The coordinates of point A are $(-1, -1)$, and the coordinates of point B are $(2, 1)$. Graph these ordered pairs in a coordinate plane. An electric current can flow along the grid lines, but it can flow only to the right or up. How many different paths could the current follow to flow from A to B? 10 paths

The coordinates of point C are $(0, 0)$, and the coordinates of point D are $(3, 2)$. Without counting them, tell how many different paths the current could follow to flow from C to D. 10 paths

Give the coordinates of two other points E and F, where the number of paths that the current could follow to flow from point E to point F is the same as the number that it could follow to flow from C to D. Answers may vary.

Additional Answers

40.

41.

Graphs of Linear Equations

9.2

Objectives: To graph linear equations by making tables of ordered pairs
To graph linear equations from their x- and y-intercepts

An equation such as $3x = 4y - 24$ is called a *linear equation*. A **linear equation** is an equation whose graph is a line.

Capsule Review

Each set of ordered pairs are solutions of the given equation. Graph the ordered pairs in a coordinate plane and then connect them.
See side column.

1. $\{(0, -2), (1, 1), (-1, -5)\}$; $y = 3x - 2$

2. $\{(-1, -1), (0, 0), (3, 3)\}$; $y - x = 0$

3. $\{(0, -3), (1, -1), (2, 1)\}$; $y - 2x = -3$

4. $\{(2, 0), (-2, -2), (4, 1)\}$; $y - \frac{1}{2}x = -1$

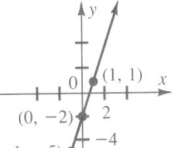

In many situations, it is important to write linear equations in *standard form.*

Linear equations (with the variables x and y) can be written in the form $Ax + By = C$, where A, B, and C are real numbers, and A and B are not both equal to 0. If A, B, and C are integers, the equation is said to be in **standard form.**

$3x - y = 2$ and $-x + y = 0$ are examples of linear equations in standard form. $y = 2x - 3$ and $y - \frac{1}{2}x = -1$ are examples of linear equations that are not in standard form. How would you write the last two equations in standard form?

To graph a linear equation, you may follow these steps:

1. Solve the equation for y.

2. Choose several values for x. Substitute each x-value in the equation and find the corresponding y-value.

3. Record the ordered-pair solutions in a table.

4. Graph the ordered pairs. Draw a line through the points.

Vocabulary
Linear equation
Standard form
x-intercept
y-intercept

Materials/Manipulatives
Computer
Geoboard
Graph paper
Graphing calculator
Straightedge
Teacher's Resource Book,
   Teaching Aids 10, 11, 12
   Transparencies 14, 15, 17, 18

BACKGROUND

In the Capsule Review, students plot points and then connect them to form a straight line. Discuss the fact that every ordered pair on the line is a solution of the equation. In this lesson, students graph linear equations by finding and graphing ordered pairs.

Additional Answers

2.

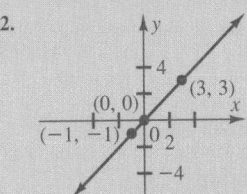

3.

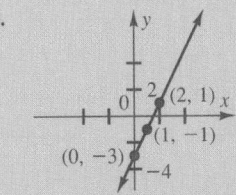

4.

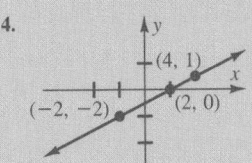

- Point out that the solution for an equation consists of the set of all ordered pairs that satisfy the equation.
- Discuss why the first step to graphing the equation is to solve for y. Students should realize that this form makes it easier to find the ordered pairs.
- Teaching Aid 10 and Transparencies 15, 17, and 18, in the *Teacher's Resource Book,* may be helpful to illustrate graphs of linear equations.
- Students who have difficulty graphing simple linear equations may benefit from hands-on activities using a geoboard.
- After students have practiced the basic concept of graphing linear equations, have them graph several exercises using a graphing calculator.

Critical Thinking

Causal Explanation In the lesson, a four-step method is given for graphing linear equations. Step 4 says to draw a line through the plotted points. Suppose a line cannot be drawn using all the plotted points. Explain what happened. *If the equation was linear, a mistake was made in finding or graphing the ordered pairs.*

CHALKBOARD EXAMPLES

- **For Example 1**
  1. Make a solution table, and graph $x - 2y = 6$. *Ordered pairs may vary.*

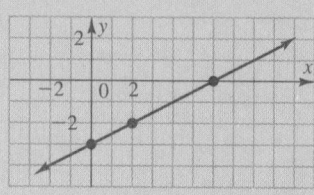

EXAMPLE 1 **Make a solution table and graph:** $3x + 4y = 12$.

1. Solve for y. $3x + 4y = 12$

$$4y = -3x + 12 \qquad \text{Subtract 3x from each side.}$$

$$y = -\frac{3}{4}x + 3 \qquad \text{Divide each side by 4.}$$

2. Choose the x-values. Solve to find corresponding y-values. This computer program may be used to generate the table of values.

```
10  PRINT "X","Y"
20  FOR X = - 4 TO 4 STEP 4
30  Y = - 3 / 4 * X + 3
40  PRINT X,Y
50  NEXT X
60  END
```

x	y
4	$-\frac{3}{4}(4) + 3 = 0$
-4	$-\frac{3}{4}(-4) + 3 = 6$
0	$-\frac{3}{4}(0) + 3 = 3$

3. Graph the ordered pairs from the above table. This computer program may be used to generate the graph.

```
10  FOR Y = 6.5 TO 0 STEP - .5
20  FOR X = - 4 TO 4 STEP .25
30  IF Y = - 3 / 4 * X + 3 THEN
       PRINT "+(";X;",";Y;")"; :X = 4: GOTO 60
40  IF X = 0 THEN PRINT "1";: GOTO 60
50  PRINT " ";
60  NEXT X: PRINT
70  NEXT Y
80  FOR X = 1 TO 8: PRINT "*---";:
       NEXT X: PRINT "*"
90  END
```

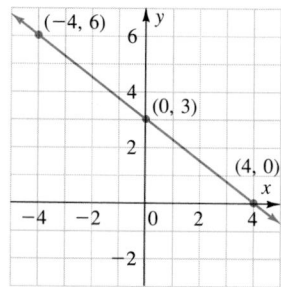

In Example 1, why do you think multiples of 4 were chosen for values of x? Do you think the coordinates of every point on the graph satisfy the equation $3x + 4y = 12$?

At the right, the graph of $3y = x - 6$ intersects the x-axis at point $P(6, 0)$. 6 is called the **x-intercept** of the graph.

The graph intersects the y-axis at point $Q(0, -2)$. -2 is called the **y-intercept** of the graph.

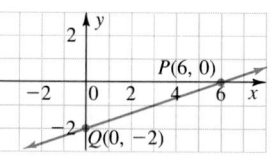

The x-intercept and y-intercept can be used to graph a linear equation. As shown in Example 2, sometimes it is helpful first to write the equation in standard form.

376 Chapter 9 Linear Equations

EXAMPLE 2   Use the intercepts to graph $x = \frac{1}{3}y + 1$.

Write the equation in standard form: $3x - y = 3$.
Substitute 0 for y to find the x-intercept. $3x - 0 = 3;$ $3x = 3;$ $x = 1$
Substitute 0 for x to find the y-intercept. $3(0) - y = 3;$ $-y = 3;$ $y = -3$
Plot the intercept points and draw the graph.   Plot A(1, 0) and B(0, -3).

The computer program will find the intercepts
to be used in graphing.

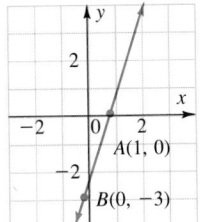

```
10 Y = 0:X = 1 / 3 * Y + 1
20 PRINT "WHEN Y = 0, X = ";X;" SO THE
   X-INTERCEPT IS A(";X;",0)"
30 X = 0:Y = 3 * X - 3
40 PRINT : PRINT "WHEN X = 0, Y = ";Y;" SO
   THE Y-INTERCEPT IS B(0,";Y;")"
50 END
```

Any third solution such as (2, 3) can be used as
a check.

When you graph an equation such as $x = -4$ in a coordinate plane, notice
that the equation places no restrictions on y. Set-builder notation may help
you to see which ordered pairs are solutions of $x = -4$.

$\{(x, y): x = -4\}$ *Read:* The set of all ordered pairs
of real numbers x and y,
such that $x = -4$.

In all ordered pair solutions of $x = -4$, the
x-coordinate is -4. The y-coordinate can be any
real number.

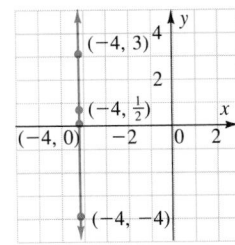

Graphing the ordered pairs in which the abscissa is
always -4 yields a graph that is parallel to the
y-axis and 4 units to the left of the y-axis.

EXAMPLE 3   **Graph $y = 3$ in a coordinate plane.**

The solution set of $y = 3$ is
$\{(x, y): y = 3\}$. Some solutions are:
$(-3, 3)$, $(0, 3)$, $\left(1\frac{1}{2}, 3\right)$, and $(3, 3)$.
The graph is parallel to the x-axis
and 3 units above the x-axis.

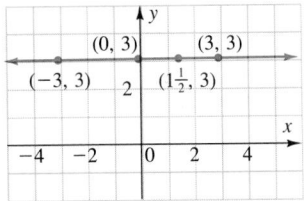

How do the solutions for the graph of $x = -4$ compare with the solutions for
the graph of $y = 3$?

9.2 Graphs of Linear Equations   **377**

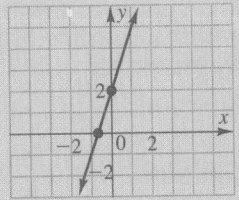
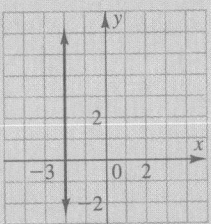
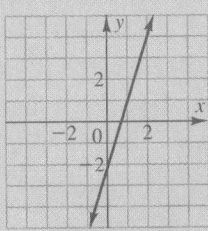

Common Error

- Students often make errors when finding ordered pairs. Suggest to these students that they should check their ordered pairs in the original equation before they plot them.
- See *Teacher's Resource Book* for additional remediation.

LESSON FOLLOW-UP

Assignment Guide

- See p. 368B for assignments.
- See *Teacher's Resource Book, Technology,* p. 19.

Lesson Quiz

Make a solution table, then graph the equation. Ordered pairs may vary.

1. $x + y = 8$ **2.** $x - 2y = 10$

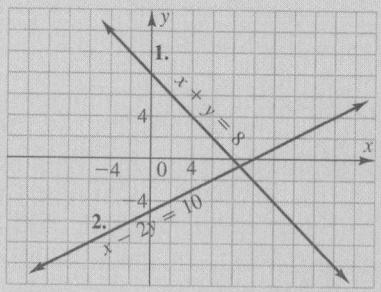

Use the *x*- and *y*-intercepts to graph the equation.

3. $x = y + 2$

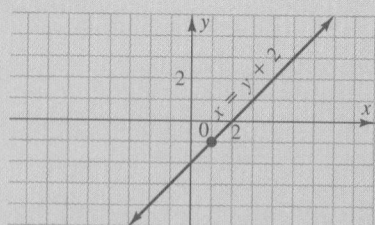

Enrichment

Are $2x - y = 3$ and $-2x + y = -3$ in standard forms of the linear equation $y = 2x - 3$? If not, why? If yes, which form is preferable and why?
Both are standard forms of the equation $y = 2x - 3$; however, it may be more convenient to write the coefficient of *x* as a positive number.

378

EXAMPLE 4 The graph of $y = -2x + 1$ is shown at the right. Find two solutions from the graph. Check these solutions.

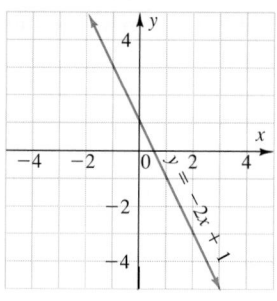

(0, 1) and (1, −1) appear to be solutions. Check by substituting these values in the equation.

(0, 1)
$y = -2x + 1$
$1 \stackrel{?}{=} -2(0) + 1$
$1 \stackrel{?}{=} 0 + 1$
$1 = 1$ ✔

(1, −1)
$y = -2x + 1$
$-1 \stackrel{?}{=} -2(1) + 1$
$-1 \stackrel{?}{=} -2 + 1$
$-1 = -1$ ✔

CLASS EXERCISES

Find the *x*- and *y*-intercepts of the graph of each equation.

1. $y - 3x = 4$
x: $-\frac{4}{3}$; *y*: 4

2. $x + y = 8$
x: 8; *y*: 8

3. $y = -7$
no *x*-intercept; *y*: −7

4. $x = 3$
x: 3; no *y*-intercept

For Discussion

5. What is the fewest number of points needed to determine a line? Why is it a good idea to locate three points when you graph an equation?
two; the third point acts as a check

6. The standard form of a linear equation is $Ax + By = C$, where *A*, *B*, and *C* are integers and *A* and *B* are not both 0. What type of graph results if $A = 0$? If $B = 0$? horizontal line; vertical line

PRACTICE EXERCISES

Make a solution table. Then graph the equation. See below pp. 378–379.

A **1.** $2x + 3y = 12$ **2.** $4x + 5y = 20$ **3.** $x - 2y = 4$ **4.** $x - 3y = 15$

Use the *x*- and *y*-intercepts to graph the equation.
See Additional Answer section beginning p. 719.

5. $x = \frac{1}{2}y + 3$ **6.** $x = \frac{2}{3}y + 5$ **7.** $2x + y = 8$ **8.** $4x + y = 16$

9. $y = \frac{2}{5}x + 2$ **10.** $y = \frac{1}{2}x + 2$ **11.** $y = \frac{1}{4}x - 1$ **12.** $y = \frac{3}{4}x - 3$

Graph each equation in a coordinate plane. Give three solutions of each.
See Additional Answer section beginning p. 719.

13. $y = 2$ **14.** $y = 0$ **15.** $x = 1$ **16.** $x = 5$

17. $2x + y = 4$ **18.** $3x + y = 9$ **19.** $y = -\frac{1}{3}x$ **20.** $y = -\frac{1}{4}x$

Additional Answers

1.
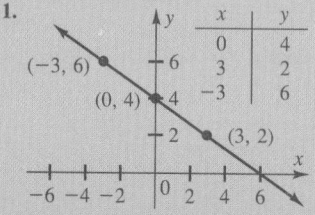

x	y
0	4
3	2
−3	6

(−3, 6)   (0, 4)   (3, 2)

2.
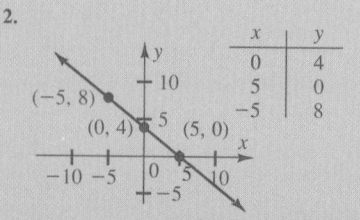

x	y
0	4
5	0
−5	8

(−5, 8)   (0, 4)   (5, 0)

Continued on p. 379.

Draw the graph to determine whether each ordered pair is a solution of $y = \frac{2}{3}x - 1$. Check your answer.

21. $(0, 1)$ no   **22.** $(3, 1)$ yes   **23.** $(-3, -3)$ yes   **24.** $(1, 0)$ no

Graph each equation.
See Additional Answer section beginning p. 719.

B   **25.** $x = -\frac{5}{2}$ **26.** $y + 6 = 0$ **27.** $y = \frac{3}{5}x - \frac{2}{5}$ **28.** $y = -\frac{1}{4}x + \frac{3}{4}$

29. $2x - y = 9$ **30.** $4x - 6y = 6$ **31.** $3y + 2x = 5$ **32.** $4y - x = 10$

Draw the graph to determine the missing coordinate of each ordered pair solution of $y = x + 3$.

C   **33.** $(0, y)$ 3   **34.** $(-2, y)$ 1   **35.** $(x, 0)$ –3   **36.** $(x, -1)$ –4

Determine the missing coordinate of the given solution.

37. $y = 3x;\ (2a^2,\ \underline{\frac{?}{6a^2}})$

38. $y = 2x + 1;\ (b^2,\ \underline{\frac{?}{2b^2 + 1}})$

39. $y = \frac{1}{2}x - 3;\ (\underline{\frac{?}{8d^4 + 6}},\ 4d^4)$

40. $y = \frac{1}{4}x + 1;\ (\underline{\frac{?}{32b^3 - 4}},\ 8b^3)$

Applications

Finance   In the equation $w = 0.25s + 75$, w (dollars) is the total weekly salary in a sales job in which there is a base salary of $75 and a 25% commission on sales s (dollars). You may wish to use a computer to help you in solving Exercises 41–42.

41. Using w as the vertical axis and s as the horizontal axis, graph this linear equation from a table of values. See Additional Answer section beginning p. 719.

42. What is the w-intercept, and what does it represent in this situation?
75; represents the weekly salary in a week in which there were no sales

DID YOU KNOW?

Why does it take longer to fly from New York to Miami than from Miami to New York?

Did you know that the **Coriolis** force plays an important role in flying?

The Coriolis force is caused by the earth's rotation, which affects the way airplanes travel.

Therefore, a plane never flys on a straight line, since it has to continuously make corrections in order to reach its destinations.

Research how these corrections are made.
Check students' work.

9.2 Graphs of Linear Equations   **379**

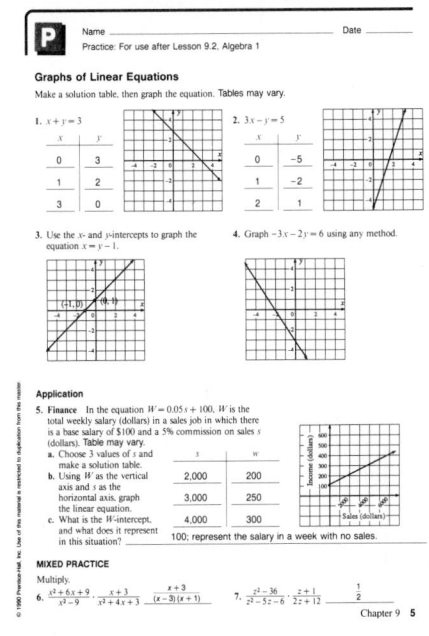
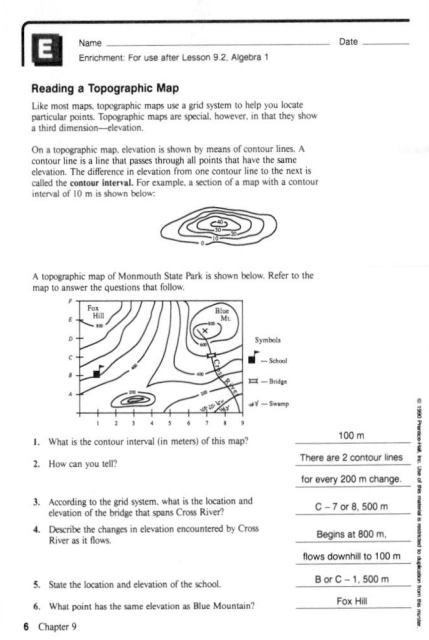
Additional Answers

3.

x	y
0	-2
4	0
-4	-4

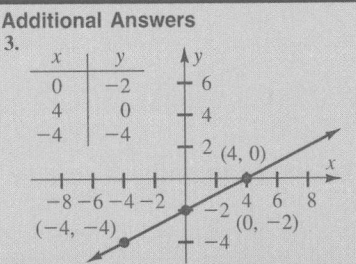

(4, 0)
(-4, -4)
(0, -2)

4.

x	y
0	-5
3	-4
6	-3

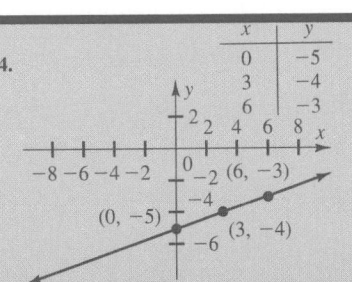

(6, -3)
(0, -5)
(3, -4)

BACKGROUND

A student's ability to organize information given in a problem, so that it can be used to solve the problem, is a key to success in this lesson. Analyze errors in the students' work and then classify specific errors.

Error Analysis Classification
1. *Misunderstanding*
   Unable to identify important mathematical ideas
2. *Misapplied strategy*
   Made error(s) in the solution process
   Error in checking

Critical Thinking

Predicting Consequences   What are some difficulties in estimating values from graphs? Values obtained from a graph are only as accurate as the graph. For example, if the graph is a rough sketch, the estimates will be only approximations.

9.3 Problem Solving Strategy: Estimate from Graphs

Graphs in the coordinate plane are often used in mathematics, science, and business to show relationships between two variables and to make predictions.

EXAMPLE   **Mrs. Clark earns $100 a week plus 3% commission on her car sales during that week. Her income can be expressed by $I = 0.03s + 100$, where I is her income and s is the amount of her sales. From a graph, estimate Mrs. Clark's income when her weekly sales are:**
a. $10,000   **b.** $22,554

Understand the Problem   **What are the given facts?**
You are given: $I = 0.03s + 100$. You are asked to graph the equation and estimate the income for sales of $10,000 and $22,554.

Plan Your Approach   **Choose a strategy.**
1. Income I depends on sales s. Label the horizontal axis s and the vertical axis I. Titles may be useful.
2. Look at the data; choose appropriate scales for the axes.
3. Graph: $I = 0.03s + 100$.

Complete the Work   **Solve.**
Units of $5000 are convenient for the horizontal axis. You can make a table of some values for (s, I). Units of $100 are convenient for the vertical axis.

s	I
0	100
5000	250
20,000	700

Interpret the Results   **Conclusion.**
Estimates from the graph: An income of $400 corresponds to $10,000 in sales. An income of about $775 corresponds to sales of $22,554.

Check your conclusions.

(10,000; 400)
$$I = 0.03s + 100$$
$$400 \stackrel{?}{=} 0.03(10,000) + 100$$
$$400 = 400 \; ✔$$

(22,554; 775)
$$I = 0.03s + 100$$
$$775 \stackrel{?}{=} 0.03(22,554) + 100$$
$$775 \approx 776.62 \quad \textit{Very close estimate}$$

380   Chapter 9 Linear Equations

CLASS EXERCISES

The graph shows how the distance a package travels is related to the amount charged by Expert Courier.

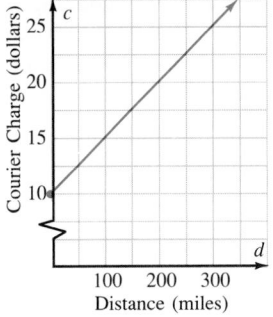

1. Estimate the cost of sending a package 250 mi.
   $22.50
2. Estimate how far you can send a package for $20.
   200 mi

Assume that the graph continues in a straight line indefinitely.

3. Estimate the cost of sending a package 600 mi. $40

Below is a rate schedule Jill developed for shoveling snow. Plot the points for the data listed in the table, then connect them.

x-axis	Time worked (hours)	1	2	3	4
y-axis	Charge (dollars)	10	15	20	25

4. How much does Jill charge for $2\frac{1}{2}$ h? for 6 h?
   $17.50 $35.00

For Discussion

5. The graphs of linear relationships involve two variables. How do you decide which variable to represent along the horizontal axis and which along the vertical axis? Explain. The given or independent variable is represented along the horizontal axis. The dependent variable is represented along the vertical axis.
6. Why should you examine the data before choosing scales for the axes of a graph? Can the two axes have different scales? Explain.
   You should examine the data so that it can be graphed within the scales chosen. The two axes may have different scales or they may be the same, depending on the data.

PRACTICE EXERCISES

The fee for renting a word processor is $25 plus $15 for each day you keep the machine. The total fee can be expressed by $F = 25 + 15d$, where F is the total fee and d is the number of days the machine is rented. Use this information for Exercises 1–4.

A 1. Complete the table.

Number of days (d)	1	2	3
Rental fee (F)	$40	?	?

$55 $70

2. Graph the solutions given in the table. Label the horizontal axis d, and the vertical axis F. Connect the points with a line. See below.

3. Use the graph to estimate the rental fee for 6 days. $115

4. Jose can spend no more than $200 in rental fees. For how many days can he rent a word processor? 11 days

9.3 Problem Solving Strategy: Estimate from Graphs   **381**

Additional Answers

2.

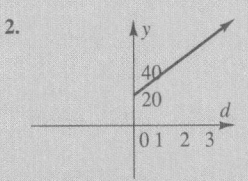

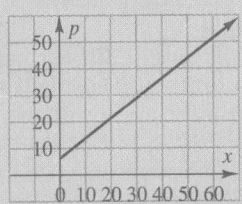

LESSON FOLLOW-UP

Common Error

- Some students have difficulty determining which variable to represent on the horizontal and vertical axes. Have these students always put the independent variable along the horizontal axis and the dependent variable along the vertical axis.
- See *Teacher's Resource Book* for additional remediation.

Assignment Guide

- See p. 368B for assignments.
- See *Teacher's Resource Book,* for Reading and Writing in Algebra activity p. 9.

Mixed Problem Solving Review

- The following skills and concepts are reviewed:
  Using polynomial equations (Ex. 3, 4)
  Solving uniform motion problems (Ex. 2, 5)
  Solving rational equations (Ex. 1, 5)
- The following problem solving strategies may be appropriate:
  Making a drawing or a table (Ex. 1–5)

Project

Have students work in cooperative groups to complete this project.

Lesson Quiz

1. In the equation $s = 10 + 0.9c$, s is the selling price (in dollars) and c is the cost (in dollars) of an article. Use a graph to estimate the selling price of articles whose costs are:
   a. $2 and **b.** $21.   a. about $12;
   b. about $30; Check students' graphs.

Enrichment

The distance an object falls due to gravity is given by the equation $s = 16t^2$, where s is the distance in feet and t is the time in seconds. Use a graph of this equation to estimate how long it takes an object to fall 50 feet.
about 1.8 s; check students' graphs

382

Sally went shopping for school clothes in Blue City. The city sales tax is 2%. Her total cost can be expressed by $C = x + 0.02x$, where C is her total cost including tax and x is the amount of her purchase in dollars. Use this information for Exercises 5–8.

5. Complete the table.

Amount of purchase (x)	$50	$100	$200
Amount of total cost (C)	$51	? $102	? $204

6. Graph the solutions in the table. Label the horizontal axis x, and the vertical axis C. Connect the points with a line. See below.

7. Use the graph to estimate the total cost of a purchase of $300. $306

8. Use the graph to estimate the total cost of a purchase of $450. $459

A company claims that a certain fertilizer multiplies the yield of cucumbers per plant by 3. The expected number of cucumbers per plant, with fertilizer, can be expressed by $C = 3p$, where C is the actual number of cucumbers per plant, with fertilizer, and p is the average number of cucumbers per plant, without fertilizer. Use this information for Exercises 9–12.

B   9. Complete the table.

Variety	A	B	C
Average number of cucumbers per plant, without fertilizer	4	10	12
Expected number of cucumbers per plant, with fertilizer	12	? 30	? 36

10. Graph the solutions given in the table. See below.

11. An actual test produced this data:

Variety	A	B	C
Average number of cucumbers per plant, without fertilizer	4	10	12
Actual number of cucumbers per plant, with fertilizer	15	28	35

On your graph for Exercise 10, graph these points in a different color. See below.

12. Does the company's claim seem justified? Yes, the claim is justified.

The power p in watts delivered to a certain element with current i in amperes is given by the equation $p = 100i - 50i^2$. Use this for Exercises 13–14.

C   13. Use 0 amps, 0.5 amp, 1 amp, 1.5 amps, and 2 amps to graph the given equation. Check students' graphs.

14. Estimate the power that corresponds to 0.25 amp and to 1.75 amps.
21.9 watts; 21.9 watts

Additional Answers

6.

10–11.

For a science project, a stone is thrown upward from the ground at a rate of 48 ft per second. Its distance d (in feet) above the ground is given by the equation $d = -16t^2 + 48t$, where t is time in seconds.

15. Use $t = 0$, $t = 0.5$, $t = 1$, $t = 1.5$, $t = 2$, and $t = 2.5$ to graph the equation. See below.

16. Use the graph to estimate when the stone will hit the ground. after 3 s

Mixed Problem Solving Review

1. The length of a rectangle is $\dfrac{2}{w + 2}$ in., and the area is $\dfrac{4}{w^2 - 4}$ in.^{2}. Find the width of the rectangle. $\dfrac{2}{w - 2}$

2. A jet plane and a prop plane leave the same airport at the same time and travel in opposite directions. The jet travels at 960 km/h and the prop plane travels at 560 km/h. In how many hours will they be 4560 km apart? 3 h

3. The lengths of two adjacent sides of a parallelogram are consecutive even integers. The perimeter of the parallelogram is 108 m. What are the dimensions of the parallelogram? 26 m and 28 m

4. The area of a rectangle is 176 cm^2. Find the dimensions of the rectangle if the length exceeds the width by 5 cm. length = 16 cm, width = 11 cm

5. Erik traveled 1120 km in 2 days. At this rate, how far would he travel in 13 days? 7280 km

PROJECT

Long before units of measure were standardized, people used parts of their bodies as units. For example, a **foot** was the distance from the end of a person's heel to the tip of the toe, and a **cubit** was the distance from the end of the middle finger to the elbow.

1. Measure and record the *foot* and the *cubit* for 20 or more different people. Use the centimeter as the unit of measure and record each pair of measures as an ordered pair: *(foot, cubit)*. Check students' work.

2. On a piece of graph paper, plot all the points for the ordered pairs that result from your measurements. (*Note:* When data is presented this way, the result is called a **scatter diagram,** or a **scatter plot.**) Check students' graphs.

3. If the points appear to cluster around a line, then a relationship may exist between the two units of measure. If they do not obviously cluster around a line, then a relationship may not exist between the two units. Look at your graph. Does it show a relationship or no relationship? Answers may vary.

9.3 Problem Solving Strategy: Estimate from Graphs **383**

Additional Answers

15.

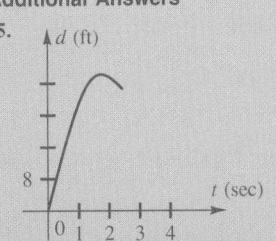

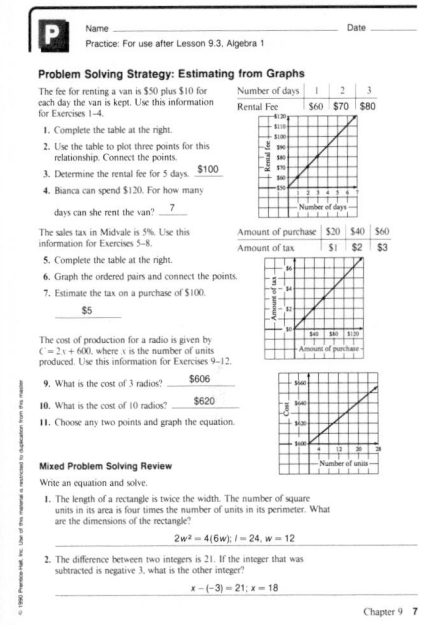
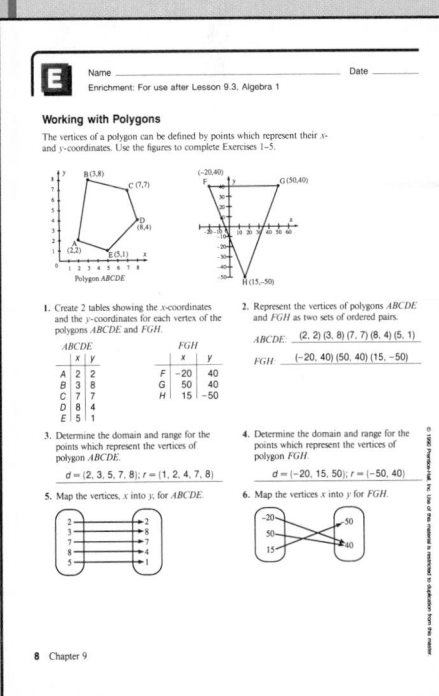
383

Vocabulary
Collinear points
Slope

Materials/Manipulatives
Graph paper
Graphing calculator
Overhead projector
Straightedge
Teacher's Resource Book,
   Teaching Aids 10, 11, 12
   Transparencies 14, 15, 16,
   17, 18

BACKGROUND

In the Capsule Review, Exercises 1–5 provide students with practice in simplifying fractions. In this lesson, students find the slope of a line by writing the ratios of vertical change to horizontal change. In some cases, it is necessary to write the ratio in simplest form.

9.4 Slope

Objectives: To find the slope of a line from its graph or from the coordinates of two points of the line
To draw a line with a given slope through a given point

Which ramp is easier to climb? Why? To describe the steepness of an incline, you can say that it rises a certain vertical distance for a given horizontal distance. Ramp A rises 6 ft for every 100 ft of horizontal run, while Ramp B rises 15 ft for every 100 ft of horizontal run.

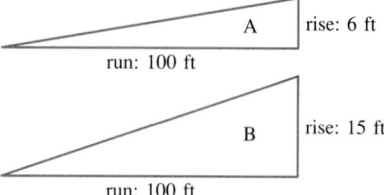

The relationship of the rise to the run can be expressed as a *ratio*.

$$\frac{\text{rise}}{\text{run}} = \frac{6}{100} = \frac{3}{50} \qquad \frac{\text{rise}}{\text{run}} = \frac{15}{100} = \frac{3}{20}$$

Capsule Review

You can use division to simplify a ratio.

EXAMPLE $\quad \dfrac{-12}{60} = \dfrac{-12 \div 12}{60 \div 12} = \dfrac{-1}{5}$, or $-\dfrac{1}{5}$

Simplify.

1. $\dfrac{24}{32} \quad \frac{3}{4}$ 2. $\dfrac{51}{17} \quad \frac{3}{1}$ 3. $\dfrac{-18}{54} \quad -\frac{1}{3}$ 4. $\dfrac{16}{-6} \quad -\frac{8}{3}$ 5. $\dfrac{-11}{-11} \quad \frac{1}{1}$

You can use the coordinates of two points of a line to determine the slope, or steepness, of the line. The **slope** of a line is the ratio of the change in *y* to the change in *x* between any two points on the line. This is often thought of as the ratio of the rise, or vertical change, to the run, or horizontal change. This is illustrated with line PQ (written $\overleftrightarrow{PQ}$).

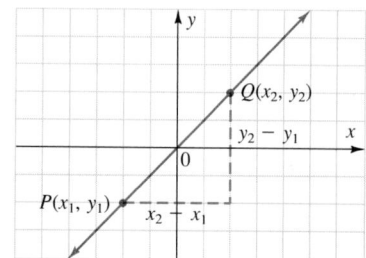

For any two points of a line, $P(x_1, y_1)$ and $Q(x_2, y_2)$, the slope m is given by the formula:

$$m = \frac{\text{rise}}{\text{run}} = \frac{\text{vertical change}}{\text{horizontal change}} = \frac{y_2 - y_1}{x_2 - x_1}, \text{ where } x_2 - x_1 \neq 0.$$

Note: It does not matter which point you call P or Q so long as you stick to your choice once it is made.

384 Chapter 9 Linear Equations

EXAMPLE 1 Find the slope of a line that contains the points $A(2, 1)$ and $B(4, 2)$.

Substitute in the formula $m = \dfrac{y_2 - y_1}{x_2 - x_1}$.

$$A(2, 1) \qquad B(4, 2)$$
$$\underset{x_1 \; y_1}{\uparrow \; \uparrow} \qquad \underset{x_2 \; y_2}{\uparrow \; \uparrow}$$

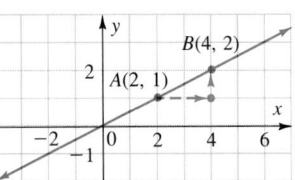

$$m = \frac{y_2 - y_1}{x_2 - x_1} = \frac{2 - 1}{4 - 2} = \frac{1}{2}$$

The slope is positive. The line slants up 1 unit for every 2-unit change to the right. Note that either point can be assigned the coordinates (x_1, y_1) or (x_2, y_2). The slope of the line will be the same. How can you show this?

EXAMPLE 2 Find the slope of a line that contains the points $C(-3, 1)$ and $D(2, -2)$.

$$C(-3, 1) \qquad D(2, -2)$$
$$\underset{x_1 \; y_1}{\uparrow \; \uparrow} \qquad \underset{x_2 \; y_2}{\uparrow \; \uparrow}$$

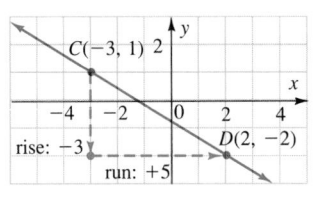

$$m = \frac{y_2 - y_1}{x_2 - x_1} = \frac{-2 - 1}{2 - (-3)}$$

$$= \frac{-3}{5} = -\frac{3}{5}$$

In Example 2, the slope is negative. The line slants down 3 units for every 5-unit change to the right.

Lines that slant up to the right have positive slopes. Lines that slant down to the right have negative slopes. In Example 3, the slopes of a horizontal line and a vertical line are considered.

EXAMPLE 3 Find the slope of:
  a. a horizontal line that contains the points $M(0, 2)$ and $N(5, 2)$
  b. a vertical line that contains the points $P(-3, 4)$ and $R(-3, 2)$

a.

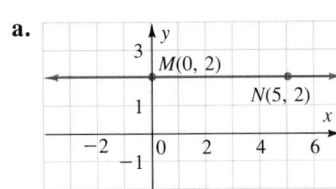

$$m = \frac{y_2 - y_1}{x_2 - x_1}$$

$$= \frac{2 - 2}{5 - 0}$$

$$= \frac{0}{5}, \text{ or } 0$$

9.4 Slope   **385**

385

- **For Example 2**

  Find the slope of the line that contains the given points.

  3. $M(6, -3)$, $N(3, -1)$ $-\frac{2}{3}$

  4. $U(5, -3)$, $V(1, 3)$ $-\frac{3}{2}$

- **For Example 3**

  Find the slope of:
  5. a horizontal line that contains $S(0, 5)$ and $T(5, 5)$. 0
  6. a vertical line that contains $X(-5, 6)$ and $Y(-5, -2)$. undefined

- **For Example 4**

  7. Through point $C(4, -2)$, draw a line with slope of -1.

  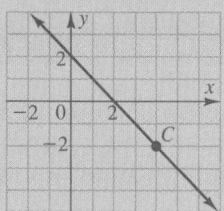

- **For Example 5**

  8. Determine if points $X(-5, -2)$, $Y(1, 1)$, and $Z(2, 6)$ are collinear. no

Common Error

- Students often confuse the values of x_1, y_1, x_2, and y_2, so that they compute the slope using the following incorrect rule: $\frac{y_2 - y_1}{x_1 - x_2}$. Students should be encouraged to write the formula first, and then substitute the values for the appropriate variables to compute the slope. You may wish to have students show that for a given line $\frac{y_2 - y_1}{x_2 - x_1}$ is the same as $\frac{y_1 - y_2}{x_1 - x_2}$.
- See *Teacher's Resource Book* for additional remediation.

b.

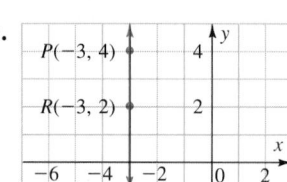

$$m = \frac{y_2 - y_1}{x_2 - x_1}$$
$$= \frac{4 - 2}{-3 - (-3)}$$
$$= \frac{2}{0}, \text{ or undefined}$$

If a line is horizontal, then its slope is 0. If a line is vertical, then its slope is undefined, or the line has no slope.

If you are given the coordinates of one point of a line and its slope, you can draw the line. The procedure is shown in Example 4.

EXAMPLE 4 **Through point $R(1, 2)$, draw a line with slope of $-\frac{3}{2}$.**

1. Plot $R(1, 2)$.

2. From R, go down 3 units (for the rise, -3), since $-\frac{3}{2} = \frac{-3}{2}$. Go to the right 2 units (for the run, 2). Mark point, S.

3. Draw a line through R and S.

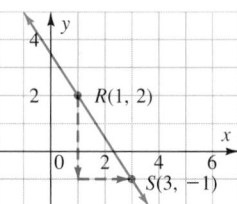

Collinear points are points that lie on the same line. If you know the coordinates of any collinear points, you can find the slope of the line and determine if any other points are also collinear. It is not necessary to draw the graph.

EXAMPLE 5 **Determine if points $A(-4, -1)$, $B(-2, 1)$, and $C(2, 5)$ are collinear.**

If the points *are* collinear, then the slopes of $\overleftrightarrow{AB}$ and $\overleftrightarrow{BC}$ will be the same.

slope of $\overleftrightarrow{AB}$

$$m = \frac{1 - (-1)}{-2 - (-4)} = \frac{2}{2}, \text{ or } 1$$

slope of $\overleftrightarrow{BC}$

$$m = \frac{5 - 1}{2 - (-2)} = \frac{4}{4}, \text{ or } 1$$

Since the slope of $\overleftrightarrow{AB}$ equals the slope of $\overleftrightarrow{BC}$, the points are collinear. Check by graphing the three points.

CLASS EXERCISES

Refer to the graph at the right. Classify the slope of the line as positive, negative, zero, or no slope.

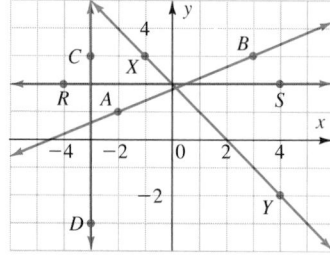

1. $\overleftrightarrow{AB}$ positive

2. $\overleftrightarrow{CD}$ no slope

3. $\overleftrightarrow{XY}$ negative

4. $\overleftrightarrow{RS}$ zero

Additional Answers Practice Exercises

19.

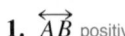

20.

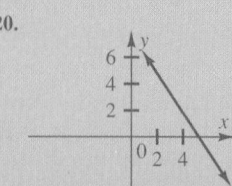

Find the slope of a line that contains the given points.

5. $A(6, 7)$; $B(1, 3)$ $\frac{4}{5}$ **6.** $R(-1, 3)$; $S(2, 4)$ $\frac{1}{3}$ **7.** $C(-2, 3)$; $D(2, 1)$ $-\frac{1}{2}$

8. $E(1, 3)$; $F(5, -3)$ $-\frac{3}{2}$ **9.** $P(-5, 2)$; $Q(3, 2)$ 0 **10.** $M(-1, 2)$; $N(-1, 4)$
no slope

PRACTICE EXERCISES

Find the slope of a line that contains the given points.

A   **1.** $A(3, 2)$, $B(5, 6)$ 2 **2.** $R(3, 8)$, $T(1, 4)$ 2 **3.** $C(2, 9)$, $D(5, 14)$ $\frac{5}{3}$

4. $E(4, 7)$, $F(7, 11)$ $\frac{4}{3}$ **5.** $M(-4, 4)$, $N(2, -5)$ $-\frac{3}{2}$ **6.** $J(-3, 1)$, $K(3, -4)$ $-\frac{5}{6}$

7. $S(-2, 1)$, $T(3, -5)$ $-\frac{6}{5}$ **8.** $P(-5, 2)$, $Q(2, -4)$ $-\frac{6}{7}$ **9.** $A(9, -2)$, $B(3, 4)$ -1

10. $R(6, -3)$, $S(1, 2)$ -1 **11.** $W(7, -1)$, $X(2, 3)$ $-\frac{4}{5}$ **12.** $G(5, -2)$, $H(4, 3)$ -5

Find the slope of a line that contains the following points. State whether it is a horizontal or vertical line.

13. $M(1, 3)$, $N(2, 3)$
0; horizontal
14. $X(0, 5)$, $Y(3, 5)$
0; horizontal
15. $P(-5, 2)$, $R(-5, 1)$
no slope; vertical
16. $J(-3, 0)$, $K(-3, 2)$
no slope; vertical
17. $A(4, 7)$, $B(3, 7)$
0; horizontal
18. $B(2, 1)$, $C(0, 1)$
0; horizontal

Through the given point, draw a line with the given slope. See below pp. 386–387.

19. $R(3, 4)$
slope $-\frac{1}{2}$
20. $P(2, 5)$
slope $-\frac{4}{3}$
21. $T(-1, 5)$
slope $-\frac{2}{3}$
22. $U(-2, 3)$
slope $-\frac{1}{3}$

The coordinates of three points are given. Use slope to determine if the points are collinear.

23. $A(-1, -5)$, $B(1, -2)$, $C(5, 4)$ yes   **24.** $X(-2, -6)$, $Y(0, -2)$, $Z(6, 10)$ yes

B   **25.** $D(-3, 4)$, $E(0, 2)$, $F(-3, 0)$ no   **26.** $G(3, 3)$, $H(1, -1)$, $I(0, 0)$ no

27. $J(-2, 1)$, $K(-2, 4)$, $L(2, 4)$ no   **28.** $M(-2, 1)$, $N(0, 4)$, $P(2, 7)$ yes

29. $R(1, -2)$, $S(-1, -5)$, $T(5, 4)$ yes   **30.** $S(-3, 4)$, $M(0, 2)$, $C(-3, 0)$ no

Find the slope, if it exists, of each side of the given figure.

31.
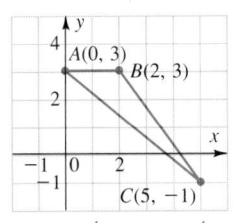
$m_{AC} = -\frac{4}{5}$; $m_{BC} = -\frac{4}{3}$; $m_{AB} = 0$

32.
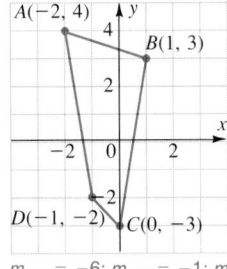
$m_{AD} = -6$; $m_{DC} = -1$; $m_{CB} = 6$; $m_{AB} = -\frac{1}{3}$

Discussion
Explain how the sign of the slope affects the graph.   If the slope is positive, the line slants upward. If the slope is negative, the line slants downward.

Critical Thinking
Observation In Example 4, discuss what would happen if you wrote $m = -\frac{3}{2}$ as $\frac{3}{-2}$. Students should discover that the second point they may locate would be $(-1, 5)$ but the line drawn is exactly the same.

Assignment Guide
- See p. 368B for assignments.
- In Exercises 37–40, students can find the answers algebraically or graphically. In Exercise 43, students should recall that the opposite sides of a parallelogram are parallel and have equal slopes.

Test Yourself
See *Teacher's Resource Book, Tests,* pp. 93–94.

Lesson Quiz
Find the slope of the line that contains the given points.

1. $X(-3, 4)$, $Y(2, -2)$ $-\frac{6}{5}$

2. $A(-5, -4)$, $B(0, -2)$ $\frac{2}{5}$

3. $W(-2, 4)$, $U(-1, 4)$ 0

4. Through the point $A(2, 4)$, draw a line with slope of $-\frac{5}{2}$.

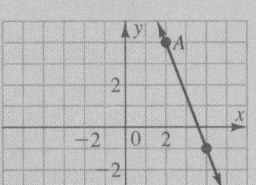

5. Use slope to determine if points $A(2, -4)$, $B(-2, -10)$,   and $C(10, 8)$ are collinear.   yes

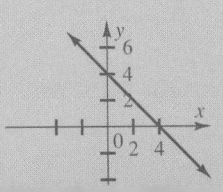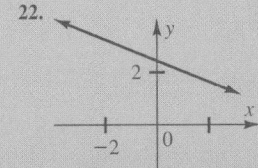

387

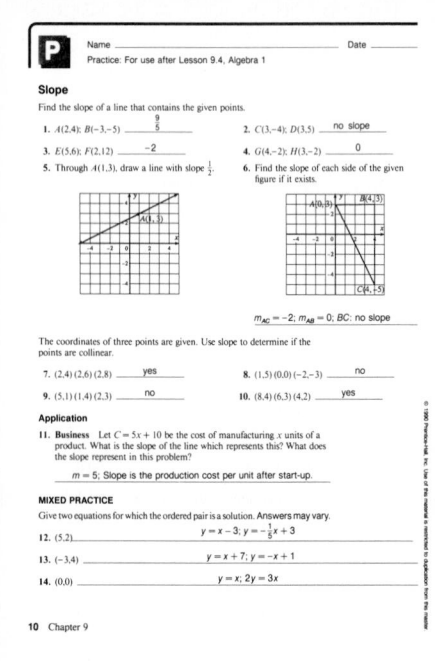
Through the given point, draw a line with the given slope. See below.

33. $P(6, -1)$
slope: -1

34. $R\left(0, \frac{1}{2}\right)$
slope: 6

35. $S\left(\frac{1}{2}, -\frac{3}{2}\right)$
slope: 0

36. $T\left(1\frac{1}{3}, -2\frac{2}{3}\right)$
slope: -3

Find the value of the missing coordinate using the given slope.

C **37.** $A(4, y)$ and $B(8, 12)$; slope: $-\frac{1}{2}$ 14

38. $C(x, -3)$ and $D(2, 1)$; slope: $\frac{1}{4}$ -14

39. $E(x, 0)$ and $F(3, 4)$; slope: 2 1

40. $G(-1, y)$ and $H(1, -1)$; slope: 3 -7

Find the slope of a line that contains the given points.

41. $A(a, 3a)$ and $B(b, 3b)$ $m_{AB} = 3$

42. $C(c, c + 4)$ and $D(d, d + 4)$
$m_{CD} = 1$

Applications

$m_{RS} = \frac{1}{2}; m_{ST} = -\frac{4}{5}; m_{TU} = \frac{2}{7-x}; m_{RU} = \frac{4}{-2-x}$

43. Geometry   The vertices of a parallelogram $RSTU$ are $R(-2, 4)$, $S(2, 6)$, $T(7, 2)$, and $U(x, 0)$. Find the slope of each side of the parallelogram. $U(3, 0)$

44. Science   If 35 cm³ of gold weigh 392 g and 21 cm³ of gold weigh 235.2 g, draw a graph with cubic centimeters of gold as the horizontal axis and grams of gold as the vertical axis. Assuming that weight and volume of gold are related through a linear equation, find the slope. What does the slope represent in this problem? $m \approx 11$; slope represents g/cm³

TEST YOURSELF

Is the given ordered pair a solution of the equation?   9.1

1. $2x + 3y = -2$; $(5, -4)$ yes

2. $y - x = 2$; $\left(\frac{1}{2}, \frac{3}{2}\right)$ no

Graph each equation. See p. 389.   9.2

3. $5y - 2x = 10$

4. $y - 3x = 9$

5. $y = -x + 1$

6. $y = \frac{1}{4}x + 2$

The amount of dog food ordered per week by the Poodle Kennel depends on how many dogs are registered. The table shows data for three weeks.   9.3

7. Graph the ordered pairs and connect the points.
See p. 389.

No. of Dogs	10	12	16
Food (pounds)	36	42	54

8. From the graph, estimate the amount of food to order for 6 dogs. 24 lb

9. How many pounds of food should be ordered for 20 dogs? 66 lb

10. If 60 pounds were ordered, how many dogs were registered that week? 18 dogs

Find the slope of a line that contains the given points.   9.4

11. $A(5, 3)$, $B(3, 2)$ $\frac{1}{2}$

12. $C(-2, -7)$, $D(4, -3)$ $\frac{2}{3}$

Additional Answers

33.

34.

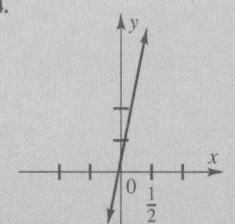

APPLICATION:
Radio Waves

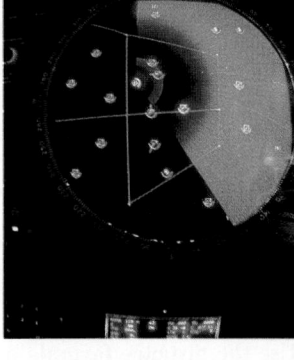

Did you know that radar is used to detect and locate fixed or moving objects? It can determine the direction, distance, height, and speed of objects that are much too far away for us to see. It can locate objects as small as insects or as large as mountains. The word radar comes from *ra*dio *d*etection *a*nd *r*anging.

Almost every radar set works by sending radio waves toward an object and receiving waves that are reflected from the object. The time it takes for the reflected waves to return indicates how far away the object is. The direction from which the reflected waves return tells the location of the object. The ability of radar to do so many tasks makes it useful for a wide variety of purposes.

Radio waves as transmitted by radar have definite frequency. They travel at the rate of 186,000 mi/s. The frequencies of such waves are measured in units called megahertz (MHz). One megahertz equals 1 million hertz (cycles per second).

EXAMPLE   How far away from each other are two boats, if a signal is sent out by one ship and returned by the other in $\frac{1}{100,000}$ s?
Hint: Use the distance formula.

Let $r = 186,000$ and $t = \frac{1}{100,000}$ and solve for d.

$$d = r \times t$$

$$= 186,000 \times \frac{1}{100,000}$$

$$= \frac{186,000 \text{ mi/s}}{100,000 \text{ s}}$$

$$= 1.86 \text{ mi}$$

The signal traveled 1.86 mi altogether. So the distance between the ships is one-half of the distance or 0.93 mi.

Application: Radio Waves   **389**

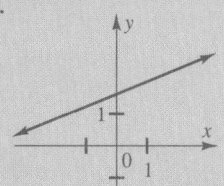
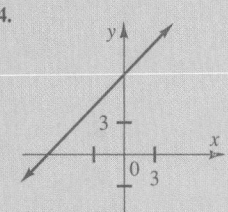
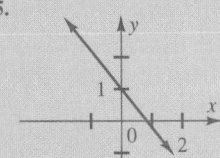
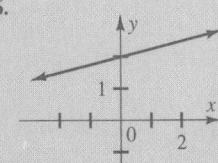
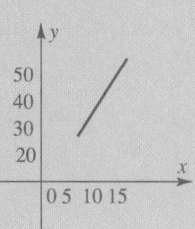
35.

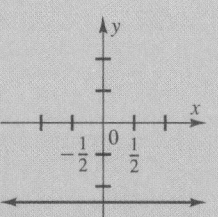

36.

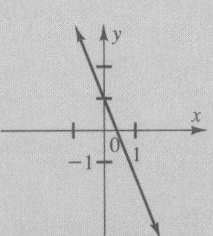

Modern radar has provided useful images from space. The Apollo 17 flight in December 1972 gathered data with radar to develop maps of the moon. In 1978, the satellite Seasat carried the first space-based imaging radar. It operated for three months. The second imaging radar was aboard the United States space shuttle Columbia during its second flight in November 1981.

Radar is influenced by the temperature, air pressure, and the water vapor content of the atmosphere. The program below gives you the radar distance and the geometric distance when you input the optical horizon distance.

```
10 INPUT "ENTER OPTICAL HORIZON DISTANCE:  ";D
20 DR = 1.07 * D:DG = DR / 1.15
30 PRINT : PRINT "RADAR DISTANCE IS ";DR
40 PRINT : PRINT "GEOMETRIC DISTANCE IS ";DG
50 END
```

Solve. Use the distance formula and the above program.

1. How far away are two boats if a signal is sent out and returns in $\frac{1}{10,000}$ of a second? 9.3 mi

2. How far must a signal travel from one ship to another to verify that they are 3.5 mi apart? 7 mi

3. Find the distance between two airplanes if a signal is sent out from one airplane and returned in 0.0002 s. 18.6 mi

4. An air traffic control tower receives a signal from an airplane 500 mi away. How many seconds does it take for the signal to reach the station? 0.0027 s

5. The moon is approximately 240,000 mi from the earth. How long does it take for a radar signal to reach the moon and return? 2.58 s

6. A satellite orbiting the earth sends a radar signal to a tracking station and receives a reply in 0.003 s. How far is the satellite from the earth? 279 mi

7. A satellite orbiting the earth at a distance of 150 mi sends a signal to a tracking station which relays the signal up to second satellite. The total time needed is 0.0014 s. How far above the earth is the second satellite? 110.4 mi

8. Calculate the radar distance and geometric distance for an optical horizon distance of:
   a. 15 mi on flat land.　**b.** 8 mi on open sea.　**c.** 100 mi on a mountain top.
   16.05 mi; 13.96 mi　　　8.56 mi; 7.44 mi　　　107 mi; 93.04 mi
9. Calculate the radar distance and geometric distance for the following optical horizon distances:
   a. Los Angeles, CA 15 mi　**b.** Ely, NV 45 mi　**c.** Jackson, MS 7 mi
   16.05 mi; 13.96 mi　　　　48.15 mi; 41.87 mi　　　7.49 mi; 6.51 mi

9.5

Slope-Intercept Form of a Linear Equation

Objectives: To use the slope-intercept form to graph a linear equation
To use slope to determine if two lines are parallel

When a linear equation such as $3x + y - 2 = 0$ is solved for y, an equivalent form of a linear equation is obtained.

Capsule Review

You can solve an equation by addition, subtraction, multiplication, or division.

EXAMPLE   Solve for y:

$$2x + 3y = 3$$
$$3y = -2x + 3 \qquad \textit{Subtract 2x from both sides.}$$
$$y = \frac{-2x + 3}{3} = -\frac{2}{3}x + 1 \qquad \textit{Divide each side by 3.}$$

Solve each equation for y.

1. $y - 2x = 8$ $y = 2x + 8$ **2.** $y + 2x = -5$ $y = -2x - 5$ **3.** $3y - x = 9$ $y = \frac{1}{3}x + 3$

4. $2y + 3x = 4$ $y = -\frac{3}{2}x + 2$ **5.** $2y + x + 5 = 0$ $y = -\frac{1}{2}x - \frac{5}{2}$ **6.** $3y + 2x - 7 = 0$ $y = -\frac{2}{3}x + \frac{7}{3}$

Look at the graphs of $y = -3x$ and $y = -3x + 2$.

$y = -3x$

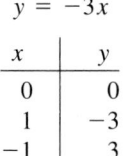

x	y
0	0
1	-3
-1	3

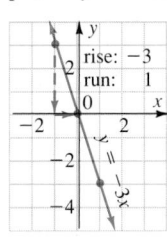

$y = -3x + 2$

x	y
0	2
1	-1
2	-4

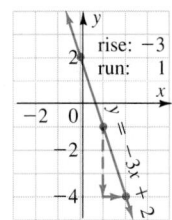

The graphs of both $y = -3x$ and $y = -3x + 2$ are lines with slope -3. The lines intersect the y-axis at different points. The y-intercept of $y = -3x$ is 0. The y-intercept of $y = -3x + 2$ is 2. This suggests the following property.

The equation $y = mx + b$ is called the **slope-intercept form** of a linear equation. The graph of the equation is a line with slope m and y-intercept b.

9.5 Slope-Intercept Form of a Linear Equation   **391**

LESSON PLAN

Vocabulary
Parallel
Slope-intercept form

Materials/Manipulatives
Graph paper
Graphing calculator
Overhead projector
Straightedge
Teacher's Resource Book,
   Teaching Aids 10, 11, 12
   Transparencies 14, 15, 16,
   17, 18

BACKGROUND

In the Capsule Review, students review solving linear equations for one variable in terms of the other. Remind students that in solving problems like Exercise 3, $\frac{1}{3}$ is distributed over the sum of $x + 9$, getting $y = \frac{1}{3}x + 3$, not $y = \frac{1}{3}x + 9$. This review prepares students to solve linear equations for y, in order to find the slope and y-intercept of a line.

- For Example 1, point out that you divide both $-4x$ and 12 by 3, so that the y-intercept is 4. Many students may think the y-intercept is 12.
- Stress the importance of students checking their graphs by using a third point.
- For Example 4, have students graph both lines on the same coordinate plane to show that the two lines are parallel. You may wish to use Teaching Aids 10, 11 and Transparencies 14, 15, 17, and 18, in the *Teacher's Resource Book*, to illustrate several examples.
- Have students use the *trace function* on a graphing calculator to find the y-intercept for several exercises.

CHALKBOARD EXAMPLES

- **For Example 1**

  Find the slope and the y-intercept of the line for the given equation.

  1. $2x - 3y = 6$ $m = \frac{2}{3}$, $b = -2$

  2. $x + 2y = 9$ $m = -\frac{1}{2}$, $b = \frac{9}{2}$

- **For Example 2**

  Write an equation of the line with the given slope and y-intercept.

  3. $m = \frac{1}{3}$, $b = 1$ $y = \frac{1}{3}x + 1$

  4. $m = -1$, $b = 0$ $y = -x$

- **For Example 3**

  5. Graph $2x + 4y = 8$.

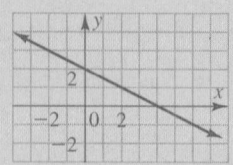

EXAMPLE 1   **Find the slope and the y-intercept of the line for the equation $4x + 3y = 12$.**

$$4x + 3y = 12 \qquad \textit{Solve for y.}$$
$$3y = -4x + 12 \qquad \textit{Subtract 4x from each side.}$$
$$y = -\frac{4}{3}x + 4 \qquad \textit{Divide each side by 3.}$$
$$\textit{The equation is in slope-intercept form.}$$
$$\underset{m}{\uparrow} \qquad \underset{b}{\uparrow}$$

The slope is $-\frac{4}{3}$; the y-intercept is 4.

EXAMPLE 2   **Write an equation of the line with slope -2 and y-intercept 0.**

$$m = -2 \text{ and } b = 0$$
$$y = mx + b$$
$$y = -2x + 0 \qquad \textit{Substitute } -2 \text{ for m and 0 for b.}$$
$$y = -2x$$

Although a linear equation can be graphed using a table of values, a more efficient method uses only the slope and y-intercept.

EXAMPLE 3   **Graph: $x - 2y = 4$**

Write the equation in the form $y = mx + b$.

$$x - 2y = 4$$
$$-2y = -x + 4$$
$$y = \frac{1}{2}x - 2 \qquad m = \frac{1}{2}; b = -2$$

1. The y-intercept is -2. Plot the point whose coordinates are $(0, -2)$.

2. From that point, use the slope, $\frac{1}{2}$, to locate another point. Go up 1 unit and 2 units to the right.

$$\text{slope} = \frac{1}{2} \begin{array}{l} \leftarrow \text{up 1} \\ \leftarrow \text{right 2} \end{array}$$

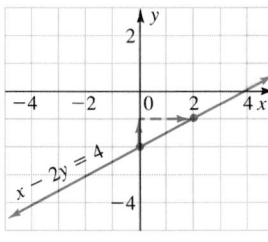

3. Draw a line through the two points.

4. Use a third point to check. Is $(-4, -4)$ a solution of $y = \frac{1}{2}x - 2$? Is the point for $(-4, -4)$ on the line?

392   Chapter 9 Linear Equations

Additional Answers

5.

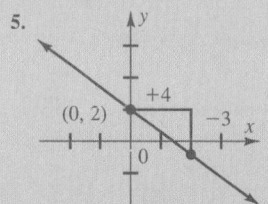

6.

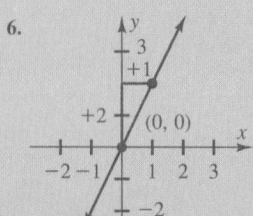

Look at the graphs of $y = x + 1$ and $y = x - 1$.

The lines seem to be *parallel*. Note that the slopes are the same, but the y-intercepts are different.

$$y = x + 1 \qquad y = x - 1$$
$$m = 1, b = 1 \qquad m = 1, b = -1$$

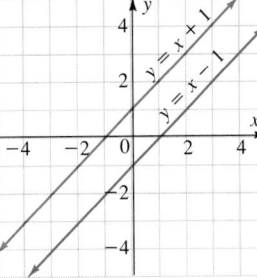

Graph $y = x + 4$. What do you notice about this line and the other two lines?

This suggests the following property.

> Two nonvertical lines have the same slope if and only if they are **parallel.**

Note that vertical lines are parallel but have slopes that are undefined.

EXAMPLE 4 **Determine whether the graphs of $y = -2x + 3$ and $4x + 2y = 5$ are parallel lines.**

Find the slope of each line.

$$y = -2x + 3 \qquad 4x + 2y = 5$$
$$\text{slope} = -2 \qquad 2y = -4x + 5$$
$$y = -2x + \frac{5}{2}$$
$$\text{slope} = -2$$

Since the lines have the same slope, they are parallel.

CLASS EXERCISES

Find the slope and the y-intercept of the line for the given equation.

1. $y = -\frac{2}{3}x$
$m = -\frac{2}{3}, b = 0$

2. $x + 5y = 10$
$m = -\frac{1}{5}, b = 2$

3. $8x - y = 2$
$m = 8, b = -2$

4. $x = 3y + 7$
$m = \frac{1}{3}, b = -\frac{7}{3}$

Graph each equation using the slope and the y-intercept. See below pp. 392–393.

5. $y = -\frac{4}{3}x + 2$ **6.** $y - 2x = 0$ **7.** $2x + 5y = 10$ **8.** $y - 4 = 0$

For Discussion

9. You have learned to draw a line with a given slope through a given point. How does this relate to using the slope and y-intercept to graph a linear equation? It is the same except that when you use the y-intercept you are locating a particular point—the point where the line intersects the y-axis.

10. Describe the relationship of the graphs of three linear equations if b is the same for all three but m is different. All three lines intersect the y-axis at the same point.

9.5 Slope-Intercept Form of a Linear Equation **393**

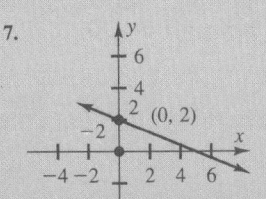
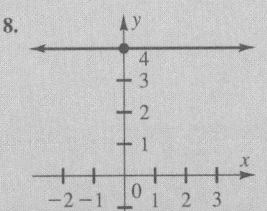
- **For Example 4**
  Determine whether the graphs of the two equations are parallel lines.
  6. $x + 2y = 7$
  $y = \frac{1}{2}x - 4$ no
  7. $y = 4$
  $y - 2 = 1$ yes

Common Error

- In using the slope-intercept method to graph a straight line, students sometimes are confused about how to locate the second point using the slope. To help them with this difficulty, stress that the slope is the $\frac{\text{rise}}{\text{run}} = \frac{\text{vertical distance}}{\text{horizontal distance}}$. Review Transparency 16, in the *Teacher's Resource Book*.
- See *Teacher's Resource Book* for additional remediation.

LESSON FOLLOW-UP

Discussion

Determine whether the graphs of $\frac{3}{4}y - \frac{1}{8}x = 2$ and $y = \frac{x}{6} + \frac{8}{3}$ are parallel lines. Yes, since the lines have the same slope.

Critical Thinking

Comparing-Contrasting In what ways are Examples 1 and 2 different? The difference in the two examples is in what is to be found. In Example 1, the equation of the line is given and slope and y-intercept are to be found. In Example 2, the process is reversed.

Assignment Guide

- See p. 368B for assignments.
- For Exercises 43–46, remind students that the slope of a line is the coefficient of x when the equation is written in the slope-intercept form.

393

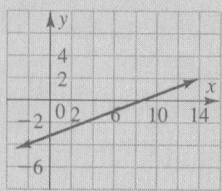
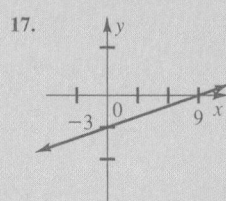
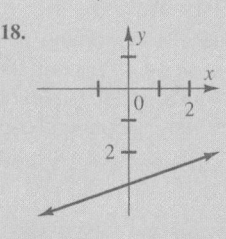
Are the graphs of the two equations parallel lines? Explain.

11. $y = 2x + 5$
$-2x + y = 9$
parallel, slopes = 2

12. $x + 3y = 7$
$y = \frac{1}{3}x - 4$
not parallel,
slopes are $\frac{1}{3}, -\frac{1}{3}$

13. $x - y = 3$
$y - x = 2$
parallel, slopes = 1

14. $y = 8$
$y + 2 = 3$
parallel, slopes = 0

PRACTICE EXERCISES

Find the slope and the y-intercept of the line for the given equation.

A **1.** $3x + 2y = 6$ $\frac{3}{2}; -3$

2. $5x + 3y = 15$ $-\frac{5}{3}; 5$

3. $x - 3y = 9$ $\frac{1}{3}; -3$

4. $x - 4y = 20$ $\frac{1}{4}; -5$

5. $y = -2x$ $-2; 0$

6. $y = -5x$ $-5; 0$

7. $y = 3x + 6$ $3; 6$

8. $y = 4x + 8$ $4; 8$

Write an equation of the line with the given slope and y-intercept.

9. $m = -2$
$b = 0$ $y = -2x$

10. $m = -5$
$b = 2$ $y = -5x + 2$

11. $m = 1$
$b = 3$ $y = x + 3$

12. $m = 4$
$b = 2$
$y = 4x + 2$

13. $m = \frac{2}{3}$
$b = 4$ $y = \frac{2}{3}x + 4$

14. $m = \frac{3}{4}$
$b = 3$ $y = \frac{3}{4}x + 3$

15. $m = 0$
$b = -1$ $y = -1$

16. $m = 0$
$b = -3$ $y = -3$

Graph each equation. See side column.

17. $x - 3y = 9$

18. $x - 6y = 18$

19. $x + 2y = 8$

20. $x + 4y = 20$

21. $3x - 2y = 4$

22. $4x - y = 2$

23. $3x = 4y$

24. $2x = 5y$

Determine whether the graphs of the two equations are parallel lines.

25. $y = -3x + 2$
$3x + 2y = 7$
not parallel

26. $x - y = 2$
$4x = 4y + 6$
parallel

27. $2x - 3y = 9$
$-4x + 6y = 12$
parallel

28. $2x = 4y - 7$
$2y = 6x + 1$
not parallel

Write the equation in slope-intercept form. Then state the slope and the y-intercept.

B **29.** $3y = 6x$
$y = 2x, m = 2, b = 0$

30. $2y = -x + 7$ $y = -\frac{1}{2}x + \frac{7}{2}, m = -\frac{1}{2}, b = \frac{7}{2}$

31. $3x - 5y = 15$ $y = \frac{3}{5}x - 3, m = \frac{3}{5}, b = -3$

32. $2x - 3y = 7$ $y = \frac{2}{3}x - \frac{7}{3}, m = \frac{2}{3}, b = -\frac{7}{3}$

33. $\frac{x}{2} = \frac{y}{5}$
$y = \frac{5}{2}x, m = \frac{5}{2}, b = 0$

34. $\frac{y}{2} - \frac{x}{3} = \frac{1}{4}$ $y = \frac{2}{3}x + \frac{1}{2}, m = \frac{2}{3}, b = \frac{1}{2}$

35. $2x + 3y = 4y$ $y = 2x, m = 2, b = 0$

36. $x + 4 = y - 1$ $y = x + 5, m = 1, b = 5$

Graph each equation using the slope and the y-intercept.
See Additional Answer section beginning p. 719.

37. $5x + 2y + 10 = 0$

38. $2y - 3x - 2 = 0$

39. $4x = 2y + 3$

40. $3x = 4y + 1$

41. $\frac{x}{2} + 6y = 15$

42. $2x - 3y = 2$

Find the value of a so that the graph of the equation has the given slope.

43. $y = 2ax + 4; m = -1$ $-\frac{1}{2}$

44. $3y = 2ax - 2; m = -2$ -3

19.

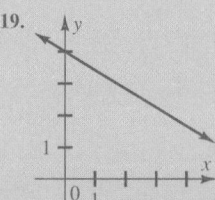

20.

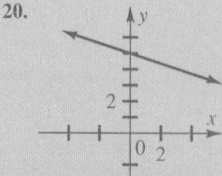

21.

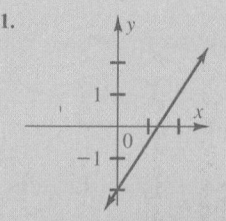

45. $ax + 2y = 3$; $m = 4$ −8

46. $y - 3ax = 5$; $m = \frac{1}{3}$ $\frac{1}{9}$

Two lines are perpendicular if the product of their slopes is -1. That is, $m_1 m_2 = -1$, where m_1 is the slope of one line and m_2 is the slope of the other line.

For each pair of equations, tell if the lines are parallel or perpendicular.

C **47.** $3x - 4y = 12$; $-6x + 8y = -4$ **48.** $2x + 3y = 8$; $4y - 3 = 6x$
  parallel   perpendicular
49. $ax + by = c$; $bx - ay = d$ **50.** $ax - by = c$; $-ax + by = d$
  perpendicular   parallel
51. Can two parallel lines have the same y-intercept? Explain.
  No; parallel lines do not intersect.
52. Can two perpendicular lines have the same y-intercept? Explain.
  Yes; perpendicular lines can intersect on the y-axis.

Applications

Computer   The following program prints a graph that enables you to estimate the temperature in either Fahrenheit or Celsius when the temperature is given in the other scale.

```
10 PRINT "FAHRENHEIT"
20 FOR C = 100 TO 0 STEP  - 5
30 F = (9 / 5) * C + 32:J = C / 5 + 2
40 IF F < 100 THEN J = J + 1
50 PRINT F; SPC( J);"* (";C;",";F;")"
60 NEXT C
70 PRINT  SPC( 5);"+5";
80 FOR I = 20 TO 100 STEP 20: PRINT "--";
90 PRINT : PRINT ; TAB( 10);"CELSIUS"
100 END
```

Use the graph to answer the following.

53. Write the equation of the line. $F = \frac{9}{5}C + 32$

54. What is the temperature Celsius if the temperature Fahrenheit is
  a. 75 24° **b.** 100 38° **c.** 207 97°

55. What is the temperature Fahrenheit if the temperature Celsius is
  a. 75 167° **b.** 100 212° **c.** 207 405°

EXTRA

The tip of the minute hand on Big Ben, the clock at the Houses of Parliament in London, England, travels 146 mi each year. Determine the number of times a year that the minute and the hour hands have the same slope when pointing in opposite directions. 8760

22.
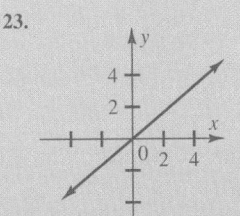

23.

24.
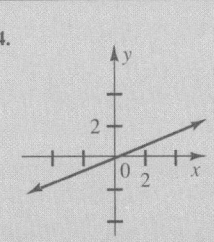

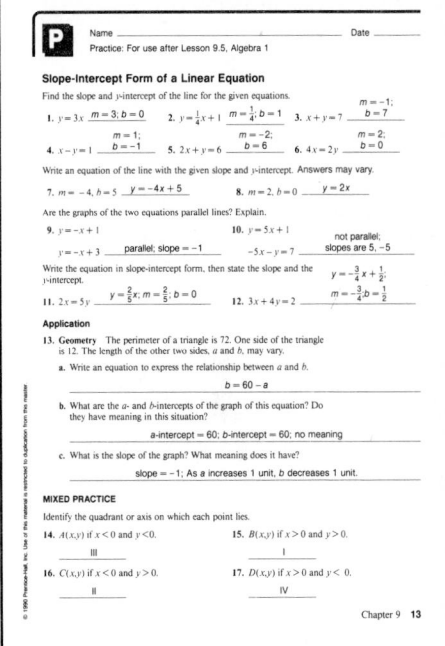
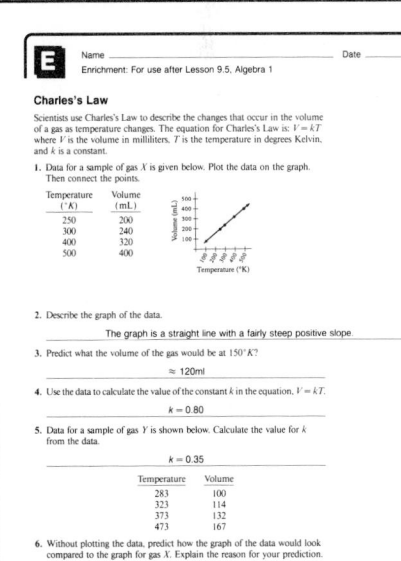

Materials/Manipulatives
Graph paper
Graphing calculator
Overhead projector
Straightedge
Teacher's Resource Book,
   Teaching Aids 10, 11, 12
   Transparencies 14, 15, 17, 18

BACKGROUND

In the Capsule Review, the students review finding slope, *y*-intercept, and *x*-intercept. In this lesson, students will use these concepts to determine equations of lines. You may wish to have students review graphing linear equations using a graphing calculator.

9.6

Equation of a Line

Objectives: To determine an equation of a line, given the slope of the line and the coordinates of one point
To determine an equation of a line, given the coordinates of two points of the line

You have been working with equations and graphs that show how two variables are related. If you have only a graph, you may be able to read enough information from the graph to write the related equation.

Capsule Review

Determine the following from the graph at the right. Use $m = \dfrac{y_2 - y_1}{x_2 - x_1}$.

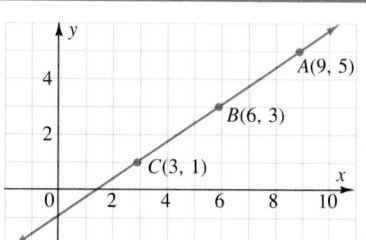

1. Slope, using A and B $\frac{2}{3}$
2. Slope, using B and C $\frac{2}{3}$
3. *y*-intercept -1 4. *x*-intercept $\frac{3}{2}$

When you can determine the *y*-intercept and the slope of a line from its graph, you can write an equation of the line.

EXAMPLE 1 **Write an equation of the given line.**

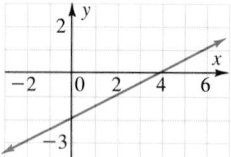

1. The line intersects the *y*-axis at the point whose coordinates are $(0, -2)$. The *y*-intercept is -2.

2. To find the slope, use two points whose coordinates you can determine, such as $(2, -1)$ and $(-2, -3)$.

$$m = \frac{y_2 - y_1}{x_2 - x_1} \qquad \underset{\underset{x_2\ \ y_2}{\uparrow\ \ \uparrow}}{(2,\ -1)} \quad \underset{\underset{x_1\ \ y_1}{\uparrow\ \ \uparrow}}{(-2,\ -3)}$$

$$= \frac{-1 - (-3)}{2 - (-2)} = \frac{2}{4} = \frac{1}{2} \qquad \text{The slope is } \frac{1}{2}.$$

3. Write the equation in slope-intercept form.

$$y = mx + b \qquad m = \frac{1}{2}; b = -2$$

$$y = \frac{1}{2}x + (-2), \text{ or } y = \frac{1}{2}x - 2$$

396   Chapter 9 Linear Equations

The linear equation in Example 1, $y = \frac{1}{2}x - 2$, can be placed in standard form. Recall that $Ax + By = C$ is the standard form of a linear equation if A, B, and C are integers and A and B are not both 0.

$$2y = x - 4 \qquad \textit{Multiply each side by 2. Subtract x from each side.}$$
$$-x + 2y = -4 \longleftarrow \textit{Standard form of the equation}$$

You can also write an equation of a line when you know only the slope and the coordinates of any point of the line.

EXAMPLE 2 **Write an equation of a line in standard form that has a slope of $\frac{2}{3}$ and contains the point $P(3, 6)$.**

1. Write the equation in slope-intercept form.

$$y = \frac{2}{3}x + b \qquad m = \frac{2}{3}$$

$$6 = \frac{2}{3}(3) + b \qquad \textit{Substitute 6 for y and 3 for x.}$$

$$6 = 2 + b$$
$$4 = b \qquad \textit{Solve for b.}$$

$$y = \frac{2}{3}x + 4 \qquad \textit{Slope-intercept form}$$

2. Change the equation to standard form.

$$y = \frac{2}{3}x + 4$$

$$3y = 2x + 12$$

$$-2x + 3y = 12$$

So, the standard form of the equation is $-2x + 3y = 12$.

An equation of a line can be determined when the coordinates of two points of the line are given.

EXAMPLE 3 **Write an equation of a line that contains points $A(-3, -2)$ and $B(5, 2)$.**

1. Find the slope of the line through the two points.

$$m = \frac{y_2 - y_1}{x_2 - x_1} \qquad \underset{\underset{x_1 \quad y_1}{\uparrow \quad \uparrow}}{A(-3, -2)} \quad \underset{\underset{x_2 \quad y_2}{\uparrow \quad \uparrow}}{B(5, 2)}$$

$$= \frac{2 - (-2)}{5 - (-3)} = \frac{4}{8}, \text{ or } \frac{1}{2}$$

The slope is $\frac{1}{2}$.

2. Write in slope-intercept form.

$$y = \frac{1}{2}x + b \qquad \textit{Substitute the coordinates of either point for x and y and solve for b.}$$

$$2 = \frac{1}{2}(5) + b$$

$$-\frac{1}{2} = b$$

$$y = \frac{1}{2}x - \frac{1}{2} \qquad \textit{Substitute } \frac{1}{2} \textit{ for m and } -\frac{1}{2} \textit{ for b.}$$

So the slope-intercept form of the equation is $y = \frac{1}{2}x - \frac{1}{2}$.

9.6 Equation of a Line **397**

TEACHING SUGGESTIONS

- Stress that an equation for a line can be found in more than one way.
- Point out that students should first write the slope-intercept form of an equation with all the known information.
- In Example 3, the standard form of the equation is $-x + 2y = -1$. Note that $x - 2y = 1$ is also considered to be in standard form by applying the property of -1 for multiplication.
- For Example 4, stress that parallel lines have equal slopes. The standard form of the equation is $-2x + y = -4$.
- Use Teaching Aids 10, 11, 12 and Transparencies 14, 15, 17, 18, in the *Teacher's Resource Book*, to illustrate the examples.

Critical Thinking

Causal Explanation In Example 3, the coordinates of point B were substituted into the equation $y = \frac{1}{2}x + b$ to find the y-intercept. Could point A have been used instead? Since the slope of the line through points A and B is $\frac{1}{2}$, the coordinates of any point on the line $y = \frac{1}{2}x + b$ may be substituted. Students can verify this by substituting $A(-3, -2)$ in $y = \frac{1}{2}x + b$ and simplifying.

CHALKBOARD EXAMPLES

- **For Example 1**
  1. Write an equation of the given line. $y = -\frac{1}{2}x - 3$

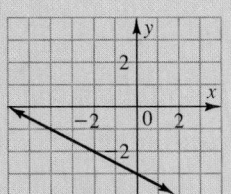

Write an equation of a line in standard form that has the given slope and contains the given point.

2. $m = \frac{3}{4}$; $P(2, 4)$
   $-3x + 4y = 10$

3. $m = -\frac{1}{2}$; $P(0, 3)$ $x + 2y = 6$

- **For Example 3**

Write an equation of a line that contains the given points.

4. $A(1, 7)$ and $B(-3, 4)$
   $y = \frac{3}{4}x + \frac{25}{4}$

5. $C(-3, -2)$ and $D(2, -6)$
   $y = -\frac{4}{5}x - \frac{22}{5}$

- **For Example 4**

Write an equation of a line that is parallel to the given line and contains the given point.

6. $y = 3x + 1$ and $P(2, -1)$
   $y = 3x - 7$

7. $x + 2y = 4$ and $P(-1, 2)$
   $y = -\frac{1}{2}x + \frac{3}{2}$

Common Error

- Students often try to memorize the steps necessary for finding an equation of a line for the different cases, and confuse the methods. Encourage these students to write the slope-intercept form of an equation $y = mx + b$ with all the known information. Then, students should determine what is to be found and in what order. Students should be encouraged to use reasoning skills rather than memorization.
- See *Teacher's Resource Book* for additional remediation.

EXAMPLE 4   Write an equation of a line that is parallel to the graph of $y = 2x - 1$ and contains $P(1, -2)$.

If lines are parallel, their slopes are equal. The slope of the graph of $y = 2x - 1$ is 2. The slopes of the two lines must be equal.

$$
\begin{array}{ll}
y = mx + b & \text{Slope-intercept form} \\
y = 2x + b & \text{It is known that } m = 2. \\
-2 = 2(1) + b & \text{Substitute the coordinates } (1, -2) \text{ for } x \text{ and } y. \\
-4 = b & \text{Solve for } b.
\end{array}
$$

So, the equation is $y = 2x - 4$.

CLASS EXERCISES

Refer to the graph at the right. Give an equation in slope-intercept form for each.

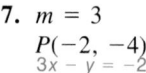

1. $\overleftrightarrow{AB}$ $y = \frac{1}{3}x + 1$ 2. $\overleftrightarrow{CD}$ $y = -2x - 2$

Give each linear equation in standard form.

3. $y = 3x - 1$
   $-3x + y = -1$

4. $y = \frac{1}{4}x + \frac{3}{8}$
   $-2x + 8y = 3$

5. $x = \frac{2}{3}y$
   $3x - 2y = 0$

6. $\frac{x}{4} + \frac{y}{3} = 8$
   $3x + 4y = 96$

Write an equation of a line in standard form given the slope and a point.

7. $m = 3$
   $P(-2, -4)$
   $3x - y = -2$

8. $m = 1$
   $R(-4, -1)$
   $x - y = -3$

9. $m = \frac{3}{4}$
   $T(1, 1)$
   $-3x + 4y = 1$

10. $m = -\frac{1}{2}$
    $V(0, 3)$
    $x + 2y = 6$

11. Write an equation in standard form of a line through $P(-3, 8)$ and $Q(-1, 12)$.
    $-2x + y = 14$

12. Write an equation in standard form of a line that is parallel to the graph of $y - 2x = 4$ and contains the point $P(2, -2)$. $-2x + y = -6$

PRACTICE EXERCISES

A   Use two points whose coordinates you can determine from the graph to find the slope. Then write an equation in slope-intercept form.

1. The line intersects the y-axis at the point $(0, -3)$. The y-intercept is -3.
   $y = \frac{3}{2}x - 3$

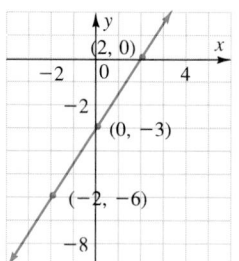

2. The line intersects the y-axis at the point (0, 4). The y-intercept is 4. $y = \frac{1}{2}x + 4$

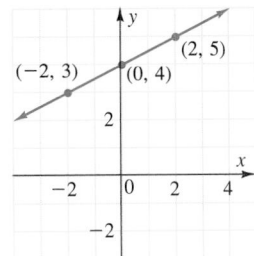

Write an equation of a line in standard form given the slope and a point.

3. $m = \frac{1}{2}$
$R(0, 0)$
$-x + 2y = 0$

4. $m = \frac{3}{2}$
$C(2, 6)$
$-3x + 2y = 6$

5. $m = -2$
$B(-1, 1)$
$2x + y = -1$

6. $m = -3$
$A(-1, 5)$
$3x + y = 2$

7. $m = -\frac{5}{4}$
$P(4, -3)$
$5x + 4y = 8$

8. $m = -\frac{1}{5}$
$Q(6, 1)$
$x + 5y = 11$

9. $m = \frac{7}{3}$
$S\left(0, -\frac{1}{6}\right)$
$-14x + 6y = -1$

10. $m = \frac{5}{2}$
$T\left(3, -\frac{1}{4}\right)$
$-10x + 4y = -31$

Write an equation in slope-intercept form that contains the given points.

11. $A(-1, -7)$
$B(2, 8)$
$y = 5x - 2$

12. $U(-2, -9)$
$V(1, 8)$ $y = \frac{17}{3}x + \frac{7}{3}$

13. $R(5, 6)$
$S(6, 9)$
$y = 3x - 9$

14. $X(3, 1)$
$Y(4, 8)$
$y = 7x - 20$

15. $T(1, 5)$
$R(-1, 11)$
$y = -3x + 8$

16. $C(2, 0)$
$D(-2, 8)$
$y = -2x + 4$

17. $L(3, 3)$
$M(-6, 9)$
$y = -\frac{2}{3}x + 5$

18. $E(7, 2)$
$F(-2, 2)$
$y = 2$

Write an equation of a line in standard form with the given characteristics.

19. The line is parallel to the graph of $y = 3x - 2$ and contains $P(2, -3)$.
$-3x + y = -9$

20. The line is parallel to the graph of $y = 3x - 5$ and contains $S(1, -4)$.
$-3x + y = -7$

B **21.** The line is parallel to the graph of $2x + 5y = 3$ and the x-intercept is -2.
$2x + 5y = -4$

22. The y-intercept of the line is $-\frac{1}{2}$, and it is parallel to the graph of $-3x + y - 4 = 0$. $-6x + 2y = -1$

Write an equation of a line in standard form that contains the given points.

23. $A(-2, -12)$
$C(5, 2)$
$-2x + y = -8$

24. $M(-6, 8)$
$N(-9, 16)$
$8x + 3y = -24$

25. $G(2, -7)$
$H(-1, -10)$
$-x + y = -9$

26. $J(5, -1)$
$K(-1, 8)$
$3x + 2y = 13$

27. $L\left(\frac{1}{2}, 0\right)$
$M\left(3, 2\frac{1}{2}\right)$
$-2x + 2y = -1$

28. $N\left(\frac{1}{3}, 1\right)$
$P\left(2\frac{2}{3}, 5\right)$
$-12x + 7y = 3$

29. $Q\left(-1\frac{1}{2}, 2\right)$
$R\left(1\frac{1}{2}, 4\right)$
$-2x + 3y = 9$

30. $S\left(-1, 1\frac{1}{2}\right)$
$T(0, 3)$
$-3x + 2y = 6$

9.6 Equation of a Line **399**

LESSON FOLLOW-UP

Assignment Guide
- See p. 368B for assignments.
- For Exercises 31–34, have students discuss their methods.

Critical Thinking
Have students answer the questions independently before discussing this activity with the class.

See *Teacher's Resource Book*, for Critical Thinking Activity, p. 9.

Lesson Quiz
1. Use the graph to determine the equation of the line. $-2x + 3y = -3$

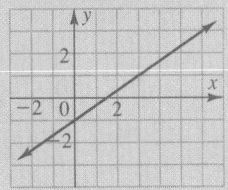

2. Write an equation of a line in standard form that has a slope of $-\frac{1}{2}$ and contains the point $P(-2, 3)$.
$x + 2y = 4$
3. Write an equation of a line in standard form that contains the points $C(-1, -3)$ and $D(4, 2)$.
$-x + y = -2$
4. Write an equation of a line in standard form that is parallel to the graph of $y = -3x + 2$ and contains $(-1, -2)$. $3x + y = -5$

Enrichment
If $0°C = 32°F$ and $100°C = 212°F$, write an equation in slope-intercept form expressing degrees Fahrenheit in terms of degrees Celsius.
$F = \frac{9}{5}C + 32$

399

P Name _____ Date _____
Practice: For use after Lesson 9.6, Algebra 1

Equation of a Line

Use the graph to determine an equation of each line. Answers may vary.

1. $\overleftrightarrow{AB}$ $y = -\frac{3}{2}x + 3$ 2. $\overleftrightarrow{CD}$ $y = -2x - 4$
3. $\overleftrightarrow{EF}$ $y = \frac{1}{3}x - \frac{10}{3}$ 4. $\overleftrightarrow{GH}$ $y = \frac{5}{6}x + \frac{4}{3}$

Write an equation in standard form of a line that has the given slope and contains the given point.

5. $m = 2$; $J(1,3)$ 6. $m = \frac{1}{2}$; $K(-4,-3)$
   $2x - y = -1$ $x - 2y = 2$

Write an equation in standard form of a line that contains the given points.

7. $L(2,5)$; $M(3,1)$ 8. $N(2,0)$; $P(0,3)$ 9. $Q(5,-2)$; $R(3,-4)$
   $4x + y = 13$ $3x + 2y = 6$ $x - y = 7$

Write an equation in standard form of a line with the given characteristics.

10. The line is parallel to the graph of $2x - y = 7$ and contains the point $S(3,4)$. $2x - y = 2$
11. The line is parallel to the graph of $4x + y = 2$ and has a y-intercept of -4. $4x + y = -4$

Application

12. **Meteorology** The relationship between degrees Celsius and degrees Fahrenheit can be stated by a linear equation. Determine that equation if 100°C corresponds to 212°F and 0°C corresponds to 32°F. (C will take the place of x and F will take the place of y.)
   $F = \frac{9}{5}C + 32$

MIXED PRACTICE

Name the ordinate in each ordered pair.

13. $(3,2)$ 2   14. $(5,-3)$ −3   15. (x,y) y

Name the abscissa in each ordered pair.

16. $(4,1)$ 4   17. $(6,2)$ 6   18. (a,b) a

16   Chapter 9

E Name _____ Date _____
Enrichment: For use after Lesson 9.6, Algebra 1

Displacement and Velocity

The motion of an object can be described in terms of displacement and velocity. Displacement is the change in position of an object relative to its starting point. Velocity is the change in position per unit of time. The relationship between displacement and velocity can be illustrated by making a distance-time graph.

1. The data chart below records the motion of swimmer A during the first minute of a race. Plot the data on the graph, then connect the points.

Time(s)	Distance(m)
0	0
10	20
20	40
30	60
40	80
50	100
60	120

2. Describe the graph of the data.
   Graph is a straight line.

3. The velocity of an object can be calculated by using the formula velocity = $\frac{distance}{time}$. Use this equation to calculate the velocity of swimmer A for each 10-second interval.
   Velocity for each interval = 2 m/s

4. Determine the slope of the line of the distance-time graph for swimmer A.
   Slope = 2

5. How does the slope of the line compare with your answer to Exercise 3?
   The slope is equal to the velocity.

6. The graph records the motion of swimmer B during the first minute of the same race. Compare the velocity of swimmer A with that of swimmer B. Explain.
   The slope of the graph for swimmer A is twice that of swimmer B. The steeper the slope the greater the velocity.

Chapter 9   17

Write an equation of a line in standard form with the given characteristics.

31. The line has a y-intercept of 3 and an x-intercept of -5. $-3x + 5y = 15$

32. The line passes through $B(-3, 7)$ and is parallel to the line through $C(1, 4)$ and $D(2, 6)$. $-2x + y = 13$

C   33. The line passes through $N(2, -5)$ and is perpendicular to the graph of $y + 3x - 8 = 0$. $-x + 3y = -17$

34. The line passes through $P(c, 4c)$ and is perpendicular to the graph of $3y + 4x = 6$. $-3x + 4y = 13c$

Write an equation of a line in slope-intercept form given the slope and a point.

35. $m = 2g$; $T(2, 7)$
   $y = 2gx + 7 - 4g$

36. $m = -5$; $U(0, -3k)$
   $y = -5x - 3k$

37. $m = \frac{1}{n}$; $V(-2, 1)$
   $y = \frac{1}{n}x + \frac{2}{n} + 1$

Applications

38. **Chemistry** The solubility s, in $\frac{g}{100}$ cm^3 of water, of sodium chlorate is 100 at 20°C and 170 at 70°C. Assuming that s and the temperature t are related through a linear equation, determine this equation. (*Hint:* s will take the place of y, and t will take the place of x in the equation $y = mx + b$.) $s = \frac{7}{5}t + 72$

CRITICAL THINKING: Predicting Consequences

Predicting results or consequences is a critical thinking skill that helps you draw conclusions about the probable effects of some event. Sometimes called "making an educated guess," it involves linking what you *know* with what you *think* will happen. Using information, data, or facts that are readily available, you can predict a logical result if the trend suggested by the information is maintained.

The slope of a line is an indicator of its relative position. If you know the slope of a line, you know something about the line. In this lesson you are given two indicators that can be used to predict whether a line rises or falls moving from left to right. What are they?
Slope is positive, the line slants up. Slope is negative, the line slants down.

You can predict how steep a line is by knowing its slope. As the slope of a line gets closer to zero, what happens to the line? As the slope increases from 0, what happens to the line? Make a general statement that helps you predict the steepness of a line. Slope of a line closer to zero, the line gets flatter. Slope increases, the line gets steeper. The greater the positive slope, the steeper the line.

Linear Inequalities in Two Variables

Objective: To graph linear inequalities in two variables

If peanuts cost \$4 a pound and cashews cost \$8 a pound, how would you draw a graph to show the different combinations of nuts you could buy for \$24 or less?

To draw such a graph, you would need to graph a *linear inequality* in two variables. A **linear inequality** relates a linear expression with inequality signs.

Capsule Review

You can write an equation for the graph of a line when given certain characteristics of the line.

EXAMPLE What is the equation of this line?

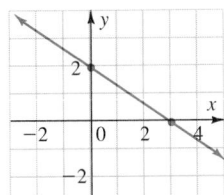

- Find the y-intercept, b. $b = 2$
- Find the slope, m. $m = -\frac{2}{3}$
- Write the equation. $y = mx + b$

$$y = -\frac{2}{3}x + 2$$
$$3y = -2x + 6$$
$$2x + 3y = 6$$

Write the equation of the line drawn.

1.

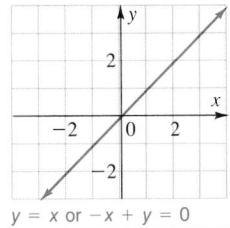

$y = x$ or $-x + y = 0$

2.

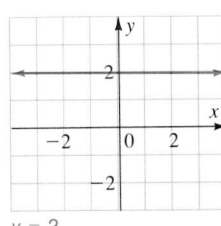

$y = 2$

3.

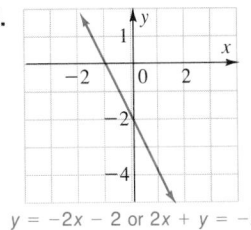

$y = -2x - 2$ or $2x + y = -2$

The graph of a linear equation separates the coordinate plane into three sets of points: points on the line, points above the line, and points below the line.

These regions are called **half-planes** and the line is called the **boundary** of each half-plane.

The graph of an inequality related to a linear equation includes all points (x, y) on one side of the line and sometimes the line as well.

9.7 Linear Inequalities in Two Variables **401**

- It is important for students to understand the methods of graphing presented in the previous lessons.
- Emphasize that the graphs of inequalities are shown by shading. An overhead projector can be useful in illustrating the shading of a graph in an open or closed half-plane. Teaching Aids 10–12 and Transparencies 14–20, in the *Teacher's Resource Book,* may be helpful to illustrate graphs of inequalities in two variables.

CHALKBOARD EXAMPLE

- **For Example 1**

  State which of the given points belong to the graph of the inequality.
  1. $y > x + 5$; $(0, 0)$, $(4, -3)$ (4, −3)
  2. $x < 5$; $(0, 4)$, $(7, 1)$ (0, 4)

- **For Example 2**

  Write the equation of the inequality whose graph is shown. Tell whether it is an open or closed half-plane.
  3.

  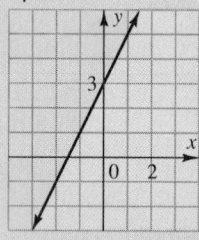

  $y \leq 2x + 3$; closed half-plane

  4.

  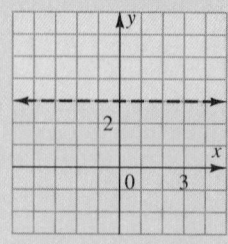

  $y > 3$; open half-plane

EXAMPLE 1   **State which of the given points belong to the graph of the inequality.**
   a. $y > x + 2$; $(-5, -1)$, $(0, 0)$ **b.** $x < 3$; $(-2, 4)$, $(3, 2)$

a. Try $(-5, -1)$.   Try $(0, 0)$.   **b.** Try $(-2, 4)$.   Try $(3, 2)$.

$y > x + 2$	$y > x + 2$	$x < 3$	$x < 3$
$-1 > -5 + 2$	$0 > 0 + 2$	$-2 < 3$	$3 < 3$
$-1 > -3$	$0 > 2$	Yes ✔	No
Yes ✔	No		

The graphs of inequalities are shown by shading. If the inequality uses $<$ or $>$, the boundary line is not part of the graph and is drawn as a dashed line. This is called an **open half-plane.** If the inequality uses $\leq$ or $\geq$, the boundary line is part of the graph and is drawn as a solid line. This is called a **closed half-plane.**

To graph a linear inequality in the two variables x and y when the coefficient of y is not zero:

- Write the given inequality as an equivalent inequality that has y alone on one side.
- Graph the related linear equation. Use a dashed line if the inequality involves $<$ or $>$. Use a solid line if the inequality involves $\leq$ or $\geq$.
- Test a point in each half-plane to see which satisfies the inequality.
- Shade the appropriate half-plane.

EXAMPLE 2   **Write the inequality whose graph is shown. Tell whether it is an open or closed half-plane.**

a.

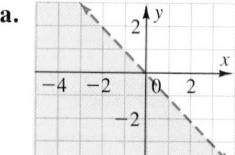

b.

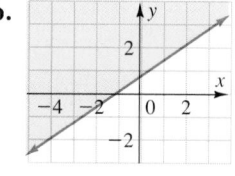

c.

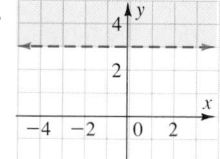

$y < -x$; open half-plane $y \geq \frac{2}{3}x + \frac{2}{3}$; closed half-plane $y > 3$; open half-plane

EXAMPLE 3   **Graph $y < 2x + 1$.**

- Draw the graph of $y = 2x + 1$ as a dashed line.
- Test a point in each half-plane.
  Try $(0, 0)$.   Try $(-1, 2)$.
  $0 < 2(0) + 1$ $2 < 2(-1) + 1$
  $0 < 1$ ✔ Yes $2 < -1$ No
- Shade the half-plane containing the point $(0, 0)$.

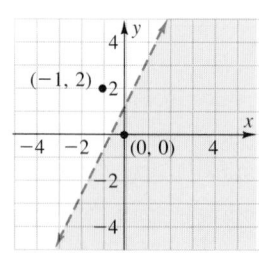

EXAMPLE 4   Graph $x \geq 2$.

- Draw the graph of $x = 2$ as a solid line.
- Test a point in each half-plane.
  Try $(0, 0)$.   Try $(3, 1)$.
  $0 \geq 2$ No $3 \geq 2$ ✔ Yes
- Shade the half-plane containing the point $(3, 1)$.

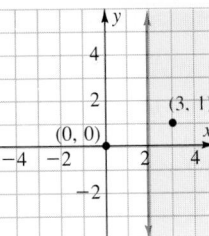

CLASS EXERCISES

State whether the given point belongs to the graph of the inequality.

1. $y > x + 1$; $(1, -1)$ no   **2.** $y \leq 2x + 4$; $(3, 2)$ yes   **3.** $y < 2x$; $(-3, -6)$ no

4. $y > 5$; $(6, -1)$ no   **5.** $x \geq -1$; $(-3, 0)$ no   **6.** $x \leq 0$; $(-1, 4)$ yes

Write the inequality whose graph is shown. Tell whether it is an open or closed half-plane.

7.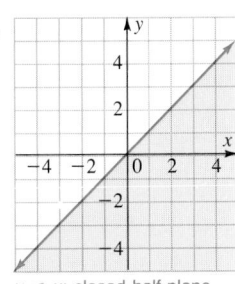

$y \leq x$; closed half-plane

8.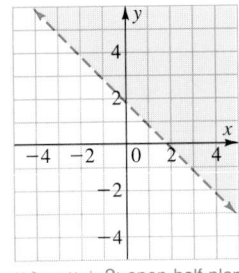

$y > -x + 2$; open half-plane

9.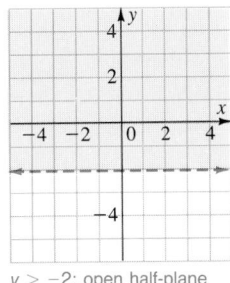

$y > -2$; open half-plane

PRACTICE EXERCISES

State which of the given points belong to the graph of the inequality.

A **1.** $y > x + 5$; $(3, 1)$, $(-6, 0)$ $(-6, 0)$ **2.** $y > x + 1$; $(3, 1)$, $(0, 2)$ $(0, 2)$

3. $y + 2 > x + 1$; $(0, 0)$, $(3, 5)$ **4.** $y + 3 \geq x + 4$; $(1, 2)$, $(3, 0)$ $(1, 2)$
$(0, 0)$, $(3, 5)$

Write the inequality whose graph is shown. Tell whether it is an open or closed half-plane.

5.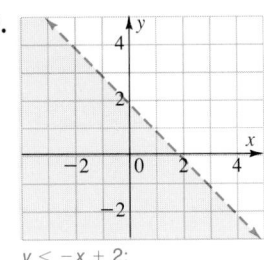

$y < -x + 2$;
open half-plane

6.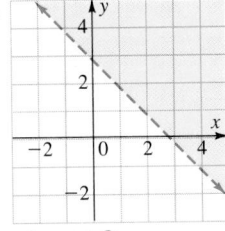

$y > -x + 3$;
open half-plane

7.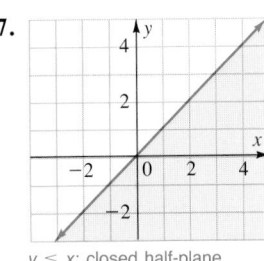

$y \leq x$; closed half-plane

9.7 Linear Inequalities in Two Variables   **403**

- **For Example 3**
  Graph.
  5. $y \geq x + 5$

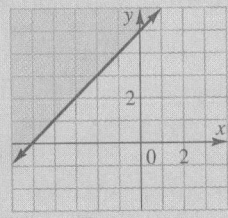

6. $y < x$

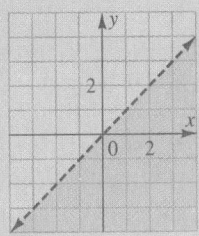

- **For Example 4**
  Graph.
  7. $x \geq 3$

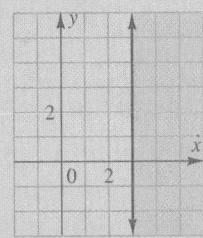

Common Error

- Students often become confused when shading graphs. They are puzzled as to which side of the line the graph should be shaded. Students who make this error should be encouraged to substitute points into the equation from each side of the line, to determine the direction of the shading.
- See *Teacher's Resource Book* for additional remediation.

403

Assignment Guide

- See p. 368B for assignments.
- See *Teacher's, Resource Book, Tests*, pp. 95–96.

Critical Thinking

Causal Explanation In Example 3, why is it necessary to test points in each half-plane?   Testing the points in each half-plane will help determine which part of the graph to shade.

Lesson Quiz

State which of the given points belong to the graph of the inequality.

1. $y > x + 3$; (0, 1), (4, 8)   (4, 8)

2. $y + 2 < x$; (0, 0), (4, 1)   (4, 1)

Graph.

3. $y \geq 1$

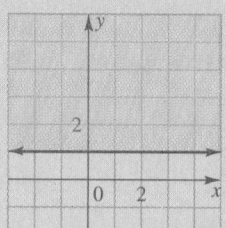

4. $y \leq 3x + 2$

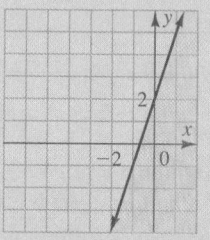

Write an equation of the inequality whose graph is shown.

5.

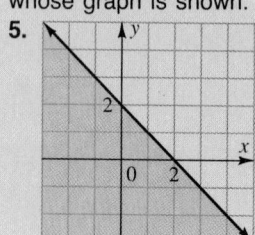

$y \leq -x + 2$

8.

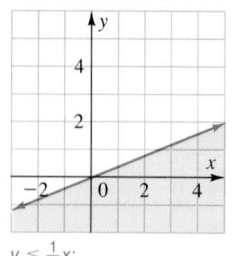

$y \leq \frac{1}{2}x$;
closed half-plane

9.

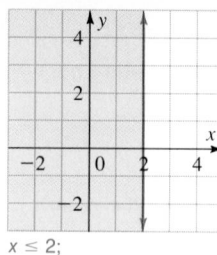

$x \leq 2$;
closed half-plane

10.

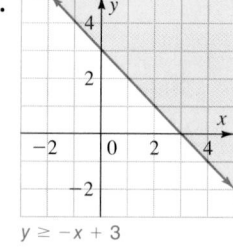

$y \leq 4$;
closed half-plane

Graph the inequality and test a point in each half-plane. Shade the half-plane containing the point.
See Additional Answer section beginning p. 719.

11. $y < 3x + 2$ **12.** $y < 4x + 1$ **13.** $y > x + 3$

14. $y > 2x + 1$ **15.** $x \geq 3$ **16.** $x \geq 5$

17. $y > 3x + 4$ **18.** $y > 2x + 5$ **19.** $y \geq 1$

20. $y \geq -4$ **21.** $y < 3x - 1$ **22.** $y < 2x - 3$

B   **23.** $y - 1 \leq x + 3$ **24.** $y - 4 \leq x + 5$ **25.** $y + 3 < x - 3$

26. $y + 2 < x - 1$ **27.** $y + 6 > 2x - 1$ **28.** $y + 3 > 3x - 4$

29. $y - 5 > 5x - 10$ **30.** $y - 3 > 4x - 9$ **31.** $y + 8 > x + 9$

Write the inequality whose graph is shown.

32.

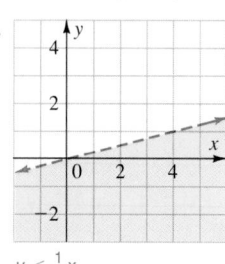

$y < \frac{1}{4}x$

33.

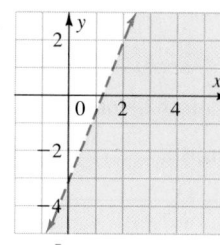

$y < \frac{5}{2}x - 3$

34.

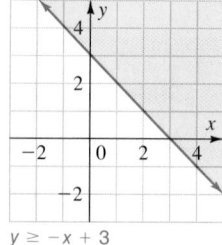

$y \geq -x + 3$

C   **35.**

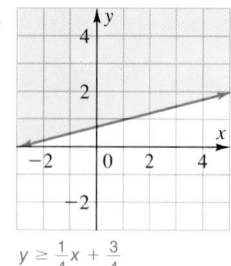

$y \geq \frac{1}{4}x + \frac{3}{4}$

36.

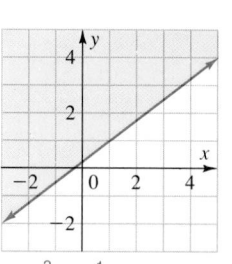

$y \geq \frac{3}{4}x + \frac{1}{4}$

37.

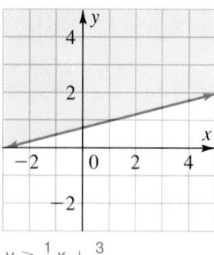

$y \geq 1$

Graph the inequality and tell whether it is an open or closed half-plane.
See Additional Answer section beginning p. 719.

38. $2y + 3 < \frac{1}{2}x + 5$ **39.** $3y + 4 < \frac{1}{3}x + 7$ **40.** $2y - 3 \geq \frac{1}{4}x + 4$

41. $4y - 1 \geq \frac{1}{8}x + 6$ **42.** $\frac{3}{5}y + 1 < \frac{1}{3}x + 2$ **43.** $\frac{2}{3}y + 2 < \frac{2}{5}x + 1$

Applications

Computer Computer programs are used in business to make decisions. A club that sells cookies or doughnuts decides to use the computer to help them decide what to sell. Use this program to help you decide.

```
10 PRINT   TAB( 15);"PROFIT MADE": PRINT
20 PRINT "DOZEN","COOKIES","DONUTS"
30 FOR I = 1 TO 12
40 C = 2.5 * I - 10
50 D = 4 * I - 25
60 PRINT I,C,D
70 NEXT I
80 END
```

44. Which product would you sell if the club members only volunteered to bring
   a. 2 dozen   **b.** 8 dozen   **c.** 10 dozen   **d.** 12 dozen
      cookies   cookies   either   donuts

45. Use the program to graph the two profit lines. Would you still answer Exercise 44a–d the same way? Why? Yes; answers may vary.

46. Nutrition Suppose that a person working at 21°C uses about 3000 calories per day, and for each 1°C increase in temperature this person uses 30 fewer calories. Find a linear equation to represent this data. Draw a graph to determine the theoretical temperature at which a person at work would need 0 calories. $y = -30x + 2370$; 79°C

TEST YOURSELF

Find the slope and the y-intercept of the line for the given equation. Then graph the equation.   9.5

1. $4x + y = 2$ $m = -4, b = 2$ **2.** $3x - 2y = 6$ $m = \frac{3}{2}, b = -3$

Write an equation in standard form of a line for each situation.   9.6

3. Slope m of line is -2, and the line contains $P(3, 2)$. $2x + y = 8$

4. Line contains the points $A(2, -1)$ and $B(3, -4)$. $3x + y = 5$

State which of the given points belong to the graph of the inequality. Graph each inequality. See Additional Answer section beginning p. 719.   9.7

5. $y > 2x + 3$; $(0, 3)$, $(1, 7)$ (1, 7)   **6.** $y < 3x - 2$; $(-1, -7)$, $(-2, 0)$ (-1, -7)

7. $y \leq x + 5$; $(0, 6)$, $(1, 3)$ (1, 3)   **8.** $y \geq \frac{1}{2}x - 4$; $(0, 4)$, $(2, -5)$ (0, 4)

9.7 Linear Inequalities in Two Variables   **405**

Teacher's Resource Book
Reteaching—Chapter 9, p. 18

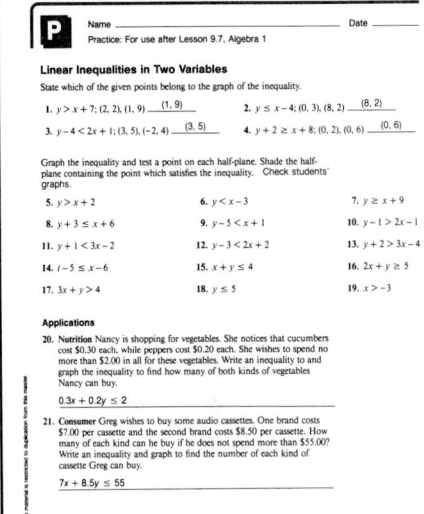

Name _____ **Date** _____
Practice: For use after Lesson 9.7, Algebra 1

Linear Inequalities in Two Variables
State which of the given points belong to the graph of the inequality.

1. $y > x + 7$; (2, 2), (1, 9) __(1, 9)__   2. $y \leq x - 4$; (0, 3), (8, 2) __(8, 2)__
3. $y - 4 < 2x + 1$; (3, 5), (-2, 4) __(3, 5)__   4. $y + 2 \geq x + 8$; (0, 2), (0, 6) __(0, 6)__

Graph the inequality and test a point on each half-plane. Shade the half-plane containing the point which satisfies the inequality. Check students' graphs.

5. $y > x + 2$ 6. $y < x - 3$ 7. $y \geq x + 9$
8. $y + 3 \leq x + 6$ 9. $y - 5 < x + 1$ 10. $y - 1 > 2x - 1$
11. $y + 1 < 3x - 2$ 12. $y - 3 < 2x + 2$ 13. $y + 2 > 3x - 4$
14. $1 - 5 \leq x - 6$ 15. $x + y \leq 4$ 16. $2x + y \geq 5$
17. $3x + y > 4$ 18. $y \leq 5$ 19. $x > -3$

Applications
20. **Nutrition** Nancy is shopping for vegetables. She notices that cucumbers cost $0.30 each, while peppers cost $0.20 each. She wishes to spend no more than $2.00 in all for these vegetables. Write an inequality and graph the inequality to find how many of both kinds of vegetables Nancy can buy.
   $0.3x + 0.2y \leq 2$

21. **Consumer** Greg wishes to buy some audio cassettes. One brand costs $7.00 per cassette and the second brand costs $8.50 per cassette. How many of each kind can he buy if he does not spend more than $55.00? Write an inequality and graph to find the number of each kind of cassette Greg can buy.
   $7x + 8.5y \leq 55$

Chapter 9   **19**

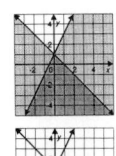

Name _____ **Date** _____
Enrichment: For use after Lesson 9.7, Algebra 1

Graphing Inequalities and Intersection
The intersection between two or more linear inequalities is called the **feasible set**. This region includes all the points (x, y) which would satisfy each individual inequality. This region is found by examining the area where both graphs of the linear inequalities overlap.

Use the intersection between the inequalities to find the feasible set for
$\begin{cases} y \leq 2x + 1 \\ y \leq -x + 1 \end{cases}$
The feasible set is the region shaded by both graphs.

This region can best be shown by only including the area where both graphs intersect. This region includes all those points (x, y) which satisfy both inequalities.

Graph the inequalities and find the feasible set. Check students' graphs.

1. $\begin{cases} y \geq x + 1 \\ y \geq 2x - 1 \end{cases}$ 2. $\begin{cases} y \leq x - 4 \\ y \leq -x - 4 \end{cases}$ 3. $\begin{cases} y \geq 2x + 4 \\ y \geq 0 \end{cases}$
4. $\begin{cases} y \geq x + 1 \\ x \geq 0 \end{cases}$ 5. $\begin{cases} y \geq -x + 3 \\ y \geq -x + 5 \\ x \geq 1 \end{cases}$ 6. $\begin{cases} y \leq -x + 2 \\ y \leq -x + 3 \\ y \geq 0 \end{cases}$

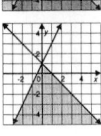

20   Chapter 9

Additional Answers

1–4.

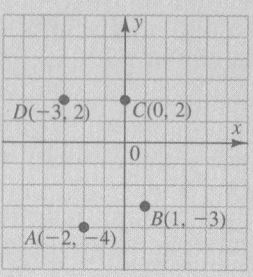

7.

x	y
0	1
2	0
-2	2

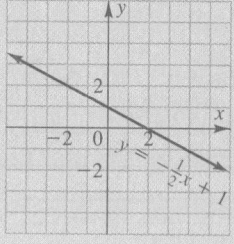

8.

x	y
0	-4
2	0
3	1

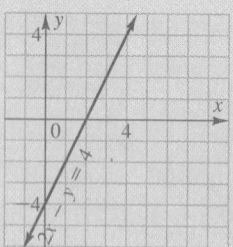

406

Vocabulary

abscissa (371)	origin (370)
boundary (401)	parallel (393)
closed half-plane (402)	quadrant (370)
collinear points (386)	slope (384)
coordinate system (370)	slope-intercept form (391)
half-plane (401)	standard form (375)
linear equation (375)	*x*-axis (370)
linear inequality (401)	*x*-intercept (376)
open half-plane (402)	*y*-axis (370)
ordinate (371)	*y*-intercept (376)

Graphing Ordered Pairs   To graph an ordered pair of numbers in the coordinate plane, move left or right from the origin for the abscissa, or *x*-coordinate, and then up or down for the ordinate, or *y*-coordinate.   9.1

Graph the points in a coordinate plane. See side column.

1. $A(-2, -4)$ **2.** $B(1, -3)$ **3.** $C(0, 2)$ **4.** $D(-3, 2)$

Finding Solutions   To determine if an ordered pair (x, y) is a solution of an equation in two variables, substitute the *x*- and *y*-coordinates in the equation to see if they produce a true sentence.

Determine which of the ordered pairs listed are solutions of the equation.

5. $2x + y = 7$; (2, 3), (4, 2) (2, 3)   **6.** $-x - y = -3$; (-3, 0), (3, 0) (3, 0)

Graphing Linear Equations   Linear equations are equations that can be written in the form $Ax + By = C$ where A, B, and C are real numbers and A and B are not both 0. If A, B, and C are integers, the equation is said to be in **standard form.** You can use several methods to graph a linear equation.   9.2

1. From a table of *x*- and *y*-values, graph at least three ordered pairs.

2. Plot points for the *x*- and *y*-intercepts. To find the *x*-intercept, let $y = 0$ and solve for *x*. To find the *y*-intercept, let $x = 0$ and solve for *y*.

Make a solution table. Then graph the equation. See side column.

7. $y = -\frac{1}{2}x + 1$ **8.** $2x - y = 4$ **9.** $3x + 2y = 6$ **10.** $x = -6$

9.

x	y
0	-3
2	0
-2	-6

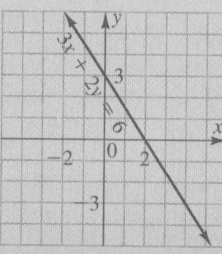

10.

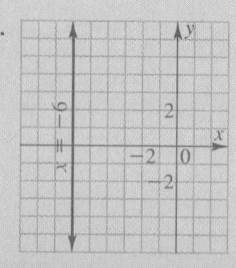

Estimating from Graphs When the data in a problem can be graphed, the graph can be used to estimate solutions to the problem.

9.3

The Fahrenheit temperature is approximately equal to the number of times a cricket chirps in 15 seconds, t, plus 39. Use this for Exercises 11–12.

11. Make a table of ordered pairs for $F = t + 39$ and graph the function.

12. If the outdoor temperature is 95°F, how many cricket chirps would you expect to hear in 15 s? 56

Slope of a Line The formula is $m = \dfrac{y_2 - y_1}{x_2 - x_1}$, where $P(x_1, y_1)$ and $Q(x_2, y_2)$ are any two points of a line and $x_2 - x_1 \neq 0$.

9.4

Find the slope of a line that contains the given points.

13. $A(-1, 5); B(1, 6)$ $\frac{1}{2}$

14. $C(-2, -4); D(1, -2)$ $\frac{2}{3}$

Through the given point, draw a line with the given slope. See side column.

15. $m = \frac{1}{4}; C(2, -2)$

16. $m = -\frac{2}{3}; D(0, 1)$

Slope-Intercept Form of a Linear Equation The slope-intercept form of an equation is $y = mx + b$, where m is the slope and b is the y-intercept.

9.5

Find the slope and the y-intercept. Then graph the equation. See side column.

17. $y = \frac{1}{2}x - 4$ 18. $y = -\frac{3}{4}x + 3$ 19. $x + 2y = 6$ 20. $3x - 5y = 15$

$m = \frac{1}{2}, b = -4$ $m = -\frac{3}{4}, b = 3$ $m = -\frac{1}{2}, b = 3$ $m = \frac{3}{5}, b = -3$

Determine whether the graphs of the two equations are parallel lines.

21. $5x - y = 1; 5x + y = 7$
not parallel

22. $2x + 3y = 2; 4x + 6y = -4$
parallel

Equation of a Line An equation can be written using the slope of the line and the coordinates of one point, or the coordinates of two points.

9.6

Write an equation in standard form.

23. The line has a slope of $\frac{2}{3}$ and contains the point $A(0, -4)$. $-2x + 3y = -12$

24. The line contains the points $P(-1, 4)$ and $Q(-4, -2)$. $-2x + y = 6$

Linear Inequalities in Two Variables The solution set of a linear inequality in two variables is an open or closed half-plane.

9.7

Graph each inequality. See Additional Answers beginning p. 719.

25. $y > x + 1$

26. $x \geq 3$

27. $y + 2x \leq 2$

15.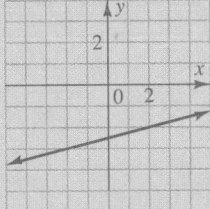

16.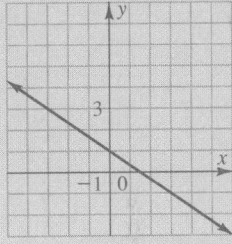

17.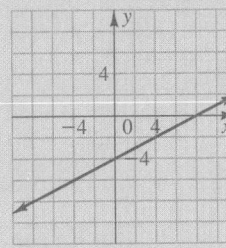

18.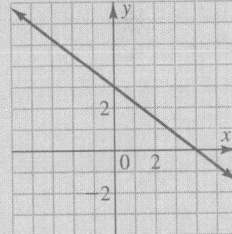

19.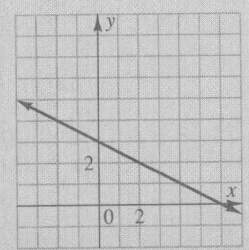

20.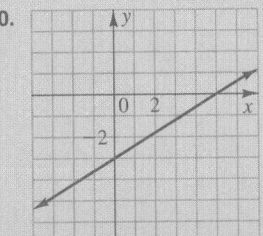

See *Teacher's Resource Book.*
- *Tests*, pp. 97–100
- *Calculator Test*, pp. 17–18

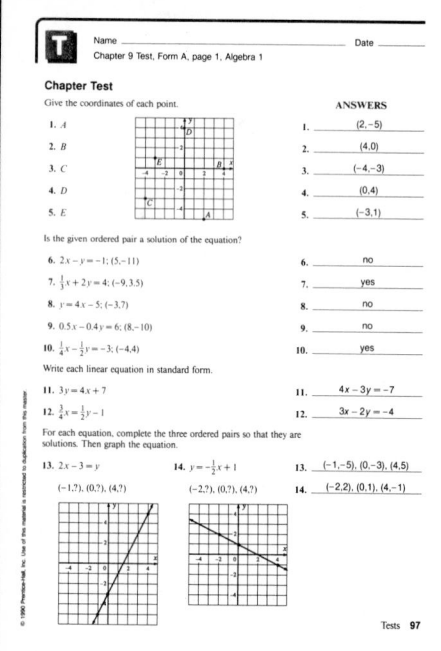

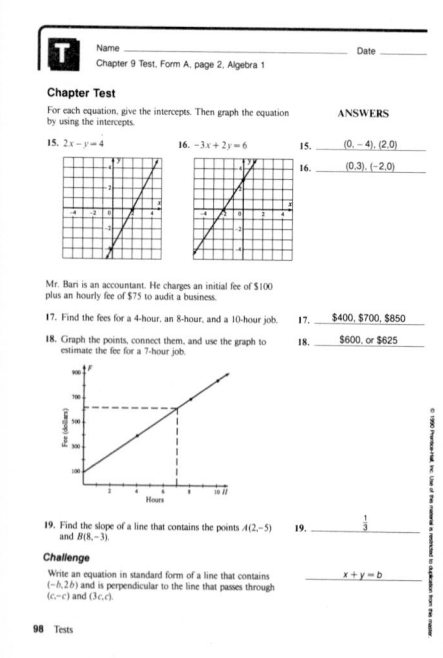

Graph the ordered pairs in a coordinate plane. See below.

1. $(2, -1)$ 2. $(1, -2)$ 3. $(5, -6)$ 4. $(-1, -4)$

5. $(0, 2)$ 6. $(3, 0)$ 7. $(-3, 0)$ 8. $(-5, 4)$

Determine which ordered pairs listed are solutions of the equation.

9. $x - 3y = 6$
   $(3, -1), (6, -1)$ (3, −1)

10. $y = \frac{1}{2}x - 4$
    $(-2, -5), (1, -3)$ (−2, −5)

Make a solution table. Then graph the equation. See below.

11. $y = 2x - 1$ 12. $y = -\frac{1}{3}x$

Use the slope and the intercepts to graph. See p. 409.

13. $3x - y = 9$ 14. $2y = 4x - 8$

15. The formula used to convert temperature from a Fahrenheit (F) scale to a Celsius (C) scale is $C = \frac{5}{9}(F - 32)$. Make a graph of the given equation using points for 32°F, −4°F, and 5°F. Use the graph to estimate the Celsius temperature corresponding to 50°F. 10°C

16. Find the slope of a line that contains the points $C(8, -3)$ and $D(4, 1)$. −1

17. Through the point $Q(0, 3)$, draw the graph of a line having a slope of 5.
Check students' graphs.

18. Write $3x + 2y = 1$ in slope-intercept form. Then graph the equation. $y = -\frac{3}{2}x + \frac{1}{2}$

19. Determine if the graphs of $y = 4x - 1$ and $16x - 4y = 12$ are parallel. parallel

20. Write an equation in standard form of a line that has slope $\frac{1}{4}$ and contains the point $C(-1, -2)$. −x + 4y = −7

21. Write an equation in standard form of a line that contains $A(-5, 6)$ and $B(1, 2)$. 2x + 3y = 8

Graph each inequality. See p. 409.

22. $y < x - 1$ 23. $y - \frac{1}{2}x \geq 1$

Challenge

Write an equation in standard form of a line that contains the point $M(a, 3a)$ and is perpendicular to the graph of $4y + 3x = 6$. −4x + 3y = 5a

408   Chapter 9 Linear Equations

Additional Answers

1–4.

5–8.

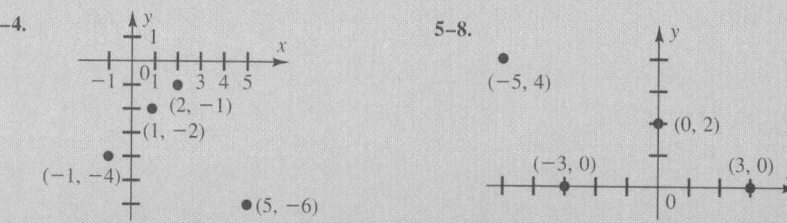

Select the best choice for each question.

1. An equation of a line through
A $P(3, 1)$ with slope of 2 is:
   A. $y = 2x - 5$ **B.** $y = 2x + 5$
   C. $y = x + 2$ **D.** $y = 2x + 1$
   E. $y = x - 2$

2. A driver gets an average of 28 mi/
B gal of gas with her car. How many
   gallons would be used on a trip of
   518 mi?
   A. 18 gal   **B.** 18.5 gal **C.** 19 gal
   D. 19.5 gal **E.** 20 gal

3. Find the value of $|3x - 2y + 4|$
D when $x = -5$ and $y = 3$.
   A. -25 **B.** 5 **C.** 13 **D.** 17 **E.** 25

4. $\dfrac{1}{x} + \dfrac{3}{2x} - \dfrac{4}{3x} =$
C
   A. 0   **B.** $\dfrac{7}{6}$ **C.** $\dfrac{7}{6x}$
   D. $\dfrac{7}{6x^2}$ **E.** $\dfrac{7}{6x^3}$

5. Find the slope of a line which
B passes through the points $P(-3, 2)$
   and $Q(1, 5)$.
   A. $-\dfrac{3}{4}$ **B.** $\dfrac{3}{4}$
   C. $-\dfrac{9}{2}$ **D.** $\dfrac{4}{3}$
   E. $-\dfrac{4}{3}$

6. Find the product of
E $(2x - 3)(3x + 2)$
   A. $6x^2 - 6$
   B. $6x^2 + 4x - 6$
   C. $6x^2 + 5x - 6$
   D. $6x^2 - 4x - 6$
   E. $6x^2 - 5x - 6$

7. An artist bought 4 tubes of paint
D for $11.95 a tube, and 3 brushes,
   one for $8.50 and the other 2 for
   $6.75 each. What was the total
   amount spent for these supplies?
   A. $68.50 **B.** $68.80 **C.** $69.50
   D. $69.80 **E.** $70.80

8. Solve for x when $\dfrac{3}{x} + \dfrac{2}{x} = \dfrac{5}{2}$
D
   A. $\dfrac{1}{2}$ **B.** 1 **C.** $1\dfrac{1}{2}$ **D.** 2 **E.** $2\dfrac{1}{2}$

9. Find the value of $\left(\dfrac{3x^2y}{2ab}\right)\left(\dfrac{4ab^2}{6xy^2}\right)$
A
   when $a = 1$, $b = -2$, $x = 3$, and
   $y = 2$.
   A. -3 **B.** -1 **C.** 1 **D.** 2 **E.** 3

10. Which of the following represents a
E   point on a line for the equation
    $2x - 3y = 8$?
    I. $A(7, 2)$
    II. $B(3, -1)$
    III. $C(-2, -4)$
    A. I only   **B.** II only
    C. III only   **D.** I, II only
    E. I, III only

11. A homeowners' loan of $4000 for a
E   new roof requires that $4500 be
    paid back by the end of one year.
    Find the annual rate of simple
    interest on the loan.
    A. 1.11%   **B.** 1.25%   **C.** 10%
    D. 11.1%   **E.** 12.5%

12. If x is 30% of y and y is 20% of z,
B   then x is what percent of z?
    A. 5 **B.** 6 **C.** 10 **D.** 50 **E.** 60

The individual comments provided about some problems can be helpful in guiding students to solve these problems.
9. Students should simplify first and then substitute the assigned values.
10. The concept that an ordered pair which satisfies an equation represents a point on a graph is an important one and should be reinforced.

See *Teacher's Resource Book,* for Preparing for Standardized Tests.

Additional Answers (cont.)

11.
x	y
0	-1
1	1
-1	-3

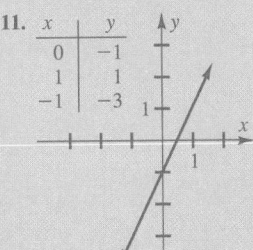

12.
x	y
0	0
3	-1
-3	1

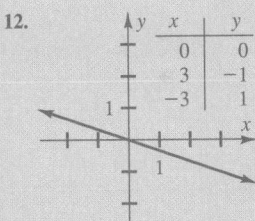

13.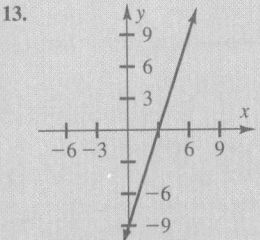

14.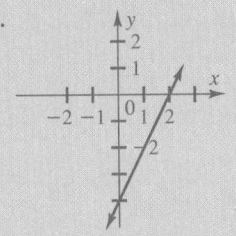

22.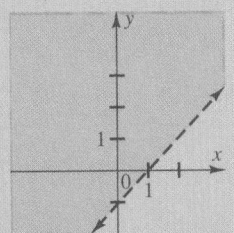

23.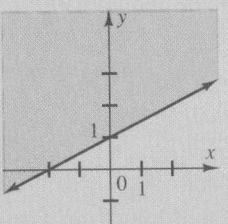

409

Maintaining Skills

The following skills and concepts are reviewed:
Graphing points and linear equations
Evaluating Expressions
Ratios and proportions

Additional Answers

7–12.

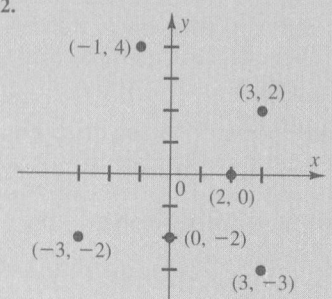

13.

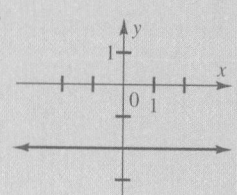

14.

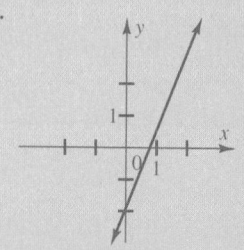

Write the coordinates for each point.

Example 1 Point A See graph.
The coordinates of A are $(-2, 3)$.

1. C $(2, 1)$ 2. B $(0, 2)$ 3. E $(1, -3)$

4. D $(2, -1)$ 5. G $(0, -2)$ 6. F $(-2, -2)$

Graph each ordered pair. See side column.

7. $(3, 2)$ 8. $(-1, 4)$ 9. $(2, 0)$

10. $(-3, -2)$ 11. $(3, -3)$ 12. $(0, -2)$

Draw a graph of each equation. See side column.

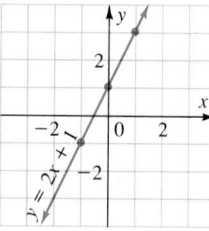

Example 2 $y = 2x + 1$
$y = 2x + 1$
$= 2(-1) + 1$
$= -2 + 1$
$= -1$

x	y
-1	-1
0	1
1	3

13. $y = -2$ 14. $y = 3x - 2$ 15. $y = 2x$ 16. $-2x + 3y = 6$

Evaluate each expression for the given value of the variable.

Example 3 $x^2 - 1, x = -4$
$x^2 - 1 = (-4)^2 - 1 = 16 - 1 = 15$

17. $3x - 2, x = -1$ -5 18. $2x + 5, x = 2$ 9 19. $-3x + 3, x = -3$ 12

20. $x^2 + 3, x = 4$ 19 21. $-2x^2 - 3, x = 2$ -11 22. $3x^2 - 2, x = -3$ 25

23. $\frac{1}{2}x^2 - 2, x = 3$ $\frac{5}{2}$ 24. $|x|, x = -2$ 2 25. $|x| - 1, x = -1$ 0

Solve.

26. At Oradell High School one hundred twenty-five students study French. Seventy-five students study Spanish. Write in simplest form the ratio of the number of students who study Spanish to the number of students who study French. $\frac{3}{5}$

27. During an election 7 out of 10 students voted for Hilary for class president. If 42 students voted for Hilary, how many students voted in the election?
60 students

28. The ratio of the number of boys to girls in the Senior High is 6 to 7. There are 350 girls in the Senior High. How many boys are there? 300 boys

410   Chapter 9 Linear Equations

15.

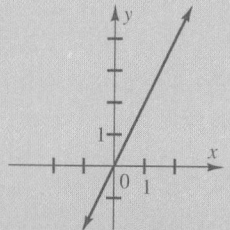

16.

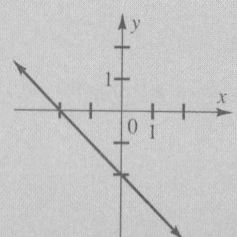

SUMMARY

In Chapter 10, students continue their work with linear equations introduced in the previous chapter and are given additional opportunities to apply their graphing skills. They learn the difference between a relation and a function, and learn how to represent each as a set of ordered pairs, a table, a mapping, or a graph. This chapter reinforces the idea that algebraic concepts can be applied to real world situations. When students learn about direct and inverse variations, they not only practice with algebraic equations, but apply their knowledge to solving real world problems as well.

After this chapter is completed, students should be able to identify a relation and tell whether or not it is a function, state its domain and range, and represent it as a set of points, a table, a mapping, a graph and, when possible, as an equation. They should be able to identify and use standard functional notation and use linear functions to solve word problems. They should also be able to apply the concept of direct and inverse variation to many real world applications.

CHAPTER OBJECTIVES

- To identify relations and functions from tables, mappings, graphs, and diagrams, and to determine their domains and ranges
- To graph relations and functions
- To use the vertical line test to determine whether or not a relation is a function
- To identify and evaluate standard functional notation
- To identify linear and constant functions, and find the value of simple composite functions
- To identify direct and inverse variations, and to solve problems involving them

Problem Solving Strategy

To solve word problems using appropriate formulas

CHAPTER HIGHLIGHTS

The *theme* of Chapter 10 is finance. This theme is addressed in the chapter's special features, which include discussions on Cost Analysis, Algebra in Accounting, and Algebra and Taxation.

PROBLEM SOLVING AND APPLICATIONS

Students are instructed to use an appropriate formula—a strategy which is essential for many problem solving situations. Many formulas are used in the studies of economics and the sciences. Since many diverse fields give rise to functions and relations, a variety of applications are given in Chapter 10.

TECHNOLOGY

Calculator

Functions and relations can be evaluated very quickly with the aid of a calculator. Likewise, problems involving direct and inverse variations may require its use.

Computer

A computer may be useful both for evaluating and graphing functions and relations.

RESOURCES

Teacher's Resource Book

- Teaching Aids 11, 13
- Transparencies 14, 21, 22, 23

STUDENT TEXT				TEACHER'S RESOURCE BOOK		
Chapter Content	Basic	Average	Enriched	R	P	E
10.1 Relations	D: 414/1-11 odd, 23	D: 415/9-17 odd, 23, 24	D: 416/13-21 odd, 23-25	1	2	3
10.2 Functions and Function Notation	D: 419/1-17 odd, 32 R: 416/2, 4, 6	D: 420/15-27 odd, 32, 33 R: 416/8, 14, 18	D: 420/23-31 odd, 32, 33 R: 416/14, 18, 22	4	5	6
10.3 Linear, Constant, and Composite Functions	D: 423/1-19 odd R: Test Yourself	D: 424/11-25 odd R: Test Yourself	D: 424/21-35 odd R: Test Yourself	7	8	9
10.4 Direct Variation	D: 428/1-13 odd, 29 R: 424/12, 14, 18	D: 428/11-23 odd, 29 R: 424/20, 22, 26	D: 428/15-27 odd, 29 R: 424/26, 30, 34	10	11	12

10.5 Inverse Variation	D: 432/1-13 odd, 27
	R: 428/8, 10, 12
	  432/2, 4, 6
		D: 432/7-17 odd, 27, 28
		R: 428/18, 20, 24
		  432/2, 4, 6
			D: 432/15-25 odd, 27, 28
			R: 428/20, 24, 28
				13	14	15

10.6 Problem Solving Strategy: Use an Appropriate Formula	D: 436/1-15 odd MPSR: 1-3 R: Test Yourself	D: 436/11-23 odd MPSR: 1-3 R: Test Yourself	D: 436/17-25 odd MPSR: 1-3 R: Test Yourself		16	17

D = Daily   R = Review   MPSR = Mixed Problem Solving Review   R = Reteaching   P = Practice   E = Enrichment

STUDENT TEXT				TEACHER'S RESOURCE BOOK	
Review And Testing	Test Yourself	424	Chapter Test	440	Spanish Chapter Summary and Review	19-20
	Test Yourself	437	Prep. for Stan. Tests	441	• Quizzes	101-104
	Chapter Sum. and Rev.	438	Cumulative Review	442	• Chapter Test (Form A)	105-106
			Extra Practice	664	• Chapter Test (Form B)	107-108
					Calculator Test	19-20
Special Features	Algebra in Taxation	416	Algebra in Accounting	429	Applications—Chapter 10	18
	Reading in Algebra	421	Extra	433	Critical Thinking	10
	Application	425	Project	436	Reading and Writing in Algebra	10
					Technology	20-21

10 Relations, Functions, and Variation

Money earned at an hourly wage is directly related to the number of hours spent on the job. As the number of hours increases, the amount of take-home pay also increases.

411

BACKGROUND

The floor of the stock exchange is one of the most active arenas for world finance. Numerous mathematical formulas are used in the various financial markets as vast fortunes are traded daily.

Vocabulary

Domain
Range
Relation
x-coordinates
y-coordinates

Materials/Manipulatives

Graph paper
Overhead projector
Straightedge

BACKGROUND

In the Capsule Review, students review reading a graph and writing the points in table form or as a set of ordered pairs. You may want to emphasize the importance of order (x, y). Remind students of the one-to-one correspondence between ordered pairs of numbers and points in a coordinate plane. In this lesson, students learn to show a relation as a set of ordered pairs in a table, as a mapping, or as a graph.

Relations

10.1

Objectives: To identify relations from tables, graphs, and diagrams
To determine the domain and range of a relation

Ernie makes extra money as a word processor. It took him 3 hours to input a 40-page report, 8 hours to input a 100-page manuscript, and $\frac{1}{2}$ hour to input a 5-page letter. The relation between the number of pages p he types and the time t it takes him to do so can be shown as $\left\{(40, 3), (100, 8), \left(5, \frac{1}{2}\right)\right\}$.
This set of ordered pairs can be represented by a *table*, by a *mapping*, or by a *graph*.

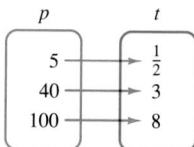

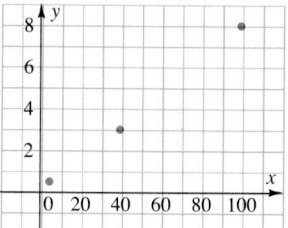

Capsule Review

The points on a graph can be shown in a table or as a set of ordered pairs.

EXAMPLE **Write the points shown on the graph in a table and as a set of ordered pairs.**

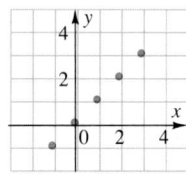

x	y
−1	−1
0	0
1	1
2	2
3	3

$\{(-1, -1); (0, 0); (1, 1);$
$(2, 2); (3, 3)\}$

1. Determine y for the points shown on the graph.

x	−3	−1	0	2	5
y	1	−1	2	0	−2

2. Write the points as a set of ordered pairs.
$\{(-3, 1), (-1, -1), (0, 2), (2, 0), (5, -2)\}$

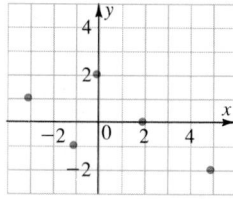

---

412 Chapter 10 Relations, Functions, and Variation

A **relation** is a set of one or more ordered pairs. It can be described in a set of ordered pairs, a graph, a mapping, or an open sentence in two variables.

The **domain** of a relation is the set of all its first elements or *x-coordinates*.

The **range** of a relation is the set of all its second elements or *y-coordinates*.

EXAMPLE 1   State the relation specified in the table below as a set of ordered pairs. State the domain and the range of this relation.

x	y
-1	0
0	1.5
1	3

Ordered pairs: $\{(-1, 0), (0, 1.5), (1, 3)\}$
Domain: $\{-1, 0, 1\}$
Range: $\{0, 1.5, 3\}$

When indicating the domain or range of a relation in set notation, use each element once.

EXAMPLE 2   State the relation specified in the mapping below as a set of ordered pairs. State the domain and the range of the relation.

Ordered pairs: $\left\{\left(0, \frac{1}{2}\right), (-2, 0), (1, 3), (-2, 3)\right\}$

Domain: $\{-2, 0, 1\}$

Range: $\left\{0, \frac{1}{2}, 3\right\}$

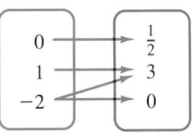

EXAMPLE 3   The graph shows the closing price of MAX stock over a period of one week. State the relation as a set of ordered pairs. State the domain and the range of the relation.

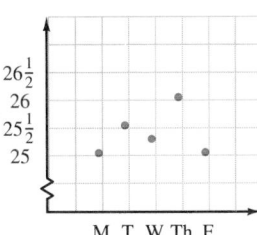

Ordered pairs: $\left\{(\text{Mon.}, 25), \left(\text{Tue.}, 25\frac{1}{2}\right), \left(\text{Wed.}, 25\frac{1}{4}\right), (\text{Thur.}, 26), (\text{Fri.}, 25)\right\}$

Domain: $\{\text{Mon., Tue., Wed., Thur., Fri.}\}$

Range: $\left\{25, 25\frac{1}{2}, 25\frac{1}{4}, 26\right\}$

10.1 Relations   **413**

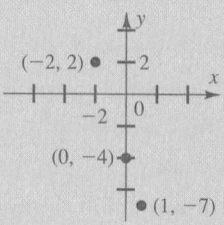
Sometimes a relation is defined by a given domain and an equation. When variables other than x and y are used, assume that the first letter in alphabetic order represents the domain.

EXAMPLE 4   **Given the domain {-2, 0, 1} of the relation $2x + y = -1$, determine the range. Graph your results.**

Rewrite $2x + y = -1$ in terms of y.

$$y = -2x - 1$$

Let $x =$ an element in the domain. Solve for y.

x	y
-2	3
0	-1
1	-3

The range is {3, -1, -3}.

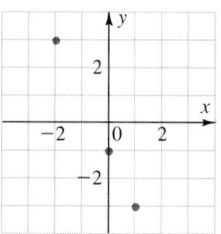

CLASS EXERCISES

1. Is the set {1, 2, 3, 4, 5} a relation? Explain.
No; it is not a set of one or more ordered pairs of numbers.
2. A grocer sells 5 lb of potatoes for $1.80. Show the relation. {(5, 1.80)}

Determine the domain and the range of the following relations.

3. (4, 1), (4, 2)
$D = \{4\}$ $R = \{1, 2\}$

6.
x	y
Sept.	$140
Oct.	$255
Nov.	$235
Dec.	$180
$D = $ {Sept., Oct., Nov., Dec.}
$R = $ {140, 180, 235, 255}

4.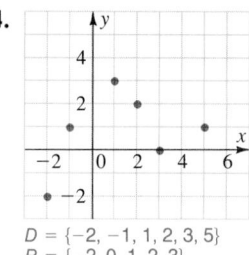
$D = \{-2, -1, 1, 2, 3, 5\}$
$R = \{-2, 0, 1, 2, 3\}$

5.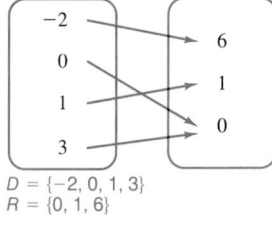
$D = \{-2, 0, 1, 3\}$
$R = \{0, 1, 6\}$

PRACTICE EXERCISES

State the relation as a set of ordered pairs. Determine the domain and the range of the relation.

A   1.
x	y
-3	5
-1	4
1	4
3	-3

2.
x	y
2	-1
5	3
7	-1
9	-7

3.
x	y
$\frac{1}{3}$	-1
0	0
$\frac{1}{3}$	2
$\frac{1}{2}$	$2\frac{1}{2}$

4.
x	y
2	-1
$2\frac{1}{2}$	0
3	-1
$3\frac{1}{2}$	$-3\frac{1}{2}$

414   Chapter 10 Relations, Functions, and Variation

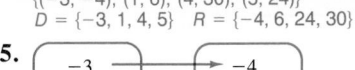

{(−3, −4), (1, 6), (4, 30), (5, 24)}
$D = \{-3, 1, 4, 5\}$ $R = \{-4, 6, 24, 30\}$

{(1, 1), (−1, 1), (2, 4), (−2, 4)}
$D = \{-2, -1, 1, 2\}$ $R = \{1, 4\}$

5.
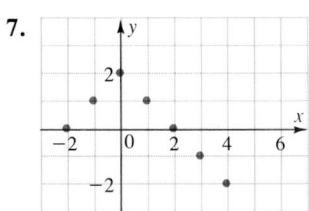

6.
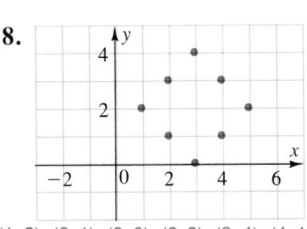

7.
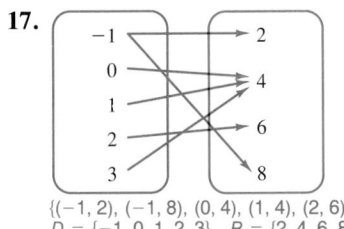

8.
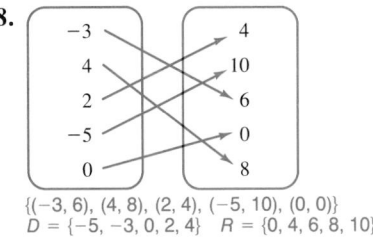

{(−2, 0), (−1, 1), (0, 2), (1, 1), (2, 0), (3, −1), (4, −2)}
$D = \{-2, -1, 0, 1, 2, 3, 4\}$ $R = \{-2, -1, 0, 1, 2\}$

{(1, 2), (2, 1), (3, 0), (2, 3), (3, 4), (4, 1), (4, 3), (5, 2)}
$D = \{1, 2, 3, 4, 5\}$ $R = \{0, 1, 2, 3, 4\}$

Given the domain $\{-1, 0, 2\}$, determine the range for each relation and graph the results.

9. $y = 3x + 5$ $R = \{2, 5, 11\}$ **10.** $y = 2x - 3$ $R = \{-5, -3, 1\}$ **11.** $y = 9 - 2x$
$R = \{5, 9, 11\}$

B

12. $x - 2y = 14$
$R = \left\{-\frac{15}{2}, -7, -6\right\}$

13. $y = \frac{x}{2} + 1$
$R = \left\{\frac{1}{2}, 1, 2\right\}$

14. $y = \frac{x}{2} - 2$
$R = \left\{-\frac{5}{2}, -2, -1\right\}$

State the relation as a set of ordered pairs. State the domain and the range. Graph the relation.

15.

Year	1890	1910	1930	1950	1970
Price of milk	$0.07	$0.08	$0.14	$0.21	$0.33

16.

Time	10 AM	11 AM	Noon	1 PM	2 PM
Stock price	$22\frac{1}{2}$	23	$23\frac{1}{4}$	$22\frac{5}{8}$	23

17.
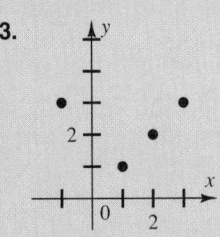

18.

{(−1, 2), (−1, 8), (0, 4), (1, 4), (2, 6), (3, 4)}
$D = \{-1, 0, 1, 2, 3\}$ $R = \{2, 4, 6, 8\}$

{(−3, 6), (4, 8), (2, 4), (−5, 10), (0, 0)}
$D = \{-5, -3, 0, 2, 4\}$ $R = \{0, 4, 6, 8, 10\}$

Given the domain $\left\{-1\frac{1}{4}, \frac{1}{2}, 2\right\}$, determine the range for each relation and graph the results.

C

19. $8x + \frac{1}{2}y = 8$ $\{-16, 8, 36\}$

20. $4x - \frac{1}{2}y = -5$ $\{0, 14, 26\}$

21. $4x - y = 2$ $\{-7, 0, 6\}$

22. $16x - 2y = -4$ $\{-8, 6, 18\}$

10.1 Relations   **415**

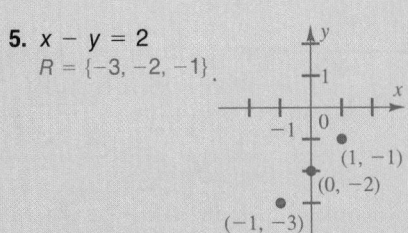
415

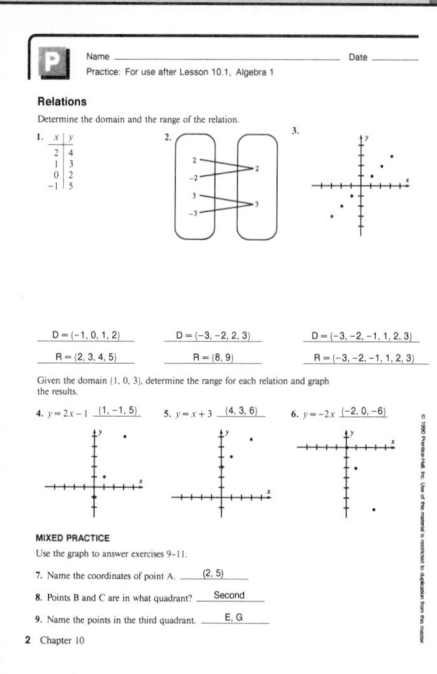

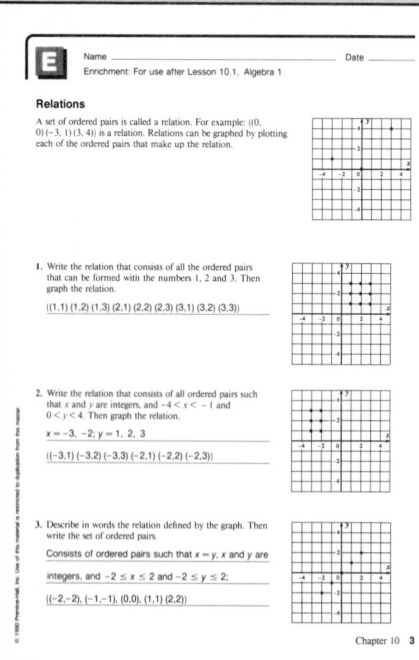

Applications

State the domain and the range of the following relations. Describe your results as a set of ordered pairs.

23. **Finance**   In the first year, Zelda made $5000 selling encyclopedias. She increased her earnings by $200 each year for the next four years.

$D = \{1, 2, 3, 4, 5\}$ $R = \{5000, 5200, 5400, 5600, 5800\}$ $\{(1, 5000), (2, 5200), (3, 5400), (4, 5600), (5, 5800)\}$

24. **Finance**   John started out at 9 AM to go door-to-door selling brushes. He sold 6 brushes an hour until 3 PM.

$\{(1, 6), (2, 12), (3, 18), (4, 24), (5, 30), (6, 36)\}$ $D = \{1, 2, 3, 4, 5, 6\}$ $R = \{6, 12, 18, 24, 30, 36\}$

25. **Meteorology**   Sun Valley was covered with 3 ft of snow when it started to snow again. The snow fell at a rate of 1 ft/h for 5 h.

$\{(1, 4), (2, 5), (3, 6), (4, 7), (5, 8)\}$ $D = \{1, 2, 3, 4, 5\}$ $R = \{4, 5, 6, 7, 8\}$

ALGEBRA IN TAXATION

Did you know that relationships play a very important role in our tax structure? There are three types of tax structures in our society:

Proportional tax   A tax in which the percentage of tax paid is the same for all incomes. An example of this is a constant or "flat rate" state income tax.

Progressive tax   A tax in which the percentage of tax paid increases as total income increases. An example of this is the federal income tax.

Regressive tax   A tax in which the percentage of tax paid decreases as total income increases. An example of this is social security tax. The amount of social security tax paid in 1989 was 7.51% of the first $48,000 earned.

1. Dan had an income of $11,000 in a state where the income tax is 2.5%. What was the amount Dan paid in taxes? $275

2. Mildred is single and earns $35,000 a year. The federal government has three tax rates shown at the right. Find the amount Mildred paid in income tax. $9800

Income is between	Then the tax rate is
$0–$15,000	15%
$15,001–$40,000	28%
above $40,001	30%

3. Marcia earned $20,000 and Alex earned $50,000. Who paid the higher percent of total income to social security?
Marcia pays 7.15%, Alex pays 6.06%.

Functions and Function Notation

Objectives: To identify functions
To understand standard function notation

Rose earns $5.00 per hour in a flower shop. The relation between her salary s and the number of hours h she works is represented in this graph. Her salary depends on how many hours she works. For 7 hours she earns $35. For $1\frac{1}{2}$ hours she earns only $7.50. The equation $s = 5h$ represents this relation.

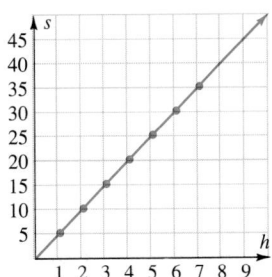

LESSON PLAN

Vocabulary
Function
Function notation
Vertical line test

Materials/Manipulatives
Graph paper
Graphing calculator
Overhead projector
Straightedge

BACKGROUND

In the Capsule Review, students are given mappings of relations and are asked to write the ordered pairs for each relation. In the lesson, students will learn that although all the exercises are relations, only Exercises 1 and 2 are functions. You may want to elicit from the students that when examining the ordered pairs in Exercises 1 and 2, no element of the domain repeats. This leads directly to the definition of function.

Capsule Review

Recall that relations are sets of ordered pairs and can be indicated by mappings. Give the relations indicated as sets of ordered pairs.

1.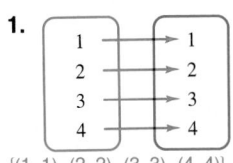

{(1, 1), (2, 2), (3, 3), (4, 4)}

2.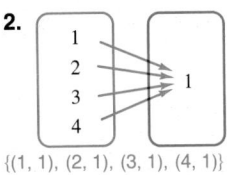

{(1, 1), (2, 1), (3, 1), (4, 1)}

3.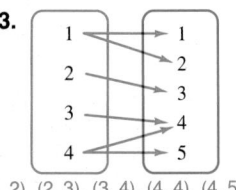

{(1, 1), (1, 2), (2, 3), (3, 4), (4, 4), (4, 5)}

A **function** is a relation in which each element of the domain is paired with *exactly* one element of the range.

EXAMPLE 1 **Tell whether each relation specifies a function. Explain.**

a. (0, −1), (2, −2), (1, −1), (1, 5), (−3, 4)

b.

Time	Temp.
1 PM	15°C
2 PM	16°C
3 PM	17°C
4 PM	19°C
5 PM	17°C

c.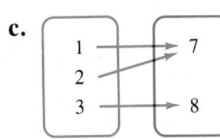

10.2 Functions and Function Notation **417**

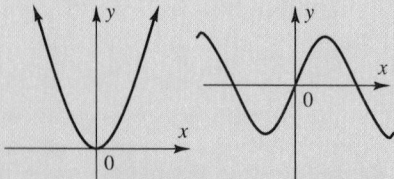 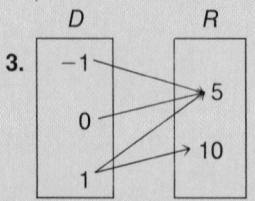
a. No; the element 1 is paired with both -1 and 5.

b. Yes; each element of time corresponds with exactly one temperature.

c. Yes; each element of the domain is paired with exactly one element of the range.

Another method for determining whether a relation is a function involves drawing a graph of the ordered pairs and then drawing vertical lines through the graph. This is called the **vertical line test.**

> ### Vertical Line Test
>
> If a vertical line intersects a graph in more than one point, then the graph is not the graph of a function.

EXAMPLE 2 **Graph each of the following relations. Use the vertical line test to determine whether each relation is a function.**

a. $(1, 4)$, $(0, 1)$, $(2, 1)$, $(3, 3)$, $(5, 0)$ **b.** $(1, 3)$, $(3, 5)$, $(3, 2)$, $(3, 0)$

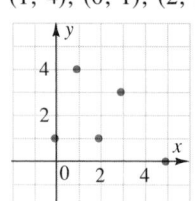   **a.** Yes.

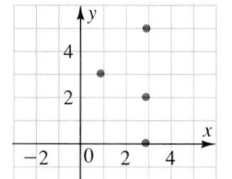   **b.** No.

For the relation to be a function, any vertical line can only pass through a single point. Example (b) is not a function while Example (a) is a function.

Functions can be specified using different types of **function notation.**

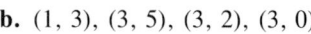

Arrow notation, $F: x \rightarrow 2x + 1$	Read: The function F that pairs x with $2x + 1$.
f of x notation: $f(x) = 2x + 1$	Read: f of x equals $2x + 1$.
Equation in two variables: $y = 2x + 1$	Explain why y is called a function of x.

All the ordered pairs of a function are in the form (x, y) or $(x, f(x))$. Note that $f(x)$ does not mean f times x; rather, it refers to the range of the function whose domain is represented by x. Letters other than f, such as F, g, G, h, and so on, are often used for *function notation.*

EXAMPLE 3 **Evaluate, given $f(x) = x - 3$ and $g(x) = x^2$.**

　a. $f(0)$ 　　　　　**b.** $g(2)$ 　　　　　**c.** $f(0) - g(2)$

　a. $f(0) = 0 - 3 = -3$ 　　**b.** $g(2) = 2^2 = 4$ 　　**c.** $f(0) - g(2) = -3 - 4 = -7$

418　　Chapter 10 Relations, Functions, and Variation

EXAMPLE 4   Evaluate, given the domain $\{-2, 0, 1\}$.

a. $y = 4x - 1$ b. $g(x) = \frac{1}{3}x^2 - 2$

a. $y = 4x - 1$

x	$4x - 1$	y
-2	$4(-2) - 1$	-9
0	$4(0) - 1$	-1
1	$4(1) - 1$	3

b. $g(x) = \frac{1}{3}x^2 - 2$

$g(-2) = \frac{1}{3}(-2)^2 - 2 = \frac{1}{3}(4) - 2 = -\frac{2}{3}$

$g(0) = \frac{1}{3}(0)^2 - 2 = -2$

$g(1) = \frac{1}{3}(1)^2 - 2 = \frac{1}{3}(1) - 2 = -\frac{5}{3}$

Some functions have a point where the graph for the function changes direction. Some of these points can be determined by examining the coefficients and constants in the function.

EXAMPLE 5   Use a graphing calculator or computer program to find the point where the graph changes direction:

a. $f(x) = |x + 2|$ b. $g(x) = |x - 3|$ c. $h(x) = |x - 4| + 2$

a. $x = -2$, $f(-2) = 0$; changes direction at $(-2, 0)$

b. $x = 3$, $f(3) = 0$; changes direction at $(3, 0)$

c. $x = 4$, $f(4) = 2$; changes direction at $(4, 2)$

CLASS EXERCISES

For Discussion

Is each relation a function? Explain.

1. (x, y) where x is each person in Los Angeles and y is the type of car that person owns. no; people may have more than one car

2. (x, y) where x is each person in your Algebra class and y is that person's birthdate. yes; each person has only one birthday

3. (x, y) where x is a person and y is that person's social security number. yes; each person has just one social security number

PRACTICE EXERCISES

Tell whether each relation specifies a function.

A   1. $\{(-3, -2), (-2, -1), (-1, 0), (0, 1), (1, 2)\}$ a function

2. $\{(5, 0), (0, 5), (5, 1), (1, 5), (5, 2), (2, 5)\}$ not a function

3. $\{(-1, -3), (4, 0), (5, 2), (2, 3), (-2, -3), (1, 1)\}$ a function

4. $\{(2.5, -1.5), (-0.5, 3), (-1.5, -5), (2.5, 2)\}$ not a function

10.2 Functions and Function Notation   **419**

419

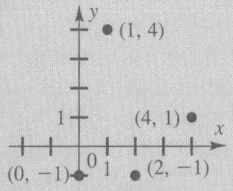

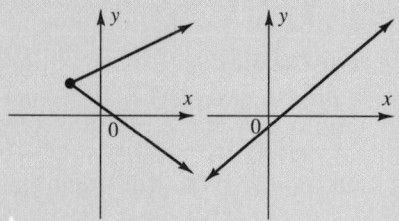
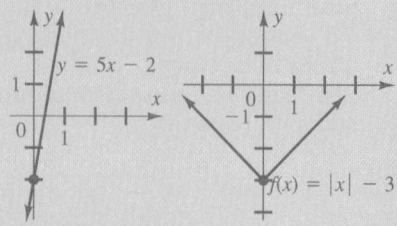
5.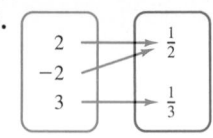
a function

6.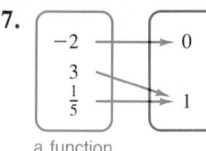
a function

7.
a function

8.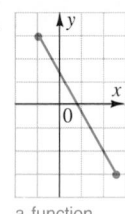
a function

9.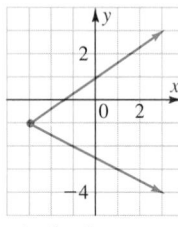
not a function

10.
not a function

11.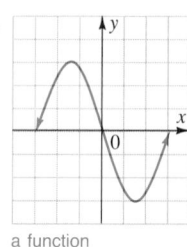
a function

Evaluate, given $f(x) = x + 2$.

12. $f(2)$ 4   **13.** $f(3)$ 5   **14.** $f(-1)$ 1   **15.** $f(-4)$ −2

Graph each relation given the domain: $\{-1, 0, 3, 6\}$. State the range and tell whether each is a function. Check students' graphs.

16. $y = x + 4$ $R = \{3, 4, 7, 10\}$; a function   **17.** $3x - y = 5$ $R = \{-8, -5, 4, 13\}$; a function

18. $f(x) = |x| + 1$ $R = \{2, 1, 4, 7\}$; a function   **19.** $f(x) = -|x - 1|$
$R = \{-2, -1, -5\}$; a function

B   **20.** $f: x \rightarrow x - 25$, domain: {all real numbers}. State the range and whether the relation is a function. $R = \{$all real numbers$\}$; a function

21. $f(x) = |x| - 1$, domain: {all real numbers}. State the range and whether the relation is a function. $R = \{$all real numbers greater than or equal to $-1\}$; a function

Evaluate given that $f(x) = x^2 + 1$ and $g(x) = 5x - 3$.

22. $f(-2)$ 5   **23.** $g(1)$ 2   **24.** $f(-2) + g(1)$ 7

25. $f(2) \times g(0)$ −15   **26.** $f(4) \times g(1)$ 34   **27.** $f(-2) - g(1)$ 3

Use a graphing calculator or a computer program to find the point where the graph changes direction.

28. $f(x) = |x + 4|$ (−4, 0)   **29.** $g(x) = |2x + 4|$ (−2, 0)   **30.** $y = |2x + 4| - 5$
(−2, −5)

C Determine the relation by evaluating for the conditions. Graph the relation and tell whether or not it is a function.

31. $3a + 2b = 1$; Domain: $\{a: -5 < \text{integers} < 5\}$ a function

32. $7j + 3k = 9$; Domain: $\{j: \text{counting numbers} < 6\}$ a function

33. $y = |x| + 2$; Range: $\{\text{integers} < 4\}$ a function

34. $y = |x| - 3$; Range: $\{\text{whole numbers} < 5\}$ a function

Applications

35. Finance Graph the closing prices of AEM stock over the period of one week: (Mon., 38), $\left(\text{Tue.}, 38\frac{1}{8}\right)$, $\left(\text{Wed.}, 35\frac{1}{4}\right)$, (Thur., 37), $\left(\text{Fri.}, 37\frac{3}{8}\right)$. Is this relation a function? yes

36. Meteorology Graph the relation between month m and average temperature t as described in this chart. Is this relation a function? yes

Average Temperatures for Anchorage, Alaska

m	Jan.	Feb.	Mar.	Apr.	May	Jun.	Jul.
t	13°F	18°F	24°F	35°F	46°F	54°F	58°F

READING IN ALGEBRA

Perhaps you read entire lines in one or two glances as a way of reading quickly. Since many sentences in a math textbook are concerned with definitions, examples, and explanations, you may miss important ideas when you "scan" a page.

Below are several statements from this book. Examine each statement and decide whether it is exactly as given in the book. If not, restate it so that it duplicates the original.

1. (page 412) The relationship between the pages he types and the time can be represented as a set of pairs, a table, or a graph.

2. (page 417) A function is a special relation where different ordered pairs have different first coordinates.

3. (page 345) A proportion is a statement with equal ratios.

4. (page 385) Recall that a line with a positive slope slants up. Lines with negative slopes slant down.

10.2 Functions and Function Notation **421**

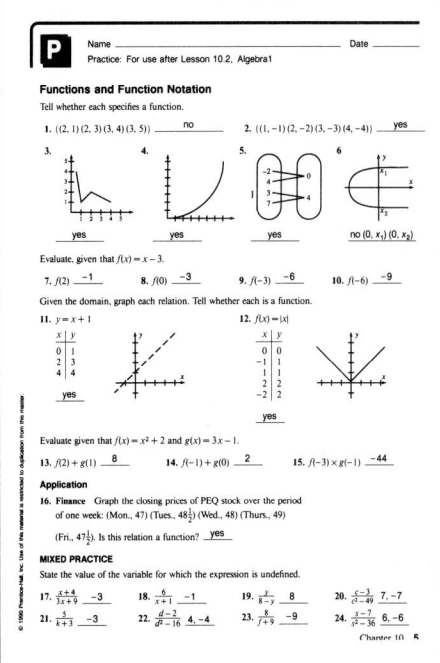
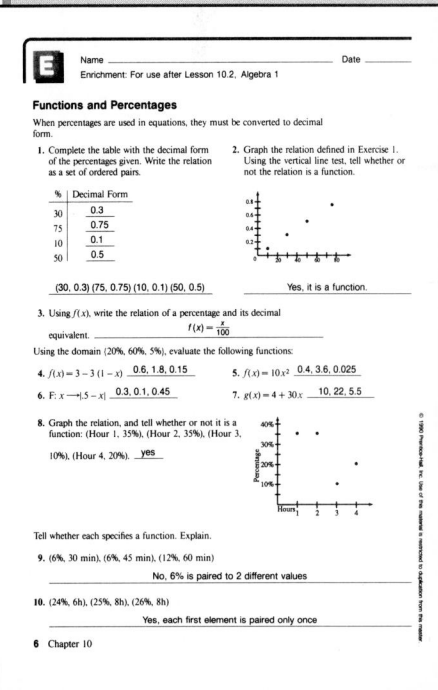

Vocabulary
Composite function
Constant function
Linear function

Materials/Manipulatives
Graph paper
Overhead projector
Straightedge
Teacher's Resource Book,
*   Transparency 21*

BACKGROUND

In the Capsule Review, students re-view finding the slope and y-intercept of a linear equation by writing it in the slope-intercept form. Before assigning the Capsule Review, you may want to review the definitions of slope and y-intercept and finding both by graphing an equation.

TEACHING SUGGESTIONS

When discussing Example 1, you may want to review the definition of func-tion. Stress that every function as-signs each member of the domain to *exactly one* member of the range. Review the role of the vertical line test for identifying functions.

CHALKBOARD EXAMPLES

• **For Example 1**
   Graph each relation. Is the relation a function? A linear function?
   1. $2x - y = 2$ yes; yes
   2. $x = 3$ no; no

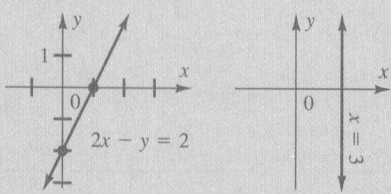

10.3

Linear, Constant, and Composite Functions

Objectives: To identify linear and constant functions from a graph
   To evaluate composite functions

Linear equations such as $y = 3x + 4$ and $y = 2$ define functions. Recall that the graph of a linear equation is a straight line.

Capsule Review

The graph of the equation $y = mx + b$ where m and b are real numbers is a line whose slope is m and whose y-intercept is b.

EXAMPLE **Use the slope and the y-intercept to graph the equation $y = -x + 3$.**

$y = -x + 3$, so the slope m is -1; the y-intercept b is 3.

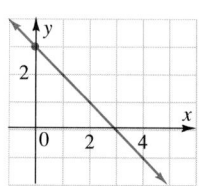

Use the slope and the y-intercept to graph the equation.

1. $x + 3y = 9$ $\begin{array}{l}m = -\frac{1}{3}\\ b = 3\end{array}$ **2.** $-5y - x = 10$ $\begin{array}{l}m = -\frac{1}{5}\\ b = -2\end{array}$ **3.** $2x - 3y = 8$ $\begin{array}{l}m = \frac{2}{3}\\ b = -\frac{8}{3}\end{array}$

A **linear function** is a special kind of function with a domain equal to the set of real numbers, whose graph is a straight line. A linear function is a function that can be defined by an equation in slope-intercept form.

$$y = mx + b \quad m = \text{slope}; \quad b = \text{y-intercept}$$

EXAMPLE 1 **Graph each relation. Is the relation a function? A linear function?**

a. $x + y = -2$

x	0	1	2
y	-2	-3	-4

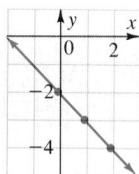

b. $y = |x| + 1$

x	2	1	0	-1	-2
y	3	2	1	2	3

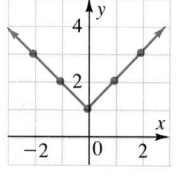

a. Yes, because the vertical line test holds. Yes, because it can be written in slope-intercept form $y = -x - 2$, where m is -1 and b is -2.

b. Yes, because the vertical line test holds. No, because the equation cannot be written in slope-intercept form (the graph is not a straight line).

422   Chapter 10 Relations, Functions, and Variation

A **constant function** is a linear function whose range contains only one element. The graph of a constant function is a horizontal line.

EXAMPLE 2 Graph each relation. Is the relation a function? A linear function? A constant function?

a. $g(x) = x - 2$ **b.** $x = -2$ **c.** $f(x) = 3$

a. Label the vertical axis $g(x)$.

x	$g(x)$
0	-2
1	-1
2	0

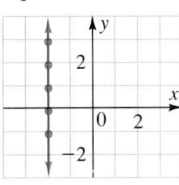

Linear function; not a constant function

b. All x values equal -2.

Not a function

c. All $f(x)$ values equal 3.

Linear function; constant function

A **composite function** combines two or more functions. To evaluate a composite function, evaluate the inner function first, then evaluate the outer function.

EXAMPLE 3 Evaluate $f(g(2))$, given $f(x) = 3x + 2$ and $g(x) = \frac{1}{2}x^2 - 1$.

First, evaluate the innermost function.

$g(2) = \frac{1}{2}(2)^2 - 1$
$= \frac{1}{2}(4) - 1$
$= 2 - 1 = 1$

Now, since $g(2)$ is 1,

$f(g(2)) = f(1)$
$= 3(1) + 2$
$= 3 + 2$
$= 5$

CLASS EXERCISES

Graph each relation. Is the relation a function? A linear function? A constant function?

1. $f(x) = 2x - 1$ **2.** $m(x) = 4$ **3.** $x = 5$
yes; yes; no   yes; yes; yes   not a function

Evaluate, given that $f(x) = 2x + 2$ and $g(x) = 6x + 5$.

4. $f(g(2))$ 36   **5.** $f(g(7))$ 96   **6.** $g(f(-1))$ 5   **7.** $g(f(-4))$ -31

PRACTICE EXERCISES

Graph each relation. Is the relation a function? A linear function? A constant function?

A   **1.** $f(x) = 3x - 2$ **2.** $G: x \rightarrow x + 7$ **3.** $f(x) = |x| + 1$ **4.** $h(x) = 2|x|$
yes; yes; no   yes; yes; no   yes; no; no   yes; no; no

10.3 Linear, Constant, and Composite Functions   **423**

- **For Example 2**
  Is the relation a function. A linear function? A constant function?
  3. $f(x) = 3x + 7$ yes; yes; no
  4. $g(x) = 6$ yes; yes; yes

- **For Example 3**
  Evaluate, given $f(x) = x - 3$ and $g(x) = 2x - 1$.
  5. $f(-1)$ -4 **6.** $g(f(-1))$ -9

Common Error

- Students often make errors when evaluating composite functions. Encourage students to note the positioning of the parentheses.
- See *Teacher's Resource Book* for additional remediation.

LESSON FOLLOW-UP

Assignment Guide
See p. 410B for assignments.

Test Yourself
See *Teacher's Resource Book,* Tests, pp. 101–102.

Critical Thinking
Classifying The graph of every linear function is a straight line. Is it true that every straight line is a graph of a linear function?   No, vertical lines are not graphs of functions.

Lesson Quiz
Graph each relation. Is the relation a function? A linear function? A constant function?
1. $g(x) = 2x + 5$ yes; yes; no
2. $y = -2$ yes; yes; yes

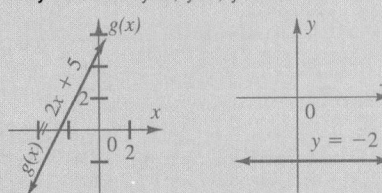

Evaluate, given $f(x) = x - 5$ and $g(x) = 3x$.
3. $g(3)$ 9   **4.** $f(g(3))$ 4

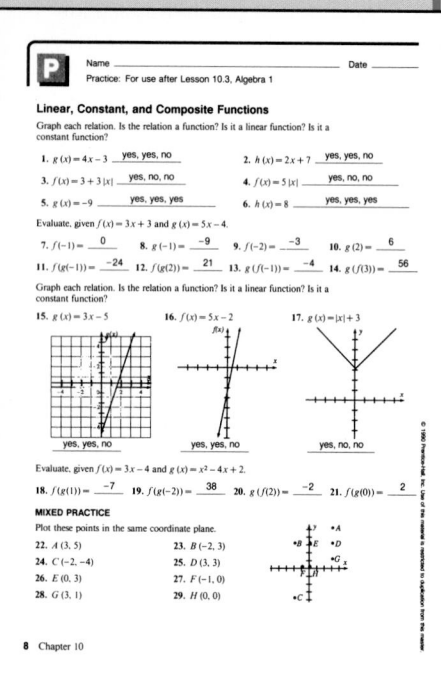

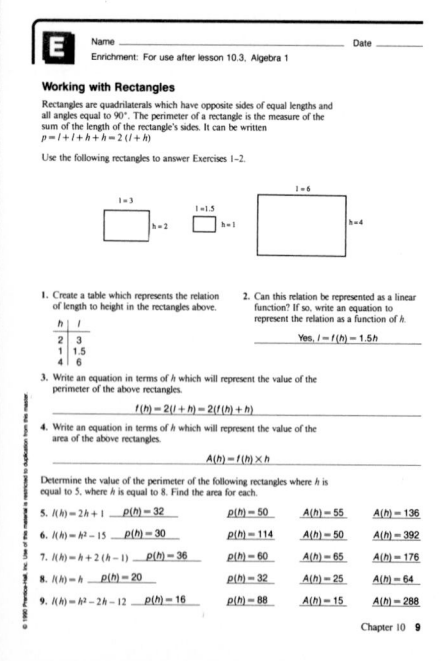

5. $f(x) = -7$
yes; yes; yes

6. $g(x) = 5$
yes; yes; yes

7. $x = 5$
not a function

8. $x = -4$
not a function

9. $f(x) = -5$
yes; yes; yes

10. $H: x \rightarrow 2$
yes; yes; yes

11. $f(x) = -\dfrac{x}{2} + 3$
yes; yes; no

12. $f(x) = \dfrac{x}{3} + 6$
yes; yes; no

Evaluate, given $f(x) = 2x + 1$ and $g(x) = 4x - 5$.

13. $f(-1)$ –1

14. $g(-1)$ –9

15. $f(-2)$ –3

16. $g(-2)$ –13

17. $f(g(1))$ –1

18. $f(g(2))$ 7

19. $g(f(3))$ 23

20. $g(f(4))$ 31

B **Graph each relation. Is the relation a function? A linear function? A constant function?**

21. $f(x) = 2x - 9$
yes; yes; no

22. $f(x) = 3x - 7$
yes; yes; no

23. $h: x \rightarrow -|x| - 3$
yes; no; no

24. $h: x \rightarrow \left|\dfrac{x}{2}\right| + 11$
yes; no; no

25. $g(x) = -4|x| + 2$
yes; no; no

26. $g(x) = -\dfrac{3}{2}|x| - 3$
yes; no; no

Evaluate, given $f(x) = 5x - 3$ and $g(x) = x^2 - 3x + 1$.

C **27.** $f(g(1))$ –8

28. $f(g(2))$ –8

29. $g(f(0))$ 19

30. $g(f(3))$ 109

31. $f(g(3))$ 2

32. $f(g(-1))$ 22

33. $g(f(1))$ –1

34. $g(f(2))$ 29

35. Evaluate $f(t(15))$, given $f(x) = |-x| - 2$ and $t(x) = \dfrac{1}{x}$. $-\dfrac{29}{15}$

36. Evaluate $g(r(-2))$, given $g(x) = |x| + x$ and $r(x) = -1.1$. 0

Applications

37. Consumer The cost of a long distance phone call of t minutes is found by using the function $f(t) = 0.75t + 1.45$. Find the cost of a 15-min phone call.
$12.70

TEST YOURSELF

Given the domain $\{-3, 0, 4\}$, state the range and graph the results. 10.1

1. $y = 2x + 3$
$R = \{-3, 3, 11\}$

2. $y = 3x - 4$
$R = \{-13, -4, 8\}$

3. $y = \dfrac{1}{4}x - 1$
$R = \left\{-\dfrac{7}{4}, -1, 0\right\}$

4. $y = \dfrac{1}{3}x + 1$
$R = \left\{0, 1, \dfrac{7}{3}\right\}$

Graph each relation. Is the relation a function? A linear function? A constant function? 10.2

5. $\{(0, 1), (1, 3), (-1, 4), (2, 5)\}$
yes; no; no

6. $\{(0, -2), (1, -1), (0, -3), (4, 2)\}$
no; no; no

7. $y = -2x + 4$
yes; yes; no

8. $y = -4$
yes; yes; yes

9. $y = |x| + 5$
yes; no; no

10. $x = -5$
no; no; no

Evaluate, given $f(x) = 3x + 2$ and $g(x) = 4x - 1$. 10.3

11. $f(-3)$ –7

12. $g(4)$ 15

13. $f(g(2))$ 23

14. $g(f(3))$ 43

APPLICATION:
Cost Analysis

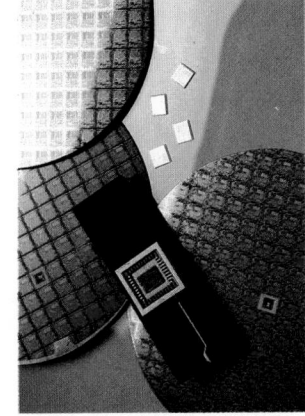

Did you know that cost analysis plays an integral part in mathematical modeling with respect to business applications? In businesses where various products are produced, a manufacturer must take fixed and variable costs into consideration. Fixed costs are costs which remain constant, while variable costs can change at any time during production.

The following example illustrates the above.

EXAMPLE   A computer manufacturer needs to purchase microchips. The supplier charges a fixed cost of $50.00 on the first 100 chips, and $0.35 as a variable cost for each chip purchased over this amount.

How much would the computer manufacturer have to pay the supplier in order to purchase 2010 chips?

$c(x)$ = cost function
   m = variable cost of $0.35 per chip after the first 100
   b = fixed cost of $50.00 on the first 100 chips
   x = amount of chips over 100 purchased
$c(x) = mx + b$

Thus the equation would be:

$$c(x) = (0.35)(1910) + 50$$
$$c(x) = 668.50 + 50$$
$$c(x) = 718.50$$

The total cost to the computer maker would be $718.50 for the purchase of 2010 microchips.

Solve.

1. The fixed cost of purchasing the first 20 televisions is $480. The variable cost per television is $12. Find the cost function $c(x)$. If 186 televisions are to be purchased, what is the total cost? $c(x) = 12x + 480; \$2472$

2. Determine the total cost of producing 190 chairs if the fixed cost of rent and taxes is $6600 and the variable cost of materials and shipping expenses is $20 per chair. $10,400

Application: Cost Analysis   **425**

Application
The discussion of cost analysis provides a vivid illustration of the everyday use of algebraic concepts in business. While the cost equations for large business operations can be complicated, many small businesses use the simple linear functions studied in this chapter.

See *Teacher's Resource Book,* Follow-up Application, p. 18.

Vocabulary
Constant of proportionality
Constant of variation
Direct variation

Materials/Manipulatives
Graph paper
Overhead projector
Straightedge
Teacher's Resource Book,
Transparency 22

BACKGROUND

In the Capsule Review, students re-view solving an equation in terms of *x*. Point out that when solving linear equations for *y*, they are actually writing them in slope-intercept form. In this lesson, students will learn a special case of a linear function, direct variation. The linear function $y = mx + b$, is a direct variation when $m = k$ (constant of variation) and $b = 0$.

10.4

Direct Variation

Objectives: To identify direct variations
To solve word problems involving direct variation

Karla earns money by waxing automobiles. She charges $15 per car. Karla waxed 2 cars on Friday, 6 cars on Saturday, and 3 cars on Sunday. How much did she earn each day?

The amount Karla earns depends on the number of cars she waxes. This is called a *direct variation*. The direct variation can be written as $y = 15x$. The constant 15 is called the **constant of variation** or the **constant of proportionality.**

	Let $x =$ number of cars waxed	Let $y =$ dollars earned
Friday	2	$30
Saturday	6	$90
Sunday	3	$45

Capsule Review

A linear equation shows how the values of *x* and *y* depend on each other.

EXAMPLE **Show how *y* depends on *x* in the equation $3x - y = 2$.**

$3x - y = 2$
$-y = -3x + 2$ · *Solve for y.*
$y = 3x - 2$

y is always 2 less than 3 times the value of *x*.

Show how *y* depends on *x* in the following equations.

$y = \frac{3}{4}x + \frac{3}{4}$

$y = x + 4$

$y = x - 2$

1. $-x + y = 4$ 　　 **2.** $\frac{1}{2}x - \frac{1}{2}y = 1$ 　　 **3.** $3x = 4y - 3$

A **direct variation** is a function in the form

$$y = kx, \, k \neq 0$$

where it is said that *y* varies directly as *x*, or *y* is directly proportional to *x*.

Direct variation is a special case of the linear function $y = mx + b$, where $m = k$ and $b = 0$.

The graph of a direct variation is a straight line with slope of k passing through the origin.

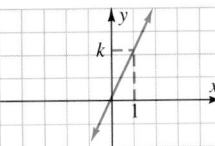

EXAMPLE 1 **For each equation, tell whether y varies directly as x. Explain.**

a. $2x + y = 0$
$\quad\quad y = -2x$

b. $\quad x = y + 1$
$\quad\quad x - 1 = y$

a. Yes; $y = -2x$ is in the form $y = kx$ with $k = -2$. (y is always negative two times x.)

b. No; $y = x - 1$ is not in the form $y = kx$.

EXAMPLE 2 **For the following table tell whether y varies directly as x. If so, name the constant of variation and the equation that shows the relationship.**

x	y
3	3.6
6.1	7.32
11	13.2

Substitute each x and y in $\frac{y}{x} = k$.

$\frac{3.6}{3} = 1.2$ $\quad$ $\frac{7.32}{6.1} = 1.2$ $\quad$ $\frac{13.2}{11} = 1.2$

y varies directly as x. $k = 1.2$ and $y = 1.2x$.

In general, given two ordered pairs (x_1, y_1) and (x_2, y_2) of the same direct variation, the constant of variation is the same for each equation: $y_1 = kx_1$ and $y_2 = kx_2$. From these equations, you can write $\frac{y_1}{x_1} = k$ and $\frac{y_2}{x_2} = k$. Then $\frac{y_1}{x_1} = \frac{y_2}{x_2}$ because each ratio equals k.

Recall that an equation which states that two ratios are equal is a proportion.

To solve a proportion use the property of proportions: if $\frac{a}{b} = \frac{c}{d}$, then $ad = bc$.

EXAMPLE 3 **The amount of rice used in a casserole recipe is directly proportional to the number of people served. If $1\frac{1}{4}$ cups of uncooked rice serve 6 people, how many cups of rice would be needed to serve a group of 40 people?**

Let r = number of cups of rice needed and p = number of people to be served. Then $r = kp$.

$\frac{r_1}{p_1} = \frac{r_2}{p_2}$ $\quad$ $\frac{r_1}{p_1} = k$ and $\frac{r_2}{p_2} = k$ $\quad\quad$ $6r = 50$ $\quad$ *Property of Proportions*

$\frac{1\frac{1}{4}}{6} = \frac{r}{40}$ $\quad$ *Substitute.* $\quad\quad\quad\quad\quad$ $r = 8\frac{1}{3}$

$8\frac{1}{3}$ cups of rice are needed.

10.4 Direct Variation **427**

- **For Example 3**

4. The amount of soda ash in a detergent varies directly as the total weight of the box. If $1\frac{1}{2}$ cups of ash are used in a 12-oz box, how many cups are needed for a 20-oz box? $2\frac{1}{2}$ c

- **For Example 4**

5. y varies directly as x. If $y = 6$ when $x = 4.5$, find x when $y = 16$. $x = 12$

LESSON FOLLOW-UP

Assignment Guide
See p. 410B for assignments.

Algebra in Accounting
Have students work in cooperative pairs.

Lesson Quiz
For each equation, tell whether y varies directly as x.

1. $y = \frac{2}{11}x$ yes
2. $y = 7x + 1$ no
3. For the table, tell whether y varies directly as x. If so, name the constant of variation and the equation that shows the relationship.
yes; 3; $y = 3x$

x	3	5	7
y	9	15	21

4. d is directly proportional to t. $d = 32$ when $t = 0.8$. Find t when $d = 256$. $t = 6.4$

Enrichment
Using the formulas for finding the circumference of a circle in terms of the radius or diameter, find all the direct variations. $C = \pi d$, so circumference is directly proportional to the diameter; $C = 2\pi r$, so circumference is directly proportional to the radius; $d = 2r$, so diameter is directly proportional to the radius.

EXAMPLE 4 y varies directly as x. If $y = 5$ when $x = 7.5$, find x when $y = 9$.

$$\frac{y_1}{x_1} = \frac{y_2}{x_2} \qquad \frac{y_1}{x_1} = k \text{ and } \frac{y_2}{x_2} = k \qquad 5x = 67.5 \qquad \textit{Property of Proportions.}$$
$$\qquad\qquad\qquad\qquad\qquad\qquad\qquad x = 13.5$$
$$\frac{5}{7.5} = \frac{9}{x} \qquad \textit{Substitute.}$$

CLASS EXERCISES

Find the constant of variation k if y varies directly as x.

1. $y = 5.1$, $x = 3$ 1.7
2. $y = 3.2$, $x = 0.8$ 4

For Discussion

Does y vary directly with x?

3. $y = \frac{1}{2}x$ yes; (2, 1), (4, 2)
4. $y = 2x + 3$ no, not in the form $y = kx$
5. $xy = 3$ no; not in the form $y = kx$

PRACTICE EXERCISES

A   **For each equation tell whether y varies directly as x.**

1. $y = \frac{4}{5}x$ yes
2. $y = \frac{7}{9}x + 1$ no
3. $y = 3x - 2$ no
4. $y = 5x$ yes

For each table tell whether y varies directly as x. If so, give the constant of variation and the equation that shows the relationship.

5.
x	1	3	5	9
y	4	12	20	36

yes; 4; $y = 4x$

6.
x	8	18	20	21
y	4	9	10	11

no

7.
x	0.6	4.5	6.3	15.6
y	0.2	1.5	2.1	5.2

yes; $\frac{1}{3}$; $y = \frac{1}{3}x$

8.
x	1.6	2.2	2.4	2.8
y	1.2	1.75	1.8	2.1

no

Solve.

9. y varies directly with x. $y = 5$ when $x = 25$. Find y when $x = 55$. 11
10. y varies directly with x. $y = 3$ when $x = 2$. Find y when $x = 34$. 51
11. B varies directly with A. $B = 4$ when $A = 150$. Find B when $A = 200$. $5\frac{1}{3}$
12. N varies directly with M. $N = 84$ when $M = 12$. Find N when $M = 14$. 98
13. y varies directly with x. $y = 5$ when $x = 6$. Find y when $x = 42$. 35
14. y varies directly with x. $y = 35$ when $x = 56$. Find y when $x = 8$. 5

B
15. E varies directly with M. $E = 110$ when $M = 17.6$. Find M when $E = 80$. 12.8
16. C varies directly as W. $C = 3.78$ when $W = 3$. Find C when $W = 4.5$. 5.67
17. W is directly proportional to L. $W = 9$ when $L = 12.5$. Find W when $L = 16.5$. 11.88
18. F is directly proportional to T. $F = 2.25$ when $T = 12$. Find F when $T = 50$. 9.375

19. l is directly proportional to w. $l = 3.9$ when $w = 3$. Find l when $w = 40$. 52

20. d is directly proportional to t. $d = 36$ when $t = 0.9$. Find d when $t = 11$. 440

21. A varies directly as l. $A = 5.4$ when $l = 1.8$. Find A when $l = 3$. 9

22. C varies directly as r. $C = 1.9$ when $r = 0.213$. Find C when $r = 10$. 89.2

23. y is directly proportional to x. $y = 2.56$ and $x = 3.2$. Find y when $x = 25$. 20

24. y is directly proportional to x. $y = 7.29$ when $x = 0.9$. Find y when $x = 1.2$. 9.72

C **25.** If y varies directly as the square of x, and $y = 1.2$ when $x = 2$, what does y equal when $x = 5$? 7.5

26. If y varies directly as the square of x, and $y = 40.5$ when $x = 9$, what does y equal when $x = 12$? 72

27. Does the area of a circle vary directly as the radius? no

28. Does a square's perimeter vary directly as the length of its side? yes

Applications

29. Finance The amount of interest earned on a savings account is directly proportional to the amount of money in the account. If $5000 earns $350 interest, how much interest is earned on $8000? $560

ALGEBRA IN ACCOUNTING

The following function uses the *straight line method* to determine the annual rate of depreciation.

$$D = \frac{C - S}{N}$$

where C = original cost N = estimated life
        S = scrap value D = the amount to be depreciated each year

EXAMPLE   A car is purchased at a cost of $9600. It is estimated that it will be used for 20 years, after which it will be worth $600 for scrap. Find the annual depreciation and the annual rate of depreciation of the car.

$$D = \frac{9600 - 600}{20} = \$450 \text{ annual depreciation}$$

$$450 \div 9600 = 4.69\% \text{ annual rate of depreciation}$$

Use the above function to solve.

A mainframe computer is purchased at a cost of $110,000. It is estimated it will be used for 5 years, after which it will have a scrap value of $10,000. Find the annual depreciation and the annual rate of depreciation. $20,000; 18.18%

10.4 Direct Variation   **429**

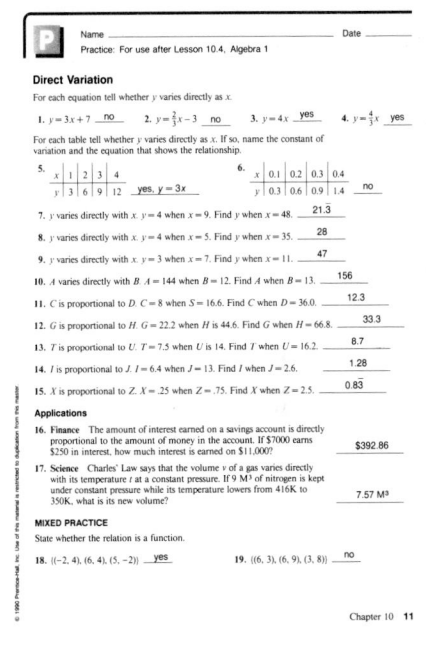
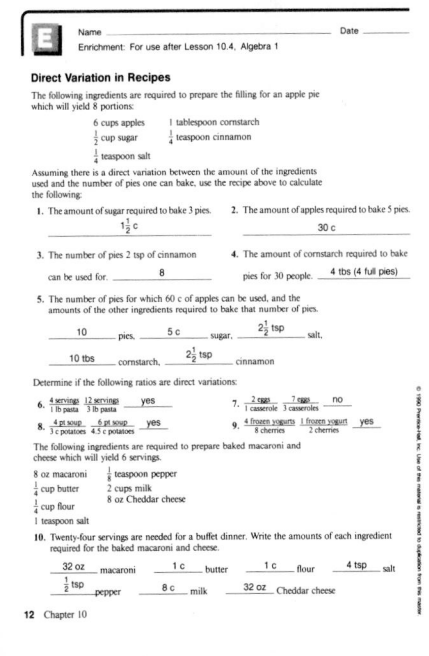

Vocabulary

Inverse variation

Materials/Manipulatives

Graph paper
Overhead projector
Straightedge
Teacher's Resource Book,
   Teaching Aid 11,
   Transparency 22, 23

BACKGROUND

In the Capsule Review, students re-view direct variation. They first evalu-ate the constant of variation for given values of x and y. Students then use the constant to write a linear function. In this lesson, inverse variation is dis-cussed. An inverse variation has a constant of variation k, but it is *not* a linear function.

Critical Thinking

Comparing–Contrasting Compare the equations $y = kx$ and $\dfrac{y_1}{y_2} = \dfrac{x_2}{x_1}$, and determine whether they describe the same types of variation. If it is known that y varies inversely with x, then $\dfrac{y_1}{y_2} = \dfrac{x_2}{x_1}$ is the same as $\dfrac{x_1}{y_2} = \dfrac{x_2}{y_1}$, which is an inverse variation. However, in some cases, specific values of x and y could hold true for a direct variation. For example, if $y_1 = -2$, $y_2 = 2$, $x_1 = 1$ and $x_2 = -1$, then $\dfrac{x_1}{x_2} = \dfrac{y_2}{y_1}$. The equation $y = kx$ is a direct variation.

Inverse Variation

10.5

Objectives: To identify inverse variations
To solve problems involving inverse variations

Ron is a SCUBA diver and he knows that as he dives the amount of pressure p increases, while the volume v of a confined gas will decrease. A relation of this type is called an *inverse variation*. This relation between pressure and volume is known as *Boyle's Law*.

Capsule Review

Determining k identifies the equation for finding any pair (x, y) related in direct proportion by that constant.

EXAMPLE **For $y = kx$, find k if $x = 3$ and $y = 7.5$. Then use k to state the equation.**

$$y = kx$$
$$7.5 = k(3) \qquad \textit{Substitute the elements of the known pair.}$$
$$2.5 = k \qquad \textit{The equation is } y = 2.5x.$$

Evaluate for k, given $y = kx$. Then use k to state the equation.

1. $x = 2$ and $y = 8$ $4; y = 4x$ **2.** $y = -3$ and $x = \dfrac{2}{3}$ $-\dfrac{9}{2}; y = -\dfrac{9}{2}x$ **3.** $x = 7$ and $y = 28$ $4; y = 4x$

An **inverse variation** is a function in the form: $xy = k$ or $y = \dfrac{k}{x}$, $k \neq 0$, where it is said that y varies inversely (or indirectly) as x, or y is inversely proportional to x. The *constant of variation* is k.

Inverse variation is not a linear function. The graph of an inverse variation is a hyperbola described by the function $xy = k$, $k \neq 0$.

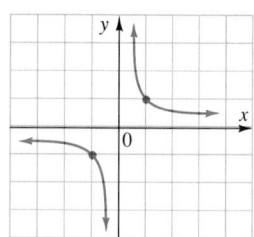

EXAMPLE 1 **From the table below tell whether y varies inversely as x. If so, name the constant of variation and the equation that shows the relationship.**

x	y
5	4.8
6.4	3.75
3	8
20	1.2

Substitute each (x, y) in $xy = k$.

$5(4.8) = 24 \qquad 6.4(3.75) = 24 \qquad 3(8) = 24 \qquad 20(1.2) = 24$

y varies inversely as x. $k = 24$; $xy = 24$

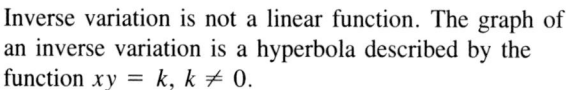

430   Chapter 10 Relations, Functions, and Variation

Suppose (x_1, y_1) and (x_2, y_2) are ordered pairs of the same inverse variation. The constant of variation would be the same for each: $x_1 \cdot y_1 = k$ and $x_2 \cdot y_2 = k$.

Therefore, $x_1 \cdot y_1 = x_2 \cdot y_2$ or $\dfrac{x_1}{x_2} = \dfrac{y_2}{y_1}$.

EXAMPLE 2 y varies indirectly as x. If $y = 3$ when $x = 10.5$, find x when $y = 9$.

$$x_1 \cdot y_1 = x_2 \cdot y_2 \qquad x_1 \cdot y_1 = k \text{ and } x_2 \cdot y_2 = k$$
$$10.5(3) = x(9) \qquad \textit{Substitute.}$$
$$31.5 = 9x$$
$$3.5 = x$$

EXAMPLE 3 **At a depth of 33 ft in salt water, the pressure is measured to be 2 atmospheres (atm). The volume of air in a container is 10 ft³. Find the volume of air in the container at a depth where the pressure is 1.25 atm.**

Let x = pressure at 33 ft and y = volume of air in the container; then $xy = k$.

$$x_1 \cdot y_1 = x_2 \cdot y_2 \qquad 20 = 1.25y$$
$$(2)(10) = (1.25)(y) \qquad 16 = y \qquad \text{The volume of air is 16 ft}^3.$$

Another example of an inverse variation is the principle of the lever. A lever is a bar that pivots about a fixed point called the fulcrum. If masses m_1 and m_2 are placed at distances d_1 and d_2 from the fulcrum and the lever is balanced, then $m_1 d_1 = m_2 d_2$.

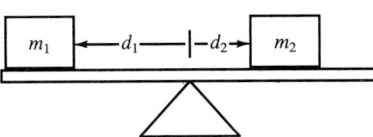

EXAMPLE 4 **Eric and Stephanie were playing on a seesaw. Eric, whose mass is 32 kg, sat 1.5 m from the fulcrum. What must be Stephanie's mass if the seesaw balanced when she sat 2 m from the fulcrum?**

Let m = mass in kg and d = distance in m; then $md = k$.
$$m_1 \cdot d_1 = m_2 \cdot d_2$$
$$32(1.5) = m_2 \cdot 2 \qquad \textit{Substitution.}$$
$$48 = m_2 \cdot 2$$
$$24 = m_2 \qquad \text{Stephanie's mass is 24 kg.}$$

CLASS EXERCISES

For each table tell whether y varies inversely as x. If so, name the constant of variation and the equation that shows the relationship.

1.

x	6	8	1.2	48
y	4	3	20	0.5

24; $xy = 24$

2.

x	3	4.5	5	1.2
y	15	10	9	38

no

10.5 Inverse Variation **431**

431

Find the constant of variation *k* if *y* varies indirectly as *x*.

3. $y = 8$, $x = 4$ 32

4. $y = 3.3$, $x = 3$ 9.9

5. $y = 8.1$, $x = 0.7$ 5.67

6. *y* varies inversely as *x*. If *y* = 6 when *x* = 0.8, find *y* when *x* = 3. 1.6

7. In a rectangle with a constant area, the width *w* is inversely proportional to the length *l*. If *w* = 9 when *l* = 32, find *w* when *l* = 2.4. 120

PRACTICE EXERCISES

For each table tell whether *y* varies inversely as *x*. If so, name the constant of variation and the equation that shows the relationship.

A

1.

x	*y*
2	6
−3	−4
12	1

yes; $xy = 12$

2.

x	*y*
9	4
−2	−18
3	12

yes; $xy = 36$

3.

x	*y*
−0.8	1.8
1.2	−1.2
−3.6	0.4

yes; $xy = -1.44$

4.

x	*y*
−1.6	0.3
0.4	7.2
2	−0.24

no

Solve.

5. *y* varies inversely as *x*. If *y* = 12 when *x* = 6, find *y* when *x* = 9. 8

6. *y* varies indirectly as *x*. If *y* = 8 when *x* = 18, find *y* when *x* = 12. 12

7. *l* is inversely proportional to *w*. If *l* = 1.6 when *w* = 30, find *l* when *w* = 12. 4

8. *s* is inversely proportional to *t*. If *s* = 25 when *t* = 8, find *s* when *t* = 0.5. 400

9. *w* varies indirectly as *l*. If *w* = 3.2 when *l* = 6, find *w* when *l* = 0.8. 24

10. *C* varies inversely as *k*. If *C* = 24 when *k* = 1.6, find *C* when *k* = 0.12. 320

11. *y* is inversely proportional to *x*. If *y* = 4.2 and *x* = 3.9, find *y* when *x* = 2.6. 6.3

12. *y* varies inversely as *x*. If *y* = 2.25 when *x* = 3.6, find *y* when *x* = 0.3. 27

13. *j* is inversely proportional to *k*. If *j* = 9 when *k* = 2.5, find *j* when *k* = 4.25. 5.29

14. *h* varies inversely as *l*. If $h = \frac{1}{4}$ when $l = \frac{1}{6}$, find *h* when $l = \frac{2}{3}$. $\frac{1}{16}$

B 15. *m* varies indirectly as the square root of *t*. If *t* = 144 when *m* = 6, find *t* when *m* = 132. $\frac{36}{121}$

16. *l* varies indirectly with z^2. If *l* = 9 when *z* = 2, find *z* when *l* = 90. 0.633

17. *n* varies inversely with the cube of *q*. If *n* = 9.3 when *q* = 4.2, find *n* when *q* = 3.2. 21.03

18. *h* varies indirectly as the square of *i*. If *h* = 4 when *i* = 1.6, find *h* when *i* = 6.2. 0.266

432 Chapter 10 Relations, Functions, and Variation

19. The volume of air in a container is 15 in.^{3} at 1.5 atm. Find the volume at 2.25 atm. 10 in.^{3}

20. The volume of air in a container is 12 m^3 at 1.75 atm. Find the pressure if the volume is 4 m^3. 5.25 atm

21. How much mass must be placed 2.5 m away from the fulcrum in order to balance a 35-kg object that is 3 m from the fulcrum? 42 kg

22. If a 60-kg object is 3 m from the fulcrum and balances a 45-kg object, how far is the 45-kg object from the fulcrum? 4 m

C 23. Two camels traveled the same distance. Do their rates of speed vary indirectly as the number of hours traveled? Explain. yes; $r_1 t_1 = r_2 t_2$

24. Two factory workers had the same gross salary per week. Do their rates of pay vary inversely as the number of hours they work? Give an example to explain your answer. yes; 20×25 h $= \$10 \times 50$ h

For Exercises 25 and 26, the rate r varies inversely as time t.

25. A distance was traveled in 5 h at 42 mi/h. The return trip was done in 6 h. What was the average speed on the return trip? 35 mi/h

26. A trip was made in a light plane traveling at 160 mi/h and took 3 h 30 min. The average speed on the return trip was 200 mi/h. How long did the return trip take? 2.8 h

Applications

27. **Geometry** If the area of a triangle stays constant, does the base of the triangle vary indirectly as the height? yes

28. **Geometry** Does the circumference of a circle vary inversely as its radius? no

EXTRA

The cost of owning a car depends upon the number of miles it is driven. D.D. kept records and found that it cost $362.00 to drive 400 mi a month and $397.00 to drive 650 mi a month. Use this information to answer these questions.

1. Assume that a linear equation is a reasonable mathematical model of the cost-distance function. Write the equation. $C = 0.14m + 306$

2. Predict the cost of driving D.D.'s car 2500 mi per month. $516, $656

3. What meaning does slope have in the case of D.D.'s car?
Tells the increase in cost per mile.

4. According to your equation, how much will it cost to drive 0 mi per month? Is that amount reasonable? $306

10.5 Inverse Variation **433**

Teacher's Resource Book
Reteaching—Chapter 10, p. 13.

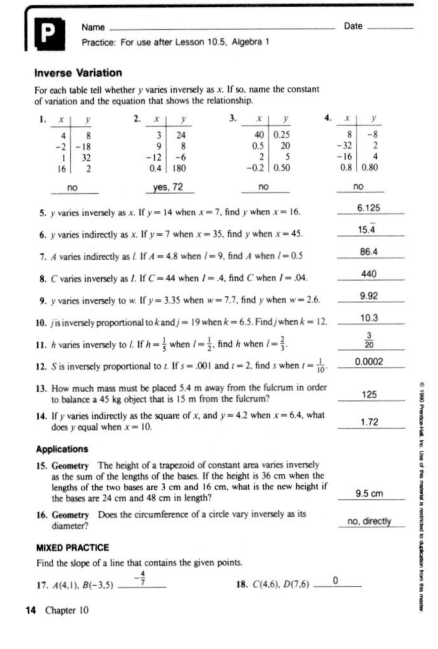

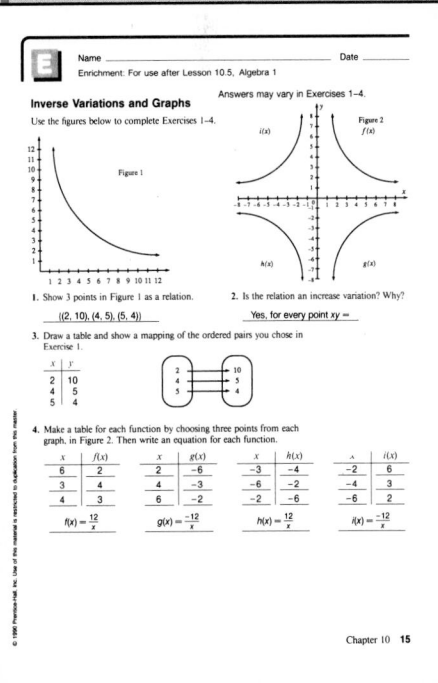

433

BACKGROUND

- In many instances, formulas have been developed to facilitate problem solving. Selecting the appropriate formula is a crucial step in the solution process of many of these problems.
- To determine a student's progress, analyze errors in the student's work and then classify specific errors.

Error Analysis Classification

1. *Misunderstanding*
   Did not understand the conditions of the problem
2. *Misapplied Strategy*
   Chose an incorrect formula
   Was inconsistent in substituting values for variables in the formula

---

10.6

Problem Solving Strategy: Use an Appropriate Formula

A formula is an equation that expresses a relationship among different variables. Mathematical formulas are used to solve problems in science, engineering, economics, business, and the social sciences. Formulas are also used in everyday life to solve consumer problems.

People working in different occupations have reference books containing formulas needed to solve specific problems. For example, an accountant uses a formula to calculate how much business equipment depreciates each year. Depreciation is the amount of decrease in the value of the equipment over a period of time.

EXAMPLE 1 **James is an accountant. He uses the formula given below to find the linear depreciation for business equipment owned by a client. Tax rules allow the property to be depreciated over a period of 10 years. If the equipment had an original cost of $10,000, find its value at the end of 3 years.**

$$V = C\left(1 - \frac{n}{N}\right)$$

where V = value at the end of n years
C = original cost
N = total number of years the equipment can be depreciated

☐ **Understand the Problem**

What are the given facts?

The equipment can be depreciated for 10 years.
The original cost was $10,000.

What are you asked to find?

You are asked to find the value of the equipment at the end of 3 yea

☐ **Plan Your Approach**

Choose a strategy.

The problem involves linear depreciation. The strategy requires applying the formula for calculating linear depreciation.

Substitute the given numbers into the formula to solve the problem.

$$V = 10,000\left(1 - \frac{3}{10}\right)$$

434   Chapter 10 Relations, Functions, and Variation

Complete the Work

Solve the equation.

$$V = 10,000\left(1 - \frac{3}{10}\right)$$

$$= 10,000\left(\frac{7}{10}\right) = 7000$$

Interpret the Results

State your answer.

The value of the equipment at the end of 3 years is $7000.

CLASS EXERCISES

Write a formula that can be used to solve a problem in each case.

1. area of a rectangle $A = lw$ **2.** area of a triangle **3.** equation of a line
$A = \frac{1}{2}bh$ $y = mx + b$

4. If Ralph bought 18 pens for $0.86 each, how much did he spend in all? $15.48

5. Use the formula $I = prt$. Determine the interest if $p = 5000, $r = 0.0825$, and $t = 4$. $1650

6. Use the linear depreciation formula given in the example to find the value V if $C = 5000, $N = 10$ yr, and $n = 3$. $3500

PRACTICE EXERCISES

Select a formula that can be used to solve a problem in each case.

1. area of a square $A = s^2$ $V = \frac{4}{3}\pi r^3$

2. circumference of a circle $C = 2\pi r$ $V = s^3$

3. linear depreciation $V = C\left(1 - \frac{n}{N}\right)$ $C = 2\pi r$

4. simple interest $I = prt$ $I = prt$

5. volume of a sphere $V = \frac{4}{3}\pi r^3$ $A = s^2$

6. volume of a cube $V = s^3$ $V = C\left(1 - \frac{n}{N}\right)$

Solve each problem.

7. Ernie bought 36 ballpoint pens for $1.12 each. How much did he spend in all? $40.32

8. A weather report gave the temperature as 20°C. Use the formula $F = \frac{9}{5}C + 32$ to find the equivalent temperature in degrees Fahrenheit. 68°F

9. Annie spent $169 for 130 tennis balls. How much did she spend for each tennis ball? $1.30

10. Robert and Mary bought 5 gallons of milk for $9.65. How much did they spend for each gallon of milk? $1.93

10.6 Problem Solving Strategy: Use an Appropriate Formula   **435**

TEACHING SUGGESTION

It is a good idea to have students make clear tables to assign values to the variables. These tables should be used after the problem is solved to check the solutions.

Critical Thinking

Discovering Patterns The formula $C = 2\pi r$ relates the circumference of a circle to its radius. Does this equation express either of the types of variation studied in this chapter, and if so, what is the constant of variation? It is a direct variation and the constant of variation is 2π.

CHALKBOARD EXAMPLES

• **For the Example**
  A certain car can be depreciated over a period of 8 years. If the original cost of the car was $12,500, use the formula in the example to find its worth after 6 years. $3125

Common Error

• Students frequently substitute the values in a problem for the wrong variables in the formula. Have these students carefully label all variables.
• See *Teacher's Resource Book* for additional remediation.

LESSON FOLLOW-UP

Discussion

What restrictions, if any, must be placed on the variables if the formula $A = \pi r^2$ is solved for r? None, the formula becomes $r = \sqrt{\frac{A}{\pi}}$, so there is no chance of 0 being in the denominator. A and r, of course, must be positive numbers.

Assignment Guide

• See p. 410B for assignments.
• See *Teacher's Resource Book,* Tests pp. 103–104.

- The following skills and concepts are reviewed:
  Solving problems involving proportions (Ex. 1)
  Using the formula for the perimeter of a rectangle (Ex. 3)
- The following problem solving strategies may be appropriate:
  Make a table (Exercises 1 and 2)
  Draw a diagram (Ex. 3)

Project

The project involves:
Researching the different interest rates offered by local banks
Determining variables for a loan of a given amount

Lesson Quiz

Solve each problem.

1. Use the formula $F = \frac{9}{5}C + 32$ to find the temperature in degrees Fahrenheit of a reading of 35°C. 95°F

2. Buzz paid $23.10 for 14 yo-yos. How much did each yo-yo cost? $1.65

3. Use the formula in the example to determine the worth of a product after 3 years if its original cost was $1800. Assume that the product can depreciate for a total of 12 years. $1350

Using the formula $s = \frac{1}{2}gt^2$, solve for g.

11. $s = 9$, $t = 1$ 18 **12.** $s = 36$, $t = 2$ 18 **13.** $s = 64$, $t = 4$ 8 **14.** $s = 81$, $t =$ 18

Use the linear depreciation formula, $V = C\left(1 - \dfrac{n}{N}\right)$, to find the value V for each set of conditions.

	C	N	n		C	N	n
15.	$5000	5 yr	1 $4000	**16.**	$20,000	4 yr	4 $0
B **17.**	$3000	3 yr	3 $0	**18.**	$15,000	10 yr	8 $3000
19.	$50,000	20 yr	15 $12,500	**20.**	$60,000	25 yr	17 $19,200

Use the formula, $V = \frac{1}{3}\pi r^2 h$ to solve for the following unknowns. Assume $\pi \approx 3.14$. This formula can be used to find the volume of a cone.

21. Find h when $V = 64$ and $r = 3$. 6.79 **22.** Find r when $h = 6$ and $V = 64$. 3.

23. Find V when $r = \frac{1}{4}$ and $h = \frac{1}{3}$. 0.0218 **24.** Find r when $h = 0.03$ and $V = 0.$ 1.49

C **25.** The ratio of the speed of an airplane to the speed of sound is called a Mach number. Find the Mach number (to one decimal place) for an airplane designed to fly at a maximum speed of 1800 mi/h. Use 740 mi/h for the speed of sound. 2.4

26. If A represents the speed of an aircraft and s represents the speed of sound, write a formula for finding the Mach number M of the aircraft. $M = \frac{A}{s}$

Mixed Problem Solving Review

1. William commutes 648 mi a week to work by car. If the car averages 18 mi/gal, how much does he spend on gasoline over a 7-week period if gasoline sells for $0.96 per gallon? $241.92

2. It takes Carlos 6 h to paint a room and 7 h for Jerome to paint the same room. How long would it take them to do the job together? 3.23 h

3. The length of a rectangle is 3 in. more than 6 times the width. If the perimeter is 48 in., find the length and the width of the rectangle. l = 21 in.; w = 3

PROJECT

Find out the interest rates offered by 5 banks in your neighborhood.
Determine the variables involved in obtaining a $5000 loan.

For each equation, tell whether *y* varies directly as *x*. Explain. 10.4

1. $3x + y = 0$
yes; $y = -3x$; in the form $y = kx$

2. $x = y + 2$
no; $x = y + 2$ is not in the form $y = kx$

3. $\frac{1}{2}x + y = 0$
yes; $y = -\frac{1}{2}x$; in the form $y = kx$

4. $y = \frac{4}{7}x + 3$
no; $y = \frac{4}{7}x + 3$ is not in the form $y = kx$

Solve.

5. *y* varies directly with *x*. If $y = 3$ when $x = 2$, find *y* when $x = 4$. 6

6. *y* varies directly with *x*. If $y = 5$ when $x = 4$, find *y* when $x = 8$. 10

For each table tell whether *y* varies inversely as *x*. If so, name the constant of variation and the equation that shows the relationship. 10.5

7.

x	y
4	3.5
5.6	2.5
20	0.7
2	7

yes; $xy = 14$

8.

x	y
6	2.5
1.2	12.5
30	0.5
3	5

yes; $xy = 15$

9.

x	y
−2.3	0.3
0.5	4.3
2	−3.2
4	2.7 no

10.

x	y
3.2	0.5
1.6	2
0.3	5
4	2 no

Solve. 10.5–10.6

11. *y* varies indirectly as *x*. If $y = 5$ when $x = 4$, find *x* when $y = 2$. 10

12. *y* varies indirectly as *x*. If $y = 8$ when $x = 10$, find *x* when $y = 5$. 16

13. Robert bought 5 albums for $8.98 each. How much did he spend in all?
$44.90

14. Dan spent $6.45 on five notebooks for school. How much did he spend for each notebook? $1.29

Given the linear depreciation formula, $V = C\left(1 - \dfrac{n}{N}\right)$, find the value of *V*, for each set of conditions.

	C	N	n	
15.	4,000	4 yr	1	$3000
16.	12,000	10 yr	8	$2400

10.6 Problem Solving Strategy: Use an Appropriate Formula **437**

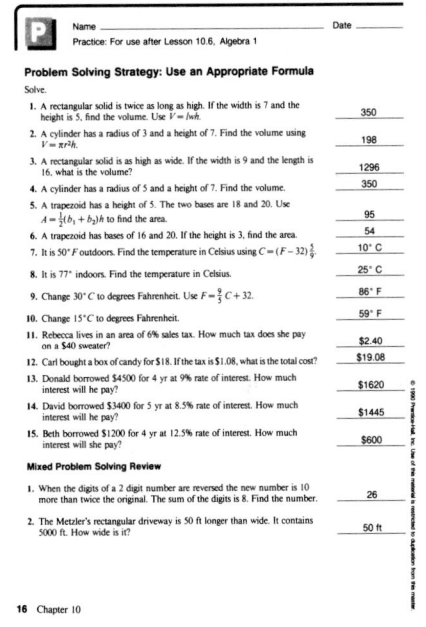

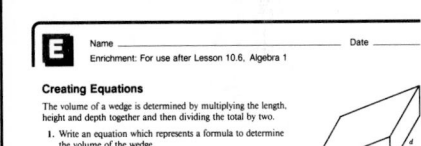

- See *Teacher's Resource Book, Spanish Chapter Summary and Review*, pp. 19–20.
- See *Extra Practice*, p. 664.

Vocabulary

composite function (423)
constant function (423)
constant of proportionality (426)
direct variation (426)
domain (413)
function (417)

function notation (420)
inverse variation (430)
linear function (422)
range (413)
relation (413)
vertical line test (418)

A **relation** is any set of ordered pairs.
The **domain** of a relation is the set of all the first elements or x-coordinates.
The **range** of a relation is the set of all the second elements or y-coordinates.
A **function** is a relation in which each element of the domain is paired with exactly one element of the range. Function notation includes, as examples:
$y = 4x$, $f(x) = 4x$, and $H: x \rightarrow 4x$.

State the relation as a set of ordered pairs. Also state the domain and the range and tell whether the relation is a function. 10.1

1.

x	2	5	2	-2
y	-2	-5	0	1

{(2, −2), (5, −5), (2, 0), (−2, 1)}
$D = \{-2, 2, 5\}$ $R = \{-2, -5, 0\}$ not a function

2.

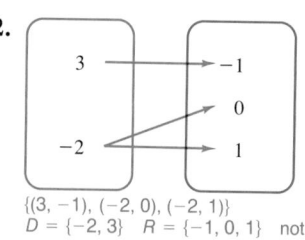

{(3, −1), (−2, 0), (−2, 1)}
$D = \{-2, 3\}$ $R = \{-1, 0, 1\}$ not a function

Vertical Line Test A relation is not a function if any vertical line can pass through the graph in more than one point.

Linear Function A set of ordered pairs whose graph is a nonvertical straight line can be defined by an equation in the slope-intercept form.

$$y = mx + b \qquad m = \text{slope}; \ b = y\text{-intercept}$$

Graph each relation and tell whether or not it is a function. If so, is it a linear function? 10.2–10.3

3. $2x + y = 4$; domain $\{-1, 0, 4\}$
a function; not a linear function

4. $y = |x|$; domain {all real numbers}
a function; not a linear function

5. $f(x) = 2x + 2$; domain {all real numbers}
a function; a linear function

6. $x = 2$
not a function

7. Graph the relation between month m and average temperature t as described in this chart. Is this relation a function? Is it a linear function? yes

Average Temperature for Eureka, California

Month (m)	Jan.	Feb.	Mar.	Apr.	May	Jun.	Jul.
Temperature (t)	47°F	49°F	48°F	49°F	52°F	55°F	56°F

8. Evaluate $f(-2) + g(0)$, given $f(x) = x^2$ and $g(x) = 2x - 1$. 3

Direct Variation A *direct variation* is a function in the form

$$y = kx, \ k \neq 0$$

where y varies directly as x, or y is directly proportional to x. The constant of variation is k.

Inverse Variation An *inverse variation* is a function in the form

$$xy = k, \ k \neq 0$$

where y varies inversely (or indirectly) as x, or y is inversely proportional to x. The constant of variation is k.

State whether y varies directly or inversely as x. Also determine the equation which shows the relationship and name the constant of variation.   10.4–10.6

inverse variation; $y = \frac{18}{x}$; 18

9. $\frac{y}{4} = x$ direct variation; $y = 4x$; 4

10.

x	36	6	8	90
y	0.5	3	2.25	0.2

11. If y varies directly with x, and $y = 5$ when $x = 25$, find y when $x = 55$. 11

12. If r is inversely proportional to t, and $r = 46$ when $t = 1.5$, find r when $t = 2$. 34.5

13. The amount of interest owed each month on a fixed mortgage varies directly as the current balance. If the balance for one month is \$65,000 and the interest owed is \$650, what is the interest owed five years later when the balance is \$48,000? \$480

14. Charles' Law says that the volume V of a gas varies directly as its temperature t at a constant pressure. If 20 L of neon is kept at a constant pressure while its temperature changes from $360°K$ to $513°K$, determine its new volume. 28.5 L

15. The length of a rectangle of constant area is inversely proportional to the width. If the length of the rectangle is 6 m and the width is 4 m, what would the length be if the width is 3 m? 8 m

See *Teacher's Resource Book.*
- *Tests,* pp. 105–108
- *Calculator Test,* pp. 19–20

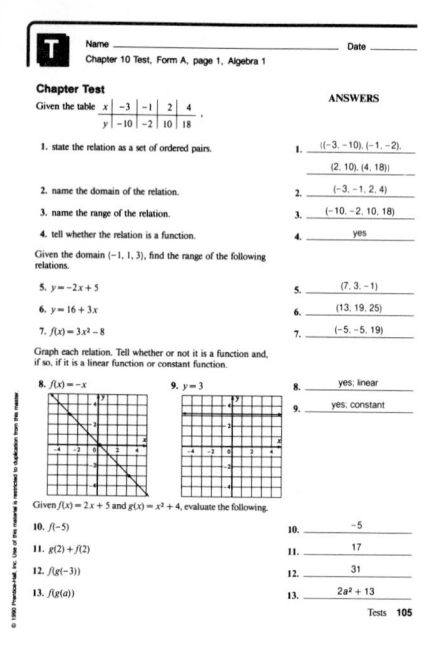

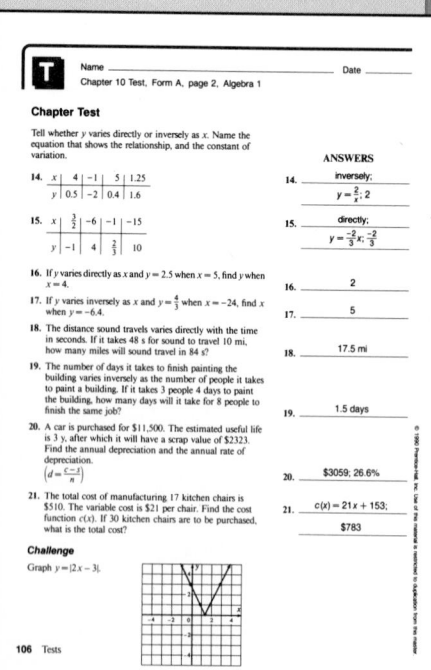

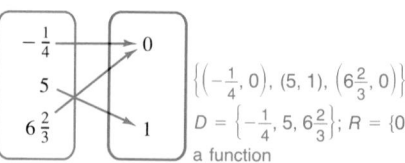

State each relation as a set of ordered pairs. Name the domain and range of each relation, and tell whether the relation is a function.

1.

x	2	5	0	−2
y	−5	−14	1	7

{(2, −5), (5, −14), (0, 1), (−2, 7)}
$D = \{−2, 0, 2, 5\}$ $R = \{−14, −5, 1, 7\}$ a function

2.

$\{(−\frac{1}{4}, 0), (5, 1), (6\frac{2}{3}, 0)\}$
$D = \{−\frac{1}{4}, 5, 6\frac{2}{3}\}; R = \{0,$
a function

Graph each relation and tell whether or not it is a function and, if so, if it is a linear function.

3. $y − 3x = 2;$
Domain: {. . . −1, 0, 1 . . .}
a function; not a linear function

4. $f(x) = 3x − 1$
Domain: {all real numbers}
a function; a linear function

5. $y = −1$
Domain: {all real number
a function; a linear function

6. Graph the closing prices of a stock over a period of one week. Is this relation a function? yes

Day	Mon.	Tue.	Wed.	Thu.	Fri.
Closing price	22	$23\frac{1}{8}$	$23\frac{1}{4}$	23	$23\frac{1}{4}$

7. Evaluate $f(0) + g(−2)$, given $f(x) = x^2 + 1$ and $g(x) = 3x$. −5

Tell whether y varies directly or inversely as x. Name the equation which shows the relationship and give the constant of variation.

8. $\frac{y}{x} = −2$ direct variation; y = −2x; −2

9.

x	18	3	4	45
y	0.5	3	2.25	0.2

inverse variation; $y = \frac{9}{x}$; 9

10. If y varies inversely as x, and $y = 6$ when $x = 9$, find y when $x = 2.7$. 20

11. If the cost of kumquats c varies directly as their weight w, and $c = 3.78$ when $w = 3$, find c when $w = 4.5$. 5.67

12. The amount of flour used in baking bread is directly proportional to the number of loaves of bread. If 6 cups of flour makes 2 loaves of bread, how many cups of flour would be used to make 5 loaves of bread? 15 cups

Challenge

1. Graph $y = |x|$; domain $\{−3 \le x \le 3\}$

2. The distance a spring stretches is directly proportional to the mass hooked onto the bottom of it. If a spring stretches 1.1 cm when holding a 3-kg weight, how far will it stretch when a 7-kg weight is hooked onto its end? 2.57 cm

Select the best choice for each question.

1. The equation of the line through
 D (4, −1) and (0, 7) is:
 A. $y = 7x + 2$
 B. $y = -7x + 2$
 C. $y = 2x + 7$
 D. $y = -2x + 7$
 E. $y = \frac{-3}{2}x + 7$

2. When $\frac{2}{3}$ of 690 is subtracted from $\frac{3}{5}$
 A of 865, the result is:
 A. 59   B. 69   C. 89
 D. 159   E. 169

3. A customer used a $100 bill to pay
 D for purchases of $29.95, $14.50,
 $8.90, $2.75, and 79¢. What did the
 customer receive in change?
 A. $42.11
 B. $42.91
 C. $43.01
 D. $43.11
 E. $43.91

4. If x varies directly as y, and if
 E $x = 12$ when $y = 33$, then what is
 the value of x when y is 198?
 A. 544.5
 B. 177
 C. 90
 D. 76
 E. 72

5. The equation for the graph of the
 A vertical line through the point
 (−1, 3) is:
 A. $x = -1$
 B. $y = -1$
 C. $x = 3$
 D. $y = 3$
 E. $y = x + 4$

6. Find the value of $f(-2)$ when
 C $f(x) = 2x^2 + 4x + 7$.
 A. −9   B. −7   C. 7
 D. 9   E. 23

7. Martha took 1 h and 15 min to ride
 D her bike the 15 mi to her cousin's
 house. She later returned by the
 same route but took 1 h and 45 min
 for the return trip. What was her
 average rate for the round trip?
 A. 8.5 mi/h
 B. 9 mi/h
 C. 9.5 mi/h
 D. 10 mi/h
 E. 10.5 mi/h

8. If the function $y = 5x - 2$ has a
 B domain restricted to $x \geq 1$, then it
 has a range of:
 A. $y \leq 3$
 B. $y \geq 3$
 C. $y \leq 1$
 D. $y \geq 1$
 E. $y = 3$

9. Of two cereals, type A contains
 D 160 mg of sodium per oz while type
 B contains 110 mg per oz. Which of
 the following would be true about
 the number of mg of sodium in a
 $1\frac{1}{2}$ oz serving of type A as compared
 to a 2 oz serving of type B?
 A. they have the same number
 B. serving A has 50 mg more
 C. serving B has 50 mg more
 D. serving A has 20 mg more
 E. serving B has 20 mg more

The individual comments provided for
some problems can guide the students in solving these problems.

1. The different methods for finding
   the equation of a line, given certain
   information, require frequent review.
9. Students have a tendency to guess
   at the answers to problems of this
   nature, and should be dissuaded
   from this.

See *Teacher's Resource Book* for
Preparing for Standardized Tests.

Additional Answers

23.
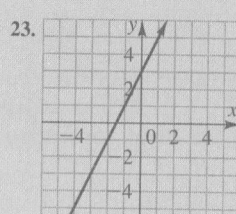

24.
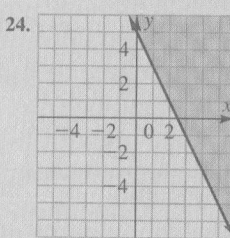

25.
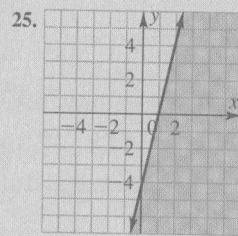

CUMULATIVE REVIEW   CHAPTERS 1–10

State the value of the variable for which the expression is undefined.   8.1

1. $\dfrac{15}{x + 3}$ -3

2. $\dfrac{4}{5y + 3}$ $-\frac{3}{5}$

3. $\dfrac{m + 2}{m^2 + 8m + 12}$ -2, -6

4. $\dfrac{s - 4}{s^2 - 16}$ -4, 4

Simplify.   8.6, 8.8

5. $\dfrac{15x^2y^4}{5xy^2}$ $3xy^2$

6. $\dfrac{24r^3s^5}{3r^2s^2}$ $8rs^3$

7. $\dfrac{14m^2 + 2mn}{14m^2n}$ $\frac{7m + n}{7mn}$

8. $\dfrac{16x^3 + 4xy}{8x^3y}$ $\frac{4x^2 + y}{2x^2y}$

9. 4 to 8 1 to 2

10. 0.3 : 2.1 1 : 7

11. 3 ft to 5 yd $\frac{1}{5}$

12. \$4.40 to \$0.22 20

13. $5 + 7x - \dfrac{3}{x}$ $\frac{7x^2 + 5x - 3}{x}$

14. $\dfrac{\dfrac{3n}{n^2} - \dfrac{1}{n}}{1 + \dfrac{3m}{n^2}}$ $\frac{2n}{n^2 + 3m}$

15. $\dfrac{\dfrac{4x}{x^2} - \dfrac{1}{x}}{1 + \dfrac{4y}{x^2}}$ $\frac{3x}{x^2 + 4y}$

Factor completely.   7.8

16. $4x^4 - 16x^2$
$4x^2(x + 2)(x - 2)$

17. $4x^2 - 4x - 15$
$(2x + 3)(2x - 5)$

18. $16x^3y^2 - 8x^2y^2 + 24x^2y^3$
$8x^2y^2(2x - 1 + 3y)$

Write an equation of a line in standard form given the following slope and/or points on the line.   9.4, 9.6

19. $m = 3$, $(0, -3)$ $-3x + y = -3$

20. $m = -\frac{1}{2}$, $(6, 0)$ $x + 2y = 6$

21. $(6, -9)$, $(4, -10)$ $x - 2y = 24$

22. $(11, -13)$, $(-9, 7)$ $x + y = -2$

Graph each equation or inequality. See side column.   9.6, 9.7

23. $y = 2x + 3$

24. $y \geq -2x + 5$

25. $y \leq 4x - 4$

Find the range of each function.   10.2

26. $f(t) = \dfrac{1}{1 + 3t}$ $D = \{-1, 0, 1\}$
$R = \left\{-\frac{1}{2}, 1, \frac{1}{4}\right\}$

27. $g: x \to x^2 - 16$ $D = \left\{-4, \frac{1}{2}, 3\right\}$
$R = \left\{0, -\frac{63}{4}, -7\right\}$

Solve.   4.3, 4.10, 5.6

28. $|2m - 3| = 17$ $\{10, -7\}$

29. $|8 - 3t| < 6$ $\left\{\frac{2}{3} < t < \frac{14}{3}\right\}$

30. $|4a - 7| \leq 1$ $\left\{\frac{3}{2} \leq a \leq 2\right\}$

31. Two trains are traveling east from the same city. Train 2 traveling at 120 mi/h leaves 1 hr after train 1. Train 1 travels at a speed of 110 mi/h. How long will it take train 2 to overtake train 1? 11 h

32. Find four consecutive even integers whose sum is 52. 10, 12, 14, 16

33. The perimeter of a rectangle is 110 cm. If the length of the rectangle is 5 cm more than the width, what are the dimensions of the rectangle?
$l = 30$ cm $w = 25$ cm

442   Chapter 10 Relations, Functions, and Variation

OVERVIEW • Chapter 11

SUMMARY

In Chapter 11, students solve systems of linear equations by using several methods. They learn how to use the graphing, substitution, addition-subtraction, and the multiplication-addition/subtraction methods to solve systems of linear equations. Students describe the graph of the system and the number of solutions by examining the slope and y-intercept of each equation. Students use their skills in solving systems of equations to solve word problems involving digits, age, money, mixtures, and wind and water currents.

After this chapter has been completed, students will be able to use their knowledge of solving a system of linear equations to graph the solution set of a system of inequalities.

CHAPTER OBJECTIVES

- To use graphs to solve systems of linear equations
- To solve a system of linear equations in two variables by the substitution method
- To solve systems of linear equations by the addition/subtraction method
- To solve appropriate systems of linear equations by using the multiplication-addition/subtraction method
- To use systems of equations to solve digit problems
- To use systems of equations to solve age problems
- To use systems of equations to solve money and mixture problems
- To use systems of equations to solve uniform-motion problems involving winds and water currents
- To graph the solution set of a system of linear inequalities

Problem Solving Strategy

To solve a problem by writing and solving a system of linear equations

CHAPTER HIGHLIGHTS

The *theme* of the chapter is business. Special features and applications demonstrate how systems of linear equations can be applied to real-world situations.

PROBLEM SOLVING AND APPLICATIONS

Problem solving and applications form an integral part of each lesson. Students use various methods of solving systems of linear equations to solve problems related to everyday experiences. In Lessons 11.3, 11.6, 11.7, 11.8, and 11.9, students use the four-step problem solving method to simplify and solve word problems.

TECHNOLOGY

Calculator

Students may use a graphing calculator or computer program to check their solutions to systems of linear equations.

Computer

The computer feature in Lesson 11.6 introduces transposition errors to students. They learn how to use a computer program to check for transposition errors.

The computer program in Lesson 11.8 generates a chart of possible combinations of dimes and quarters that add up to a specified amount.

RESOURCES

Teacher's Resource Book

- Teaching Aids 5, 14, 15

- Transparencies 7, 14, 15, 17, 18, 19, 20, 24

STUDENT TEXT

TEACHER'S RESOURCE BOOK

Chapter Content	Basic	Average	Enriched	R	P	E
11.1 Graphing Systems of Linear Equations	D: 446/1-29 odd, 49, 50 R: 447/4, 12, 14	D: 446/1-41 odd, 49-52 R: 447/6, 14, 22	D: 447/31-47 odd, 49-53	1	2	3
11.2 The Substitution Method	D: 453/1-27 odd, 50 R: 447/2, 6, 14	D: 453/1-41 odd, 50, 51 R: 447/20, 24, 26	D: 453/37-49 odd, 50, 51 R: 448/32, 34, 40	4	5	6
11.3 Problem Solving Strategy: Writing a Linear System	D: 457/1-11 odd MPSR 1-3 R: 453/2, 8, 14	D: 457/1-13 odd MPSR 1-3 R: 453/26, 28, 51	D: 457/7-17 odd MPSR 1-3 R: 453/36, 38, 51		7	8
11.4 The Addition/Subtraction Method	D: 461/1-23 odd, 46, 47 R: 457/2, 4, 6 461/4, 6, 12	D: 461/1-37 odd, 44-48 R: 457/8, 10, 12 461/8, 10, 18	D: 461/27-45 odd, 46-49 R: 457/8, 10, 12	9	10	11
11.5 The Multiplication-Addition/Subtraction Method	D: 465/1-21 odd, 35 R: 461/2, 8, 10 Test Yourself	D: 465/1-27 odd, 35, 36 R: Test Yourself	D: 465/19-33 odd, 35, 36 R: Test Yourself	12	13	14
11.6 Problem Solving: Digit Problems	D: 468/1-11 odd R: 465/2, 4, 10	D: 468/1-15 odd R: 465/16, 22, 24	D: 469/9-15 odd R: 465/28, 30, 32		15	16
11.7 Problem Solving: Age Problems	D: 471/1-15 odd R: 468/2, 4, 6	D: 471/1-23 odd R: 468/6, 8, 12	D: 472/11-27 odd R: 469/8, 10, 12		17	18
11.8 Problem Solving: Money and Mixture Problems	D: 476/1-13 odd, 21 R: 471/4, 8, 10	D: 476/1-14 odd, 21, 22 R: 472/16, 18, 20	D: 477/1-14 odd, 21-23 R: 472/20, 22, 24		19	20
11.9 Problem Solving: Wind and Water Current Problems	D: 481/1-15 odd R: 476/2, 4, 6	D: 481/1-19 odd R: 476/4, 8, 10	D: 481/6-21 odd R: 477/6, 8, 10		21	22
11.10 Graphing Systems of Linear Inequalities	D: 485/1-15 odd, 34 R: 481/6, 8, 10	D: 485/1-27 odd, 34, 35 R: Test Yourself	D: 485/17-33 odd, 34, 35 R: Test Yourself	23	24	25

D = Daily   R = Review   MPSR = Mixed Problem Solving Review   R = Reteaching   P = Practice   E = Enrichment

	STUDENT TEXT				**TEACHER'S RESOURCE BOOK**	
Review	Test Yourself	466	Chapter Test	490	Spanish Chapter Summary and Review	21-22
And	Test Yourself	487	Prep. for Stan. Tests	491	• Quizzes	113-116
Testing	Chapter Sum. and Rev.	488	Maintaining Skills	492	• Chapter Test (Form A)	117-118
			Extra Practice	665	• Chapter Test (Form B)	119-120
					Calculator Test	21-22
Special	Career	449	Algebra in Bookkeeping	469	Applications—Chapter 11	26
Features	Application	450	Extra	473	Critical Thinking	11
	Writing in Algebra	454	Biography	478	Reading and Writing in Algebra	11
	Project	458	Career	483		
	Extra	462				

11 Systems of Linear Equations

Large corporations as well as small companies need managers with good skills in business mathematics. Projecting the maximum profit and minimum cost involves an understanding of linear systems of equations.

443

Vocabulary
Consistent
Dependent system
Inconsistent
Independent System
Parallel lines
Simultaneous equations
System of linear equations

Materials/Manipulatives
Computer graphing paper
Graph paper
Graphing calculator
Overhead projector
Straightedge
Teacher's Resource Book,
  Teaching Aids 10, 11, 12
  Transparencies 14, 15, 17, 18

BACKGROUND

In the Capsule Review, the exercises review graphing linear equations using any method. The Example illustrates graphing a linear equation using the intercept method. Encourage students to use the method that is most appropriate. You may wish to have students explain their choice of a particular method. For example, in Exercise 3, the slope-intercept method would be more appropriate. For students having difficulty graphing, you may wish to have them review Chapter 9. In this lesson, students solve systems of linear equations, also known as simultaneous equations, by graphing.

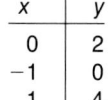

Graphing Systems of Linear Equations

11.1

Objective: To use graphs to solve systems of linear equations

The graph of a linear equation in two variables is a line in the coordinate plane. The coordinates of any point on the line are said to belong to the solution set of the equation.

Capsule Review

The ability to locate and plot key points is an essential skill in graphing equations.

EXAMPLE   Graph $y - 2x = 2$

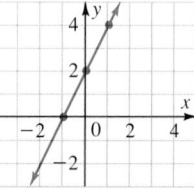

x	y
0	2
−1	0
1	4

One way to graph $y - 2x = 2$ is to use the x- and y-intercepts. That is, plot the points with coordinates (0, 2) and (−1, 0). As a check, plot a third ordered pair that satisfies the equation.

Graph the linear equations. See Additional Answer section beginning p. 719.

1. $y = -x + 4$ **2.** $y = -2x + 1$ **3.** $x - y = -3$ **4.** $2y + 5x = 0$

Two (or more) linear equations using the same variables form a **system of linear equations.** Such equations are commonly known as **simultaneous equations.** Graphing is one method of solving such a system. Solving a system of equations means to determine the point of intersection of the lines.

EXAMPLE 1   Solve by graphing: $\begin{cases} x - y = 2 \\ x + y = 8 \end{cases}$

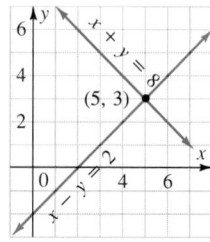

From the graph the point of intersection of the system of linear equations has the coordinates (5, 3). This point is the only solution of the system.

$x - y = 2$	$x + y = 8$
$5 - 3 \overset{?}{=} 2$	$5 + 3 \overset{?}{=} 8$
$2 = 2$ ✔	$8 = 8$ ✔

Systems of equations with at least one solution are called **consistent.** If the graph of each equation is different, the system is known as an **independent system.** So, the system in the above example is considered to be both an *independent* and *consistent system.*

Some systems of linear equations have more than one solution.

EXAMPLE 2   Solve by graphing: $\begin{cases} x - y = 3 \\ 4x - 4y = 12 \end{cases}$

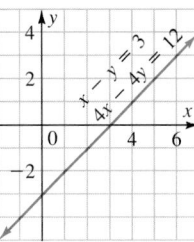

The graphs are the same line, that is, they coincide. The coordinates of any point on the line satisfy both equations, so this system *has infinitely many solutions.* This type of system is known as a **dependent** and **consistent system.** By dividing each side of the equation, $4x - 4y = 12$ by 4, you can show that the equations are equivalent.

You can state the solution as the set of all points on the line $x - y = 3$, or in symbols write:

$$\{(x, y): x - y = 3\}$$

Some systems have no solutions, as shown in Example 3.

EXAMPLE 3   Solve by graphing: $\begin{cases} x + 2y = 6 \\ x = 10 - 2y \end{cases}$

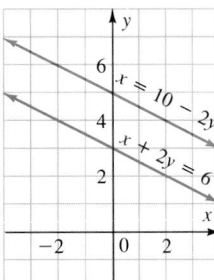

The lines do not intersect. They are parallel lines. Since the lines have no points in common, the system of equations has no solution and therefore can be classified as an **independent** and **inconsistent system.**

What can you tell about a system of equations without graphing? Consider the equations in Examples 1, 2, and 3 written in slope-intercept form, $y = mx + b$.

Example 1	**Example 2**	**Example 3**
$\begin{cases} y = x - 2 \\ y = -x + 8 \end{cases}$	$\begin{cases} y = x - 3 \\ y = x - 3 \end{cases}$	$\begin{cases} y = -\frac{1}{2}x + 3 \\ y = -\frac{1}{2}x + 5 \end{cases}$

The table below describes the nature of the graphs of these equations.

Slope m	y-intercept b	Graph of the system	Number of solutions
Different	Different or Same	Intersecting lines	One
Same	Same	Same line	Infinitely many
Same	Different	Parallel lines	None

Using this table, what generalizations can be made about lines that intersect? that coincide? that are parallel? In what ways does this relate to the solution sets of their equations?

11.1 Graphing Systems of Linear Equations   **445**

TEACHING SUGGESTIONS

- Encourage students to label each line when solving a system of equations by graphing.
- Using the examples, emphasize that two lines in a plane either intersect, coincide, or are parallel.
- Note that in Example 2, the solution is expressed in set-builder notation.
- Encourage students to answer the questions about the table on p. 445. Stress the relationship of the slope *m* and the *y*-intercept *b* to the graph and the number of solutions of the system. Point out that a system of linear equations in two variables can have a unique solution, infinitely many solutions, or no solution.
- Point out that a system with at least one solution is consistent, and one with no solution is inconsistent. Also, a system with infinitely many solutions is dependent, and one with exactly one or no solution is independent.
- Use Teaching Aids 10–12, and Transparencies 14, 15, 17, and 18, in the *Teacher's Resource Book*, to illustrate several examples for the table on p. 445. This will help students to have a better understanding of graphing systems of linear equations.

- **For Example 1**

  Solve by graphing:

  1. $\begin{cases} x + y = 2 \\ x - y = 2 \end{cases}$ (2, 0)

  2. $\begin{cases} y = -x \\ y = x + 4 \end{cases}$ (−2, 2)

- **For Example 2**

  Solve by graphing:

  3. $\begin{cases} y - x = 1 \\ 2x - 2y = -2 \end{cases}$
     $\{(x, y): x - y = -1\}$

  4. $\begin{cases} y = -x + 3 \\ 2y = -2x + 6 \end{cases}$
     $\{(x, y): x + y = 3\}$

- **For Example 3**

  Solve by graphing:

  5. $\begin{cases} 2y - 6x = 4 \\ y = 3x + 5 \end{cases}$ no solution

  6. $\begin{cases} y + x = 3 \\ x = -y + 2 \end{cases}$ no solution

- **For Example 4**

  Without graphing, describe the graph, and tell the number of solutions.

  7. $\begin{cases} 2x + y = -3 \\ 2y + 6 = -4x \end{cases}$
     same line; infinitely many solutions

  8. $\begin{cases} 2y = 3x \\ 2y - 3x = 8 \end{cases}$
     parallel lines; no solution

Common Error

- Some students may attempt to identify the slope and y-intercept of a linear equation without putting it in the form $y = mx + b$. Emphasize the importance of writing the equation in the form $y = mx + b$ when describing the graph and determining the number of solutions of the given system. You may also want to review Lesson 9.5.
- See *Teacher's Resource Book* for additional remediation.

446

EXAMPLE 4 **Without graphing, describe the graph and determine the number of solutions:** $\begin{cases} 4x - y = 2 \\ x - \frac{1}{2}y = 1 \end{cases}$

Write each equation in $y = mx + b$ form. Compare the slopes and the y-intercepts.

| $4x - y = 2$ | $y = 4x - 2$ | $m_1 = 4;\ b_1 = -2$ |
| $x - \frac{1}{2}y = 1$ | $y = 2x - 2$ | $m_2 = 2;\ b_2 = -2$ |

The slopes are different. The y-intercepts are the same. The graphs are intersecting lines with one solution, $(0, -2)$. You can use a computer or graphing calculator to check your conclusion. Graph $4x - y = 2$ and then graph $x - \frac{1}{2}y = 1$ on the same grid. The lines intersect and there is one solution.

CLASS EXERCISES

Using the graphs given, find the solution of each system. Then check the solution in each equation of the system.

1. $\begin{cases} y = x + 2 \\ y = 3x - 2 \end{cases}$ (2, 4)

2. $\begin{cases} y = 3x - 2 \\ x - y = 4 \end{cases}$ (−1, −5)

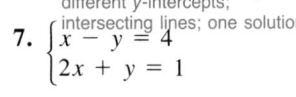

Solve by graphing. Check students' graphs.

3. $\begin{cases} 2x + y = 4 \\ 2y = 8 - 4x \end{cases}$
   $\{(x, y): 2x + y = 4\}$

4. $\begin{cases} x + y = 9 \\ 3x + 3y = 18 \end{cases}$
   no solution

Without graphing, describe the graphs of the system, and determine the number of solutions.

5. $\begin{cases} y = 3x + 6 \\ y = 3x \end{cases}$ same slope; different y-intercept; parallel lines; no solution

6. $\begin{cases} 2y = -x + 2 \\ -2y = x - 2 \end{cases}$ same slope; same y-intercept; same line; infinitely many solutions

7. $\begin{cases} x - y = 4 \\ 2x + y = 1 \end{cases}$ different slopes; different y-intercepts; intersecting lines; one solution

8. $\begin{cases} y = \frac{1}{2}x + 4 \\ 2y = x - 6 \end{cases}$ same slope; different y-intercept; parallel lines; no solution

9. $\begin{cases} 4y = -3x + 5 \\ 2y = -x - 4 \end{cases}$ different slopes; different y-intercepts; intersecting lines; one solution

10. $\begin{cases} 5y = 15x + 10 \\ y = 3x + 2 \end{cases}$ same slope; same y-intercept; same line; infinitely many solutions

For Discussion

11. What kinds of systems would be difficult to solve by graphing?
    systems with non-integer solutions or nonlinear systems

PRACTICE EXERCISES

Solve by graphing. Check students' graphs.

A 1. $\begin{cases} x - y = 6 \\ 2x + y = 3 \end{cases}$ (3, −3)

2. $\begin{cases} x + 2y = 8 \\ x - y = -4 \end{cases}$ (0, 4)

3. $\begin{cases} x + 2y = -4 \\ 2x + 4y = -8 \end{cases}$
   $\{(x, y): x + 2y = -4\}$

4. $\begin{cases} x - y = 5 \\ 3x - 3y = 15 \end{cases}$
$\{(x, y): x - y = 5\}$

5. $\begin{cases} 2x - y = 6 \\ 2x - y = 1 \end{cases}$ no solution

6. $\begin{cases} y = 3x - 1 \\ y = 3x + 2 \end{cases}$
no solution

7. $\begin{cases} y - 2x = 4 \\ y + \frac{1}{3}x = -3 \end{cases}$ $(-3, -2)$

8. $\begin{cases} y - 2x = -6 \\ y - \frac{2}{3}x = 2 \end{cases}$ $(6, 6)$

9. $\begin{cases} y = -\frac{1}{2}x + 2 \\ y = -\frac{1}{2}x - 4 \end{cases}$
no solution

10. $\begin{cases} y = \frac{3}{4}x - 3 \\ y = \frac{3}{4}x + 1 \end{cases}$ no solution

11. $\begin{cases} y = -2x \\ x = -2y + 6 \end{cases}$ $(-2, 4)$

12. $\begin{cases} y = 3x - 1 \\ x = \frac{1}{4}y \end{cases}$ $(-1, -4)$

For each graph explain why the system shown is independent and consistent, independent and inconsistent, or dependent and consistent.

13.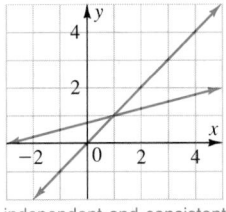
independent and consistent

14.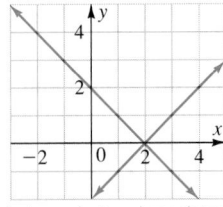
independent and consistent

15.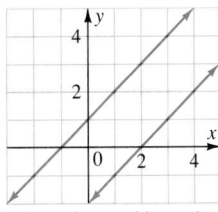
independent and inconsistent

16.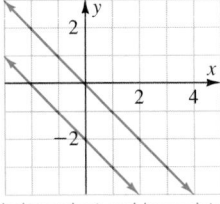
independent and inconsistent

17.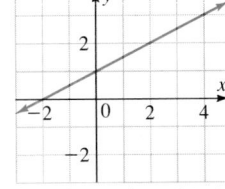
dependent and consistent

18.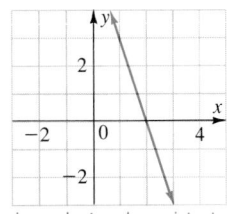
dependent and consistent

19.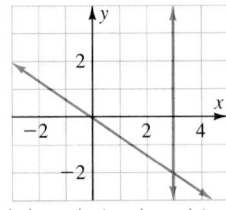
independent and consistent

20.
independent and consistent

21.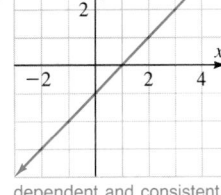
dependent and consistent

22.
dependent and consistent

23.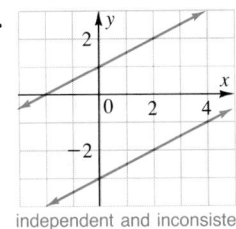
independent and inconsistent

24.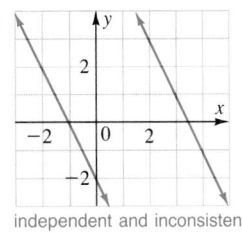
independent and inconsistent

11.1 Graphing Systems of Linear Equations **447**

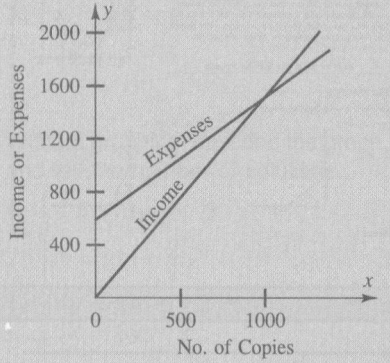
APPLICATION: Break-Even Point

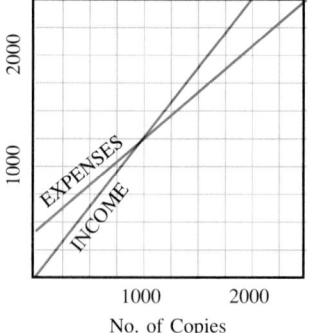

No. of Copies

Did you know that graphing systems of linear equations can be used to determine profit and loss? The Franklins are thinking of publishing a newsletter for coin collectors. They determine that the expenses for research and writing will be $400. They then add the expenses for printing and mailing. The formula they devise for the total expenses *y* of printing and mailing *x* copies is $y = 400 + 0.85x$.

They plan to sell the newsletter for $1.25 per copy. Thus, their formula for the total income is $y = 1.25x$.

The Franklins graph the two equations. The point at which their income begins to exceed their expenses is the break-even point. What is the *x*-coordinate of the break-even point, and what does it represent? What is the *y*-coordinate of the break-even point, and what does it represent?

EXERCISES

Use the graph above for Exercises 1 and 2.

1. What is the loss if only 500 copies are sold during the first month? $200

2. What is the profit if 1500 copies are sold during the second month? $200

After the first year, the Franklins find that their expenses have increased. A better formula for their expenses now is $y = 600 + 0.9x$. The Franklins increase the price of the newsletter to $1.50, which gives the formula $y = 1.5x$ for their income.

3. Make a graph to show the new break-even point. See side column.

4. How many copies must be sold before there is a profit? 1000

5. If one month after their price increase the Franklins sell only 300 copies of their newsletter, what will be their loss for the month? $420

6. In a few months, if the Franklins are selling an average of 2000 copies a month, what will be their average profit per month? $600

The Substitution Method

Objective: To solve a system of linear equations in two variables by the substitution method

If the solution of a system of equations involves fractions, it may be difficult to accurately read these values from a graph. Algebraic methods are used to provide more accurate solutions to linear systems than the graphing method.

Capsule Review

Isolating the variable is a key part of solving equations using certain algebraic methods.

EXAMPLE **Solve for x:** $y - x = 9$
$$-x = 9 - y$$
$$x = y - 9$$

Solve the equation for the indicated variable.

1. $x - y = 3$; y $\quad y = x - 3$

2. $x - 2y = 4$; y $\quad y = \frac{x}{2} - 2$

3. $2x - 3y = 5$; x $\quad x = \frac{3}{2}y + \frac{5}{2}$

4. $3y - x = 9$; x $\quad x = 3y - 9$

5. $\frac{x}{2} = \frac{y}{4}$; y $\quad y = 2x$

6. $\frac{1}{2}x = 4y$; x $\quad x = 8y$

The **substitution method** is one technique that can be used to solve a system of linear equations. The key to this method of solving a system of equations is the elimination of one of the variables. In this method the variable selected is eliminated by substitution.

The Substitution Method

- In either equation, solve for one variable in terms of the other.
- Substitute for that variable in the other equation. Solve.
- Substitute the result from Step 2 in either equation. Solve for the other variable.
- Check the solution in both original equations.

LESSON PLAN

Vocabulary
Substitution method

Materials/Manipulatives
Computer graphing paper
Graphing calculator
Overhead projector
Straightedge

BACKGROUND

In the Capsule Review, Exercises 1–6 review solving an equation for one variable in terms of another. Some students may forget to divide each term by the coefficient of the indicated variable. In this lesson, students must solve an equation for one variable in terms of the other as a first step in solving a system of linear equations (sometimes called simultaneous equations).

- Emphasize that the substitution method is one of the algebraic methods used to solve systems of equations. Note that other ways to solve a system algebraically are shown in Lessons 11.4 and 11.5. Point out to students that the substitution method is easier to use when the coefficient of one of the variables is 1 or −1.
- You may need to remind students that most of the time it is best to solve for the positive value of the variable.
- Remind students that solutions are written as ordered pairs in alphabetical order.
- In Example 1, point out that it is faster to find x using the equation $x - y = 3$.
- When discussing Example 2, have students discover that it is easiest to solve the first equation for b as a first step, since the coefficient is −1. Point out what happens when there is no solution. You may want to have students prove the answer graphically.

CHALKBOARD EXAMPLES

- **For Example 1**
  Solve:
  1. $\begin{cases} x + y = 4 \\ 3x - 2y = 1 \end{cases}$ $\left(\frac{9}{5}, \frac{11}{5}\right)$
  2. $\begin{cases} y - x = -1 \\ x + 2y = -3 \end{cases}$ $\left(-\frac{1}{3}, -\frac{4}{3}\right)$

- **For Example 2**
  Solve:
  3. $\begin{cases} 2c + 3d = 7 \\ 6c - d = 1 \end{cases}$ $\left(\frac{1}{2}, 2\right)$
  4. $\begin{cases} 4a + 3b = 1 \\ 4a = -5 - 3b \end{cases}$ no solution

EXAMPLE 1 **Solve:** $\begin{cases} x - y = 3 \\ 2x - 3y = 5.5 \end{cases}$

In the first equation, if $x - y = 3$, then $x = y + 3$. Why?

$2x - 3y = 5.5$	*Restate the second equation of the system.*
$2(y + 3) - 3y = 5.5$	*Substitute $y + 3$ for x.*
$2y + 6 - 3y = 5.5$	*Solve for y.*
$-y = -0.5$	*Multiply each side by -1.*
$y = 0.5$	

Replace y with 0.5 in either equation.

$x - y = 3$	*Solve for x.*
$x - 0.5 = 3$	
$x = 3.5$	

Check the solution (3.5, 0.5) in both equations. Why is it easier to use the first equation in solving for x?

Look at the linear equations in Example 2. How would you begin? Why?

EXAMPLE 2 **Solve:** $\begin{cases} 2a - b = -4 \\ 4a = 7 + 2b \end{cases}$

In the first equation, if $2a - b = -4$, then $b = 2a + 4$.

$4a = 7 + 2b$	*Restate the second equation.*
$4a = 7 + 2(2a + 4)$	*Substitute $2a + 4$ for b.*
$4a = 7 + 4a + 8$	*Solve for a.*
$4a = 4a + 15$	
$0 \neq 15$	There is no solution.

Some systems lend themselves more to the substitution method than others. This method is best used when the coefficient of one of the variables is 1 or −1.

CLASS EXERCISES

Solve by substitution. Check the results in the original equations.

1. $\begin{cases} y = 2x \\ 7x - y = 35 \end{cases}$
(7, 14)

2. $\begin{cases} a + 3b = 5 \\ 2a - 4b = -5 \end{cases}$
$\left(\frac{1}{2}, \frac{3}{2}\right)$

3. $\begin{cases} 3m + 6n = -15 \\ 2m - 3n = 4 \end{cases}$
(−1, −2)

4. $\begin{cases} 5g - 2f = -8 \\ 3f + 5g = -3 \end{cases}$
$\left(1, -\frac{6}{5}\right)$

For Discussion

5. What happens when you try to solve these systems? Give the solution sets of each system.

   a. $\begin{cases} 3x - y = -2 \\ y = 3x + 2 \end{cases}$
   $\{(x, y): -3x + y = 2\}$

   b. $\begin{cases} 3u - v = 0 \\ 6u - 2v = 5 \end{cases}$
   no solution

PRACTICE EXERCISES

Solve by the substitution method. Check your results.

A

1. $\begin{cases} x - y = 0 \\ x + y = 2 \end{cases}$ (1, 1)

2. $\begin{cases} x + 3y = -4 \\ y + x = 0 \end{cases}$ (2, -2)

3. $\begin{cases} 3u - v = 17 \\ v + 2u = 8 \end{cases}$ (5, -2)

4. $\begin{cases} 5 = p + 5q \\ p + q = -3 \end{cases}$ (-5, 2)

5. $\begin{cases} 3x + 2y = 9 \\ x + y = 3 \end{cases}$ (3, 0)

6. $\begin{cases} x + 3y = -4 \\ 2y + 3x = 3 \end{cases}$ $\left(\frac{17}{7}, -\frac{15}{7}\right)$

7. $\begin{cases} 2y - 3x = 4 \\ x = -2 \end{cases}$ (-2, -1)

8. $\begin{cases} y = 3 \\ 2x = 5y + 7 \end{cases}$ (11, 3)

9. $\begin{cases} 2d = 5e \\ e - 3d = -13 \end{cases}$ (5, 2)

10. $\begin{cases} 5g = 3f + 6 \\ g - 2f = 46 \end{cases}$ (-32, -18)

11. $\begin{cases} k = 10 - 2j \\ k = 4j + 36 \end{cases}$ $\left(-\frac{13}{3}, \frac{56}{3}\right)$

12. $\begin{cases} n = 39 - 3m \\ n = 2m - 61 \end{cases}$ (20, -21)

13. $\begin{cases} 25r - 10q = 100 \\ 5q + 15r = 60 \end{cases}$ (0, 4)

14. $\begin{cases} 10m - 5n = -20 \\ 10n - 40m = 80 \end{cases}$ (-2, 0)

15. $\begin{cases} 3c + 4d = 6 \\ d - 6c = 6 \end{cases}$ $\left(-\frac{2}{3}, 2\right)$

16. $\begin{cases} 12e + 5f = 5 \\ f + 18e = 14 \end{cases}$ $\left(\frac{5}{6}, -1\right)$

17. $\begin{cases} 4y - x = 2 \\ -2x + 12y = 17 \end{cases}$ $\left(11, \frac{13}{4}\right)$

18. $\begin{cases} 18x = y - 10 \\ 18x = 30y + 19 \end{cases}$ $\left(-\frac{11}{18}, -1\right)$

19. $\begin{cases} 3y + x = -1 \\ x = -3y \end{cases}$ no solution

20. $\begin{cases} y - x = 4 \\ x + 3 = y \end{cases}$ no solution

21. $\begin{cases} 5b - 2 = 2a \\ 3a + 6 = 25b \end{cases}$ $\left(-\frac{4}{7}, \frac{6}{35}\right)$

22. $\begin{cases} 4d - c = -3 \\ 2c - 6 = 8d \end{cases}$ $\{(c, d): c - 4d = 3\}$

23. $\begin{cases} 4s - 3t = 8 \\ 2s + t = -1 \end{cases}$ $\left(\frac{1}{2}, -2\right)$

24. $\begin{cases} j + 6k = 0 \\ 4j - 3k = 9 \end{cases}$ $\left(2, -\frac{1}{3}\right)$

B **25.** $\begin{cases} 5e - 7f = 1 \\ 4e - 2f = 16 \end{cases}$ $\left(\frac{55}{9}, \frac{38}{9}\right)$

26. $\begin{cases} 13h - 10g = 45 \\ 6g - 3h = -3 \end{cases}$ (2, 5)

27. $\begin{cases} 20x - 15y = 17 \\ x = y + 1 \end{cases}$ $\left(\frac{2}{5}, -\frac{3}{5}\right)$

28. $\begin{cases} 8x - 1 = 4y \\ 3x = y + 1 \end{cases}$ $\left(\frac{3}{4}, \frac{5}{4}\right)$

29. $\begin{cases} 2x - 3y = 19 \\ 5y - 2x = -37 \end{cases}$ (-4, -9)

30. $\begin{cases} 3y + 5x = -3 \\ 2x - 3y = -30 \end{cases}$ $\left(-\frac{33}{7}, \frac{48}{7}\right)$

31. $\begin{cases} 15n = -270m \\ 15m + 2n = -7 \end{cases}$ $\left(\frac{1}{3}, -6\right)$

32. $\begin{cases} -5r + 14t = 13 \\ -9r = -72t \end{cases}$ $\left(-4, -\frac{1}{2}\right)$

33. $\begin{cases} 2x - y = 1 \\ 2x - 5y = -1 \end{cases}$ $\left(\frac{3}{4}, \frac{1}{2}\right)$

34. $\begin{cases} 12y - 3x = 11 \\ x - 2y = -2 \end{cases}$ $\left(-\frac{1}{3}, \frac{5}{6}\right)$

35. $\begin{cases} 4v + 3u = -6 \\ 5v - 6u = -27 \end{cases}$ (2, -3)

36. $\begin{cases} 2s - 5t = 6 \\ 4s + 3t = -1 \end{cases}$ $\left(\frac{1}{2}, -1\right)$

37. $\begin{cases} 5x - 7y = -21 \\ 14y - 5x = 22 \end{cases}$ $\left(-4, \frac{1}{7}\right)$

38. $\begin{cases} 5x - 2y = 4 \\ 8y + 15x = 2\frac{2}{3} \end{cases}$ $\left(\frac{8}{15}, -\frac{2}{3}\right)$

39. $\begin{cases} 2a + 3b = 5a - 6 \\ 4a - 2b - 8 = 2b \end{cases}$ $\{(a, b): a - b = 2\}$

40. $\begin{cases} 5d + 4c + 7 = 3d - 1 \\ -7c + 2d - 12 = 6 - 8c \end{cases}$ $\left(-\frac{26}{3}, \frac{40}{3}\right)$

41. $\begin{cases} -4a + 3b - 5 = 2a - 5 \\ -8b + 2a + 3 = 10 - 6b \end{cases}$ $\left(-\frac{7}{2}, -7\right)$

C **42.** $\begin{cases} \frac{1}{4}(3x - 4) = -\frac{1}{2}(2y - x) \\ -(y - 3x) = 2x - y \end{cases}$ (0, 1)

43. $\begin{cases} 3(y - 2x) = 5(y - 2x) - 8 \\ -\frac{1}{3}(x - 5y) = (y - x) - 4 \end{cases}$ $\left(-\frac{10}{3}, -\frac{8}{3}\right)$

44. $\begin{cases} \frac{1}{3}(r - 1) = \frac{1}{2}(3r + s) \\ \dfrac{r - s}{4} = 1 \end{cases}$ (1, -3)

45. $\begin{cases} \frac{2}{3}(2x + 1) - \frac{3}{2}(3y - 1) = -1 \\ \dfrac{y - 3x}{2} = -1 \end{cases}$ (1, 1)

11.2 The Substitution Method **453**

Common Error

- When solving a system of equations, some students may think that the solution for the system is correct if it satisfies one of the equations. Stress the importance of checking the solution in each equation.
- See *Teacher's Resource Book* for additional remediation.

LESSON FOLLOW-UP

Discussion

Discuss the advantages or disadvantages of the substitution method versus the graphical method for the following system.

$$\begin{cases} 3x + 2y = 550 \\ x = \frac{4}{5}y \end{cases}$$

The substitution method is easier to use in this case because one equation is solved for *x*.

Assignment Guide

- See p. 442B for assignments.
- For Exercise 51, use a graphing calculator or a computer program.
- See *Teacher's Resource Book,* for Critical Thinking activity p. 11.

Critical Thinking

Causal Explanation In Example 2, the conclusion is made that the system has no solution. Explain why there is no solution.   There are no values of *a* and *b* that can make $4a = 7 + 2b$ a true statement.

Lesson Quiz

Solve by the substitution method. Check your results.

1. $\begin{cases} x + y = 1 \\ 2x - 3y = 5 \end{cases}$ $\left(\frac{8}{5}, -\frac{3}{5}\right)$

2. $\begin{cases} 3c - d = 13 \\ 2d + 3c = 16 \end{cases}$ $\left(\frac{14}{3}, 1\right)$

3. $\begin{cases} 26a = 24b + 90 \\ 12b = 6a - 10 \end{cases}$ $\left(5, \frac{10}{6}\right)$

4. $\begin{cases} 3a = -6b + 42 \\ 3b = -2a + 23 \end{cases}$ (4, 5)

453

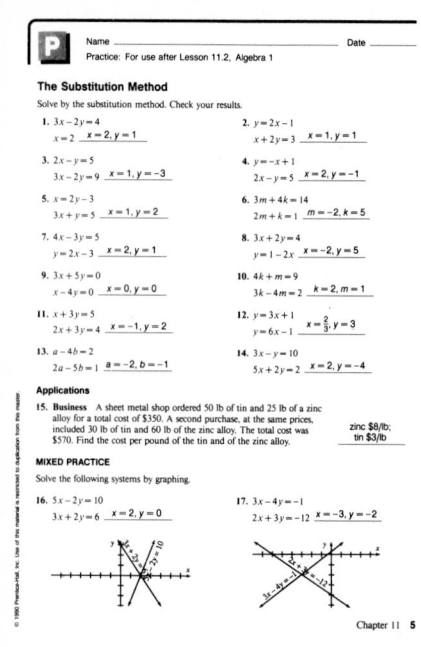

46. $\begin{cases} \dfrac{j + 4k}{3} = -2 \\ -\dfrac{1}{4}(j + 2) = \dfrac{1}{2}(j + 2k) \end{cases}$ (2, −2)

47. $\begin{cases} \dfrac{-2y - x}{3} = 1 \\ \dfrac{3}{4}(1 - 5x) - \dfrac{1}{3}(2y - 1) = 4 \end{cases}$ $\left(-\dfrac{23}{41}, -\dfrac{50}{41}\right)$

The equations of the following systems are not linear. However, if c is substituted for $\dfrac{1}{x}$ and d for $\dfrac{1}{y}$, the equations become linear in c and d. In each, substitute c for $\dfrac{1}{x}$ and d for $\dfrac{1}{y}$. Then solve.

48. $\begin{cases} \dfrac{1}{x} + \dfrac{1}{y} = \dfrac{1}{3} \\ \dfrac{2}{x} - \dfrac{3}{y} = \dfrac{1}{4} \end{cases}$ (4, 12)

49. $\begin{cases} \dfrac{1}{x} - \dfrac{1}{y} = -\dfrac{5}{6} \\ \dfrac{3}{x} + \dfrac{2}{y} = -\dfrac{5}{6} \end{cases}$ (−2, 3)

Applications

50. Business An accounting student took a test of verbal skills and a test of mathematical skills. Her total score was 1250, and her math score was 200 more than the verbal. Find the two scores by solving the system:

$$\begin{cases} x + y = 1250 \\ x = y + 200 \end{cases}$$

verbal 525
math 725

51. Calculator Graph Exercises 25–41 using a graphing calculator or using a computer graphing program. Check the answers you got using the substitution method with the solutions that the graph indicates.
Check students' graphs.

WRITING IN ALGEBRA

Write an algebraic expression for each of the following.

1. After buying a newspaper, you have x dimes and y nickels. Write their total value in cents. (*Hint:* If x represents the number of dimes, then $10x$ represents the total value.) $10x + 5y$

2. You have x dimes and twice as many quarters. Write the total value of your quarters in cents. $50x$

3. If t represents the digit in the tens place of a two-digit number and u represents the digit in the ones place, write the number. $10t + u$

4. If h represents the hundreds digit in a three-digit number, t the tens digit, and 5 the ones digit, write the number. $100h + 10t + 5$

5. You sell t tickets at \$5 each. Your friend sells 10 more such tickets. Write the total number of dollars collected by your friend. $5(t + 10)$

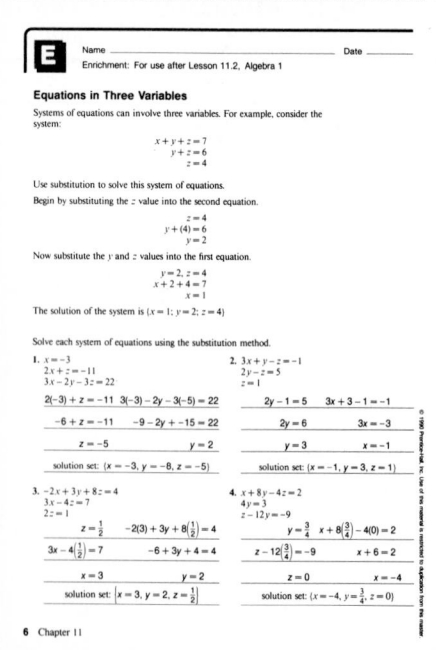

454 Chapter 11 Systems of Linear Equations

Problem Solving Strategy:
Write a Linear System to Solve a Problem

LESSON PLAN

Materials/Manipulatives
Graph paper
Overhead projector
Straightedge

BACKGROUND

A key to success in this lesson is the students' ability to organize and understand the information given in the problem. Analyze students' errors to determine their misunderstanding of the problem.

Error Analysis Classification
1. *Misunderstanding*
   Failed to read the problem
   Misinterpreted the point in the question
2. *Misapplied Strategy*
   Wrote an incorrect equation
   Failed to complete the solution process
   Did not interpret the solution correctly

When a problem requires that you find two numbers, you may find it easier to solve the problem by using a system of equations. To solve, assign different variables to the two unknown numbers, write two equations, and then solve the system.

EXAMPLE 1   Arkville paid a contractor to have a rectangular grassplot fenced in. One side of the plot ran along a roadway, and the special fencing for this side cost $10/ft. Fencing for the other three sides cost $5/ft. The contractor claimed that the perimeter of the plot was 1740 ft, and his bill amounted to $11,325. If his calculations were correct, what are the dimensions of the plot?

Understand the Problem

What is given?
The perimeter of a rectangular plot is 1740 ft. Fencing along one side cost $10/ft and along the other sides $5/ft. The total cost of fencing was $11,325.

You are asked to find the length and width of the plot.

Plan Your Approach

Choose a strategy.
Draw a diagram.

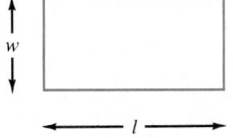

Let l = the length (in ft)
w = the width (in ft)

Write a system of equations.

$$\begin{cases} 2l + 2w = 1740 \\ 10l + 5l + 5w + 5w = 11{,}325 \end{cases}$$

The perimeter is 1740 ft.
The terms on the left represent the cost of fencing all four sides.

11.3 Problem Solving Strategy: Write a Linear System to Solve a Problem   **455**

- In this lesson, students learn how to write a linear system of equations to solve a problem. Encourage students to use the four-step method for solving problems.
- Remind students of the importance of reading each question carefully. After finding a solution to the system of equations, emphasize that it is important to check the solution against the facts in the problem.
- Point out that an accurate drawing of the information given in the problem is a key to solving the problem. You may want to use an overhead projector to illustrate Example 1.

Critical Thinking

Observation Choose one key idea given in the problem that would be helpful in solving the problem.

Answers may vary. Possible answer given: The plot is rectangular. This choice provides relationships between the sides of the plot, which allows the equation to be derived and used to solve the problem.

CHALKBOARD EXAMPLE

- **For the Example**
  The perimeter of a rectangular garden is 126 ft. The length of the rectangle is twice the width. Find the dimensions of the plot. $l = 42$ ft $w = 21$ ft

---

☐ **Complete the Work**

Solve the system of equations.

To simplify the system, divide each side of the first equation by 2. Combine like terms in the second equation, and then divide each side by 5.

$$\begin{cases} 2l + 2w = 1740 \\ 10l + 5l + 5w + 5w = 11{,}325 \to 15l + 10w = 11{,}325 \end{cases} \to \begin{cases} l + w = 870 \\ 3l + 2w = 226 \end{cases}$$

The simplified system to be solved is:

$l + w = 870$ *Solve the first equation for l.*

     $l = 870 - w$

$3l + 2w = 2265$ *Substitute $870 - w$ for l in the second equation.*

$3(870 - w) + 2w = 2265$ *Solve for w.*

$2610 - 3w + 2w = 2265$

         $w = 345$

$l + w = 870$ *Substitute 345 for w in the first equation.*

$l + 345 = 870$ *Solve for l.*

     $l = 525$

☐ **Interpret the Results**

State your conclusion.

The width is 345 ft, and the length is 525 ft.
Check your conclusion.
Do these dimensions give a perimeter of 1740 ft?

$$2(525) + 2(345) \stackrel{?}{=} 1740$$
$$1740 = 1740 ✔$$

Do these dimensions give a total fencing cost of $11,325?

$$10(525) + 5(525) + 5(345) + 5(345) \stackrel{?}{=} 11{,}325$$
$$11{,}325 = 11{,}325 ✔$$

CLASS EXERCISES

Write a system of linear equations for the problem. Do not solve.

1. One positive number equals 3 times another number. The difference between the numbers is 10. Find the numbers. $x = 3y$
$x - y = 10$

2. Twenty-six students entered their projects in the science fair. The number of girls was 4 fewer than twice the number of boys. How many boys entered their science projects in the fair? $g + b = 26$
$g = 2b - 4$

3. The perimeter of an isosceles triangle is 48 in. The length of the base is 1 in. less than half the length of one of the two equal sides. Find the lengths of the sides of the triangle. $2s + b = 48$
$b = \frac{1}{2}s - 1$

Solve the problem by writing and solving a system of equations.

1. The length of a rectangle is 2 ft less than three times the width. If the perimeter is 68 ft, what are the dimensions of the rectangle? *l* = 25 ft, *w* = 9 ft

2. The perimeter of a rectangle is 10 m. Twice the width is equal to one-half the length. Find the length and the width. *l* = 4 m, *w* = 1 m

3. The sum of two numbers is 48. If the smaller number is subtracted from the larger, the difference is 12. Find the numbers. 30, 18

4. Find two numbers whose sum is −64, if twice the first is 1 more than the second. −21, −43

5. Said's father has 13 more than 5 times as many coins in his antique coin collection as Said has. The total number of coins in both collections is 247. How many coins does each one have? Said 39; Said's father 208

6. Bella and Irina together sold 137 tickets for a benefit concert. If Irina sold 10 fewer than twice as many as Bella, how many tickets did each girl sell? Bella 49; Irina 88

7. For a mathematics project, 27 students were divided into two groups. One group had 3 more than twice the number of students in the other. How many students were in each group? 8, 19

8. A 50-ft rope is cut into two pieces. The length of one piece is 9 times the length of the other. What is the length of the longer piece? 45 ft

9. Find two positive numbers if one is $\frac{2}{3}$ the other, and their difference is 5. 15, 10

10. One number is 4 more than half of another. The difference between the two numbers is 2. Find these numbers. 6, 4 or 10, 12

11. Last year Zachary received $469.75 interest from two investments. The interest rates were 7.5% on one account and 8% on the other. If the total amount invested was $6000, how much was invested at each rate? $3950 at 8%; $2050 at 7.5%

12. The federal tax on a $12,000 salary was 8 times the state tax. If the combined taxes were $2700, find the state's share of taxes. $300

13. Leila left home at noon, traveling at 24 mi/h. An hour later her brother Josh, driving 36 mi/h, set out to overtake her. How long did it take him? (*Hint:* Let *l* = Leila's time in h, let *j* = Josh's time in h.) 2 h

14. It took Henri 50 h of cycling to finish his bike tour. On the return trip over the same route, he increased his cycling rate by 1 mi/h and took only 45 h. What was his rate on the return trip? 10 mi/h

11.3 Problem Solving Strategy: Write a Linear System to Solve a Problem   **457**

Common Error

- Students often make errors in assigning variables to the unknown quantities and then write incorrect equations. Encourage students to read each problem carefully, write down all given information, and assign variables to unknown quantities in order to write correct equations.
- See *Teacher's Resource Book* for additional remediation.

LESSON FOLLOW-UP

Assignment Guide

See p. 442B for assignments.

Mixed Problem Solving Review

- The following skills and concepts are reviewed:
  Solving mixture problems (Ex. 1)
  Solving uniform motion problems (Ex. 2)
  Solving work problems (Ex. 3)
- The following problem solving strategies may be appropriate:
  Making a drawing or table (Ex. 1–3)
  Writing an equation or inequality (Ex. 1–3)

Lesson Quiz

Solve.

1. The length of a rectangle is three times its width. If the perimeter of the rectangle is 56 ft, find the dimensions of the rectangle. *l* = 21 ft *w* = 7 ft

2. The sum of two numbers is 7. If the second number is subtracted from twice the first, the difference is 5. Find the numbers. 4, 3

3. The difference of two numbers is 5. If the sum of four times the first number and the second is 50, find the numbers. 11, 6 or 9, 14

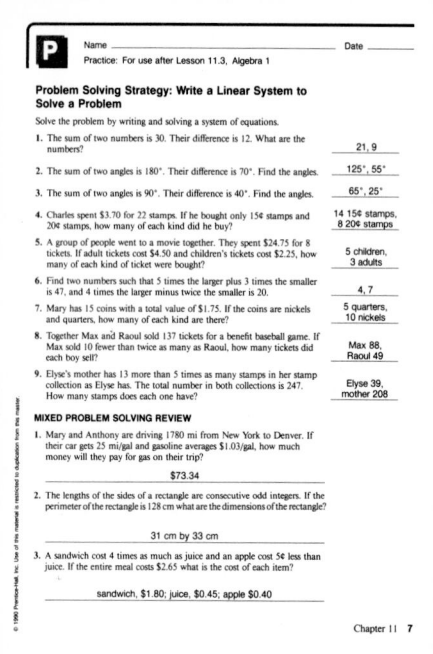

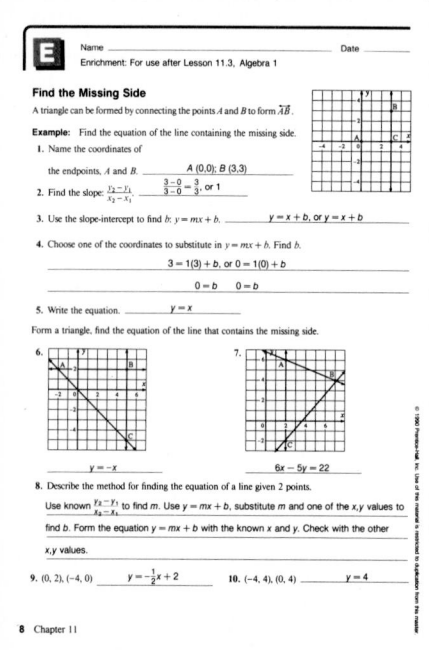

C **15.** If the length of one pair of opposite sides of a rectangle were doubled and the other pair of opposite sides were each decreased by 14 m, the new rectangle would be a square with a perimeter of 84 m. Find the rectangle's original dimensions. $l = 35$ m, $w = 10.5$ m

16. If the length of one pair of opposite sides of a square were tripled and the other pair were each increased by 7 cm, the new figure would be a rectangle with a perimeter of 96 cm. Find the dimensions of the original square. 10.25 cm by 10.25 cm

17. Alice and Jeanine live 18 blocks apart in opposite directions from the Coles Sports Center. If Alice lives 3 more blocks than $\frac{1}{4}$ as far from the center as Jeanine does, how far does Alice live from the sports center? 6 blocks

Mixed Problem Solving Review

1. If you add 2.5 L of water to 10 L of a 10% solution of salt in water, what will be the percent of salt in the new solution? 8%

2. On a round trip of 70 mi each way Diana averaged 7 mi/h more on the return trip, which took 30 min less than the trip going of $2\frac{1}{2}$ h. Find her two speeds. $r_1 = 28$ mi/h; $r_2 = 35$ mi/h

3. Ian has one job at which he must work a 20 h/wk at $4.50/h. He may also work at a second job which pays $6.25/h. If he must earn at least $160 this week, how long must he work at the second job? at least 11.2 h

PROJECT

In this lesson some of the problems that you solved by writing a system of equations were the same types you solved using a single variable and one equation. Which method do you prefer? Why? Solve the following word problems with a partner. One student should use one equation to solve the problem. The other student should use a system of equations. Take turns using the two methods. Discuss your preferences.

1. The denominator of a fraction is 12 more than its numerator. If 5 is subtracted from both numerator and denominator, the new fraction reduces to $\frac{2}{3}$. Find the original fraction. $\frac{29}{41}$

2. One number is 30% more than the other. If their sum is 161, find the two numbers. 70, 91

3. Working together, two girls can finish a job in 4 days. If one girl works alone for 8 days, the other girl can then finish the job by herself in 2 days. How long would it take each girl working alone? $g_1 = 12$ days; $g_2 = 6$ days

458   Chapter 11 Systems of Linear Equations

The Addition/Subtraction Method

Objective: To solve systems of linear equations by the addition subtraction method

The substitution method is one algebraic method for solving simultaneous equations. Another is the **addition/subtraction method,** in which a new equation is formed by adding or subtracting the equations in the system. The new equation contains just one of the original variables and can be solved for that variable. Before using this technique, the equations of the system should be in standard form: $Ax + By = C$, where A, B, and C are integers and both A and B do not equal zero.

Capsule Review

EXAMPLE   Rewrite $4 - x = 3y$ in standard form.

$$-x - 3y = -4 \quad \textit{Subtract 4 and 3y from each side.}$$
$$\text{or} \quad x + 3y = 4 \quad \textit{Multiply each side by } -1.$$

Rewrite the following equations in standard form.

1. $5x + 4 = -9y$ **2.** $y = -3x - 5$ $3x + y = -5$ **3.** $14 - x = 0$ $x = 14$
$5x + 9y = -4$

The Addition/Subtraction Method

- Add or subtract the given equations to eliminate one variable.
- Solve the resulting equation for the remaining variable.
- Replace the value of the known variable in one of the original equations to find the value of the unknown variable.
- Check the solution in both original equations.

EXAMPLE 1   Solve by the addition method: $\begin{cases} x + y = 6 \\ x - y = 2 \end{cases}$

$$\begin{cases} x + y = 6 \\ x - y = 2 \end{cases}$$
$$\overline{2x = 8} \quad \textit{Add the equations to eliminate the y-terms.}$$
$$x = 4 \quad \textit{Solve for x.}$$

$$x + y = 6 \quad \textit{Replace x with 4 in either original equation.}$$
$$4 + y = 6 \quad \textit{Solve for y.}$$
$$y = 2$$

So, the solution is $(4, 2)$.

LESSON PLAN

Vocabulary
Addition/subtraction method

Materials/Manipulatives
Calculators

BACKGROUND

In the Capsule Review, the exercises review writing linear equations in standard form. For an equation to be in standard form, A, B, and C must be integers and $Ax + By = C$. In this lesson, students use the addition/ subtraction method to solve systems of linear equations. Each equation in the system is written in standard form before using the addition/subtraction method.

Critical Thinking
Causal Explanation   In the Capsule Review, the equation $4 - x = 3y$ is to be written in standard form. The text has an answer of $-x - 3y = -4$ or $x + 3y = 4$. Are both of these equations in standard form? Explain.
Yes; the value of A, B, and C are integers in both forms of the equation.

Check the solution $(4, 2)$ in both equations:

$$x + y = 6 \qquad\qquad x - y = 2$$
$$4 + 2 \overset{?}{=} 6 \qquad\qquad 4 - 2 \overset{?}{=} 2$$
$$6 = 6 \;\checkmark \qquad\qquad 2 = 2 \;\checkmark$$

In the next example, one equation is rewritten in standard form then one of the variables of the system is eliminated by subtraction.

EXAMPLE 2 **Solve:** $\begin{cases} 8m + 12n = 50 \\ 12n = 3m - 27 \end{cases}$

$$\begin{cases} 8m + 12n = 50 \\ -3m + 12n = -27 \end{cases} \quad \textit{Express the second equation in standard form.}$$

$$\begin{array}{ll} 11m \qquad\quad = 77 & \textit{Subtract the equations to eliminate the n-terms.} \\ \qquad m = 7 & \textit{Solve for m.} \end{array}$$

$$\begin{array}{ll} 12n = 3m - 27 & \textit{Replace m with 7 in either original equation.} \\ 12n = 3(7) - 27 \\ 12n = 21 - 27 & \textit{Solve for n.} \\ 12n = -6 \\ \quad n = -\dfrac{1}{2} \end{array}$$

The check of the solution $\left(7, -\dfrac{1}{2}\right)$ is left for you.

Notice that in Example 1 the coefficients of y are opposites, and in Example 2 the coefficients of n are the same. The addition/subtraction method can be used whenever the two equations have the same or opposite coefficients for one of the variables. This method works best when the equations are in standard form.

CLASS EXERCISES

Tell whether addition or subtraction is appropriate. Give the resulting one-variable equation. Then solve the system.

1. $\begin{cases} x + y = 4 \\ x - y = -10 \end{cases}$
   addition; $2x = 6$; $(-3, 7)$

2. $\begin{cases} x + y = 4 \\ 2x + y = 5 \end{cases}$
   subtraction; $-x = -1$; $(1, 3)$

3. $\begin{cases} -7a + b = 1 \\ 3 - 3b = 7a \end{cases}$
   subtraction; $4b = 4$; $(0, 1)$

4. $\begin{cases} 2p - q = 1 \\ 2p - q = -3 \end{cases}$
   subtraction; $0 = 4$; no solution

5. $\begin{cases} 3m - 4n = 1 \\ 3m - 2n = -1 \end{cases}$
   subtraction; $-2n = 2$; $(-1, -1)$

6. $\begin{cases} 9s + 4t = -13 \\ -9s = \dfrac{1}{2}t - 1 \end{cases}$
   addition; $\dfrac{7}{2}t = -14$; $\left(\dfrac{1}{3}, -4\right)$

7. Use the substitution method for Class Exercise 1, and show that it gives the same result as the addition method. Check students' work.

For Discussion

8. Explain why either the addition or subtraction method can be used to solve the system $-3x + y = -3$ and $3x + y = 9$.
The addition can be used to solve for y and the subtraction can be used to solve for x.

9. The subtraction method produces no solution in Class Exercise 4. Why?
There is no ordered pair which satisfies the system.

PRACTICE EXERCISES

Solve by the addition/subtraction method.

A

1. $\begin{cases} x - y = -8 \\ x + y = 12 \end{cases}$ (2, 10)

2. $\begin{cases} x + y = 10 \\ x - y = -2 \end{cases}$ (4, 6)

3. $\begin{cases} a + b = 0 \\ a - b = -6 \end{cases}$ (−3, 3)

4. $\begin{cases} a - b = -14 \\ a + b = -4 \end{cases}$ (−9, 5)

5. $\begin{cases} p + q = -2 \\ q = p + 10 \end{cases}$ (−6, 4)

6. $\begin{cases} q = 16 + p \\ -p - q = 0 \end{cases}$ (−8, 8)

7. $\begin{cases} 3a - b = 21 \\ 2a + b = 4 \end{cases}$ (5, −6)

8. $\begin{cases} 7s + t = 22 \\ 5s - t = 14 \end{cases}$ (3, 1)

9. $\begin{cases} m - 4n = 6 \\ m - 2n = 18 \end{cases}$ (30, 6)

10. $\begin{cases} 7g + h = 42 \\ -3g + h = -8 \end{cases}$ (5, 7)

11. $\begin{cases} 3j - k = -10 \\ -5j - k = 14 \end{cases}$ (−3, 1)

12. $\begin{cases} -v + 5w = 12 \\ -v - 3w = -4 \end{cases}$ (−2, 2)

13. $\begin{cases} 3y = -5 - 2x \\ 7x - 3y = 23 \end{cases}$ (2, −3)

14. $\begin{cases} -2m - n = 5 \\ -2m - 3n = -7 \end{cases}$ $\left(-\frac{11}{2}, 6\right)$

15. $\begin{cases} 2a - b = 1 \\ b = 2a - 1 \end{cases}$
{(a, b): 2a − b = 1}

16. $\begin{cases} 3x + 8y = -7 \\ -8y = 7 + 3x \end{cases}$
{(x, y): 3x + 8y = −7}

17. $\begin{cases} 3x - y = 8 \\ \frac{1}{3}y - 3x = \frac{2}{3} \end{cases}$ $\left(-\frac{5}{3}, -13\right)$

18. $\begin{cases} 2p - 3q = 11 \\ \frac{1}{3}q - 2p = 1 \end{cases}$ $\left(-\frac{5}{4}, -\frac{9}{2}\right)$

19. $\begin{cases} 2c + 5d = 44 \\ -6c + 5d = 8 \end{cases}$ $\left(\frac{9}{2}, 7\right)$

20. $\begin{cases} 4a - 7b = 3 \\ 16a - 7b = 12 \end{cases}$ $\left(\frac{3}{4}, 0\right)$

21. $\begin{cases} 6a - 5b = 6 \\ -5b + 7a = 7 \end{cases}$ (1, 0)

B

22. $\begin{cases} 4g - 2h = -14 \\ 5h = 4g + 32 \end{cases}$ $\left(-\frac{1}{2}, 6\right)$

23. $\begin{cases} 2m - 5n = 17 \\ 6m = 5n + 1 \end{cases}$ (−4, −5)

24. $\begin{cases} -7a + 4b = 13 \\ 2b = 3 + 7a \end{cases}$ (1, 5)

25. $\begin{cases} -7c + 2d = 31 \\ -17c = 17 + 2d \end{cases}$ $\left(-2, \frac{17}{2}\right)$

26. $\begin{cases} y = -3x + 1 \\ 5x - 2 = -y \end{cases}$ $\left(\frac{1}{2}, -\frac{1}{2}\right)$

27. $\begin{cases} 2x = y + 1 \\ 5y - 2x = 1 \end{cases}$ $\left(\frac{3}{4}, \frac{1}{2}\right)$

28. $\begin{cases} 3d = 3 - 4c \\ c = 1 - 3d \end{cases}$ $\left(\frac{2}{3}, \frac{1}{9}\right)$

29. $\begin{cases} 4e = 5 + 2f \\ 6f = 9 - 4e \end{cases}$ $\left(\frac{3}{2}, \frac{1}{2}\right)$

30. $\begin{cases} 0.4a - 0.2b = -1.4 \\ 0.4a - 0.5b = -3.2 \end{cases}$
(−0.5, 6)

31. $\begin{cases} -0.7p + 0.2q = 3.1 \\ -1.7p - 0.2q = 1.7 \end{cases}$
(−2, 8.5)

32. $\begin{cases} 2v + 3w = 6 \\ 2v - 27w = 18 \end{cases}$ $\left(\frac{18}{5}, -\frac{2}{5}\right)$

33. $\begin{cases} 12j + 5k = 76 \\ 4j = 52 - 5k \end{cases}$ (3, 8)

34. $\begin{cases} 0.12x - 1.2y = 3.024 \\ 1.34x - 1.2y = 6.928 \end{cases}$ (3.2, −2.2)

35. $\begin{cases} 2.3x - 0.45y = 7.99 \\ -2.3x + 1.6y = -4.31 \end{cases}$ (4.1, 3.2)

36. $\begin{cases} \frac{3}{2}x + \frac{5}{4}y = \frac{18}{13} \\ -\frac{3}{2}x + \frac{3}{4}y = \frac{8}{13} \end{cases}$ $\left(\frac{7}{78}, 1\right)$

37. $\begin{cases} 6r + \frac{3}{7}s = \frac{19}{3} \\ r + \frac{3}{7}s = \frac{4}{3} \end{cases}$ $\left(1, \frac{7}{9}\right)$

Common Error

- Some students may have difficulty determining when to add or subtract the equations in a system. For these students show that the addition method is used when the coefficients of like terms are opposites of each other, as is shown in Example 1. The subtraction method is used when the coefficients of like terms are the same, as is shown in Example 2. Have students work in small groups and compare answers. Encourage them to check their solutions.
- See *Teacher's Resource Book* for additional remediation.

LESSON FOLLOW-UP

Critical Thinking

Causal Explanation Explain why it does not matter which of the original equations the solution is substituted in. The assumption is that if there is at least one ordered pair which satisfies one of the equations, it must also satisfy the other in order to be a common solution. Emphasize, though, that students should check by substituting in both equations.

Assignment Guide

- See p. 442B for assignments.
- For Exercises 30–35, have students check their solutions using a calculator.

Lesson Quiz

Solve by the addition/subtraction method.

1. $\begin{cases} x + y = 10 \\ x - y = -2 \end{cases}$ (4, 6)

2. $\begin{cases} 10x = 2y + 6 \\ x - 2y = -6 \end{cases}$ $\left(\frac{4}{3}, \frac{11}{3}\right)$

3. $\begin{cases} \frac{a}{2} + \frac{b}{3} = 1 \\ 3a = 6 - 2b \end{cases}$
{(a, b): 3a = 6 − 2b}

4. $\begin{cases} 6d = -8c \\ 3c = 3 - 6d \end{cases}$ $\left(-\frac{3}{5}, \frac{4}{5}\right)$

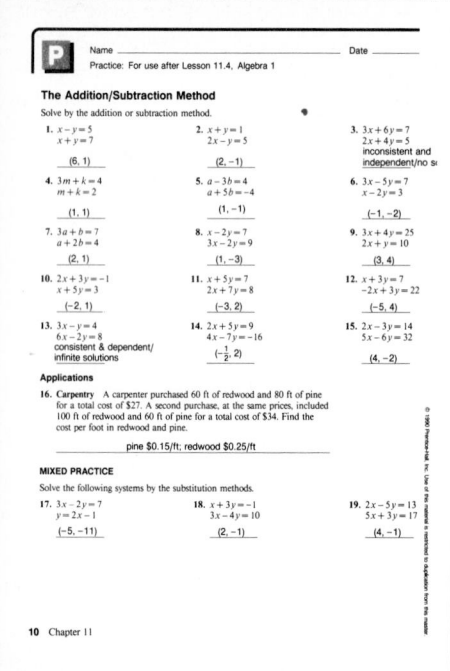

C

38. $\begin{cases} \dfrac{m + n}{2} = \dfrac{3n - 2}{2} \\ \dfrac{3n + 8}{2} = -\left(\dfrac{m + n}{2}\right) \end{cases}$ $(-4, -1)$

39. $\begin{cases} \dfrac{f + 3}{2} + g = 2 \\ g - \dfrac{f + 3}{2} = -5 \end{cases}$ $\left(4, -\dfrac{3}{2}\right)$

40. $\begin{cases} \dfrac{p + 2}{3} = q + 3 \\ 4q = \dfrac{p + 2}{3} \end{cases}$ $(10, 1)$

41. $\begin{cases} \dfrac{2j + 3}{9} = k + 6 \\ -3k = \dfrac{2j + 3}{9} \end{cases}$ $\left(\dfrac{75}{4}, -\dfrac{3}{2}\right)$

In Exercises 42–45, substitute c for $\dfrac{1}{x}$, d for $\dfrac{1}{y}$ to solve for x and y.

42. $\begin{cases} \dfrac{6}{x} + \dfrac{4}{y} = 16 \\ \dfrac{3}{x} - \dfrac{4}{y} = 2 \end{cases}$ $\left(\dfrac{1}{2}, 1\right)$

43. $\begin{cases} \dfrac{8}{x} - \dfrac{2}{y} = -2 \\ \dfrac{8}{x} + \dfrac{7}{y} = 25 \end{cases}$ $\left(2, \dfrac{1}{3}\right)$

44. $\begin{cases} \dfrac{1}{x} + \dfrac{3}{y} = 1 \\ -\dfrac{4}{x} + \dfrac{3}{y} = -3 \end{cases}$ $\left(\dfrac{5}{4}, 15\right)$

45. $\begin{cases} -\dfrac{5}{x} + \dfrac{2}{y} = 3 \\ \dfrac{5}{x} - \dfrac{3}{y} = -4 \end{cases}$ $(-5, 1)$

Applications

Use a system of equations to solve.

46. Agriculture The Allens grow only soybeans and corn on their 240-acre farm. This year they plan to plant 80 more acres of soybeans than of corn. How many acres will they plant of each crop? 80 acres of corn
160 acres of soybeans

47. Agriculture The Bensons are planting an apple orchard on their farm. They decide to grow 85 acres of wheat along with some acres of apples. If they had doubled the size of the orchard there would have been only 60 acres of wheat. How large is the orchard they planted? 25 acres

48. Science Two batteries produce a total voltage of 4.5 v. The difference in their voltage is 1.5 v. Determine the voltages of the two batteries. 3 v, 1.5 v

49. Engineering When analyzing a certain electric circuit, an electric engineer found these equations, $3i_1 + 4i_2 = 3$ and $3i_1 - 5i_2 = -6$. Solve for the electric currents i_1 and i_2 (in amperes). $-\dfrac{1}{3}$ amp; 1 amp

EXTRA

The graphs of these equations form a triangle. Find the vertices of the triangle. Then find the area of the triangle. (0, 0); (6, 0); (−6, 12); 36

$x + y = 6$
$2x + y = 0$
$y = 0$

The Multiplication-Addition/Subtraction Method

Objective: To solve appropriate systems of linear equations by using the multiplication-addition/subtraction method

Sometimes the substitution method and the addition/subtraction method are not the most effective ways of solving simultaneous equations. Consider a system such as:

$$\begin{cases} 3x - 2y = -12 \\ 5x + 4y = 2 \end{cases}$$

Adding or subtracting will not result in an equation in just one variable, since neither the x nor the y terms are the same or opposites. If necessary, the substitution method can always be used. What is the difficulty?

Note that the addition method could be used to solve the system if both sides of the first equation were multiplied by 2. The resulting equation is an **equivalent system of equations.**

$$\begin{cases} 6x - 4y = -24 \\ 5x + 4y = 2 \end{cases}$$

Equivalent systems may look different but must have the same solution. Compare this second system of equations with the one above. Are the two systems equivalent?

Capsule Review

In using multiplication with the addition/subtraction method, it is important to remember to multiply both sides of the equation using the multiplication property of equality.

EXAMPLE   **Multiply:** $x - 2y = 3$ by 4
$$4(x - 2y) = 4(3)$$
$$4x - 8y = 12$$

Multiply each side of the equation by the given integer.

1. $2m + 5n = 1$ by 3 $\quad 6m + 15n = 3$

2. $5p - q = 2$ by -1 $\quad -5p + q = -2$

3. $-3s + 6t = -8$ by -2 $\quad 6s - 12t = 16$

4. $-4x - 7y = -2$ by -5 $\quad 20x + 35y = 10$

The main idea in solving a system of equations by the **multiplication-addition/subtraction method** is to use the multiplication property of equality on one or both of the original equations.

11.5 The Multiplication-Addition/Subtraction Method   **463**

LESSON PLAN

Vocabulary
Multiplication-addition/subtraction method

Materials/Manipulatives
Calculators

BACKGROUND

In the Capsule Review, the exercises review transforming a linear equation into an equivalent equation by using the multiplication property of equality. Remind students that the two equations are equivalent since they have the same solution. In this lesson, students use the multiplication property of equality on one or both equations in a linear system of equations in order to solve it.

- Stress the importance of multiplying *each* term on both sides of the equation by the same number to produce an equivalent equation.
- Stress that sometimes it is necessary to multiply *one* equation and sometimes *both* equations in order to solve the system.
- Remind students to find the value of each variable and to check each solution in the *original* equations.
- For Exercises 1–27, you may want students to check their solutions using a calculator.

CHALKBOARD EXAMPLES

For Exercises 1–4, solve.

- **For Example 1**
  1. $\begin{cases} 4a + 3b = -1 \\ 5a + 6b = -8 \end{cases}$ $(2, -3)$
  2. $\begin{cases} 6m - 3n = 12 \\ 5m = n + 1 \end{cases}$ $(-1, -6)$

- **For Example 2**
  3. $\begin{cases} 3u + 7v = 5 \\ 2u + 8v = 10 \end{cases}$ $(-3, 2)$
  4. $\begin{cases} 3a + 2b = 6 \\ 4a + 3b = 7 \end{cases}$ $(4, -3)$

Common Errors

- Some students may attempt to solve a system by adding or subtracting first. Point out that in these examples, if you add or subtract first, no variable is eliminated. Stress the importance of eliminating one of the variables.
- Some students may have trouble determining which number to multiply by in each equation. Review the concept of least common multiples with these students.
- See *Teacher's Resource Book* for additional remediation.

EXAMPLE 1 **Solve:** $\begin{cases} 3a - 4b = 18 \\ a + 2b = -4 \end{cases}$

The *b*-terms may be eliminated. If the second equation is multiplied by 2, the coefficients of the *b*-terms will each be 4.

$$\begin{cases} 3a - 4b = 18 \\ a + 2b = -4 \end{cases} \longrightarrow \begin{array}{c} 3a - 4b = 18 \\ 2(a + 2b = -4) \end{array} \longrightarrow \begin{array}{c} 3a - 4b = 18 \\ 2a + 4b = -8 \end{array}$$

$$\begin{array}{ll} 3a - 4b = 18 \\ 2a + 4b = -8 & \text{\textit{Add to eliminate the b-terms.}} \\ \hline \quad\quad 5a = 10 & \text{\textit{Solve for a.}} \\ \quad\quad\quad a = 2 \end{array}$$

$$\begin{array}{ll} a + 2b = -4 & \text{\textit{Replace a with 2 in either equation.}} \\ 2 + 2b = -4 & \text{\textit{Solve for b.}} \\ \quad\quad 2b = -6 \\ \quad\quad\quad b = -3 \end{array}$$

The solution is $(2, -3)$. How would you check?

EXAMPLE 2 **Solve:** $\begin{cases} 4x + 15y = 7 \\ 9y = -6x + 21 \end{cases}$

$$\begin{cases} 4x + 15y = 7 \\ 6x + 9y = 21 \end{cases} \quad \text{\textit{Write the second equation in standard form.}}$$

The *x*-terms may be eliminated. If the first equation is multiplied by 3 and the second equation by 2, the coefficients of the *x*-terms will each be 12.

$$\begin{cases} 4x + 15y = 7 \\ 6x + 9y = 21 \end{cases} \longrightarrow \begin{array}{c} 3(4x + 15y) = 3(7) \\ 2(6x + 9y) = 2(21) \end{array} \longrightarrow \begin{array}{c} 12x + 45y = 21 \\ 12x + 18y = 42 \end{array}$$

$$\begin{array}{ll} 12x + 45y = 21 \\ 12x + 18y = 42 & \text{\textit{Subtract to eliminate the x-terms.}} \\ \hline \quad\quad 27y = -21 & \text{\textit{Solve for y.}} \\ \quad\quad\quad y = \dfrac{-21}{27} = -\dfrac{7}{9} \end{array}$$

$$\begin{array}{ll} 9y = -6x + 21 & \text{\textit{Replace y with } } -\dfrac{7}{9} \text{ \textit{in either original equation.}} \\ 9\left(-\dfrac{7}{9}\right) = -6x + 21 & \text{\textit{Solve for x.}} \\ -7 = -6x + 21 \\ -28 = -6x \\ \dfrac{-28}{-6} = \dfrac{14}{3} = x \end{array}$$

The check of the solution $\left(\dfrac{14}{3}, -\dfrac{7}{9}\right)$ is left for you.

CLASS EXERCISES

For each system, write an equivalent system in which addition or subtraction of the two equations will eliminate (a) the first variable and (b) the second variable. Then solve. Check students' work.

1. $\begin{cases} a + 2b = 4 \\ a + 3b = -2 \end{cases}$ (16, −6)

2. $\begin{cases} 2x - y = 4 \\ x + 3y = 16 \end{cases}$ (4, 4)

3. $\begin{cases} 2a - 3b = -4 \\ -6a + 9b = -15 \end{cases}$
no solution

4. $\begin{cases} 3s - 7t = 13 \\ 6s + 5t = 7 \end{cases}$ (2, −1)

5. $\begin{cases} 8x + 3y = 13 \\ 3x + 2y = 11 \end{cases}$ (−1, 7)

6. $\begin{cases} 4c - 15d = -13 \\ 6c + 10d = 13 \end{cases}$ $\left(\frac{1}{2}, 1\right)$

7. Explain how multiplication can be used with the addition/subtraction method to solve the system:

$$\begin{cases} 7x + 9y = 3 \\ 5x + 4y = 1 \end{cases}$$
Multiply the first equation by 5.
Multiply the second equation by 7.
Subtract the second equation from the first.
Solve for y. Substitute the value of y back into an original equation and solve for x.

PRACTICE EXERCISES

Solve by the multiplication with addition or subtraction method.

A **1.** $\begin{cases} 3a - 4b = 1 \\ 12a - b = \end{cases}$ (−1, −1)

2. $\begin{cases} -5c + 3d = -16 \\ -10c + d = -22 \end{cases}$ (2, −2)

3. $\begin{cases} 8u - 4v = 16 \\ 4u + 5v = 22 \end{cases}$ (3, 2)

4. $\begin{cases} -5m + 3n \\ -2m - 5n = 0 \end{cases}$ (5, −2)

5. $\begin{cases} -3e + 4f = -6 \\ 5e \quad 6f = 8 \end{cases}$ (−2, −3)

6. $\begin{cases} 5k + 3l = 17 \\ 2k - 9l = 17 \end{cases}$ (4, −1)

7. $\begin{cases} 8r - 5s = -11 \\ 3s = 4r - 11 \end{cases}$ (−22, −33)

8. $\begin{cases} 9p + 4q = -17 \\ 12q = -3 - 3p \end{cases}$ $\left(-2, \frac{1}{4}\right)$

9. $\begin{cases} 3x - 2y = 6 \\ 5x + 7y = 41 \end{cases}$ (4, 3)

10. $\begin{cases} 5m - 2n = 8 \\ 3m - 5n = 1 \end{cases}$ (2, 1)

11. $\begin{cases} 7a - 3b = -9 \\ 9b - 4a = -24 \end{cases}$ (−3, −4)

12. $\begin{cases} -3x + 4y = -6 \\ -6y + 5x = 8 \end{cases}$
(−2, −3)

13. $\begin{cases} 8c - 3d = 5 \\ 16c + 9d = 5 \end{cases}$ $\left(\frac{1}{2}, -\frac{1}{3}\right)$

14. $\begin{cases} 3s - 8t = 4 \\ 9s - 4t = 5 \end{cases}$ $\left(\frac{2}{5}, -\frac{7}{20}\right)$

15. $\begin{cases} 3x = y + 1 \\ -9x + 2y = -5 \end{cases}$
(1, 2)

B **16.** $\begin{cases} 2a + 5b = 6 \\ 3a = 10b + 2 \end{cases}$ $\left(2, \frac{2}{5}\right)$

17. $\begin{cases} u = 4v \\ 3u + 2v = 7 \end{cases}$ $\left(2, \frac{1}{2}\right)$

18. $\begin{cases} p = 2q \\ 2p + 6q = 5 \end{cases}$ $\left(1, \frac{1}{2}\right)$

19. $\begin{cases} 6m + 12n = 7 \\ 8m - 15n = -1 \end{cases}$ $\left(\frac{1}{2}, \frac{1}{3}\right)$

20. $\begin{cases} 10r - 9s = 18 \\ 6s + 2r = 1 \end{cases}$ $\left(\frac{3}{2}, -\frac{1}{3}\right)$

21. $\begin{cases} 2(p + 3) = 3 - q \\ 3(p - 1) = q - 4 \end{cases}$
$\left(-\frac{4}{5}, -\frac{7}{5}\right)$

22. $\begin{cases} 4(x + 3) = 3y + 7 \\ 2(y - 5) = x + 5 \end{cases}$ (7, 11)

23. $\begin{cases} c - 2d = 500 \\ 0.03c + 0.02d = 51 \end{cases}$
(1400, 450)

24. $\begin{cases} 3e - 2f = -80 \\ 0.05e - 0.03f = 2 \end{cases}$
(640, 1000)

25. $\begin{cases} \dfrac{3m + 2n}{4} = -5m + n \\ 2n - 23m = 5 \end{cases}$
no solution

26. $\begin{cases} \dfrac{7u - 4v}{2} = 5v \\ 5 + v = 7u \end{cases}$ $\left(\frac{10}{13}, \frac{5}{13}\right)$

27. $\begin{cases} \dfrac{-2a + b}{5} = \dfrac{4a - 2b}{3} \\ \dfrac{a + 2}{3} = \dfrac{1 - b}{9} \end{cases}$
(−1, −2)

11.5 The Multiplication-Addition/Subtraction Method **465**

LESSON FOLLOW-UP

Critical Thinking

Comparing-Contrasting Explain how the Multiplication-Addition/Subtraction Method and the Addition/Subtraction Method are alike and different. The methods are the same once the coefficients of one of the variables are the same, or opposite, in the equations of the system. They are different in that the Multiplication-Addition/Subtraction method is used when neither pair of coefficients is the same (or opposite) in the two equations, as they were in problems in the previous lesson.

Assignment Guide

See p. 442B for assignments.

Test Yourself

See *Teacher's Resource Book*, Tests, pp. 113–114.

See *Teacher's Resource Book*, for Reading and Writing in Algebra activity p. 11.

Lesson Quiz

Solve by the multiplication-addition/ subtraction method.

1. $\begin{cases} 5a + 6b = 1 \\ 3a + 2b = -1 \end{cases}$ (−1, 1)

2. $\begin{cases} 2x + 3y = 4 \\ 3x - 2y = 3 \end{cases}$ $\left(\frac{17}{13}, \frac{6}{13}\right)$

3. $\begin{cases} 4a = 3b + 15 \\ 2b - a = 0 \end{cases}$ (6, 3)

4. $\begin{cases} 2.4 - 0.3x = 0.4y \\ 5x - 2 = 6y \end{cases}$ (4, 3)

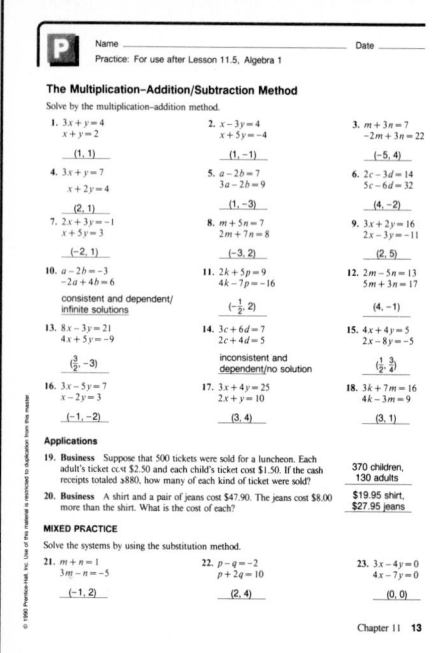

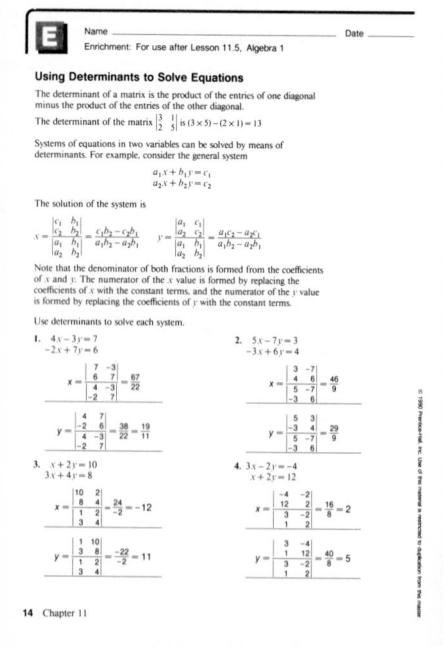

C **28.** $\begin{cases} \dfrac{1}{x} + \dfrac{1}{y} = 5 \\ \dfrac{2}{x} + \dfrac{3}{y} = 13 \end{cases}$ $\left(\dfrac{1}{2}, \dfrac{1}{3}\right)$

29. $\begin{cases} \dfrac{1}{x} - \dfrac{2}{y} = 8 \\ \dfrac{3}{x} + \dfrac{1}{y} = 10 \end{cases}$ $\left(\dfrac{1}{4}, -\dfrac{1}{2}\right)$

30. $\begin{cases} \dfrac{1}{x} + \dfrac{3}{y} = 10 \\ \dfrac{2}{x} + \dfrac{1}{y} = 6 \end{cases}$ $\left(\dfrac{5}{8}, \dfrac{5}{14}\right)$

Solve the following systems in terms of coefficients a, b, and c.

31. $\begin{cases} ax + y = c \\ x + by = c \end{cases}$ $x = \dfrac{c(1-b)}{1-ab}$ $y = \dfrac{c(1-a)}{1-ab}$

32. $\begin{cases} ax + y = c \\ ax + by = 0 \end{cases}$ $x = -\dfrac{bc}{a(1-b)}$ $y = \dfrac{c}{1-b}$

33. $\begin{cases} ax + y = c \\ ax + y = 0 \end{cases}$ $\{(x, y): ax + y = c \text{ and } c = 0\}$

34. $(-1, 1)$ and $(3, -15)$ are two solutions of the nonlinear equation $y = ax^2 + b$. Find a and b. $(-2, 3)$

Applications

35. Business A department store is having a sale on women's shoes. The shoes are selling for $20 and $25 a pair. At the end of the day the total receipts for the sale of 55 pairs of shoes were $1250. If x and y represent the numbers of pairs of $20 and $25 shoes respectively, find x by solving the system: $20x + 25y = 1250$ and $x + y = 55$. 25

36. Food Preparation The cafeteria usually makes 112 cups of orange-pineapple fruit punch. One Friday the amount of orange juice was tripled, and the pineapple juice was doubled to make a total of 274 c of punch. How many cups of the two juices were used on that Friday? 150 c of orange juice
124 c of pineapple juice

TEST YOURSELF

Describe the graph and tell the number of solutions. Verify by graphing. 11.1

1. $\begin{cases} x + y = 6 \\ 2x - y = 3 \end{cases}$
intersecting lines; one solution

2. $\begin{cases} x + y = 6 \\ \dfrac{1}{2}x + \dfrac{1}{2}y = 3 \end{cases}$
same line; infinitely many solutions

3. $\begin{cases} 3x + y = 1 \\ x + \dfrac{1}{2}y = -1 \end{cases}$
intersecting lines; one solution

Solve by an appropriate method of your choice: substitution, addition, subtraction, or multiplication-addition/subtraction. 11.2–11.5

4. $\begin{cases} 2x + y = -10 \\ x + 3y = 0 \end{cases}$ $(-6, 2)$

5. $\begin{cases} 3x + 2y = 10 \\ x - 2y = 14 \end{cases}$ $(6, -4)$

6. $\begin{cases} 4x - 3y = 15 \\ x + y = 9 \end{cases}$ $(6, 3)$

7. $\begin{cases} \dfrac{1}{3}x = -\dfrac{1}{3}y + 4 \\ \dfrac{8}{3} = x + \dfrac{1}{3}y \end{cases}$ $(-2, 14)$

8. $\begin{cases} -\dfrac{2}{3}y + 2x = -1 \\ \dfrac{1}{3}y + x = \dfrac{1}{2} \end{cases}$ $\left(0, \dfrac{3}{2}\right)$

9. A marketing firm budgets $33,000 each year for advertising. It spends twice as much money on advertisements in newspapers as in magazines. How much does it spend on advertising in newspapers? in magazines?
$22,000; $11,000

466 Chapter 11 Systems of Linear Equations

Problem Solving: Digit Problems

Objective: To use systems of equations to solve digit problems

Digit problems are problems involving the digits of a number. The number 25 consists of the digit 2 in the tens place and the digit 5 in the ones place. What happens when the digits of a number are reversed?

Number	Expanded Notation	Reversed Digits	Expanded Notation
25	$2 \cdot 10 + 5 \cdot 1$	52	$5 \cdot 10 + 2 \cdot 1$
48	$4 \cdot 10 + 8 \cdot 1$	84	$8 \cdot 10 + 4 \cdot 1$
tu	$10t + u$	ut	$10u + t$

In general, if $10t + u$ is the original number, then $10u + t$ is the number with the digits reversed.

EXAMPLE The sum of the digits of a two-digit number is 8. If the digits are reversed, the new number is 18 more than the original number. Find the original number.

Understand the Problem

Find a two-digit number that satisfies these conditions.

1. The sum of the digits is 8.
2. When the digits are reversed, the new number is 18 more than the original number.

Plan Your Approach

Write a system of equations.

$$\begin{cases} t + u = 8 \\ 10u + t = (10t + u) + 18 \end{cases}$$

The sum of the digits is 8.

The number with the digits reversed is 18 more than the original number.

Complete the Work

Solve the system by the easiest method.

$$\begin{cases} t + u = 8 \longrightarrow \\ 10u + t = 10t + u + 18 \longrightarrow -9t + 9u = 18 \end{cases} \begin{cases} t + u = 8 \\ -t + u = 2 \end{cases}$$

$$2u = 10$$
$$u = 5$$

Now find the value of t.

$$t + u = 8$$
$$t + 5 = 8$$
$$t = 3$$

BACKGROUND

To solve a problem successfully, students must be able to organize the information in the problem in a way that will allow them to write systems of equations easily. Making a list of conditions is stressed in this lesson as a way of organizing the given information. Students may encounter difficulty in many different areas. You can do an error analysis of the students' work to determine how they are proceeding. Then classify and correct specific student errors.

Error Analysis Classification

1. *Misunderstanding*
   Misread the problem
2. *Misapplied Strategy*
   Wrote an incorrect equation
   Failed to complete the solution
   Did not interpret the solution correctly

Critical Thinking

Reasoning Explain why the sum of the digits of a two-digit number can be represented by either $t + u$ or $u + t$; however, the number itself can only be represented by $10t + u$ and not $10u + t$. The sum of the digits of a two-digit number can be expressed by $t + u$ or $u + t$ because the integers in the tens and units places are being added and addition of integers is commutative; however, the actual two-digit number must be represented as $10t + u$ or $u + 10t$ because place value is needed.

TEACHING SUGGESTIONS

- Point out the difference in the representation of 25 and 52 in expanded notation. Have students note what happens when the digits are reversed. You may wish to discuss why numbers like 25 and 52 have different values, but their digits have the same sum.
- Emphasize why a two-digit integer cannot be represented by tu.
- Stress the difference between the representation of a two-digit number, $10t + u$, and the number with digits reversed, $10u + t$.

CHALKBOARD EXAMPLE

- **For the Example**

  Find the original number described by the problem.

  1. The sum of the digits of a two-digit number is 14. If the digits are reversed, the new number is 36 less than the original. 95
  2. The units digit is twice the tens digit. If the digits are interchanged, the new number is 18 more than the original number. 24

LESSON FOLLOW-UP

Assignment Guide

- See p. 442B for assignments.
- Exercise 14 requires writing three equations to solve.

Lesson Quiz

Find the original two-digit number described by the problem.

1. The sum of the digits is 11. The original number decreased by 9 equals the number formed when the digits are reversed. 65
2. Twice the tens digit of a number increased by the units digit is 13. If the digits are interchanged, the new number is 36 more than the original. 37

 **Interpret the Results**

The number $(10t + u)$ is 35.
Check the number in the word problem.
Find the sum of the digits. $3 + 5 = 8$
Reverse the digits. $53 \overset{?}{=} 35 + 18$
    $53 = 53$ ✔

CLASS EXERCISES

Write an equation for each word sentence.

1. The sum of the digits is 9. $t + u = 9$
2. The units digit is 4 more than the tens digit. $t + 4 = u$
3. The tens digit is half the units digit. $t = \frac{1}{2}u$
4. The number with its digits reversed is 9 more than the original number. $10u + t = 10t + u + 9$

Solve the system of equations to find the number from the Class Exercises above.

5. Exercises 1 and 3 36
6. Exercises 3 and 4 12
7. Exercises 1 and 4 45
8. Exercises 2 and 3 48

PRACTICE EXERCISES

Find the original two-digit number described by the problem.

A
1. The sum of the digits is 6. The number is 6 times its units digit. 24
2. The sum of the digits is 6. Reversing the digits gives a new number that is 18 less than the original. 42
3. The units digit is 3 times the tens digit. When the digits are reversed, the new number is 54 more than the original. 39
4. The units digit is 3 times the tens digit. The number is 12 more than the tens digit. 13
5. The units digit exceeds the tens digit by 6. The number is 10 more than 9 times the tens digit. 28
6. The sum of the digits is 12. The number is 1 more than 8 times its units digit. 57
7. The sum of the digits is 10. The original number decreased by 54 equals the number formed when the digits are reversed. 82
8. The sum of the digits is 12. The original number increased by 36 equals the number formed when the digits are reversed. 48

468   Chapter 11 Systems of Linear Equations

9. Twice the tens digit of a number increased by the units digit is 22. If the digits are reversed, the new number is 45 less than the original. 94

B 10. Three times the units digit is 2 less than the tens digit. If the digits are reversed, the new number is 54 less than the original. 82

11. The sum of the digits is 11. If the digits are reversed, the original number is 7 more than twice the new number. 83

12. A number is 9 more than the sum of its digits. If the digits are reversed, the new number is 3 less than 4 times the original. 16

13. A number is 7 times the sum of its digits. If the digits are reversed, the new number is 30 less than twice the original. 21

C 14. The hundreds digit of a three-digit number equals the sum of the tens and units digits. The units digit is twice the tens digit. The difference between the number and the new number with reversed digits is 297. 936

15. Write a single equation in digits t and u that has just one solution.
Answers may vary. $t + u = 1$

16. Write a two-digit integer problem that has no solution.
Answers may vary. One possible solution: $t = 3u$; $10u + t = \frac{1}{2}(10t + u)$

ALGEBRA IN BOOKKEEPING

When two digits in a number are turned around, it is called a **transposition.** In bookkeeping, the bookkeeper often has to check for **transposition errors.** To see if there is an error the bookkeeper subtracts the figure in question from the figure he/she obtained. If the difference is divisible by 9, there is usually a transposition error. This computer program checks for transposition errors.

```
10 INPUT "ENTER A THREE DIGIT
        NUMBER:  ";N
20 NH =   INT (N / 100):NT =  INT
        ((N - NH * 100) / 10)
30 ND = (N - NH * 100 - NT * 10)
40 Y1 = ND * 100 + NT * 10 + NH
50 Y2 = NH * 100 + ND * 10 + NT
60 Y3 = NT * 100 + NH * 10 + ND
70 PRINT "NUMBER"; TAB( 15);"DIFFERENCE";
        TAB( 30);"DIFF/9"
80 PRINT N: PRINT Y1,N - Y1,(N - Y1) / 9
90 PRINT Y2,N - Y2,(N - Y2) / 9
100 PRINT Y3,N - Y3,(N - Y3) / 9
110 END
```

Exercises

1. Is it possible to use the first transposed number printed by the program to prove that the difference between any three-digit number and the number with the digits reversed is divisible by 99? Yes

2. Run the program several times, and then explain what Y1 in line 40, Y2 in line 50, and Y3 in line 60 mean.
Y1, Y2, and Y3 show the different combinations of transposition errors.

11.6 Problem Solving: Digit Problems   **469**

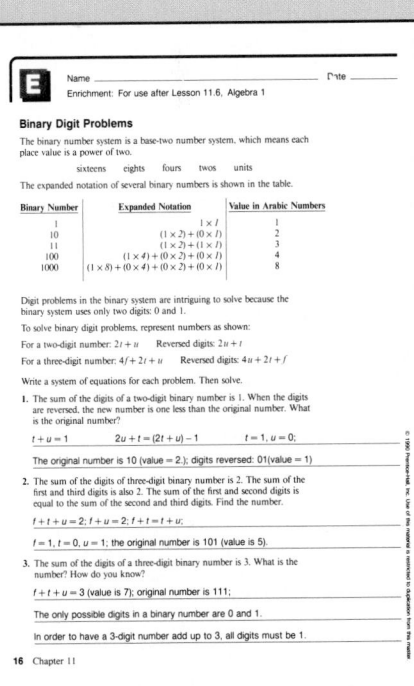

BACKGROUND

To solve a problem successfully, students must be able to organize the information in the problem in a way that will allow them to write systems of equations easily. Using a table to organize the given information is stressed in this lesson. Students may encounter difficulty in many different areas. You can do an error analysis of the students' work to determine how they are proceeding. Then, classify and correct specific student errors.

Error Analysis Classification

1. *Misunderstanding*
   Misread the problem
   Incorrectly organized the information in a table
2. *Misapplied Strategy*
   Wrote an incorrect equation
   Used the wrong formula or applied it incorrectly
   Failed to complete the solution
   Did not interpret the solution correctly

11.7

Problem Solving: Age Problems

Objective: To use systems of equations to solve age problems

Kim's father is now $2\frac{1}{2}$ times as old as Kim. Ten years ago he was 4 times as old as Kim was.

This type of problem can readily be solved by setting up a system of equations to represent the two statements. Think of algebraic expressions to represent the two ages.

EXAMPLE   Reread the problem above about Kim and her father. Find their present ages.

◻ **Understand the Problem**

Two facts about the relationship between the ages of Kim and her father are given.

Now: Kim's father's age is $2\frac{1}{2}$ times Kim's age.
10 yr ago: Kim's father's age was 4 times Kim's age.

◻ **Plan Your Approach**

Represent the variables.
Let k = Kim's age now.
Let f = Kim's father's age now.
Make a table to show their ages in terms of the variables. Then translate the two age relationships into a system of equations:

	Age now	Age 10 yr ago
Kim	k	$k - 10$
Father	f	$f - 10$

$$\begin{cases} f = 2\frac{1}{2}k \\ f - 10 = 4(k - 10) \end{cases}$$

◻ **Complete the Work**

$$\begin{cases} f = 2\frac{1}{2}k \longrightarrow f = \frac{5}{2}k \\ f - 10 = 4(k - 10) \longrightarrow f - 10 = 4k - 40 \end{cases}$$

Substitute $f = \frac{5}{2}k$ into the second equation. Solve for k.

$$\frac{5}{2}k - 10 = 4k - 40$$

$5k - 20 = 8k - 80$	*Multiply each side by 2.*
$-3k = -60$	*Subtract 8k and add 20 to each side.*
$k = 20$	*Divide each side by −3.*

If $k = 20$, then $f = \frac{5}{2}k = \frac{5}{2}(20) = 50$.

470   Chapter 11 Systems of Linear Equations

| | Interpret the Results | Conclusion: Kim is 20 years old; her father is 50 years old. Check: $50 = 2\frac{1}{2}(20)$. Ten years ago Kim was 10, her father 40, so Kim's father was then 4 times as old as Kim. |

CLASS EXERCISES

1. The headings for each column in the table are given. Complete the table.

Ages of Two Students

	Age 8 years ago	Age 5 years ago	Age 2 years ago	Present age	Age in 1 year	Age in 4 years	Age in 7 years
Anne	$\underline{?}\,a - 8$	$\underline{?}\,a - 5$	$a - 2$	a	$a + \underline{1?}$	$a + 4$	$\underline{?}\,a + 7$
Bill	$b - 8$	$\underline{?}\,b - 5$	$b - 2$	$\underline{?}\,b$	$b + \underline{1?}$	$b + 4$	$b + 7$

Use entries from the table above to write an equation for the statements.

2. Anne is 3 years younger than Bill. $b - 3 = a$

3. Eight years ago Bill was twice as old as Anne. $b - 8 = 2(a - 8)$

4. In 4 years Anne will be $\frac{5}{6}$ as old as Bill. $a + 4 = \frac{5}{6}(b + 4)$

5. Seven years from now Bill's age will be $\frac{7}{6}$ of Anne's age. $b + 7 = \frac{7}{6}(a + 7)$

6. The sum of their present ages is 25. $a + b = 25$

Solve systems consisting of the equations from the Class Exercises above.

7. Exercises 2 and 6
Anne 11 yr
Bill 14 yr

8. Exercises 2 and 3
Anne 11 yr
Bill 14 yr

9. Exercises 4 and 5
Anne 11 yr
Bill 14 yr

PRACTICE EXERCISES

Write and solve a system of linear equations to find the present ages.

A

1. Cordell is twice as old as Beth. Eight years ago he was 3 times as old. Cordell 32 yr
Beth 16 yr

2. Dawn is 3 years older than Lois. Four years ago Dawn was twice as old as Lois. Dawn 10 yr
Lois 7 yr

3. Mario's age is 2 years more than twice Nadia's age. In 9 years her age will be $\frac{2}{3}$ of his. Mario 12 yr
Nadia 5 yr

4. Tanya's younger brother's age is $\frac{3}{4}$ of hers. In 7 years the sum of their ages will be 28. Tanya 8 yr
Brother 6 yr

5. Two years ago Adam was 6 times as old as his son. In 3 years he will be $3\frac{1}{2}$ times as old. Adam 32 yr
Son 7 yr

11.7 Problem Solving: Age Problems **471**

471

Critical Thinking

Observation Explain what *a* and *b* represent in the class exercises. *a is Anne's present age, and b is Bill's present age.*

Assignment Guide

See p. 442B for assignments.

Lesson Quiz

Write and solve a system of linear equations to find the present ages.

1. John is three times as old as Teresa. In 3 years the sum of their ages will be 54. How old is each now? *John: 36 yr; Teresa: 12 yr*

2. One-fourth the sum of Alex's age and Judy's age is 9. Four years ago, Alex was $2\frac{1}{2}$ times as old as Judy. How old is each one now? *Judy: 12 yr; Alex: 24 yr*

Enrichment

If you square a number and subtract the result from 10 you get the second number. Doubling the number gives the same result as subtracting the second number from 2. What are the numbers? *−2, 6 or 4, −6*

6. Six years ago Bob was 4 times as old as Peri. In 9 years he will be $\frac{3}{2}$ as old. *Bob 18 yr* *Peri 9 yr*

7. Sarat is 4 years younger than his brother Akhil. Fourteen years ago Akhil was twice as old as Sarat. *Sarat 18 yr* *Akhil 22 yr*

8. In 2 years Peter will be twice as old as his sister Eve. The sum of their present ages is 26. *Eve 8 yr* *Peter 18 yr*

9. Lauren is 18 years younger than Joyce. Twelve years ago Joyce was 4 times as old as Lauren was. *Lauren 18 yr* *Joyce 36 yr*

10. In 3 years Rufus will be $\frac{2}{3}$ the age of Jason. The sum of their present ages is 44. *Rufus 17 yr* *Jason 27 yr*

11. Six years ago the sum of Harvey's and Carol's ages was 71. Harvey is 27 years older than Carol. *Carol 28 yr* *Harvey 55 yr*

12. 21 years ago Alvin was 11 times older than Tomio. The sum of their present ages is 54. *Alvin 32 yr* *Tomio 22 yr*

13. Mary is 9 years older than Seth. In a year she will be 3 times as old as he is. *Mary $12\frac{1}{2}$ yr; Seth $3\frac{1}{2}$ yr*

14. Roz is twice as old as Gerry. In 5 years the sum of their ages will be 28. *Roz 12 yr* *Gerry 6 yr*

15. Susan is 3 times as old as Randi. One-fourth the sum of their ages is 8. *Randi 8 yr* *Susan 24 yr*

16. The sum of the ages of Ira and Sofia is 26. The difference between 4 times Sofia's age and twice Ira's age is 8. *Ira 16 yr* *Sofia 10 yr*

B 17. In 1945, Liz was twice as old as Bill. That same year the difference in their ages was 18 years. In what year was each born? *Liz 1909* *Bill 1927*

18. In 1987, Joy was 3 times as old as Ali. If Ali was born 8 years after Joy, what age will each be in 1999? *Ali 16 yr* *Joy 24 yr*

19. Six years ago Bill was 17 years younger than twice Ann's age. Now their combined age is 100 years. Find their present ages. *Bill 59 yr* *Ann 41 yr*

20. Patty was 3 times as old as Tom in 1982. In 1986, the difference in their ages was 4 years. Find their ages now. *Answers will vary according to the current year.*

21. The sum of Spero's and Chris's ages is 50 years. In $2\frac{1}{2}$ years Spero will be $\frac{5}{6}$ of Chris's age. Find their present ages. *Spero $22\frac{1}{2}$ yr; Chris $27\frac{1}{2}$ yr*

22. Presently, Susie is $\frac{3}{4}$ of Weiva's age. In 4 years she will be $\frac{4}{5}$ of Weiva's age. Find their present ages. *Weiva 16 yr* *Susie 12 yr*

23. Armando is $1\frac{1}{3}$ times as old as Zelda. Five years ago his age was $1\frac{1}{2}$ hers. Find Armando's age now. *Armando 20 yr*

24. Nina's age is $\frac{2}{3}$ of Liu's. Four years ago Liu's age was $\frac{5}{3}$ of Nina's. What is Nina's age now? Nina 16 yr

Solve by using a system of three equations in three variables.

C **25.** The sum of all Emma's and Vangie's books equals 45. One fourth of Kim's books are equal to twelve less than Emma's books. Kim's books are equal to $\frac{8}{5}$ of Emma's. Find the present number of books for each person. Emma: 20; Kim: 32; Vangie: 25

26. Diana had three classes this semester, history, mathematics, and English. Her total grade points for all three classes was 255. Her history grade was 10 more points than her English grade. Her mathematics grade was 95 points less than twice her history grade. What grade did she receive in each class? What was her grade-point average?
history: 90; mathematics: 85; English: 80; average: 85

27. Thirteen years ago Mary's age was $\frac{5}{17}$ of Grace's age. Two years from now Mary will be $\frac{1}{2}$ of Jim's age. Together all their ages add up to 118. Find their ages five years from now. Mary = 23 yr; Grace = 47 yr; Jim = 48 yr

EXTRA

A **palindrome** sentence reads the same backward as forward. Solve the systems of equations to decode the palindromes. Each solution corresponds to a point on the graph. The letter for the point replaces the number of the system in the coded palindrome.

1. $x + y - 6 = 0$
$x - 4 = y$ (5, 1)

2. $x + y = 2$
$2y - 10 = x$ (-2, 4)

3. $2x + 3y - 8 = 0$
$3x + y = 5$ (1, 2)

4. $2x + 3y + 5 = 0$
$5x + 3y = 1$ (2, -3)

5. $4x + 3y = -2$
$8x = 2y + 12$ (1, -2)

6. $2y = 5x - 11$
$3x + 5y = 19$ (3, 2)

7. $2x + 5y - 18 = 0$
$y - 5x + 18 = 0$ (4, 2)

8. $3x + y = 10$
$y + 2x = 7$ (3, 1)

9. $4x = 2y + 20$
$x + 5y = -17$ (3, -4)

10. $4x = 7 - 3y$
$4y = 12 - 4x$ (-2, 5)

Palindrome 1: 2–1 8–9 1–9 9–10–5–7–5–10–9–9 1–9 8 1–2
MA   IS   AS   SELFLESS   AS   I   AM
Palindrome 2: 1 2–1–3, 1 4–5–1–3, 1 6–1–3–1–5, 4–1–3–1–2–1
A MAN,   A PLAN,   A CANAL,   PANAMA

11.7 Problem Solving: Age Problems   **473**

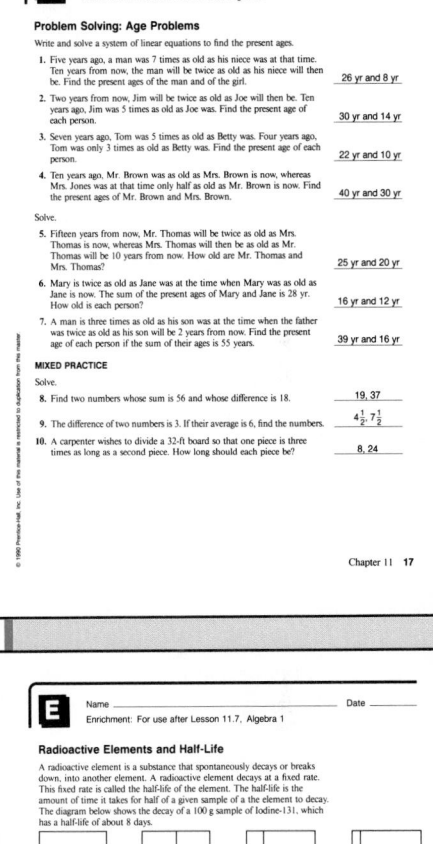

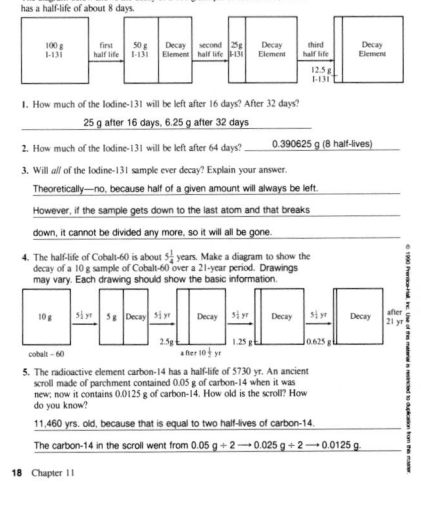

Materials/Manipulatives
Computer
Overhead projector
Teacher's Resource Book,
  Teaching Aid 5,
  Transparency 7

BACKGROUND

To solve a problem successfully, students must be able to organize the information given in the problem in a way that will allow them to write systems of equations easily. Using a table to organize the given information is stressed in this lesson. Students may encounter difficulty in many different areas. Do an error analysis of the students' work and then classify and correct specific errors.

Error Analysis Classification
1. *Misunderstanding*
   Misread the problem
   Incorrectly organized the information in a table
2. *Misapplied Strategy*
   Wrote an incorrect equation
   Used the wrong formula or applied it incorrectly
   Failed to complete the solution
   Did not interpret the solution correctly

11.8

Problem Solving: Money and Mixture Problems

Objective: To use systems of equations to solve money and mixture problems

Randy has 83 coins worth $10.70. Some are dimes and the rest are quarters. By trial and error, it is possible to find how many of each coin he has, although it would probably take a long time. Using algebraic equations might prove easier.

EXAMPLE 1 **Use a system of equations to find how many of each kind of coin is in the mixture described above.**

□ **Understand the Problem**   There are 83 coins in all, consisting only of dimes and quarters. The value of the coins, in dollars, is $10.70. (In cents, the value of the coins is 1070¢.)

□ **Plan Your Approach**

Let d = the number of dimes.

Let q = the number of quarters.

Organize the information in terms of the variables.

No. of Coins	Value of Each (¢)	Total Value
d	10	$10d$
q	25	$25q$
83		1070

Use the first and third columns:
$$\begin{cases} d + q = 83 \\ 10d + 25q = 1070 \end{cases}$$

Use the multiplication-addition/subtraction method to solve the system.

□ **Complete the Work**

$d + q = 83 \rightarrow \begin{cases} -10d - 10q = -830 \\ \underline{10d + 25q = 1070} \end{cases}$ *Multiply each side by -10.*

$ 15q = 240$ *Add to eliminate the d-terms.*

$ q = 16$

If $q = 16$ and $d + q = 83$, then $d = 83 - 16$, or 67.

□ **Interpret the Results**   Conclusion: There are 16 quarters and 67 dimes.
Check: 16 quarters and 67 dimes make a total of 83 coins.
Value in cents: $16(25) + 67(10) = 400 + 670 = 1070$
So, there are 67 dimes and 16 quarters.

474   Chapter 11 Systems of Linear Equations

EXAMPLE 2 A chemist has two alcohol-in-water solutions: a 20% alcohol solution and a 50% alcohol solution. He needs 12 L of a solution that is 45% alcohol. How many liters of the two starting solutions should he mix?

Understand the Problem How many liters of the 20% alcohol solution and of the 50% alcohol solution must be mixed to produce 12 L of a 45% solution?

Plan Your Approach Let x = number of liters of 20% alcohol solution.
Let y = number of liters of 50% alcohol solution.

	No. of liters of solution	No. of liters of alcohol
20% solution	x	$0.20x$
50% solution	y	$0.50y$
45% solution	12	$0.45(12)$

The amount of pure alcohol in the first two solutions, $0.20x + 0.50y$, must equal the alcohol in the new solution, $0.45(12)$. Write two equations; solve by substitution.

Complete the Work From the table: $\begin{cases} x + y = 12 \longrightarrow x = 12 - y \\ 0.20x + 0.50y = 0.45(12) \rightarrow 20x + 50y = 45(12) \end{cases}$

$20x + 50y = 45(12)$ *Solve by substitution.*
$20(12 - y) + 50y = 540$ *Substitute $12 - y$ for x.*
$2(12 - y) + 5y = 54$ *Divide each side by 10.*
$24 - 2y + 5y = 54$ *Solve for y.*
$y = 10$

If $x + y = 12$ and $y = 10$, then $x = 12 - 10$, or 2.

Interpret the Results Conclusion: 2 L of 20% solution and 10 L of 50% solution are required to make 12 L of 45% solution.

Check: $0.20(2) + 0.50(10) \overset{?}{=} 0.45(12)$
$0.4 + 5 \overset{?}{=} 0.45(12)$
$5.4 = 5.4$ ✓

CLASS EXERCISES

Write an algebraic expression for each word sentence. Use the following information.

h = number of lb of hazelnuts at $4.98/lb, and c = number of lb of cashews at $6.50/lb.

1. What is the total number of pounds of nuts? $h + c$

2. What is the value of the hazelnuts in dollars? in cents? $4.98h$; $498h$

11.8 Problem Solving: Money and Mixture Problems   **475**

Critical Thinking

Analyzing Whole-Part Relationships
Tables, graphs, equations, and pictures are means of modeling the conditions of a problem. Draw a picture model of the conditions presented in Example 2. Answers may vary. Possible answer given:

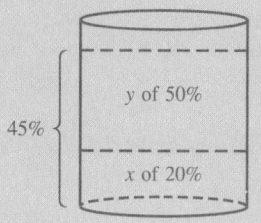

45% { y of 50% / x of 20%

3. What is the value of the cashews in dollars? in cents? $6.50c$; $650c$

4. What is the total value of the nuts? $4.98h + 6.50c$ (in dollars)

5. Write a system of equations for this problem. A 15-lb mixture of hazelnuts and cashews is worth $5.79/lb. How many pounds of each kind does the mixture contain? $h(4.98) + c(6.50) = (5.79)(15)$
   $h + c = 15$

6. What is the advantage of expressing the values of the nuts in cents? no calculations with decimals

x = amount of money (dollars) invested at 7.5% annual interest, and
y = amount of money (dollars) invested at 8% annual interest.

7. What yearly interest (dollars) is earned on the 7.5% investment? $0.075x$

8. What yearly interest (dollars) is earned on both investments? $0.075x + 0.08y$

9. What is the total amount of money invested? $x + y$

10. Give a system of equations for this problem: part of $17,000 was invested at 7.5% annual interest and the remainder at 8.0%. If the combined annual interest was $1347.50, how much was invested at each rate?
    $x + y = 17,000$
    $0.075x + 0.08y = 1347.50$

PRACTICE EXERCISES

Write a system of equations, then solve.

A

1. George saves nickels and dimes for tolls. If he has 28 coins worth $2.60, how many are nickels and how many are dimes? 24 dimes 4 nickels

2. Lorena has 26 coins in nickels and quarters, which are worth a total of $3.10. How many of each coin does she have? 17 nickels 9 quarters

3. Movie tickets cost $6 for adults and $2 for children under twelve. If 175 tickets were sold, with cash receipts of $750, how many children's tickets were sold? 75

4. To raise funds, a school sells two kinds of raffle tickets, some for $6, others for $1.50. Sales for both amounted to $822. If 371 tickets were sold, how many were $1.50 tickets? 312

5. The health food store wishes to blend peanuts that cost $1.20/lb with raisins that cost $2.10/lb to make 50 lb of a mixture that costs $1.47/lb. How many pounds of peanuts and of raisins are needed? 35 lb of peanuts; 15 lb of raisins

6. A 100 kg mixture of $0.69/kg pinto beans and $0.89/kg kidney beans is valued at $81. How many kilograms of each does it contain? 40 kg of pinto beans; 60 kg of kidney beans

7. Part of an investment of $32,000 earns 7.5% annual interest; the rest earns 9%. If the annual interest from both is $2670, how much is invested at the higher rate? $18,000

8. The total annual interest from two bank accounts is $481. One account earns 5.9% annual interest and the other earns 6.75%. If the two accounts contain a total of $7600, how much is in the account at the lower interest? $3764.40

9. A bank teller has a total of 124 bills in fives and tens. The total value of the money is $840. How many of each kind does he have? 44 tens
80 fives

10. In a cash register there are 87 bills, $5 and $1 bills only. If their value is $179, how many of each kind of bill are there? 23 fives
64 ones

11. Mrs. Chavis has twice as much money invested at 7.5% as she has at 6.0%. The yearly income from both investments is $840. How much has she invested at each rate? $4000 at 6%
$8000 at 7.5%

B 12. In a laboratory a pharmacist has 30% and 80% alcohol solutions. She needs 100 mL of a 50% alcohol solution. How many milliliters of the 30% and 80% solutions should she mix? 60 mL of 30%
40 mL of 80%

13. A dairy has milk that is 4% butterfat and cream that is 40% butterfat. To make 36 gal of a mixture that is 20% butterfat, how many gallons of milk and cream must be used? 16 gal of cream
20 gal of milk

14. The number of $2 raffle tickets printed is $3\frac{1}{2}$ times the number of $5 tickets. If all the tickets are sold, receipts from the $5 tickets will be $500 less than those from the $2 tickets. How many $5 tickets were printed? 250

15. The attendance at a school football game was 350. Tickets for adults cost $2.25, compared to $1.00 for children. If the total receipts were $600, how many children and adults attended? 150 children; 200 adults

16. In order to get a thicker sauce, a restaurant owner combines a sauce that is 70% tomato paste with the original sauce, which is 40% tomato paste. How much of each should be used to make 5 L of the new 60% tomato paste sauce? $1\frac{2}{3}$ L of 40%; $3\frac{1}{3}$ L of 70%

17. Walnuts cost $9.95/lb, while peanuts cost $6.50/lb. If there are 3 less lb of peanuts than there are walnuts, how many lb of each are there in a box which costs $62.75? 5 lb walnuts
2 lb peanuts

18. Rosa has $3.10 in nickels and dimes. She has 10 fewer nickels than she has dimes. How many dimes and nickels does she have? 24 dimes
14 nickels

C 19. A collection of 90 coins, pennies, nickels, and dimes, has a value of $2.85. If there are twice as many pennies as there are nickels and dimes combined, how many pennies, dimes, and nickels are there?
60 pennies; 15 nickels, 15 dimes

20. Miquel invested $10,000 in 3 banks. He invested the same amount of money in two banks, which gave him a 6% yearly interest rate. The third bank gave him a rate of 7% for one year. If he made $640 in interest after 1 year, how much did he invest in each bank?
First bank $3000; Second bank $3000; Third bank $4000

11.8 Problem Solving: Money and Mixture Problems **477**

LESSON FOLLOW-UP

Assignment Guide
• See p. 442B for assignments.
• You may want to review simple interest before beginning the Class Exercises

Project
You may have students work in groups to do some research on crystals.

Lesson Quiz
Write a system of equations, then solve.
1. There are 51 more dimes than quarters in a collection of coins worth $10.70. How many coins of each kind are there? 67 dimes; 16 quarters

2. A businessman invests $10,000 in two different bank notes. One note pays an annual simple interest rate of 5% and the other pays 5.5%. If he earned $520 interest in the first year, how much did he invest in each bank note? $6000 at 5%; $4000 at 5.5%

3. A pharmacist needs 1000 mL of a 10% solution. She has only 5% and 25% solutions available. How many milliliters of each solution should she mix to obtain the desired solution? 750 mL of 5%; 250 mL of 25%

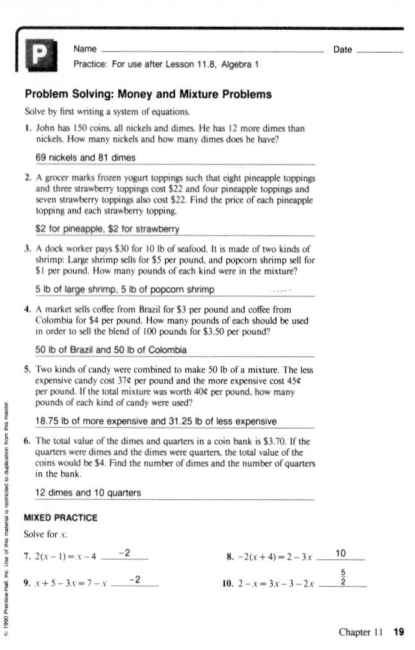

Name _____ Date _____
Practice: For use after Lesson 11.8, Algebra 1

Problem Solving: Money and Mixture Problems

Solve by first writing a system of equations.

1. John has 150 coins, all nickels and dimes. He has 12 more dimes than nickels. How many nickels and how many dimes does he have?

   69 nickels and 81 dimes

2. A grocer marks frozen yogurt toppings such that eight pineapple toppings and three strawberry toppings cost $22 and four pineapple toppings and seven strawberry toppings also cost $22. Find the price of each pineapple topping and each strawberry topping.

   $2 for pineapple, $2 for strawberry

3. A dock worker pays $30 for 10 lb of seafood. It is made of two kinds of shrimp: Large shrimp sells for $5 per pound, and popcorn shrimp sell for $1 per pound. How many pounds of each kind were in the mixture?

   5 lb of large shrimp, 5 lb of popcorn shrimp

4. A market sells coffee from Brazil for $3 per pound and coffee from Colombia for $4 per pound. How many pounds of each should be used in order to sell the blend of 100 pounds for $3.50 per pound?

   50 lb of Brazil and 50 lb of Colombia

5. Two kinds of candy were combined to make 50 lb of a mixture. The less expensive candy cost 37¢ per pound and the more expensive cost 45¢ per pound. If the total mixture was worth 40¢ per pound, how many pounds of each kind of candy were used?

   18.75 lb of more expensive and 31.25 lb of less expensive

6. The total value of the dimes and quarters in a coin bank is $3.70. If the quarters were dimes and the dimes were quarters, the total value of the coins would be $4. Find the number of dimes and the number of quarters in the bank.

   12 dimes and 10 quarters

MIXED PRACTICE

Solve for x.

7. $2(x - 1) = x - 4$ -2 8. $-2(x + 4) = 2 - 3x$ 10

9. $x + 5 - 3x = 7 - x$ -2 10. $2 - x = 3x - 3 - 2x$ $\frac{5}{2}$

Chapter 11   **19**

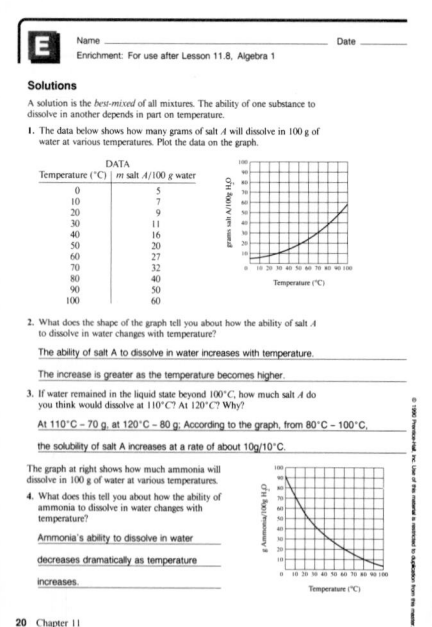

Name _____ Date _____
Enrichment: For use after Lesson 11.8, Algebra 1

Solutions

A solution is the *best-mixed* of all mixtures. The ability of one substance to dissolve in another depends in part on temperature.

1. The data below show how many grams of salt *A* will dissolve in 100 g of water at various temperatures. Plot the data on the graph.

DATA	
Temperature (°C)	m salt A/100 g water
0	5
10	7
20	9
30	11
40	16
50	20
60	27
70	32
80	40
90	50
100	60

2. What does the shape of the graph tell you about how the ability of salt *A* to dissolve in water changes with temperature?

   The ability of salt A to dissolve in water increases with temperature.

   The increase is greater as the temperature becomes higher.

3. If water remained in the liquid state beyond 100°C, how much salt *A* do you think would dissolve at 110°C? At 120°C? Why?

   At 110°C – 70 g, at 120°C – 80 g; According to the graph, from 80°C – 100°C,

   the solubility of salt A increases at a rate of about 10g/10°C.

   The graph at right shows how much ammonia will dissolve in 100 g of water at various temperatures.

4. What does this tell you about the ability of ammonia to dissolve in water changes with temperature?

   Ammonia's ability to dissolve in water

   decreases dramatically as temperature

   increases.

20   Chapter 11

Applications

Computer   Bill does not like to carry more than $1.50 in change. More than eight coins tear holes in his pockets. The computer program at the right will generate a chart of the possible combinations of dimes and quarters that Bill can carry.

```
10 PRINT "QUARTERS","DIMES","TOTAL"
20 D = 0
30 FOR Q = 8 TO 0 STEP  - 1
40 QT = Q * .25:DT = D * .10
50 PRINT Q;"   $";QT,D;"   $";DT,"   $";QT + DT
60 D = D + 1: NEXT Q
70 END
```

Solve.

21. What is the least number of quarters and dimes that Bill can carry and have $1.25? What are the coins?   3 quarters and 5 dimes

22. If Bill carried all dimes, how many would he need to carry to have as much money as if he carried all quarters?   15 dimes = 6 quarters

23. How many of each coin should Bill carry if he wants to have an equal amount of money for each coin?   2 quarters, 5 dimes

---

BIOGRAPHY

Sonja Corvin-Kowalewski was born in Moscow in 1850. By the time she was 18, her progress in the study of mathematics was so rapid that she enrolled in the University of Heidelberg for advanced studies. At age 20 she became a student of Karl Weierstrass, the father of modern analysis, with whom she did considerable work on the refraction of light in crystalline media. In 1888, her paper ''On the Rotation of a Solid Body About a Fixed Point'' won the coveted Bordin Prize of the French Academy of Sciences. She taught at the University of Stockholm from 1889 until she died, at 41, during a flu epidemic.

An Investigation

Kowalewski's interest in crystals may have been generated by the fact that crystals, including snowflakes, provide striking examples of symmetry and other important mathematical principles. Do some research on crystals, and prepare a report on this natural phenomenon. Check students' work.

11.9

Problem Solving: Wind and Water Current Problems

Objective: To use systems of equations to solve uniform-motion problems involving winds and water currents

Cal and Marty were about to start a round trip cycling race on a windy day. "Because of the wind, our times won't be as good as they are on a calm day," Cal said.

"You're wrong," said Marty. "It will slow us down when we head into the wind, but it will help us when the wind is at our backs, and so it won't make any difference."

Which boy is right?

LESSON PLAN

Materials/Manipulatives
*Teacher's Resource Book,
Transparency 24*

BACKGROUND

To solve a problem successfully, students must be able to organize the information given in the problem in a way that will allow them to write systems of equations easily. Use a table and/or diagram to organize the given information in a problem. Students may encounter difficulty in many different areas. Do an error analysis of the students' work, then classify and correct specific errors.

Error Analysis Classification
1. *Misunderstanding*
   Misread the problem
   Incorrectly organized the information in a table
2. *Misapplied Strategy*
   Wrote an incorrect equation
   Used the wrong formula or applied it incorrectly
   Failed to complete the solution
   Did not interpret the solution correctly

EXAMPLE 1 **Supply numbers to consider Cal's and Marty's opinions. Assume that they are making a 60-mi round trip, that with no wind they can average 15 mi/h on their bicycles, and that there is a constant wind of 5 mi/h.**

Understand the Problem   For half the round trip they head directly into the wind. Their rate is $15 - 5$, or 10 mi/h. For half the trip the wind blows in the same direction they are traveling. Their rate then is $15 + 5$, or 20 mi/h.

Plan Your Approach   Use the distance formula, distance = rate × time, to find the average rate of speed with the wind blowing. Compare this with the given rate of speed with no wind.

Make a rate-time-distance table to determine the time it would take to cycle each part of the trip when the wind is blowing. Then use the total time and the total distance to find the average rate of speed for the round trip.

Let t_1 = time against wind.
Let t_2 = time with wind.
$t_1 + t_2$ = total time.

	r	×	t	=	d
Against wind	$15 - 5$		t_1		30
With wind	$15 + 5$		t_2		30

Write equations to find t_1 and t_2.

11.9 Problem Solving: Wind and Water Current Problems   **479**

TEACHING SUGGESTIONS

- In Lesson 4.10 students used linear equations with one unknown to solve problems that involve uniform motion. Students may need to review this section before beginning Lesson 11.9.
- Using the examples, stress how tables and/or diagrams are used to solve each problem.
- In Example 1, point out the use of the subscripts on t_1 and t_2. Remind students that each expression represents time.
- In the water current problems, like Example 2, encourage students to draw a diagram to show that going downstream, the boat is traveling with the current and going upstream, the boat is traveling against the current. Use Transparency 24, in the *Teacher's Resource Book,* to illustrate examples of wind and water current problems.

CHALKBOARD EXAMPLES

- **For Example 1**
  1. A small aircraft flew 260 mi in 2 h with the wind. Flying against the wind, the aircraft flew 180 mi in 2 h. Find the rate of the plane in calm air and the rate of the wind. rate of the plane in calm air: 110 mi/h; rate of wind: 20 mi/h
  2. A cyclist travels 60 mi round trip in a 3 mi/h wind. Find the average rate of speed for the trip if the cyclist can travel 12 mi/h with no wind. 11.25 mi/h

Complete the Work

$$(15 - 5)t_1 = 30 \qquad (15 + 5)t_2 = 30$$
$$10t_1 = 30 \qquad 20t_2 = 30$$
$$t_1 = \frac{30}{10} = 3 \qquad t_2 = \frac{30}{20}, \text{ or } \frac{3}{2}$$

Find the total time: $t_1 + t_2 = 3 + \frac{3}{2}$, or $\frac{9}{2}$

Substitute the total time, $\frac{9}{2}$, to find the rate of speed for the total distance with the wind blowing: $r \cdot \frac{9}{2} = 60$, or $r = 13.\overline{3}$

Interpret the Results

$13.\overline{3}$ mi/h is less than 15 mi/h for the round trip. Cal was right. On a windy day the average rate of speed for a round trip is less than on a day with no wind.

The distance formula and systems of equations can be used to solve water-current problems.

EXAMPLE 2 **It takes 2 h for a boat to travel 28 mi downstream. The same boat can travel 18 mi upstream in 3 h. Find the rate of speed of the boat in still water and the rate of the current.**

Understand the Problem

Draw a diagram.   downstream ⟵——— boat ———⟶ upstream
                              ⟵——— current

The boat travels with the current when it goes downstream. Thus, the rate the boat travels downstream is the rate of the boat in still water plus the rate of the current. What is the rate of speed of the boat when it travels upstream?

Plan Your Approach

Make a table to show a system of equations. Then solve.
Let r = rate of speed of the boat in still water.
Let c = rate of current.

	r	$\times$ t	$=$ d
Downstream	$r + c$	2	28
Upstream	$r - c$	3	18

Complete the Work

$$\begin{cases} (r + c)2 = 28 \rightarrow r + c = 14 \\ (r - c)3 = 18 \rightarrow \underline{r - c = 6} \end{cases}$$
$$2r = 20 \qquad \textit{Add the equations.}$$
$$r = 10$$

Substitute 10 for r, and solve for c: $(r + c)2 = 28$
$$c = 4$$

480   Chapter 11 Systems of Linear Equations

Interpret the Results	Conclusion: The rate of the boat in still water is 10 mi/h. The rate of the current is 4 mi/h.
	The check is left for you.

CLASS EXERCISES

Complete the table. Write a system of equations. Then solve.

1. An airplane averages 255 mi/h with no wind. How long will it take the airplane to travel 2160 mi flying against a 15 mi/h wind? How long does it take the airplane to travel the same distance flying with the wind? Find the average rate of speed for the round trip.

	Rate	× Time	= Distance
Against wind	? 240	t_1 9	2160
With wind	? 270	t_2 8	2160 254.1 mi/h

2. A boat takes 3 h to go 24 mi upstream and 3 h to go 36 mi downstream. Find the speed of the current and the rate of the speed of the boat in still water.

	Rate	× Time	= Distance
Downstream	? $r + c$	? 3	36 2 mi/h— current
Upstream	? $r - c$	? 3	24 10 mi/h— still water

PRACTICE EXERCISES

A

1. A small aircraft flies a 2160-mi round trip in a 45 mi/h wind. Find the average rate of speed for the trip if the aircraft can fly 225 mi/h with no wind. 216 mi/h

2. A cyclist travels a 90-mi round trip in a 3 mi/h wind. Find the average rate of speed for the trip if the cyclist can travel 12 mi/h with no wind. 11.25 mi/h

3. A crew rowing with the current traveled 16 mi in 2 h; against the current, the crew rowed 8 mi in 2 h. Find the rate of rowing in still water and the rate of the current. 6 mi/h; 2 mi/h

4. Traveling with the wind, a plane flew 4000 km in 5 h. Against the wind the plane only flew 3000 km in the same time. Find the rate of speed of the plane in calm air and the speed of the wind. 700 km/h; 100 km/h

5. A boat travels 12 km upstream in 2 h. If the return trip takes 1 h, find the rate of speed of the boat in calm water. 9 km/h

11.9 Problem Solving: Wind and Water Current Problems **481**

For Example 2

3. Paddling with the current, Jan can go 24 mi in 3 h. Against the current, it takes her 4 h to go the same distance. Find Jan's rate in calm water and the rate of the current. Jan's rate in calm water: 7 mi/h; rate of current: 1 mi/h

4. A crew can row 30 km downstream in $1\frac{1}{2}$ h. Rowing upstream against the current, the crew traveled 12 km in $1\frac{1}{2}$ h.

Find the rate of the crew in still water and the rate of the current. rate of crew in still water: 14 km/h; rate of current: 6 km/h

Common Error

• Many students have difficulty setting up word problems involving uniform motion. For these students, making a chart should be required. Watch carefully how these students work Exercises 1 and 2 in the Class Exercises. You may wish to have students work in small groups and analyze each problem.

• See *Teacher's Resource Book* for additional remediation.

Critical Thinking

Classifying Explain what the term "uniform motion" means. Uniform motion means that the *rate* (speed) of motion does not vary.

Assignment Guide

See p. 442B for assignments.

Career

Students learn about geophysicists and their work. Have students work together to gather data on environmental conditions in their neighborhood.

Lesson Quiz

1. A plane takes 4 h to fly a certain distance with a headwind of 20 mi/h. The return trip against the headwind takes $4\frac{3}{4}$ h. Find the speed of the plane in calm air.
   233.3 mi/h

2. A rowing team rowed 16 mi downstream in 2 h. Rowing upstream against the current, the team rowed 8 mi in 2 h. Find the rate of the rowing team in still water and the rate of the current. rate of rowing team: 6 mi/h; rate of current: 2 mi/h

Enrichment

Solve Example 2 on page 480 by graphing. Check students' graphs.

6. A plane travels 1200 mi with the wind in 2 h. The return trip against the wind takes 3 h. Find the rate of speed of the plane in calm air. 500 mi/h

7. A plane traveled 2400 km in 4 h with a tailwind. However, returning against the same wind took 1 h longer. Find the plane's airspeed and the wind speed. 540 km/h; 60 km/h

8. Flying a propeller plane against a headwind for 700 mi, Sandy took 5 h to reach the city. He flew with the tailwind when he made the return trip in $3\frac{1}{2}$ h. What was the wind speed? 30 mi/h

9. Natasha rowed upstream 28 mi in 7 h and traveled the same distance downstream in 4 h. What was her rate without the current? $5\frac{1}{2}$ mi/h

10. Pam swims downstream for 10 mi in 2 h. The return trip upstream takes four times as long. What is the rate of the current? 1.875 mi/h

11. Traveling at 14 mi/h, Noah makes a 140-mi bike trip against the wind. He covers the same distance at 20 mi/h with the wind. Find his total time traveled. 17 h

12. Bjorn traveled 100 mi on his motorcycle in 2 h with the wind. It took him 3 hours to return the same distance against the wind. Find the rate of the wind. $8\frac{1}{3}$ mi/h

13. Against prevailing headwinds, a pilot calculates his flight as 6 h for a distance of 2100 mi. The return trip with the wind would require 1 h less. Find the rate of speed of the plane with no wind. 385 mi/h

14. With a tailwind, a plane flew 300 mi in 40 min. With no change in wind, the return trip took 5 min more. Find the rate of the wind in mi/h. 25 mi/h

B 15. A riverboat travels 10 km upstream in 50 min. The riverboat travels 15 km downstream in 45 min. Find the rate of speed of the boat in calm water in km/h. 16 km/h

16. A swimmer swims upstream at 40 m/min and downstream at twice the rate. How fast can she swim in still water? 60 m/min

17. A steamboat travels 8.4 mi downstream in 3 h. Traveling upstream, it can travel $\frac{3}{7}$ of the distance in the same time. What is the rate of the current and the rate of the steamboat in still water? 2 mi/h; 0.8 mi/h

18. A canoe covers a distance of 40 mi downstream in 6 h. Returning upstream, it takes the canoe 3 times as long to cover $\frac{3}{5}$ of the distance. Find the rate of the current and the rate of the canoe in still water. $2\frac{2}{3}$ mi/h; 4 mi/h

482   Chapter 11 Systems of Linear Equations

19. Flying for 5 h against the wind, François makes a journey of 180 km in his ultralight. With the wind the ultralight makes the same trip in 3 h. Find the rate of speed of the wind. 12km/h

20. An eagle flies 300 mi in 8 h with the wind. It flies only $\frac{1}{3}$ of the distance in 7 h against the wind. Find the rate of the eagle in the air against the wind. $14\frac{2}{7}$ mi/h

C **21.** It takes a salmon the same time to swim a distance upstream that it takes to swim twice that distance downstream. If the salmon swims at a rate r and the rate of the current is c, find the relationship between the two rates. $\frac{2d}{t} - c = \frac{d}{t} + c$

22. A plane travels with the wind at a mi/h and travels against the wind at b mi/h. Find the rate of the wind and the rate of speed of the plane in still air in terms of a and b. $\frac{a+b}{2}$ still air rate; $a - \frac{a+b}{2}$ winds' rate

CAREER: Geophysicist

A **geophysicist** is a person who specializes in the branch of science that deals with the physics of the Earth. This includes weather, winds, tides, earthquakes, volcanoes, and their effect on Earth. The data gathered and studied by geophysicists are often used to improve the environment in which we live, and to help us live more safely and comfortably in an environment over which we may have little control.

Most geophysicists specialize in one area of geophysics, such as climatology (the study of climate and climatic phenomena), meteorology (the study of the atmosphere and atmospheric phenomena), and seismology (the study of earthquakes and related phenomena).

If you are curious about the physical environment, enjoy collecting and analyzing data, and like mathematics and science, then you may be interested in becoming a geophysicist.

An Investigation

An earthquake sends shock waves through the earth. A primary wave travels at a rate of 5 mi/s, and a secondary wave, which starts at the same time, travels at a rate of 3 mi/s. A seismologist working in a seismic station notes that the time between the primary and secondary waves of an earthquake was 16 s. Using the distance formula $d = rt$, the scientist writes and solves two equations to determine how far from the station the earthquake occurred. What two equations did the scientist write? How far from the station was the earthquake? $d = (5 \text{ mi/s})(s)$; $d = (3 \text{ mi/s})(s + 16)$; 120mi

11.9 Problem Solving: Wind and Water Current Problems **483**

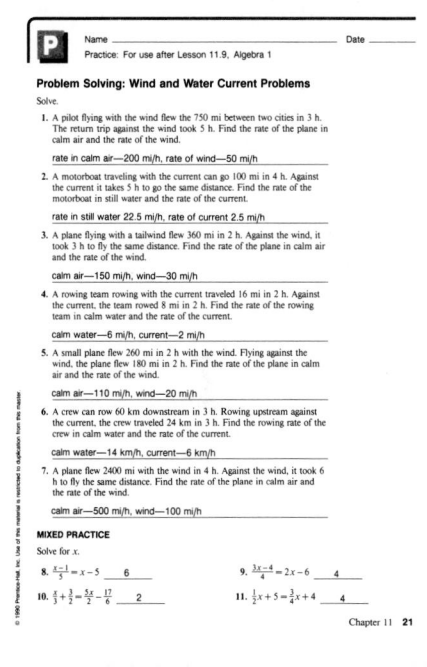

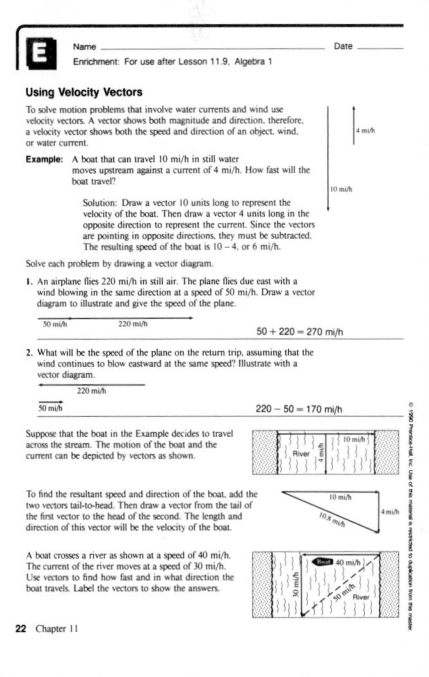

BACKGROUND

In the Capsule Review, students practice graphing linear inequalities. Compare the use of a solid line in Capsule Review, Exercise 1 with the use of broken lines in Capsule Review, Exercise 2. In this lesson, students will graph inequalities to solve systems of linear inequalities.

Critical Thinking

Discovering Relationships Explain the use of a dotted line to graph the region $y > -4x + 2$, and the use of a solid line to graph the region $y \leq x - 4$. Both regions are bounded by lines. A dotted line is used to graph the boundary when the boundary is *not* a part of the region. A solid line is used to graph the boundary when the boundary *is* a part of the region.

Additional Answers

1.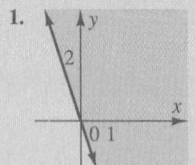

2.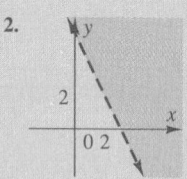

3.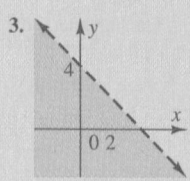

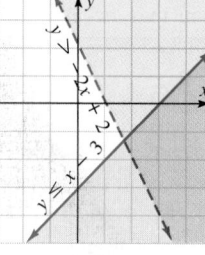

11.10 Graphing Systems of Linear Inequalities

Objective: To graph the solution set of a system of linear inequalities

In order to analyze ways of maximizing profits and minimizing costs, some companies use graphs of *systems of linear inequalities*. A **system of linear inequalities** involves two or more linear inequalities. Such a system can often be solved by graphing.

Capsule Review

To graph an inequality, it is important to graph the related equality first.

Graph each inequality. See side column.

1. $y \leq -3x$ 2. $2x + y < 6$ 3. $2x + 3y > 12$

To solve a system of linear inequalities in two variables x and y, first solve each inequality for y.

EXAMPLE Graph the solution of the system $\begin{cases} 2x + y > 2 \\ x - y \geq 3 \end{cases}$

$2x + y > 2$ $x - y \geq 3$ *Reverse the direction of the*
  $y > -2x + 2$ $-y \geq -x + 3$ *inequality when you multiply or*
                        $y \leq x - 3$ *divide by a negative number.*

Graph $y > -2x + 2$.
First, graph $y = -2x + 2$. Use a broken line since the graph of $y > -2x + 2$ does not include the line. Shade the region above the line to represent the graph of $y > -2x + 2$.

Graph $y \leq x - 3$ in the same coordinate plane. First graph $y = x - 3$. Use a solid line since $y \leq x - 3$ includes points on the line. Shade the region below the line to represent the graph of $y \leq x - 3$.

The graph of the solution is shaded in both colors and is the intersection of the inequalities. The solution includes points on the boundary line $y = x - 3$, but not on the boundary line $y = -2x + 2$.

484   Chapter 11 Systems of Linear Equations

CLASS EXERCISES

Tell which region, *A*, *B*, *C*, or *D*, is the graph of the system of inequalities.

1. $\begin{cases} x < 0 \\ y < 0 \end{cases}$ C

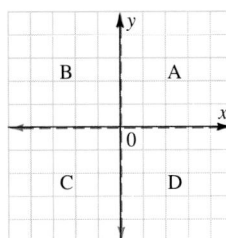

2. $\begin{cases} x \geq -1 \\ y \geq 1 \end{cases}$ A

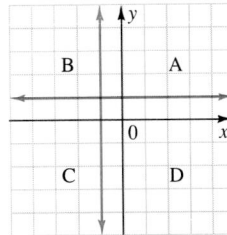

3. $\begin{cases} x \geq 2 \\ y < 3 \end{cases}$ D

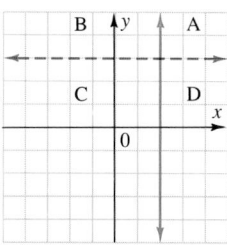

4. $\begin{cases} x < -2 \\ y > -2 \end{cases}$ B

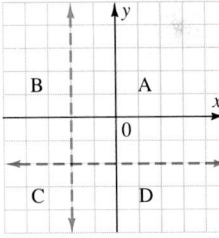

Determine whether the ordered pair is a solution of the system $x + y \leq 6$ and $x - y < 1$.

5. $(1, -3)$ no   **6.** $(1, 2)$ yes   **7.** $(0, 0)$ yes   **8.** $(6, 0)$ no

9. $(-2, 1)$ yes   **10.** $(7, 1)$ no   **11.** $(8, 6)$ no   **12.** $(-3, -1)$ yes

For Discussion

13. In the Example on page 484, each equation divides the coordinate plane into three sets.

s_1: The set of points on the line
s_2: The set of points for which the *greater than* relation holds
s_3: The set of points for which the *less than* relation holds

Use these three sets to describe the solution of the system $2x + y > 2$ and $x - y \geq 3$. s_1: $y = x - 3$; $x > \frac{5}{3}$ s_3: $y < x - 3$; $x > \frac{5}{3}$

s_2: $y > -2x + 2$; $x > \frac{5}{3}$

11.10 Graphing Systems of Linear Inequalities   **485**

TEACHING SUGGESTIONS

- Use the example to stress the procedure used to solve a system of inequalities. Transparencies 15 and 17–20, in the *Teacher's Resource Book,* may also be helpful in doing so.
- Point out why the inequality symbol was reversed in $-y \geq -x + 3$ when it was divided by -1.
- Relate the symbols $>, <, \geq,$ and $\leq$ with the inclusion or exclusion of the boundary lines on the graph.

CHALKBOARD EXAMPLE

- **For the Example**
  Graph the solution of each system.
  1. $\begin{cases} 3x + y > 3 \\ x - y \geq 1 \end{cases}$

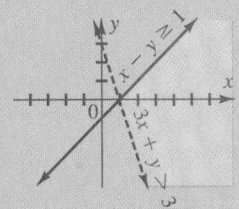

  2. $\begin{cases} y < -2x \\ x \leq 2 \end{cases}$

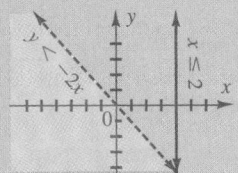

Common Error

- Many students make errors in graphing. Students demonstrating this problem should review Lesson 9.7.
- See *Teacher's Resource Book* for additional remediation.

LESSON FOLLOW-UP

Assignment Guide
See p. 442B for assignments.

Lesson Quiz

Graph the system of inequalities and
indicate the solution by shading.

1. $\begin{cases} x \le 2 \\ y \ge -1 \end{cases}$

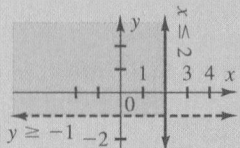

2. $\begin{cases} y < 3x - 1 \\ y \ge 4 - 2x \end{cases}$

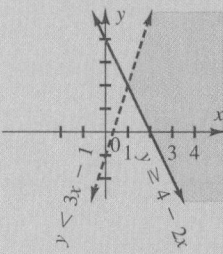

3. $\begin{cases} x + y > 5 \\ 3x - y < 3 \end{cases}$

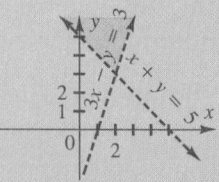

Enrichment

Solve this system of equations by any
method you have learned thus far.

$\begin{cases} x = 7 - y - z \\ 2x = y - z + 4 \\ 3x = -2y - z + 11 \end{cases}$ (1, 2, 4)

PRACTICE EXERCISES

**Graph the system of inequalities, and indicate the solution of the system
by shading.** See Additional Answer section beginning p. 719.

A **1.** $\begin{cases} x \le 1 \\ y \ge 4 \end{cases}$ 　 **2.** $\begin{cases} x \ge 2 \\ y \le 3 \end{cases}$ 　 **3.** $\begin{cases} y \ge 0 \\ x > 0 \end{cases}$ 　 **4.** $\begin{cases} y < -2 \\ x \le 2 \end{cases}$

5. $\begin{cases} y \le 2x \\ x > 1 \end{cases}$ 　 **6.** $\begin{cases} y > x \\ x < -2 \end{cases}$ 　 **7.** $\begin{cases} y > 1 - x \\ x \le -1 \end{cases}$ 　 **8.** $\begin{cases} y < 2 - x \\ x > 4 \end{cases}$

9. $\begin{cases} y < x + 3 \\ y < 5 - 2x \end{cases}$ 　 **10.** $\begin{cases} y < 5x - 1 \\ y \ge 7 - 3x \end{cases}$ 　 **11.** $\begin{cases} y - x \le 5 \\ y > 2x \end{cases}$ 　 **12.** $\begin{cases} y < -3x \\ x > 4 \end{cases}$

13. $\begin{cases} x + y > 5 \\ 2x - y < 4 \end{cases}$ 　 **14.** $\begin{cases} x + y > 2 \\ 2x - y \le 1 \end{cases}$ 　 **15.** $\begin{cases} y > 4x + 2 \\ x \le 4 \end{cases}$ 　 **16.** $\begin{cases} y \le 4x - 3 \\ x > 3 \end{cases}$

B **17.** $\begin{cases} 3x + y \ge 0 \\ 2x - y \le -4 \end{cases}$ 　 **18.** $\begin{cases} 2x + y \le 4 \\ 3x - y > 6 \end{cases}$ 　 **19.** $\begin{cases} 4x - y < 4 \\ x + 2y < 2 \end{cases}$ 　 **20.** $\begin{cases} x + y > 0 \\ x - 3y > 3 \end{cases}$

21. $\begin{cases} x - 2y < 3 \\ 2x + y > 8 \end{cases}$ 　 **22.** $\begin{cases} x + 2y > 4 \\ 2x - y > 6 \end{cases}$ 　 **23.** $\begin{cases} 2x \ge y + 3 \\ x < 3 - 2y \end{cases}$ 　 **24.** $\begin{cases} 3 < 2x - y \\ x - 3y \le 4 \end{cases}$

25. $\begin{cases} 2x - y \le 3 \\ x - \frac{1}{3}y > 1 \end{cases}$ 　 **26.** $\begin{cases} 5x - y > 6 \\ 2x - \frac{1}{2}y \le 3 \end{cases}$ 　 **27.** $\begin{cases} 3y - x + 1 \le 0 \\ x - y - 1 > 0 \end{cases}$

**A system of inequalities may contain more than two inequalities. Graph
the system.** See Additional Answer section beginning p. 719.

C **28.** $\begin{cases} 3y - x + 1 \le 0 \\ x + 2y - 3 \ge 0 \\ x - y - 1 > 0 \end{cases}$ 　 **29.** $\begin{cases} 4x + 5 > y \\ x - 4 \le 2y \\ 4y \le -5x + 20 \end{cases}$ 　 **30.** $\begin{cases} 3x + 2 \ge 2y \\ 2x - 8 > 4y \\ -4y < x - 4 \end{cases}$

31. $\begin{cases} \frac{1}{2}x - y > 3 \\ 3x - \frac{3}{2}y \ge -1 \\ y < 4 \end{cases}$ 　 **32.** $\begin{cases} x - 4y < 4 \\ \frac{1}{3}x - 2y \ge 2 \\ -x + \frac{1}{2}y \ge -2 \end{cases}$ 　 **33.** $\begin{cases} x > \frac{1}{2}y + 1 \\ -\frac{2}{3}x \le 2y - 5 \\ \frac{5}{6}y \ge -4x + 2 \end{cases}$

Applications

Write a system of two inequalities. Solve and then graph the solution.

34. Office Administration Two typists are working on a statistical report.
To finish on time, together they need to type between 20 and 30 pages
per day. This is the first time typist A has typed material that contains
mostly numbers, so she may be expected to type no more than $\frac{2}{3}$ as
many pages as typist B. On the graph, find at least two acceptable
combinations of typing output that the typists might produce in a day.
Answers may vary. One possible solution is A: 10 pg/d, B: 15 pg/d. A $\le \frac{2}{3}$B, A + B < 30, A + B > 20.

35. Agriculture Some land on a farm is to be fenced as a feeder lot for cattle. The farmer wants the distance around the lot to be no more than 2600 ft. The length should be greater than 800 ft. From the graph, name two sets of dimensions for the feeder lot that satisfy the farmer's requirements. Must the graph be shown in all four quadrants of the coordinate plane? $l = 900$ ft, $w = 400$ ft or $l = 1000$ ft, $w = 300$ ft $2l + 2w \leq 2600$; $l > 800$.

TEST YOURSELF

Find the original number described in the problem. 11.6

1. The sum of the digits is 11. Reversing the digits gives a new number that is 9 more than the original. 56

2. The tens digit is twice the units digit. Reversing the digits gives a new number that is 27 less than the original. 63

Write and solve a system of linear equations to find the present ages. 11.7

3. Robert is four years older than Dawn. Seven years ago Dawn was $\frac{3}{4}$ as old as Robert. Robert 23 yr, Dawn 19 yr

4. Greg is three times as old as Jane. Five years ago he was five times as old. Greg 30 yr, Jane 10 yr

Solve by first writing a system of equations. 11.8–11.9

5. Anne Marie has 52 coins in dimes and quarters, which are worth $6.25. How many of each coin does she have? 7 quarters, 45 dimes

6. John has a total of 9 stamps, which consist of 25¢ and 2¢ stamps. If his stamps have a value of $1.10, how many of each stamp does he have? 4 25¢ stamps; 5 2¢ stamps

7. A car travels a 240 mi round trip in a 15 mi/h wind. Find the average rate of speed for the trip if the car travels 45 mi/h with no wind. 40 mi/h

8. It takes 4 h for a boat to travel 56 mi downstream. The same boat can travel 36 mi upstream in 6 h. Find the rate of speed of the boat in still water and the rate of the current. 10 mi/h still water, 4 mi/h current

Graph the system of inequalities, and indicate the solution of the system by shading. See Additional Answer section beginning p. 719. 11.10

9. $\begin{cases} x \leq 3 \\ y \geq 1 \end{cases}$

10. $\begin{cases} x \geq 2 \\ y \leq 3 \end{cases}$

11. $\begin{cases} y \geq 1 - 2x \\ x > y \end{cases}$

12. $\begin{cases} y > -4 - x \\ 3y - x \leq 3 \end{cases}$

11.10 Graphing Systems of Linear Inequalities **487**

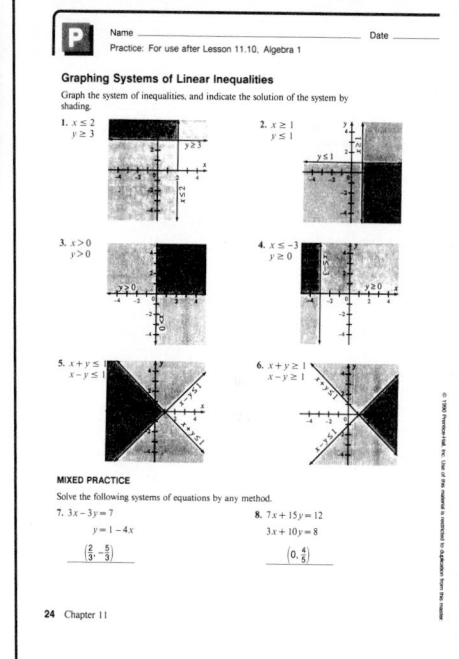

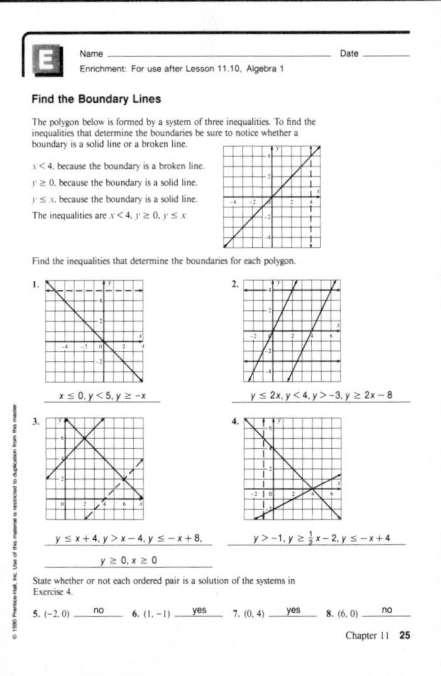

Additional Answers

1.

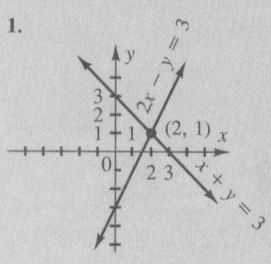

2.

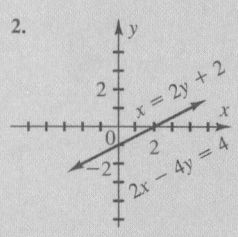

3.

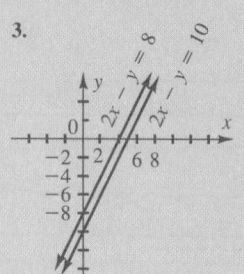

Vocabulary

consistent system (444)	independent system (444)
dependent system (445)	simultaneous equations (444)
equivalent systems (463)	system of linear equations (444)
inconsistent system (445)	system of linear inequalities (484)

The Graphing Method   To solve a system of linear equations by graphing,   **11.1**
graph both equations in the same coordinate plane. The coordinates of any
point of intersection of the lines are a solution of the system.

Solve by graphing. State the number of solutions and describe the system.

1. $\begin{cases} x + y = 3 \\ 2x - y = 3 \end{cases}$ **2.** $\begin{cases} x = 2y + 2 \\ 2x - 4y = 4 \end{cases}$ **3.** $\begin{cases} 2x - y = 10 \\ 2x - y = 8 \end{cases}$

(2, 1); 1 solution; lines intersect   infinite number of solutions; same line   no solution; parallel lines

The Substitution Method   To solve a system of linear equations by   **11.2**
substitution:

- In either equation solve for one variable in terms of the other.
- Substitute for that variable in the other equation. Solve.
- Find the corresponding value of the other variable and check the solution.

Solve by the substitution method.

4. $\begin{cases} y = 2x \\ x + 2y = 8 \end{cases}$ $\left(\frac{8}{5}, \frac{16}{5}\right)$ **5.** $\begin{cases} 2r + 3s = 27 \\ 4r - s = 9 \end{cases}$ $\left(\frac{27}{7}, \frac{45}{7}\right)$ **6.** $\begin{cases} \frac{1}{4}c - d = -1 \\ 4c + 3d = 22 \end{cases}$ (4, 2)

Mixed Problems   To solve problems that involve two unknowns and two   **11.3**
conditions, use the four problem solving steps. Assign two variables to the
unknowns, translate the given statements into a system of equations, and
solve the system.

7. The perimeter of a triangular sign is 21 ft. If the lengths of two sides are
equal and the third side is 3 ft longer than one of the equal sides, find
the lengths of the three sides.   6 ft, 6 ft, 9 ft

The Addition/Subtraction Method   To solve a system of linear equations   **11.4**
using the addition/subtraction method:

- add or subtract the equations to eliminate one of the variables.
- solve the resulting equation for the remaining variable.
- replace that value in either equation, and solve for the unknown variable.
- check the solution.

Solve by the addition/subtraction method.

8. $\begin{cases} 2a + b = 8 \\ a - b = 4 \end{cases}$ (4, 0)

9. $\begin{cases} 3p = 13 - q \\ 2p - q = 2 \end{cases}$ (3, 4)

10. $\begin{cases} \frac{1}{2}m - \frac{1}{2}n = 10 \\ \frac{3}{4}m + \frac{1}{2}n = 20 \end{cases}$
(24, 4)

The Multiplication-Addition/Subtraction Method   To solve a system   **11.5**
of equations by the multiplication-addition/subtraction method, multiply one
or both equations to produce an equivalent system in which the coefficients
of one variable are the same or additive inverses of one another. Then use
the addition/subtraction method.

Solve by the multiplication-addition/subtraction method.

11. $\begin{cases} x + 4y = 17 \\ 3x + 2y = 6 \end{cases}$ $\left(-1, \frac{9}{2}\right)$

12. $\begin{cases} 6a + 7b = -33 \\ 5a - 4b = 2 \end{cases}$ (−2, −3)

13. $\begin{cases} \frac{1}{4}c + d = \frac{7}{2} \\ \frac{1}{2}c - \frac{1}{4}d = 1 \end{cases}$ $\left(\frac{10}{3}, \frac{8}{3}\right)$

Digit Problems   To solve problems involving two-digit integers, use two   **11.6**
variables to represent the digits, write a system of equations to describe the
relationships between them, and solve the system.

14. The sum of the digits of a two-digit number is 5. If the digits are
interchanged, the new number is 13 more than twice the original. Find
the original number. 14

Age Problems, Money and Mixture Problems, Wind and Water-   **11.7–11.9**
Current Problems   To solve these types of problems, translate the
statements into a system of equations, and solve the system.

15. The ages of two sisters, Sue and Amy, total 35 yr. In 5 yr, Sue will
be twice as old as Amy. How old is each now? Sue 25 yr
Amy 10 yr

16. Ed spent $3.40 for 22 stamps. If he bought only 25-cent and 10-cent
stamps, how many of each kind did he buy? 14 10¢ stamps
8 25¢ stamps

17. It takes a boat $1\frac{1}{2}$ hr to go 12 mi downstream and 6 hr to return. Find
the rate of speed of the boat in still water and the speed of the current.
5 mi/h; 3 mi/h

Solving Systems of Inequalities   To solve a system of inequalities,   **11.10**
graph each inequality on the same coordinate plane. The solution of the
system is the double-shaded area, which is the intersection of the inequalities.

Solve by graphing. See side column.

18. $\begin{cases} x < -1 \\ y > 3 \end{cases}$

19. $\begin{cases} y \le x + 4 \\ x + 2y \ge 5 \end{cases}$

20. $\begin{cases} x + 2y < -4 \\ 2x - y < -3 \end{cases}$

Summary and Review   **489**

 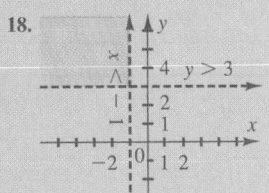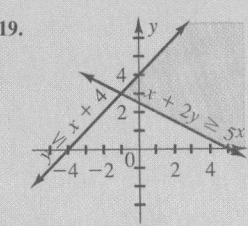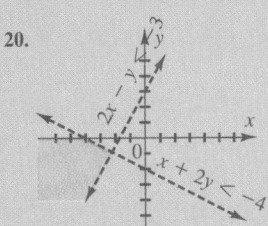

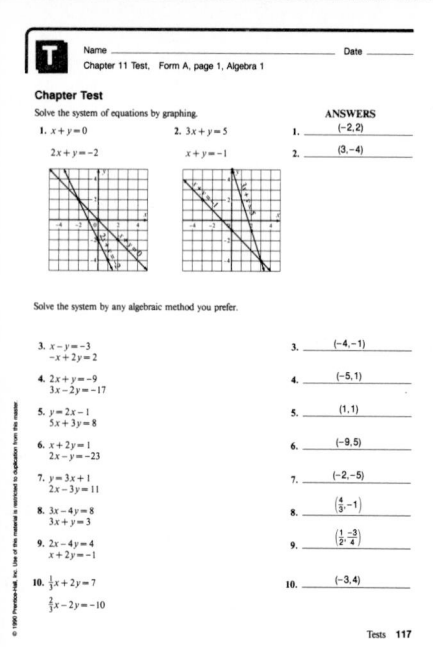

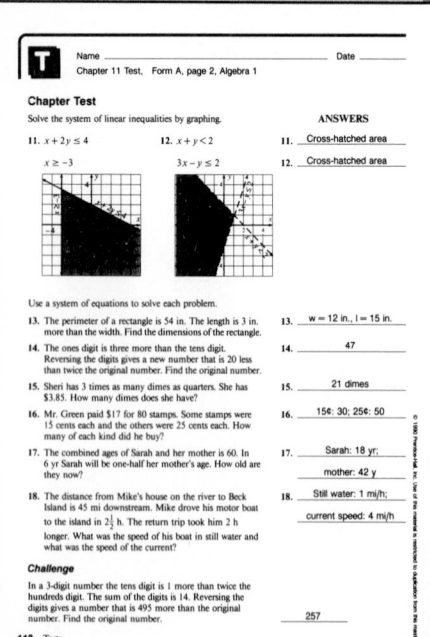

Solve the system of equations by graphing. Check students' graphs.

1. $\begin{cases} 3x - y = 4 \\ -9x + 3y = -12 \end{cases}$
$\{(x, y): 3x - y = 4\}$

2. $\begin{cases} x + 2y = -2 \\ x - y = 4 \end{cases}$ $(2, -2)$

3. $\begin{cases} x + 2y = 6 \\ x + y = -1 \end{cases}$ $(-8, 7)$

Solve the system by any algebraic method you prefer.

4. $\begin{cases} x - y = 1 \\ y = 2x - 3 \end{cases}$ $(2, 1)$

5. $\begin{cases} x + y = 2 \\ 3x - 2y = -9 \end{cases}$ $(-1, 3)$

6. $\begin{cases} 2x + y = 0 \\ y = \dfrac{x}{3} \end{cases}$ $(0, 0)$

7. $\begin{cases} 2x - y = -1 \\ 3x = y + 2 \end{cases}$ $(3, 7)$

8. $\begin{cases} \dfrac{x}{3} - \dfrac{y}{2} = 6 \\ \dfrac{x}{2} + \dfrac{y}{8} = 2 \end{cases}$ $(6, -8)$

9. $\begin{cases} 5x = 4y - 7 \\ 8y = 6x + 2 \end{cases}$ $(-3, -2)$

Solve the system of linear inequalities by graphing. Check students' graphs.
See Additional Answer section beginning p. 719.

10. $\begin{cases} 2x + y < -4 \\ x \geq 1 \end{cases}$

11. $\begin{cases} y \leq -2x \\ x > -2y + 6 \end{cases}$

12. $\begin{cases} 2x + y < 0 \\ 2x - y < -6 \end{cases}$

Use a system of equations to solve the problem.

13. The sum of the digits of a two-digit number is 9. If the digits are reversed, the new number is 45 more than the original number. Find the two-digit number. 27

14. A store sells cashews for $4.40/lb and peanuts for $1.20/lb. How many lb of each can be bought to get exactly 3 lb of nuts for $6? 2.25-lb peanuts 0.75-lb cashews

15. A barge travels 16 mi upstream in 4 h. On the return trip it takes 2 h to travel the same distance with the current. Find the rate of speed of the barge in still water and the speed of the stream's current. 6 mi/h; 2 mi/h

16. Allen is 4 yr older than his brother Randy. Three years ago, Allen was twice as old as Randy. How old is each now? Allen 11 yr Randy 7 yr

Challenge

1. The jetstream is the wind that blows across the country from west to east. A jet plane flying directly against the jetstream makes an 800-mi nonstop trip from Kennedy Airport to O'Hare Airport in 2 h. The jet plane makes the return trip in 1 h 36 min with the jetstream directly behind it. Find the speed of the jetstream. 50 mi/h

Comments provided for certain problems can assist students in solving them.

Select the best choice for each question.

1. Find the value of $2ab(3a^2 - 5b)^2$
 B when $a = -3$ and $b = 5$.
  A. -1470
  B. -120
  C. -100
  D. 100
  E. 120

2. What is the value of x in the
 C system of equations:
$$\begin{cases} 2x - 7y = 8 \\ x - 4y = 3 \end{cases}$$

  A. 2 B. 5 C. 11 D. 17 E. $21\frac{1}{4}$

3. In his small motorboat it takes Sam
 E 5 h to go 30 mi up the river, but
  he can return down the river in
  only 3 h. What is the rate, in mi/h,
  of the river?
  A. 8 B. 6 C. 5 D. 4 E. 2

4. Solve the equation:
 A
  $3(x + 7) + 5(2x - 4) = 11(x - 3)$
  A. -17
  B. -16
  C. 16
  D. 17
  E. 33

5. Three years ago, Martin's age was
 C one half his sister's age. If the sum
  of their ages today is 21, how old
  is Martin now?
  A. 4 B. 5 C. 8 D. 10 E. 13

6. $\dfrac{54.81}{2.7} = \dfrac{?}{}$
 B
  A. 2.03 B. 20.3 C. 203
  D. 2.3 E. 23

7. An equation of a line through
 C P(4, 3) and Q(5, 5) is:
  A. $y = 2x - 11$
  B. $y = -2x + 11$
  C. $y = 2x - 5$
  D. $y = -2x + 5$
  E. $y = 2x + 11$

8. Sara purchased 3 cassette tapes at
 C $7.90 each, 1 video tape for
  $22.50, and 4 blank cassette tapes
  for $1.95 each. How much sales
  tax, at 6%, was added to the total?
  A. $0.32 B. $0.33 C. $3.24
  D. $3.27 E. $5.40

9. The sum of the digits of a two-digit
 E number is 11. If the digits are
  reversed, the new number is 27
  more than the original number.
  What is the units digit of the
  original number?
  A. 3 B. 4 C. 5 D. 6 E. 7

10. Some boys wanted to make shelves
 E for their clubhouse, and after
  measuring the space, decided each
  shelf should be a board 18 in. long
  and 6 in. wide. They found three
  boards, one measuring 2 ft × 12 in.,
  another 20 in. × 6 in., and the
  third one 38 in. × 8 in. Using a
  saw and these boards, how many
  shelves can they make?
  A. 0 B. 2 C. 3 D. 4 E. 5

11. Find the coordinates of the point
 D of intersection of the graphs of
  $y = 3x - 1$ and $2x + y = 9$.
  A. (1, 2) B. (−1, −4) C. (0, 9)
  D. (2, 5) E. (3, 3)

1. Although this problem could be worked by first multiplying out the algebraic expressions and then substituting the values for *a* and *b*, it would involve more calculations.

5. This could also be solved using one linear equation. If Martin's age now is *x*, then his sister is $21 - x$ years old now. Then,
$$x - 3 = \tfrac{1}{2}(21 - x - 3)$$
$$2x - 6 = 18 - x$$
$$3x = 24$$
$$x = 8$$

10. Encourage students to draw a picture illustrating how each board can be cut.

11. The addition-subtraction method could also be used to solve this system of equations using
$$\begin{cases} 3x - y = 1. \\ 2x + y = 9 \end{cases}$$

See *Teacher's Resource Book,* for Preparing for Standardized Tests.

Maintaining Skills

The following skills and concepts are reviewed:

Solving mathematical sentences using the correct order of operation

Finding square roots

Multiplying using the FOIL Method

Solving problems involving measurements

Perform the indicated operations.

Example 1 $1.2 \cdot 2 + 5.3 - 4.2 \div 7 + 3 \cdot 5$

$\underline{1.2 \cdot 2} + 5.3 - \underline{4.2 \div 7} + \underline{3 \cdot 5}$ *Do all multiplications and divisions from left to right.*

$= 2.4 + 5.3 - 0.6 + 15$ *Now do all additions and subtractions from left to right.*

$= 22.1$

1.   729.58
  + 3.46
  ‾‾‾‾‾‾
  733.04

2.   345.15
  + 5.98
  ‾‾‾‾‾‾
  351.13

3.   238.98
  − 23.07
  ‾‾‾‾‾‾
  215.91

4.   765.39
  − 36.09
  ‾‾‾‾‾‾
  729.3

5. $5.24 \cdot 2 \div 2.62 + 4$ 8   **6.** $25.6 \div 8 \cdot 3.2 + 2$ 12.24   **7.** $50.5 - 4 \cdot 1.2 \div 6 + 3$ 52.7

Simplify.

Example 2 $\sqrt{900}$

$= \sqrt{9} \cdot \sqrt{100}$
$= 3 \cdot 10 = 30$

8. $\sqrt{25}$ 5   **9.** $\sqrt{36}$ 6   **10.** $\sqrt{400}$ 20   **11.** $\sqrt{625}$ 25

12. $\sqrt{144}$ 12   **13.** $\sqrt{225}$ 15   **14.** $\sqrt{0.04}$ 0.2   **15.** $\sqrt{0.09}$ 0.3

Multiply.

Example 3 $(a + 3)(a - 2)$

$$(a + 3)(a - 2) = (a + 3)(a - 2) = a^2 - 2a + 3a - 6 = a^2 + a - 6$$

16. $(a - 5)(a + 5)$ $a^2 - 25$ **17.** $(y - 3)(y - 4)$ $y^2 - 7y + 12$

18. $(2x + 6)(x - 3)$ $2x^2 - 18$ **19.** $(3b + 5)(b - 2)$ $3b^2 - b - 10$

20. $(2m + 4)(3m - 2)$ $6m^2 + 8m - 8$ **21.** $(3x + 2)(4x - 5)$ $12x^2 - 7x - 10$

Solve.

22. Sam is 185 cm tall. Otis is 1.5 m tall. What is the difference in their heights? 35 cm

23. Box A weighs 3 lb 8 oz. Box B weighs 4 lb 9 oz. What is the combined weight of the boxes? 8 lb 1 oz

OVERVIEW • Chapter 12

SUMMARY

In Chapter 12, students learn more about rational and irrational numbers. Students are also introduced to the concepts and skills involved in simplifying radicals and solving equations with radicals. The major focus of this chapter is on square roots. Using the problem solving strategies, students will solve problems involving square roots. In particular, students will use two applications of square roots: the Pythagorean theorem and the distance formula.

After this chapter is completed, students should be able to add, subtract, multiply, and divide radicals and express answers in simplest form. They should also be able to find the square root of a number by using a square root table, the divide-and-average method, and a calculator. A primary goal of this chapter is to prepare students for using radicals in solving quadratic equations in Chapter 13.

CHAPTER OBJECTIVES

- To find the square roots of numbers with rational square roots
- To approximate irrational square roots
- To write rational numbers in decimal or fraction form
- To simplify square roots
- To simplify square roots containing variable expressions
- To simplify sums and differences of radicals
- To simplify products and quotients of radicals
- To solve simple radical equations
- To use the Pythagorean theorem to find the length of a leg or the length of the hypotenuse of a right triangle
- To find the distance between any two points in the coordinate plane

Problem Solving Strategy

To introduce the use of coordinate geometry

CHAPTER HIGHLIGHTS

The *theme* of Chapter 12 is electronic manufacturing. The chapter's special features show how the concepts of radicals are utilized in electronics. Electronic manufacturers integrate many mathematical concepts such as manipulating radicals into their work as shown in this chapter.

PROBLEM SOLVING AND APPLICATIONS

Problem solving and applications form an integral part of each lesson. Students combine concepts from algebra and geometry by using the coordinate plane. In Lesson 12.11, students learn how to find the midpoint of segments without being given any measurements.

TECHNOLOGY

Calculator

Students learn how to use a calculator to find the positive (or principal) square root of a number by pressing the $\sqrt{}$ key. They may use a calculator to compare their estimations of square roots.

Computer

The computer feature in Lesson 12.3 provides a program to approximate the square root of any positive number using only addition and division. In Lesson 12.10, students are introduced to a computer program that will find the lengths of each side of a figure. Students should learn how the distance formula is applied in this program.

RESOURCES

Teacher's Resource Book

- Teaching Aids 12, 15
- Transparencies 10, 12, 15, 17, 18, 25, 26, 27, 28, 29

STUDENT TEXT				TEACHER'S RESOURCE BOOK		
Chapter Content	Basic	Average	Enriched	R	P	E
12.1 Square Roots	D: 496/1-13 odd, 35	D: 496/1-25 odd, 35	D: 496/15-33 odd, 35	1	2	3
12.2 Irrational Square Roots	D: 499/1-15 odd, 29 R: 496/2, 8, 10	D: 499/1-23 odd, 29-30 R: 496/4, 12, 14	D: 499/17-27 odd, 29-30 R: 496/16, 22, 30	4	5	6
12.3 Decimal Forms of Rational Numbers	D: 502/1-15 odd, 32 R: 499/2, 4, 6	D: 502/1-27 odd, 32 R: 499/6, 10, 12	D: 502/17-31 odd, 32 R: 499/18, 22, 24	7	8	9
12.4 Simplifying Square Roots	D: 505/1-27 odd, 51 R: 502/2, 6, 8	D: 505/1-43 odd, 51, 52 R: 502/6, 10, 14	D: 505/29-49 odd, 51-53 R: 502/18, 22, 24	10	11	12
12.5 Addition and Subtraction of Radicals	D: 510/1-17 odd, 37 R: 505/4, 14, 26	D: 510/1-31 odd, 37, 38 R: 505/6, 18, 42	D: 511/19-35 odd, 37, 38 R: 505/30, 38, 48	13	14	15
12.6 Multiplication of Radicals	D: 514/1-19 odd, 43-46 R: Test Yourself	D: 514/1-35 odd, 43-48 R: Test Yourself	D: 514/21-41 odd, 43-50 R: Test Yourself	16	17	18
12.7 Division of Radicals	D: 518/1-23 odd, 43, 44 R: 514/2, 10, 18	D: 518/1-35 odd, 43-45 R: 514/6, 16, 34	D: 518/25-41 odd, 43-46 R: 514/22, 32, 40	19	20	21
12.8 Solving Radical Equations	D: 522/1-23 odd, 42-44 R: 518/2, 10, 22	D: 522/1-35 odd, 43-45 R: 518/6, 18, 32 522/2, 10, 14	D: 522/25-41 odd, 42-46 R: 518/26, 30, 40	22	23	24
12.9 The Pythagorean Theorem	D: 526/1-11 odd, 19-21 R: 522/4, 14, 22	D: 526/1-15 odd, 19-23 R: 522/8, 16, 34	D: 526/13-17 odd, 19-24 R: 522/26, 34, 40	25	26	27
12.10 The Distance Formula	D: 530/1-11 odd, 25 R: 526/2, 8, 10	D: 530/1-19 odd, 25 R: 526/2, 10, 14	D: 530/13-23 odd, 25 R: 526/14, 16	28	29	30
12.11 Problem Solving Strategy: Using Coordinate Geometry	D: 532/1-7 odd MPSR 1-4 R: Test Yourself	D: 532/1-13 odd MPSR 1-4 R: Test Yourself	D: 533/9-17 odd MPSR 1-4 R: Test Yourself		31	32

D = Daily R = Review MPSR = Mixed Problem Solving Review   R = Reteaching P = Practice E = Enrichment

	STUDENT TEXT				TEACHER'S RESOURCE BOOK	
Reviewing And Testing	Test Yourself	515	Chapter Test	538	Spanish Chapter Summary and Review	23-24
	Test Yourself	535	Prep. for Stan. Tests	539	• Quizzes	121-124
	Chapter Sum. and Review	536	Cumulative Review	540	• Chapter Test (Form A)	125-126
			Extra Practice	666	• Chapter Test (Form B)	127-128
Special Features	Historical Note	496	Biography	511	Calculator Test	23-24
	Algebra in Industry	499	Extra	519, 523	Applications—Chapter 12	33
	Extra	502	Did You Know?	527	Critical Thinking	12
	Algebra in Police Science	506	Logical Reasoning	530	Reading and Writing in Algebra	12
	Application	507	Project	535	Technology	22

12 Radicals

Knowledge gained through technology is changing how we live and work in many ways. Mathematics plays an important role in the application of this knowledge to solve practical problems.

493

BACKGROUND

In electronic manufacturing, many types of equations and formulas are used. Electronic manufacturers perform various calculations involving small numbers. Many of their calculations require the use of radicals. It is essential to have a strong background in mathematics in order to successfully complete various electronic tasks.

Vocabulary
Positive square root
Radical
Radicand
Radical sign
Square root

Materials/Manipulatives
Calculators
Teacher's Resource Book,
  Teaching Aid 5

BACKGROUND

In the Capsule Review, the exercises illustrate the concept of squaring a number. For Exercise 2, you may wish to discuss the difference between $(-2)^2$ and -2^2. For Exercise 8, some students may write the answer as $(ab)^2$. You may want to discuss why this is correct. In this lesson, students find the square root of a number, that is, they perform the inverse of squaring a number.

Critical Thinking

• *Discovering Relationships* Use a dictionary to find the derivation of the word *radical*. Then, find at least two nonmathematical uses of the word. Which one has the closest relation to the mathematical meaning? *Radical* is derived from the Latin word *radicalis* meaning "having roots" and from the French word *radix* meaning "a root." Answers may vary for the uses of the word. Some examples are "one who follows extreme principles," and "arising from the root or base of the stem."

• *Causal Explanation* Explain why there are no square roots of negative real numbers. Negative numbers do not have square roots in the real number system. The square of every real number is either positive or zero.

| 12.1 | # Square Roots |

Objective: To find the square roots of numbers with rational square roots

A landscape architect wants to use 121 tiles, each one foot square, to create a square patio. Since $11^2 = 11 \times 11 = 121$, the architect can make a square patio that has 11 tiles on each side.

Subtracting a number is the inverse of adding the number and dividing by a nonzero number is the inverse of multiplying by the number. The inverse of squaring a number is finding the *square root*, $\sqrt{121} = 11$.

Capsule Review

Simplify.

1. 4^2 16   **2.** $(-2)^2$ 4   **3.** $\left(\dfrac{1}{2}\right)^2$ $\frac{1}{4}$ **4.** 12^2 144

Write in exponential form.

5. $\left(-\dfrac{1}{3}\right)\left(-\dfrac{1}{3}\right)$ $\left(-\frac{1}{3}\right)^2$ **6.** $(-4)(-4)$ $(-4)^2$ **7.** $s \cdot s$ s^2 **8.** $a \cdot a \cdot b \cdot b$ $a^2 b^2$

If $x^2 = y$, then x is called a **square root** of y. Since $11^2 = 121$, then 11 is a square root of 121. However, $(-11)^2 = 121$, and -11 is also a square root of 121. Every positive real number has two square roots, one positive and one negative. Does every negative real number have two square roots?

To indicate the **positive** (or **principal**) **square root** of a number y, write $\sqrt{y}$. The symbol $\sqrt{}$ is called a **radical sign.** An expression like $\sqrt{25}$ is a **radical,** and the number under the radical sign is a **radicand.**

To indicate the negative square root of a number y, write $-\sqrt{y}$. The expression $\pm\sqrt{y}$ indicates both square roots of y. For example, $\sqrt{9} = 3$, $-\sqrt{9} = -3$, and $\pm\sqrt{9} = \pm 3$. When using your calculator, pressing the $\sqrt{}$ key will give the positive (or principal) square root.

EXAMPLE 1 **Find the indicated square root:** **a.** $\sqrt{64}$ **b.** $-\sqrt{\frac{1}{9}}$ **c.** $\pm\sqrt{0.81}$

a. $\sqrt{64} = 8$ **b.** $-\sqrt{\frac{1}{9}} = -\frac{1}{3}$ **c.** $\pm\sqrt{0.81} = \pm 0.9$

An important property of square roots is suggested by the following:
$\sqrt{100} = 10$ and $\sqrt{25} \cdot \sqrt{4} = \sqrt{5^2} \cdot \sqrt{2^2} = 5 \cdot 2 = 10$. Therefore,
$\sqrt{100} = \sqrt{25} \cdot \sqrt{4}$.

Product Property of Square Roots

For all real numbers m and n, where $m \geq 0$ and $n \geq 0$,
$$\sqrt{mn} = \sqrt{m} \cdot \sqrt{n}$$

A similar property for division of square roots is suggested by the following:
$\sqrt{\frac{36}{9}} = \sqrt{4} = 2$ and $\frac{\sqrt{36}}{\sqrt{9}} = \frac{6}{3} = 2$. Therefore, $\sqrt{\frac{36}{9}} = \frac{\sqrt{36}}{\sqrt{9}}$.

Quotient Property of Square Roots

For all real numbers m and n, where $m \geq 0$ and $n > 0$, $\sqrt{\frac{m}{n}} = \frac{\sqrt{m}}{\sqrt{n}}$

Use one of the two properties of square roots to find the square root of a number.

EXAMPLE 2 **Simplify. Do not use a calculator.**

a. $\sqrt{1156}$ **b.** $\sqrt{\frac{1296}{169}}$ **c.** $-\sqrt{2.56}$

a. $\sqrt{1156}$
$= \sqrt{4 \cdot 289}$
$= \sqrt{2^2 \cdot 17^2}$
$= \sqrt{2^2} \cdot \sqrt{17^2}$
$= 2 \cdot 17$
$= 34$

b. $\sqrt{\frac{1296}{169}}$
$= \frac{\sqrt{4^2 \cdot 9^2}}{\sqrt{169}}$
$= \frac{\sqrt{4^2} \cdot \sqrt{9^2}}{\sqrt{13^2}}$
$= \frac{4 \cdot 9}{13}$
$= \frac{36}{13}$

c. $-\sqrt{2.56}$
$= -\sqrt{\frac{256}{100}}$
$= -\frac{\sqrt{256}}{\sqrt{100}}$
$= -\frac{\sqrt{4^2} \cdot \sqrt{4^2}}{\sqrt{10^2}}$
$= -\frac{4 \cdot 4}{10}$
$= -\frac{16}{10}$, or -1.6

12.1 Square Roots **495**

TEACHING SUGGESTIONS

- Some students may have difficulty recognizing perfect squares. You may wish to use Teaching Aid 15, in the *Teacher's Resource Book*, to become familiar with the squares of integers.
- Students can "discover" the two properties by using calculators. They can also use calculators to check their answers.
- When discussing the two properties, tell students that m and n do not have to be perfect squares.

CHALKBOARD EXAMPLES

- **For Example 1**
  Find the indicated square root:
  1. $\sqrt{36}$ 6 **2.** $-\sqrt{\frac{1}{16}}$ $-\frac{1}{4}$

- **For Example 2**
  Simplify.
  3. $\sqrt{1024}$ 32 **4.** $\sqrt{\frac{900}{2500}}$ $\frac{3}{5}$

Common Error

- Many students incorrectly place the decimal point when finding the square root of decimal numbers. Students should check the placement of the decimal point by multiplying the number of decimal places in the answer by 2. This should be the number of decimal places in the radicand.
- See *Teacher's Resource Book* for additional remediation.

LESSON FOLLOW-UP

Assignment Guide
See p. 492B for assignments.

Lesson Quiz
Find the indicated square roots.
1. $\pm\sqrt{225}$ ± 15 **2.** $-\sqrt{\frac{9}{81}}$ $-\frac{1}{3}$
3. $\sqrt{0.2304}$ 0.48 **4.** $\sqrt{\frac{0.36}{1.21}}$ $\frac{6}{11}$

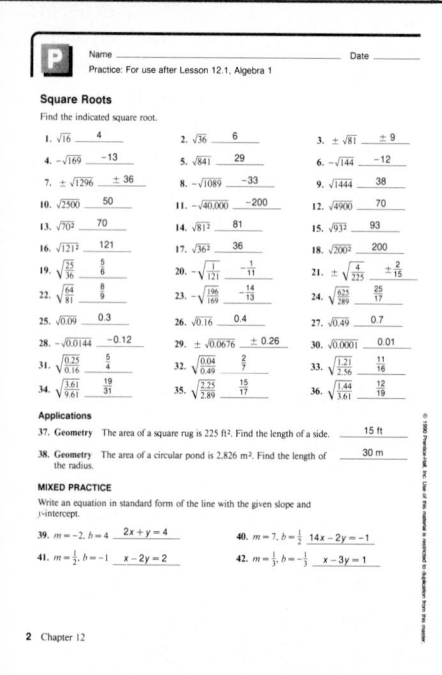

CLASS EXERCISES

Find the indicated square roots.

1. $\sqrt{49}$ 7 **2.** $-\sqrt{121}$ −11 **3.** $\pm\sqrt{144}$ ±12 **4.** $\pm\sqrt{289}$ ±17 **5.** $\sqrt{5^2}$ 5

6. $\sqrt{9^2}$ 9 **7.** $\sqrt{\dfrac{1}{49}}$ $\frac{1}{7}$ **8.** $-\sqrt{\dfrac{1}{16}}$ $-\frac{1}{4}$ **9.** $\pm\sqrt{1600}$ ±40 **10.** $\pm\sqrt{576}$ ±24

PRACTICE EXERCISES

Find the indicated square roots.

A **1.** $\sqrt{25}$ 5 **2.** $-\sqrt{81}$ −9 **3.** $-\sqrt{256}$ −16 **4.** $\sqrt{361}$ 19 **5.** $\sqrt{\dfrac{4}{9}}$ $\frac{2}{3}$

6. $\pm\sqrt{\dfrac{16}{25}}$ $\pm\frac{4}{5}$ **7.** $-\sqrt{\dfrac{1}{144}}$ $-\frac{1}{12}$ **8.** $\sqrt{\dfrac{1}{121}}$ $\frac{1}{11}$ **9.** $\pm\sqrt{\dfrac{144}{225}}$ $\pm\frac{4}{5}$ **10.** $\pm\sqrt{\dfrac{196}{361}}$ $\pm\frac{14}{19}$

11. $-\sqrt{10,000}$ −100 **12.** $-\sqrt{90,000}$ −300 **13.** $\sqrt{1089}$ 33 **14.** $\sqrt{784}$ 28

B **15.** $\sqrt{0.01}$ 0.1 **16.** $\sqrt{0.04}$ 0.2 **17.** $\sqrt{0.64}$ 0.8 **18.** $\sqrt{0.25}$ 0.5

19. $-\sqrt{1.96}$ −1.4 **20.** $\sqrt{2.89}$ 1.7 **21.** $\sqrt{0.0009}$ 0.03 **22.** $\sqrt{0.0025}$ 0.05

23. $\pm\sqrt{0.0625}$ ±0.25 **24.** $\pm\sqrt{0.0196}$ ±0.14 **25.** $\sqrt{0.1296}$ 0.36 **26.** $\sqrt{0.1089}$ 0.33

C **27.** $\sqrt{\dfrac{0.25}{0.09}}$ $\frac{5}{3}$ **28.** $\sqrt{\dfrac{0.01}{0.81}}$ $\frac{1}{9}$ **29.** $\sqrt{\dfrac{1.44}{2.25}}$ $\frac{4}{5}$ **30.** $\sqrt{\dfrac{1.21}{3.61}}$ $\frac{11}{19}$

31. $\sqrt[4]{81}$ 3 **32.** $\sqrt[4]{10,000}$ 10 **33.** $\sqrt[3]{125}$ 5 **34.** $\sqrt[3]{64}$ 4

Applications

35. Physics The approximate time t (in seconds) that it takes an object to fall a distance d (in ft) under the influence of gravity is given by the formula $t = \sqrt{\dfrac{d}{16}}$. Find the time it takes an object to fall 144 ft. 3 s

HISTORICAL NOTE

Figurate numbers are a subset of the counting numbers.

1. Diagram the next three triangular numbers.
15, 21, 28

2. Diagram the next three square numbers.
25, 36, 49

3. The Greek mathematician Pythagoras and his followers suggested that any square number greater than 1 is the sum of two successive triangular numbers. Draw diagrams to show that this is true for the square numbers shown here.
Check students' diagram.

Triangular Numbers

1 3 6 10, . . .

Square Numbers

1 4 9 16, . . .

Irrational Square Roots

Objective: To approximate irrational square roots

An artist has 68 square marble tiles.
The artist wants to use all of the tiles to
create a square mosaic design. Assuming
that no open spaces are left and that no
tiles are broken, is this possible?

Since there is no integer a such that
$a^2 = 68$, the artist cannot use all 68 tiles
to make a square design.

Because 68 is not the square of an integer, its square root is not a rational
number. The square root of 68 is an *irrational number*. An **irrational
number** is a real number that cannot be written in the form $\frac{m}{n}$, where m and
n are integers and $n \neq 0$. Some examples are $\sqrt{2}$, $\sqrt{5}$, $\sqrt{13}$, and π.

Capsule Review

Graph each of these sets of numbers on a number line.
See Additional Answer section beginning p. 719.

1. $\{-5, 5, 1, -1, 0\}$ **2.** $\{0, 1, 2, 3, \ldots\}$ **3.** {positive integers}

4. $\left\{2.5, -1.5, 3\frac{3}{4}, -0.5, -\frac{1}{4}\right\}$ **5.** {odd integers}

The set of real numbers is made up of rational numbers and irrational
numbers. If you were to graph all rational numbers and irrational numbers on
the number line, the graph would be continuous, or complete. This property
of the real numbers is called the *completeness property*.

The **completeness property** states that there is a one-to-one correspondence
between the real numbers and the points of a number line.

Irrational square roots are often left in radical form, but for some problems it
may be necessary to approximate the square roots. You probably will use a
calculator to find decimal approximations of irrational square roots. You can,
however, use a square-root table such as the one on page 670. It lists decimal
values for the square roots of integers from 1 through 150. A calculator gives
a closer approximation of the square root.

12.2 Irrational Square Roots   **497**

LESSON PLAN

Vocabulary
Completeness Property
Irrational number

Materials/Manipulatives
Calculators
Square-root table

BACKGROUND

- In the Capsule Review, students
  graph rational numbers on a number line. Students who have difficulty recognizing rational and irrational numbers should review
  Lesson 1.1. In this lesson, students
  learn that there is a one-to-one
  correspondence between the real
  numbers and the points of a number line. Also, students approximate the square root of an irrational number.
- The divide-and-average method
  for approximating irrational square
  roots was developed by the Greek
  mathematician and scientist, Hero.

TEACHING SUGGESTIONS

- Emphasize that a real number is
  either rational or irrational but not
  both.
- Students should understand that
  the square root of an irrational
  number can only be an approximation, for which there is no exact
  fraction or decimal equivalent.
- Point out that the fastest and most
  accurate method of finding the
  square root of an irrational number
  is by using a calculator.
- When discussing Example 2, have
  students divide 75 by 8.66 in Step
  4. Discuss that the quotient
  ≈ 8.661 matches the divisor to the
  hundredths place.

EXAMPLE 1 **Approximate $\sqrt{68}$ to the nearest hundredth. Use the square-root table.**

n	n^2	$\sqrt{n}$
67	4489	8.185
68 ⟶	4624 ⟶	8.246
69	4761	8.307

$\sqrt{68} \approx 8.246$, or 8.25 to the nearest hundredth

Another method for approximating irrational square roots is called the *divide-and-average method*.

EXAMPLE 2 **Approximate $\sqrt{75}$ using the divide-and-average method.**

Step 1 75 is between 64 and 81; therefore, $\sqrt{75}$ is between $\sqrt{64}$ and $\sqrt{81}$.

$64 < 75 < 81$
$8 < \sqrt{75} < 9$

Step 2 75 is closer to 81 than to 64, and so 9 is a closer approximation of $\sqrt{75}$. Therefore, divide 75 by 9. Divide until the quotient has one more decimal place than the divisor.

$9)\overline{75.0} \quad 8.3$

Step 3 Find the average of 9 and 8.3. The average should have the same number of decimal places as the quotient.

$\dfrac{9 + 8.3}{2} = \dfrac{17.3}{2} \approx 8.7$

Step 4 Repeat steps 2 and 3 using the average 8.7 as the divisor.

$8.7)\overline{75.000} \quad 8.62 \qquad \dfrac{8.7 + 8.62}{2} = \dfrac{17.32}{2} = 8.66$

So, $\sqrt{75} \approx 8.66$. If the steps were repeated would you get a closer approximation? Each successive repetition yields a number closer to, but never equal to, the irrational number. This illustrates the **density property** of real numbers, which states that between any two real numbers there is another real number.

CLASS EXERCISES

Use the square-root table on page 670 to approximate the square root. Then, compare your answers using a calculator.

1. $\sqrt{3}$ 1.732 **2.** $\sqrt{2}$ 1.414 **3.** $\sqrt{27}$ 5.196 **4.** $\sqrt{58}$ 7.616 **5.** $\sqrt{31}$ 5.568

6. $\sqrt{97}$ 9.849 **7.** $\sqrt{85}$ 9.220 **8.** $\sqrt{19}$ 4.359 **9.** $\sqrt{45}$ 6.708 **10.** $\sqrt{76}$ 8.718

Use the divide-and-average method to approximate the square root.

11. $\sqrt{50}$ 7.07 **12.** $\sqrt{79}$ 8.89 **13.** $\sqrt{18.5}$ 4.30 **14.** $\sqrt{5.9}$ 2.43 **15.** $\sqrt{39.5}$ 6.28

498   Chapter 12 Radicals

PRACTICE EXERCISES

A Approximate the square root to the nearest tenth using the divide-and-average method.

1. $\sqrt{5}$ 2.2   **2.** $\sqrt{8}$ 2.8   **3.** $\sqrt{22}$ 4.7   **4.** $\sqrt{17}$ 4.1

5. $\sqrt{83}$ 9.1   **6.** $\sqrt{67}$ 8.2   **7.** $\sqrt{95}$ 9.7   **8.** $\sqrt{59}$ 7.7

9. $\sqrt{27}$ 5.2   **10.** $\sqrt{32}$ 5.7   **11.** $\sqrt{15}$ 3.9   **12.** $\sqrt{12}$ 3.5

13. $\sqrt{99}$ 9.9   **14.** $\sqrt{86}$ 9.3   **15.** $\sqrt{19.5}$ 4.4   **16.** $\sqrt{17.7}$ 4.2

B **17.** $\sqrt{149}$ 12.2   **18.** $\sqrt{165}$ 12.8   **19.** $\sqrt{127}$ 11.3   **20.** $\sqrt{105}$ 10.2

21. $\sqrt{71.5}$ 8.5   **22.** $\sqrt{9.5}$ 3.1   **23.** $\sqrt{4.51}$ 2.1   **24.** $\sqrt{58.9}$ 7.7

C Use the divide-average-method to compute the following to two decimal places of accuracy.

25. $\sqrt{40,098.52}$ 200.25   **26.** $\sqrt{95,000}$ 308.22   **27.** $\sqrt{0.432}$ 0.66   **28.** $\sqrt{0.915}$ 0.96

Applications

29. Geometry The area of a square rug is 48 ft². What is the approximate length of one side of the rug? 6.93 ft

30. Geometry The length of a rectangular poster is 3 times the width. The area of the rectangle is 192 in². Find the dimensions of the poster.
$l = 24$ in., $w = 8$ in.

ALGEBRA IN INDUSTRY

In the printing industry, printers often use a measurement unit called an *em* to measure the available type space on a page. This unit is helpful when computing printing costs. An *em* is the area occupied by the letter M in any type size. The size of the em, of course, varies with the size of the type. In 6-point type there are 144 ems in the square inch; in 12-point type only 36. The formula for finding the cost of composition is:

$$C = \frac{T}{E} \times H$$

where C = cost of composition, E = total ems set per hour, T = total ems set, and H = hourly wage. Use the formula to find the cost of setting type for the following book.

A total of 16,800,000 ems are needed to set the type for an encyclopedia. The compositor works at a rate of 3500 em/h and charges $42.50 per hour. $204,000

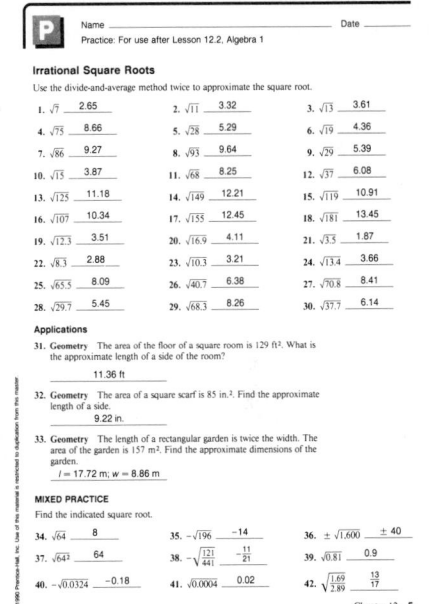

BACKGROUND

In the Capsule Review, students show that terminating decimals and mixed fractions are rational numbers by writing them in the form $\frac{m}{n}$, where m and n are integers and $n \neq 0$. In this lesson, the definition of rational numbers is extended to include repeating decimals.

TEACHING SUGGESTIONS

- Point out that decimals that do not terminate or repeat are called irrational numbers, for example, π.
- For Example 1, point out the meaning of the notation in writing 0.833 . . . and in writing $0.8\overline{3}$.
- For Examples 2 and 3, make sure students understand how to determine the power of 10 by which to multiply.
- Have students check their results using a calculator.

12.3

Decimal Forms of Rational Numbers

Objective: To write rational numbers in decimal or fraction form

A carpenter has two boards. One is $\frac{3}{4}$ in. thick. The other is $1\frac{5}{16}$ in. thick. If the carpenter uses a calculator to find the total thickness, she changes the fractions to decimals.

The rational numbers $\frac{3}{4}$ and $1\frac{5}{16}$ can be expressed as **terminating decimals.**

$\frac{3}{4} = 0.75$ and $1\frac{5}{16} = 1.3125$. The division results in a zero remainder.

Capsule Review

Show that the number is a rational number.

1. $8.3 \frac{83}{10}$
2. $1.5 \frac{3}{2}$
3. $4 \frac{4}{1}$
4. $0 \frac{0}{1}$

5. $-2\frac{1}{2} \frac{-5}{2}$
6. $-1\frac{3}{4} \frac{-7}{4}$
7. $6.01 \frac{601}{100}$
8. $5.99 \frac{599}{100}$

Not every rational number can be expressed as a terminating decimal. Some rational numbers are represented by **repeating decimals.** However, *every* rational number can be expressed as either a terminating or a repeating decimal.

EXAMPLE 1   **Divide to express $\frac{5}{6}$ as a decimal.**

$$\frac{5}{6} \longrightarrow 6\overline{)\begin{array}{l} 0.833 \\ 5.000 \end{array}}$$

Notice that the digit 3 repeats in the quotient and that the remainder 2 also repeats.

$$
\begin{array}{r}
0.833 \\
6\,)\,5.000 \\
\underline{4\ 8} \\
20 \\
\underline{18} \\
20 \\
\underline{18} \\
2
\end{array}
$$

So, $\frac{5}{6} = 0.8333 \ldots , = 0.8\overline{3}$.   *The bar shows the repeating digit or block of digits.*

500   Chapter 12 Radicals

EXAMPLE 2 Write $0.\overline{45}$ in the form $\frac{m}{n}$, where m and n are integers, $n \neq 0$.

Let $x = 0.\overline{45}$.

$100x = 45.\overline{45}$ *Multiply each side by 10^2, or 100, because two digits repeat.*

$\underline{x = 0.\overline{45}}$ *Subtract $x = 0.\overline{45}$ from $100x = 45.\overline{45}$.*

$99x = 45.00$

$x = \dfrac{45}{99}$, or $\dfrac{5}{11}$ *Solve for x.*

So, $0.\overline{45} = \dfrac{5}{11}$.

EXAMPLE 3 Write $0.5\overline{3}$ in the form $\frac{m}{n}$, where m and n are integers, $n \neq 0$.

Let $x = 0.5\overline{3}$.

$10x = 5.\overline{33}$ *Multiply each side by 10^1, or 10, because one digit*

$\underline{x = 0.5\overline{3}}$ *repeats.*

$9x = 4.80$ *Subtract $x = 0.5\overline{3}$ from $10x = 5.\overline{33}$.*

$x = \dfrac{4.8}{9} = \dfrac{48}{90} = \dfrac{8}{15}$ *Solve for x.* $\dfrac{4.8}{9} = \dfrac{4.8(10)}{9(10)} = \dfrac{48}{90}$

So, $0.5\overline{3} = \dfrac{8}{15}$.

CLASS EXERCISES

Express each rational number as a terminating or repeating decimal.

1. $\frac{5}{8}$ 0.625   **2.** $-\frac{5}{2}$ −2.5   **3.** $-\frac{1}{6}$ $-0.1\overline{6}$ **4.** $\frac{2}{9}$ $0.\overline{2}$

Write each decimal in the form $\frac{m}{n}$, where m and n are integers, $n \neq 0$.

5. 0.75 $\frac{3}{4}$ **6.** 1.8 $\frac{9}{5}$ **7.** $0.\overline{6}$ $\frac{2}{3}$ **8.** $0.8\overline{3}$ $\frac{5}{6}$

PRACTICE EXERCISES

Express each rational number as a decimal.

A   **1.** $\frac{1}{8}$ 0.125   **2.** $\frac{7}{2}$ 3.5   **3.** $\frac{7}{3}$ $2.\overline{3}$ **4.** $\frac{2}{3}$ $0.\overline{6}$ **5.** $-\frac{5}{4}$ −1.25   **6.** $\frac{8}{5}$ 1.6

     7. $\frac{4}{9}$ $0.\overline{4}$ **8.** $-\frac{5}{11}$ $-0.\overline{45}$ **9.** $-\frac{51}{4}$ −12.75   **10.** $\frac{37}{8}$ 4.625   **11.** $\frac{5}{33}$ $0.\overline{15}$ **12.** $-\frac{8}{11}$ $-0.\overline{72}$

Write each decimal in the form $\frac{m}{n}$, where m and n are integers, $n \neq 0$.

13. 2.33 $\frac{233}{100}$ **14.** -1.6 $\frac{-8}{5}$ **15.** $0.\overline{3}$ $\frac{1}{3}$ **16.** $0.\overline{1}$ $\frac{1}{9}$

12.3 Decimal Forms of Rational Numbers   **501**

501

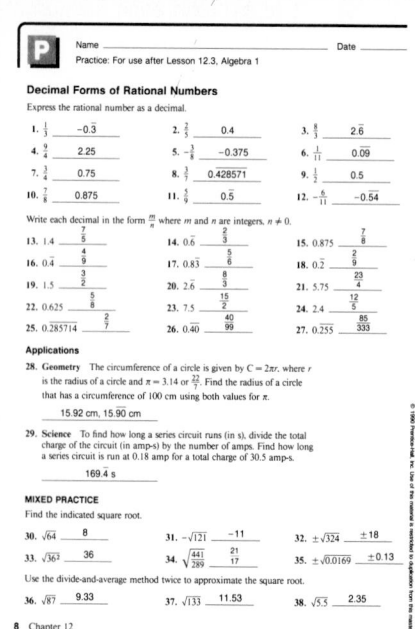

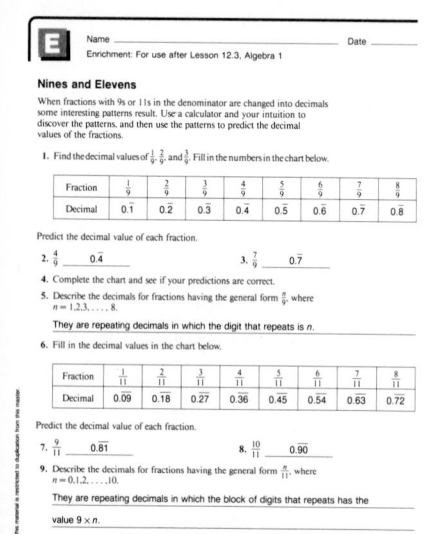

B **17.** $0.\overline{27}$ $\frac{3}{11}$ **18.** $0.\overline{45}$ $\frac{5}{11}$ **19.** $1.\overline{1213}$ $\frac{11212}{9999}$ **20.** $-5.2\overline{3}$ $\frac{-157}{30}$

21. $0.\overline{325}$ $\frac{325}{999}$ **22.** $0.\overline{125}$ $\frac{125}{999}$ **23.** $0.\overline{142857}$ $\frac{1}{7}$ **24.** $0.\overline{857142}$ $\frac{6}{7}$

Write each number in the form $\frac{m}{n}$, and then find their sum.

25. $\frac{2}{3}$; $0.\overline{3}$ $\frac{2}{3}, \frac{1}{3}, 1$ **26.** $0.\overline{36}$; $\frac{7}{11}$ $\frac{4}{11}, \frac{7}{11}, 1$ **27.** $\frac{1}{18}$; 0.38 $\frac{1}{18}, \frac{7}{18}, \frac{4}{9}$ **28.** $\frac{5}{7}$; $0.\overline{285714}$ $\frac{5}{7}, \frac{2}{7}, 1$

C **29.** The rational numbers $\frac{1}{20}$ and $\frac{3}{125}$ can be expressed as terminating decimals. Write the prime factorization of each denominator. What pattern do you observe? The prime factors are all 2s or 5s.

30. The rational numbers $\frac{1}{6}$, $\frac{5}{12}$, and $\frac{1}{11}$ can be expressed as repeating decimals. Write the prime factorization of each denominator. Do factors other than 2 or 5 occur? $6 = 2 \cdot 3$; $12 = 2 \cdot 2 \cdot 3$; 11 is prime; yes.

31. Use the information in Exercises 29–30 to make a general rule for determining, without dividing, whether a rational number in simplest form will be a terminating or a repeating decimal. A rational number represents a terminating decimal if the prime factors of its denominator consist of only the factors 2 and/or 5. A rational number represents a repeating decimal if the prime factors of its denominator include factors other than 2 and/or 5.

Applications

32. **Electricity** To find how long a series circuit runs (in s), divide the total charge of the circuit (in amp × s) by the number of amps. Find how long a student runs a series circuit at 0.12 amp for a total charge of 20.2 amp × s. $168.\overline{3}$ s

EXTRA

Newton's Method, named after Sir Isaac Newton (1642–1727), provides a way to approximate the square root of any positive number using only addition and division. This computer program applies Newton's method five times and prints each approximation.

```
10 INPUT "APPROXIMATE THE SQUARE ROOT OF
      WHAT POSITIVE NUMBER?  ";N: PRINT
20 INPUT "FIRST APPROXIMATION:  ";W: PRINT
30 FOR I = 1 TO 5
40 X = (W + N / W) / 2
50 PRINT X
60 W = X
70 NEXT I
80 END
```

Tell how the outcome of the program is changed if line 40 is replaced by
See below.

1. 40 X = INT(((W + N/W)/2) * 10 + 0.05)/10

2. 40 X = INT(((W + N/W)/2) * 100 + 0.005)/100

3. What is the relationship between this method and the divide and average method? Is one more accurate than the other? If so, which one?

Additional Answers
1. This line will round the approximation to the nearest tenth.
2. This line will round the approximation to the nearest hundredth.
3. Both methods find the approximation of a square root. Newton's Method is more accurate.

Simplifying Square Roots

Objectives: To simplify square roots
To simplify square roots containing variable expressions

LESSON PLAN

Materials/Manipulatives
Calculators
Teacher's Resource Book,
Teaching Aid 15

Electricians use the formula $V = \sqrt{WR}$, where V is voltage, W is power in watts, and R is resistance in ohms. If an appliance uses 150 watts and has a resistance of 20 ohms, what voltage does the appliance need?

Substituting the values for W and R:

$$V = \sqrt{150 \cdot 20}$$
$$= \sqrt{3000}$$

However, 3000 is not the square of an integer.

When a radicand is not the square of an integer, you may use the product and quotient properties of square roots to *simplify* a square-root radical.

BACKGROUND

In the Capsule Review, students review finding the square root of a perfect square. You may want to remind students that every positive real number has two square roots, one positive and one negative. Exercises 5 and 6 indicate the negative square root of 6400 and 8100, respectively. Discuss the product and quotient properties of square roots when doing the exercises in the Capsule Review. In this lesson, these properties are used when students simplify numerical square roots. These properties are also used when students simplify square roots of numbers that are not perfect squares of variable expressions.

Capsule Review

Find the indicated square root.

1. $\sqrt{900}$ 30   2. $\sqrt{3600}$ 60   3. $\sqrt{100}$ 10   4. $\sqrt{144}$ 12   5. $-\sqrt{6400}$ -80

6. $-\sqrt{8100}$ -90 7. $\sqrt{\dfrac{1}{400}}$ $\frac{1}{20}$ 8. $\sqrt{\dfrac{1}{900}}$ $\frac{1}{30}$ 9. $\sqrt{\dfrac{2500}{49}}$ $\frac{50}{7}$ 10. $\sqrt{\dfrac{9}{1600}}$ $\frac{3}{40}$

An expression that contains a square-root radical is in *simplest form* if

• the radicand contains no square factor other than 1 and no fractions, and
• no denominator contains a radical.

EXAMPLE 1   Simplify: $\sqrt{3000}$

$\sqrt{3000} = \sqrt{100 \cdot 30}$ *The greatest square factor of 3000 is 100.*
$= \sqrt{100} \cdot \sqrt{30}$ *Use the product property of square roots.*
$= 10\sqrt{30}$

From Example 1, you see that the voltage needed by the appliance described at the beginning of the lesson is $10\sqrt{30}$ volts.

12.4 Simplifying Square Roots   **503**

- Some students may have difficulty finding the greatest square factor of a number. Have them review Teaching Aid 15, in the *Teacher's Resource Book*.
- Stress the importance of using absolute values as needed when simplifying radicals with variables. Remind students that if x is negative, then $\sqrt{x}$ is undefined for real numbers.
- In Example 4, some students may have difficulty solving the inequality. Have students check the answer in the original inequality.

Critical Thinking

Predicting Consequences If m is even, then $\sqrt{x^m} = |x^{\frac{m}{2}}|$. What happens when m is odd?   If m is odd, then $\sqrt{x^m} = x^{\frac{m-1}{2}}\sqrt{x}$.

CHALKBOARD EXAMPLES

- **For Example 1**
  Simplify.
  1. $\sqrt{96}$ $4\sqrt{6}$ 2. $\sqrt{363}$ $11\sqrt{3}$
  3. $\sqrt{845}$ $13\sqrt{5}$
  4. $\sqrt{5000}$ $50\sqrt{2}$

- **For Example 2**
  Simplify.
  5. $\sqrt{98x^3}$ $7x\sqrt{2x}$
  6. $\sqrt{75a^8}$ $5|a|^4\sqrt{3}$
  7. $\sqrt{162b^2}$ $9b\sqrt{2}$

- **For Example 3**
  Evaluate each radical for the given value of the variable. Simplify, if possible.
  8. $\sqrt{3x-5}$, $x = 1$
     $\sqrt{-2}$; not a real number
  9. $\sqrt{5x+7}$, $x = 4$ $3\sqrt{3}$

- **For Example 4**
  For what values of m will each radical be a real number?
  10. $\sqrt{-m+4}$ $m \leq 4$
  11. $\sqrt{3-2m}$ $m \leq \frac{3}{2}$

You know that $\sqrt{6^2} = 6$, but $\sqrt{x^2} = x$ is true only when x is positive or zero. For example: $\sqrt{(-6)^2} \neq -6$, since $\sqrt{(-6)^2} = \sqrt{36} = 6$. However, the following property is true for *all* real numbers.

> For any real number n, $\sqrt{n^2} = |n|$.

EXAMPLE 2   Simplify: a. $\sqrt{72y^2}$ **b.** $\sqrt{27x^3}$ **c.** $\sqrt{50a^6}$

a. $\sqrt{72y^2} = \sqrt{36 \cdot 2 \cdot y^2}$ *The greatest perfect square factor of $72y^2$ is $36y^2$.*
$\qquad = \sqrt{36y^2} \cdot \sqrt{2}$ *Product property of square roots*
$\qquad = 6|y|\sqrt{2}$ *Absolute value symbols ensure that $\sqrt{y^2}$ is positive.*

b. $\sqrt{27x^3} = \sqrt{9x^2 \cdot 3x}$ *Find the greatest square factor of $27x^3$.*
$\qquad = \sqrt{9x^2} \cdot \sqrt{3x}$ *Product property of square roots*
$\qquad = 3x\sqrt{3x}$ *No absolute value symbols are needed. If x were negative, $\sqrt{27x^3}$ would be undefined.*

From now on in this text, unless stated otherwise, you can assume that all variables in a radicand are *greater than* or *equal* to zero. Therefore, absolute value notation may be omitted.

c. $\sqrt{50a^6} = \sqrt{25a^6 \cdot 2}$ *Find the greatest square factor of $50a^6$.*
$\qquad = \sqrt{25a^6} \cdot \sqrt{2}$ *Product property of square roots.*
$\qquad = 5a^3\sqrt{2}$

EXAMPLE 3   Evaluate $\sqrt{2n - 10}$:   a. for $n = 3$ b. for $n = 9$

a. $\sqrt{2n - 10}$
$\quad = \sqrt{2 \cdot 3 - 10}$ *Replace n with 3.*
$\quad = \sqrt{6 - 10}$
$\quad = \sqrt{-4}$

For $n = 3$, $\sqrt{2n - 10} = \sqrt{-4}$, which is not a real number.

b. $\sqrt{2n - 10}$
$\quad = \sqrt{2 \cdot 9 - 10}$ *Replace n with 9.*
$\quad = \sqrt{18 - 10}$
$\quad = \sqrt{8}$
$\quad = \sqrt{4} \cdot \sqrt{2}$, or $2\sqrt{2}$

For $n = 9$, $\sqrt{2n - 10} = 2\sqrt{2}$.

To find values of y that make a radical expression like $\sqrt{-2y - 5}$ a real number, find values of y that make the radicand nonnegative.

EXAMPLE 4   For what values of y will $\sqrt{-2y - 5}$ be a real number?

$\qquad -2y - 5 \geq 0$ *The radicand must be nonnegative.*
$\qquad\quad -2y \geq 5$
$\qquad\qquad y \leq -\frac{5}{2}$

For $y \leq -\frac{5}{2}$, $\sqrt{-2y - 5}$ is a real number.

CLASS EXERCISES

Assume that the variable may be positive or negative, then tell why each radical is not in the simplest form and simplify.

1. $\sqrt{20}$ $2\sqrt{5}$
4 is a factor.

2. $\sqrt{27}$ $3\sqrt{3}$
9 is a factor.

3. $\sqrt{18x^3}$ $3|x|\sqrt{2x}$
$9x^2$ is a factor.

4. $\sqrt{45b^4}$ $3b^2\sqrt{5}$
$9b^4$ is a factor.

Evaluate for $a = 3$. Then simplify, if possible.

5. $\sqrt{a+9}$ $2\sqrt{3}$

6. $\sqrt{2a-3}$ $\sqrt{3}$

7. $\sqrt{-5a-10}$
$\sqrt{-25}$; not a real no.

8. $\sqrt{3a-1}$ $2\sqrt{2}$

For what values of x will each radical represent a real number?

9. $\sqrt{3x-9}$ $x \geq 3$

10. $\sqrt{2x+5}$ $x \geq -\frac{5}{2}$

11. $\sqrt{-2x-7}$
$x \leq -\frac{7}{2}$

12. $\sqrt{-x+4}$ $x \leq 4$

PRACTICE EXERCISES

Evaluate for the given value of the variable. Then simplify, if possible.

A **1.** $\sqrt{c-7}$, $c = 15$ $2\sqrt{2}$

2. $\sqrt{5x-6}$, $x = -6$
$\sqrt{-36}$; not a real no.

3. $\sqrt{3a+6}$, $a = 7$ $3\sqrt{3}$

Find the values of x that make each radical expression a real number.

4. $\sqrt{5x-10}$ $x \geq 2$

5. $\sqrt{2x+7}$ $x \geq -\frac{7}{2}$

6. $\sqrt{-4x+2}$ $x \leq \frac{1}{2}$

7. $\sqrt{-3x-9}$
$x \leq -3$

Simplify and assume all variables are greater than or equal to zero.

8. $\sqrt{24}$ $2\sqrt{6}$

9. $\sqrt{48}$ $4\sqrt{3}$

10. $\sqrt{98}$ $7\sqrt{2}$

11. $\sqrt{54}$ $3\sqrt{6}$

12. $\sqrt{288}$ $12\sqrt{2}$

13. $\sqrt{150}$ $5\sqrt{6}$

14. $\sqrt{784}$ 28

15. $\sqrt{1000}$ $10\sqrt{10}$

16. $\sqrt{200x^2}$ $10x\sqrt{2}$

17. $\sqrt{75x^4}$ $5x^2\sqrt{3}$

18. $\sqrt{63x^3}$ $3x\sqrt{7x}$

19. $\sqrt{300x^6}$ $10x^3\sqrt{3}$

20. $\sqrt{8b^8}$ $2b^4\sqrt{2}$

21. $\sqrt{12y^{12}}$ $2y^6\sqrt{3}$

22. $\sqrt{5c^5}$ $c^2\sqrt{5c}$

23. $\sqrt{15d^7}$ $d^3\sqrt{15d}$

24. $-\sqrt{120m^6}$
$-2m^3\sqrt{30}$

25. $-\sqrt{125x^{16}}$ $-5x^8\sqrt{5}$

26. $\sqrt{100b^9}$ $10b^4\sqrt{b}$

27. $\sqrt{144p^8}$ $12p^4$

B **28.** $\sqrt{a^2b}$ $a\sqrt{b}$

29. $\sqrt{x^4y}$ $x^2\sqrt{y}$

30. $\sqrt{m^4n^6}$ m^2n^3

31. $\sqrt{p^{12}q^{10}}$ p^6q^5

32. $\sqrt{320x^5}$ $8x^2\sqrt{5x}$

33. $\sqrt{243x^{13}}$ $9x^6\sqrt{3x}$

34. $-\sqrt{128n^9}$
$-8n^4\sqrt{2n}$

35. $-\sqrt{150a^{11}}$
$-5a^5\sqrt{6a}$

36. $\sqrt{88a^4}$ $2a^2\sqrt{22}$

37. $\sqrt{500r^7}$ $10r^3\sqrt{5r}$

38. $\sqrt{720a^{12}}$ $12a^6\sqrt{5}$

39. $\sqrt{\frac{36}{49}x^5y}$ $\frac{6}{7}x^2\sqrt{xy}$

40. $-\sqrt{\frac{100}{64}a^3}$ $-\frac{5}{4}a\sqrt{a}$

41. $\sqrt{0.09c^5}$ $0.3c^2\sqrt{c}$

42. $\sqrt{0.04p^9}$ $0.2p^4\sqrt{p}$

43. $\sqrt{0.16m^3}$
$0.4m\sqrt{m}$

C **44.** $\sqrt{\sqrt{144}}$ $2\sqrt{3}$

45. $\sqrt{\sqrt{324}}$ $3\sqrt{2}$

46. $\sqrt{\sqrt{625}}$ 5

47. $\sqrt{\sqrt{10,000}}$ 10

48. $\sqrt{x^2+4x+4}$ $x+2$

49. $\sqrt{a^2-6a+9}$ $a-3$

50. $\sqrt{9x^2+6x+1}$ $3x+1$

12.4 Simplifying Square Roots   **505**

LESSON FOLLOW-UP

Assignment Guide

See p. 492B for assignments.

Lesson Quiz

Simplify.
1. $\sqrt{125y^8}$ $5|y|^4\sqrt{5}$
2. $\sqrt{x^5y^2}$ $x^2y\sqrt{x}$

Evaluate each radical for the given value of the variable. Simplify, if possible.
5. $\sqrt{a+3}$, $a = 25$ $2\sqrt{7}$
6. $\sqrt{-2a-6}$, $a = 2$ $\sqrt{-10}$; not a real number

Find the values of x that will make each radical a real number.
7. $\sqrt{-3x+6}$ $x \leq 2$
8. $\sqrt{2x-5}$ $x \geq \frac{5}{2}$

Enrichment

Write $8^{\frac{1}{2}}$ and $a^{\frac{3}{2}}$ using a radical. Simplify. How are these related? $\sqrt{8}$; $2\sqrt{2}$; $\sqrt{a^3}$; $a\sqrt{a}$; both use the rule $a^{\frac{m}{n}} = \sqrt[n]{a^m}$, $8 = 2^3$.

505

Name _____ Date _____
Practice: For use after Lesson 12.4, Algebra 1

Simplifying Square Roots

Evaluate for the given rule of the variable. Then simplify, if possible.

1. $\sqrt{k+3}$, $k=6$ ___ 3
2. $\sqrt{x-1}$, $x=17$ ___ 4
3. $\sqrt{3y+4}$, $y=7$ ___ 5
4. $\sqrt{m+5}$, $m=44$ ___ 7
5. $\sqrt{p-2}$, $p=9$ ___ $\sqrt{7}$
6. $\sqrt{6w+1}$, $w=-2$ ___ not a real number

Find the values of x that make each radical a real number.

7. $\sqrt{2x+1}$ ___ $x \geq -\frac{1}{2}$
8. $\sqrt{4x-3}$ ___ $x \geq \frac{3}{4}$
9. $\sqrt{x+2}$ ___ $x \geq -2$
10. $\sqrt{2x-5}$ ___ $x \geq \frac{5}{2}$

Simplify.

11. $\sqrt{75}$ ___ $5\sqrt{3}$
12. $\sqrt{8}$ ___ $2\sqrt{2}$
13. $\sqrt{27}$ ___ $3\sqrt{3}$
14. $\sqrt{48}$ ___ $4\sqrt{3}$
15. $\sqrt{12}$ ___ $2\sqrt{3}$
16. $\sqrt{250}$ ___ $5\sqrt{10}$
17. $\sqrt{100x^2}$ ___ $10x$
18. $\sqrt{49x^4}$ ___ $7x^2$
19. $\sqrt{64m^6}$ ___ $8m^3$
20. $\sqrt{5c^3}$ ___ $c^2\sqrt{5c}$
21. $\sqrt{9k^{10}}$ ___ $3k^5$
22. $\sqrt{121m^3}$ ___ $11m^2\sqrt{m}$
23. $\sqrt{400z^{13}}$ ___ $20z^6\sqrt{2}$
24. $\sqrt{x^8y}$ ___ x^3y^4
25. $\sqrt{98w^{15}}$ ___ $7w^7\sqrt{2w}$
26. $\sqrt{4x^5y^3w}$ ___ $2x^2y^2\sqrt{xyw}$
27. $\sqrt{144k^9m^3}$ ___ $12k^4m^3\sqrt{km}$
28. $\sqrt{24x^5y^5z^6}$ ___ $2xy^2z^4\sqrt{6xyz}$

Applications

29. **Physics** The formula for the distance a body falls from rest is $d = \frac{1}{2}gt^2$, where d is the distance, g is the force of gravity, and t is the elapsed time. Find t if $g = 32$ ft/s² and $d = 64$ ft. ___ 2s

30. **Geometry** Find the length of the side of a square whose area is 128 in.² ___ 11.31 in.

MIXED PRACTICE

Write each decimal in the form $\frac{m}{n}$ where m and n are integers, $n \neq 0$.

31. 3.8 ___ $\frac{19}{5}$
32. 0.5 ___ $\frac{5}{9}$
33. 0.35 ___ $\frac{35}{99}$

Chapter 12 **11**

12 Chapter 12

Name _____ Date _____
Enrichment: For use after Lesson 12.4, Algebra 1

Perfect Hypercubes

If you multiply an integer by itself four times, the result is a perfect hypercube. For example, the number 256 is perfect hypercube because

$4 \times 4 \times 4 \times 4 = 256$

1. List all the perfect hypercubes between the numbers 1 and 1000.

1, 16, 81, 256, 625

Write the perfect hypercubes for each of the following integers.

2. 8 ___ 4096
3. 10 ___ 10,000
4. 11 ___ 14,641
5. 12 ___ 20,736
6. 15 ___ 50,625
7. 20 ___ 160,000

There are five perfect hypercubes, written either vertically, horizontally, or diagonally hidden in the puzzle below. Find the numbers, and then write each as an integer raised to the fourth power (for example, $256 = 4^4$).

8. ___ $16 = 2^4$
9. ___ $1296 = 6^4$
10. ___ $256 = 4^4$
11. ___ $2401 = 7^4$
12. ___ $6561 = 9^4$

1	6		2
2		2	4
9		5	0
6	5	6	1

13. Listed below are the first nine powers of 10. Circle the numbers that are perfect hypercubes.

10   100   1,800   (10,000)   100,000   1,000,000
10,000,000   (100,000,000)   1,000,000,000

14. Based on your observations, devise a shortcut for determining whether a power of ten is a perfect hypercube.

The power of ten and the number of 0s must be a multiple of 4.

15. Use your method to predict the next power of 10 that is a perfect hypercube.

10^{12}, or 1,000,000,000,000

Applications

51. **Physics** A formula in physics that can be used to determine the velocity v in feet per second of an object (neglecting air resistance) after it has fallen a certain distance is $v = \sqrt{64h}$, where h is the distance the object has fallen in feet. Find the velocity of an object after it has fallen 128 ft. $64\sqrt{2}$ ft/sec

52. **Geometry** Find the length of a side of a square whose area is 125 in.². $5\sqrt{5}$ in.

53. **Physics** The formula $T = 2\pi\sqrt{\dfrac{L}{32}}$ gives the time T (in seconds) required for a pendulum to make one complete swing back and forth. If L is 8 ft (the length of the pendulum), how long does it take the pendulum to make one complete swing? π sec

ALGEBRA IN POLICE SCIENCE

Did you know that the approximate speed of a car prior to an accident can be determined from the skid marks left by the car? An investigating officer will use the formula $S = 2\sqrt{5f}$, where S represents the speed in mi/h and f represents the length of the skid mark in ft.

EXAMPLE An automobile involved in an accident left skid marks 135 ft in length. What was the approximate speed of the car prior to the accident?

$S = 2\sqrt{5f}$
$S = 2\sqrt{5(135)}$ *Substitute the value that you know.*
$S = 2\sqrt{675}$ *Simplify.*
$\quad = 2\sqrt{3(9)(25)}$
$\quad = 30\sqrt{3}$
$S \approx 30(1.73) \approx 51.9$ *Use an approximation for $\sqrt{3}$.*

So, the approximate speed of the car was 51.9 mi/h.

Give the approximate speed of the car, to the nearest whole mi/h, for each of the following skid marks.

1. 25 ft
22 mi/h
2. 80 ft
40 mi/h
3. 125 ft
50 mi/h
4. 175 ft
59 mi/h
5. 200 ft
63 mi/h

506 Chapter 12 Radicals

APPLICATION:
Image Formation

Did you know that photography, the art of taking quality photographs, involves many mathematical computations that people often take for granted? One such calculation concerns the focal length of a camera. The focal length of a camera is the distance between the center of the lens and the focal point. The size of the image formed on the film depends upon the focal length of the lens. The shorter the focal length of the lens, the smaller the image.

A formula can be used to find the focal length of a camera lens:

$$\frac{1}{p} + \frac{1}{q} = \frac{1}{f}$$

where p is the object distance, q the image distance, and f the focal length.

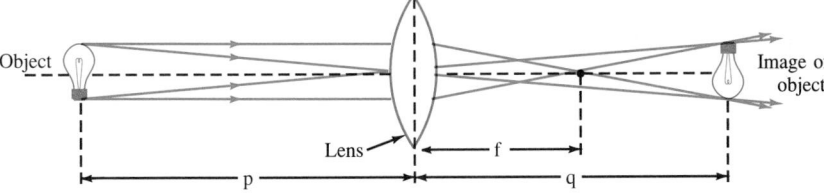

When an object is placed on one side of a converging lens beyond the principal focus, a real image will be formed on the opposite side of the lens. If the object is moved closer to the focal point, the image will be formed farther away from the lens and will be bigger. One way of accurately determining the position of an image is to use the lens formula.

If a camera with an image distance of 4 cm is held 64 cm from an object, what is the focal length of the camera?

$$\frac{1}{64} + \frac{1}{4} = \frac{1}{f}; \quad f = \frac{64}{17} \approx 3.76$$

The focal length is approximately 4 cm.

Application
Students are introduced to the way mathematics is integrated into many professions like photography. They are shown how mathematical formulas are used to calculate the focal length of a camera lens. This method of solving problems involving focal length is then extended to solving problems using a nomogram. Using a nomogram is an alternate method of solving certain types of equations.

See *Teacher's Resource Book,* Follow-up Application, p. 33.

Another way to solve problems of the form $\frac{1}{a} + \frac{1}{b} = \frac{1}{c}$ is to use a **nomogram.** A nomogram is a graph which usually contains three scales graduated for different variables.

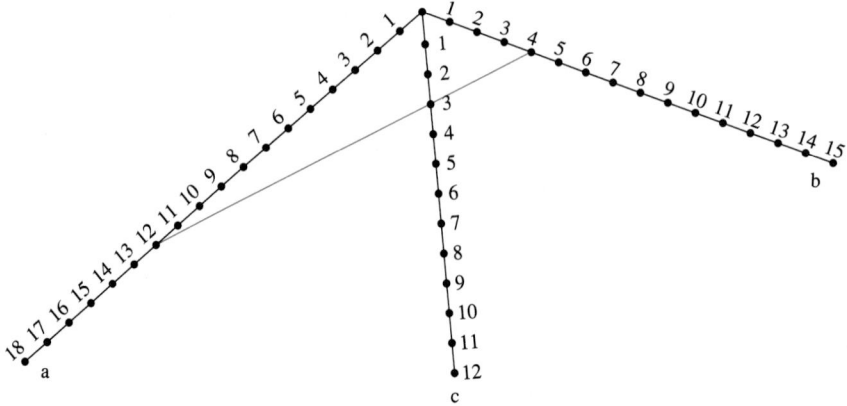

When a straight line connects values of any two points, the related value may be read directly from the third at the point intersected by the line. For example, to solve $\frac{1}{12} + \frac{1}{4} = \frac{1}{c}$, follow these steps:

- Copy the nomogram above.
- Locate the point 12 on the *a* scale.
- Locate the point 4 on the *b* scale.
- Connect them with a straight line.

Notice that this line intersects the *c* scale at the point 3. Thus, it is clear from the nomogram that $\frac{1}{12} + \frac{1}{4} = \frac{1}{3}$. How would you check this?

Use your Nomogram in the manner shown to solve each of the following. Check your answers algebraically.

1. $\frac{1}{6} + \frac{1}{3} = \frac{1}{c}$ 2

2. $\frac{1}{15} + \frac{1}{b} = \frac{1}{6}$ 10

3. $\frac{1}{a} + \frac{1}{9} = \frac{1}{6}$ 18

4. A camera with an image distance of 5 cm is held 70 cm from an object. What is the focal length of the camera? $\frac{14}{3}$ cm

5. Mike took a picture of an object that was 66 cm away. His camera has a focal length of $\frac{66}{23}$ cm. What is the image distance of the picture? 3 cm

Addition and Subtraction of Radicals

Objective: To simplify sums and differences of radicals

LESSON PLAN

Vocabulary
Like radicals
Unlike radicals

Materials/Manipulatives
Calculators
Overhead projector

Adding and subtracting radical expressions is very similar to adding and subtracting *similar terms* of polynomials. Like radicals are like similar terms.

Like Radicals	Unlike Radicals
$-\sqrt{3}$ and $-2\sqrt{3}$	$\sqrt{3}$ and $\sqrt{7}$
$5\sqrt{x}$ and $6\sqrt{x}$	$-\sqrt{x}$ and $2\sqrt{y}$

Capsule Review

EXAMPLES   **a.** $-x^2y + 5x^2y = 4x^2y$ **b.** $4mn^2 + 3m^2n$

Like terms   Unlike terms cannot
be combined.

Simplify. If not possible, explain why.

1. $12m^3 - 9m^3$ $3m^3$

2. $3a^2b + 6a^2b$ $9a^2b$

3. $r^2s - 4rs^2$ unlike terms

4. $5x + 2x^2 - 2x + x^2$
$3x^2 + 3x$

5. $3y^3 - y + 2y^3 + 8y$
$5y^3 + 7y$

6. $9a^2b^3 - 8b^3 + 2a^2$
unlike terms

BACKGROUND

In the Capsule Review, the exercises focus on adding and subtracting monomials. Students who are having difficulty should review Lessons 2.4 and 6.6. In this lesson, students learn to add and subtract radical expressions. They learn to group like radicals just as they learned to combine like terms previously.

You add or subtract radicals in the same way you combine like terms; that is, you use the distributive property.

EXAMPLE 1   **Simplify:** $\sqrt{3} - 2\sqrt{5} + 5\sqrt{3}$.

$$\sqrt{3} - 2\sqrt{5} + 5\sqrt{3}$$
$$= (\sqrt{3} + 5\sqrt{3}) - 2\sqrt{5} \qquad \textit{Group like radicals.}$$
$$= (1 + 5)\sqrt{3} - 2\sqrt{5} \qquad \textit{Use the distributive property.}$$
$$= 6\sqrt{3} - 2\sqrt{5}$$

TEACHING SUGGESTIONS

- Point out how the distributive property is used to simplify sums and differences of radicals. In Example 1, you may wish to draw an analogy with simplifying polynomials using an overhead projector.
- Stress that you should simplify radicals before combining like radicals.
- Remind students that when working with radicals here we assume all variables represent nonnegative numbers.

The expression $6\sqrt{3} - 2\sqrt{5}$ is in its simplest radical form since $6\sqrt{3}$ and $2\sqrt{5}$ are unlike radicals and therefore, cannot be combined. As with other expressions like $2x - 3x$, you can add or subtract radicals if they are similar. Two or more radicals are similar if their radicands are identical. In all other cases the radicals are dissimilar or unlike.

In Example 2, to add or subtract some radicals, you must write each one in simplest form. Then, you can combine the like radicals.

12.5 Addition and Subtraction of Radicals   **509**

Critical Thinking

Comparing-Contrasting Compare and contrast Examples 2 and 3. Answers may vary. Differ: Example 2 has no variable, whereas Example 3 does; Example 2 simplifies to two terms, whereas Example 3 simplifies to one. Alike: Each term is written in simplest form, terms are regrouped, and like terms are combined.

CHALKBOARD EXAMPLES

For Exercises 1–3, simplify.

- **For Example 1**
  1. $4\sqrt{2} + \sqrt{2} - 2\sqrt{5}$ $5\sqrt{2} - 2\sqrt{5}$

- **For Example 2**
  2. $5\sqrt{12} - \sqrt{48} - 2\sqrt{27}$ 0

- **For Example 3**
  3. $\sqrt{54ab^2} - 2\sqrt{6ab^2} + \sqrt{24ab^2}$ $3b\sqrt{6a}$

Common Error

- In simplifying sums and differences of radicals, students sometimes think that they can add or subtract radicands. Caution students that $3\sqrt{5} + 5\sqrt{3} \ne 8\sqrt{8}$.
- See *Teacher's Resource Book* for additional remediation.

LESSON FOLLOW-UP

Assignment Guide

- See p. 492B for assignments.
- You may have students use a calculator to simplify Practice Exercises 1–12.

Lesson Quiz

Perform the indicated operations. Assume that all variables represent positive real numbers.
1. $2\sqrt{3} - 3\sqrt{7} - 5\sqrt{3}$
   $-3\sqrt{3} - 3\sqrt{7}$
2. $2\sqrt{28} + \sqrt{63} - 3\sqrt{112}$
   $-5\sqrt{7}$
3. $\sqrt{64b^3} - \sqrt{25b^3} - \sqrt{4b^3}$
   $b\sqrt{b}$
4. $\sqrt{72m^3n^2} + \sqrt{98m^3n^2} - 2\sqrt{50m^3n^2}$ $3mn\sqrt{2m}$

510

EXAMPLE 2 Simplify: $\sqrt{54} + 2\sqrt{40} - 3\sqrt{96}$.

$$\begin{aligned}
&\sqrt{54} + 2\sqrt{40} - 3\sqrt{96} \\
&= \sqrt{9 \cdot 6} + 2\sqrt{4 \cdot 10} - 3\sqrt{16 \cdot 6} \quad &&\textit{Write each radical in} \\
&= 3\sqrt{6} + 2 \cdot 2\sqrt{10} - 3 \cdot 4\sqrt{6} \quad &&\textit{simplest form.} \\
&= 3\sqrt{6} + 4\sqrt{10} - 12\sqrt{6} \\
&= (3\sqrt{6} - 12\sqrt{6}) + 4\sqrt{10} \quad &&\textit{Group like radicals.} \\
&= (3 - 12)\sqrt{6} + 4\sqrt{10} \quad &&\textit{Use the distributive property.} \\
&= -9\sqrt{6} + 4\sqrt{10}
\end{aligned}$$

Recall that, you may assume all radicals with variables represent nonnegative numbers unless stated otherwise.

EXAMPLE 3 Simplify: $\sqrt{18x^2y} - \sqrt{8x^2y} + \sqrt{50x^2y}$.

$$\begin{aligned}
&\sqrt{18x^2y} - \sqrt{8x^2y} + \sqrt{50x^2y} \\
&= \sqrt{9x^2 \cdot 2y} - \sqrt{4x^2 \cdot 2y} + \sqrt{25x^2 \cdot 2y} \\
&= 3x\sqrt{2y} - 2x\sqrt{2y} + 5x\sqrt{2y} \\
&= (3x - 2x + 5x)\sqrt{2y} \\
&= 6x\sqrt{2y}
\end{aligned}$$

CLASS EXERCISES

Simplify. Assume that all variables represent nonnegative real numbers.

1. $5\sqrt{2} + \sqrt{2}$ $6\sqrt{2}$ 2. $\sqrt{3} - 4\sqrt{3}$ $-3\sqrt{3}$ 3. $-5\sqrt{a} + 2\sqrt{a}$ $-3\sqrt{a}$

4. $\sqrt{x} - 6\sqrt{x}$ $-5\sqrt{x}$ 5. $\sqrt{6} - 4\sqrt{6}$ $-3\sqrt{6}$ 6. $-\sqrt{10} + \sqrt{7} - 3\sqrt{7}$ $-\sqrt{10} - 2\sqrt{7}$

7. $\sqrt{16y} - \sqrt{y}$ $3\sqrt{y}$ 8. $-5\sqrt{b} + \sqrt{4b}$ $-3\sqrt{b}$ 9. $\sqrt{75} + 2\sqrt{27} - \sqrt{12}$ $9\sqrt{3}$

10. $-\sqrt{80} - 3\sqrt{45} + \sqrt{20}$ $-11\sqrt{5}$ 11. $\sqrt{12x^3} + 2\sqrt{27x^3}$ $8x\sqrt{3x}$ 12. $2\sqrt{28y^3} + \sqrt{63y^3}$ $7y\sqrt{7y}$

PRACTICE EXERCISES

Perform the indicated operations. Assume that all variables represent nonnegative real numbers and simplify.

A   1. $8\sqrt{5} - 3\sqrt{5}$ $5\sqrt{5}$ 2. $-2\sqrt{2} - \sqrt{2}$ $-3\sqrt{2}$ 3. $6\sqrt{10} + \sqrt{10}$ $7\sqrt{10}$

4. $-4\sqrt{7} + 3\sqrt{7}$ $-\sqrt{7}$ 5. $2\sqrt{27} + 3\sqrt{16}$ $6\sqrt{3} + 12$ 6. $3\sqrt{18} - \sqrt{25}$ $9\sqrt{2} - 5$

7. $6\sqrt{3} - 4\sqrt{5} - \sqrt{3}$ $5\sqrt{3} - 4\sqrt{5}$ 8. $-\sqrt{7} - 7\sqrt{3} + 4\sqrt{7}$ $3\sqrt{7} - 7\sqrt{3}$

9. $\sqrt{8} + 2\sqrt{50} - \sqrt{18}$ $9\sqrt{2}$ 10. $2\sqrt{12} - \sqrt{48} + 3\sqrt{27}$ $9\sqrt{3}$

11. $8\sqrt{72} - 3\sqrt{8} - \sqrt{98}$ $35\sqrt{2}$ 12. $-5\sqrt{80} + \sqrt{125} + 10\sqrt{45}$ $15\sqrt{5}$

13. $\sqrt{9x} - \sqrt{16x} + \sqrt{25x}$ $4\sqrt{x}$ 14. $3\sqrt{36a} + \sqrt{100a} - 2\sqrt{64a}$ $12\sqrt{a}$

510   Chapter 12 Radicals

15. $\sqrt{12x} - \sqrt{27x} + \sqrt{48x}$ $3\sqrt{3x}$ **16.** $\sqrt{18y} - 2\sqrt{32y} - \sqrt{50y}$ $-10\sqrt{2y}$

17. $4\sqrt{54} - \sqrt{6} + 5\sqrt{24}$ $21\sqrt{6}$ **18.** $2\sqrt{250} - 3\sqrt{640} - 5\sqrt{10}$ $-19\sqrt{10}$

B   **19.** $\sqrt{100x^2y} - \sqrt{144x^2y} - 5\sqrt{x^2y}$ $-7x\sqrt{y}$ **20.** $-3\sqrt{81ab^2} + 2\sqrt{ab^2} - 5\sqrt{9ab^2}$
                                                                                      $-40b\sqrt{a}$

21. $\sqrt{72xy^2} - 2\sqrt{98xy^2}$ $-8y\sqrt{2x}$ **22.** $-3\sqrt{125c^4d} + \sqrt{80c^4d}$ $-11c^2\sqrt{5d}$

23. $4\sqrt{320a^3} - 2\sqrt{180a^3}$ $20a\sqrt{5a}$ **24.** $\sqrt{44x^5} + \sqrt{99x^5}$ $5x^2\sqrt{11x}$

25. $\sqrt{175a^2b} - 3\sqrt{112a^2b}$ $-7a\sqrt{7b}$ **26.** $-5\sqrt{192rs^3} + 2\sqrt{300rs^3}$ $-20s\sqrt{3rs}$

27. $5\sqrt{176} - 3\sqrt{99} + 4\sqrt{162}$ $11\sqrt{11} + 36\sqrt{2}$ **28.** $-3\sqrt{200} + 2\sqrt{147} - \sqrt{338}$
                                                                                  $-43\sqrt{2} + 14\sqrt{3}$

29. $\sqrt{\dfrac{3}{4}} - 2\sqrt{\dfrac{3}{4}}$ $-\dfrac{1}{2}\sqrt{3}$ **30.** $-3\sqrt{\dfrac{5}{16}} - 5\sqrt{\dfrac{5}{16}}$ $-2\sqrt{5}$

31. $\sqrt{\dfrac{5xy^2}{9}} - \sqrt{\dfrac{5xy^2}{4}}$ $-\dfrac{y}{6}\sqrt{5x}$ **32.** $-\sqrt{\dfrac{5t^3}{16}} + \sqrt{\dfrac{5t^3}{36}}$ $-\dfrac{t}{12}\sqrt{5t}$

C   **33.** $a\sqrt{ab^3} + ab\sqrt{ab} - b\sqrt{a^3b}$ $ab\sqrt{ab}$ **34.** $3x\sqrt{25x^3} - x\sqrt{4x^3} + 3x\sqrt{9x^3}$
                                                                                    $22x^2\sqrt{x}$

35. $y\sqrt{8x^5} + xy\sqrt{18x^3} - x\sqrt{50x^3y^2}$ 0 **36.** $a\sqrt{27a^3} - b\sqrt{48b^3} - a^2\sqrt{75a}$
                                                                                    $-2a^2\sqrt{3a} - 4b^2\sqrt{3b}$

Applications

37. Geometry   Find the perimeter of a square whose side has a length of $\sqrt{125}$ cm. $20\sqrt{5}$ cm

38. Geometry   Find the perimeter of a triangle whose sides measure $4\sqrt{2}$ cm, $4\sqrt{6}$ cm, and $8\sqrt{2}$ cm.
$12\sqrt{2} + 4\sqrt{6}$ cm

BIOGRAPHY

Amalie (Emmy) Noether, born in Erlanger, Germany, on March 23, 1882, is considered to be the most creative abstract algebraist of modern times. In 1907, she earned her Ph.D. degree *summa cum laude* from the University of Erlanger. In 1915 she went to the University of Göttingen, where she was persuaded to remain by the eminent mathematicians *David Hilbert* and *Felix Klein.*

The real extent of her work cannot be accurately judged from her papers, because much of her work during this period appeared in the publications of her students and colleagues. In 1933 Noether left Germany for the United States, where she became a visiting professor of mathematics at Bryn Mawr College in Pennsylvania. She also lectured and conducted research at the Institute for Advanced Study in Princeton, New Jersey. The names of Noether, Hilbert, and Klein are among the most prominent of those active in establishing new frontiers in modern mathematics. Research one of these mathematicians and be prepared to present your findings in a group discussion.
Answers may vary.

Teacher's Resource Book
Reteaching—Chapter 12, p. 13

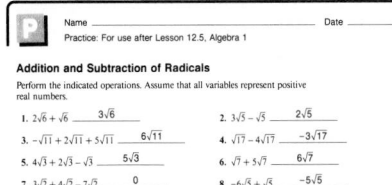

BACKGROUND

In the Capsule Review, students review simplifying radicals with and without variables. You may want to ask students why the variables represent nonnegative numbers. In this lesson, students multiply radicals with and without variables and then write the product in simplest form.

Critical Thinking

Reasoning by Analogies Two properties of real numbers involving square roots have been discussed. When n is a real number, $\sqrt{n^2} = |n|$ and $(\sqrt{n})^2 = n$, if $n \geq 0$. What, if any, conclusions can you derive from these properties? When n is restricted to nonnegative real numbers, $n \geq 0$, $\sqrt{n^2} = (\sqrt{n})^2$.

12.6

Multiplication of Radicals

Objective: To simplify products of radicals

To simplify expressions containing square roots, you used the product property of square roots: $\sqrt{mn} = \sqrt{m} \cdot \sqrt{n}$ for any real numbers where $m \geq 0$, $n \geq 0$.

According to the *symmetric property of equality*, $\sqrt{m} \cdot \sqrt{n} = \sqrt{mn}$. This means that you can use the product property to multiply radicals.

Capsule Review

Simplify. Assume that the variables represent nonnegative real numbers.

1. $\sqrt{625}$ 25   **2.** $\sqrt{900}$ 30   **3.** $\sqrt{54}$ $3\sqrt{6}$ **4.** $\sqrt{63}$ $3\sqrt{7}$

5. $\sqrt{r^4 s^5}$ $r^2 s^2 \sqrt{s}$ **6.** $\sqrt{a^3 b^{10}}$ $ab^5\sqrt{a}$ **7.** $\sqrt{8x^3 y^7}$ $2xy^3\sqrt{2xy}$ **8.** $\sqrt{27c^2 d}$ $3c\sqrt{3d}$

The *commutative* and *associative properties* for multiplication are also used when multiplying radicals.

EXAMPLE 1   **Multiply and simplify:** $2\sqrt{6} \cdot 3\sqrt{2}$

$$
\begin{aligned}
2\sqrt{6} \cdot 3\sqrt{2} &= (2 \cdot 3) \cdot (\sqrt{6} \cdot \sqrt{2}) &&\textit{Commutative and associative properties}\\
&= 6 \cdot (\sqrt{6} \cdot \sqrt{2}) &&\sqrt{m} \cdot \sqrt{n} = \sqrt{mn}\\
&= 6\sqrt{12}\\
&= 6\sqrt{4 \cdot 3} &&\textit{Simplify: } \sqrt{12}\\
&= 6\sqrt{4} \cdot \sqrt{3} &&\sqrt{mn} = \sqrt{m} \cdot \sqrt{n}\\
&= 6 \cdot 2\sqrt{3} = 12\sqrt{3}
\end{aligned}
$$

It is sometimes easier to simplify a radical before you multiply.

EXAMPLE 2   **Simplify:** $-5\sqrt{8x} \cdot 4\sqrt{3x}$

$$
\begin{aligned}
-5\sqrt{8x} \cdot 4\sqrt{3x} &= (-5 \cdot 4) \cdot (\sqrt{8x} \cdot \sqrt{3x})\\
&= -20 \cdot (\sqrt{4 \cdot 2x} \cdot \sqrt{3x}) &&\textit{Simplify: } \sqrt{8x}\\
&= -20 \cdot 2\sqrt{2x} \cdot \sqrt{3x} &&\sqrt{4 \cdot 2x} = \sqrt{4} \cdot \sqrt{2x} = 2\sqrt{2x}\\
&= -40\sqrt{6x^2} &&\sqrt{2x} \cdot \sqrt{3x} = \sqrt{6x^2}\\
&= -40\sqrt{x^2} \cdot \sqrt{6} &&\textit{Simplify: } \sqrt{6x^2}\\
&= -40x\sqrt{6}
\end{aligned}
$$

512   Chapter 12 Radicals

You can also use the distributive property to simplify products of expressions that contain radicals.

EXAMPLE 3 Simplify: $\sqrt{2}(5 + 3\sqrt{6})$

$$\begin{aligned}
\sqrt{2}(5 + 3\sqrt{6}) &= \sqrt{2} \cdot 5 + \sqrt{2} \cdot 3\sqrt{6} \qquad \textit{Use the distributive property.}\\
&= 5\sqrt{2} + 3\sqrt{12}\\
&= 5\sqrt{2} + 3\sqrt{4} \cdot \sqrt{3} \qquad \textit{Simplify: } 3\sqrt{12}\\
&= 5\sqrt{2} + 3 \cdot 2\sqrt{3}\\
&= 5\sqrt{2} + 6\sqrt{3}
\end{aligned}$$

In this example, notice that $5\sqrt{2} + 6\sqrt{3}$ is in simplest form because $\sqrt{2}$ and $\sqrt{3}$ are unlike radicals.

Recall that you used the FOIL method to multiply two binomials. You can also use FOIL to multiply binomials that contain radicals.

EXAMPLE 4 Simplify: $(2 + 3\sqrt{7})(3 - 2\sqrt{7})$

$$(2 + 3\sqrt{7})(3 - 2\sqrt{7}) = (2 + 3\sqrt{7})(3 - 2\sqrt{7})$$

$$\begin{aligned}
&= 2 \cdot 3 - 2 \cdot 2\sqrt{7} + 3\sqrt{7} \cdot 3 - 3\sqrt{7} \cdot 2\sqrt{7}\\
&= 6 - 4\sqrt{7} + 9\sqrt{7} - 6\sqrt{7} \cdot \sqrt{7}\\
&= 6 + 5\sqrt{7} - 6(\sqrt{7})^2 \qquad \textit{Combine like radicals.}\\
&= 6 + 5\sqrt{7} - 6 \cdot 7 \qquad \textit{Simplify: } (\sqrt{7})^2\\
&= -36 + 5\sqrt{7}
\end{aligned}$$

In this example, notice that $\sqrt{7} \cdot \sqrt{7} = 7$, since $\sqrt{7} \cdot \sqrt{7} = (\sqrt{7})^2$. This suggests the following property.

> For all nonnegative real numbers n, $(\sqrt{n})^2 = n$.

EXAMPLE 5 Simplify: $(2 + \sqrt{3})(2 - \sqrt{3})$

$$\begin{aligned}
(2 + \sqrt{3})(2 - \sqrt{3}) &= 2^2 - (\sqrt{3})^2 \qquad \textit{Recall: } (m + n)(m - n) = m^2 - n^2\\
&= 4 - 3\\
&= 1
\end{aligned}$$

12.6 Multiplication of Radicals **513**

514

Common Errors

- When multiplying radicals, students sometimes forget to simplify. Some students may benefit from keeping a table of perfect squares for reference.
- Students sometimes forget to combine like terms when multiplying binomials containing radicals. For example, in Example 4, remind students that $-4\sqrt{7}$ and $9\sqrt{7}$ are like radicals and must be combined if the answer is to be expressed in simplest form. Review multiplying polynomials.
- Draw parallels between multiplying expressions with polynomials and multiplying expressions with radicals.
- See *Teacher's Resource Book* for additional remediation.

LESSON FOLLOW-UP

Assignment Guide

- See p. 492B for assignments.
- See *Teacher's Resource Book,* for Critical Thinking activity, p. 12.

Test Yourself

See *Teacher's Resource Book, Tests,* pp. 121–122.

Lesson Quiz

Multiply and simplify.
1. $-3\sqrt{6} \cdot 2\sqrt{3}$ $-18\sqrt{2}$
2. $4\sqrt{7y} \cdot \sqrt{8y}$ $8y\sqrt{14}$
3. $\sqrt{2}(2 - 3\sqrt{6})$ $2\sqrt{2} - 6\sqrt{3}$
4. $(3\sqrt{5}) - 4)(2\sqrt{5} + 1)$ $26 - 5\sqrt{5}$
5. $(\sqrt{2} + 3)(\sqrt{2} - 3)$ -7

Enrichment

Assume that a, b, and c are rational numbers, $c \geq 0$, and c is not a square of an integer. Are $b\sqrt{c}$, $a + \sqrt{c}$, and $a + b\sqrt{c}$ rational or irrational numbers? Explain. All are irrational. None can be written in the form $\frac{m}{n}$ where m and n are integers and $n \neq 0$.

CLASS EXERCISES

Multiply and simplify.

1. $\sqrt{5} \cdot \sqrt{10}$ $5\sqrt{2}$
2. $(\sqrt{2})(-\sqrt{6})$ $-2\sqrt{3}$
3. $(3\sqrt{2})^2$ 18
4. $(-5\sqrt{3})^2$ 75
5. $-2\sqrt{7y} \cdot 3\sqrt{8y}$ $-12y\sqrt{14}$
6. $\sqrt{2x} \cdot \sqrt{24x}$ $4x\sqrt{3}$
7. $-\sqrt{3}(5 + 2\sqrt{3})$ $-5\sqrt{3} - 6$
8. $\sqrt{2}(2\sqrt{6} - 3)$ $4\sqrt{3} - 3\sqrt{2}$
9. $(5 - 2\sqrt{6})(2 + 3\sqrt{6})$ $-26 + 11\sqrt{6}$
10. $(4 + 3\sqrt{7})(3 - 4\sqrt{7})$ $-72 - 7\sqrt{7}$
11. $(3 - \sqrt{5})(3 + \sqrt{5})$ 4
12. $(\sqrt{3} - 7)(\sqrt{3} + 7)$ -46

For Discussion

13. In Example 5, $(2 + \sqrt{3})(2 - \sqrt{3}) = 1$, which is a rational number. Explain why the product of two binomials of the form $a + \sqrt{b}$ and $a - \sqrt{b}$ is always rational. The sum of the two terms that contain irrational numbers, $-a\sqrt{b}$ and $a\sqrt{b}$, will always be zero.
14. Explain and show how multiplying radical expressions is like multiplying polynomials. See below.

PRACTICE EXERCISES

Multiply and simplify.

A
1. $\sqrt{2} \cdot \sqrt{8}$ 4
2. $\sqrt{12} \cdot \sqrt{3}$ 6
3. $\sqrt{4} \cdot \sqrt{3}$ $2\sqrt{3}$
4. $\sqrt{25} \cdot \sqrt{2}$ $5\sqrt{2}$
5. $(\sqrt{7})^2$ 7
6. $(-\sqrt{5})^2$ 5
7. $3\sqrt{50} \cdot \sqrt{2}$ 30
8. $2\sqrt{3} \cdot \sqrt{30}$ $6\sqrt{10}$
9. $-5\sqrt{6} \cdot 2\sqrt{3}$ $-30\sqrt{2}$
10. $3\sqrt{3} \cdot 5\sqrt{15}$ $45\sqrt{5}$
11. $2\sqrt{7} \cdot 3\sqrt{3}$ $6\sqrt{21}$
12. $-5\sqrt{5} \cdot 4\sqrt{6}$ $-20\sqrt{30}$
13. $3\sqrt{5} \cdot 4\sqrt{70}$ $60\sqrt{14}$
14. $7\sqrt{14} \cdot 2\sqrt{7}$ $98\sqrt{2}$
15. $\sqrt{\frac{3}{5}} \cdot \sqrt{\frac{5}{3}}$ 1
16. $\sqrt{\frac{9}{2}} \cdot \sqrt{\frac{2}{3}}$ $\sqrt{3}$
17. $3\sqrt{12x} \cdot 2\sqrt{2x}$ $12x\sqrt{6}$
18. $6\sqrt{5a} \cdot 4\sqrt{10a}$ $120a\sqrt{2}$
19. $(3\sqrt{n})^2$ $9n$
20. $(-2\sqrt{m})^2$ $4m$

B
21. $\sqrt{3}(4 + \sqrt{3})$ $4\sqrt{3} + 3$
22. $\sqrt{5}(\sqrt{5} - 3)$ $5 - 3\sqrt{5}$
23. $\sqrt{6}(\sqrt{6} - 2)$ $6 - 2\sqrt{6}$
24. $\sqrt{2}(2 + \sqrt{2})$ $2\sqrt{2} + 2$
25. $(3\sqrt{2} + 1)(2\sqrt{2} - 3)$ $9 - 7\sqrt{2}$
26. $(5 - 4\sqrt{3})(4 + 5\sqrt{3})$ $-40 + 9\sqrt{3}$
27. $(6 - \sqrt{7})(6 + \sqrt{7})$ 29
28. $(\sqrt{3} - 4)(\sqrt{3} + 4)$ -13
29. $\sqrt{2ab} \cdot 3\sqrt{6ab}$ $6ab\sqrt{3}$
30. $-2\sqrt{8xy} \cdot \sqrt{3xy}$ $-4xy\sqrt{6}$
31. $\sqrt{c^2d} \cdot \sqrt{de^3}$ $cde\sqrt{e}$
32. $\sqrt{a^5b} \cdot \sqrt{bc^5}$ $a^2bc^2\sqrt{ac}$
33. $5a\sqrt{\frac{a}{b}} \cdot \sqrt{\frac{a}{b}}$ $\frac{5a^2}{b}$
34. $3r\sqrt{\frac{4r}{s}} \cdot \sqrt{\frac{r}{s}}$ $\frac{6r^2}{s}$
35. $(3\sqrt{7} + 2)^2$ $67 + 12\sqrt{7}$
36. $(5 - 2\sqrt{6})^2$ $49 - 20\sqrt{6}$

C
37. $(3 - \sqrt{3})(4 + \sqrt{2})$ $12 + 3\sqrt{2} - 4\sqrt{3} - \sqrt{6}$
38. $(\sqrt{5} + 2)(\sqrt{6} - 4)$ $\sqrt{30} - 4\sqrt{5} + 2\sqrt{6} - 8$
39. $(\sqrt{x} + 2\sqrt{y})^2$ $x + 4\sqrt{xy} + 4y$
40. $(5\sqrt{u} + 2\sqrt{v})^2$ $25u + 20\sqrt{uv} + 4v$
41. $(2\sqrt{m} - 3\sqrt{n})(4\sqrt{m} + \sqrt{n})$ $8m - 10\sqrt{mn} - 3n$
42. $(\sqrt{x} + 4\sqrt{y})(5\sqrt{x} - 2\sqrt{y})$ $5x + 18\sqrt{xy} - 8y$

514   Chapter 12 Radicals

Additional Answers
Class Exercises
14. Multiplying radical expressions is like multiplying a binomial. The FOIL method may be used when multiplying radical expressions. For example, $(2 + \sqrt{5})(2 - \sqrt{5}) = 4 - 2\sqrt{5} + 2\sqrt{5} - 5 = 4 - 5 = -1$.

Applications

Geometry Find the area of each of the following figures. Express answers in simplest form.

43. A triangle whose base is $2\sqrt{3}$ m and whose height is $2\sqrt{2}$ m. $2\sqrt{6}$ m²

44. A rectangle whose length measures $\dfrac{5\sqrt{2} + 3}{3}$ cm and whose width measures $\dfrac{3\sqrt{2} - 2}{5}$ cm. $\dfrac{24 - \sqrt{2}}{15}$ cm²

45. A square whose side is $4\sqrt{x}$ ft. $16x$ ft²

46. A trapezoid whose height and upper base each are $\sqrt{x}$ m and whose lower base is $2\sqrt{y}$ m. $\left[\text{Hint: } A = \dfrac{1}{2}h(b_1 + b_2)\right]$ $\dfrac{1}{2}x + \sqrt{xy}$ m²

Number Problems Write an equation for each word sentence. Do not solve.

47. The square root of a number squared is 12. $\sqrt{x^2} = 12$

48. The product of 20 and the square root of the sum of 5 and some number is equal to 100. $20\sqrt{5 + x} = 100$

49. When 3 is subtracted from the square root of the product of 2 and some number the result is 7. $\sqrt{2x} - 3 = 7$

50. The product of 4 and the square root of the product of 3 and some number is 24. $4\sqrt{3x} = 24$

TEST YOURSELF

Approximate the square root using the divide-and-average method. 12.2

1. $\sqrt{45}$ 6.71

2. $\sqrt{80}$ 8.94

Write each rational number as a common fraction. 12.3

3. $0.\overline{3}$ $\dfrac{1}{3}$

4. $0.\overline{12}$ $\dfrac{4}{33}$

Simplify. 12.1, 12.4

5. $\sqrt{196}$ 14

6. $-\sqrt{90{,}000}$ -300

7. $\sqrt{\dfrac{25}{16}}$ $\dfrac{5}{4}$

8. $\pm\sqrt{\dfrac{4}{81}}$ $\pm\dfrac{2}{9}$

9. $-\sqrt{48}$ $-4\sqrt{3}$

10. $\sqrt{63y^2}$ $3y\sqrt{7}$

11. $\sqrt{25x^3}$ $5x\sqrt{x}$

12. $\sqrt{\dfrac{64}{9}}$ $\dfrac{8}{3}$

Perform the indicated operations. 12.5–12.6

13. $6\sqrt{2} - 4\sqrt{7} - \sqrt{2}$ $5\sqrt{2} - 4\sqrt{7}$

14. $\sqrt{8} - 2\sqrt{50} + \sqrt{18}$ $-5\sqrt{2}$

15. $3\sqrt{6} \cdot 4\sqrt{2}$ $24\sqrt{3}$

16. $\sqrt{3}(2 - 2\sqrt{6})$ $2\sqrt{3} - 6\sqrt{2}$

12.6 Multiplication of Radicals **515**

Teacher's Resource Book
Reteaching—Chapter 12, p. 16

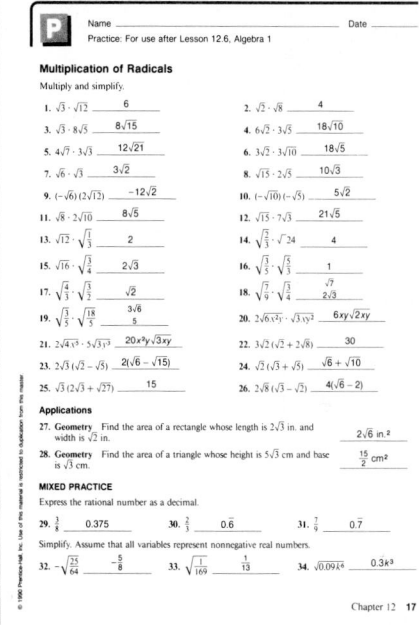

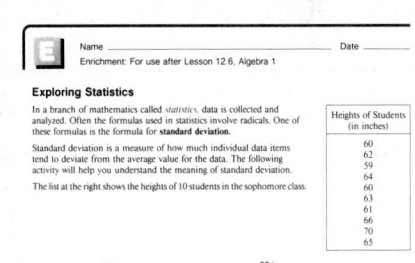

BACKGROUND

In the Capsule Review, students simplify radical expressions that contain perfect square numbers. In Exercises 1–8, the quotient property of square roots is used. In this lesson, students use this property to simplify irrational square roots.

12.7

Division of Radicals

Objective: To simplify quotients of radicals

Recall the quotient property of square roots; that is, for any real numbers $m \geq 0$ and $n > 0$,

$$\sqrt{\frac{m}{n}} = \frac{\sqrt{m}}{\sqrt{n}}$$

You have already used this property to simplify radical expressions that contain perfect square numbers.

Capsule Review

Simplify.

1. $\sqrt{\frac{4}{9}}$ $\frac{2}{3}$

2. $-\sqrt{\frac{16}{25}}$ $-\frac{4}{5}$

3. $\sqrt{\frac{64}{49}}$ $\frac{8}{7}$

4. $\sqrt{\frac{1}{144}}$ $\frac{1}{12}$

5. $-\sqrt{\frac{1}{100}}$ $-\frac{1}{10}$

6. $\sqrt{\frac{36}{121}}$ $\frac{6}{11}$

7. $\sqrt{\frac{225}{81}}$ $\frac{5}{3}$

8. $\sqrt{\frac{4z^8}{100}}$ $0.2z^4$

The quotient property of square roots also applies when you simplify irrational square roots. Recall that an expression in simplest form cannot have a radical in the denominator.

EXAMPLE 1 **Simplify:** $\sqrt{\frac{2}{3}}$

$$\sqrt{\frac{2}{3}} = \frac{\sqrt{2}}{\sqrt{3}} = \frac{\sqrt{2} \cdot \sqrt{3}}{\sqrt{3} \cdot \sqrt{3}} \qquad \textit{Multiply by 1 in the form } \frac{\sqrt{3}}{\sqrt{3}}.$$

$$= \frac{\sqrt{6}}{\sqrt{9}}$$

$$= \frac{\sqrt{6}}{3}, \text{ or } \frac{1}{3}\sqrt{6}$$

Changing a fraction such as $\frac{\sqrt{2}}{\sqrt{3}}$ (with an irrational denominator) into a fraction such as $\frac{\sqrt{6}}{3}$ (with a rational denominator) is called **rationalizing the denominator.** Examples 2 and 3 show how to rationalize a denominator that contains variables.

516   Chapter 12 Radicals

EXAMPLE 2 **Simplify:** $\sqrt{\dfrac{1}{x^7}}$

$$\sqrt{\frac{1}{x^7}} = \frac{\sqrt{1}}{\sqrt{x^7}}$$

$$= \frac{\sqrt{1} \cdot \sqrt{x}}{\sqrt{x^7} \cdot \sqrt{x}}$$

$$= \frac{\sqrt{x}}{\sqrt{x^8}} = \frac{\sqrt{x}}{x^4}$$

Notice that multiplying by $\dfrac{\sqrt{x}}{\sqrt{x}}$ gives an equivalent rational expression without a radical in the denominator.

Sometimes it is easier to simplify the expression before rationalizing the denominator.

EXAMPLE 3 **Simplify:** $\dfrac{\sqrt{24x^2y}}{\sqrt{3xy^2}}$

$$\frac{\sqrt{24x^2y}}{\sqrt{3xy^2}} = \sqrt{\frac{24x^2y}{3xy^2}} = \sqrt{\frac{8x}{y}} = \frac{\sqrt{4} \cdot \sqrt{2x}}{\sqrt{y}} = \frac{2\sqrt{2x} \cdot \sqrt{y}}{\sqrt{y} \cdot \sqrt{y}} \qquad \textit{Multiply by 1 in the form } \frac{\sqrt{y}}{\sqrt{y}}.$$

$$= \frac{2\sqrt{2xy}}{\sqrt{y^2}} = \frac{2\sqrt{2xy}}{y}$$

The radical expression $3 - 2\sqrt{2}$ is called the *conjugate* of $3 + 2\sqrt{2}$. In general, if m and n are nonnegative, then the binomials $a\sqrt{m} + b\sqrt{n}$ and $a\sqrt{m} - b\sqrt{n}$ are **conjugates** of each other. Notice that conjugates are the sum and the difference of the same two terms.

You can use conjugates to rationalize denominators containing binomial radical expressions.

EXAMPLE 4 **Rationalize the denominator:** $\dfrac{2\sqrt{5} - 3}{3 + 2\sqrt{2}}$

$$\frac{2\sqrt{5} - 3}{3 + 2\sqrt{2}} = \frac{2\sqrt{5} - 3}{3 + 2\sqrt{2}} \cdot \frac{3 - 2\sqrt{2}}{3 - 2\sqrt{2}} \qquad \textit{Multiply the numerator and the denominator by the conjugate of } 3 + 2\sqrt{2}.$$

$$= \frac{(2\sqrt{5} - 3)(3 - 2\sqrt{2})}{(3 + 2\sqrt{2})(3 - 2\sqrt{2})}$$

$$= \frac{6\sqrt{5} - 4\sqrt{10} - 9 + 6\sqrt{2}}{9 - 4 \cdot 2} \qquad \textit{Use FOIL to multiply in the numerator.}$$
$$\textit{(3 + 2\sqrt{2})(3 - 2\sqrt{2}) = (3)^2 - (2\sqrt{2})^2}$$

$$= \frac{6\sqrt{5} - 4\sqrt{10} - 9 + 6\sqrt{2}}{1}$$

$$= 6\sqrt{5} - 4\sqrt{10} - 9 + 6\sqrt{2}$$

CLASS EXERCISES

Rationalize the denominator and simplify.

1. $\sqrt{\dfrac{1}{5}}$ $\dfrac{\sqrt{5}}{5}$, or $\dfrac{1}{5}\sqrt{5}$ 2. $\sqrt{\dfrac{1}{2}}$ $\dfrac{\sqrt{2}}{2}$, or $\dfrac{1}{2}\sqrt{2}$ 3. $\dfrac{\sqrt{2}}{\sqrt{5}}$ $\dfrac{\sqrt{10}}{5}$, or $\dfrac{1}{5}\sqrt{10}$ 4. $\dfrac{\sqrt{3}}{\sqrt{7}}$ $\dfrac{\sqrt{21}}{7}$, or $\dfrac{1}{7}\sqrt{21}$

5. $\dfrac{2\sqrt{2}}{\sqrt{18}}$ $\dfrac{2}{3}$ 6. $\dfrac{3\sqrt{2}}{4\sqrt{32}}$ $\dfrac{3}{16}$ 7. $\sqrt{\dfrac{4}{x}}$ $\dfrac{2\sqrt{x}}{x}$, or $\dfrac{2}{x}\sqrt{x}$ 8. $\sqrt{\dfrac{9}{b^3}}$ $\dfrac{3\sqrt{b}}{b^2}$, or $\dfrac{3}{b^2}\sqrt{b}$

Write the conjugate of each binomial.

9. $1 - \sqrt{2}$
$1 + \sqrt{2}$
10. $2 + \sqrt{3}$
$2 - \sqrt{3}$
11. $5 + 3\sqrt{5}$
$5 - 3\sqrt{5}$
12. $4 - 2\sqrt{7}$
$4 + 2\sqrt{7}$

PRACTICE EXERCISES

Rationalize the denominator and simplify.

A 1. $\sqrt{\dfrac{2}{11}}$ $\dfrac{\sqrt{22}}{11}$ 2. $\sqrt{\dfrac{3}{10}}$ $\dfrac{\sqrt{30}}{10}$ 3. $-2\sqrt{\dfrac{1}{2}}$ $-\sqrt{2}$ 4. $-3\sqrt{\dfrac{1}{3}}$ $-\sqrt{3}$

5. $\dfrac{3\sqrt{8}}{\sqrt{3}}$ $2\sqrt{6}$ 6. $\dfrac{2\sqrt{12}}{-\sqrt{5}}$ $-\dfrac{4}{5}\sqrt{15}$ 7. $\dfrac{-\sqrt{90}}{\sqrt{10}}$ -3 8. $\dfrac{\sqrt{75}}{2\sqrt{3}}$ $\dfrac{5}{2}$

9. $\dfrac{5\sqrt{2}}{3\sqrt{6}}$ $\dfrac{5}{9}\sqrt{3}$ 10. $\dfrac{4\sqrt{3}}{2\sqrt{8}}$ $\dfrac{\sqrt{6}}{2}$ 11. $\dfrac{-3\sqrt{5}}{4\sqrt{15}}$ $-\dfrac{\sqrt{3}}{4}$ 12. $\dfrac{6\sqrt{6}}{-2\sqrt{30}}$ $-\dfrac{3\sqrt{5}}{5}$

13. $\sqrt{\dfrac{16}{y}}$ $\dfrac{4\sqrt{y}}{y}$ 14. $\sqrt{\dfrac{25}{a}}$ $\dfrac{5\sqrt{a}}{a}$ 15. $\sqrt{\dfrac{8}{x}}$ $\dfrac{2\sqrt{2x}}{x}$ 16. $\sqrt{\dfrac{12}{b}}$ $\dfrac{2\sqrt{3b}}{b}$

17. $\dfrac{3}{\sqrt{a^3}}$ $\dfrac{3\sqrt{a}}{a^2}$ 18. $\dfrac{-5}{\sqrt{x^5}}$ $\dfrac{-5\sqrt{x}}{x^3}$ 19. $\dfrac{-2}{3\sqrt{y^3}}$ $\dfrac{-2\sqrt{y}}{3y^2}$ 20. $\dfrac{\sqrt{3}}{\sqrt{12m}}$ $\dfrac{\sqrt{m}}{2m}$

21. $\sqrt{\dfrac{24c^3}{6c}}$ $2c$ 22. $\sqrt{\dfrac{27x^5}{3x}}$ $3x^2$ 23. $\dfrac{\sqrt{a^3b^4}}{\sqrt{ab}}$ $ab\sqrt{b}$ 24. $\dfrac{\sqrt{cd}}{\sqrt{c^3d^3}}$ $\dfrac{1}{cd}$

B 25. $\dfrac{5}{3 - \sqrt{2}}$ $\dfrac{15 + 5\sqrt{2}}{7}$ 26. $\dfrac{-6}{5 + \sqrt{7}}$ $\dfrac{-5 + \sqrt{7}}{3}$ 27. $\dfrac{-3}{\sqrt{5} - 1}$ $\dfrac{-3\sqrt{5} - 3}{4}$ 28. $\dfrac{2}{\sqrt{6} + 3}$ $\dfrac{2\sqrt{6} - 6}{-3}$

29. $\dfrac{\sqrt{5} - 1}{\sqrt{5} + 3}$ $-2 + \sqrt{5}$ 30. $\dfrac{\sqrt{6} + 3}{\sqrt{6} - 4}$ $\dfrac{18 + 7\sqrt{6}}{-10}$

31. $\dfrac{2 + \sqrt{3}}{1 - \sqrt{5}}$ $\dfrac{2 + 2\sqrt{5} + \sqrt{3} + \sqrt{15}}{-4}$ 32. $\dfrac{4 - \sqrt{3}}{2 + \sqrt{7}}$ $\dfrac{8 - 4\sqrt{7} - 2\sqrt{3} + \sqrt{21}}{-3}$

33. $\dfrac{-5}{2\sqrt{11} + 2}$ $\dfrac{-\sqrt{11} + 1}{4}$ 34. $\dfrac{-7}{3\sqrt{10} - 5}$ $\dfrac{-21\sqrt{10} - 35}{65}$

35. $\dfrac{1 - 3\sqrt{7}}{3\sqrt{3} + 2}$ $\dfrac{3\sqrt{3} - 2 - 9\sqrt{21} + 6\sqrt{7}}{23}$ 36. $\dfrac{3\sqrt{2} + 2}{3 - 2\sqrt{5}}$ $\dfrac{9\sqrt{2} + 6\sqrt{10} + 6 + 4\sqrt{5}}{-11}$

C **37.** $\dfrac{2\sqrt{7} + 3\sqrt{5}}{3\sqrt{7} - 2\sqrt{5}}$ $\dfrac{72 + 13\sqrt{35}}{43}$ **38.** $\dfrac{5\sqrt{2} - \sqrt{3}}{\sqrt{2} + 3\sqrt{3}}$ $\dfrac{19 - 16\sqrt{6}}{-25}$

39. $\dfrac{\sqrt{x} - \sqrt{y}}{\sqrt{x}}$ $\dfrac{x - \sqrt{xy}}{x}$ **40.** $\dfrac{\sqrt{x} + 2\sqrt{y}}{5\sqrt{x}}$ $\dfrac{x + 2\sqrt{xy}}{5x}$

41. $\dfrac{2\sqrt{x} - 3}{\sqrt{x} + 1}$ $\dfrac{2x - 5\sqrt{x} + 3}{x - 1}$ **42.** $\dfrac{3\sqrt{x} + 4\sqrt{y}}{3\sqrt{x} - 4\sqrt{y}}$ $\dfrac{9x + 24\sqrt{xy} + 16y}{9x - 16y}$

Applications

Solve. Express answers in simplest form.

43. Chemistry The ratio of the rates of diffusion of two gases is given by the formula $\dfrac{r_1}{r_2} = \dfrac{\sqrt{m_1}}{\sqrt{m_2}}$ where m_1 and m_2 are masses of the molecules of the gases. Find $\dfrac{r_1}{r_2}$ if $m_1 = 25$ units and $m_2 = 80$ units. $\dfrac{\sqrt{5}}{4}$

44. Physics The period T in seconds of a pendulum of length L in feet is given by the formula $T = 2\pi\sqrt{\dfrac{L}{32}}$. Find the period of a pendulum 4 ft long. $\pi\dfrac{\sqrt{2}}{2}$ s

45. Number Problem The square root of a number divided by the square root of the product of 4 and the number is $\dfrac{1}{2}$. all positive real numbers

46. Number Problem The square root of the product of 5 and some number divided by the square root of the product of 20 and the number squared is $\dfrac{1}{2}$. 1

EXTRA

Tell whether each statement is true or false. If false, tell why.

1. $\sqrt{36n} = \sqrt{36} \cdot \sqrt{n}$ true   **2.** $\dfrac{5}{6} = 0.\overline{83}$ false; $\dfrac{5}{6} = 0.8\overline{3}$

3. $\sqrt{36} = -6$ false; $\sqrt{36} = 6$, the positive root   **4.** $\sqrt{20} = 4\sqrt{5}$ false; $\sqrt{20} = \sqrt{4}\sqrt{5} = 2\sqrt{5}$

5. $(3 + \sqrt{2})^2 = 11 + 6\sqrt{2}$ true   **6.** $2\sqrt{5} \cdot 3\sqrt{6} = 6\sqrt{11}$ false; $2\sqrt{5} \cdot 3\sqrt{6} = 6\sqrt{30}$

7. The simplest form of $\sqrt{\dfrac{1}{8}}$ is $\dfrac{\sqrt{8}}{8}$. false; $\dfrac{\sqrt{8}}{8} = \dfrac{\sqrt{4} \cdot \sqrt{2}}{8} = \dfrac{2\sqrt{2}}{8} = \dfrac{\sqrt{2}}{4}$

8. The simplest form of $\dfrac{\sqrt{25}}{\sqrt{7}}$ is $\dfrac{5\sqrt{7}}{7}$. true

12.7 Division of Radicals   **519**

Teacher's Resource Book
Reteaching—Chapter 12, p. 19

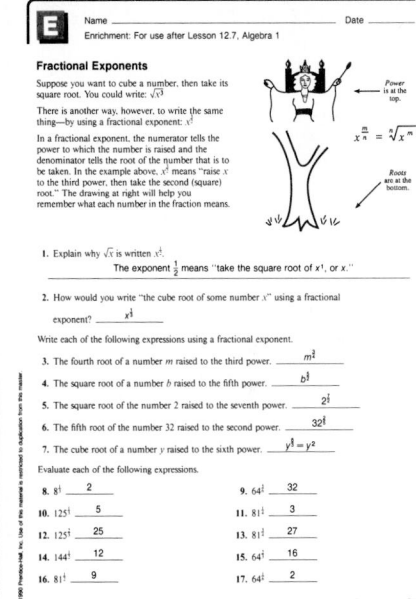

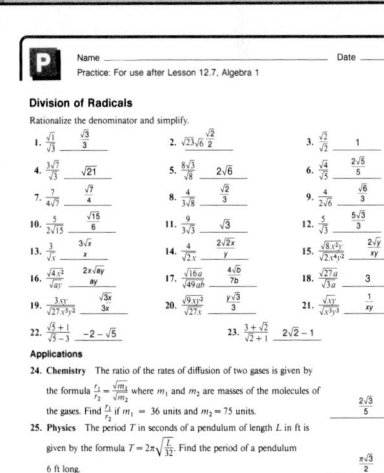

BACKGROUND

In the Capsule Review, students find the values of x that make a given radical a real number. In Exercises 2 and 3, some students may not reverse the inequality symbol when dividing both sides by a negative number. Emphasize that if $\sqrt{x}$ is a real number, then $x \geq 0$. In this lesson, this concept is applied when students solve equations containing radicals.

Critical Thinking

Classifying What is the derivation of the word *extraneous*? Relate the meaning to the mathematical use of the word. The Latin derivation is *extraneus*, meaning "strange." In mathematics, an extraneous root is not a solution; that is, it does not satisfy the equation.

12.8	# Solving Radical Equations

Objective: To solve simple radical equations

Many scientific formulas contain radicals. For example, the velocity (in ft/s) of an object (disregarding air resistance) after it has fallen a certain distance is given by the formula $v = \sqrt{2gh}$, where g is the acceleration of gravity and h is the distance (in ft) the object has fallen. The equation $v = \sqrt{2gh}$ is called a *radical equation*.

Capsule Review

For what values of x is the radical a real number?

EXAMPLE $\sqrt{2x + 6}$

$$2x + 6 \geq 0 \qquad \text{\small $\sqrt{2x + 6}$ is a real number if $2x + 6$ is nonnegative.}$$
$$2x \geq -6 \qquad \text{\small Solve for x.}$$
$$x \geq -3$$

So, $\sqrt{2x + 6}$ is a real number when $x \geq -3$.

1. $\sqrt{3x - 9}$ $x \geq 3$ **2.** $\sqrt{-2x + 5}$ $x \leq \frac{5}{2}$ **3.** $\sqrt{18 - 5x}$ $x \leq \frac{18}{5}$ **4.** $\sqrt{6 + 3x}$ $x \geq -2$

A **radical equation** is an equation that contains radicals with variables in the radicand. To solve such an equation:

• Isolate the radical on one side of the equation and combine any like terms.
• Square both sides of the equation to eliminate the radical.
• Repeat steps 1 and 2, if necessary.

EXAMPLE 1   **Solve and check:** $3 + \sqrt{a - 1} = 5$

$$3 + \sqrt{a - 1} = 5$$
$$\sqrt{a - 1} = 5 - 3 \qquad \text{\small Isolate the radical by subtracting 3 from each side.}$$
$$(\sqrt{a - 1})^2 = (2)^2 \qquad \text{\small Combine like terms: $5 - 3 = 2$; then square each side.}$$
$$a - 1 = 4 \qquad \qquad \text{\small $(\sqrt{n})^2 = n, n \geq 0$}$$
$$a = 5$$

520   Chapter 12 Radicals

Check: $3 + \sqrt{a - 1} = 5$

$3 + \sqrt{5 - 1} \stackrel{?}{=} 5$ *Replace a with 5.*

$3 + \sqrt{4} \stackrel{?}{=} 5$

$3 + 2 \stackrel{?}{=} 5$

$5 = 5$ ✔

The solution is 5.

You can square each side of an equation anytime it is convenient to do so, as long as you check all solutions in the original equation.

EXAMPLE 2   Solve and check: $0 = 8 + 4\sqrt{x}$

$0 = 8 + 4\sqrt{x}$

$-8 = 4\sqrt{x}$ *Isolate the term that contains the radical.*

$-2 = \sqrt{x}$ *Divide each side by 4.*

$(-2)^2 = (\sqrt{x})^2$ *Square each side.*

$4 = x$ *$(\sqrt{n})^2 = n, n \geq 0$*

Check: $0 \stackrel{?}{=} 8 + 4\sqrt{4}$

$0 \stackrel{?}{=} 8 + 4 \cdot 2$

$0 \neq 16$

The equation $0 = 8 + 4\sqrt{x}$ has no real number solution.

In this example, the simplified equation $-2 = \sqrt{x}$ is obtained. Explain why there is no real number solution for this equation.

When an equation is solved by squaring, an *extraneous solution* may be introduced. Recall from Chapter 8 an extraneous solution will not check in the original equation.

EXAMPLE 3   Solve and check: $\sqrt{5t^2 - 16} = t$

$\sqrt{5t^2 - 16} = t$

$(\sqrt{5t^2 - 16})^2 = (t)^2$ *Square each side.*

$5t^2 - 16 = t^2$

$4t^2 = 16$

$t^2 = 4$

$t = 2 \text{ or } t = -2$

Check:

$\sqrt{5(2)^2 - 16} \stackrel{?}{=} 2$ $\sqrt{5(-2)^2 - 16} \stackrel{?}{=} -2$

$\sqrt{5(4) - 16} \stackrel{?}{=} 2$ $\sqrt{5(4) - 16} \stackrel{?}{=} -2$

$\sqrt{20 - 16} \stackrel{?}{=} 2$ $\sqrt{20 - 16} \stackrel{?}{=} -2$

$\sqrt{4} \stackrel{?}{=} 2$ $\sqrt{4} \stackrel{?}{=} -2$

$2 = 2$ ✔ $2 \neq -2$

The solution is 2. -2 is an extraneous solution.

CLASS EXERCISES

Solve and check.

1. $\sqrt{x} = 5$

2. $\sqrt{q} = 12$

3. $\sqrt{2b} = 16$

4. $\sqrt{3y} = 9$

5. $2\sqrt{3t} = 4$

6. $3\sqrt{5p} = 6$

12.8 Solving Radical Equations   **521**

TEACHING SUGGESTIONS

- Stress the importance of isolating the radical on one side of the equation and combining like terms, if possible, before squaring. Point out how squaring a radical eliminates the square root; that is, $(\sqrt{n})^2 = n, n \geq 0$.
- Show how extraneous solutions may be introduced by squaring. Emphasize the importance of checking the apparent solutions in the original equation.
- You may have students use a calculator to check their solutions.

CHALKBOARD EXAMPLES

For Exercises 1–6, solve and check.

- **For Example 1**

  1. $\sqrt{2x - 1} - 3 = 1$ $\frac{17}{2}$

  2. $8 = \sqrt{\frac{3n}{4}} - 1$ 108

- **For Example 2**

  3. $0 = 6 + 2\sqrt{x}$ no solution

  4. $\sqrt{\frac{2m}{3}} + 7 = 5$ no solution

- **For Example 3**

  5. $\sqrt{3y^2 - 2} = y$ 1

  6. $\sqrt{4m^2} = \sqrt{m^2 + 27}$ 3, −3

Common Error

- Some students may square both sides of the equation before isolating the radical. You may wish to show them that squaring both sides of the radical equation before isolating the radical results in a new equation that is more complicated than the original.
- See *Teacher's Resource Book* for additional remediation.

Discussion

Explain how you would solve $\sqrt{3x - 5} = \sqrt{x + 5}$. Square both sides of the equation and then solve for x.

Assignment Guide

- See p. 492B for assignments.
- In problems like Exercise 29, some students may square the binomial $y + 1$ incorrectly.
- See *Teacher's Resource Book,* for Reading and Writing in Algebra activity, p. 12.

Extra

This feature affords the students the opportunity to solve real world problems involving radical equations. They are introduced to the formula $V = 3.5\sqrt{h}$. Make sure students understand what each variable represents in the formula before solving the exercises.

Lesson Quiz

Solve and check.
1. $5 - \sqrt{x - 2} = 4$ 3
2. $4 + \sqrt{x - 3} = 6$ 7
3. $5 + 5\sqrt{m} = 0$ no solution
4. $0 = 8 - 4\sqrt{y}$ 4
5. $\sqrt{4n^2 - 15} = n$ $\sqrt{5}$
6. $\sqrt{4x^2 - 27} = x$ 3

State each equation in the form needed before squaring each side. Then give the equation obtained by squaring.

7. $\sqrt{2x + 1} = 3$
   $2x + 1 = 9$

8. $\sqrt{3a - 1} = 2$
   $3a - 1 = 4$

9. $\sqrt{4y + 1} + 3 = 2$
   $\sqrt{4y + 1} = -1,\ 4y + 1 = 1$

10. $\sqrt{3c + 1} - 4 = 1$
    $\sqrt{3c + 1} = 5,\ 3c + 1 = 25$

11. $0 = 3 - 2\sqrt{y}$
    $-3 = -2\sqrt{y},\ 4y = 9$

12. $6 - 3\sqrt{2x} = 0$
    $\sqrt{2x} = 2,\ 2x = 4$

PRACTICE EXERCISES

Solve and check.

A

1. $\sqrt{y} = 8$ 64

2. $\sqrt{a} = 9$ 81

3. $\sqrt{3m} = 18$ 108

4. $\sqrt{4x} = 8$ 16

5. $\sqrt{n} = \dfrac{1}{4}$ $\dfrac{1}{16}$

6. $\sqrt{m} = \dfrac{2}{3}$ $\dfrac{4}{9}$

7. $\sqrt{\dfrac{x}{3}} = 2$ 12

8. $\sqrt{\dfrac{b}{7}} = 3$ 63

9. $\sqrt{y - 2} = 3$ 11

10. $\sqrt{a + 4} = 6$ 32

11. $\sqrt{4x} - 4 = 0$ 4

12. $0 = \sqrt{2z} - 9$ $\dfrac{81}{2}$

13. $6 + \sqrt{m} = 5$
    no solution

14. $10 + 2\sqrt{b} = 0$
    no solution

15. $6 - 3\sqrt{y} = 0$ 4

16. $8 - \sqrt{a} = 1$ 49

17. $\sqrt{5x - 1} + 3 = 7$ $\dfrac{17}{5}$

18. $\sqrt{3x + 4} + 1 = 4$ $\dfrac{5}{3}$

19. $\sqrt{6m - 1} - 5 = -2$ $\dfrac{5}{3}$

20. $\sqrt{2x - 3} - 2 = 4$ $\dfrac{39}{2}$

21. $7 - 3\sqrt{2b} = 1$ 2

22. $5 - 2\sqrt{y} = 2$ $\dfrac{9}{4}$

23. $\sqrt{\dfrac{2m}{3}} + 5 = 7$ 6

24. $9 = \sqrt{\dfrac{5n}{4}} - 1$ 80

B

25. $\sqrt{x} = 3\sqrt{2}$ 18

26. $\sqrt{t} = 2\sqrt{5}$ 20

27. $\sqrt{5y^2 - 7} = 2y$ $\sqrt{7}$

28. $\sqrt{3n^2 + 12} = 3n$ $\sqrt{2}$

29. $\sqrt{y^2 + 3} = y + 1$ 1

30. $t - 5 = \sqrt{t^2 - 35}$ 6

31. $\sqrt{2x - 3} = \sqrt{3x - 2}$
    no solution

32. $\sqrt{3y - 5} = \sqrt{5y - 3}$
    no solution

33. $\sqrt{2b + 1} = \sqrt{4b + 7}$
    no solution

34. $2\sqrt{5a - 1} = 3\sqrt{2a + 4}$ 20

35. $\sqrt{3y + 4} = y - 2$ 7

36. $m - 4 = \sqrt{2m - 5}$ 7

C

37. $\sqrt{y} + 2 = \sqrt{y + 16}$ 9

38. $\sqrt{x - 1} = 2 - \sqrt{x}$ $\dfrac{25}{16}$

Cube both sides. Solve for a.

Example: $\sqrt[3]{7a + 5} = 3 \longrightarrow 7a + 5 = 27 \longrightarrow a = \dfrac{22}{7}$

39. $\sqrt[3]{2x + 3} = 7$ 170

40. $\sqrt[3]{3y + 5} = \sqrt[3]{5 - 2y}$ 0

41. Explain why cubing both sides of cubic-root equations will not produce extraneous solutions.   Cubing a number does not change its sign.

522   Chapter 12 Radicals

Applications

42. Number Problem The square root of $\frac{1}{5}$ of a number is 5. Find the number. 125

43. Number Problem When 5 times a number is decreased by 2, the square root of the result is 6. Find the number. $\frac{38}{5}$

44. Physics In $v = \sqrt{2gh}$, find the value of h if $v = 18$ ft/s and $g = 32$ ft/s^2. $\frac{81}{16}$ ft

45. Physics The time t in seconds that it takes an object to fall a distance of d ft from rest is given by the formula $t = \sqrt{\dfrac{2d}{g}}$ where g is the acceleration due to gravity. Solve for d. Find the value of d when $g = 32$ ft/s^2 and $t = 3$ s. 144 ft

46. Physics The period (T) of a pendulum is the time needed to swing side to side and back. The period is given by the formula $T = 2\pi\sqrt{\dfrac{l}{980}}$, where l is the length of a pendulum in centimeters. Find the length of the pendulum given a period of 1 s and $\pi \approx 3.14$. 25 cm

EXTRA

When you were younger, you discovered that you could see farther if you climbed a tree. The higher you climbed, the farther you could see. There is a formula for this:

$$V = 3.5\sqrt{h}$$

where h is your height, in meters, above the ground, and V is the distance, in kilometers, that you can see.

Solve. Round your answer to the nearest whole number.

1. How far could you see if you climbed 7 m to the top of a tree? 9 km

2. Suppose that you wanted to see a distance of 21 km. How tall a tree should you climb to do this? 36 m

3. Suppose that you could see a distance of 55 km if you stood on the roof of a building. To the nearest meter, how tall is the building? 247 m

4. Suppose that you are flying in an airplane at an altitude of 8 km. How far could you see from the window of the plane? 313 km

5. Suppose that the plane in Exercise 4 loses altitude and that you could then see a distance of about 200 km. How much altitude did the plane lose? 4735 m

Teacher's Resource Book
Reteaching—Chapter 12, p. 22

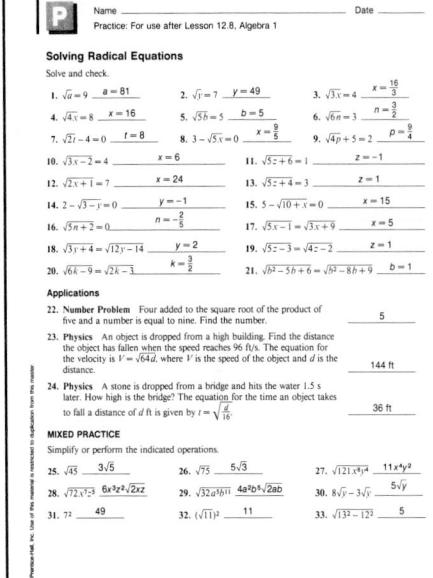

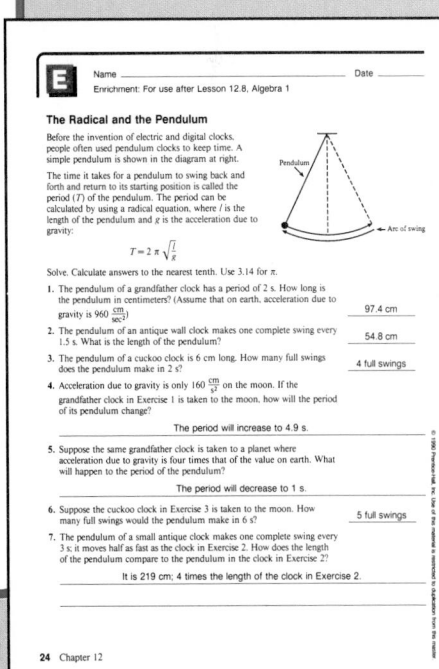

Vocabulary
Hypotenuse
Legs
Pythagorean theorem

Materials/Manipulatives
Calculators
Coordinate grid
Overhead projector
Square-root table
Teacher's Resource Book,
Teaching Aid 12,
Transparencies 26, 28

BACKGROUND

In the Capsule Review, students review finding squares and square roots. In this lesson, students use this skill when solving for the unknown in the Pythagorean theorem, $c^2 = a^2 + b^2$.

Critical Thinking

Classifying In Example 2, two special right triangles are discussed, a 45–45–90 triangle and a 30–60–90 triangle. What is the easiest way to draw each of these triangles? A 45–45–90 triangle can be formed by drawing a diagonal of a square. A 30–60–90 triangle can be formed by drawing an altitude in an equilateral triangle.

12.9 The Pythagorean Theorem

Objective: To use the Pythagorean theorem to find the length of a leg or the length of the hypotenuse of a right triangle

In physics, two forces that pull at right angles and the resultant force are represented by a rectangle with a diagonal, as shown at the right. The magnitude of this resultant force can be calculated by thinking of the rectangle as being divided into two right triangles. The calculations involve powers and square roots.

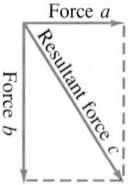

Capsule Review

Simplify.

1. 6^2 36
2. $3^2 + 2^2$ 13
3. $10^2 - 8^2$ 36
4. 18^2 324

5. $\sqrt{36}$ 6
6. $\sqrt{81}$ 9
7. $\sqrt{13^2 - 5^2}$ 12
8. $\sqrt{3^2 + 4^2}$ 5

9. $(\sqrt{3})^2$ 3
10. $(\sqrt{11})^2$ 11
11. $(x + 1)^2$
    $x^2 + 2x + 1$
12. $(y - 2)^2$
    $y^2 - 4y + 4$

In a right triangle, the side opposite the right angle is the longest side. It is called the **hypotenuse.** The other two sides are called the **legs** of the triangle.

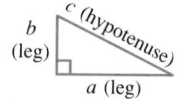

From the work of a Greek named Pythagoras and the members of his secret society came an important right-angled triangle property called the *Pythagorean theorem.* This theorem relates the squares on the sides of a right triangle and thus describes the relationship of the lengths of those sides.

> ### The Pythagorean Theorem
>
> In a right triangle, the square of the length of the hypotenuse is equal to the sum of the squares of the lengths of the two legs.
>
> $$c^2 = a^2 + b^2$$

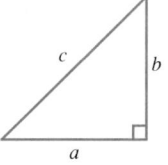

The *Pythagorean theorem* is an important mathematical tool for solving problems in surveying, carpentry, and navigation. It also provides mathematicians with insight in finding the square and square roots of a number.

524   Chapter 12 Radicals

EXAMPLE 1 Two forces, $a = 6$ lb and $b = 8$ lb, pull at right angles. Find the resultant force, c.

$c^2 = a^2 + b^2$
$c^2 = 6^2 + 8^2$ *Replace a with 6 and b with 8.*
$c^2 = 36 + 64$
$c^2 = 100$ *Since $c^2 = 100$, $c = 10$ or $c = -10$.*
$c = 10$ *The length must be positive.*

force a

force b

force c

So, the resultant force is 10 lb.

In geometry, two special right triangles are often used. They are referred to as the 45-45-90 triangle and the 30-60-90 triangle. The numbers are the measures, in degrees, of the angles of the triangles.

EXAMPLE 2 Find the length of the unknown side to the nearest tenth. Use the table on page 670 or a calculator.

a.

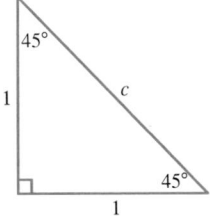

45°
1
c
45°
1

b.

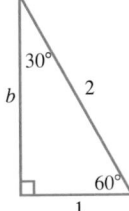

30°
b
2
60°
1

a. $c^2 = a^2 + b^2$
$c^2 = 1^2 + 1^2$ *Solve for c^2*
$c^2 = 2$ *Since $c^2 = 2$, $c = \sqrt{2}$*
      or $c = -\sqrt{2}$.
$c = \sqrt{2}$ *The length, c, cannot be*
      negative.
$c \approx 1.4$ *Use a table or calculator.*

b. $c^2 = a^2 + b^2$
$2^2 = 1^2 + b^2$ *Solve for b^2.*
$4 = 1 + b^2$
$3 = b^2$
$\sqrt{3} = b$
$1.7 \approx b$

When you know the lengths of the three sides of a triangle, you can determine whether it is a right triangle by using the *converse* of the Pythagorean theorem: If $a^2 + b^2 = c^2$, then the triangle is a right triangle.

EXAMPLE 3 The lengths of the sides of a triangle are 4, 5, and 8. Determine whether the triangle is a right triangle.

$a^2 + b^2 = c^2$
$4^2 + 5^2 \stackrel{?}{=} 8^2$ *Substitute: $a = 4$, $b = 5$, $c = 8$*
$16 + 25 \stackrel{?}{=} 64$
$41 \neq 64$ So, the triangle is not a right triangle.

12.9 The Pythagorean Theorem   **525**

525

LESSON FOLLOW-UP

Assignment Guide

- See p. 492B for assignments.
- The text suggests that a calculator or a table of square roots be used for some exercises.
- Use Transparency 28, in the *Teacher's Resource Book*, for Exercise 17, to show a suggested proof of the Pythagorean theorem.
- See *Teacher's Resource Book, Technology*, p. 22.

Lesson Quiz

Use the Pythagorean theorem, $c^2 = a^2 + b^2$, to find the missing length to the nearest tenth. Use the table on page 670 or a calculator.

1. $a = \sqrt{3}$, $b = 1$, $c =$ ___   2
2. $a = 18$, $c = 30$, $b =$ ___   24
3. $a = 1.2$, $b = 1.6$, $c =$ ___   2.0

The lengths of three sides of a triangle are given. Is the triangle a right triangle?

4. $\sqrt{2}$, $\sqrt{2}$, 4   no

5. $2\sqrt{\frac{1}{3}}$, 2, 4   no

Enrichment

In this lesson, the converse of the Pythagorean theorem is discussed. Give three mathematical statements and their converses. Show whether converses are true or false.   Answers will vary. One possible answer is given.

Statement: If a and b are even numbers, then the sum of a and b is even.

Converse: If the sum of a and b is even, then a and b are even numbers.

Although the statement is true, the converse is false. For example, if the sum of a and b is 8, a could be 5 and b could be 3.

CLASS EXERCISES

Use the Pythagorean theorem, $c^2 = a^2 + b^2$, to find the missing length.

1. $a = 6$, $b = 8$, $c =$? 10
2. $a = 10$, $b = 24$, $c =$? 26
3. $a = 5$, $c = 13$, $b =$? 12
4. $b = 4$, $c = 5$, $a =$? 3
5. $a = 2$, $c = \sqrt{13}$, $b =$? 3
6. $a = \sqrt{5}$, $b = \sqrt{5}$, $c =$? $\sqrt{10}$

PRACTICE EXERCISES

Use the Pythagorean theorem, $c^2 = a^2 + b^2$, to find the missing length to the nearest tenth. Use the table on page 670 or a calculator.

A

1. $a = 3$, $b = 4$, $c =$? 5
2. $a = 5$, $b = 12$, $c =$? 13
3. $a = 10$, $c = 19$, $b =$? 16.2
4. $b = 8$, $c = 24$, $a =$? 22.6
5. $a = 4$, $b = 9$, $c =$? 9.8
6. $a = 7$, $b = 5$, $c =$? 8.6
7. $b = 10$, $c = 13$, $a =$? 8.3
8. $a = 40$, $c = 41$, $b =$? 9

The lengths of three sides of a triangle are given. Is it a right triangle?

9. 3, 4, 6 no
10. 18, 15, 23 no
11. 1, 1, $\sqrt{2}$ yes
12. 1, $\sqrt{3}$, 2 yes

Use $c^2 = a^2 + b^2$ to find the missing length to the nearest tenth. Use the table on page 670 or a calculator.

B

13. $a = 0.8$, $b = 0.6$, $c =$? 1
14. $a = 2.4$, $b = 1.0$, $c =$? 2.6
15. $a = \frac{1}{5}$, $c = \frac{1}{3}$, $b =$? $0.2\overline{6}$ or $\frac{4}{15}$
16. $a = 2\frac{1}{2}$, $c = 6\frac{1}{2}$, $b =$? 6

The diagrams below suggest a proof of the Pythagorean theorem. Each figure shows a square with side of length $(a + b)$.

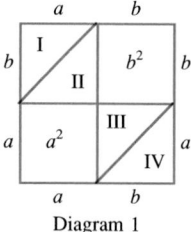
Diagram 1

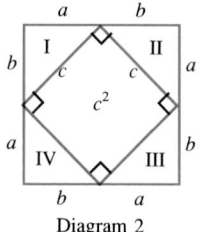
Diagram 2

C 17. In Diagram 1, show that $(a + b)^2 = a^2 + b^2 + 4\left(\frac{1}{2}ab\right)$. See below.

In Diagram 2, show that $(a + b)^2 = c^2 + 4\left(\frac{1}{2}ab\right)$.

18. Use the equations in Exercise 17 to verify the Pythagorean theorem.
See below.

526   Chapter 12 Radicals

---

17. Diagram 1: Area of large square = Areas of 2 small squares + Areas of 4 small triangles, so $(a + b)^2 = a^2 + b^2 + 4\left(\frac{1}{2}ab\right)$. Diagram 2: Area of blue square =

Area of red square + Areas of 4 small triangles, so $(a + b)^2 = c^2 + 4\left(\frac{1}{2}ab\right)$.

18. $(a + b)^2 = a^2 + b^2 + 4\left(\frac{1}{2}ab\right)$, so $a^2 + b^2 = (a + b)^2 - 4\left(\frac{1}{2}ab\right)$. Also, $(a + b)^2 = c^2 + 4\left(\frac{1}{2}ab\right)$, so $c^2 = (a + b)^2 - 4\left(\frac{1}{2}ab\right)$. Therefore, by the transitive property, $a^2 + b^2 = c^2$.

Applications

Solve. Round the answer to the nearest tenth.

19. Construction A carpenter braces an 8 × 15 ft wall by nailing a board diagonally across the wall. How long is the bracing board? 17 ft

20. Physics Two jeeps at a 90° angle to each other try to pull a third car out of the snow. If one jeep exerts a force of 600 lb and the other exerts a force of 800 lb, what is the resulting force on the car stuck in snow? 1000 lb

21. Geometry The diagonal of a square is $8\sqrt{2}$ cm. Find the length of a side of the square. 8 cm

22. Sports A hiker leaves her camp in the morning. How far is she from camp after walking 5 mi due west and then 7 mi due north? 8.6 mi

23. Geometry The lengths of the sides of a right triangle are given by three consecutive integers. Find the lengths of the sides. 3, 4, 5

24. Construction A wire is stretched from the top of a 4-ft pole to the top of a 9-ft fence. If the pole and fence are 10 ft apart, how long is the wire? 11.2 ft

DID YOU KNOW?

The gaps between the rails on a railroad track are deliberately placed there for the safety of the train. These are called *expansion gaps* and allow the rails to expand when the temperature rises. Without such gaps, the track would buckle and rise off the ground.

1. Suppose a 20-ft piece of rail expands 1 in. during a hot spell. If there were no expansion gaps between the rails, about how high off the ground would the rail rise? (*Hint:* Use the Pythagorean theorem and right triangles to estimate the height.) Before expansion, the rail is 240 in. long. After expansion, it is 241 in. long. Find h. ≈11 in.

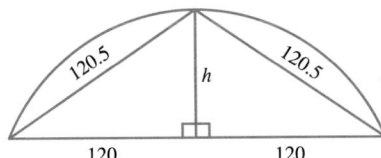

2. To make the ride smoother for passengers riding a train, it is desirable not to have too many gaps. Suppose rails are 50 ft long. If a rail expands 1 in. during a temperature change, how far off the ground would it rise if there were no expansion gaps? ≈17 in.

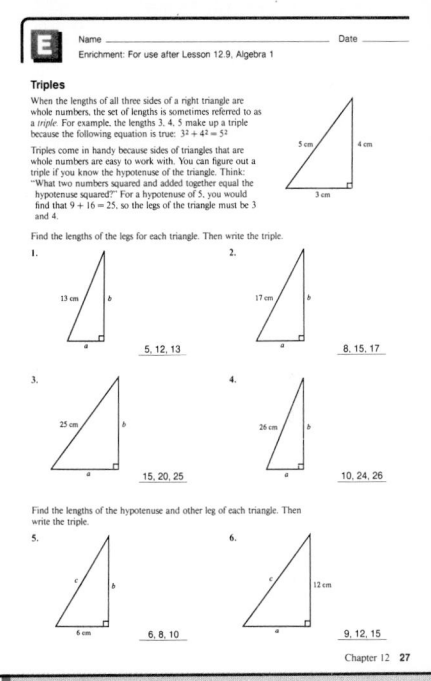

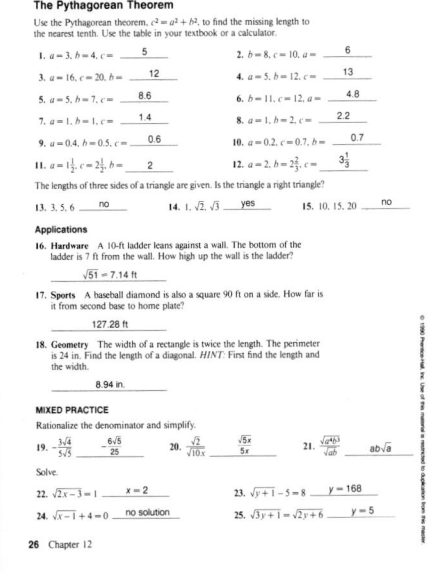

Materials/Manipulatives
Coordinate graph paper
Overhead projector
Straightedge
Teacher's Resource Book,
Teaching Aid 12,
Transparency 15, 27

BACKGROUND

In the Capsule Review, Exercises 1–6 review finding the distance between two points on a number line. In this lesson, this concept is extended to find the distance between two points in the coordinate plane.

TEACHING SUGGESTIONS

• Stress the relationship between the distance formula and the Pythagorean theorem. You may wish to point out to students that the distance formula is an application of the theorem.

• Emphasize that the distance formula can be used for any points in the coordinate plane. You may wish to use Teaching Aid 12 and Transparency 15, in the *Teacher's Resource Book,* to illustrate several examples of the use of the distance formula.

12.10

The Distance Formula

Objective: To find the distance between any two points in the coordinate plane

A city planner is making a map for a new subdivision that will be laid out in square blocks. Various locations are labeled with ordered pairs, just as points in the coordinate plane are labeled. If two locations are labeled $A(3, 5)$ and $B(9, 2)$, what is the distance between the points?

In Lesson 5.6, you found the distance between two points on a number line. This is important to recall before studying the *distance formula.*

Capsule Review

Find the distance between the given points on a number line.

EXAMPLE $A(-5)$ and $B(2)$

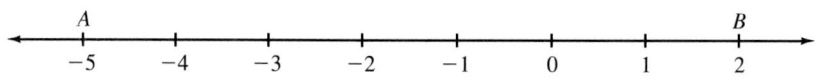

$$|2 - (-5)| = |2 + 5| = 7, \text{ or } |-5 - 2| = |-7| = 7$$

The distance between A and B is 7 units.

1. $R(2)$ and $S(5)$ 3   **2.** $C(7)$ and $D(3)$ 4   **3.** $X(8)$ and $Y(-1)$ 9

4. $E(-5)$ and $F(1)$ 6   **5.** $A(-5)$ and $D(-4)$ 1   **6.** $P(-2)$ and $Q(-13)$ 11

In the coordinate plane, you can think of the axes and the lines parallel to the axes as number lines.

For the lines parallel to the
x-axis:

$DE = |1 - 5| = |5 - 1| = 4$
$FG = |1 - 5| = |5 - 1| = 4$

For the lines parallel to the
y-axis:

$DF = |4 - 1| = |1 - 4| = 3$
$EG = |4 - 1| = |1 - 4| = 3$

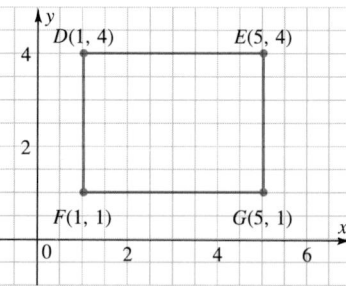

528   Chapter 12 Radicals

To find the distance between two points A and B not on the x-axis, y-axis, or a line parallel to either axis, you can use the Pythagorean theorem.

$$(AB)^2 = (AC)^2 + (CB)^2$$
$$AB = \sqrt{(AC)^2 + (CB)^2}$$
$$= \sqrt{(5 - 2)^2 + (9 - 3)^2}$$
$$= \sqrt{3^2 + 6^2}$$
$$= \sqrt{9 + 36} = \sqrt{45} = 3\sqrt{5}$$

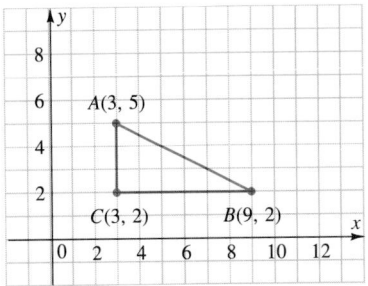

So, the distance between A and B on the city planner's map is $3\sqrt{5}$ units. This method can be generalized as follows:

Distance Formula

For any points $P_1(x_1, y_1)$ and $P_2(x_2, y_2)$ in the coordinate plane, the distance d between the points is given by

$$d = \sqrt{(x_2 - x_1)^2 + (y_2 - y_1)^2}$$

EXAMPLE Find the distance between $E(-4, 2)$ and $F(5, 4)$.

$$d = \sqrt{(x_2 - x_1)^2 + (y_2 - y_1)^2}$$
$$d = \sqrt{(-4 - 5)^2 + (2 - 4)^2}$$
$$d = \sqrt{(-9)^2 + (-2)^2}$$
$$d = \sqrt{81 + 4}$$
$$d = \sqrt{85}$$

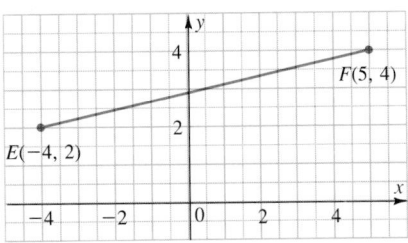

The distance between $E(-4, 2)$ and $F(5, 4)$ is $\sqrt{85}$.

CLASS EXERCISES

State the values of x_1, x_2, y_1, and y_2 for each pair of points. Then find the distance.

1. $A(0, 0)$, $B(-3, 4)$
   0, -3, 0, 4; 5
2. $P(5, 12)$, $Q(0, 0)$
   5, 0, 12, 0; 13
3. $R(2, 2)$, $T(5, -2)$
   2, 5, 2, -2; 5
4. $C(1, 4)$, $D(6, 9)$
   1, 6, 4, 9; $5\sqrt{2}$
5. $X(3, 1)$, $Y(-1, 6)$
   3, -1, 1, 6; $\sqrt{41}$
6. $E(5, 6)$, $F(4, -1)$
   5, 4, 6, -1; $5\sqrt{2}$

For Discussion

7. When using the distance formula, does it matter which point has coordinates (x_1, y_1) or (x_2, y_2)? Explain. no; squaring the difference makes the signs irrelevant

12.10 The Distance Formula **529**

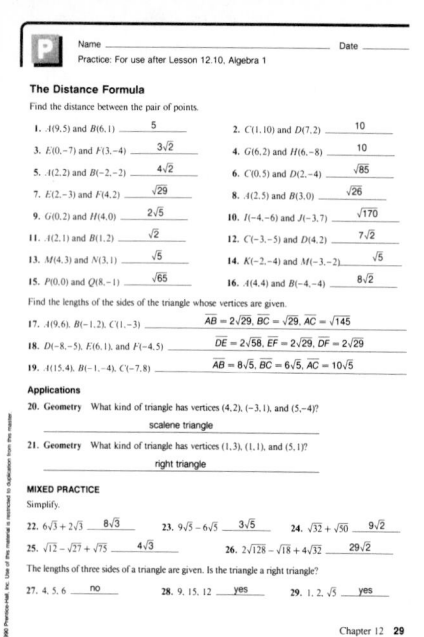

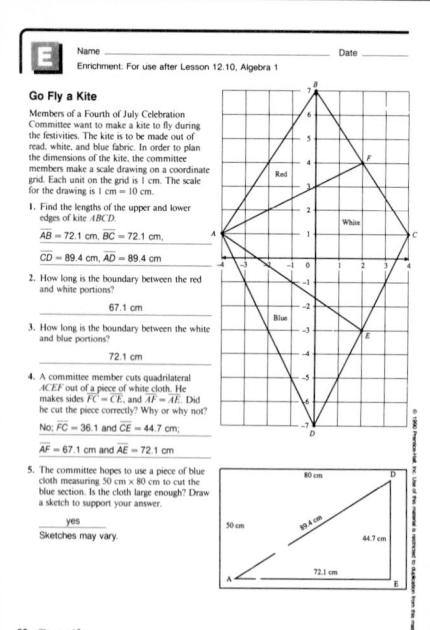

PRACTICE EXERCISES

Find the distance between each pair of points.

A

1. $A(1, 2)$, $B(4, -2)$ 5

2. $R(4, 2)$, $T(-2, 10)$ 10

3. $P(4, -2)$, $Q(-2, 4)$ $6\sqrt{2}$

4. $X(-6, -2)$, $Y(-5, 4)$ $\sqrt{37}$

5. $L(-5, 1)$, $M(7, 6)$ 13

6. $E(5, 13)$, $F(5, -1)$ 14

7. $E(3, 1)$, $F(-2, -1)$ $\sqrt{29}$

8. $A(-5, 0)$, $B(-9, 6)$ $2\sqrt{13}$

9. $C(10, 8)$, $D(2, -3)$ $\sqrt{185}$

10. $P(7, -9)$, $Q(4, -3)$ $3\sqrt{5}$

11. $S(8, -10)$, $T(3, 2)$ 13

12. $A(-2, 4)$, $B(7, -8)$ 15

Find the lengths of the sides of the triangle whose vertices are given.

B

13. $A(0, 0)$, $B(8, 0)$, $C(4, 3)$
$AB = 2\sqrt{2}$, $BC = 5$, $AC = 5$

14. $R(-1, 7)$, $S(0, 0)$, $T(8, 4)$
$RS = 5\sqrt{2}$, $ST = 4\sqrt{5}$, $RT = 3\sqrt{10}$

15. $X(-4, 2)$, $Y(-1, 6)$, $Z(5, 4)$
$XY = 5$, $YZ = 2\sqrt{10}$, $XZ = \sqrt{85}$

16. $D(1, 5)$, $E(5, 5)$ $F(5, 1)$
$DE = 4$, $EF = 4$, $DF = 4\sqrt{2}$

17. $A(3, 6)$, $B(-1, 3)$, $C(5, -5)$
$AB = 5$, $BC = 10$, $AC = 5\sqrt{5}$

18. $R(7, -3)$, $S(0, 4)$, $T(8, -1)$
$RS = 7\sqrt{2}$, $ST = \sqrt{89}$, $RT = \sqrt{5}$

19. $M(-7, 5)$, $N(-7, -7)$, $P(2, -7)$
$MN = 12$, $NP = 9$, $MP = 15$

20. $J(6, 3)$, $K(9, 7)$, $L(10, 0)$
$JK = 5$, $KL = 5\sqrt{2}$, $JL = 5$

C

21. The distance between two points with coordinates $(1, 1)$ and $(4, y)$ is 5. Find all possible values for y. 5 or -3

22. The distance between two points with coordinates $(2, -1)$ and $(x, 3)$ is 5. Find all possible values for x. 5 or -1

23. Can the point with coordinates $(-2, 4)$ be the center of a circle that passes through the points with coordinates $(1, 0)$, $(-5, 0)$, and $(1, 8)$? yes

Applications

24. Computer   The distance formula has many applications in coordinate geometry. Use it to prove that quadrilateral *ABCD* is a rhombus. $A(6, 5)$, $B(2, 2)$, $C(9, 1)$ and $D(5, -2)$. This computer program will find the lengths of each side of the figure. See below.

```
10  PRINT "ENTER THE COORDINATES FOR"
20  INPUT "POINT A:  ";AX,AY
30  INPUT "POINT B:  ";BX,BY
40  INPUT "POINT C:  ";CX,CY
50  INPUT "POINT D:  ";DX,DY
60  S1 = SQR ((AX - BX) ^ 2 + (AY - BY) ^ 2)
70  S2 = SQR ((BX - CX) ^ 2 + (BY - CY) ^ 2)
80  S3 = SQR ((CX - DX) ^ 2 + (CY - DY) ^ 2)
90  S4 = SQR ((DX - AX) ^ 2 + (DY - AY) ^ 2)
100 PRINT : PRINT "SIDE AB IS ";S1
110 PRINT "SIDE BC IS ";S2
120 PRINT "SIDE CD IS ";S3
130 PRINT "SIDE DA IS ";S4
140 END
```

LOGICAL REASONING

A geometric figure is formed by the four lines whose equations are:

$$y = x \qquad y = -x$$
$$y = x - 4 \qquad y = -x + 4$$

What kind of geometric figure is it? What is its area? Square, A = 8 sq. units

Additional Answers

24. The quadrilateral is a rhombus since $AB = BC = CD = AD$.

Problem Solving Strategy: Use Coordinate Geometry

LESSON PLAN

Materials/Manipulatives
Coordinate graph paper
Overhead projector
Straightedge
Teacher's Resource Book,
  Teaching Aid 10,
  Transparencies 15, 17, 18

Coordinate geometry combines concepts from algebra and geometry by using the coordinate plane. Certain kinds of problems are more easily solved by this approach than by either algebra or geometry alone.

Given a line segment, how can the midpoint of the segment be found without measurement?

EXAMPLE Find the midpoint M of segment RP given the endpoints of your choice; for this example, use the points $(-4, -1)$ and $(6, 5)$.

Understand the Problem

What are the given facts?
Segment RP has endpoints of $(-4, -1)$ and $(6, 5)$.

What are you asked to find?
The coordinates of the midpoint $M(x, y)$.

Plan Your Approach

Choose a strategy.
The strategy is to use a right triangle and the lengths of the sides of the triangle to locate the x- and y-coordinates for the midpoint M.

- Plot the points R and P,
  then draw a right triangle
  RSP. The coordinates of S
  are $(6, -1)$. Why?
- Draw lines parallel to the
  x- and y-axes from M to
  sides RS and SP.
- Then A is the midpoint of
  RS and B is the midpoint
  of SP.

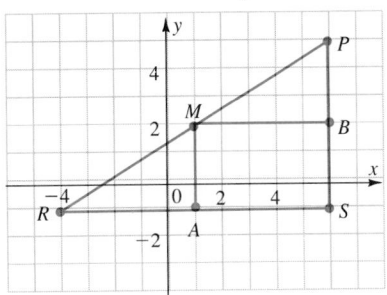

Complete the Work

Locate the values of A and B.
Since A is the midpoint of RS, then $RA = AS$. Since B is the midpoint of SP, then $SB = BP$.

$$\text{length of } RX = \text{distance from } R(-4, -1) \text{ to } A(x, -1)$$
$$= |x - (-4)|$$

BACKGROUND

A student's ability to organize information given in a problem, so that it can be used to solve the problem, is a key to success in this lesson. To determine a student's progress, analyze errors in the student's work and then classify specific errors.

Error Analysis Classification
1. *Misunderstanding*
   Failed to understand the underlying concept of the problem
2. *Misapplied strategy*
   Wrote an incorrect equation/ formula
   Made error(s) in the solution process

- Before doing the example, have students graph vertical, horizontal, and oblique lines on coordinate graph paper. Then have them find the coordinates of the midpoint of each line. Use Teaching Aid 10 and Transparencies 15, 17, 18 in the *Teacher's Resource Book,* to graph several lines and find the midpoint of each line.
- Before discussing Class Exercise 7, you may want to show that it is true for a specific triangle. For example, in triangle *RST,* *R*(0, 0), *S*(0, 1), and *T*(1, 0), the midpoint *P* of the hypotenuse is the same distance from *R, S,* and *T.*
- Special emphasis should be placed on Step 4 of the problem solving process, Interpret the Results. Students should check that their work in Step 3 agrees with the conditions stated in the problem. For example, students should check that the computed lengths are equal.

Since x is the larger value, the statement can be written as

$$x - (-4)$$

The lengths of each segment can be determined by subtracting the smaller coordinate from the larger coordinate.

$RA = x - (-4)$ and $AS = 6 - x$ $\qquad$ $SB = y - (-1)$ and $BP = 5 - y$

$x + 4 = 6 - x$ *Solve for x.* $\qquad$ $y + 1 = 5 - y$ *Solve for y.*

$\qquad 2x = 2$ $\qquad\qquad\qquad\qquad\qquad$ $2y = 4$

$\qquad x = 1$ $\qquad\qquad\qquad\qquad\qquad\quad$ $y = 2$

Interpret the Results   **State your answer.**

The coordinates of midpoint M are (1, 2). Notice that given $R(-4, -1)$ and $P(6, 5)$, the midpoint coordinates, (1, 2), are the averages of the x- and y-coordinates. How would you show this?

For this example, the endpoints of segment RP were given. If the endpoints were any coordinates (x_1, y_1) and (x_2, y_2), then the midpoint could be found using the average of the x- and y-coordinates.

$$M\left(\frac{x_1 + x_2}{2}, \frac{y_1 + y_2}{2}\right)$$

CLASS EXERCISES

Find the coordinates of the midpoints of the segments with the following endpoints.

1. (2, 4) and (8, −4) (5, 0) $\qquad\qquad$ **2.** (−4, 3) and (6, −11) (1, −4)

3. (−5, 2) and (7, 7) $\left(1, 4\frac{1}{2}\right)$ $\qquad\quad$ **4.** (−6, 0) and (0, 6) (−3, 3)

5. (x, 0) and (0, y) $\left(\frac{x}{2}, \frac{y}{2}\right)$ $\qquad\quad$ **6.** (2a, b) and (6a, −4b) $\left(4a, -\frac{3b}{2}\right)$

For Discussion

7. How would you use the midpoint formula to show that the midpoint of the hypotenuse of a right triangle is equidistant from the three vertices? Find the coordinates of the midpoint, then use the distance formula to find the distances to the vertices.

PRACTICE EXERCISES

Find the midpoints of the segments with the following endpoints.

A   **1.** (−6, 4) and (−4, 6) (−5, 5) $\qquad\qquad$ **2.** (−4, −1) and (−1, −4) $\left(-2\frac{1}{2}, -2\frac{1}{2}\right)$

$\quad$ **3.** (−7, 3) and (−5, 3) (−6, 3) $\qquad\qquad$ **4.** (5, −2) and (8, −2) $\left(6\frac{1}{2}, -2\right)$

$\quad$ **5.** (1, 7) and (−8, −3) $\left(-3\frac{1}{2}, 2\right)$ $\qquad\quad$ **6.** (−5, 2) and (−7, 5) $\left(-6, 3\frac{1}{2}\right)$

$\quad$ **7.** (2a, b) and (a, 2b) $\left(\frac{3a}{2}, \frac{3b}{2}\right)$ $\qquad\quad$ **8.** (3a, −3b) and (−2a, −3b) $\left(\frac{a}{2}, -3b\right)$

532 $\quad$ Chapter 12 Radicals

Write the missing coordinates of the labeled points using the given points.

9.

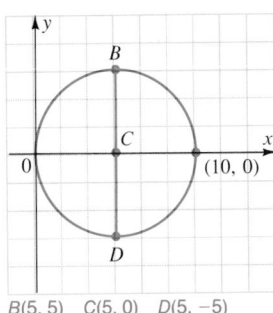

B(5, 5)   C(5, 0)   D(5, −5)

10.

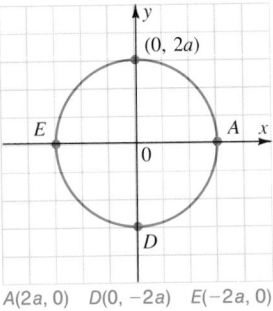

A(2a, 0)   D(0, −2a)   E(−2a, 0)

Complete each statement in order to show that the diagonals are equal in length.

11.

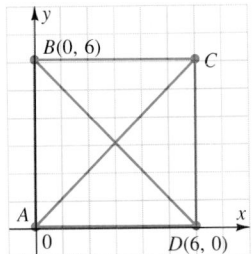

a. The coordinates of C are __?__. (6, 6)
b. The length of segment AC is __?__. $6\sqrt{2}$
c. The length of segment BD is __?__. $6\sqrt{2}$
d. What statement can be made concerning the length of the diagonals of a square?
  are the same

12.

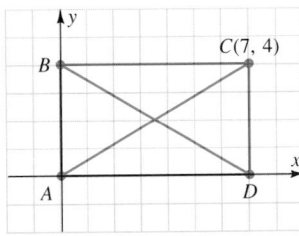

a. The coordinates of B are __?__. (0, 4)
b. The coordinates of D are __?__. (7, 0)
c. The length of segment AC is __?__. $\sqrt{53}$
d. The length of segment BD is __?__. $\sqrt{53}$
e. What statement can be made about the diagonals of a rectangle?
  are the same

13. Use the square in Exercise 11 to show that the diagonals of a square bisect each other. That is, show that the diagonals have the same midpoint.
$M_{AC} = M_{BD} = (3, 3)$; check students' work.

14. For Exercise 12, show that the diagonals of the rectangle have the same midpoint. $M_{AC} = M_{BD} = \left(\frac{7}{2}, 2\right)$; check students' work.

15. Triangle ABC has vertices $A(−2, 1)$, $B(5, 2)$, and $C(1, −2)$. Find the length of each side of the triangle. Is it a right triangle? Explain. $AC = 3\sqrt{2}$; $BC = 4\sqrt{2}$; $AB = 5\sqrt{2}$; yes; $(AB)^2 = (AC)^2 + (BC)^2$.

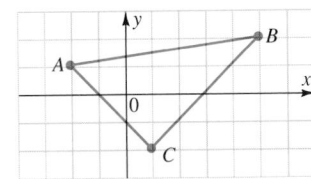

• **For the Example**
Complete each statement to show that the diagonals are equal in length.

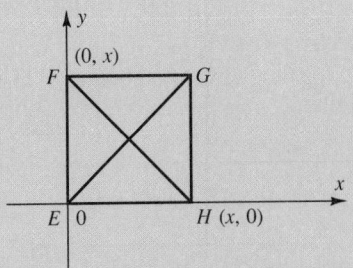

1. The coordinates of G are __?__.
  (x, x)
2. The length of EG is __?__. $\sqrt{2}x$
3. The length of FH is __?__. $\sqrt{2}x$

LESSON FOLLOW-UP

Critical Thinking
Causal Explanation Two boats leave the point (0, 0) at the same time. How far apart are they after the first boat reaches the point (16, 0) and the second boat reaches the point (0, 5)? Students should use their knowledge of coordinate geometry and the distance formula to compute the distance, $\sqrt{281}$.

Project

Have students work in groups to re-search other famous mathematicians.

Lesson Quiz

Complete each statement to show that the diagonals are equal in length.

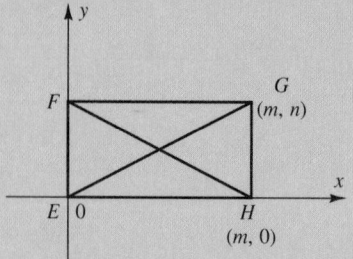

1. The coordinates of E are ？.
(0, 0)

2. The coordinates of F are ？.
(0, n)

3. The length of EG is ？. $\sqrt{m^2 + n^2}$

4. The length of FH is ？. $\sqrt{m^2 + n^2}$

In a circle, the center is $O(m, n)$ and r is its radius. $P(x, y)$ is any point on the circle.

5. Use the distance formula to represent the length of the radius.
$\sqrt{(x - m)^2 + (y - n)^2}$

6. Write the equation of a circle with center (m, n) and radius r.
$(x - m)^2 + (y - n)^2 = r^2$

Mixed Problem Solving Review

Solving mixture problems (Ex. 1, 4)
Solving problems involving per-cents (Ex. 2, 4)
Solving Current problems (Ex. 3)
• The following problem solving strategies may be appropriate:
Drawing a table or a diagram (Ex. 1–4)

Test Yourself

See *Teacher's Resource Book, Tests,* pp. 123–124.

534

For Exercises 16–17, find:

16.

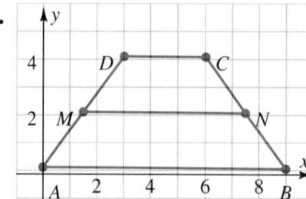

a. the midpoint M of $\overline{AD}$ $\left(1\frac{1}{2}, 2\right)$
b. the midpoint N of $\overline{BC}$ $\left(7\frac{1}{2}, 2\right)$
c. the length of $\overline{MN}$ 6
d. the length of $\overline{CD}$ 3
e. the length of $\overline{AB}$ 9
f. a statement that can be made concerning MN and $AB + CD$ $6 = \frac{1}{2}(3 + 9)$

17.

a. the midpoint K of $\overline{PQ}$ (4, 0)
b. the midpoint J of $\overline{QR}$ (7, 3)
c. the length of $\overline{JK}$ $3\sqrt{2}$
d. the length of $\overline{PR}$ $6\sqrt{2}$
e. a statement that can be made concerning JK and PR $3\sqrt{2} = \frac{1}{2}(6\sqrt{2})$

C 18. The perpendicular bisector of a line segment intersects the segment's midpoint at right angles. Any point lying in the perpendicular bisector is equidistant from the endpoints of the segment. In the figure line PQ is the perpendicular bisector of segment AB.

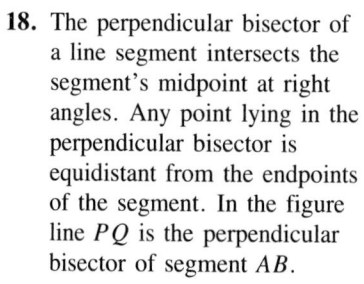
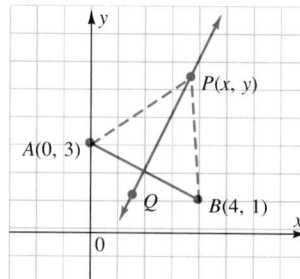

a. Using the coordinates of $A(0, 3)$ and $P(x, y)$, find the length of segment AP. $AP = \sqrt{x^2 + (y - 3)^2}$
b. Using the coordinates of $B(4, 1)$ and $P(x, y)$, find the length of segment BP. $BP = \sqrt{(x - 4)^2 + (y - 1)^2}$ $\sqrt{x^2 + (y - 3)^2} = \sqrt{(x - 4)^2 + (y - 1)^2}$
c. Using the lengths of segments AP and BP, write an equation that expresses the fact that P is equidistant from A and B.
d. Square both sides of the equations, and simplify. What is your resulting equation? $y = 2x - 2$

Mixed Problem Solving Review

1. How many kilograms of pinto beans costing \$1.29/kg and how many kilograms of garbanzos at \$1.59/kg should be mixed to make 27 kg of a mixture valued at \$38.43? 15 kg pinto beans, 12 kg garbanzo beans

2. Suki's age is now 75% of her brother's. Seven years ago his age was 50% greater than hers. How old is each one now? Suki 21 yr, brother 28 yr

3. Canoeing downstream for 2 h Josh travels 11 mi. Traveling upstream for the same time he goes only 7 mi. How fast does he go in still water? 4.5 mi/h

4. How many milliliters of water must be mixed with 25 ml of a 15% solution of alcohol in water to get a 10% solution? 12.5 mL

PROJECT

René Descartes, a mathematician of the 1600s, provided the foundation for coordinate geometry, and Sir Isaac Newton was famous for his development of calculus. Newton wrote to a friend, "If I have seen farther than Descartes, it is because I have stood on the shoulders of giants." Research why he might have made such a statement. Answers may vary.

TEST YOURSELF

Simplify.   12.7

1. $\sqrt{\dfrac{4}{8}}$ $\dfrac{\sqrt{2}}{2}$

2. $\dfrac{5}{3 - \sqrt{2}}$ $\dfrac{15 + 5\sqrt{2}}{7}$

3. $\sqrt{t^2 + 6t + 9}$ $t + 3$

4. $\dfrac{\sqrt{48x^3y^2}}{\sqrt{3xy}}$ $4x\sqrt{y}$

5. $\dfrac{-3\sqrt{5}}{4 - \sqrt{15}}$ $-12\sqrt{5} - 15\sqrt{3}$

6. $\dfrac{5}{2 - \sqrt{3}}$ $10 + 5\sqrt{3}$

Find the solution to each of the following equations.   12.8

7. $\sqrt{10t^2 - 16} = t$ $\frac{4}{3}$

8. $\sqrt{9a^2 - 6a + 1} = 0$ $\frac{1}{3}$

9. $\sqrt{12x - 35} = x$ 7, 5

10. $\sqrt{-5h + 3} = \sqrt{2h}$ $\frac{1}{2}$

Determine the value of x for each of the following triangles.   12.9

11.
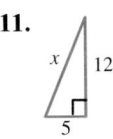
x 12
5
13

12.
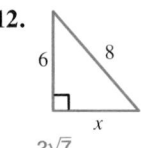
6 8
x
$2\sqrt{7}$

13.
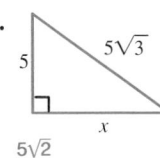
5 $5\sqrt{3}$
x
$5\sqrt{2}$

Find the distance and midpoint for each of the following pairs   12.10–12.11
of points.

14. $A(10, 7)$, $B(-3, 4)$ $\sqrt{178}$; $\left(3\frac{1}{2}, 5\frac{1}{2}\right)$

15. $A(8, -10)$, $B(3, 5)$ $5\sqrt{10}$; $\left(5\frac{1}{2}, -2\frac{1}{2}\right)$

12.11 Problem Solving Strategy: Use Coordinate Geometry **535**

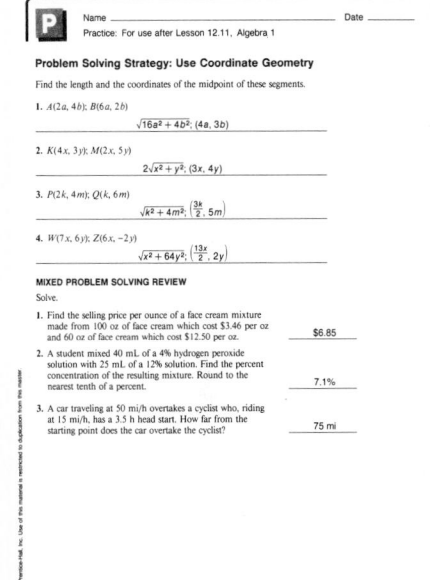
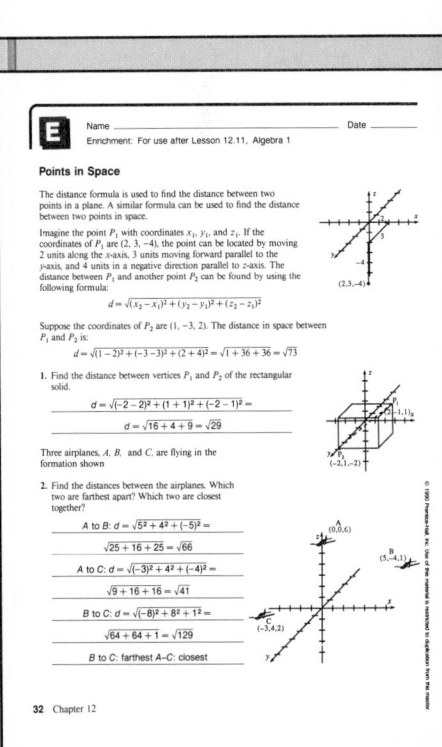

- See *Teacher's Resource Book, Spanish Chapter Summary and Review*, pp. 23–24.
- See Extra Practice, p. 666.

CHAPTER 12 SUMMARY AND REVIEW

Vocabulary

completeness property (497)	radical equation (520)
conjugate (517)	radical sign (494)
density property (498)	radicand (494)
hypotenuse (524)	rationalizing the denominator (516)
irrational number (497)	repeating decimal (500)
leg (524)	square root (494)
principal square root (494)	terminating decimal (500)
radical (494)	

Square Roots   If $x^2 = y$, then x is called a square root of y.   **12.1**

Product and Quotient Properties of Square Roots

For all real numbers m and n where $m \geq 0$ and $n \geq 0$, $\sqrt{mn} = \sqrt{m} \cdot \sqrt{n}$

For all real numbers m and n where $m \geq 0$ and $n > 0$, $\sqrt{\dfrac{m}{n}} = \dfrac{\sqrt{m}}{\sqrt{n}}$.

Find the principal square root.

1. $\sqrt{25}$ 5   **2.** $\sqrt{\dfrac{4}{9}}$ $\dfrac{2}{3}$ **3.** $\sqrt{\dfrac{81}{36}}$ $\dfrac{3}{2}$ **4.** $\sqrt{900}$ 30

Irrational Square Roots   An irrational number is a real number that   **12.2**
cannot be written in the form $\dfrac{m}{n}$, where m and n are integers and $n \neq 0$.

Use the square-root table on page 670 to approximate the square root.

5. $\sqrt{5}$ 2.236   **6.** $\sqrt{10}$ 3.162   **7.** $\sqrt{89}$ 9.434   **8.** $\sqrt{60}$ 7.746

Use the divide-and-average method to the nearest hundredth to approximate the square root.

9. $\sqrt{8}$ 2.83   **10.** $\sqrt{17}$ 4.12   **11.** $\sqrt{27}$ 5.20   **12.** $\sqrt{86}$ 9.27

Decimal Form of Rational Numbers   A rational number can be written   **12.3**
in the form $\dfrac{m}{n}$, where m and n are integers, $n \neq 0$. A rational number can
also be written as a terminating or repeating decimal.

Write each rational number as a terminating or repeating decimal.

13. $-\dfrac{7}{2}$ -3.5 **14.** $\dfrac{1}{9}$ $0.\overline{1}$ **15.** $\dfrac{5}{6}$ $0.8\overline{3}$

Write each decimal in the form $\dfrac{m}{n}$, where m and n are integers, $n \neq 0$.

16. 0.25 $\frac{1}{4}$

17. $0.\overline{6}$ $\frac{2}{3}$

18. $0.\overline{54}$ $\frac{6}{11}$

Simplifying Square Roots An expression that contains a square root is in *simplest form* when: The radicand contains no square factors other than 1, and no fractions. No denominator contains a radical.　12.4

Simplify.

19. $\sqrt{20}$ $2\sqrt{5}$

20. $\sqrt{45}$ $3\sqrt{5}$

21. $\sqrt{98x^2}$ $7x\sqrt{2}$

22. $\sqrt{12y^3}$ $2y\sqrt{3y}$

Combining Square Roots Only like square roots can be simplified using addition or subtraction. Use the Product and Quotient Properties to multiply and divide.　12.5–12.7

Perform the indicated operations.

23. $\sqrt{5} + 2\sqrt{6} - 4\sqrt{5}$　$-3\sqrt{5} + 2\sqrt{6}$

24. $-5\sqrt{6x} \cdot 2\sqrt{3x}$　$-30x\sqrt{2}$

25. $\sqrt{3}(2\sqrt{2} - 5)$　$2\sqrt{6} - 5\sqrt{3}$

26. $(2 - 3\sqrt{5})(3 + 2\sqrt{5})$　$-24 - 5\sqrt{5}$

27. $\dfrac{\sqrt{3}}{\sqrt{5}}$　$\frac{\sqrt{15}}{5}$

28. $\dfrac{1 + \sqrt{5}}{2 - \sqrt{5}}$　$-7 - 3\sqrt{5}$

Solving Radical Equations To solve a radical equation, isolate the radical and then square each side of the equation.　12.8

Solve.

29. $\sqrt{3x - 1} = 4$　$\frac{17}{3}$

30. $0 = 6 + 2\sqrt{x}$　no solution

31. $\sqrt{2y + 1} + 2 = 5$　4

Pythagorean Theorem In a right triangle, the square of the hypotenuse is equal to the sum of the squares of the legs: $c^2 = a^2 + b^2$.　12.9

If c is the hypotenuse, find the length of the unknown side.

32. $a = 10,\ b = 24,\ c = ?$　26

33. $a = 1,\ c = \sqrt{2},\ b = ?$　1

Distance Formula $d = \sqrt{(x_2 - x_1)^2 + (y_2 - y_1)^2}$　12.10

Find the distance between the given points.

34. $A(0, 9)$ and $B(0, -12)$　21

35. $X(-3, 7)$ and $Y(-9, -6)$　$\sqrt{205}$

Use Coordinate Geometry Many problems in geometry can be solved using algebraic techniques.　12.11

36. A rectangle has vertices at $(0, 0)$, $(-3, 3)$, $(3, 9)$, and $(6, 6)$. Find the length and the midpoint of each diagonal. $3\sqrt{10};\ \left(1\frac{1}{2}, 4\frac{1}{2}\right)$

Summary and Review　**537**

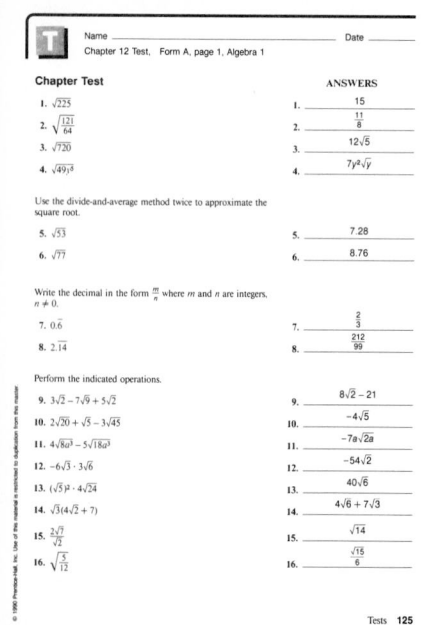

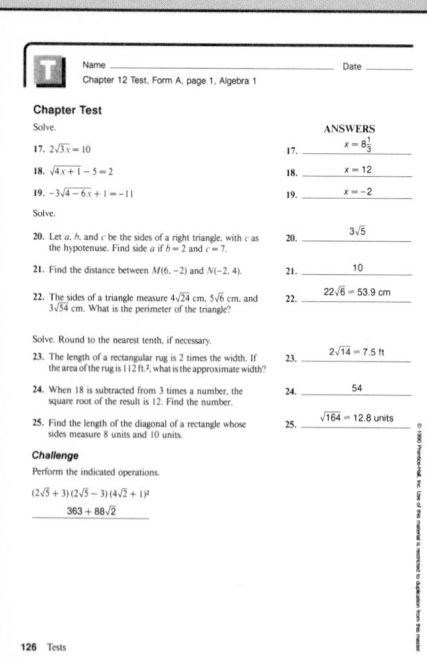

CHAPTER 12 TEST

Simplify.

1. $\sqrt{\dfrac{100}{49}}$ $\dfrac{10}{7}$

2. $\sqrt{900}$ 30

3. $\sqrt{450}$ $15\sqrt{2}$

4. $\sqrt{27y^3}$ $3y\sqrt{3y}$

5. Use the divide-and-average method to approximate $\sqrt{24}$.   ≈4.89

Write each decimal in the form $\dfrac{m}{n}$ **where m and n are integers, $n \neq 0$.**

6. $0.\overline{3}$ $\dfrac{1}{3}$

7. $1.\overline{45}$ $\dfrac{16}{11}$

Perform the indicated operations.

8. $2\sqrt{3} - 4\sqrt{3} + 5\sqrt{4}$ $-2\sqrt{3} + 10$

9. $\sqrt{12b^2} - \sqrt{27b^2}$ $-b\sqrt{3}$

10. $3\sqrt{6} \cdot 2\sqrt{3}$ $18\sqrt{2}$

11. $\sqrt{2}(2\sqrt{5} - 3)$ $2\sqrt{10} - 3\sqrt{2}$

12. $\dfrac{\sqrt{5}}{\sqrt{8}}$ $\dfrac{\sqrt{10}}{4}$

13. $\sqrt{\dfrac{2}{3}}$ $\dfrac{\sqrt{6}}{3}$

Solve.

14. $2\sqrt{2x + 1} = 8$ $\dfrac{15}{2}$

15. $\sqrt{3x - 1} + 2 = 7$ $\dfrac{26}{3}$

16. If c is the hypotenuse of a right triangle, find b when $a = 2$ and $c = 4$. $2\sqrt{3}$

17. Find the distance between $A(-2, 4)$ and $B(7, -8)$.   15

18. A triangle has vertices at $(-4, 0)$, $(4, 0)$, and $(0, 8)$. Find the midpoint of each side of the triangle. $(0, 0)$; $(2, 4)$; $(-2, 4)$

19. A rectangle has sides with lengths of 6 and 9. Find the lengths of the diagonals of this rectangle. $3\sqrt{13}$

Solve. Round to the nearest tenth, if necessary.

20. Find the perimeter and area of a rectangle whose length is $5\sqrt{y}$ ft and whose width is $2\sqrt{y}$ ft. $P = 14\sqrt{y}$ ft; $A = 10y$ ft^2

21. When 5 is subtracted from the square root of twice a number, the result is 61. Find the number.   2178

22. What length of wire is needed to reach from the top of a 3.5 m pole to a point 1.5 m from the base of the pole?   3.8 m

Challenge

In dealing with the theory of vibratory motion in physics, the equation $a^2 - 2al + k^2 = 0$ is derived. Show that $a = l \pm \sqrt{l^2 - k^2}$ are both solutions of the equation.

538   Chapter 12 Radicals

Additional Answers

Challenge

$(l + \sqrt{l^2 - k^2})^2 - 2l(l + \sqrt{l^2 - k^2}) + k^2 = 0$ and
$(l - \sqrt{l^2 - k^2})^2 - 2l(l - \sqrt{l^2 - k^2}) + k^2 = 0$.

Select the best choice for each question.

1. When simplified, $\sqrt{18x^3y^2} =$
   B
   A. $2xy\sqrt{3x}$ B. $3xy\sqrt{2x}$
   C. $2xy\sqrt{3}$ D. $3xy\sqrt{2}$
   E. $9xy\sqrt{x}$

2. In 1987, the towns in one county
   D spent the following amounts for education:

$6,472,891	$4,989,300
$1,473,600	$12,394,000
$3,456,863	$947,965

   To the nearest million, what was the total spent for education by these six towns?
   A. $27 million   B. $28 million
   C. $29 million   D. $30 million
   E. $31 million

3. $\sqrt{2809}$ equals
   C
   A. 43   B. 47   C. 53
   D. 57   E. 63

4. $\sqrt{162} + \sqrt{50} - 3\sqrt{8} =$
   E
   A. $6 - \sqrt{2}$ B. $2\sqrt{5} - 3\sqrt{2}$
   C. $20\sqrt{2}$ D. $9\sqrt{2}$
   E. $8\sqrt{2}$

5. Find the better price: a bicycle
   D advertised at 30% off on a list price of $348 or one advertised at 25% off on a list price of $295?
   A. $73.75   B. $104.40
   C. $209.97   D. $221.25
   E. $243.60

6. Solve for x: $\sqrt{2x - 5} = 3$
   E
   A. 3   B. 4   C. 5
   D. 6   E. 7

7. What fraction is equivalent to the
   B decimal 1.125?
   A. $\frac{45}{4}$ B. $\frac{9}{8}$ C. $\frac{6}{5}$
   D. $\frac{5}{6}$ E. $\frac{9}{80}$

8. Paul has been assigned a term
   C paper which is to be 20 pages long. He typed his first draft and found he had only 15 pages. What per cent of the term paper did he have left to write?
   A. 5%   B. 20%   C. 25%
   D. $33\frac{1}{3}$%   E. 75%

9. Solve for x:
   A
   $$\frac{3}{x + 1} - \frac{2}{x} = \frac{2}{x + 1}$$
   A. -2 B. -1 C. 0
   D. 1   E. 2

10. Use $a^2 + b^2 = c^2$ to find b when
    A $a = 24$ and $c = 25$.
    A. 7   B. 8   C. 51
    D. 49   E. 51

11. If the circle has a radius of 14 cm
    D and one side of the square is 16 cm, what is the area of the shaded portion? (Use $\frac{22}{7}$ as an approximation for π.)
    A. 1232 sq cm
    B. 976 sq cm
    C. 616 sq cm
    D. 360 sq cm
    E. 106 sq cm

The individual comments provided about some problems can be helpful in guiding students to solve these problems.

2. Since all the answer choices are close in amounts, students should add the actual amounts and then round the sum. Students may also round addends to the nearest ten-thousand and then add.

7. Answer choices A, D, and E can be eliminated immediately, since they are either less than 1 or greater than 10.

See *Teacher's Resource Book,* for Preparing for Standardized Tests.

See *Teacher's Resource Book, Cumulative Test,* pp. 133–136.

CUMULATIVE REVIEW (CHAPTERS 1–12)

Write the numbers in order from least to greatest. $-\sqrt{\frac{9}{16}}, -\frac{1}{3}, 0, \frac{1}{2}, \sqrt{\frac{4}{9}}$ 1.2

1. $\sqrt{4}, 6, 3, -2$ -2, $\sqrt{4}$, 3, 6

2. $-\frac{1}{3}, \sqrt{\frac{4}{9}}, 0, -\sqrt{\frac{9}{16}}, \frac{1}{2}$

Match the equation or inequality in exercises 3–7 with its solution set a–e.   5.2, 5.6, 11.5

3. $\frac{1}{x^2} - \frac{2}{3x} = \frac{5}{3}$ B

4. $|x| - 3 = -2$ E

5. $2 < 5 - 3x < 8$ A

6. $2x - 3 > -1$ C

7. $\begin{cases} -7y + 6 = x \\ 3x + y = -2 \end{cases}$ D

a. $\{x: -1 < x < 1\}$

b. $\left\{-1, \frac{3}{5}\right\}$

c. {all real numbers greater than 1}

d. $\{(-1, 1)\}$

e. $\{-1, 1\}$

Solve each equation, inequality, or system.   4.4, 5.6, 11.2, 12.8

8. $15x = 5(x - 4)$ -2

9. $6 - \frac{3}{4}a > 3$ a < 4

10. $|2y - 1| = 5$ -2; 3

11. $m - \frac{3}{4} = \frac{5m}{8}$ 2

12. $\frac{2}{3}t - 1 = 7$ 12

13. $\begin{cases} 2c + 3d = 14 \\ 4c - 3d = 10 \end{cases}$ (4, 2)

14. $z^2 - 9z = 0$ 0, 9

15. $\frac{3}{b + 2} = \frac{1}{b - 2}$ 4

16. $6 + \sqrt{n - 3} = 2$ no solution

17. $4r - 5(r + 1) = -(3r - 2) + 5$ 6

18. $-9 \le -3n$ and $-3n < 6$ -2 < n ≤ 3

19. $g^2 + 2g - 15 = 0$ -5, 3

20. $\sqrt{3w + 1} = 3\sqrt{2w - 1}$ $\frac{2}{3}$

Solve. Use the table on the right.   10.4

21. ABC Roofing charges $25 plus a certain amount per hour. How much does ABC Roofing charge per hour? $15

22. Tin Roofing charges by the hour. How much does Tin Roofing charge per hour? $20

Cost of Job				
Time worked	1 h	2 h	3 h	4 h
ABC Roofing	$40	$55	?	?
Tin Roofing	$20	$40	?	?

23. How long must a job be for both to charge the same amount? 5 h

24. Complete the table.

70	85
60	80

Simplify. Assume that no variable equals zero. **2.5, 6.4, 8.1, 8.6, 12.4**

25. $|-\sqrt{36}|$ 6

26. $-\left[-\left(-\frac{1}{3}\right)\right]$ $-\frac{1}{3}$

27. $\sqrt{\dfrac{9}{144}}$ $\frac{1}{4}$

28. $(1.2 \times 10^{-3})^2$ 1.44×10^{-6} **29.** $(3p^2q)(2pq^3)$ $6p^3q^4$

30. $(c - d)^2 - d^2$
$c^2 - 2cd$

31. $\dfrac{-6a^5b^2}{9a^3b^3}$ $\frac{-2a^2}{3b}$

32. $\dfrac{-2}{3\sqrt{2x}}$ $-\frac{\sqrt{2x}}{3x}$

33. $\dfrac{3 - m}{m^2 - m - 6}$ $-\frac{1}{m+2}$

34. $\dfrac{z^2 - 4}{3z + 6}$ $\frac{z-2}{3}$

35. $\dfrac{s + t}{\dfrac{3}{s} + \dfrac{3}{t}}$ $\frac{st}{3}$

36. $\sqrt{12x^3y}$ $2x\sqrt{3xy}$

37. $2(\sqrt{3^2 + 1})^2 - 3(\sqrt{2^2 - 1})$
$20 - 3\sqrt{3}$

38. $2[(h - 3)^2] + 2[h - (-3)^2]$
$2h(h - 5)$

Write the equation for each line in slope-intercept form. **9.4, 9.6**

39. The line represented by $x - 2y = 6$. $y = \frac{1}{2}x - 3$

40. The line that has slope -2 and contains the point $P\ (1, 1)$. $y = -2x + 3$

41. The line that contains the points $A\ (-1, -2)$ and $B\ (1, 4)$. $y = 3x + 1$

Factor completely. If a polynomial cannot be factored, write prime. **7.3–7.5**

42. $m^2 - 11m + 18$
$(m - 2)(m - 9)$

43. $12x^2y^2 - 9xy^2$
$3xy^2(4x - 3)$

44. $4a^6 + 12a^3 + 9$
$(2a^3 + 3)^2$

45. $a^3 + 23$ Prime

46. $2b^2 - 9b - 18$
$(2b + 3)(b - 6)$

47. $3p^3 + 9p^2 + 3p$
$3p(p^2 + 3p + 1)$

48. $xy - 3y - 2x + 6$ $(y - 2)(x - 3)$

49. $3m + 6n - 2m^2 - 4mn$
$(m + 2n)(3 - 2m)$

The fee for renting a computer is $45 plus $25 for each day you keep the machine. Use this information for Exercises 50–53. **9.3**

50. Complete this table.

Number of days	1	2	3
Rental fee	$70	? $95	? $120

51. Use the table to graph three points for this relationship. Draw a line through the points. See side column.

52. Use the graph to determine the rental fee for 5 days. $170

53. Jan can spend $220. For how many days can he rent a computer? 7 days

Evaluate each expression if $a = -\frac{1}{2}$, $b = 4$, and $c = -\frac{3}{4}$. **2.2, 7.4, 8.7, 12.4, 12.7**

54. $[(a + c)b]^2 - 1$ 24

55. $\sqrt{b} \div a$ -4

56. $b + c \div a$ $5\frac{1}{2}$

57. $\sqrt{-b \div a}$ $2\sqrt{2}$

58. $(a^2 + c)(a^2 - c)$ $-\frac{1}{2}$

59. $\sqrt{(a - c)b}$ 1

60. $\dfrac{a^2b}{a + b}$ $\frac{2}{7}$

61. $\sqrt{\dfrac{-a\sqrt{b}}{(a - c)^2}}$ 4

62. $\sqrt{b} + \dfrac{c - a^2}{b}$ $1\frac{3}{4}$

Cumulative Review **541**

51.
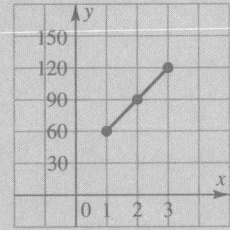

Perform the indicated operation.　　　　6.1, 6.6, 6.7, 8.1, 8.2, 8.3, 12.4, 12.5

63. $(0.6 \div 0.3)^2$ 4

64. $\sqrt{0.25} - (0.2)^2$ 0.46

65. $-0.8 - (-\sqrt{0.36})$ -0.2

66. $(-2a^2d)(5a^3d^2)$ $-10a^5d^3$

67. $(-3m^2n^3)^2$ $9m^4n^6$

68. $(3t - 2)^2$ $9t^2 - 12t + 4$

69. $\dfrac{p + 2}{p + 1} \cdot \dfrac{p^2 - 1}{p^2 - 4}$ $\dfrac{p - 1}{p - 2}$

70. $\dfrac{12x^3y^2}{4x^5yz}$ $\dfrac{3y}{x^2z}$

71. $\dfrac{c^2 - 9}{c - 1} \div c - 3$ $\dfrac{c + 3}{c - 1}$

72. $\dfrac{2h}{h^2 - 1} - \dfrac{1}{h + 1}$ $\dfrac{1}{h - 1}$

73. $\sqrt{2}(3 + 2\sqrt{10})$ $3\sqrt{2} + 4\sqrt{5}$

74. $\dfrac{-3\sqrt{14}}{\sqrt{63}}$ $-\sqrt{2}$

75. $(5r^2 + 2r) - (3r^2 - 4r + 1)$ $2r^2 + 6r - 1$

76. $(-b^3 + 3b^2 - 2)(-3b^2)$ $3b^5 - 9b^4 + 6b^2$

77. $3x(y^2 + 2y) - 2y(xy + 2x)$ $xy^2 + 2xy$

78. $\sqrt{25x^2y} - \sqrt{9x^2y} + \sqrt{36x^2y}$ $8x\sqrt{y}$

Determine the range for each given domain $\{-2, 0, 1\}$.　　　　10.1

79. $y = 2x - 3$ $\{-7, -3, -1\}$

80. $y = x^2 + 1$ $\{5, 1, 2\}$

81. $\frac{1}{2}y = \frac{1}{4}x + 3$ $\{5, 6, 6\frac{1}{2}\}$

82. $\frac{1}{3}y = x + \frac{1}{6}$ $\{-5\frac{1}{2}, 6, 6\frac{1}{2}\}$

Solve.　　　　4.3, 4.5, 8.6, 8.9, 10.4, 10.5, 11.1, 11.9

83. The cost of apples c varies directly with their weight w. If $c = \$1.29$ when $w = 3$, find c when $w = 5$. $2.15

84. Find three consecutive odd integers such that the first times the second is 1 more than 2 times the third. 3, 5, 7 or −3, −1, 1

85. A crew rowing with the current traveled 18 mi in 2 h and against the current, the crew rowed 10 mi in 2 h. Find the rate of the crew in still water and the rate of the current. rate of crew 7 mi/h; rate of current 2 mi/h

86. Ben earned \$127.50 in annual simple interest on an investment of \$1500. What annual interest rate was paid? 8.5%

87. The length of a rectangle is 4 less than twice its width. If the perimeter is 52 ft, what are the dimensions of the rectangle? $w = 10$ ft; $l = 16$ ft

88. If a bus traveling at 50 mi/h takes 6 h to travel from San Francisco to Fresno, and a train takes 4 h to travel the same distance, does the rate vary indirectly as the time? If so, what is the constant of variation? 300

89. The width of a rectangle is $\dfrac{2w + 8}{(w + 2)(w - 2)}$ in., and the area is $\dfrac{4}{w^2 - 4}$ in². Find the length of the rectangle. $l = \dfrac{2}{w + 4}$

90. Find two positive numbers that differ by 3 and whose reciprocals have a sum of $\frac{8}{9}$. $\frac{3}{2}, \frac{9}{2}$

OVERVIEW • Chapter 13

SUMMARY

The concept of quadratic functions was just introduced in Chapter 10. In this chapter, students learn to solve quadratic equations by using the square-root property, completing the square, and using the quadratic formula. Students also review solving quadratic equations by factoring. Students are introduced to the relationships among the solutions of a quadratic equation, the discriminant, and the graph of the related quadratic function. Finally, students write quadratic equations and use various methods to solve word problems.

After this chapter is completed, students should be able to solve quadratic equations by choosing an appropriate procedure, and to graph quadratic functions. They should also be able to solve word problems involving quadratic functions.

CHAPTER OBJECTIVES

- To solve quadratic equations using the square-root property, by completing the square, using the quadratic formula, and using graphs of quadratic functions

- To write a quadratic equation to solve a word problem

- To choose the most appropriate method for solving a quadratic equation

- To use the discriminant to determine the number and the nature of the solutions of a quadratic equation

- To write a quadratic equation given the sum and the product of the solutions of the equation

- To graph a quadratic function

Problem Solving Strategy

To solve a word problem using a function

CHAPTER HIGHLIGHTS

The *theme* of Chapter 13 is construction and design. The chapter's features and art show how construction and design use the concepts of quadratic equations and quadratic functions.

PROBLEM SOLVING AND APPLICATIONS

Real-world problems are solved by using various functions, a strategy that will prove very useful in later math courses. Models which require quadratic functions are presented as models which require linear functions. A common application of quadratic functions to physics is featured after Lesson 13.5. Applications from many other areas are presented in each lesson, showing the different fields which give rise to quadratic relationships.

TECHNOLOGY

Calculator

Solutions to quadratic functions can be verified easily with a calculator. This is especially true for irrational solutions. Problems which require the quadratic formula can often be done more quickly with a calculator.

Computer

A program for solving problems involving projectile motion is given in the physics application. The quadratic formula is also a good candidate for programming.

RESOURCES

Teacher's Resource Book

- Teaching Aids 10, 11, 12, 16

- Transparencies 14, 15, 30

STUDENT TEXT

TEACHER'S RESOURCE BOOK

Chapter Content	Basic	Average	Enriched	R	P	E
13.1 Quadratic Equations with Perfect Squares	D: 545/1-27 odd, 56	D: 545/21-45 odd, 56 R: 546/18, 22, 26	D: 545/37-55 odd, 56 R: 546/36, 40, 44	1	2	3
13.2 Completing the Square	D: 549/1-17 odd, 43 R: 545/18, 22, 26	D: 550/13-29 odd, 43, 44 R: 546/36, 40, 44	D: 550/25-41 odd, 43, 44 R: 546/46, 50, 54	4	5	6
13.3 The Quadratic Formula	D: 552/1-23 odd, 43 R: 549/10, 14, 18	D: 553/17-35 odd, 43, 44 R: 550/22, 26, 30 553/16, 20, 24	D: 553/25-41 odd, 43, 44 R: 550/32, 38, 42 553/28, 32, 36	7	8	9
13.4 Mixed Practice: Solving Quadratic Equations by Any Method	D: 555/1-15 odd, 35, 36 R: 553/16, 20, 24 Test Yourself	D: 555/13-27 odd, 35-39 R: 553/28, 32, 36 Test Yourself	D: 555/19-33 odd, 35-41 R: 553/34, 38, 42 Test Yourself	10	11	12
13.5 Graphing Quadratic Functions	D: 560/1-15 odd, 34 R: 555/8, 12, 16	D: 561/1-27 odd, 34, 35 R: 555/20, 24, 28 561/2, 8, 10	D: 561/19-33 odd, 34, 35 R: 555/26, 30, 34 561/10, 14, 16	13	14	15
13.6 The Discriminant	D: 566/1-11 odd, 25 R: 560/8, 12, 16	D: 566/9-19 odd, 25, 26 R: 561/20, 24, 28	D: 566/13-23 odd, 25, 26 R: 561/24, 28, 30	16	17	18
13.7 Problem Solving Strategy: Using a Function	D: 569/1-9 odd MPSR: 1-4 R: 566/10, 14, 18	D: 570/9-15 odd MPSR: 1-4 R: 566/14, 18, 22	D: 570/11-17 odd MPSR: 1-4 R: 566/16, 20, 24		19	20
13.8 The Sum and Product of the Solutions	D: 574/1-15 odd, 30 R: Test Yourself	D: 574/11-23 odd, 30, 31 R: Test Yourself	D: 574/17-29 odd, 30, 31 R: Test Yourself	21	22	23

D = Daily   R = Review   MPSR = Mixed Problem Solving Review   R = Reteaching   P = Practice   E = Enrichment

STUDENT TEXT				**TEACHER'S RESOURCE BOOK**	
Review	Test Yourself	556	Prep. for Stan. Tests	579	Spanish Chapter Summary and Review	25-26
And	Test Yourself	575	Maintaining Skills	580	• Quizzes	137-140
Testing	Chapter Sum. and Rev.	576	Extra Practice	667	• Chapter Test (Form A)	141-142
	Chapter Test	578			• Chapter Test (Form B)	143-144
					Calculator Test	25-26
Special	Historical Note	546	Application	562	Applications—Chapter 13	24
Features	Math Club Activity	550	Logical Reasoning	566	Critical Thinking	13
	Did You Know?	553	Project	571	Reading and Writing in Algebra	13
	Math Club Activity	561			Technology	23-25

13 Quadratic Equations and Functions

Designing and constructing uniquely shaped buildings involves solving various kinds of problems. For example, quadratic equations can be used to find the strengths and weaknesses of circular and rectangular beam configurations.

543

BACKGROUND

In the planning and construction of buildings, many types of equations and functions are used. Although linear equations are commonly used, quadratic equations and functions are applied in the various industries related to building design and construction.

LESSON PLAN

Vocabulary
Perfect square
Quadratic equation
Square-root property

Materials/Manipulatives
Calculators

BACKGROUND

In the Capsule Review, the exercises focus on finding the square root of expressions of the form ax^2 and $(ax - b)^2$. You may wish to remind students why all variables are assumed to be nonnegative.

TEACHING SUGGESTIONS

- Using Examples 1–3, point out that the solutions of these quadratic equations depend on the value of k. In Example 1, the value of k is not a perfect square, so its square root is irrational. In Example 2, the value of k is a perfect square, so the square root of k is rational. In Example 3, $k < 0$, so there is no real number solution.
- Point out that students may use their calculator or a Table of Square Roots to obtain decimal approximations for irrational roots.

Critical Thinking

Causal Explanation $(x - 1)^2 = 0$ has only one solution, $x = 1$. Explain why. $(x - 1)^2 = 0$ is considered to have two equal solutions: $x = 1$ and $x = 1$; 1 is said to be a double solution. This can be seen in the form $x - 1 = \pm\sqrt{0}$, or $x = 1 + \sqrt{0}$ and $x = 1 - \sqrt{0}$.

13.1

Quadratic Equations with Perfect Squares

Objective: To solve quadratic equations involving perfect-square expressions

A contractor has 225 square paving stones to cover a square outdoor area. Each stone is one square foot. The contractor can find the number of paving stones for one side by solving the quadratic equation, $x^2 = 225$. The property of square roots can be useful in solving quadratic equations of the form $x^2 = k$ or $(ax + b)^2 = k$, where $k \geq 0$.

Capsule Review

Recall that if $x^2 = y$, then x is called the square root of y.

Find the square root. Assume all variables are nonnegative.

1. $4x^2$ ±2x   **2.** $16y^2$ ±4y   **3.** $25m^2n^2$ ±5mn   **4.** $(3y - 1)^2$ ±(3y − 1)

An algebraic expression like $4x^2$ or $(3y - 1)^2$ is called a **perfect square.** When an equation contains a perfect square on one side and a nonnegative constant on the other, you can use the square-root property.

┌───┐

Square-Root Property

If $x^2 = k$, then $x = +\sqrt{k}$ or $x = -\sqrt{k}$ for any real number k, $k \geq 0$.

└───┘

EXAMPLE 1   Solve: $4x^2 = 20$

$$4x^2 = 20$$
$$x^2 = 5 \qquad \text{\textit{Divide each side by 4.}}$$
$$x = \pm\sqrt{5} \qquad \text{\textit{Apply the square-root property.}}$$

Check:

$4x^2 = 20$	$4x^2 = 20$
$4(\sqrt{5})^2 \overset{?}{=} 20$	$4(-\sqrt{5})^2 \overset{?}{=} 20$
$4(5) \overset{?}{=} 20$	$4(5) \overset{?}{=} 20$
$20 = 20$ ✔	$20 = 20$ ✔

The solutions are $\pm\sqrt{5}$. Use your calculator to find decimal approximations for the solutions.

EXAMPLE 2 Solve: $(y - 7)^2 = 64$

$(y - 7)^2 = 64$ *Take the square root of each side of the equation.*
$y - 7 = \pm 8$

$y - 7 = 8$ | $y - 7 = -8$
$ y = 15$ | $y = -1$

Check: $(y - 7)^2 = 64$ | $(y - 7)^2 = 64$
$(15 - 7)^2 \stackrel{?}{=} 64$ | $[(-1) - 7]^2 \stackrel{?}{=} 64$
$8^2 \stackrel{?}{=} 64$ | $(-8)^2 \stackrel{?}{=} 64$
$64 = 64$ ✓ | $64 = 64$ ✓

The solutions are 15 and -1.

EXAMPLE 3 Solve: $7(2n - 1)^2 + 10 = 3.$

$7(2n - 1)^2 + 10 = 3$
$7(2n - 1)^2 = -7$
$(2n - 1)^2 = -1$ *No real solution*

If you try to compute $\sqrt{-1}$ on your calculator, the display will indicate an error. There is no real number solution since the square of any real number is always a nonnegative real number.

CLASS EXERCISES

Solve. Express all radicals in simplest form.

1. $5x^2 = 30$ $\pm\sqrt{6}$ **2.** $n^2 = \frac{9}{16}$ $\pm\frac{3}{4}$ **3.** $3(x - 5)^2 = 75$ 10; 0

4. $(x - 2)^2 = 7$ $2 \pm \sqrt{7}$ **5.** $5(m + 3)^2 = 25$ $-3 \pm \sqrt{5}$ **6.** $4(x + 4)^2 = 256$ -12; 4

PRACTICE EXERCISES

Solve. Express all radicals in simplest form.

A   **1.** $p^2 = \frac{4}{25}$ $\pm\frac{2}{5}$ **2.** $n^2 = \frac{1}{100}$ $\pm\frac{1}{10}$ **3.** $x^2 = 49$ ± 7

4. $y^2 = 64$ ± 8 **5.** $3x^2 = 18$ $\pm\sqrt{6}$ **6.** $5m^2 = 35$ $\pm\sqrt{7}$

7. $2n^2 = 16$ $\pm 2\sqrt{2}$ **8.** $4y^2 = 48$ $\pm 2\sqrt{3}$ **9.** $x^2 - 15 = 0$ $\pm\sqrt{15}$

10. $y^2 - 10 = 0$ $\pm\sqrt{10}$ **11.** $2n^2 - 6 = 0$ $\pm\sqrt{3}$ **12.** $3m^2 - 15 = 0$ $\pm\sqrt{5}$

13. $4x^2 + 9 = 0$ **14.** $6y^2 + 24 = 0$ **15.** $3p^2 - 5 = 7$ ± 2
    no real solutions   no real solutions
16. $2n^2 - 13 = -1$ $\pm\sqrt{6}$ **17.** $8m^2 - 40 = 0$ $\pm\sqrt{5}$ **18.** $6z^2 - 42 = 0$ $\pm\sqrt{7}$

19. $(x - 1)^2 = 9$ 4, -2 **20.** $(y - 3)^2 = 36$ 9, -3 **21.** $(2x + 1)^2 = 16$ $\frac{3}{2}, -\frac{5}{2}$

22. $(3z + 2)^2 = 4$ 0, $-\frac{4}{3}$ **23.** $5(2x - 1)^2 = 45$ 2, -1 **24.** $6(3y + 2)^2 = 24$
                                                                          0, $-\frac{4}{3}$

13.1 Quadratic Equations with Perfect Squares   **545**

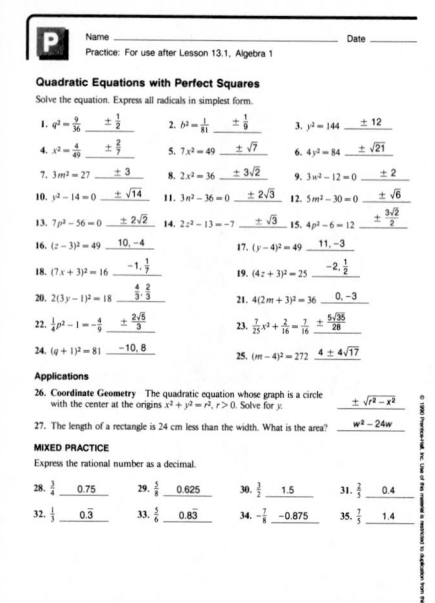

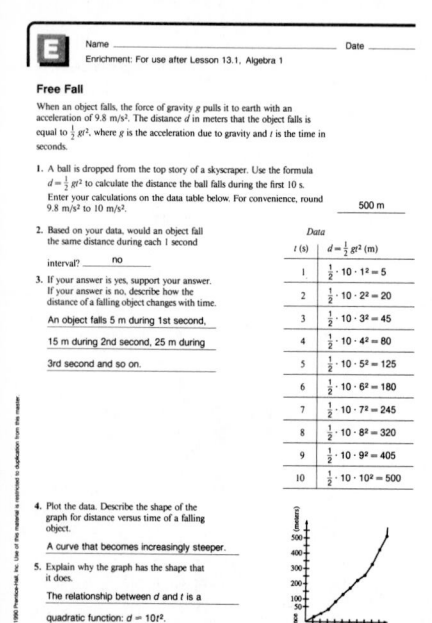

25. $\frac{1}{9}p^2 - 1 = -\frac{3}{4}$ $\pm\frac{3}{2}$

26. $\frac{4}{25}n^2 + \frac{6}{16} = \frac{15}{16}$ $\pm\frac{15}{8}$

27. $(x + 1)^2 = 72$ $-1 \pm 6\sqrt{2}$

B 28. $(n - 9)^2 = 27$ $9 \pm 3\sqrt{3}$

29. $\left(m + \frac{2}{3}\right)^2 = \frac{1}{9}$ $-\frac{1}{3}, -1$

30. $\left(n + \frac{3}{4}\right)^2 = \frac{1}{16}$ $-\frac{1}{2}, -1$

31. $\left(t + \frac{2}{3}\right)^2 = \frac{5}{9}$ $\frac{-2 \pm \sqrt{5}}{3}$

32. $\left(y + \frac{3}{4}\right)^2 = \frac{3}{16}$ $\frac{-3 \pm \sqrt{3}}{4}$

33. $2(5x + 1)^2 = 50$ $-\frac{6}{5}, \frac{4}{5}$

34. $3(2s + 4)^2 = 36$ $-2 \pm \sqrt{3}$

35. $5(z - 3)^2 = 35$ $3 \pm \sqrt{7}$

36. $7(m + 4)^2 = 70$ $-4 \pm \sqrt{10}$

37. $(x - 5)^2 + 3 = 27$ $5 + 2\sqrt{6}$

38. $(z + 3)^2 - 5 = 49$ $-3 \pm -3\sqrt{6}$

39. $2(3x - 5)^2 + 3 = 7$ $\frac{\pm\sqrt{2} + 5}{3}$

40. $3(2t + 7)^2 + 1 = 37$ $\frac{-7 \pm 2\sqrt{3}}{2}$

41. $3(2p + 1)^2 + 5 = 59$ $\frac{\pm3\sqrt{2} - 1}{2}$

42. $5(6m - 5)^2 - 3 = 57$ $\frac{\pm2\sqrt{3} + 5}{6}$

43. $6(2r + 3)^2 - 5 = 85$ $\frac{\pm\sqrt{15} - 3}{2}$

44. $\left(x - \frac{3}{5}\right)^2 - \frac{7}{9} = -\frac{1}{3}$ $-\frac{1}{15}, \frac{19}{15}$

45. $\left(y - \frac{1}{3}\right)^2 - \frac{5}{8} = -\frac{1}{2}$ $\frac{1}{3} \pm \frac{\sqrt{2}}{4}$

C 46. $5\left(x - \frac{1}{3}\right)^2 + \frac{1}{2} = \frac{3}{5}$ $\frac{1}{3} \pm \frac{\sqrt{2}}{10}$

47. $5\left(z - \frac{1}{2}\right)^2 + \frac{1}{3} = \frac{3}{4}$ $\frac{1}{2} \pm \frac{\sqrt{3}}{6}$

48. $x^2 + 2x + 1 = 4$ $1, -3$

49. $y^2 - 4y + 4 = 25$ $7, -3$

50. $25x^2 - 10x + 1 = 16$ $1, -\frac{3}{5}$

51. $16m^2 + 24m + 9 = 9$ $0, -\frac{3}{2}$

52. $x^2 + x + \frac{1}{4} = 4$ $\frac{3}{2}, -\frac{5}{2}$

53. $y^2 - 18y + 81 = 25$ $4, 14$

54. $y^2 - 12y + 36 = 84$ $6 \pm 2\sqrt{21}$

55. $b^2 + 14b + 42 = -7$ -7

Applications

Solve by the square-root property.

56. **Coordinate Geometry** The quadratic equation whose graph is a circle with the center at the origin is $x^2 + y^2 = r^2$, $r > 0$. Solve for x. $x = \pm\sqrt{r^2 - y^2}$

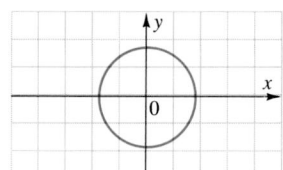

▌ HISTORICAL NOTE

The Palantine Anthology is a book of problems dating back to 500 A.D. The following problem was found in this book. Try to solve it.

> Brickmaker: I must finish this house soon. Today is cloudless and I need only a few more bricks. I have all I need but three hundred. I know you could make that many by yourself in one day. Your son will quit work when he makes 200. Your son-in-law will quit when he makes 250. The three of you working together, how soon can you have my bricks ready? $\frac{2}{5}$ of a day

Completing the Square

Objective: To solve quadratic equations by completing the square

Vocabulary
Complete the square

Materials/Manipulatives
Calculators

The product of two numbers is 40. The larger number exceeds the smaller one by 6. What equation can you use to determine the two numbers?

The equation $x(x + 6) = x^2 + 6x = 40$ is different from those of the form you solved in the preceding lesson because $x^2 + 6x$ is not a perfect square.

Capsule Review

Recall that an expression of the form $ax^2 + bx + c$ is a perfect-square trinomial if it can be factored into two identical binomial factors.

EXAMPLE **a.** $x^2 + 6x + 9 = (x + 3)(x + 3) = (x + 3)^2$

b. $x^2 - \dfrac{2}{3}x + \dfrac{1}{9} = \left(x - \dfrac{1}{3}\right)\left(x - \dfrac{1}{3}\right) = \left(x - \dfrac{1}{3}\right)^2$

Tell which of the following are perfect-square trinomials and factor them.

1. $x^2 + 4x + 4$ yes; $(x + 2)^2$ **2.** $4m^2 + 12m + 9$ **3.** $y^2 + y + 1$ no
yes; $(2m + 3)^2$

4. $z^2 - \dfrac{2}{5}z + \dfrac{1}{25}$ yes; $\left(z - \dfrac{1}{5}\right)^2$ **5.** $n^2 - n + \dfrac{1}{4}$ yes; $\left(n - \dfrac{1}{2}\right)^2$ **6.** $49p^2 - 28p + 4$
yes; $(7p - 2)^2$

7. $x^2 - x + 1$ no   **8.** $n^2 - \dfrac{4}{5}n + \dfrac{4}{25}$ yes; $\left(n - \dfrac{2}{5}\right)^2$ **9.** $c^2 - \dfrac{3}{2}c + \dfrac{9}{16}$
yes; $\left(c - \dfrac{3}{4}\right)^2$

BACKGROUND

In the Capsule Review, students must recognize and factor perfect-square trinomials. Students who are having difficulty should be referred to Chapter 7. In this lesson, students complete the square to solve quadratic equations that can be transformed into equations that contain a perfect square.

Critical Thinking

Comparing-Contrasting   Compare and contrast $2x^2 - 12x = 3$ and $x^2 + 8x - 7 = 0$. Each is a quadratic equation and can be solved by completing the square; however, the coefficient of the x^2-terms are different.

Study the perfect square at the right. In the expanded form of the square, notice that the coefficient of the first term is 1 and that the constant term is the square of one-half the coefficient of the term of the first degree.

$$(n - 6)^2 = n^2 - 12n + 36$$
$$36 = \left(\dfrac{1}{2} \cdot -12\right)^2$$

This fact can be used to develop a procedure for finding the value of c that makes $ax^2 + bx + c$ a perfect square.

To **complete the square** for $ax^2 + bx + \underline{\ ?\ }$:

* If $a \neq 1$, then divide the expression by a.
* Find one-half of the coefficient of x.
* Square the value obtained.
* Add the squared result to $x^2 + \dfrac{b}{a}x$.

Completing the square is one method of solving quadratic equations that works whether or not the equation can be factored. That is, it works for all quadratic equations.

13.2 Completing the Square   **547**

- Using Example 1, stress the steps involved in completing the square. Point out that the coefficient of x^2 is 1, and that students are looking for a value of c that makes $x^2 - 8x + c$ a perfect square trinomial.
- In Example 4, emphasize that before completing the square to solve the quadratic equation, the equation should be in the form $ax^2 + bx = c$, where $a = 1$.
- Have students use a calculator to check their solutions.

CHALKBOARD EXAMPLES

- **For Example 1**

Find the value of c to complete the square.

1. $y^2 - 12y + c$ 36
2. $x^2 - \frac{3}{2}x + c$ $\frac{9}{16}$

Solve by completing the square for Exercises 3–9. Express all radicals in simplest form.

- **For Example 2**
3. $x^2 + 6x = 27$ 3, −9
4. $y^2 - 10y = -24$ 4, 6

- **For Example 3**
5. $p^2 - p - 3\frac{3}{4} = 0$ $-\frac{3}{2}, \frac{5}{2}$
6. $n^2 - 2n - \frac{1}{3} = 0$ $\frac{3 \pm 2\sqrt{3}}{3}$

- **For Example 4**
7. $7x^2 - 14x - 28 = 0$ $1 \pm \sqrt{5}$
8. $2y^2 - 2y - 2 = 0$ $\frac{1 \pm \sqrt{5}}{2}$
9. $2z^2 + 12z + 8 = 0$ $-3 \pm \sqrt{5}$

Common Error

- Remind students to add the term $\left(\frac{1}{2} \cdot \frac{b}{a}\right)^2$ to both sides of the equation when they are completing the square. Students who frequently make this error should write out each step in words and check their answers.
- See *Teacher's Resource Book* for additional remediation.

548

EXAMPLE 1   **Find the value of c to complete the square for $x^2 - 8x + c$.**

Using the procedure given, the coefficient of x^2 is 1, and $\frac{1}{2}(-8) = -4$. The term to be added to $x^2 - 8x$ is $(-4)^2$ or 16. Therefore, $x^2 - 8x + 16$ is equal to $(x - 4)^2$, which is a perfect square.

EXAMPLE 2   **Solve $x^2 + 6x = 40$ by completing the square.**

$$x^2 + 6x = 40$$ *Complete the square.*
$$x^2 + 6x + 9 = 40 + 9$$ *Take one-half of the coefficient of x, square it, and add the result to both sides of the equation.*
   $\frac{1}{2}(6) = 3;\ 3^2 = 9$

$$(x + 3)^2 = 49$$ *Write $x^2 + 6x + 9$ as a perfect square.*

$x + 3 = 7$ | $x + 3 = -7$ *Solve the equation.*
$x = 4$ | $x = -10$

The solutions are 4 and -10. The check is left for you.

Example 2 shows the solution to the problem posed at the beginning of this lesson. If $x = 4$, then $x + 6 = 10$, so 4 and 10 is one answer. If $x = -10$, then $x + 6 = -4$, so -10 and -4 is another answer. Both pairs of numbers, 4, 10 and -4, -10, have a product of 40, and the larger number of each pair is 6 more than the smaller.

EXAMPLE 3   **Solve $y^2 - y - \frac{3}{4} = 0$ by completing the square.**

$$y^2 - y - \frac{3}{4} = 0$$

$$y^2 - y = \frac{3}{4}$$ *Add $\frac{3}{4}$ to each side.*

$$y^2 - y + \frac{1}{4} = \frac{3}{4} + \frac{1}{4}$$ *Complete the square: $\frac{1}{2}(-1) = -\frac{1}{2}$, and $\left(-\frac{1}{2}\right)^2 = \frac{1}{4}$. Add $\frac{1}{4}$ to each side of the equation.*

$$\left(y - \frac{1}{2}\right)^2 = 1$$ *Write $y^2 - y + \frac{1}{4}$ as a perfect square.*

$y - \frac{1}{2} = 1$ | $y - \frac{1}{2} = -1$ *Solve the equation.*
$y = \frac{3}{2}$ | $y = -\frac{1}{2}$

The solutions are $\frac{3}{2}$ and $-\frac{1}{2}$. The check is left for you.

Although the method of completing the square always works for solving quadratic equations, it is sometimes faster to solve equations by factoring. So, try factoring first, and if necessary try completing the square.

Before completing the square to solve a quadratic equation, make sure the equation is in the form $ax^2 + bx = c$ and then divide through by a.

548   Chapter 13 Quadratic Equations and Functions

EXAMPLE 4 Solve $2t^2 + 3t - 4 = 0$ by completing the square.

$2t^2 + 3t - 4 = 0$

$2t^2 + 3t = 4$ *Add 4 to each side.*

$t^2 + \frac{3}{2}t = 2$ *Divide each term by 2.*

$t^2 + \frac{3}{2}t + \frac{9}{16} = 2 + \frac{9}{16}$ *Complete the square. Since $\frac{1}{2}\left(\frac{3}{2}\right) = \frac{3}{4}$ and*

          $\left(\frac{3}{4}\right)^2 = \frac{9}{16}$, add $\frac{9}{16}$ to each side of the equation.

$\left(t + \frac{3}{4}\right)^2 = \frac{41}{16}$ *Write as a perfect square.*

$t + \frac{3}{4} = \frac{1}{4}\sqrt{41}$ $\Big|$ $t + \frac{3}{4} = -\frac{1}{4}\sqrt{41}$

$t = \dfrac{-3 + \sqrt{41}}{4}$ $\Big|$ $t = \dfrac{-3 - \sqrt{41}}{4}$

The solutions are $\dfrac{-3 + \sqrt{41}}{4}$ and $\dfrac{-3 - \sqrt{41}}{4}$. The check is left for you.

The computer program below can also be used to solve Example 4.

```
10 INPUT "FOR AT^2 + BT + C = 0, ENTER A,B,C:  ";A,B,C: PRINT
20 B = B / A:C =  - C / A
30 PRINT "T^2 + ";B;"T = ";C
40 N = ((1 / 2) * B) ^ 2
50 PRINT "T^2 + ";B;"T + ";N;" = ";C;" + ";N
60 PRINT "(T + ";(1 / 2) * B;")" ^ 2 = ";C + N
70 PRINT : PRINT "THE SOLUTIONS ARE "; SQR (C + N) - (1 / 2) * B;
   " AND "; -  SQR (C + N) - (1 / 2) * B
80 END
```

Compare these solutions with the results obtained using a calculator or the table on page 670.

CLASS EXERCISES

Find the value of c to complete the square.

1. $y^2 + 10y + c$ 25   **2.** $x^2 - 6x + c$ 9   **3.** $p^2 - \frac{2}{3}p + c$ $\frac{1}{9}$

Solve by completing the square.

4. $x^2 - 8x = -15$ 3, 5   **5.** $z^2 + 18z + 56 = 0$ **6.** $4n^2 = 4n + 1$ $\frac{1 \pm \sqrt{2}}{2}$
                                           −4, −14

PRACTICE EXERCISES

Find the value of c to complete the square.

A   **1.** $m^2 + 8m + c$ 16   **2.** $t^2 + 12t + c$ 36   **3.** $y^2 - 10y + c$ 25

Discussion

Examine the figure. Explain what must be added to the figure to make it a 6-by-6 square. Prove your answer algebraically.

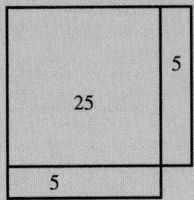

A square of area 1; $5^2 + 2 \cdot 5 + 1 = (5 + 1)^2 = 6^2$

Assignment Guide

See p. 542B for assignments.

Math Club Activity

For students who are having difficulty, analyze the differences between the two situations by making two tables.

Lesson Quiz

Find the value of c to complete the square.

1. $a^2 + a + c$ $\frac{1}{4}$

2. $y^2 + \frac{1}{2}y + c$ $\frac{1}{16}$

Solve by completing the square. Express all radicals in simplest form.

3. $y^2 + 4y = 5$ −5, 1
4. $x^2 - 4x + 1 = 0$ $2 \pm \sqrt{3}$
5. $2m^2 - 5m - 4 = 0$ $\frac{5 \pm \sqrt{57}}{4}$

Enrichment

Explain what values of b would make $4x^2 - bx + 1$ a perfect trinomial.   4

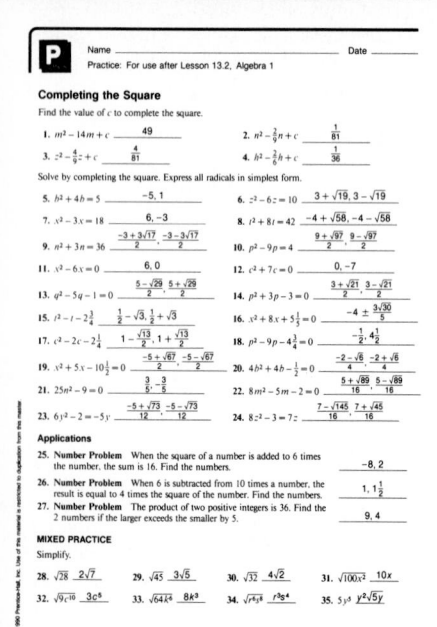

Solve by completing the square. Express all radicals in simplest form.

4. $y^2 + 3y = 3$ $\frac{-3 \pm \sqrt{21}}{2}$ 5. $b^2 - 4b = 5$ $-1, 5$ 6. $x^2 - 2x = 15$ $-3, 5$

7. $z^2 + 12z = 45$ $-15, 3$ 8. $h^2 + 12h = 28$ $-14, 2$ 9. $t^2 + 4t = 12$ $-6, 2$

10. $t^2 - 5t = 2\frac{3}{4}$ $-\frac{1}{2}, \frac{11}{2}$ 11. $y^2 + 7y = 7\frac{3}{4}$ $-\frac{7}{2} \pm 2\sqrt{5}$ 12. $x^2 + 3x = -1$ $\frac{-3 \pm \sqrt{5}}{2}$

13. $m^2 - 3m = -1$ $\frac{3 \pm \sqrt{5}}{2}$ 14. $x^2 + 3x = 0$ $-3, 0$ 15. $c^2 + 5c = 0$ $0, -5$

16. $r^2 - 6r + 5 = 0$ $1, 5$ 17. $p^2 + 8p - 9 = 0$ $-9, 1$ 18. $t^2 - 3t - 10 = 0$ $5, -2$

B 19. $p^2 + 5p + 6 = 0$ $-3, -2$ 20. $n^2 - 3n + \frac{5}{4} = 0$ $\frac{1}{2}, \frac{5}{2}$ 21. $r^2 - r - 3\frac{3}{4} = 0$ $\frac{5}{2}, -\frac{3}{2}$

22. $x^2 - 4x + 2 = 0$ $2 \pm \sqrt{2}$ 23. $4y^2 - 6y - \frac{1}{2} = 0$ $\frac{3 \pm \sqrt{11}}{4}$ 24. $3b^2 - 12b - 1 = 0$ $2 \pm \frac{\sqrt{39}}{3}$

25. $5p^2 - 10p = -4$ $1 \pm \frac{\sqrt{5}}{5}$ 26. $2t^2 - 5t = 4$ $\frac{5 \pm \sqrt{57}}{4}$ 27. $2c^2 + c = 5$ $\frac{-1 \pm \sqrt{41}}{4}$

28. $2z^2 - 10z = 3$ $\frac{5 \pm \sqrt{31}}{2}$ 29. $2n^2 + 10n - 3 = 0$ $\frac{-5 \pm \sqrt{31}}{2}$ 30. $2m^2 - m - 5 = 0$ $\frac{1 \pm \sqrt{41}}{4}$

C 31. $3n^2 - 8n + 4 = 0$ $\frac{2}{3}, 2$ 32. $2x^2 - 5x - 12 = 0$ $-\frac{3}{2}, 4$ 33. $2y^2 + 1 = -5y$ $\frac{-5 \pm \sqrt{17}}{4}$

34. $3z^2 - 1 = 4z$ $\frac{2 \pm \sqrt{7}}{3}$ 35. $3y^2 = 10 + 5y$ $\frac{5 \pm \sqrt{145}}{6}$ 36. $6b^2 = 10b - 3$ $\frac{5 \pm \sqrt{7}}{3}$

37. $1 + \frac{2}{y^2} = \frac{7}{2y}$ $\frac{7 \pm \sqrt{17}}{4}$ 38. $\frac{3}{y - 2} - \frac{1}{y - 1} = 2$ $2 \pm \frac{\sqrt{6}}{2}$ 39. $y^2 + by = -1$ $\frac{-b \pm \sqrt{b^2 - 4}}{2}$

40. $x^2 + bx = -2$ $\frac{-b \pm \sqrt{b^2 - 8}}{2}$ 41. $x^2 + bx + c = 0$ $\frac{-b \pm \sqrt{b^2 - 4c}}{2}$ 42. $ax^2 + bx + c = 0$ $\frac{-b \pm \sqrt{b^2 - 4ac}}{2a}$

Applications

Number Problems Solve each of the following.

43. When twice a number is added to the square of the number, the sum is 3. Find the number. -3 or 1

44. When 4 is subtracted from 9 times a number, the result is equal to twice the square of the number. Find the number. 4 or $\frac{1}{2}$

MATH CLUB ACTIVITY

When Kevin was 25, he began saving $1800 a year at 7% compounded annually. After 10 years, he stopped saving but left all the deposits and compound interest in his account until he was 62.

Marie didn't begin saving until she was 35. She saved $1800 a year at 7% compounded annually until she was 62. She also left the deposits and compound interest in her account.

Who had more in their account at age 62? If you deposit P dollars at r percent interest (expressed as a decimal), the amount A in the account after t years is given by the formula $A = P(1 + r)^t$. You may wish to use a calculator. Kevin

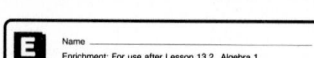

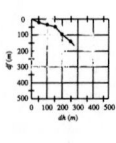

The Quadratic Formula

Objective: To develop the quadratic formula and to use it in solving quadratic equations

In the preceding lessons you learned that quadratic equations of the form $ax^2 + bx + c = 0$ can be solved by factoring, by using the square root property, or by completing the square. These same techniques can be used to solve any equation of the form $ax^2 + bx + c = 0$ where $a \neq 0$.

Capsule Review

Write the following equations in the form $ax^2 + bx + c = 0$.

1. $3x^2 - 5 = 7x$
$3x^2 - 7x - 5 = 0$

2. $4x^2 = x$
$4x^2 - x = 0$

3. $-7 = x^2$
$x^2 + 7 = 0$

4. $-2(x + 5)^2 = 3x$
$-2x^2 - 23x - 50 = 0$

Solve $ax^2 + bx + c = 0$ by completing the square.

$$ax^2 + bx + c = 0$$

$$ax^2 + bx = -c \qquad \textit{Subtract c from each side.}$$

$$x^2 + \frac{b}{a}x = \frac{-c}{a} \qquad \textit{Divide each term by a.}$$

$$x^2 + \frac{b}{a}x + \frac{b^2}{4a^2} = \frac{-c}{a} + \frac{b^2}{4a^2} \qquad \textit{Complete the square. } \left(\frac{1}{2} \cdot \frac{b}{a}\right)^2 = \frac{b^2}{4a^2},$$

$$\textit{so add } \frac{b^2}{4a^2} \textit{ to each side of the equation.}$$

$$\left(x + \frac{b}{2a}\right)^2 = \frac{b^2 - 4ac}{4a^2} \qquad \textit{Write the left side as a perfect square, and the right side as a single fraction.}$$

$$x + \frac{b}{2a} = \pm\sqrt{\frac{b^2 - 4ac}{4a^2}} \qquad \textit{Take the square root of each side.}$$

$$x = -\frac{b}{2a} \pm \frac{\sqrt{b^2 - 4ac}}{2a} \qquad \textit{Solve for x.}$$

$$x = \frac{-b \pm \sqrt{b^2 - 4ac}}{2a} \qquad \textit{Simplify.}$$

The solutions are $\dfrac{-b + \sqrt{b^2 - 4ac}}{2a}$ and $\dfrac{-b - \sqrt{b^2 - 4ac}}{2a}$.

The solutions for the quadratic equation $ax^2 + bx + c = 0$ lead to the *quadratic formula.*

13.3 The Quadratic Formula **551**

LESSON PLAN

Vocabulary
Quadratic equation
Quadratic formula

Materials/Manipulatives
Overhead projector

BACKGROUND

In the Capsule Review, students re-write quadratic equations in standard form. In this lesson, students must write equations in standard form before using the quadratic formula to solve the equation. In Exercise 4, some students may make the error of distributing the -2 first. Explain why this is incorrect.

TEACHING SUGGESTIONS

- You may want to use an overhead projector and a transparency to illustrate how the Quadratic Formula is developed by completing the square.
- In solving quadratic equations using the formula, emphasize the following steps.
  1. Write the equation in standard form, $ax^2 + bx + c = 0$.
  2. Identify the values of a, b, and c.
  3. Write the quadratic formula.
  4. Substitute the values for a, b, and c in the formula.
  5. Simplify to solve for x.
- Some students may ask what happens when $b^2 - 4ac < 0$. Note that this question is related to Exercise 4 in the Class Exercises. You may point out that for equations for which $b^2 - 4ac < 0$, there are no real solutions because the square root of a negative number does not exist among the real numbers.

Solve, using the quadratic formula.
1. $3x^2 - 9x - 30 = 0$ $-2, 5$

2. $4y^2 - 4y = 7$ $\dfrac{1 \pm 2\sqrt{2}}{2}$

3. $3c^2 = -2c + 3$ $\dfrac{-1 \pm \sqrt{10}}{3}$

Common Error

- Students often confuse the values of a, b, and c if they forget to first write the equation in standard form. Students may also make an error when the equation does not have a linear term or a constant. Point out in these cases that $b = 0$, $c = 0$, or sometimes, both b and c can equal 0.
- See *Teacher's Resource Book* for additional remediation.

LESSON FOLLOW-UP

Critical Thinking

Analyzing Relationships What happens when $b^2 - 4ac = 0$ in the quadratic formula? Find a quadratic equation for which $b^2 - 4ac = 0$. The two solutions are equal. Answers may vary for the equations. For example, $x^2 + 2x + 1 = 0$. Some students, realizing the solutions are equal, may write $(x - r)^2 = 0$ or $x^2 - 2rx + r^2 = 0$, where r is any real number.

Assignment Guide

See p. 542B for assignments.

Lesson Quiz

Solve, using the quadratic formula.
1. $a^2 + 8a + 7 = 0$ $-1, -7$

2. $t^2 + \dfrac{3}{2}t = \dfrac{5}{2}$ $1, -\dfrac{5}{2}$

3. $2x^2 = 7x - 2$ $\dfrac{7 \pm \sqrt{33}}{4}$

4. $3m^2 + 10m = -5$ $\dfrac{-5 \pm \sqrt{10}}{3}$

Enrichment

Have students solve for x using the $(3x + a)^2 = (2x - a)^2$ $0, -2a$

> **Quadratic Formula**
>
> If $ax^2 + bx + c = 0$, where a, b, and c are real numbers and $a \neq 0$, then
> $$x = \frac{-b \pm \sqrt{b^2 - 4ac}}{2a}.$$

EXAMPLE Solve $5x^2 = 10x - 4$ using the quadratic formula.

$5x^2 = 10x - 4 \rightarrow 5x^2 - 10x + 4 = 0$

$x = \dfrac{-b \pm \sqrt{b^2 - 4ac}}{2a}$

$x = \dfrac{-(-10) \pm \sqrt{(-10)^2 - 4(5)(4)}}{2(5)}$ *$a = 5$, $b = -10$, and $c = 4$.*

$x = \dfrac{10 \pm \sqrt{100 - 80}}{10}$ *Simplify.*

$x = \dfrac{10 \pm \sqrt{20}}{10}$

$x = \dfrac{10 \pm 2\sqrt{5}}{10}$ *Use the Product Property of Square Roots.*

$x = \dfrac{5 \pm \sqrt{5}}{5}$ *Reduce.*

The solutions are $\dfrac{5 + \sqrt{5}}{5}$ and $\dfrac{5 - \sqrt{5}}{5}$. The check is left for you.

CLASS EXERCISES

State the values of a, b, and c. Then use the quadratic equation to solve.

1. $x^2 + 6x + 1 = 0$
$a = 1$, $b = 6$, $c = 1$; $-3 \pm 2\sqrt{2}$

2. $3x^2 - 4x = 7$
$a = 3$, $b = -4$, $c = -7$; $-1, \frac{7}{3}$

3. $5y = y^2$
$a = 1$, $b = -5$, $c = 0$; $5, 0$

For Discussion

4. What will happen if $4ac > b^2$ in the quadratic formula?
A negative radicand will result and there will be no real solutions.

PRACTICE EXERCISES

Solve by using the quadratic formula.

A 1. $x^2 + 5x + 6 = 0$ $-3, -2$ 2. $y^2 - y - 6 = 0$ $3, -2$ 3. $c^2 - 3c - 10 = 0$
$5, -2$

4. $m^2 + 6m + 8 = 0$ $-4, -2$ 5. $p^2 - 9p = -18$ $6, 3$ 6. $t^2 - 3t = -2$ $2, 1$

7. $3y^2 - 3y - 1 = 0$ $\frac{3 \pm \sqrt{21}}{6}$ 8. $2n^2 - 5n - 12 = 0$ $4, -\frac{3}{2}$ 9. $4x^2 - 12x = -9$ $\frac{3}{2}$

10. $5b^2 - 4b = 33$ $\;3, -\frac{11}{5}$ **11.** $x^2 - 2x = 10$ $\;1 \pm \sqrt{11}$ **12.** $3x^2 - 8x = -2$ $\;\dfrac{4 \pm \sqrt{10}}{3}$

13. $6x^2 + 7x - 5 = 0$ $\;\frac{1}{2}, -\frac{5}{3}$ **14.** $2p^2 + 5p + 3 = 0$ $\;-\frac{3}{2}, -1$ **15.** $2y^2 + 3y - 1 = 0$ $\;\dfrac{-3 \pm \sqrt{17}}{4}$

16. $3n^2 - 4n - 2 = 0$ $\;\dfrac{2 \pm \sqrt{10}}{3}$ **17.** $3z^2 - 8z = -4$ $\;\frac{2}{3}, 2$ **18.** $6y^2 - y = 2$ $\;\frac{2}{3}, -\frac{1}{2}$

19. $m^2 + 6m - 10 = 0$ $\;-3 \pm \sqrt{19}$ **20.** $m^2 + 4m - 6 = 0$ $\;-2 \pm \sqrt{10}$ **21.** $c^2 = -7c - 5$ $\;\dfrac{-7 \pm \sqrt{29}}{2}$

22. $2p^2 = 5 - 4p$ $\;\dfrac{-2 \pm \sqrt{14}}{2}$ **23.** $2b^2 - 5 = 2b$ $\;\dfrac{1 \pm \sqrt{11}}{2}$ **24.** $5n^2 - 2 = 8n$ $\;\dfrac{4 \pm \sqrt{26}}{5}$

B   **25.** $(2t + 3)(t + 4) = 1$ $\;\dfrac{-11 \pm \sqrt{33}}{4}$ **26.** $(2x - 5)(x + 1) = 2$ $\;\dfrac{3 \pm \sqrt{65}}{4}$ **27.** $\dfrac{2y^2}{3} - y = \dfrac{-1}{6}$ $\;\dfrac{3 \pm \sqrt{5}}{4}$

28. $\dfrac{m^2}{3} - m = \dfrac{-1}{2}$ $\;\dfrac{3 \pm \sqrt{3}}{2}$ **29.** $\dfrac{x^2}{3} - \dfrac{3}{2} = \dfrac{x}{2}$ $\;3, -\frac{3}{2}$ **30.** $\dfrac{c^2}{3} - \dfrac{1}{2} = \dfrac{5c}{6}$ $\;-\frac{1}{2}, 3$

31. $\dfrac{x - 1}{2x} = \dfrac{x + 1}{x - 2}$ $\;\dfrac{-5 \pm \sqrt{33}}{2}$ **32.** $\dfrac{x - 4}{x} = \dfrac{3}{x + 2}$ $\;\dfrac{5 \pm \sqrt{57}}{2}$ **33.** $1 + \dfrac{2}{c^2} = \dfrac{7}{2c}$ $\;\dfrac{7 \pm \sqrt{17}}{4}$

34. $\dfrac{1}{y} - \dfrac{2}{y^2} = -6$ $\;\frac{1}{2}, -\frac{2}{3}$ **35.** $\dfrac{x^2}{x - 2} + 3 = \dfrac{2x}{x - 2}$ $\;-3, 2$ **36.** $\dfrac{3}{m - 2} - 2 = \dfrac{1}{m - 1}$ $\;\dfrac{4 \pm \sqrt{6}}{2}$

Use the quadratic formula to solve the equation for x.

C   **37.** $4x - x^2 + k^2 = 0$ $\;-2 \pm \sqrt{4 - k^2}$ **38.** $x^2 + 2xk + k^2 = 0$ $\;-k$

39. $\dfrac{x^2}{a} + \dfrac{x}{b} = -\dfrac{1}{c}$ $\;\dfrac{-ac \pm \sqrt{ac(ac - 4b^2)}}{2bc}$ **40.** $\dfrac{x^2}{a} - \dfrac{1}{c} = \dfrac{5x}{b}$ $\;\dfrac{5ac \pm \sqrt{ac(25ac + 4b^2)}}{2bc}$

41. $(2x + a)^2 = (x + a) + 6$ $\;\dfrac{-4a + 1 \pm \sqrt{8a + 97}}{8}$ **42.** $(x - b)^2 = (x - b) + 4$ $\;\dfrac{2b + 1 \pm \sqrt{17}}{2}$

Applications

43. Geometry If the length of a rectangle is one foot less than the width and the area is 12 ft^2, find the dimensions. $\;w = 4 \text{ ft}; l = 3 \text{ ft}$

44. Number Problem Find two consecutive integers such that 3 times the square of the first is equal to 7 more than 5 times the second. $\;3, 4$

DID YOU KNOW?

Projectile motion makes a parabolic path of any object fired and maintaining a constant speed. The height y of the path and the horizontal distance x the projectile travels can be determined by a quadratic equation. For example, $y = -\dfrac{1}{16}x^2 + 2x$ represents the path of a fired projectile. Assuming that the starting point is $(0, 0)$, the horizontal distance traveled of 32 ft is found by solving the equation.

Solve for the horizontal distances of these projectiles if their paths are represented by the following quadratic equations.

1. $y = -10x^2 + 10x$ $\;1 \text{ ft}$ **2.** $y = -2x^2 + 36x$ $\;1\frac{1}{2} \text{ ft}$ **3.** $y = -4x^2 + 75x$ $\;4 \text{ ft}$

Teacher's Resource Book

Reteaching—Chapter 13, p. 7.

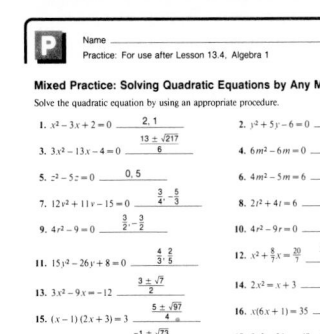

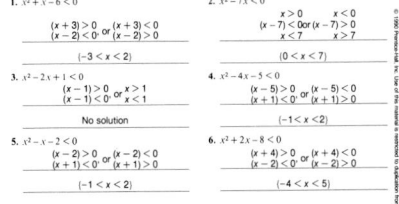

13.4 Mixed Practice: Solving Quadratic Equations by Any Method

Objective: To choose the best method for solving a quadratic equation

This table summarizes the procedures for solving quadratic equations. It can help you decide which is the best method for solving a particular quadratic equation.

METHODS FOR SOLVING QUADRATIC EQUATIONS

Method	Can Be Used	Best to Use
Factoring	sometimes	If the constant term is 0, or if $ax^2 + bx + c$ can be factored.
Square-Root Property	sometimes	For equations of the form $x^2 = k$ or $(ax + b)^2 = k$, $k \geq 0$.
Completing the square	always	For equations of the form $x^2 + bx + c = 0$, where b is even.
Quadratic Formula	always	For any equation of the form $ax^2 + bx + c = 0$.

EXAMPLE Choose a method for solving each equation. Explain your choice. Then solve.

a. $3m^2 + 2m = 8$ **b.** $y^2 - 8y = 2$ **c.** $(2x - 1)^2 = 9$ **d.** $3x^2 + 5x - 6 = 0$

a.

$$3m^2 + 2m = 8$$
$$3m^2 + 2m - 8 = 0 \qquad \text{\textit{Write in the form } ax}^2 + bx + c = 0.$$
$$(3m - 4)(m + 2) = 0 \qquad \text{\textit{Factor the left side.}}$$
$$3m - 4 = 0 \quad | \quad m + 2 = 0 \qquad \text{\textit{Solve for m.}}$$
$$m = \frac{4}{3} \qquad\qquad m = -2$$

b. $y^2 - 8y = 2$

$$(y - 4)^2 = 18 \qquad \text{\textit{Since b is even, use completing the square.}}$$
$$y - 4 = \pm\sqrt{18} \qquad \text{\textit{Solve for y.}}$$
$$y = 4 \pm 3\sqrt{2}$$

c. $(2x - 1)^2 = 9$ \qquad \textit{It is in the form } $(ax + b)^2 = k$, $k \geq 0$.

$$2x - 1 = \pm 3 \qquad \text{\textit{Use the square-root property.}}$$
$$2x - 1 = 3 \quad | \quad 2x - 1 = -3$$
$$x = 2 \quad | \quad x = -1$$

554 Chapter 13 Quadratic Equations and Functions

d. $3x^2 + 5x - 6 = 0$ *Use the quadratic formula.*

$$x = \frac{-5 \pm \sqrt{5^2 - 4(3)(-6)}}{2(3)} \qquad x = \frac{-b \pm \sqrt{b^2 - 4ac}}{2a}$$

$$x = \frac{-5 \pm \sqrt{97}}{6}$$

The check for the solution of each equation is left for you.

CLASS EXERCISES

Choose an appropriate method for solving each equation. Explain.
Answers may vary.

1. $x^2 = \dfrac{5}{9}$

2. $(3y + 7)^2 = 1$

3. $x^2 + 5x + 6 = 0$

4. $t^2 - 4t + 1 = 0$

5. $a^2 - 6a = -8$

6. $2m^2 + 5m = 7$

7. $n^2 - n - 1 = 0$

8. $x^2 + 7x - 16 = 0$

9. $3m^2 - 5m = 0$

10. $2r^2 + 3r = 9$

11. $4x^2 = \dfrac{9}{25}$

12. $(5x - 4)^2 = 25$

13. Use a calculator to solve this equation: $175x^2 - 250x - 225 = 0$ $\frac{5 \pm 2\sqrt{22}}{7}$

For Discussion

14. Why can both completing the square and the quadratic formula be used to solve all quadratic equations (assuming $b^2 - 4ac \geq 0$)? See below.

15. Why do you think it is stated, in the table at the beginning of the lesson, that the square root property can only *sometimes* be used?
Not all quadratics are of the form $x^2 = k$ or $(ax + b)^2 = k$.

PRACTICE EXERCISES

Solve the quadratic equation by using an appropriate method.

A **1.** $x^2 - x - 2 = 0$ $2, -1$

2. $y^2 - 6y + 9 = 0$ 3

3. $6m^2 = 72$ $\pm 2\sqrt{3}$

4. $4x^2 = 80$ $\pm 2\sqrt{5}$

5. $z^2 - 4z = -3$ $3, 1$

6. $x^2 + 8x = 20$ $2, -10$

7. $4x^2 + 3x - 1 = 0$ $-1, \frac{1}{4}$

8. $2x^2 + 5x + 3 = 0$ $-\frac{3}{2}, -1$

9. $3t^2 - 2t = 0$ $0, \frac{2}{3}$

10. $4x^2 - 20 = 0$ $\pm\sqrt{5}$

11. $x^2 + \dfrac{1}{6}x = \dfrac{1}{6}$ $\frac{1}{3}, -\frac{1}{2}$

12. $m^2 - \dfrac{7}{6}m = \dfrac{1}{2}$ $-\frac{1}{3}, \frac{3}{2}$

13. $n^2 = 45 + 12n$ $15, -3$

14. $15 - 14t = t^2$ $1, -15$

15. $2x^2 - 9x = -8$ $\frac{9 \pm \sqrt{17}}{4}$

B **16.** $2x^2 + 7x = 9$ $1, -\frac{9}{2}$

17. $(3x - 2)^2 = 10$ $\frac{\pm\sqrt{10} + 2}{3}$

18. $(4t - 1)^2 = 15$ $\frac{1 \pm \sqrt{15}}{4}$

19. $4x^2 - 4x + 1 = 45$ $\frac{1 \pm 3\sqrt{5}}{2}$

20. $9y^2 + 42y + 49 = 32$ $\frac{-7 \pm 4\sqrt{2}}{3}$

21. $2x^2 = 6x - 3$ $\frac{3 \pm \sqrt{3}}{2}$

22. $3 - 2m = 3m^2$ $\frac{-1 \pm \sqrt{10}}{3}$

23. $5 - \dfrac{3}{x} = \dfrac{2}{x^2}$ $-\frac{2}{5}, 1$

24. $3 + \dfrac{2}{m} = \dfrac{4}{m^2}$ $\frac{-1 \pm \sqrt{13}}{3}$

25. $(n - 4)^2 - 3(n - 4) = 10$ $9, 2$

26. $(2y + 5)^2 = -7(2y + 5) - 6$ $-3, -\frac{11}{2}$

27. $(3x - 8)^2 = (2x - 5)^2$ $\frac{13}{5}; -3$

28. $(4x + 6)^2 = (2x + 4)^2$ $-\frac{5}{3}; -1$

13.4 Mixed Practice: Solving Quadratic Equations by Any Method **555**

TEACHING SUGGESTIONS

- Point out that since factoring and the use of the square-root property only work sometimes, these methods are limited to particular cases.
- Point out that even though completing the square can be used for any quadratic equation, it is a cumbersome method to use when b is odd.

CHALKBOARD EXAMPLES

- **For the Example**
  Solve the quadratic equation by using an appropriate method.
  1. $3y^2 - 5y = 2$ $-\frac{1}{3}, 2$
  2. $2x^2 = 4x + 3$ $\frac{2 \pm \sqrt{10}}{2}$

Common Error

- Some students may get in the habit of using only the quadratic formula to solve quadratic equations, and then making an arithmetical error when evaluating it. Stress the importance of examining the given equation and determining which method will be easiest to use.
- See *Teacher's Resource Book* for additional remediation.

LESSON FOLLOW-UP

Assignment Guide

- See p. 542B for assignments.
- See *Teacher's Resource Book,* for Critical Thinking activity p. 13.

Test Yourself

See *Teacher's Resource Book,* Tests, pp. 137–138.

Lesson Quiz

Solve the quadratic equation by using an appropriate method.
1. $2n^2 = 18$ ± 3
2. $4(x - 1)^2 = 20$ $1 \pm \sqrt{5}$
3. $3a^2 + 2a = 3$ $\frac{-1 \pm \sqrt{10}}{3}$
4. $4m^2 + 12m = -5$ $-\frac{1}{2}, -\frac{5}{2}$

555

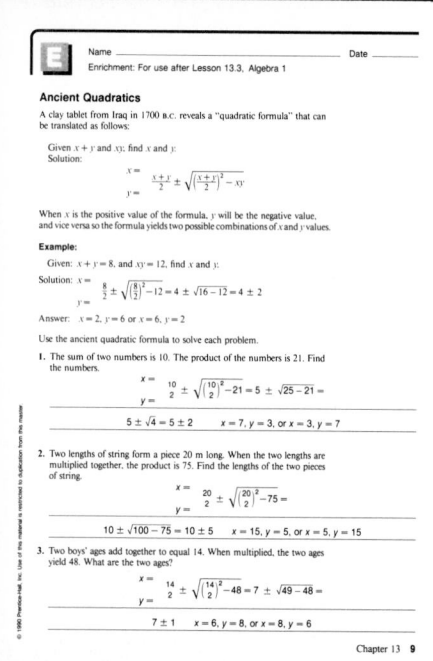

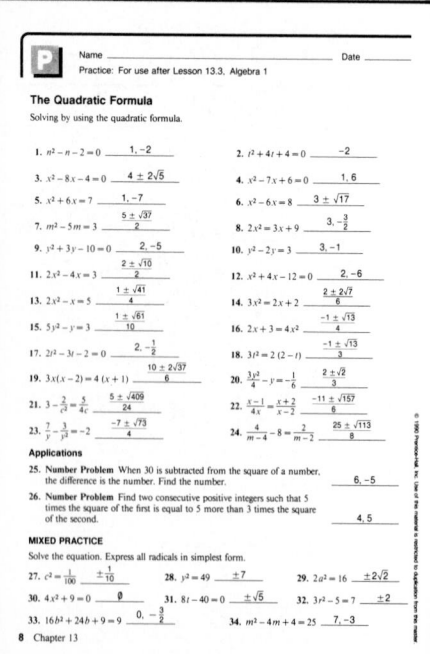

Solve for x in terms of the other variable.

C

29. $2b^2x^2 - 3bx = -1$ $\frac{1}{b}, \frac{1}{2b}$

30. $x^2 - cx = 2c^2$ $-c, 2c$

31. $(x - b)^2 + 5(x - b) + 4 = 0$ $b - 1, b - 4$

32. $(x - a)^2 + (x + a)^2 = 5a$ $\frac{\pm\sqrt{2a(5 - 2a)}}{2}$

33. $\left(\dfrac{1}{4}x - \dfrac{1}{16}b\right)^2 = \dfrac{1}{36}$ $\frac{3b \pm 8}{12}$

34. $\left(\dfrac{1}{3}x + \dfrac{1}{4}a\right)^2 = \dfrac{1}{9}$ $\frac{-3a \pm 4}{4}$

Applications

35. Physics The distance s traveled by an object with acceleration a in time t is given by the equation $s = \dfrac{1}{2}at^2$. Solve for t, when $s = 64$ ft and $a = 32$ ft/s^2. 2 s

36. Physics A projectile is shot vertically up in the air. Its distance s, in ft, after t seconds is given by the equation $s = 96t - 16t^2$. Find the values of t, to the nearest hundredth of a second, when $s = 96$ ft. 1.27 s; 4.73 s

37. Construction The length of a rectangular floor is twice the width. The area of the floor is 32 ft^2. What are the dimensions of the room? l = 8 ft; w = 4 ft

38. Number Problem Find two consecutive even integers whose product is 224. 14, 16; −16, −14

39. Number Problem Find an integer such that the square of the integer is 81 less than 18 times the integer. 9

40. Landscaping The length of a rectangular garden exceeds three times the width by 4 m. The area of the garden is 24 m^2. Find the length and width to the nearest hundredth of a meter. l = 10.72 m; w = 2.24 m

41. Number Problem Three times the square of a number equals 2 times the number. Find the number(s). $\frac{2}{3}$; 0

TEST YOURSELF

Solve by using the square-root property. 13.1

1. $5x^2 = 40$ $\pm 2\sqrt{2}$

2. $6(3z - 2)^2 = 24$ 0, $\frac{4}{3}$

Solve by completing the square. 13.2

3. $m^2 - 2m - 3 = 0$ 3, −1

4. $2x^2 - 4x = -1$ $\frac{2 \pm \sqrt{2}}{2}$

Solve by using the quadratic formula. 13.3

5. $x^2 - 2x = 5$ $1 \pm \sqrt{6}$

6. $2n^2 - 8n = -5$ $\frac{4 \pm \sqrt{6}}{2}$

Solve by using an appropriate method. 13.4

7. $4t^2 - 9 = 0$ $\pm\frac{3}{2}$

8. $y^2 - 2y = 3$ 3, −1

9. $3x^2 + 5x - 2 = 0$ $-2; \frac{1}{3}$

10. $m^2 + 4m = 9$ $-2 \pm \sqrt{13}$

Graphing Quadratic Functions

Objectives: To graph quadratic functions
To use graphs of quadratic functions to solve quadratic equations

Arrow Company finds that its profit y for producing x units is given by the equation $y = x^2 + 2x - 3$.

(Number of units, Profit)
(x, y)

Profit changes as the number of units change. That is, the amount of profit is a function of the number of units.

A function f given by the equation $f(x) = ax^2 + bx + c$, where a, b, and c are real numbers, and $a \neq 0$, is a **quadratic function.**

$y = f(x) = x^2 + 2x - 3$ is a quadratic function. The graph of the function will enable Arrow Company to determine for what values of x its profit y will be zero.

Capsule Review

You can use the slope and y-intercept to graph equations.

Give the slope and y-intercept of the graph of each of the following linear functions. Then draw its graph.
See Additional Answer section beginning p. 719.

1. $f(x) = 2x + 1$

x	−2	−1	0	1	2
$f(x)$	?	?	?	?	? 2, 1
	−3	−1	1	3	5

2. $g(x) = -x + 1$

x	−4	−2	0	2	4
$g(x)$	?	?	?	?	? −1, 1
	5	3	1	−1	−3

3. $h(x) = 5x$ 5, 0   **4.** $f(x) = -x$ −1, 0   **5.** $h(x) = 3$ 0, 3   **6.** $g(x) = -\dfrac{1}{2}$
0, −$\frac{1}{2}$

One way to graph a quadratic equation is to find several ordered pairs that satisfy the equation, then graph the ordered pairs on a coordinate plane and connect the points with a smooth curve.

LESSON PLAN

Vocabulary
Axis of symmetry
Maximum point
Minimum point
Parabola
Quadratic function
Vertex

Materials/Manipulatives
Calculators
Computer
Graph paper
Overhead projector
Teacher's Resource Book,
   Teaching Aid 16,
   Transparencies 14, 15, 30

BACKGROUND

In the Capsule Review, Exercises 1 and 2 review finding ordered pairs for a given linear function. You may wish to have students review the concept of a function and function notation in Chapter 10. In Exercises 1–6, students find the slope and y-intercept of a linear function, and graph the line associated with the linear function. In this lesson, students graph quadratic functions. They use the vertex, axis of symmetry, and x-intercepts to graph the parabola associated with the quadratic function.

- In Example 1, point out that by examining the graph of the quadratic function $f(x) = x^2 + 2x - 3$, students should discover two points where $f(x) = 0$. The two points, $(-3, 0)$ and $(1, 0)$, are called the x-intercepts.
- Stress that the graphs of quadratic functions presented in this lesson are always a parabola.
- Using Examples 1 and 2, point out that the coefficient of the x^2 term determines whether the parabola opens upward or downward. This determines whether the function has a minimum or a maximum point.
- Encourage students to draw the axis of symmetry to check the vertex of the graph and the graph itself. Use Teaching Aid 16 and Transparencies 14, 15, 30, in the *Teacher's Resource Book,* to illustrate several parabolas.

Critical Thinking

Analysis In Example 1, the parabola has a minimum value. Does it have a maximum value? Why or why not? No. Y-values continuously increase as x-decreases from -1 or increases from -1. In theory, there is no maximum value; however, real-world circumstances may effect a company's profit.

CHALKBOARD EXAMPLES

- **For Example 1**

Use graphing to find the values of x for which each function is zero.

1. $y = f(x) = -x^2 + 2x + 3$
$-1, 3$

2. $y = g(x) = x^2 + 5x + 4$
$-1, -4$

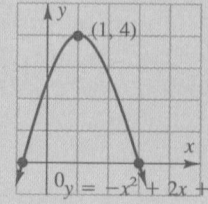

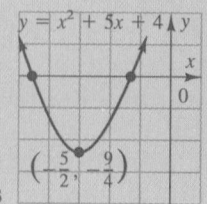

EXAMPLE 1 Use graphing to find the values of x for which $y = f(x) = x^2 + 2x - 3$ is zero.

A calculator can be used to evaluate the function for each value of x.

x	$x^2 + 2x - 3$	y
-4	$(-4)^2 + 2(-4) - 3$	5
-3	$(-3)^2 + 2(-3) - 3$	0
-2	$(-2)^2 + 2(-2) - 3$	-3
-1	$(-1)^2 + 2(-1) - 3$	-4
0	$(0)^2 + 2(0) - 3$	-3
1	$(1)^2 + 2(1) - 3$	0
2	$(2)^2 + 2(2) - 3$	5

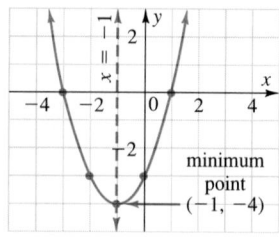

So, $y = f(x) = x^2 + 2x - 3$ is zero when $x = -3$ and $x = 1$.

The graph in Example 1 shows that the values of x for which the company's profit is 0 are -3 and 1. Since manufacturing -3 units is not a reasonable answer, -3 is not a reasonable solution. The company can conclude that it makes a profit on every unit after the first.

The curve of $y = f(x) = x^2 + 2x - 3$ is a parabola. A **parabola** is a graph of a quadratic function. The x-coordinate of a point where the curve intersects the x-axis, the point where $y = f(x) = 0$, is called an *x-intercept.*

EXAMPLE 2 Graph $y = g(x) = -x^2 - 2x.$

x	y
-3	-3
-2	0
-1	1
0	0
1	-3

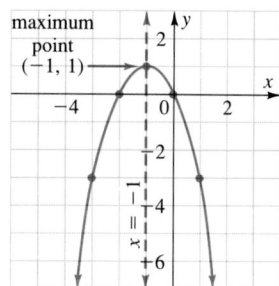

The parabola in Example 1 opens upward and has a **minimum** (lowest) **point** at $(-1, -4)$. The parabola in Example 2 opens downward and has a **maximum** (highest) **point** at $(-1, 1)$. These examples suggest the following:

> For any quadratic function $f(x) = ax^2 + bx + c, a \neq 0$:
> - If a is positive, the parabola opens upward.
> - If a is negative, the parabola opens downward.

558   Chapter 13 Quadratic Equations and Functions

The minimum or maximum point of a parabola is called the **vertex.** In Examples 1 and 2, notice that the x-coordinate of the vertex of each parabola is −1. In each example, it is the average of the x-coordinates of the points where the parabola intersects the x-axis, that is where $y = f(x) = 0$.

For $y = f(x) = x^2 + 2x − 3$ For $y = g(x) = −x^2 − 2x$

$(−3, 0), (1, 0)$ $(−2, 0), (0, 0)$

$\dfrac{−3 + 1}{2} = \dfrac{−2}{2} = −1$ $\dfrac{−2 + 0}{2} = −1$

But in each example, $−\dfrac{b}{2a}$ also equals −1. This leads to the following:

> The x-coordinate of the vertex of a parabola, the graph of a quadratic function $f(x) = ax^2 + bx + c, a \neq 0$, is $−\dfrac{b}{2a}$.

If you folded the curves in Example 1 and Example 2 along the line $x = −1$, the two halves of the parabola would coincide. In each example, the vertical line, $x = −1$, is called the *axis of symmetry*. Notice that the axis of symmetry passes through the vertex, or *turning point*, of the parabola.

> For a parabola with the equation $f(x) = ax^2 + bx + c, a \neq 0$, the equation of the **axis of symmetry** is $x = −\dfrac{b}{2a}$.

It is helpful to use the vertex and the axis of symmetry to graph a quadratic function.

EXAMPLE 3   **Find the vertex, the axis of symmetry, and six points on the parabola $h(x) = x^2 + 6x + 8$. Graph the equation.**

a. $x = −\dfrac{b}{2a} = −\dfrac{6}{2} = −3$ *The x-coordinate of the vertex of the parabola.*

$y = (−3)^2 + 6(−3) + 8$ *Substitute −3 for x to find the y-coordinate of*
$= −1$ *the vertex.*

Therefore the vertex is $(−3, −1)$.

b. $x = −\dfrac{b}{2a} = −\dfrac{6}{2} = −3$ *The axis of symmetry passes through the vertex.*

Therefore, $x = −3$ is the axis of symmetry.

13.5 Graphing Quadratic Functions   **559**

• **For Example 2**
Graph.
3. $y = f(x) = 4x + x^2$
4. $y = g(x) = −x^2 − 2x + 3$

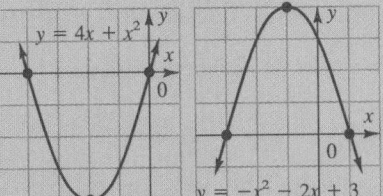

• **For Example 3**
Find the vertex, axis of symmetry, and six points to graph the equation.
5. $y = h(x) = x^2 − 6x + 5$

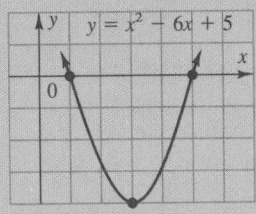

vertex is $(3, −4); x = 3$
6. $y = g(x) = −x^2 + 4x − 3$

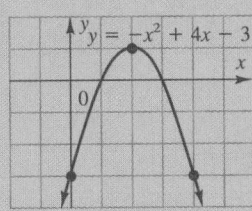

vertex is $(2, 1); x = 2$

Common Error
• Some students may become confused when finding the maximum or minimum point of a parabola. Remind these students that if *a* is positive in the quadratic function, the parabola has a minimum point. If *a* is negative, the parabola has a maximum point.
• See *Teacher's Resource Book* for additional remediation.

Discussion

For any quadratic function $f(x) = ax^2 + bx + c$, $a \neq 0$, if a is positive the parabola opens upward, and if a is negative the parabola opens downward. What happens if $a = 0$? If $a = 0$, the function is a linear function.

Assignment Guide

- See p. 542B for assignments
- See *Teacher's Resource Book, Technology*, pp. 23–25.

Lesson Quiz

State whether the graph of each equation opens upward or downward.
1. $y = 2x^2 - 4x$ upward
2. $y = -3x^2 + 4x + 1$ downward

Find the vertex, the axis of symmetry, and the x-intercepts. Use each to graph the following equations.
3. $f(x) = 2x - x^2$
   vertex is $(1, 1)$; $x = 1$; $0, 2$

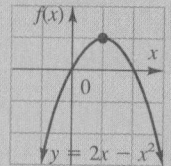

4. $g(x) = 15 + 8x + x^2$
   vertex is $(-4, -1)$; $x = -4$; $-3, -5$

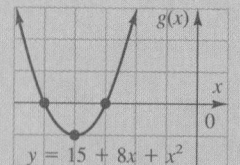

Enrichment

Discuss the similarities and differences between the graphs:

$$y = x^2 - 2x + 1$$
$$y \geq x^2 - 2x + 1$$
$$y \leq x^2 - 2x + 1$$

In each graph, the parabola is the same, namely $y = x^2 - 2x + 1$. The inequality symbols determine the region that is to be shaded.

560

c. Make a table. Since the points, except the vertex, occur in pairs that have the same $h(x)$-coordinate, choose three values of x that are greater than -3 and three values of x that are less than -3.

x	$h(x)$
-6	8
-5	3
-4	0
-3	-1
-2	0
-1	3
0	8

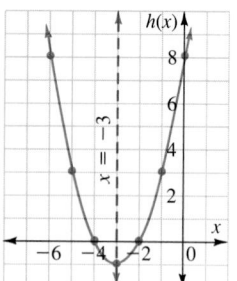

CLASS EXERCISES

Tell whether the graph of each function opens upward or downward. Then tell whether there is a minimum or a maximum point.

1. $g(x) = 2x^2$
   upward; minimum pt.
2. $h(x) = 2x - x^2$
   downward; maximum pt.
3. $g(x) = x^2 + 3x + 4$
   upward; minimum pt.

Find the vertex and the axis of symmetry of each function.

4. $g(x) = x^2 - \frac{1}{2}x - \frac{4}{12}$ $\left(\frac{1}{2}, -\frac{49}{12}\right)$; $x = \frac{1}{2}$
5. $f(x) = 3 - 2x - x^2$ $(-1, 4)$; $x = -1$
6. $h(x) = 3x^2$ $(0, 0)$; $x = 0$
7. $h(x) = 4 - x^2$ $(0, 4)$; $x = 0$
8. $g(x) = x^2 - 9$ $(0, -9)$; $x = 0$
9. $f(x) = x^2 + x$ $\left(-\frac{1}{2}, -\frac{1}{4}\right)$; $x = -\frac{1}{2}$

For Discussion

10. Graph the following on the same set of axes. You may use a graphing calculator or a computer graphing program. See below.

$$y = x^2 + 2x \qquad y = x^2 + 2x + 4 \qquad y = x^2 + 2x - 3$$

How does the value of c in $y = ax^2 + bx + c$ affect the graph?
If c is positive, each point is c units above the corresponding point on $y = ax^2 + bx$. If c is negative, each point is c units below the corresponding point.

PRACTICE EXERCISES

Graph each equation. State whether the parabola opens upward or downward and if it has a minimum or maximum point. Check students' graphs.
See Additional Answer section beginning p. 719.

A
1. $y = x^2$
   upward; minimum pt.
2. $y = 2x^2$
   upward; minimum pt.
3. $y = x^2 - 2x - 3$
   upward; minimum pt.
4. $y = x^2 - 5x - 6$
   upward; minimum pt.
5. $y = x^2 + 4x$
   upward; minimum pt.
6. $y = x^2 - 6x$
   upward; minimum pt.
7. $y = 4 - x^2$
   downward; maximum pt.
8. $y = 1 - x^2$
   downward; maximum pt.
9. $y = x^2 - 1$
   upward; minimum pt.
10. $y = x^2 - 9$
    upward; minimum pt.
11. $y = 3 - x^2$
    downward; maximum pt.
12. $y = 5 + x^2$
    upward; minimum pt.

Additional Answers   10.

Find the vertex, the axis of symmetry, and the x-intercepts. Use each to graph the following equations. Check students' graphs.

13. $s(x) = x^2 + 3x + 2 \left(-\frac{3}{2}, -\frac{1}{4}\right); x = -\frac{3}{2};$ $-1, -2$ **14.** $g(x) = x^2 - 2x + 1$ $(1, 0); x = 1$

15. $r(x) = x^2 + 5x + 8 \left(-\frac{5}{2}, \frac{7}{4}\right); x = -\frac{5}{2};$ none **16.** $f(x) = x^2 - 4x + 5$ $(2, 1); x = 2;$ none

B **17.** $h(x) = 7 - 6x - x^2$ $(-3, 16); x = -3; -7, 1$ **18.** $f(x) = 5 - 4x - x^2$ $(-2, 9); x = -2; -5, 1$

19. $g(x) = 5 + 3x - 2x^2 \left(\frac{3}{4}, \frac{49}{8}\right); x = \frac{3}{4};$ $\frac{5}{2}, -1$ **20.** $h(x) = 10 - x - 3x^2$ $\left(-\frac{1}{6}, \frac{121}{12}\right); x = -\frac{1}{6}; \frac{5}{3}, -2$

21. $f(x) = -\frac{1}{2}x^2 - 5$ $(0, -5); x = 0;$ none **22.** $g(x) = -2 + \frac{1}{2}x^2$ $(0, -2); x = 0; \pm 2$

23. $m(x) = \frac{3}{4}x^2 + 2$ $(0, 2); x = 0;$ none **24.** $r(x) = \frac{1}{5}x^2 + 3$ $(0, 3); x = 0;$ none

25. $g(x) = (x + 2)^2$ $(-2, 0); x = -2; -2$ **26.** $f(x) = (x + 3)^2$ $(-3, 0); x = -3; -3$

27. $h(x) = (x + 1)^2 - 5$ $(-1, -5); x = -1; -1 \pm \sqrt{5}$ **28.** $r(x) = (x + 4)^2 - 3$ $(-4, -3); x = -4; -4 \pm \sqrt{3}$

C **29.** $g(x) = -2(x + 3)^2 - 4$ $(-3, -4); x = -3;$ none **30.** $h(x) = -4\left(x + \frac{1}{2}\right)^2 - 4$ $\left(-\frac{1}{2}, -4\right); x = -\frac{1}{2};$ none

Graph each equation. State whether the parabola opens upward or downward and if it has a minimum or maximum point.
See below.

31. $y = 5(x - 2)^2 + 3$ upward; minimum pt. **32.** $y = 3(x - 4)^2 + 5$ upward; minimum pt. **33.** $y = -2(x - 5)^2 - 15$ downward; maximum pt.

Applications

Solve graphically.

34. Business The total profit p made by an engineering firm is given by the equation $p = x^2 - 25x + 5000$. Graph the equation. Find the minimum profit made by the company. $4843.75

35. Physics A projectile is propelled upward. Its distance s, in ft, after t seconds is given by the function $s = f(t) = 96t - 16t^2$. Graph the function. Find the maximum height reached by this projectile. 144 ft

---

MATH CLUB ACTIVITY

Can This Hiker Be Saved?

On a hiking trip, you are $\frac{2}{3}$ the distance across a stream when you spot a bear approaching. You assume it is approaching at 0.75 km/h. You can just escape by running at a uniform speed to either side of the stream. What must your speed be? 0.5 km/h

13.5 Graphing Quadratic Functions **561**

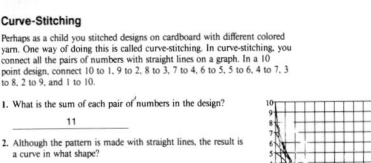
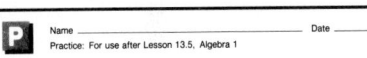
Additional Answers

31.

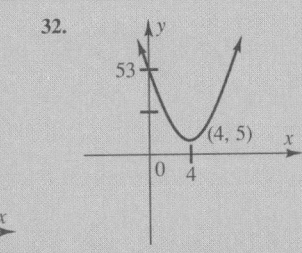

32.

33.

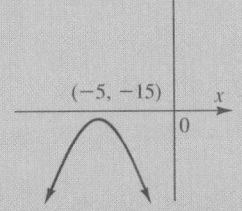

Application

The purpose of this application is to give students an appreciation for a common application of quadratic functions. Teachers can use a discussion of the motion of projectiles to help students better understand how the graph of a parabola behaves.

See *Teacher's Resource Book,* Follow-up Application, p. 24.

APPLICATION: Physics

Did you know that today computers are used to track projectiles of many forms, such as rockets and satellites?

Applications of projectile motion often occur in physics and are greatly aided by the use of computers. When a rocket is launched it is necessary to know how long it will take to land, how high it goes, and how much time it takes the rocket to go a specified distance.

It was Galileo who first accurately described projectile motion. He often used mathematics to help him analyze physical science. Galileo proved in the 1600's that when a frictionless object is projected from the ground, it takes the same amount of time to go up as it does to come down.

The path that the object traces is a parabola, represented by the function:

$$H(t) = -\frac{1}{2}gt^2 + vt$$

where $H(t)$ = height
   t = time
   g = force of gravity
   v = initial speed

The force of gravity for the earth is 32 ft/s^2, while our moon has a force of gravity of 5.32 ft/s^2. The forces of gravity for other planets in our solar system include:

Planet	Gravity (ft/s^2)
Venus	28.8
Mars	12.2
Jupiter	82.6
Saturn	35.5

The following computer program enables you to find the answer to the three questions involved with tracking a rocket launched from earth with an initial speed of 100 ft/sec. Since the program is quite simple and straightforward, it will be necessary to refine the input in repeated runs to give more precise information.

```
10 INPUT "ENTER THE BEGINNING TIME, THE ESTIMATED TIME AND
      THE TIME INCREMENT:   '';B,E,I: PRINT
20 PRINT "TIME","DISTANCE": PRINT "_____","_____"
30 FOR X = B TO E STEP I
40 PRINT X, - 16 * X ^ 2 + 100 * X
50 NEXT X
60 END
```

Use the following steps when running the program.

1. Estimate how long it will take the rocket to land. Enter the beginning time (0), the estimated time to land (say 7 or 8) and the time increment (start with 1 and refine it in later RUNs.) Repeat this step until the rocket reaches a distance of 0 again.

2. Choose a beginning and ending time that you think surround the peak of the rocket height. Enter the time and a decimal increment. Do repeated RUNs until you get the peak height. You can tell which value is the peak because the values around it are symmetric and smaller.

3. Use this program to determine how much time is needed for the rocket to cover a certain distance.

EXERCISES

1. A rocket is propelled upward at a speed of 120 ft/sec. Change line 40 to be

$$40 \text{ PRINT X}, -.5*32*X\text{^}2 + 120*X$$

in the above program to answer these questions:

   a. How high does it go? 224 ft
   b. How long is it in the air? 4 s
   c. How many seconds does it take for the rocket to reach 100 ft? ≈1 s

2. Revise line 40 so that the same rocket can be tracked when it is launched from the surface of the moon ($g = 5.32$).

   a. How high does it go? 1353.975 ft
   b. How long will it take before it reaches the surface again? 45.1127 s
   c. How does this data compare with the data of the earth launch?
   Rocket goes higher and stays up longer.

3. Investigate the force of gravity for other planets and revise the computer program to track a rocket launched from there. Check students' work.

Vocabulary
Discriminant
Root
Solution

Materials/Manipulatives
Overhead projector
Teacher's Resource Book,
  Teaching Aids 10, 11, 12,
  Transparencies 14, 15, 30

BACKGROUND

In the Capsule Review, Exercises 1–6 review solving quadratic equations by using the quadratic formula.

TEACHING SUGGESTIONS

• Using the Examples, point out the relationship between the solution of a quadratic equation and the graph of the related quadratic function.

• Emphasize the relationship between the value of the discriminant and the nature of the solutions of the equation. Stress that the value of the discriminant gives the number of roots of $ax^2 + bx + c = 0$, and the number of x-intercepts of the related parabola, $y = ax^2 + bx + c$. Teaching Aids 10, 11, 12 and Transparencies 14, 15 and 30, in the *Teacher's Resource Book*, may be used to illustrate the value of the discriminant and the nature of the solutions of a quadratic equation.

Critical Thinking

Causal Explanation If the discriminant of a quadratic equation is negative, the equation has no real solutions or roots. Does that mean the equation has no solutions or roots? Explain. The solutions or roots are not real numbers.

13.6

The Discriminant

Objective: To use the discriminant to determine the nature and number of solutions of a quadratic equation

You have solved quadratic equations by several methods and found that there may be two distinct solutions (or real roots), one solution, or no real solution. Without actually solving, you can find this information by using a part of the quadratic formula.

Capsule Review

To solve $ax^2 + bx + c = 0$, $a \neq 0$, use the quadratic formula:

$$x = \frac{-b \pm \sqrt{b^2 - 4ac}}{2a}$$

Use the quadratic formula to solve.

1. $t^2 - 3t - 10 = 0$ 5, −2

2. $2y^2 + 4y = 3$ $\frac{-2 \pm \sqrt{10}}{2}$

3. $12x^2 - 4x - 3 = 0$ $\frac{1 \pm \sqrt{10}}{6}$

4. $m^2 - 10m + 25 = 0$ 5

5. $6t^2 - 1 = 0$ $\frac{\pm\sqrt{6}}{6}$

6. $z^2 + 4 = 0$ no solution

In the quadratic formula, the algebraic expression $b^2 - 4ac$ is called the **discriminant.** The *discriminant* determines the nature and number of solutions of a quadratic equation.

EXAMPLE 1 **Solve $x^2 + 3x - 5 = 0$, and graph $y = x^2 + 3x - 5$.**

$x^2 + 3x - 5 = 0$

$$x = \frac{-b \pm \sqrt{b^2 - 4ac}}{2a}$$

$$= \frac{-3 \pm \sqrt{3^2 - 4(1)(-5)}}{2(1)}$$

$$= \frac{-3 \pm \sqrt{9 + 20}}{2}$$

$$= \frac{-3 \pm \sqrt{29}}{2}$$

$y = x^2 + 3x - 5$

x	y
−4	−1
−3	−5
−2	−7
−1.5	−7.25
−1	−7
0	−5
1	−1

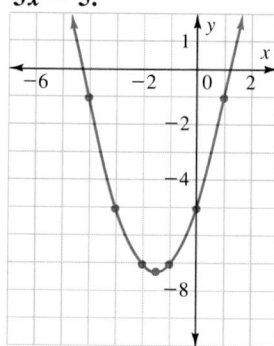

There are two real solutions.

$\frac{-3 + \sqrt{29}}{2}$ and $\frac{-3 - \sqrt{29}}{2}$. Notice that $b^2 - 4ac > 0$.

There are two x-intercepts.

EXAMPLE 2   Solve $x^2 - 2x + 1 = 0$, and graph $y = x^2 - 2x + 1$.

$x^2 - 2x + 1 = 0$

$$x = \frac{-b \pm \sqrt{b^2 - 4ac}}{2a}$$

$$= \frac{-(-2) \pm \sqrt{(-2)^2 - 4(1)(1)}}{2(1)}$$

$$= \frac{2 \pm \sqrt{4 - 4}}{2} = \frac{2 \pm 0}{2}, \text{ or } 1$$

There is one real solution. Notice that $b^2 - 4ac = 0$.

$y = x^2 - 2x + 1$

x	y
-1	4
0	1
1	0
2	1
3	4

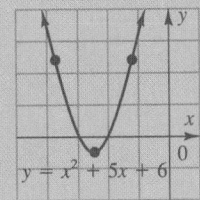

There is one x-intercept.

EXAMPLE 3   Solve $x^2 + 2x + 3 = 0$, and graph $y = x^2 + 2x + 3$.

$x^2 + 2x + 3 = 0$

$$x = \frac{-b \pm \sqrt{b^2 - 4ac}}{2a}$$

$$= \frac{-2 \pm \sqrt{(2)^2 - 4(1)(3)}}{2(1)}$$

$$= \frac{-2 \pm \sqrt{4 - 12}}{2}$$

$$= \frac{-2 \pm \sqrt{-8}}{2}, \text{ or } -1 \pm \sqrt{-2}$$

$y = x^2 + 2x + 3$

x	y
-3	6
-2	3
-1	2
0	3
1	6

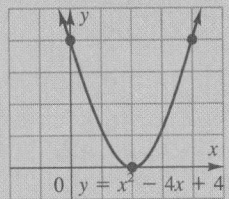

There are no real solutions. Why? Notice that $b^2 - 4ac < 0$. There are no x-intercepts.

Look for a relationship between the value of the discriminant and the nature of the solutions of the equation.

$b^2 - 4ac$	Nature of the solutions of $ax^2 + bx + c = 0$	No. of x-intercepts
Positive	Two distinct, real solutions	2
Zero	One distinct, real solution (double solution)	1
Negative	No real solutions	0

EXAMPLE 4   Use the discriminant to determine the nature of the solutions of the equation:
   a. $-x^2 + 3 = 0$ **b.** $-x^2 + 4x - 5 = 0$

a. $-x^2 + 3 = 0$
   $b^2 - 4ac = 0^2 - 4(-1)(3) = 12$ *Substitute: $a = -1$, $b = 0$, $c = 3$*
   Since $12 > 0$, there are two distinct real solutions.

b. $-x^2 + 4x - 5 = 0$
   $b^2 - 4ac = (4)^2 - 4(-1)(-5) = -4$ *Substitute: $a = -1$, $b = 4$, $c = -5$*
   Since $-4 < 0$, there are no real solutions.

13.6 The Discriminant   **565**

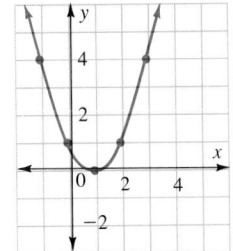
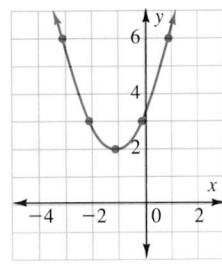
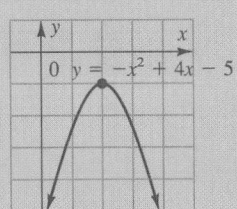

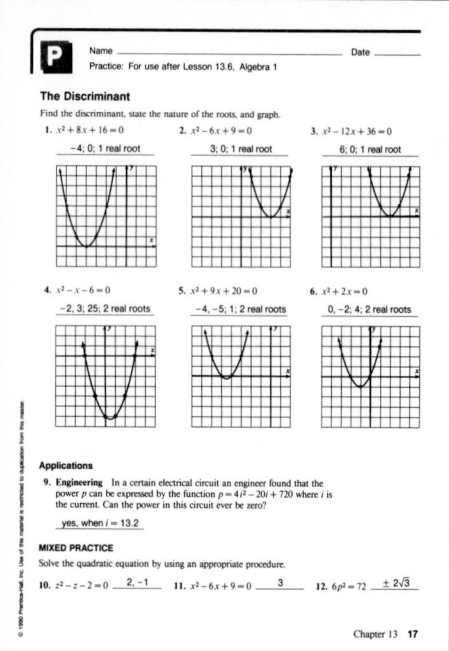

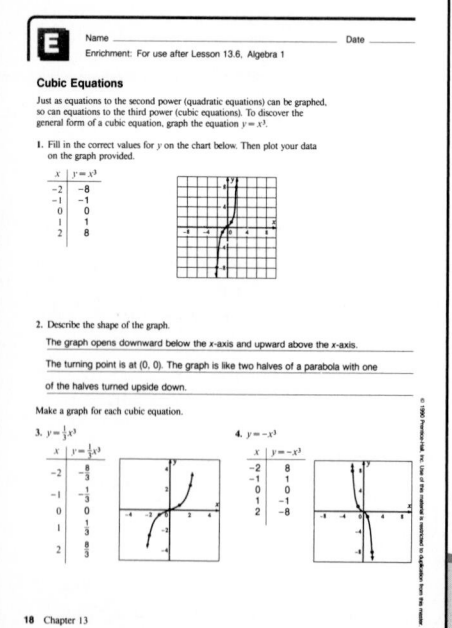

CLASS EXERCISES

Find the value of the discriminant. Then state the nature of the solutions.

1. $x^2 - 1 = 0$
4; 2 real solutions

2. $x^2 + 4 = 0$
-16; no real solutions

3. $x^2 - 6x + 9 = 0$
0; one real solution

4. $x^2 + 4x + 3 = 0$
4; 2 real solutions

5. $-2x^2 + 3x - 2 = 0$
-7; no real solutions

6. $4x^2 - 20x + 25 = 0$
0; one real solution

PRACTICE EXERCISES

Find the value of the discriminant, and state the nature of the solutions.

A

1. $x^2 + 2x - 15 = 0$
64; 2 real solutions

2. $x^2 - 5x + 4 = 0$
9; 2 real solutions

3. $x^2 - 8x + 16 = 0$
0; 1 real solution

4. $x^2 - 10x + 25 = 0$
0; 1 real solution

5. $x^2 + 4x - 6 = 0$
40; 2 real solutions

6. $x^2 - x - 3 = 0$
13; 2 real solutions

7. $2x^2 - 3x + 2 = 0$
-7; no real solutions

8. $3x^2 - 4x + 5 = 0$
-44; no real solutions

9. $-2x^2 + 7x - 3 = 0$
25; 2 real solutions

10. $-2x^2 - 3x + 2 = 0$
25; 2 real solutions

11. $-6x^2 + 5x - 4 = 0$
-71; no real solutions

12. $4x^2 - 3x + 3 = 0$
-39; no real solutions

B

13. $4x^2 + 12x = -9$
0; 1 real solution

14. $9x^2 - 30x = -25$
0; 1 real solution

15. $\frac{3}{2}x^2 = 4x - \frac{1}{2}$
13; 2 real solutions

16. $x^2 + 3x = 3$
21; 2 real solutions

17. $2x^2 + \frac{1}{2}x + \frac{2}{3} = 0$
$\frac{-61}{12}$; no real solutions

18. $\frac{1}{5}x^2 - \frac{5}{4}x - 1 = 0$
$\frac{189}{80}$; 2 real solutions

Without graphing, find the number of x-intercepts for each function.

19. $f(x) = 9 - 12x - 4x^2$ 2

20. $f(x) = -16 - 40x + 25x^2$ 2

C

21. $f(x) = x^2 + \frac{1}{2}x - \frac{17}{4}$ 2

22. $f(x) = -\frac{1}{2}x^2 - x - \frac{11}{6}$ 0

23. $f(x) = 4x^2 - kx + 625$ if $|k| > 100$ 2 **24.** $f(x) = kx^2 - 8x + 3$ if $k > 5\frac{1}{3}$ 0

Applications

25. Engineering   In a certain electrical circuit an engineer found that the power p can be expressed by the function $p = 2i^2 - 60i + 480$ where i is the current. Can the power in this circuit ever be zero? no

26. Finance   A rental agency uses the formula $T = 5400 + 300x - 50x^2$ to find its total income when x units are rented. Can they expect their total ever to equal $7000? no

LOGICAL REASONING

The formula $2D = n(n - 3)$ tells how many diagonals D in a polygon of n sides. An architect designs a building with 14 diagonals. How many sides does the building have? 7

566   Chapter 13 Quadratic Equations and Functions

Problem Solving Strategy: Use a Function

LESSON PLAN

Vocabulary
Linear function
Quadratic function

Materials/Manipulatives
Graph paper
Overhead projector
Straightedge
Teacher's Resource Book,
Teaching Aids 10, 11, 12,
Transparencies 14, 15

Martin's monthly income is $500 plus 5% of his sales. His income i can be written as a function of his sales s (in dollars).

$$i = f(s) = 0.05s + 500 \qquad \text{Do you recognize this as a linear function?}$$

In this situation, the slope of 0.05 is the rate at which Martin's income increases or decreases for a change in sales. There is a $0.05 income rise for every dollar increase in sales. The i-intercept, 500, refers to the $500 he earns if he makes no sales (if $s = 0$).

EXAMPLE 1 The table shows the prices and net weights of boxes of Apple Wheat Crackles. Recall that in a linear function, the slope is constant.

Weight (oz) w	8	20	40
Price ($) p	1.55	3.35	6.35

a. Confirm that the price p is a linear function of the weight w.
b. Write this function for the price $f(w)$.

Using the slope and intercepts, what can you tell about the function?

Understand the Problem

What are the given facts?
From a chart of ordered pairs of weight and prices, you should show that the ordered pairs belong to a linear function, and then write the function. You must then interpret the meaning of the slope and intercepts for this situation.

Plan Your Approach

Choose a strategy.
a. Show that the slope is constant.
b. Use the slope and one ordered pair to find the p-intercept. Write the function in the form $f(w) = p = mx + b$.

Complete the Work

Solve.
a. For (8, 1.55) and (20, 3.35):
$$m = \frac{3.35 - 1.55}{20 - 8} = \frac{1.80}{12} = 0.15$$

For (20, 3.35) and (40, 6.35):
$$m = \frac{6.35 - 3.35}{40 - 20} = \frac{3.00}{20} = 0.15$$

13.7 Problem Solving Strategy: Use a Function **567**

BACKGROUND

To solve these problems successfully, students must understand the concepts of linear and quadratic functions. Students are expected to solve equations, find the slope and intercepts, and find ordered pairs for these functions. Students may encounter difficulty in many different areas. You can do an error analysis of the student's work to determine how a student is proceeding; then classify and correct specific student errors.

Error Analysis Classification
1. *Misunderstanding*
   Failed to understand the concept of function
   Failed to understand the relationship between a linear function, the slope, and the intercept
   Failed to understand the relationship between a quadratic function, the vertex, and the intercept
2. *Misapplied Strategy*
   Wrote an incorrect equation
   Did not interpret the results correctly
   Failed to complete the solution

TEACHING SUGGESTIONS

- It may be necessary to review the basic concept of function developed in Chapter 10. Review with students that a function consists of a domain, a range, and a rule that tells how to associate the domain and the range. Every function, whether linear or quadratic, assigns each member of the domain to exactly one member of the range.
- Use an overhead projector Teaching Aids 10, 11, 12, and Transparencies 14, 15, in the *Teacher's Resource Book,* to illustrate the graphs of Examples 1 and 2. Have students use graph paper and a straightedge to follow along.
- In Example 1, review the general equation of a line $y = mx + b$, where m is the slope and b is the y-intercept. Point out that the slope must be constant if the function is linear.
- Some students may benefit from graphing Examples 1 and 2, as an aid to interpreting the problem solving situation.
- In Example 2, remind students that for a quadratic function in the form $ax^2 + bx + c$, where $a \neq 0$, the x-coordinate of the vertex of the parabola is $-\dfrac{b}{2a}$. If a is positive, the vertex is a minimum point. If a is negative, the vertex is a maximum point.

Critical Thinking

Discovering Relationships The lesson introduction discusses Martin's monthly income, which is given by the function $i = f(s) = 0.05 + 500$. Martin's income is composed of 2 parts, $0.05s$ and 500. What is Martin's line of work? Provide an interpretation of these two parts as sources of income.

salesperson; $0.05s$ is a commission of 5% of his sales (s) in dollars. 500 is his base salary, which he receives whether or not he sells anything.

---

b. $f(w) = p = 0.15w + b$
Use (20, 3.35) to find b.
$3.35 = 0.15(20) + b$
$3.35 = 3.00 + b$
$b = 0.35$
$f(w) = p = 0.15w + 0.35$

Interpret the Results **State your conclusion.**
The slope 0.15 is the increase in price per 1 oz increase in weight. The w-intercept has no meaning since weight cannot be negative. The price intercept $0.35 is the price of zero ounces; it could be the packaging cost.

Quadratic functions, as well as linear functions, frequently serve as mathematical models. Such a model enables you to make predictions and often provides a better understanding of the situation.

EXAMPLE 2 Lia Design Company produces a special drawing tool. As the company produces a larger number of tools, the profit per tool increases. However, beyond a certain number, complications in the manufacturing procedure reverse this advantage. The company finds that the following quadratic function is a formula that approximates the profit per tool p for the number made n.

$$p = f(n) = -0.00025n^2 + 0.105n - 1.025$$

a. Find the profit per tool if 145 tools are made.
b. Find the number of tools the Lia Design Company made if the profit was $7.50 per tool.
c. How many tools should be produced to make the most profit? What is the maximum profit?
d. At what point does the Lia Design Company start to lose money on this venture?

Understand the Problem **What are the given facts?**
Analyze the given quadratic function to answer questions **(a)** through **(d)**.

Plan Your Approach **Choose a strategy.**
Use your understanding of quadratic functions.
a. Substitute 145 for n, and find $f(145)$.
b. Substitute 7.5 for p [or $f(n)$], and find n.
c. Since the coefficient of n^2 is negative, the function will have a maximum value. You must find the vertex point.
d. For what value of n does $p = 0$? Set $f(n) = 0$, and solve.

Complete the Work	**Solve.** **a.** $f(145) = 8.94$ **b.** Solving the quadratic equation for $p = 7.5$, $n = 110$ or 310. **c.** $-\dfrac{b}{2a} = -\dfrac{0.105}{2(-0.00025)} = 210 = n$ Substitute 210 for n and find the p-coordinate for the vertex. $f(210) = 10.00$ The vertex is (210, 10). **d.** If $f(n) = 0$, $n = 10$ or 410.
Interpret the Results	**State your conclusion.** **a.** If 145 tools are made, the profit per tool will be $8.94. **b.** If the profit was $7.50 per tool, the number made was 110 or 310. **c.** Making 210 tools permits the maximum profit, $10 per tool. **d.** The company loses money if they make fewer than 10 or more than 410 tools.

CLASS EXERCISES

1. Write a function to express Susan's income if she receives a base salary of $12,000 and a 15% commission on her sales. $i = 0.15s + 12,000$

A State highway department gives estimates for the cost of constructing a particular kind of highway.

No. miles of highway m	6	9	15
Cost (millions of $) c	8.3	12.2	20.0

2. Show that cost is a linear function of the number of miles constructed. $m = 1.3$

3. Write the cost c as a function of the number of miles n. $c = 1.3n + 0.5$

4. What are the meaning of the slope and intercepts in this situation?
The slope 1.3 is the increase in cost per 1 mile. The intercept 0.5 is the cost at zero miles.

PRACTICE EXERCISES

In the relationships shown, first determine whether each is a linear function. If so, then write the function with the upper variable as a function of the lower. Tell the meaning of slopes and intercepts.

A
1. The costs of different weights of pure silver

Cost ($) c	58	70	78
No. oz w	3	18	28

linear function; $c = 0.8w + 55.6$;
slope is $0.80 increase for each ounce.
c-intercept is the constant cost of production.

2. The temperature at various times on the same day not a linear function

Temp. (°F) t	65	67	70
Time h	2 pm	5 pm	9 pm

13.7 Problem Solving Strategy: Use a Function **569**

CHALKBOARD EXAMPLES

• **For Example 1**

The chart shows the distance traveled in different times.

Distance (d)	200	320	400
Time (t)	1.5	3.6	5.0

1. Confirm that the distance (d) is a linear function of the time (t).
constant slope $m = \dfrac{120}{2.1} = \dfrac{40}{0.7}$

2. Write this function for the distance, $f(t)$. $f(t) = \dfrac{120}{2.1}t + 114.28$

3. Using the slope and intercepts, what can you tell about the function? The slope represents the rate of speed, $\dfrac{d}{t}$. The y-intercept is the number of miles traveled at the start of the problem.

• **For Example 2**

The Soho Student Tour Company offers one week tours of Washington in small groups. While some of Soho's costs per person go down as the number on the tour increases, other costs go up because they must reserve rooms in another motel and rent extra vans. Soho has a function that enables them to predict their profit per student. If x is the number of students on the tour, and $f(x)$ is the profit ($) per student, $f(x) = -0.6x^2 + 18x - 45$.

4. What is Soho's profit per student if there are 17 students on the tour? $87.60

5. If the profit was $75/student, how many students were there? 10 or 20

6. Find the number of students which will give Soho the largest profit per student. What is the maximum profit? 15; $90

7. The company will offer tours as long as they do not lose money. What is the least or greatest number of students they accept? 3, 27

569

Assignment Guide

See p. 542B for assignments.

Mixed Problem Solving Review

- The following skills and concepts are reviewed:
  Using percents in problem solving situations (Ex. 1)
  Solving work and motion problems (Ex. 2)
  Using linear functions in problem solving situations (Ex. 3)
  Solving digit problems (Ex. 4)
- The following problem solving strategies may be appropriate:
  Writing an equation (Ex. 1–4)
  Drawing a diagram (Ex. 1)

Project

The project involves:
Using the function for predicting the height of a projectile

Making a table to represent the function

Using the table to make predictions

Lesson Quiz

Assume that a linear relationship exists between the variables. Use the appropriate function to solve each problem.

1. If a lawyer charges $130 for $1\frac{1}{2}$ h work and $325 for 4 h work, how much would she charge for 6 h work? $481

2. If a health club charges $100 for a 1-month membership and $150 for a 3-month membership, how much would it charge for a 12-month membership? $375

The height of a rocket is given by the formula $h = -5t^2 + 55t + 50$, in terms of time, t.

3. How long would it take the rocket to reach a height of 100?
   1 unit of time

4. What is the maximum height of the rocket? 201.25 units

570

---

3. linear function; $c = 0.24h + 1.52$; slope is $0.24 increase for each hour. c-intercept is basic cost of $1.52.

3. The cost of lighting a field for different lengths of time

Cost ($) c	1.88	3.02	4.35
Hours h	1.5	6.3	11.9

4. The price of different weights of a rare perfume

Price ($) p	4.56	6.12	9.63
Grams g	0.5	2.1	5.7

4. linear function; $p = 0.98g + 4.1$; slope is a $0.98 increase for each gram. p-intercept $4.10 is the basic price

Write a linear function to describe each of the following situations.

5. The total cost of belonging to a health club if there is an initial fee of $75 in addition to the monthly charge of $24.50 $c = 24.5m + 75$

6. The cost of consulting a lawyer if there is a base charge of $35 in addition to the hourly charge of $55 $c = 55h + 35$

7. The number of gallons of solvent left in a 55 gal drum if it suddenly develops a leak through which liquid escapes at the rate of one qt/h $g = -\frac{1}{4}h + 55$

8. The volume of alcohol in a flask, if it initially held 3.00 L and is filling at the rate of 2.5 mL/min $v = 2.5x + 3000$

Assume that a linear relationship exists between the variables. Use the appropriate function to solve the problem.

9. If a designer charged $150 for $2\frac{1}{2}$ h consultation and $325 for 6 h, how long was your consultation, if you were charged $200? 3.5 h

10. If a biologist measures 80 cricket chirps/min at 60°F and 144 chirps/min at 76°F, at what temperature should he expect 180 chirps/min? 85°

B   One would expect that the more walnut trees planted per acre, the higher the yield of walnuts. However, beyond a certain number of trees per acre, the trees crowd one another, and the yield drops. A state agricultural department estimates that the yield in bushels of walnuts per tree can be given as a function of the number of trees per acre t by the formula: $f(t) = -0.01t^2 + 0.8t$.

11. What yield should 30 trees per acre give? 15 bushels per tree

12. How many trees per acre should produce a yield of 16 bu/tree? 40

13. What number of trees per acre gives the greatest yield? What is this maximum yield? 40 trees; 16 bushels per tree

14. What does the t-intercept represent in this situation? What does the $f(t)$ intercept represent? $f(t)$ intercept: number of the yield when no trees planted
    t-intercept: number of trees when there is no yield

A student newspaper currently has 500 subscriber's who pay $6.00/yr. The editors assume that for each $0.25 price decrease, they would sell 50 more subscriptions.

15. On this assumption, write a function for their annual receipts in terms of the number x of $0.25 price decreases. $R(x) = (6 - .25x)(500 + 50x)$

16. What number of $0.25 decreases produces the maximum receipts? What is this maximum? 7 decreases; $3612.50

Sponsors of a design show believe 600 people will attend if the price per ticket is $6.00. They assume that 25 fewer people will attend for each $0.50 increase in ticket price.

17. On this assumption, write a function for the ticket sales in terms of the number x of $0.50 price increases. $s(x) = (6 + 0.5x)(600 - 25x)$

18. What number of $0.50 increases produces the maximum ticket sales? What is this maximum? 6 increases; $4050

Mixed Problem Solving Review

1. If one pair of opposite sides of a square is made 10% longer and the other pair is made 15% shorter, the resulting rectangle will have a perimeter of 234. What is the perimeter of the original square? 240

2. One printer can do a job alone in 3 h. With a second printer also working on this job, it takes 2 h. How long would it take the second printer alone? 6 h

3. Write a linear function for the total cost of cable television if the installation charge is $35 and the monthly fee is $15. If you have paid a total of $125, how many months have you been connected? 6

4. Find a two-digit number if its tens' digit is 2 more than its units' digit and the number with the digits reversed is $\frac{4}{7}$ of the original. 42

PROJECT

The quadratic function $h(t) = 150t - 5t^2$ can be used to predict the height in meters of a small rocket launched with an initial velocity of 150 m/sec. t is the number of seconds after launching. Construct a table as shown below for $t = 0$ to 20. Graph the ordered pairs, $(t, h(t))$. Check students' graphs.

t	$h(t)$
0	0
1	145
2	280
3	405

1. What kind of curve is the graph? parabola

2. What is the maximum height reached by the rocket? 1125 m

3. After how many seconds does the rocket hit the ground? 30 s

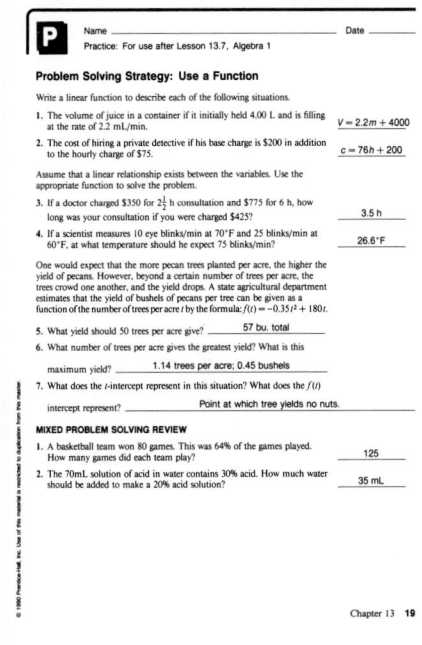

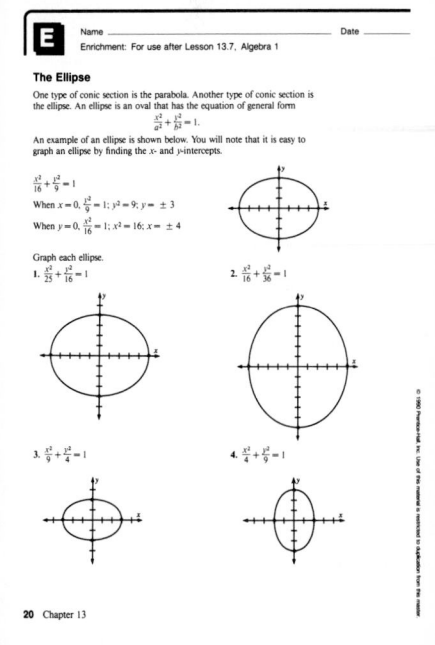

13.7 Problem Solving Strategy: Use a Function **571**

13.8

The Sum and Product of the Solutions

Objective: To use the sum and product of the solutions of a quadratic equation to write the equation

To determine, without solving, if two numbers are the solutions of a quadratic equation

Suppose you know that the solutions of a quadratic equation are 3 and -5. Could you work backwards to write the equation? Think of the two factors from which the solutions must come. $x = 3$ comes from $(x - 3)$, and $x = -5$ from $(x + 5)$. The equation is $(x - 3)(x + 5) = 0$ or $x^2 + 2x - 15 = 0$.

Capsule Review

Recall that factoring is helpful in determining the solutions of an equation.

Find the solutions of these equations.

1. $x^2 - 5x + 6 = 0$ 2, 3 **2.** $x^2 + 9x + 14 = 0$ $-2, -7$ **3.** $x^2 + 11x = 0$ 0, -11

The equation $x^2 + 2x - 15 = 0$ has solutions 3 and -5. Examine the sum and product of these solutions.

The sum of the solutions is $3 + (-5) = -2$.
The product of the solutions is $3(-5) = -15$.

opposite of the sum of solutions

$$x^2 + 2x - 15 = 0$$

product of the solutions

In general, if the solutions of a quadratic equation are s_1 and s_2, then the equation can be written as $(x - s_1)(x - s_2) = 0$, or as:

$$x^2 - (s_1 + s_2)x + s_1 s_2 = 0$$

opposite of the sum of the solutions   *product of the solutions*

Consider the standard form of a quadratic equation, $ax^2 + bx + c = 0$.

Divide each side by a: $x^2 + \dfrac{b}{a}x + \dfrac{c}{a} = 0$

572   Chapter 13 Quadratic Equations and Functions

Compare this equation with the equation $x^2 - (s_1 + s_2)x + s_1 s_2 = 0$. The coefficients of corresponding terms must be the same. This means:

$$\frac{b}{a} = -(s_1 + s_2), \text{ and } \frac{c}{a} = s_1 s_2.$$

These relationships can be used to write the quadratic equation whose solutions are given.

EXAMPLE 1   Write a quadratic equation whose solutions are $\frac{4}{5}$ and -1.

$\frac{b}{a} = -\left[\frac{4}{5} + (-1)\right] = \frac{1}{5}$ *The opposite of the sum of the solutions*

$\frac{c}{a} = \left(\frac{4}{5}\right)(-1) = -\frac{4}{5}$ *Product of the solutions*

$x^2 + \frac{1}{5}x - \frac{4}{5} = 0$ $x^2 + \frac{b}{a}x + \frac{c}{a} = 0$

How else can the equation $x^2 + \frac{1}{5}x - \frac{4}{5} = 0$ be written?

The sum and product relationship provide a method of checking the solutions of a quadratic equation without solving.

EXAMPLE 2   Determine whether $\frac{7}{4}$ and -2 are solutions of $4x^2 + x - 14 = 0$.

$-(s_1 + s_2) = -\left[\frac{7}{4} + (-2)\right] = \frac{1}{4}$

Does $\frac{1}{4} = \frac{b}{a}$ from the equation?

$\frac{1}{4} = \frac{1}{4}$ ✔

$s_1 s_2 = \frac{7}{4}(-2) = -\frac{7}{2}$

Does $-\frac{7}{2} = \frac{c}{a}$ from the equation?

$-\frac{7}{2} \stackrel{?}{=} -\frac{14}{4}$

$-\frac{7}{2} = -\frac{7}{2}$ ✔

$\frac{7}{4}$ and -2 are solutions of $4x^2 + x - 14 = 0$

CLASS EXERCISES

Without solving, find the sum and product of the solutions of each equation.

1. $x^2 + 4x - 12 = 0$ **2.** $y^2 - 6y + 8 = 0$ 6; 8   **3.** $p^2 - 3p = 10$ 3; -10
    $-4; -12$

TEACHING SUGGESTIONS

- Emphasize that for any quadratic equation of the form $x^2 + \frac{b}{a}x + \frac{c}{a} = 0$, the coefficient of the x term, $\frac{b}{a}$, is the opposite of the sum of the solutions, and the constant term $\frac{c}{a}$ is the product of the solutions.
- Use Example 1 to show how to write a quadratic equation whose solutions are given. Stress that the opposite of the sum of the roots is the coefficient of x, that is, $s_1 + s_2 = -\frac{b}{a}$.

- In Example 2, the equation is given and students are asked to determine whether the numbers given are the solutions of the given equation. You may wish to remind students to divide each term of the equation by 4 to verify the solutions: $4x^2 + x - 14 = 0$ becomes $x^2 + \frac{1}{4}x - \frac{14}{4} = 0$.

- In Example 2, discuss the advantages of the method shown as opposed to using the substitution method.

Critical Thinking
Analyzing Relationships   Example 1 shows how to derive a quadratic equation with given solutions by using the sum and product of the solutions. Given the two solutions, is there another method to derive the equation? Write the equation in the form $(x - s_1)(x - s_2) = 0$, and expand.

CHALKBOARD EXAMPLES

- **For Example 1**
  Write a quadratic equation that has the given solutions.
  1. $\frac{2}{3}, 3$ $x^2 - \frac{11}{3}x + 2 = 0$
  2. $-2, 1$ $x^2 + x - 2 = 0$

573

For Example 2

Determine if the numbers are solutions of the given equation.

3. $\frac{1}{3}$, -2; $3x^2 + 5x = 2$ yes

4. $-\frac{1}{2}$, -5; $2x^2 + 11x + 5 = 0$

yes

LESSON FOLLOW-UP

Assignment Guide

- See p. 542B for assignments.
- Emphasize that students should use the methods used in the lesson. Stress that some of the exercises should be done mentally.
- See *Teacher's Resource Book*, for Reading and Writing in Algebra activity, p. 13.

Test Yourself

See *Teacher's Resource Book*, Tests, pp. 139–140.

Lesson Quiz

Write a quadratic equation that has the given solutions.

1. $\frac{3}{4}$, 1 $x^2 - \frac{7}{4}x + \frac{3}{4} = 0$

2. $\frac{1}{3}$, -3 $x^2 + \frac{8}{3}x - 1 = 0$

3. 0, 5 $x^2 - 5x = 0$

Determine if the numbers are solutions of the given equation.

4. $\frac{1}{5}$, -7; $5a^2 + 34a - 7 = 0$ yes

5. $\frac{7}{5}$, 3; $5x^2 - 22x + 21 = 0$ yes

6. $\frac{2}{3}$, $-\frac{5}{2}$; $6y^2 + 11y - 10 = 0$

yes

Enrichment

A particular equation is known to have solutions of -2 and -3. Is the equation necessarily quadratic? Explain. The equation is not necessarily quadratic; for example, $x^3 + 4x^2 + x - 6 = 0$ has -2 and -3 as solutions, but it also has 1 as a solution. Also, $x^3 + 7x^2 + 16x + 12 = 0$ has -2 and -3 as solutions, but -2 is a double solution.

574

---

4. $3m^2 + 9m + 6 = 0$
$-3; 2$

5. $x^2 + 5x = 0$ $-5; 0$

6. $2n^2 - 10n = 12$
$5; -6$

Write a quadratic equation that has the given solutions.

7. 1, -2
$x^2 + x - 2 = 0$

8. -2, -3
$x^2 + 5x + 6 = 0$

9. $-\frac{1}{3}$, 1
$3x^2 - 2x - 1 = 0$

10. 3, $-\frac{3}{2}$
$2x^2 - 3x - 9 = 0$

For Discussion

11. If the only solution to a quadratic equation is -4, what are the sum and product of its solutions? $-8; 16$

PRACTICE EXERCISES

Write a quadratic equation in standard form that has the given solutions.

A
1. 1, 3
$x^2 - 4x + 3 = 0$

2. 3, 6
$x^2 - 9x + 18 = 0$

3. -2, 6
$x^2 - 4x - 12 = 0$

4. -3, 2
$x^2 + x - 6 = 0$

5. -5, -1
$x^2 + 6x + 5 = 0$

6. -1, -2
$x^2 + 3x + 2 = 0$

7. -5, 0
$x^2 + 5x = 0$

8. 0, 3
$x^2 - 3x = 0$

9. -3, $\frac{4}{5}$
$5x^2 + 11x - 12 = 0$

10. $-\frac{1}{2}$, 2
$2x^2 - 3x - 2 = 0$

11. $\frac{2}{3}$, 1
$3x^2 - 5x + 2 = 0$

12. $-\frac{3}{2}$, 3
$2x^2 - 3x - 9 = 0$

Determine if the numbers are solutions of the given equation.

13. -4, 4; $x^2 - 16 = 0$ yes

14. 3, -3; $x^2 + 9 = 0$ no

15. -2, -1; $x^2 - 3x + 2 = 0$ no

16. -3, -4; $x^2 + 7x + 12 = 0$ yes

Write a quadratic equation that has the given solutions.

B
17. $-\frac{5}{2}$, $\frac{5}{2}$
$4x^2 - 25 = 0$

18. $\frac{2}{3}$, $-\frac{2}{3}$
$9x^2 - 4 = 0$

19. $-\frac{3}{2}$, $\frac{4}{3}$
$6x^2 + x - 12 = 0$

20. $\frac{3}{2}$, $-\frac{1}{2}$
$4x^2 - 4x - 3 = 0$

21. $1 + \sqrt{6}$, $1 - \sqrt{6}$ $x^2 - 2x - 5 = 0$

22. $-2 + \sqrt{3}$, $-2 - \sqrt{3}$ $x^2 + 4x + 1 = 0$

Determine if the numbers are solutions of the given equation.

23. $-\frac{7}{2}$, 5; $2x^2 - 3x = 35$ yes

24. 1, $-\frac{2}{3}$; $3 = 6x^2 - x$ no

C
25. $1 \pm \sqrt{2}$; $z^2 - z - 1 = 0$ no

26. $5 \pm \sqrt{5}$; $y^2 - 10y + 20 = 0$ yes

27. $\frac{-3 \pm \sqrt{5}}{2}$; $p^2 + 3p = -1$ yes

28. $\frac{1 \pm \sqrt{7}}{3}$; $3r^2 - 2r = 2$ yes

Show that the following statements are true. $\left(\textit{Hint:} \text{ The solutions of a quadratic equation are } \dfrac{-b \pm \sqrt{b^2 - 4ac}}{2a}.\right)$

29. Sum of the solutions is $-\dfrac{b}{a}$.

$\dfrac{-b + \sqrt{b^2 - 4ac}}{2a} + \dfrac{-b - \sqrt{b^2 - 4ac}}{2a} = \dfrac{-2b}{2a} = \dfrac{-b}{a}$

30. Product of the solutions is $\dfrac{c}{a}$.

$\left(\dfrac{-b + \sqrt{b^2 - 4ac}}{2a}\right)\left(\dfrac{-b - \sqrt{b^2 - 4ac}}{2a}\right)$

$= \dfrac{b^2 - (b^2 - 4ac)}{4a^2} = \dfrac{4ac}{4a^2} = \dfrac{c}{a}$

Applications

31. Engineering An engineer thinks that $1 \pm \sqrt{5}$ are solutions of the equation $x^2 - 2x = 4$. Determine if these are solutions of the given equation. yes

32. Business In 1990 a financial officer projects from the equation $p = -x^2 - 20x + 300$, that his company will show a 0 profit in the year 2000. Determine if he is correct. yes

33. Engineering A research engineer proposes that a rocket which follows a path represented by the equation $y = -16t^2 - 256t + 4096$ has solutions of $-8 \pm 8\sqrt{5}$. Determine if this is correct. yes

TEST YOURSELF

Find the vertex and the axis of symmetry of each equation.   13.5

1. $y = x^2$ (0, 0); x = 0   **2.** $y = 5 - x^2$ (0, 5); x = 0   **3.** $y = x^2 - 2x$ (1, −1); x = 1

Tell whether the graph of each function opens upward or downward. Then tell whether there is a minimum or a maximum point.

4. $g(x) = \frac{1}{4}x^2$
upward; minimum pt.

5. $f(x) = 3x - x^2$
downward; maximum pt.

6. $h(x) = x^2 + 2x + 3$
upward; minimum pt.

Find the value of the discriminant, and state the nature of the solutions.   13.6

7. $x^2 - 3x + 4 = 0$
−7; no real solutions

8. $4y^2 + 12y + 9 = 0$
0; 1 real solution

9. $2z^2 - 5z = 12$
121; 2 real solutions

The Villo Travel Agency offers a vacation package to the Carribean at a discount rate. They figure that the amount of profit per person can be determined by the function: $f(x) = 40x - x^2$, where x is the number of people.

Use the quadratic function to solve these problems.   13.7

10. What is Villo's profit/person if 15 people were to go to the Carribean? $375

11. If the profit was $351/person, how many people went to the Carribean?
27 or 13 people

12. Find the number of people which will give Villo's the largest profit/person. What is the maximum profit? 20 people; $400 profit

13. What is the least or greatest number of people they can accept and not lose any money? 0 people or 40 people

For each equation, find the sum and product of its solutions.   13.8

14. $m^2 + 7m + 9 = 0$
−7; 9

15. $2n^2 - 4n = 5$ 2; −2.5

16. $5r^2 = 4r$ $\frac{4}{5}$; 0

13.8 The Sum and Product of the Solutions   **575**

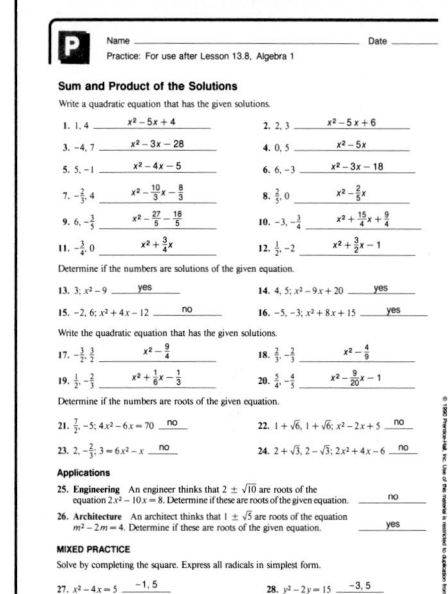
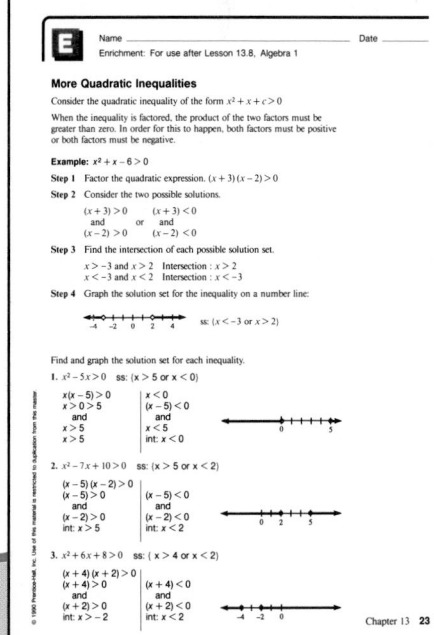

CHAPTER 13 SUMMARY AND REVIEW

Vocabulary

axis of symmetry (559)
completing the square (547)
discriminant (564)
maximum point (558)
minimum point (558)

parabola (558)
perfect square (544)
quadratic formula (552)
quadratic function (557)
vertex (559)

Using Perfect Square Quadratics   To solve quadratic equations of the   **13.1**
form $x^2 = k$ and $(ax + b)^2 = k$, where $k \geq 0$, use the square-root property:
if $x^2 = k$, then $x = +\sqrt{k}$ or $x = -\sqrt{k}$.

Solve by using the square-root property.

1. $4p^2 = 80$ $\pm 2\sqrt{5}$ **2.** $(y - 1)^2 = 9$ $4, -2$ **3.** $(m + 3)^2 - 4 = 32$
$-9, 3$

Using Completing the Square   To complete the square for $ax^2 + bx + \underline{?}$: **13.2**
• If $a \neq 1$, then divide the equation by a.
• find one-half of the coefficient of x,
• square the value,
• add the squared result to $x^2 + \dfrac{b}{a}x$.

Solve by completing the square.

4. $x^2 + 4x - 12 = 0$ $2, -6$ **5.** $y^2 - 6y - 5 = 0$ **6.** $2z^2 - 4 = 5$ $\frac{\pm 3\sqrt{2}}{2}$
$3 \pm \sqrt{14}$

Using the Quadratic Formula   To solve any quadratic equation of the   **13.3**
form $ax^2 + bx + c = 0$, you can use the quadratic formula:

$$x = \frac{-b \pm \sqrt{b^2 - 4ac}}{2a}.$$

Solve by using the quadratic formula.

7. $3x^2 + 7x + 3 = 0$ **8.** $4z^2 = 20z - 5$ $\frac{5 \pm 2\sqrt{5}}{2}$ **9.** $4p^2 - 6p = -9$
$\frac{-7 \pm \sqrt{13}}{6}$ no real solutions

Solving Quadratic Equations by Any Method   You can use factoring,   **13.4**
the square-root property, completing the square, or the quadratic formula to
solve quadratic equations.

Solve each quadratic equation by using an appropriate method.

10. $4t^2 - 8t = 0$ $0, 2$ **11.** $5x^2 = 30$ $\pm\sqrt{6}$ **12.** $(y + 3)^2 = 16$
$1, -7$
13. $3p^2 + 1 = 10p$ $\frac{5 \pm \sqrt{22}}{3}$ **14.** $k^2 + 10k + 30 = 0$ **15.** $m^2 + 5m - 24 = 0$
no real solutions $-8, 3$

576   Chapter 13 Quadratic Equations and Functions

Graphing a Quadratic Function, $f(x) = ax^2 + bx + c$, $a \neq 0$ One   13.5
way to graph a quadratic function is to find several ordered pairs that satisfy
the equation, plot the ordered pairs, and then connect the points with a
smooth curve.

**Graph the function. Find its x-intercepts. Tell whether there is a
maximum or a minimum point. Determine the axis of symmetry.**

16. $y = x^2$
    0; minimum pt.; $x = 0$

17. $y = 1 - x^2$
    1, −1; maximum pt.; $x = 0$

18. $y = x^2 - 2x + 1$
    1; minimum pt.; $x = 1$

Determining the Nature of the Solutions In the quadratic formula,   13.6
$b^2 - 4ac$ is called the discriminant. There is a relationship between the value
of the discriminant and the nature of the solutions of a quadratic equation.

Find the value of the discriminant, and state the nature of the solutions.

19. $y^2 + 4y - 12 = 0$
    64; 2 real solutions

20. $x^2 = 14x - 49$
    0; 1 real solution

21. $c^2 - 2c + 25 = 0$
    −96; no real solution

Using the Sum and Product of the Solutions of a Quadratic   13.8
Equation To write a quadratic equation in the general form
$ax^2 + bx + c = 0$, when the solutions, s_1 and s_2, of the equation are given,
use these facts:

- When the equation is written as $x^2 + \dfrac{b}{a}x + \dfrac{c}{a} = 0$, the coefficient of the

  x term, $\dfrac{b}{a}$, is the opposite of the sum of the solutions. That is $-(s_1 + s_2) = \dfrac{b}{a}$.

- The constant term, $\dfrac{c}{a}$, is the product of the solutions. That is $s_1 s_2 = \dfrac{c}{a}$.

Write a quadratic equation in standard form with the given solutions.

22. 8, −1
    $x^2 - 7x - 8 = 0$

23. −6, −5
    $x^2 + 11x + 30 = 0$

24. $\dfrac{4}{5}$, −1
    $5x^2 + x - 4 = 0$

25. $\dfrac{10}{3}$, $\dfrac{-5}{2}$
    $6x^2 - 5x - 50 = 0$

Using a Function to Solve a Problem Quadratic functions, as well as   13.7
linear functions, frequently serve as mathematical models. Such models enable
you to make predictions and often provide better understanding of the situation.

Use the function to solve the problem.

26. The Sundries Company uses the function $f(x) = -0.6x^2 + 15x - 4$ to
determine their profits/sale. Find the amount of sales (x) that will give
the Sundries Company the largest profit/sale. What is the maximum
profit per sale? 12.5, $89.75

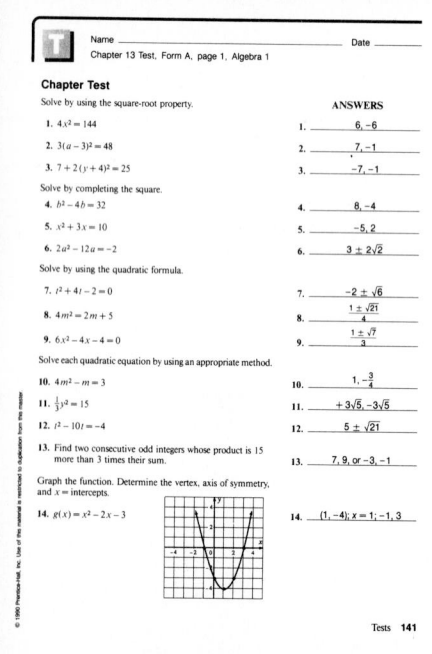

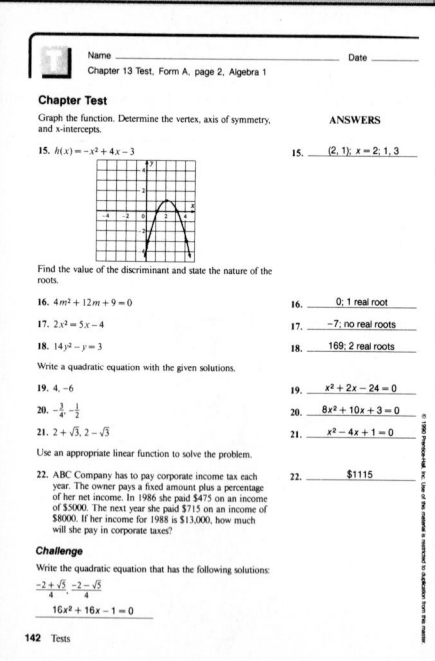

Solve by using the square-root property.

1. $2x^2 = 24$ $\pm 2\sqrt{3}$

2. $2(y - 1)^2 = 50$ $6, -4$

Solve by completing the square.

3. $c^2 - 2c = 15$ $-3, 5$

4. $2m^2 + 10m - 3 = 0$ $\dfrac{-5 \pm \sqrt{31}}{2}$

Solve by using the quadratic formula.

5. $6x^2 + 7x - 5 = 0$ $\dfrac{1}{2}, -\dfrac{5}{3}$

6. $2n^2 - 5 = 2n$ $\dfrac{1 \pm \sqrt{11}}{2}$

Solve each quadratic equation by using an appropriate method.

7. $m^2 - 6m - 7 = 0$ $7, -1$

8. $p^2 + \dfrac{p}{6} - \dfrac{1}{6} = 0$ $\dfrac{1}{3}, -\dfrac{1}{2}$

Graph the function. Find its x-intercepts. Tell whether there is a minimum or a maximum point. Determine the axis of symmetry.

Check students' graphs.

9. $y = x^2 - x - 12$
4, -3; minimum point; $x = \dfrac{1}{2}$

10. $y = -x^2 - 2$
no x-intercepts; maximum point; $x = 0$

Find the value of the discriminant, and state the nature of the roots.

11. $p^2 - 8p + 16 = 0$
0; 1 real solution

12. $2y^2 + 7y - 3 = 0$
73; 2 real solutions

13. $3x^2 = 2x - 5$
-56; no real solutions

Write a quadratic equation in standard form with the given solutions.

14. 3, 2 $x^2 - 5x + 6 = 0$

15. $\dfrac{5}{2}, -\dfrac{9}{4}$ $8x^2 - 2x - 45 = 0$

16. $-\dfrac{2}{3}, 0$
$3x^2 + 2x = 0$

Use the appropriate function to solve.

17. The length of a rectangle is 5 ft more than twice its width. Find the dimensions, to the nearest tenth of a foot, if the rectangle has an area of 20 ft². $l = 9.3$ ft; $2 = 2.2$ ft

18. The ABC Tile Company uses the function $f(x) = 115x - x^2$ to determine their profit/sale. How many sales (x) did they have if they had a profit of \$3300 per sale? 55 per sale or 60

Challenge

19. Solve graphically: $y > x^2$
$y \le 4$

Check students' graphs.

Select the best choices for each question.

1. If $4x^2 + kx + 16$ is a perfect
   D square trinomial then k could equal:
   A. 0   **B.** 4   **C.** 8
   D. 16   **E.** 32

2. What value of x will make the
   B following three ratios equal?

   $$\frac{64}{144}, \frac{x}{108}, \frac{12}{27}$$

   A. 40   **B.** 48   **C.** 52
   D. 56   **E.** 60

3.   10.08
   A $\times\ 0.05$

   A. 0.504   **B.** 5.04   **C.** 0.054
   D. 0.540   **E.** 5.40

4. Solve the equation:
   A $2x - 3 = 5x + 18$
   A. -7 **B.** -5 **C.** -3
   D. 5   **E.** 7

5. Find the value of $|3x + 2y|$ when
   B $x = -4$ and $y = 5$.
   A. 0   **B.** 2
   C. 3   **D.** 7
   E. 22

6. Solve for x: $2x + 5 = \sqrt{7}$
   E **A.** 1
   B. 22
   C. $\dfrac{5 - \sqrt{7}}{2}$
   D. $\dfrac{5 + \sqrt{7}}{2}$
   E. $\dfrac{\sqrt{7} - 5}{2}$

7. Solve for x:
   D $5x - 7 < 3x + 11$.

   A. $x < \dfrac{1}{2}$ **B.** $x < 2$

   C. $x > 2$ **D.** $x < 9$

   E. $x > 9$

8. What is the prime factorization of
   B 180?
   A. $2^3 \cdot 3 \cdot 5$ **B.** $2^2 \cdot 3^2 \cdot 5$
   C. $2 \cdot 3^3 \cdot 5$ **D.** $2^2 \cdot 9 \cdot 5$
   E. $2 \cdot 3 \cdot 6 \cdot 5$

9. Solve for x: $x^2 - 7x - 18 = 0$
   B **A.** -2 or -9
   B. -2 or 9
   C. 2 or -9
   D. 2 or 9
   E. $\pm 3\sqrt{2}$

10. Find the value of
    C $5a^3b + 2a^2b^2 - 3ab^3$ when
    $a = -1$ and $b = 2$.
    A. 42   **B.** 26   **C.** 22
    D. -22 **E.** -26

11. Tom started typing his history paper
    B at 6:48 p.m. and finished at
    10:15 p.m. that evening. How long
    did it take him to type the paper?
    A. 3 h 17 min
    B. 3 h 27 min
    C. 4 h 3 min
    D. 4 h 27 min
    E. 4 h 33 min

12. The product of two positive
    E consecutive odd integers is 195.
    Find the smaller one.
    A. 41   **B.** 39   **C.** 17   **D.** 15
    E. None of the above.

The individual comments provided about some problems can be helpful in guiding students to solve these problems.

2. Problems like this one can easily be done by cross-multiplying using either of the known fractions.
8. Stress that answers D and E are immediately eliminated because they contain factors that are not prime.

See *Teacher's Resource Book,* for Preparing for Standardized Tests.

Maintaining Skills

The following skills and concepts are reviewed:
Order of real numbers
Reading graphs
Squaring decimals
Using probability

MAINTAINING SKILLS

Order each set of numbers from least to greatest.

Example 1 Write in order: $-5, 0, -2, 3, 1$
A number line can help.
Answer: $-5, -2, 0, 1, 3$

1. $4, -1, -3, 2, -4$
$-4, -3, -1, 2, 4$
2. $0, -1.5, -1, -1.75, -2$
$-2, -1.75, -1.5, -1, 0$
3. $-3.0, 2.8, 2.08, 2.88, -3.1$
$-3.1, -3.0, 2.08, 2.8, 2.88$
4. $\frac{1}{4}, \frac{1}{3}, -\frac{3}{4}, -\frac{2}{3}, 0$ $-\frac{3}{4}, -\frac{2}{3}, 0, \frac{1}{4}, \frac{1}{3}$
5. $\frac{5}{6}, \frac{7}{8}, -\frac{3}{5}, -\frac{2}{3}, -\frac{4}{7}$ $-\frac{2}{3}, -\frac{3}{5}, -\frac{4}{7}, \frac{5}{6}, \frac{7}{8}$
6. $\frac{3}{4}, 0.7, -\frac{2}{3}, -0.6, -\frac{1}{2}$
$-\frac{2}{3}, -0.6, -\frac{1}{2}, 0.7, \frac{3}{4}$

Use the bar graph to solve each word problem.

7. How many records were sold in December? 450

8. In which month were the fewest number of records sold? Jan.

9. How many more records were sold in March then in January? 200

10. How many records were sold from November through March? 1300

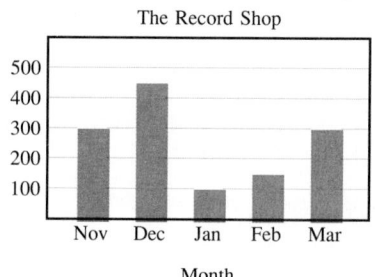

Simplify.

Example 2 $(-3.5)^2$
$(-3.5)^2 = (-3.5)(-3.5) = 12.25$

11. $(1.8)^2$ 3.24 12. $(0.7)^2$ 0.49 13. $(-2.6)^2$ 6.76 14. $-(3.2)^2$ −10.24 15. $-(-4.9)^2$ −24.01
16. $(1.2)^2$ 1.44 17. $(-5.1)^2$ 26.01 18. $-(6.5)^2$ −42.25 19. $-(-8.3)^2$ −68.89 20. $(7.4)^2$ 54.76

Find the probability of choosing at random a marble of the given color.

Example 3 $P(\text{red}) = \dfrac{\text{number of red marbles}}{\text{total number of marbles}}$
$= \frac{2}{10} = \frac{1}{5}$

21. $P(\text{blue})$ $\frac{3}{10}$ 22. $P(\text{green})$ $\frac{1}{2}$ 23. $P(\text{not blue})$ $\frac{7}{10}$ 24. $P(\text{not green})$ $\frac{1}{2}$

OVERVIEW • Chapter 14

SUMMARY

In Chapter 14, students get acquainted with Statistics and Probability, an area of mathematics which is becoming more and more important in today's world. Students learn to analyze data in a variety of ways, including finding measures of central tendency (such as the mode, median and mean) and measures of variability (such as the range, variance and standard deviation). They also learn to set up a frequency distribution table from given data and then represent it in a histogram.

After this chapter is completed, students should be able to analyze a given set of data by finding measures of central tendency and measures of variability, by setting up a frequency distribution table, or by drawing a histogram or other graph. They should be able to solve a variety of problems involving probability and odds, including those where the events are independent, dependent, mutually exclusive, or inclusive.

CHAPTER OBJECTIVES

- To find the mode, median, and mean from data and from a frequency distribution
- To make a frequency distribution table from data
- To make a histogram from a frequency distribution table
- To compute the range, variance, and standard deviation of a set of data
- To determine the probability of an event and of the complement event for a random experiment
- To solve problems involving probability
- To solve problems involving independent, dependent, mutually exclusive, and inclusive events

Problem Solving Strategy

To solve problems by drawing Venn diagrams to represent sets

CHAPTER HIGHLIGHTS

The *theme* of Chapter 14 is demography. The chapter's special features show how demography utilizes the concepts of probability and statistics.

PROBLEM SOLVING AND APPLICATIONS

Problem solving and applications form an integral part of each lesson. Students look for patterns, work backwards, and use diagrams, tables, and graphs to solve many real world problem situations. Students use the problem solving strategy in Lesson 14.5, drawing a diagram, to solve many complex problems.

TECHNOLOGY

Calculator

Students learn how to find the mean of a set of data by using a calculator in scientific mode.

Computer

The computer program in Lesson 14.3 provides a table of computations for the variance and the standard deviation from the mean. Students learn how to manipulate the program to find the variance and standard deviation.

RESOURCE

Teacher's Resource Book

- Teaching Aid 17
- Transparency 31

STUDENT TEXT

Chapter Content	Basic	Average	Enriched	R	P	E
14.1 Statistics: Measures of Central Tendency	D: 584/1-7 odd, 18	D: 584/1-11 odd, 18-19	D: 584/9-17 odd, 18-20	1	2	3
14.2 Statistics: Graphing Data	D: 588/1-9 odd, 20 R: 584/2, 6	D: 588/1-17 odd, 19, 20 R: 584/2, 4, 8	D: 588/11-17 odd, 19, 20 R: 584/12, 18	4	5	6
14.3 Statistics: Measures of Variability	D: 592/1-3 odd, 8 R: Test Yourself	D: 592/1-7 odd, 8, 9 R: Test Yourself	D: 593/5-7 odd, 8, 9 R: Test Yourself	7	8	9
14.4 Simple Probability	D: 598/1-15 odd, 31 R: 592/2	D: 598/1-25 odd, 31, 32 R: 592/2, 4, 6	D: 599/17-29 odd, 31, 32 R: 593/6	10	11	12

14.5 Problem Solving Strategy: Draw a Diagram	D: 602/1
	    MPSR 1-6
	R: 598/2, 14
		D: 602/3
		    MPSR 1-6
		R: 598/4, 24
			D: 602/5
			    MPSR 1-6
			R: 598/18, 26
					13	14

14.6 Probability: Compound Events	D: 606/1-17 odd, 31 R: Test Yourself	D: 606/1-25 odd, 31, 32 R: Test Yourself	D: 606/19-29 odd, 31, 32 R: 602/5 Test Yourself		15	16

D = Daily   R = Review   MPSR = Mixed Problem Solving Review   R = Reteaching   P = 'Practice   E = Enrichment

	STUDENT TEXT				TEACHER'S RESOURCE BOOK	
Review	Test Yourself	593	Chapter Test	610	Spanish Chapter Summary and Review	27-28
And	Test Yourself	607	Prep. for Stan. Tests	611	• Quizzes	145-148
Testing	Chapter Sum. and Rev.	608	Cumulative Review	612	• Chapter Test (Form A)	149-150
			Extra Practice	668	• Chapter Test (Form B)	151-152
					Calculator Test	27-28
Special	Algebra in Demography	585	Math Club Activity	599	Applications—Chapter 14	17
Features	Extra	589	Project	602	Critical Thinking	14
	Application	594			Reading and Writing in Algebra	14
					Technology	26-27

14 Statistics and Probability

The collection and analysis of information concerning population is called demography. This type of information provides insight into many areas such as voting patterns, career development, marriage trends, or academic achievement.

581

BACKGROUND

Demographers deal with the distribution and vital statistics of populations. This involves using many complex formulas, tables, and graphs. Chapter 14 will demonstrate how probability and statistics are integrated into real world situations.

14.1 Statistics: Measures of Central Tendency

Objective: To find the mode, median, and mean from data and from frequency distributions

Statistics is the collection, organization, analysis, and interpretation of numerical information, called *data*. Before attempting to analyze a set of data, it is a common practice to order the numbers, either from least to greatest or greatest to least.

Capsule Review

A number line shows the order of real numbers.

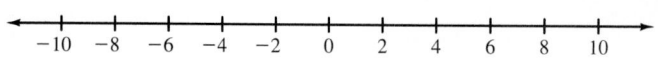

List the numbers in order from least to greatest.

1. 4, −5, 6, −1, −2, 0, 7, 9, −11
−11, −5, −2, −1, 0, 4, 6, 7, 9

2. 1.2, −3.2, −4, 5.8, 3
−4, −3.2, 1.2, 3, 5.8

3. $3\frac{1}{2}$, 3, $-3\frac{1}{2}$, $-\frac{1}{2}$, 0, -3
$-3\frac{1}{2}$, −3, $-\frac{1}{2}$, 0, 3, $3\frac{1}{2}$

4. −6.08, 6.1, 6.0, 6.12, −6.10
−6.10, −6.08, 6.0, 6.1, 6.12

Some specific characteristics of a set of data can be obtained by using *measures of central tendency*. A **measure of central tendency** is a statistic (a number) that is in some way representative or typical of a set of data. The *mode, median,* and *mean* are measures of central tendency.

> A **mode** of a set of data is a number in the set that occurs most often.
>
> A **median** of a set of data is the middle number in the set when the numbers are arranged in order from least to greatest.
>
> The **mean** of a set of data consisting of *n* numbers is the sum of the numbers in the set divided by *n*.

For a given set of data, there is exactly one mean and exactly one median. However, the set may have one, more than one, or no modes.

582 Chapter 14 Statistics and Probability

EXAMPLE 1

Brand	A	B	C	D	E	F	G	H	I	J
Price in cents	68	59	73	89	68	94	69	89	68	89

Mode: Order the data   59, 68, 68, 68, 69, 73, 89, 89, 89, 94
Both 68 and 89 appear three times; there are two modes.

Mean: $\dfrac{59 + 68 + 68 + 68 + 69 + 73 + 89 + 89 + 89 + 94}{10} = \dfrac{766}{10} \approx 77$

In the statistics mode your calculator keeps track of the number of entries. You may wish to use a calculator to display the mean.

Median: For 10 values (an even number), there is no one middle number. Find the mean of the two middle numbers: $\dfrac{69 + 73}{2} = 71$

Data can be summarized in a table called a **frequency distribution.** Each number is matched with its frequency, the number of times it occurs.

EXAMPLE 2 **The distribution of scores earned by 60 students on a 10-point quiz are shown below. Find the mode, median, and mean.**

Score	Frequency	Frequency × Score
1	1	$1 \times 1 = 1$
2	2	$2 \times 2 = 4$
3	2	$2 \times 3 = 6$
4	5	$5 \times 4 = 20$
5	4	$4 \times 5 = 20$
6	5	$5 \times 6 = 30$
7	13	$13 \times 7 = 91$
8	11	$11 \times 8 = 88$
9	9	$9 \times 9 = 81$
10	8	$8 \times 10 = 80$
Total	60 (students)	421 (all scores)

Mode: The mode is 7, because its frequency, 13, is the highest.

Median: In a list of 60, the middle scores are the 30th and 31st score. Add down the frequency column until the sum is greater than 31: $1 + 2 + 2 + 5 + 4 + 5 + 13 = 32$. The 30th and 31st scores are both 7 so the median is 7.

Mean: $\dfrac{\text{Total of all scores} \longrightarrow}{\text{Number of students} \longrightarrow} \dfrac{421}{60} = 7.0$, to the nearest tenth

14.1 Statistics: Measures of Central Tendency   **583**

TEACHING SUGGESTIONS

- Write a collection of test grades on the board. (You might choose an actual set from your class grade book.) Ask students to describe the characteristics of the set of grades. Ask if there is *one* number which could represent them all. Ask why or why not.
- Some students might have difficulty distinguishing the difference between mean, median, and mode. Have them explain in their own words what each term means.
- Have students use a calculator to check their results.

CHALKBOARD EXAMPLES

- **For Example 1**

  Find the mode, mean, and median. Round to the nearest tenth.

  1. The test scores of 10 students at Kennedy High School: 98, 88, 93, 79, 97, 93, 99, 98, 93, 88   mode: 93; mean: 92.6; median 93

  2. The ages of men on a community basketball team: 22, 44, 26, 32, 33, 26, 28, 30, 26, 40   mode: 26; mean: 30.7; median: 29

- **For Example 2**

  3. The distribution of hours of television watched by 65 students over a weekend are shown below. Find the mode, median, and mean.

Hours	Frequency	Frequency × hr
0	2	$2 \times 0 = 0$
2	2	$2 \times 2 = 4$
4	3	$3 \times 4 = 12$
7	4	$4 \times 7 = 28$
9	6	$6 \times 9 = 54$
10	10	$10 \times 10 = 100$
11	13	$13 \times 11 = 143$
12	12	$12 \times 12 = 144$
14	9	$9 \times 14 = 126$
15	3	$3 \times 15 = 45$
20	1	$1 \times 20 = 20$
Total	65 students	676 hr

mode: 11; median: 11; mean: 10.4

Common Error

- Students often confuse mode, median, and mean. Have students write a definition of each in their own words. You might ask students to generate a set of ten (10) numbers for which the mode, median, and mean are different. Follow up with a class discussion where students share their definitions and examples.
- See *Teacher's Resource Book* for additional remediation.

LESSON FOLLOW-UP

Assignment Guide
- See p. 580B for assignments.
- See *Teacher's Resource Book,* for Critical Thinking activity, p. 14.

Lesson Quiz
Find the mode, mean, and median. Round to the nearest tenth.
1. The price in cents of 10 different bars of soap: 53, 57, 62, 58, 57, 59, 53, 56, 60, 61 mode: 53, 57; median: 57.5; mean: 57.6
2. The heights in inches of the Santa Maria High School soccer team's players: 72, 70, 75, 68, 72, 66, 67, 73, 72, 70, 69, 69 mode: 72; median: 70; mean: 70.3
3. The distribution of the cars driven per household over a weekend are shown below. mode: 1; median: 1; mean: 1.6

Cars	Frequency	Frequency × cars
0	1	0
1	8	8
2	3	6
3	2	6
4	1	4
Total 15		24

Enrichment
The number of hours 10 students spent doing homework: $1\frac{3}{4}$, 2, $2\frac{1}{4}$, $2\frac{1}{4}$, $1\frac{1}{4}$, $1\frac{1}{2}$, 2, $1\frac{3}{4}$, $2\frac{1}{4}$, 3. Find the mode, median, and mean. mode $2\frac{1}{4}$; median 2; mean 2

584

CLASS EXERCISES

Find the mode, median, and mean.
(A) (B) (C)
1. Number of eggs found in Mallard duck nests at the Tenafly Nature Center: 7, 9, 9, 8, 11, 9, 8, 10, 10 A: 9 B: 9 C: 9

This table shows the frequency distribution of gas mileage for some new car models.

2. What is the mode? 24 and 26
3. What is the median to the nearest tenth? 25.5
4. What is the mean to the nearest tenth? 25.4

mi/gal	× Frequency	= Total
24	3	72
25	2	50
26	3	78
27	2	54
Sum	10	254

PRACTICE EXERCISES

Find the mode, median, and mean. Round to the nearest tenth.
(A) (B) (C)

A
1. The price in cents of 10 brands of a pint-size orange juice: 69, 71, 68, 70, 65, 71, 67, 71, 69, 67 A: 71 B: 69 C: 68.8
2. The ages in years of players on the Oakwood Acorns Basketball Team: 22, 23, 28, 33, 24, 27, 24, 26, 23, 26, 25, 29, 21, 30 A: 23, 24, 26 B: 25.5 C: 25.8
3. The weights in pounds of linemen on the Ferndale High School football team: 159, 167, 171, 162, 155, 183, 168, 153, 164, 148 A: None B: 163 C: 163
4. The number of students attending the high schools in Wexford County: 539, 495, 517, 525, 400, 560, 478 A: None B: 517 C: 502
5. Margot's weekly weight losses in pounds following the Doctors Diet: 2.1, 1.8, 1.1, 1.5, 1.4, 1.4, 1.3, 1.5, 1.2, 1.7, 1.2 A: 1.2, 1.4, 1.5 B: 1.4 C: 1.5
6. Lengths in centimeters of mature Canada geese found in the Meadville Town Park: 35.2, 42.6, 41.0, 37.2, 34.5, 36.8, 41.0, 37.9, 42.1, 41.5 A: 41.0 B: 39.45 C: 39.0

7. This table shows the number of children per family.

Children	× Frequency	= Total
0	9	0
1	10	10
2	14	28
3	10	30
4	4	16
5	2	10
6	1	6
Sum	50	100

A: 2 B: 2 C: 2

8. This table shows runs scored this season by a little league team.

Score	× Frequency	= Total
0	2	0
1	8	8
2	4	8
3	5	15
4	2	8
7	2	14
10	1	10
12	1	12
Sum	25	75

A: 1 B: 2 C: 3

584   Chapter 14 Statistics and Probability

B

9. Change one number in the set {7, 12, 19, 16} so that the median is 12.
   16 to 12 or 19 to 12 or change 12 to 8.
10. Insert a number in the set {2, 9, 11, 16} so that the median of the new set is the same as that of the original. Insert 10

11. Find *n* so that the mean of the set {6, 8, *n*, 10, 16} is 13. n = 25

12. Find *n* so that the mean of the set {18, 35, *n*, 9, 15} is 17. n = 8

Tell how the mean, median, and mode are affected by these changes.

C

13. Each number in a set of numbers is decreased by 8.
    All three measures will decrease by 8.
14. Each number in a set of numbers is increased by 4.
    All three measures will increase by 4.
15. Each number in a set of numbers is halved.
    All three measures will be halved.
16. Each number in a set of numbers is squared.
    The mode is squared. The mean is not squared. The median may or may not be squared.
17. The mean of 30 bowling scores is 145. If the four lowest and the four highest scores are removed, the mean of the remaining scores is 148. What is the mean of the scores removed? 136.75

Applications

Identify the measure of central tendency that is being used.

18. **Geography** Half the continents in the world have an area that is less than South America. median

19. **Business** The most popular shirt size at Jay's Stash is large. mode

20. **Education** The average test score in English for the district is 82. mean

---

ALGEBRA IN DEMOGRAPHY

Measures of central tendency are used in forecasting population growths, weather prediction, and analysis of data.

The population of San Antonio, Texas for 1900–1980 is given at the right.

1. How has the population changed since 1900?
   increased by a factor of 14 since 1900

2. What was the mean population for the years 1950, 1960, 1970, and 1980? 609,048.25

Year	Population
1900	53,321
1950	408,442
1960	587,718
1970	654,153
1980	785,880

3. Based on the information in the table, would you expect the population to increase or decrease from 1980–2000? increase

4. Research how the population where you live has changed.

5. What was the average population for your town or city since 1900?
   Answers may vary.

14.1 Statistics: Measures of Central Tendency **585**

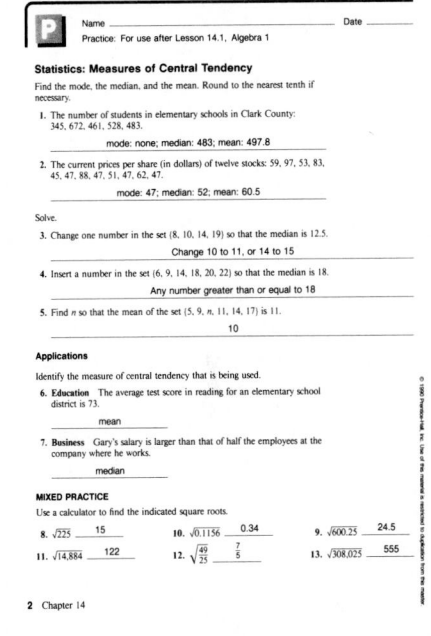

BACKGROUND

In the Capsule Review, students find the mode, median, and mean for data listed in ascending order. This review helps prepare students for this lesson.

You might want to point out to students that the mode can be found even when the data is not numerical. The median is used when the data at each extreme is not important and the mean is used when every number is important.

Critical Thinking

Observation Examine the intervals used in the frequency table in Example 1. What characteristics of the intervals do you observe? Explain.
The intervals are uniform in size and do not overlap. There are no gaps between intervals and each integral covers the entire range of data points.

14.2 Statistics: Graphing Data

Objectives: To make a frequency distribution table from data
To make a histogram from a frequency distribution table

To communicate information about data quickly, statisticians frequently display the data in a graph. Graphs provide a visual interpretation of the data. One type of graph commonly used is called a *histogram*. A **histogram** is a bar graph of a frequency distribution.

Capsule Review

Recall that in a set of data the mode is the number occurring most frequently, the median is the middle number, and the mean is the average of the numbers.

For this set of data find:
70, 70, 71, 71, 72, 72, 72, 72, 73, 73, 73, 74, 74, 75, 75, 76, 77, 78.

1. the mode.72   **2.** the median.73   **3.** the mean.73.2

For certain data, in order to construct a histogram, you must first organize the data into a frequency distribution table which shows the data grouped into intervals.

EXAMPLE 1 **The speeds of cars as they passed a checkpoint are shown. Make a frequency distribution table for the data. Locate the median from the frequency distribution table.**

31	46	37	45	30	51	41	38
44	47	26	32	38	39	44	25
37	46	51	34	35	33	28	37
38	41	33	48	36	31	36	39
43	46	33	42	40	34	34	41

- Order the speeds in convenient intervals.
- Tally the data.
- Count the tallies and write the frequencies.
- Total the frequencies.

Intervals (mi/h)	Tally	Frequency
25–29	///	3
30–34	⊬⊤ ⊬⊤	10
35–39	⊬⊤ ⊬⊤ /	11
40–44	⊬⊤ ///	8
45–49	⊬⊤ /	6
50–54	//	2
	Total	40

The median speed is the mean of the 20th and 21st values, which are in the 35–39 mi/h speed interval.

EXAMPLE 2 Make a histogram for the data in the frequency table of Example 1.

- List frequencies on the vertical axis.
- List speeds, in intervals, on the horizontal axis.
- Draw bars with no space between. The height of the bar is determined by the frequency.
- Note that, on this graph, only the lower values of each interval are labeled on the axis. For example, for 50 to 54 only 50 is written.

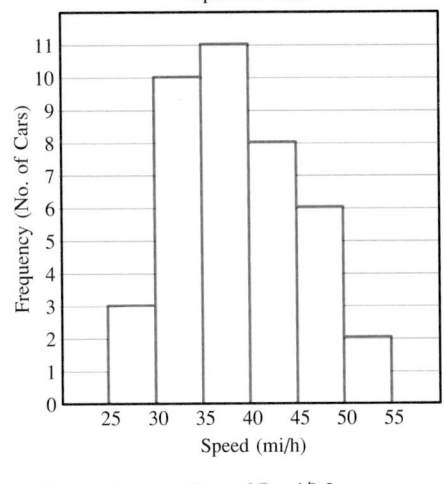

Speed of Cars

a. Which interval represents the speed at which most cars were driven?
The tallest bar shows the mode of the interval. Most cars were driven from 35 to 39 mi/h.

b. What percent of the cars were driven at speeds less than 35 mi/h?
The graph shows 13 cars at less than 35 mi/h. $\frac{13}{40} = 0.325$ or 32.5%

Graphs such as histograms are often preferred to tables of numbers because they are more interesting and easier to interpret. Can you tell the precise mean, mode, or median from the graph? Why?

CLASS EXERCISES

The Algebra I midterm test scores for 30 students at the Martin Luther King High School are listed at the right.

71	85	70	75	76
83	61	69	80	70
88	67	72	73	90
99	72	64	82	76
100	75	68	96	84
94	81	87	74	79

1. Make a frequency distribution table that shows the scores. Use intervals 60–64, 65–69, ... See below.

2. Make a histogram from your frequency distribution table. See below.

3. About what percent of the students earned a 70 or more? $83\frac{1}{3}$%

At an airport parking lot the following number of cars were parked overnight during a 25 day period (numbers are in hundreds).

1.5	1.0	1.2	1.5	1.7
2.3	1.8	1.9	1.3	1.5
1.6	2.2	1.8	1.9	1.9
1.7	1.4	1.3	2.0	2.2
2.5	2.0	1.9	1.4	1.4

4. Make a histogram from the data. Use intervals 1.0–1.4, 1.5–1.9, ... Check students' graphs.

5. From the histogram state the mode and median, then calculate the mean using all the data. A: 1.5–1.9 B: 1.5–1.9 C: 1.7

14.2 Statistics: Graphing Data **587**

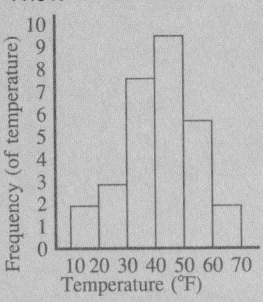

Common Error

- Some students may have difficulty in interpreting data from a frequency distribution table and/or histogram. Have these students make their histogram on graph paper so they can interpret what each unit/interval represents. Ask questions from the frequency distribution table and then refer to the histogram.
- See *Teacher's Resource Book* for additional remediation.

LESSON FOLLOW-UP

Assignment Guide
- See p. 580B for assignments.
- Have students use a calculator to check their results.

Lesson Quiz

The following is a list of the ages of 35 people who bought cars from Zelda's Used Cars: 25, 22, 21, 19, 27, 33, 41, 18, 32, 31, 23, 25, 26, 22, 19, 20, 31, 42, 44, 37, 25, 26, 28, 23, 32, 32, 19, 20, 43, 43, 27, 20, 30, 37, 38

1. Construct a frequency distribution table that shows the ages in 5 year intervals.

Intervals	Tally	Frequency
18–22	⋺⋺	10
23–27	⋺IIII	9
28–32	⋺II	7
33–37	III	3
38–42	III	3
43–47	III	3
	Total	35

2. Find the mean and the interval that contains the median. 28.6; 23–27
3. What percent of the people who bought cars are between 23 and 33 years old? 45.7%

For Discussion

6. What other graphical displays can be used to present statistical data? Use examples from magazines or newspapers. Pie charts, bar graphs, or line graphs.

PRACTICE EXERCISES

A **The 30 students whose midterm scores are listed in the Class Exercises took a year-end test. Their scores are at the right.**

76	88	82	92	68
75	68	58	62	55
77	52	70	74	66
60	67	48	65	77
79	69	70	57	63
92	84	77	88	70

1. Make a frequency distribution table that shows the scores in 5-point intervals, use 45–49, 50–54, ... See below.

2. Find the interval that contains the median. 70–74

3. Use your calculator to find the mean score. 70.96

4. Make a histogram of the year-end scores. See below.

5. From the histogram in Exercise 4, how many students earned at least a 70? 16 students

The ABC Manufacturing Company employs 35 people. The age of each employee is given at the right.

18	20	17	20	24
28	25	19	20	26
34	38	40	45	44
36	42	50	52	54
38	40	42	48	62
51	49	34	37	41
63	64	60	35	45

6. Make a frequency distribution table that shows the ages in 10-year intervals of 10–19, 20–29, ... See Additional Answer section beginning p. 719.

7. Find the interval that contains the median. 40–49

8. Use your calculator to find the mean age. 38.9 yrs

9. Make a histogram of the employees' ages. See Additional Answer section beginning p. 719.

10. What percent of the employees are between 20 and 39 years old, inclusive? 40%

B **In January 98 students worked on a class project to earn money for the class trip. This histogram displays the results.**

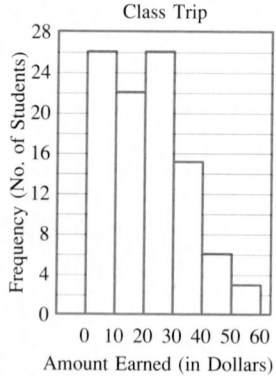

11. What percent of those in the entire class earned less than $30 for the trip? 75.5%

12. In which interval is the median earnings? $20–29

13. What percentage of students earned above the median interval? below the median interval? 24.5%; 49%

14. Give the interval(s) that contains the mode(s) for the data. $0–9; $20–29

Additional Answer

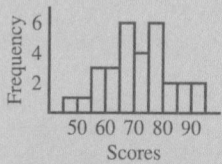

For exercises 15 and 16, 25 students recorded the number of hours a television news program was viewed in their homes.

6	10	1	4	5
0	7	9	3	11
7	4	2	6	8
4	2	5	3	9
5	8	12	15	6

15. Make a frequency distribution and find the mode, median, and mean.
mode: 4, 5, 6; median: 6; mean: 6.1; check students' table.

16. Make a histogram to show the data. See below.

C 17. Construct a histogram from which the mean, mode, and median are all in the same interval. Check students' graphs.

18. Construct a histogram with a mode, median, and mean in different intervals. Explain your work. Check students' graphs.

Applications

19. **Geography** The 13 greatest known depths in the seas and oceans of the world, to the nearest 100 ft are:

12,000; 12,300; 12,400; 12,400; 15,200; 15,700; 16,500; 18,500; 22,800; 22,800; 24,500; 30,200; 35,800

Show the data in a frequency distribution table. Then construct a histogram from the table.
See Additional Answer section beginning p. 719.

20. **Demography** It has been projected that in the year 2100 the population, in millions, of 20 countries will be:

632, 571, 509, 376, 356, 316, 309, 297, 293, 196, 173, 168, 164, 139, 128, 125, 120, 116, 112, 111

Show the data in a frequency distribution table. Then construct a histogram from the table.
See Additional Answer section beginning p. 719.

EXTRA

The mayor of a town with a population of 10,000 people wants to know how many of the people will support a bill she plans to propose at a council meeting next week. Since it is impossible to ask each person, she plans to conduct a survey. A reasonable estimate for support of the bill can be obtained if the people are selected in a random manner.

The mayor's staff conducts a telephone survey of 300 people chosen at random from the town's telephone directory. An analysis of the responses reveals that 228 of the 300 people support the bill. The mayor concludes that it is reasonable to expect 7600 people to support her bill. Is she right? Can you justify the position? Describe at least two methods the mayor's staff might have used to make the selections random.
yes, 76% of the people in the survey support the mayor's bill.

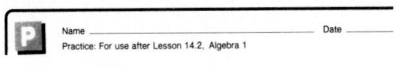

P Name _____ Date _____
Practice: For use after Lesson 14.2, Algebra 1

Statistics: Graphing Data

These numbers represent the ages of 30 employees at the Locktown Key factory: 28, 65, 22, 26, 34, 38, 62, 20, 21, 25, 33, 30, 49, 35, 41, 40, 28, 23, 21, 27, 29, 34, 30, 26, 23, 23, 31, 39, 53, and 57.

1. Make a frequency distribution table and a histogram.

Age	Tally	Frequency
20–29	ℍℍ ℍℍ IIII	14
30–39	ℍℍ IIII	9
40–49	IIII	3
50–59	II	2
60–69	II	2

2. Find the interval that contains the median age. 30–39
3. Use a calculator to find the mean age. 33.76

Application

Geography The areas, in thousands of square miles, of the provinces and territories of Canada are: 157; 2; 21; 28; 595; 413; 251; 252; 255; 366; 187; 1323.

4. Make a frequency distribution table and a histogram.

Area	Tally	Frequency
0–249	ℍℍ	5
250–499	ℍℍ	5
500–749	I	1
750–999		0
1000–1499	I	1

MIXED PRACTICE

Use the divide-and-average method twice to approximate the square root to the nearest hundredth.

5. $\sqrt{42}$ 6.48 6. $\sqrt{58}$ 7.62 7. $\sqrt{102}$ 10.10

Chapter 14 **5**

E Name _____ Date _____
Enrichment: For use after Lesson 14.2, Algebra 1

Circle Graphs

One way of displaying statistical data is with a circle graph. A circle graph is useful when you want to show the relationship of parts to a whole. For this reason, percentages are usually used on a circle graph.

Suppose you want to show the percentage of students in a school who have maintained certain grade point averages. A circle graph of the data might look like the one below.

1. Are measures of central tendency clear on a circle graph? No
Explain. Mean calculated by using weighted values according to percents. Mode cannot be determined for interval data. Median can be determined in some cases.

2. If 78 is considered an average grade, would you say that students in this school are generally above average or below average academically? Support your answer.
Below average, over half the students (55%) have grade point averages below 78.

3. The data below indicates the marital status of citizens over 18 years of age in Camden City. Calculate the percentage for each category. Draw a circle graph to display the data. Remember, the size of the portion of the circle must correspond to the percentage of the data for each category. Check students' graphs.

Marital Status	Frequency
Married	10,890
Single (never married)	6050
Divorced	3630
Widowed	1210
Separated	2420

6 Chapter 14

Additional Answer 16.

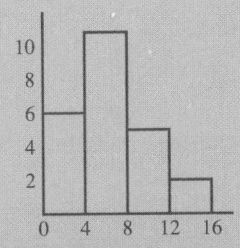

Vocabulary
Range
Standard deviation
Variance

Materials/Manipulatives
Calculators
Overhead projector

BACKGROUND

- The Capsule Review offers students an opportunity to review finding the square roots of numbers. Remind students that $\sqrt{x^2} = x$ is true only when x is positive or zero; for example, $\sqrt{(-5)^2} \neq -5$, that is $\sqrt{(-5)^2} = \sqrt{25} = 5$.
- This review prepares students for their work with standard deviation.

Critical Thinking

Observation How does the distribution of the two sets of data on p. 590 differ? The two sets of data differ in that the wages for Department A cluster around the data at each extreme, whereas the wages in Department B cluster around the middle (mean).

14.3

Statistics: Measures of Variability

Objective: To compute the range, variance, and standard deviation of a set of data

The **range** of a set of data is the difference between the greatest number and the least number in the set. The range gives you a measure of the spread, or *variability,* of the numbers. Since the range is computed from only two values, it is not always representative of the entire set of data.

To get a better picture of variability, you can use other statistical measures. These measures involve the use of square roots.

Capsule Review

Recall the Square-Root Property, if $x^2 = k$, then $x = \pm\sqrt{k}$, for any real number k, $k \geq 0$.

EXAMPLES $\sqrt{36} = 6$ $\sqrt{4^2} = 4$ $\sqrt{(-3)^2} = 3$ $\sqrt{0.49} = 0.7$

Find the principal (positive) square root.

1. 100 10   **2.** $\frac{1}{64}$ $\frac{1}{8}$ **3.** 1.21 1.1   **4.** $(-144)^2$ 144   **5.** $\left(\frac{-9}{16}\right)^2$ $\frac{9}{16}$

The frequency distributions for two sets of data are shown below. They have the same range and mean, but the data are distributed differently.

Weekly Wages for Department A				Weekly Wages for Department B		
Wages	Frequency	Freq. × Wages		Wages	Frequency	Freq. × Wages
$100	4	$ 400		$100	1	$ 100
200	0	0		200	0	0
300	1	300		300	4	1200
400	1	400		400	4	1600
500	0	0		500	0	0
600	4	2400		600	1	600
Total	10	$3500		Total	10	$3500

Range: $600 − $100 = $500   Range: $600 − $100 = $500

Mean: $3500 ÷ 10 = $350   Mean: $3500 ÷ 10 = $350

How does the distribution of the two sets of data differ? Which department has a greater extreme of wages? In which department do more people receive wages close to the mean?

590 Chapter 14 Statistics and Probability

One way to describe how much a set of data varies from the mean is by its *standard deviation* (symbol σ, pronounced "sigma"). The **standard deviation** measures how much each value in the data differs from the mean of the data. A larger standard deviation indicates that most of the values in the data do not cluster around the mean. A smaller standard deviation indicates that most of the values in the data do cluster around the mean.

To find a standard deviation:

• Compute the deviation (difference) of each number from the mean of the set.
• Compute the square of each deviation.
• Multiply each squared deviation by the corresponding frequency.
• Compute the sum of the squared deviations.
• Compute the mean of the sum; this is called the **variance.**
• Find the principal square root of the variance. The result is the standard deviation.

EXAMPLE 1 **Find the standard deviation from the mean ($350) for the wages earned in Department A and in Department B, as listed in the frequency distribution tables on page 590.**

Department A			Department B		
Income	Deviation from Mean	Freq. × (Dev.)^2	Income	Deviation from Mean	Freq. × (Dev.)^2
$100	−250	4(62,500)	$100	−250	1(62,500)
300	−50	1(2500)	300	−50	4(2500)
400	50	1(2500)	400	50	4(2500)
600	250	4(62,500)	600	250	1(62,500)
	Sum of squares	505,000		Sum of squares	145,000

$$\sigma = \sqrt{\frac{\text{sum of squares}}{\text{frequency}}}$$

$$\sigma = \sqrt{\frac{505,000}{10}}$$

$\sigma = \sqrt{50,500}$, or $225 to nearest dollar

Variance = $50,500
Standard deviation = $225

$$\sigma = \sqrt{\frac{\text{sum of squares}}{\text{frequency}}}$$

$$\sigma = \sqrt{\frac{145,000}{10}}$$

$\sigma = \sqrt{14,500}$, or $120 to nearest dollar

Variance = $14,500
Standard deviation = $120

In Example 1, the smaller standard deviation for Department B shows that more incomes in Department B, than in Department A, cluster around the mean. Note that the range was the same for both departments ($500). The range is computed by using only the greatest and least numbers, whereas the standard deviation is computed by using all of the data. This makes the standard deviation a more precise and informative measure of variability than the range.

14.3 Statistics: Measures of Variability   **591**

591

EXAMPLE 2 **In the 10 Major League All-Star baseball games, the winning teams scored the following numbers of runs: 3, 3, 4, 4, 5, 6, 7, 7, 7, 13. Find the measures of central tendency: mode, median, and mean. Find the measures of variability: range, variance, and standard deviation.**

Mode: 7 runs per game

Median: $\dfrac{5 + 6}{2} = 5.5$ runs per game

Mean: $\dfrac{3 + 3 + 4 + 4 + 5 + 6 + 7 + 7 + 7 + 13}{10} = \dfrac{59}{10}$, or 5.9 runs/game

Range: $13 - 3 = 10$

You can use a computer program to generate the table of computations for the variance and the standard deviation from the mean of 5.9. The statistics mode on a calculator will also provide a useful means for computing the measures of variability.

This table shows computations for the variance and the standard deviation from the mean of 5.9.

Variance: $\dfrac{78.90}{10} = 7.89$

Standard Deviation:
$\sigma = \sqrt{7.89} = 2.81$, to the nearest hundredth

Runs	Deviation from Mean	Freq. × (Dev.)²
3	$3 - 5.9 = -2.9$	2(8.41)
4	$4 - 5.9 = -1.9$	2(3.61)
5	$5 - 5.9 = -0.9$	1(0.81)
6	$6 - 5.9 = 0.1$	1(0.01)
7	$7 - 5.9 = 1.1$	3(1.21)
13	$13 - 5.9 = 7.1$	1(50.41)

Sum of squares 78.90

CLASS EXERCISES

The 10 families in an apartment building have these numbers of pets: 1, 2, 3, 0, 1, 0, 1, 6, 2, 4.

1. Find the measures of central tendency.
mean: 2; mode: 1; median: 1.5

2. Find the measures of variability.
range: 6; variance: 3.2; std. deviation: 1.8

PRACTICE EXERCISES

A **To the nearest dollar, find the variance and the standard deviation from the mean for the wages in each department.**

1.   Department C

Wages	100	150	200	250
Frequency	5	2	1	2

variance: $3500
std. deviation: $59.16

2.   Department D

Wages	100	150	200	250
Frequency	4	5	0	1

variance: $1900
std. deviation: $43.59

For each set of data, find the measures of central tendency: mode, median, and mean. Find the measures of variability: range, variance, and standard deviation.

(A)   (B)

(C)

3. The noontime temperature readings in degrees Celsius for 7 days:
   9, 12, 8, 10, 5, 8, 11. A: 8 B: 9 C: 9 D: 7 E: 4.6 F: 2.1

(D)   (E)   (F)

4. The hourly wages of Company XYZ:
   $7, $10, $10, $11, $12, $12, $14, $20. A: 10, 12 B: 11.5 C: 12 D: 13 E: 12.8 F: 3.6

B 5. The noontime barometer readings for 7 days:
   30.1, 29.0, 29.4, 29.6, 29.9, 29.0, 29.4.
   A: 29.0, 29.4 B: 29.4 C: 29.5 D: 1.1 E: 0.2 F: 0.4

6. The population of a city during the past 10 years:
   23,000; 26,000; 32,000; 45,000; 52,000; 50,000; 47,000; 46,000; 42,000; 37,000.
   A: none B: 43,500 C: 40,000 D: 29,000 E: 91,600,000 F: 9570.8

C 7. The earnings per share of a stock during a 10-month period:
   $4.29, $4.78, $5.06, $6.45, $6.32, $5.12, $3.25, $2.86, $2.08, $1.76.
   A: none B: $4.54 C: $4.20 D: $4.69 E: $2.46 F: $1.57

Applications

8. **Health** The amount of protein in grams in 3-oz servings of several types of fish and seafood are: bluefish, 22; clams, 11; crabmeat, 24; salmon, 17; sardines, 20; shrimp, 17; tuna, 24. What is the mean and the standard deviation for this set of data? 19.3, 4.3

9. **Business** From 1981 through 1985, XYZ Communications earned $21,000, $24,000, $30,000, $25,000, and $30,000. Find the mean and standard deviation. mean: $26,000; standard deviation: $3521.36

TEST YOURSELF

1. The mean of 24 students' test scores is 74. If the two lowest scores of 60 and 62 along with the two highest scores of 97 and 92 were removed, find the mean of the remaining scores. 73.25   **14.1**

The ages of the employees at the HELP Manufacturing Company are: 18, 25, 35, 28, 20, 21, 41, 38, 30, 25, 19, 24, 19, 22, 28, 33, 37, 38, 22, 21, 25, 19, 29, 40.

2. Find the mode, the median, and the mean for the data.
   mode: 19, 25; median: 25; mean: 27
3. Draw a histogram of the data using five-year intervals. What percentage of the employees are under 25? See below. 42%   **14.2**

4. Find the range, the variance, and the standard deviation for the data.   **14.3**
   range: 23; variance: 44.2; std. deviation: 6.7
5. The number of cars passing through a busy intersection each hour over a 24 h period are given as follows:

80	60	60	20	10	10	40	70
140	100	70	120	130	80	70	40
50	85	100	95	70	80	75	70

Find the mean and standard deviation for the data. mean: 71.9; standard deviation: 32.9

Additional Answers 3.

[Histogram: x-axis "Ages" from 0 to 45 in 5-year intervals; y-axis "Frequency" from 0 to 10]

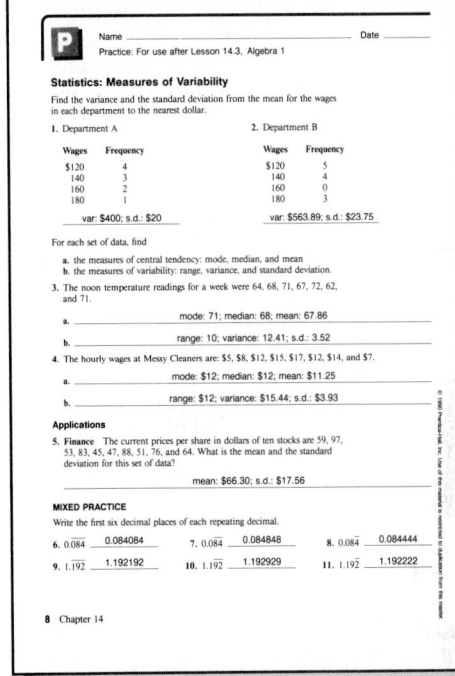

APPLICATION: Scattergrams

A scattergram is a dot or point graph
of data. A scattergram can show how
two sets of data vary relative one
to the other.

The table shows the population of
New York State in millions. The
scattergram plots the population
count against the year.

Year	1790	1820	1850	1880	1910	1940
No.	0.3	1.4	3.1	5.1	9.1	13.5

Statisticians try to draw a *line of
best fit*, a line having the same
number of points above and
below it.

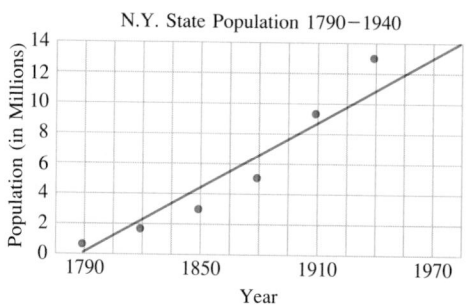

Here as the years increase, the
population also increases. The
upward slant or positive slope of
the line of best fit indicates a
positive correlation. A positive
correlation might indicate that
one variable will have a positive
influence on the other variable.

The scattergram on the right
shows the relationship between
years and death rates. As the
years have passed, the number of
deaths per thousand has
decreased in the United States.
The downward slant or negative
slope indicates a *negative
correlation*.

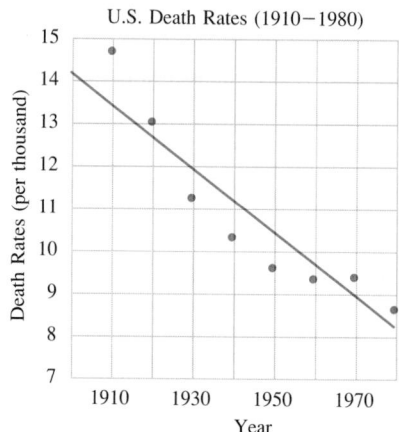

In some cases, no line of best fit
can be drawn. In such cases there
may be no correlation between
the two sets of data.

1. From the scattergram below, what can you conclude about the data? Find the slope of the line of best fit. As the age increases the height also increases. The upward slant of the best fit line indicates a positive correlation. Slope is $\frac{3}{4}$.

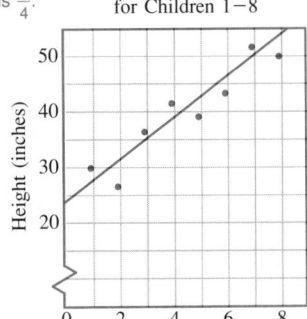

Average Height
for Children 1–8

2.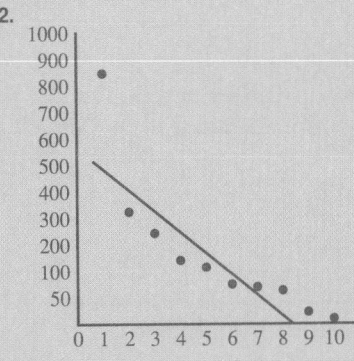

3.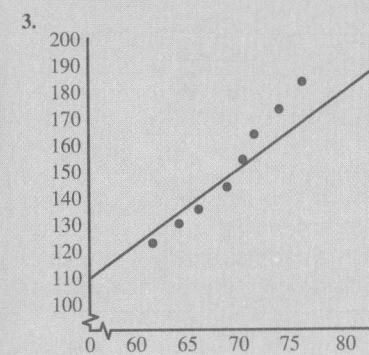

2. Draw a scattergram of the data for workers and number of hours to complete a job. Can a line of best fit be drawn? What is the correlation between the two sets of data? See side column; yes; negative correlation

Workers	0–1	1–2	2–3	3–4	4–5	5–6	6–7	7–8	8–9	9–10
Hours	860	345	262	168	105	88	68	56	42	6

3. From the following frequency distribution table, draw a scattergram of the data. Can a line of best fit be drawn? Is there a positive or negative correlation between the two sets of data? See side column; yes; positive correlation

Height	62″	64″	66″	68″	70″	72″	74″	76″
Weight	123	130	136	145	154	162	171	181

4. Draw a scattergram from the following table. What type of correlation can be found between the two sets of data? Can the number of immigrants from Spain to the United States be estimated for 1981–90? Why or why not? No correlation; cannot predict the immigration for 1981–1990.

Years	1931–40	1941–50	1951–60	1961–70	1971–80
Immigration	3,258	2,898	7,894	44,659	34,141

5. Refer to the scattergram on page 594 which showed the relationship between years and death rates. Make a frequency distribution table representing the two sets of data. Check students' tables.

6. Work with a partner and design your own statistical experiment. Use the techniques you have learned to describe the data, and explain how you and your partner can use data to predict trends. Answers may vary.

Vocabulary

Complementary events
Equally likely event
Odds
Outcome
Probability
Sample space
Trial

Materials/Manipulatives

Colored paper
Coins
Overhead projector

BACKGROUND

- In the Capsule Review, students practice writing a ratio as a fraction, a decimal, and then a percent. This review prepares them for finding probabilities and odds.
- Review the procedure for simplifying complex fractions, and then have students write these ratios as fractions.

Critical Thinking

Causal Explanation Explain what it means to say that a coin is a "fair coin." The coin is not weighted or altered so as to bias the outcome of a toss of the coin; heads or tails are equally likely outcomes when a coin is tossed.

14.4

Simple Probability

Objectives: To determine the probability of an event and of the complementary event for a random experiment
To solve problems involving probability

The Italian mathematician Girolamo Cardano (1501–1576) helped to develop the field of *probability*. **Probability** measures the likelihood that a particular event will occur. The measures are expressed as ratios.

Capsule Review

EXAMPLE   Write the ratio 4 out of 10 as a fraction in simplest form and as a percent.

$$\frac{4}{10} = \frac{2}{5}$$ *Write as a fraction. Simplify.*

$$= 0.40 \text{ or } 40\%.$$ *Divide to find the percent.*

Write each ratio as a fraction in simplest form and as a percent.

1. 15 to 25 $\frac{3}{5}$ or 60%   **2.** 18 out of 48 $\frac{3}{8}$ or 37.5%   **3.** 28 to 49 $\frac{4}{7}$ or 57.1%   **4.** 48 to 64 $\frac{3}{4}$ or 75%

In probability, each repetition of an experiment is a **trial.** A possible result of each trial is called an **outcome.** When you toss a fair coin, the two possible outcomes are *heads (H)* or *tails (T)*. The probability of tossing heads is 1 out of 2 possible outcomes.

$$\text{Probability (heads)} = \frac{1}{2} \text{ or } P(\text{H}) = \frac{1}{2}$$

$$\text{Probability (of an event)} = \frac{\text{number of favorable outcomes}}{\text{total number of possible outcomes}}$$

When the possible outcomes have the same chance of occurring, they are described as **equally likely;** they occur at *random*. The set of all possible outcomes is called the **sample space.** The sample space for tossing a coin is heads or tails. An **event** is any of the possible outcomes, including all or none.

596   Chapter 14 Statistics and Probability

EXAMPLE 1 A box contains 12 buttons, identical in size and shape but not in color. There are 2 blue, 3 yellow, 6 black, and 1 white. Find the probability of selecting:

a. a blue button   **b.** a blue or yellow button

c. a green button   **d.** a blue, yellow, black, or white button

a. $P(\text{blue}) = \dfrac{2}{12}$ ← number of blue buttons
                    ← total number of buttons

           $= \dfrac{1}{6}$ *Simplify.*

b. $P(\text{blue or yellow}) = \dfrac{5}{12}$ ← *There are 2 blues and 3 yellows*

c. $P(\text{green}) = 0$. There are no green buttons.

d. $P(\text{blue, yellow, black, or white}) = \dfrac{12}{12} = 1$

The probability of an event that is impossible is 0. The probability of an event that is certain to happen is 1. All other probabilities are between 0 and 1. In general, for any probability $P(E)$,

$$0 \le P(E) \le 1$$

In a random experiment, the two situations—that an event does occur and that the event does not occur—are **complementary events.**

In Example 1, $P(\text{blue})$ and $P(\text{not blue})$ are complementary events.

$$P(\text{blue}) = \frac{1}{6} \qquad P(\text{not blue}) = \frac{5}{6} \qquad \text{Note: } \frac{1}{6} + \frac{5}{6} = 1$$

The sum of the probability of an event $P(E)$ and the probability of its complement written as $P(\overline{E})$, is 1. $P(E) + P(\overline{E}) = 1$

Odds are a ratio that compares the probability of an event to the probability of its complement. *Odds of 2 to 1 for* means that the probability of the event occurring is $\frac{2}{3}$. *Odds of 2 to 1 against* means that the probability of the event not occurring is $\frac{2}{3}$.

EXAMPLE 2 The table below shows the SAT math scores for 186 seniors at Garrison High School. If one senior is chosen at random, find

a. the probability that the student had a score between 501 and 600

b. the odds that the student scored between 301 and 500

Score	201–300	301–400	401–500	501–600	601–700	701–800
Students	2	15	35	62	42	30

14.4 Simple Probability   **597**

597

Common Error

- Students may make errors in calculating the probability of events. Check students' work and demonstrate how the sum of the probabilities must equal 1.
- See *Teacher's Resource Book* for additional remediation.

LESSON FOLLOW-UP

Assignment Guide

- See p. 580B for assignments.
- See *Teacher's Resource Book, Technology,* pp. 26–27.

Lesson Quiz

The numbers 1–10 are written on 10 red, 10 white, 10 blue, and 10 yellow tags. The tags are mixed together in a bag and one is selected at random. Find each.

1. P(red) $\frac{1}{4}$ **2.** P(7) $\frac{1}{10}$

3. P(white or yellow) $\frac{1}{2}$

4. P(3 or 8) $\frac{1}{5}$

5. P(less than 4) $\frac{3}{10}$

6. P($\overline{6}$) $\frac{1}{9}$ **7.** Odds (blue) 1 to 3

8. Odds (6) 1 to 9

Use the table for problems 9–12.

No. of Days Rained

Jan.	Feb.	March	April	May	June	July
18	16	12	15	7	6	4

9. P(rainy day in January) $\frac{18}{31}$

10. Odds (rainy day in July) 4 to 27

11. P(clear day in April) $\frac{1}{2}$

12. Odds (clear day in June) 4 to 1

Enrichment

A math class has 4 freshman, 23 sophomores, 10 juniors, and 5 seniors. One student is selected at random, and the student's status is determined. Find P(junior or senior). $\frac{5}{14}$

598

a. P(scored 501–600) $= \frac{62}{186}$ ←———— Number of students scoring 501–600
←———— Total number of students

$= \frac{1}{3}$ *Simplify.*

$= 33\frac{1}{3}\%$ *Write as a percent.*

There is a probability of $\frac{1}{3}$ or a $33\frac{1}{3}\%$ chance that a senior chosen at random scored between 501–600.

b. Odds of scoring 301–500 $= \dfrac{\frac{50}{186}}{\frac{136}{186}}$ ←———— *probability of scoring 301–500*
←———— *probability of not scoring 301–500*

$= \frac{50}{136} = \frac{25}{68}$

The odds in favor of picking a senior who scored between 301–500 are 25 to 68.

CLASS EXERCISES

The numbers 1–5 are written on five red and five yellow tags (one number on each tag). The 10 tags are placed in a bag and are thoroughly mixed. One tag is picked at random. Find each probability.

1. $P(\text{red})\frac{1}{2}$ **2.** $P(5)\frac{1}{5}$ **3.** $P(\text{yellow }4)\frac{1}{10}$

4. $P(\text{red or yellow})$ 1   **5.** $P(1 \text{ or } 2)\frac{2}{5}$ **6.** $P(\text{even number})\frac{2}{5}$

7. $P(8)$ 0   **8.** $P(3)\frac{1}{5}$ **9.** $P(\text{not a red }3)\frac{9}{10}$

For Discussion

10. Does $P(\overline{E}) = 1 - P(E)$? Explain.
True, because $P(E)$ and $P(\overline{E})$ are the only two possible situations. Therefore, their sum is 1.

11. Are the Odds of E equal to $\dfrac{P(E)}{1 - P(E)}$? Explain.
True, because odds are defined as $\dfrac{P(E)}{P(\overline{E})}$. Therefore, if $P(\overline{E}) = 1 - P(E)$, then Odds(E) $= \dfrac{P(E)}{1 - P(E)}$.

PRACTICE EXERCISES

The numbers 1–8 are written on eight red, eight white, and eight blue tags (one number on each tag). The tags are placed in a bag and are thoroughly mixed. One tag is picked at random. Find each probability.

A

1. $P(\text{blue})\frac{1}{3}$ **2.** $P(\text{white})\frac{1}{3}$ **3.** $P(6)\frac{1}{8}$

4. $P(2)\frac{1}{8}$ **5.** $P(\text{red or blue})\frac{2}{3}$ **6.** $P(\text{blue or white})\frac{2}{3}$

7. $P(3 \text{ or } 4)\frac{1}{4}$ **8.** $P(9 \text{ or } 0)$ 0   **9.** $P(\text{greater than }6)\frac{1}{4}$

10. $P(\text{less than }6)\frac{5}{8}$ **11.** $P(\overline{7})\frac{7}{8}$ **12.** $P(\overline{5})\frac{7}{8}$

Use the table for Exercises 13–18.

13. P(rainy day in July) $\frac{5}{31}$

14. P(rainy day in May) $\frac{10}{31}$

15. Odds for rainy day in April 7 to 8 for.

16. Odds against rainy day in September 7 to 3 against.

B 17. P(clear day in August) $\frac{24}{31}$

18. Odds against rainy day in June 7 to 3 against.

Precipitation					
Apr.	May	June	July	Aug.	Sep.
14	10	9	5	7	9

A letter is chosen at random from the word *favorable*. Find the probability of each event.

19. P(consonant) $\frac{5}{9}$

20. P(vowel) $\frac{4}{9}$

21. P(the letter **a**) $\frac{2}{9}$

22. P(the letter **v**) $\frac{1}{9}$

23. P(the letters **a** or **e**) $\frac{1}{3}$

24. P(the letters **b** or **l**) $\frac{2}{9}$

25. P(the letter **y**) 0

26. P(the letter **z**) 0

Use the frequency table. Find each probability.

C 27. P(red) $\frac{1}{2}$

28. P(red or green) $\frac{5}{6}$

29. $P(\overline{\text{green}})$ $\frac{2}{3}$

30. P(red or blue) $\frac{1}{2}$

Color	Frequency
red	12
green	8
blue	4

Applications

31. **Testing** A question on a multiple-choice test has four possible answers. What are the odds against guessing the correct answer? 3 to 1 against.

32. **Finance** Rufus has four $1 bills, two $5 bills, and one $10 bill in his wallet. He takes out a bill without looking. What is the probability that it will be a $5 bill? a $10 bill? $\frac{2}{7}$; $\frac{1}{7}$

MATH CLUB ACTIVITY

This type of question was asked on the Annual High School Mathematics Examination. See if you can solve it.

There are two cards with the same size and shape. One is red on both sides and the other is red on one side and blue on the other. The cards have the same probability of being selected. In other words, the probability is $\frac{1}{2}$. One of the cards is selected and placed on a table. The side of the card on the table that you can see is red. What is the probability that the other side of the card is also red? $\frac{1}{2}$

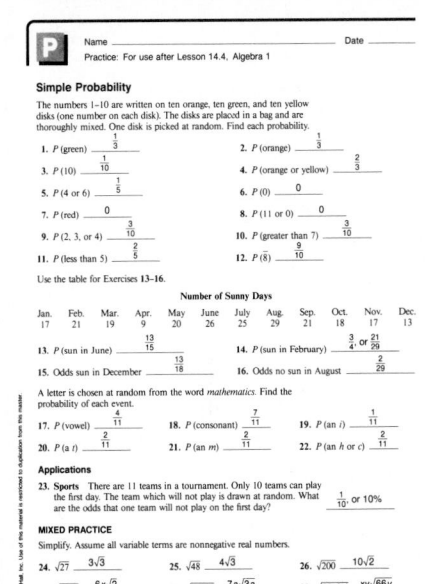

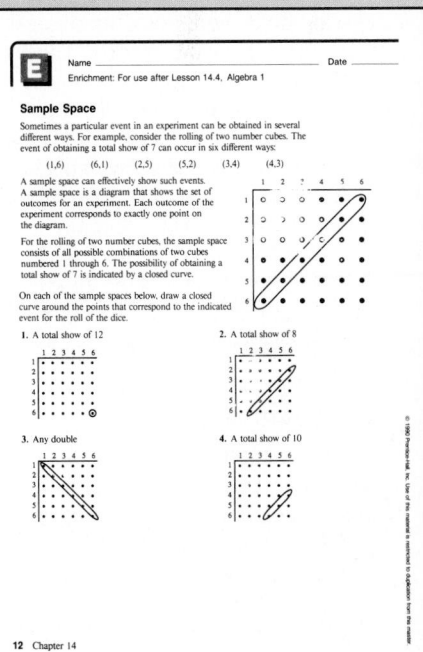

BACKGROUND

A key to success in solving problems in this lesson is for a student to read a problem and gather the given data correctly using a diagram. Before introducing this lesson, you may want to review some basic probability.

Error Analysis Classification

1. *Misunderstanding*
   Failed to understand the underlying concept of the problem
2. *Misapplied Strategy*
   Labeled and filled in the Venn diagram incorrectly
   Wrote an incorrect ratio

TEACHING SUGGESTIONS

- Explain that Venn diagrams are used for counting purposes. They are helpful in finding the probabilities in complex problem situations.
- Ask a variety of questions. For example: Are you wearing something blue? white? red? blue and white? Draw a Venn diagram to describe the data. You may wish to use Teaching Aid 17, in the *Teacher's Resource Book,* and an overhead projector to illustrate this example.

CHALKBOARD EXAMPLES

- **For the Example**
  A survey of the classes students were taking at Hahira High School revealed 90 taking gym, 60 taking Algebra and 50 taking Physical Science. 30 take both gym and Algebra, 20 take Algebra and Physical Science, 15 take gym and Physical Science, and 10 taking all three. What is the probability of a person only taking Algebra? $\frac{4}{29}$

600

14.5

Problem Solving Strategy: Draw a Diagram

A **Venn diagram** is a pictorial representation of sets. It is used for counting purposes. In this counting technique, each person or object is counted once.

EXAMPLE 1 A survey was taken of the types of magazines people read. 90 people read news magazines; 70 people read sports magazines; 40 people read business magazines; 30 people read news and sports magazines; 20 people read news and business magazines; 10 people read sports and business magazines; and 10 people read all three. If one of the people surveyed is selected at random, what is the probability the person reads only a news magazine?

▢ **Understand the Problem**

What are the given facts?
Of the 90 people who read a news magazine, 30 people read a news magazine and a sports magazine; 20 people read a news magazine and a business magazine; and 10 people read all three.

What are you asked to find?
The probability that a person selected at random from the survey reads *only* a news magazine.

▢ **Plan Your Approach**

Choose a strategy.
Draw a Venn diagram. Let each circle represent people who read news, sports, and business magazines.

▢ **Complete the Work**

Draw a diagram. Work backwards.
Place the 10 people who read all three magazines in the intersection of the three circles. Since 10 people who read news and business magazines have already been placed in the intersection of the three sets, write 10 in the intersection of news and business only. Explain how the other numbers were placed.

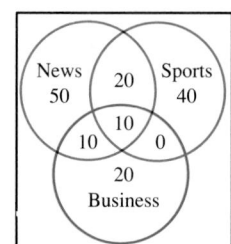

The diagram shows that 50 people of the 150 surveyed read only news magazines.

$$P(\text{only news}) = \frac{50}{150} \text{ or } \frac{1}{3}$$

State your answer.

The probability that a person selected at random from the survey reads *only* a news magazine is $\frac{1}{3}$ or $33\frac{1}{3}\%$.

Check your answer.

Find the probability of the complement.

$P(not \text{ only news}) = \frac{100}{150}$ ⟵ $40 + 20 + 20 + 10 + 10$

$= \frac{2}{3}$

Note: $\frac{1}{3} + \frac{2}{3} = \frac{3}{3}$ or 1 $P(E) + P(\overline{E}) = 1$

Since the sum is 1, the probability of $\frac{1}{3}$ is correct.

CLASS EXERCISES

Use a Venn diagram to solve.

1. The following number of students studied Spanish, French, and/or German in high school: 20 studied Spanish; 15 studied French; 10 studied German; 8 studied Spanish and French; 6 studied Spanish and German; 4 studied French and German; 1 studied all three. If a student is selected at random, what is the probability the student studied only Spanish and French. $\frac{1}{4}$

2. In a recent poll, several parents were asked what sport(s) they preferred to watch: a total of 8 preferred football, 7 liked basketball, 3 chose golf, 7 preferred football and basketball, and 2 liked to watch all of them. If one of the parents is chosen at random, what is the probability the parent preferred only golf? $\frac{1}{9}$

PRACTICE EXERCISES

Use a Venn diagram to solve.

A

1. Students were asked what kind of pet they had:
   28 had a dog.
   15 had a cat.
   8 had a dog and a cat.
   What is the probability that a randomly selected student will have only a cat? $\frac{1}{5}$

2. Students were asked whether they drank milk or juice with lunch:
   50 drank milk.
   30 drank juice.
   20 drank milk and juice.
   What is the probability that a randomly selected student will only drink milk? $\frac{1}{2}$

Critical Thinking

Causal Explanation Explain the purpose of a Venn diagram in solving problems. They are particularly useful in visualizing relationships between sets. They serve as a tool for modeling information, helping to classify and sort the information into recognizable sets.

Assignment Guide

See p. 580B for assignments.

Mixed Problem Solving Review

The following skills and concepts are reviewed.
Writing an equation (Ex. 1–6)
Solving age problems (Ex. 2)
Solving work problems (Ex. 4)
Solving mixture problems (Ex. 5)
Solving current problems (Ex. 6)
Solving problems involving inverse variations
The following problem solving strategies may be appropriate:
Drawing a diagram or a table (Ex. 1–6)

Project

Have students work in groups to conduct a survey and draw a Venn diagram to display their results.

Lesson Quiz

Use a Venn diagram to solve.

Students were asked what they had for breakfast: 23 had cereal; 18 had toast; 9 had both.
1. What is the probability that a randomly selected student will have eaten both for breakfast? $\frac{9}{32}$

Students were asked how they got to school during the school year: 34 went by car; 27 by bike; 13 walking; 7 by car and/or bike; 2 by car or walking; 6 by bike or walking; 1 by car, bike, or walking.
2. What is the probability that a randomly selected person only walked to school all year? $\frac{1}{10}$

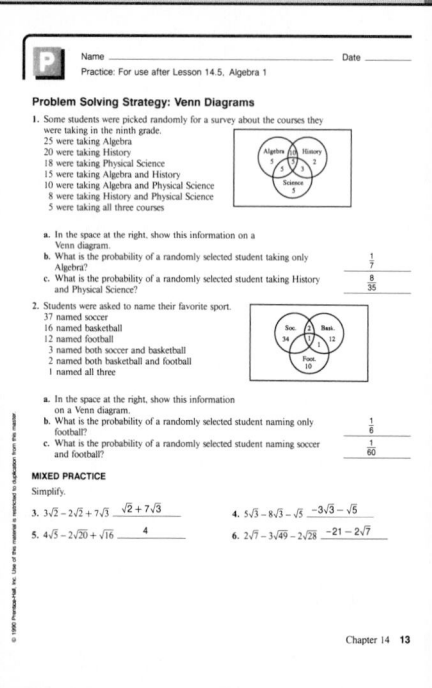

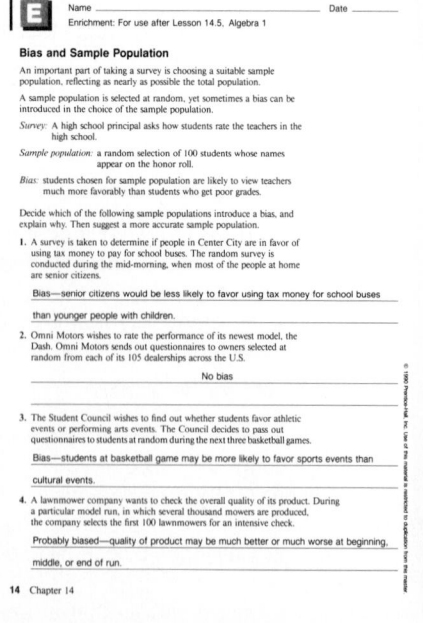

B **3.** Here are the results of a luncheon survey:

83 people had soup.
72 people had chicken.
54 people had salad.
27 people had soup and chicken.
23 people had soup and salad.
12 people had chicken and salad.
10 people had all three.

A person at the luncheon is selected at random. What is the probability the person had soup, chicken, and salad? $\frac{10}{157}$

4. Here is a list of track meet participations:

42 students ran.
28 students jumped.
8 students pole vaulted.
12 students ran and jumped.
2 students ran and pole vaulted.
6 students jumped and pole vaulted.
2 students did all three.

A member of the team is selected at random. What is the probability the member only jumped and pole vaulted? $\frac{1}{15}$

C **5.** The following number of campers chose these activities: 32 chose swimming; 32 chose boating; 20 chose hiking; 15 chose swimming and boating; 12 chose swimming and hiking; 11 chose boating and hiking; and 8 chose all three. What is the probability that a camper selected at random chose swimming and boating or boating and hiking? $\frac{1}{3}$

Mixed Problem Solving Review

1. The length of a room is 3 ft longer than its width. What are the dimensions of the room if the area is 108 ft^2? $w = 9$ ft; $l = 12$ ft

2. Al's father is 3 times as old as Al is. 5 years ago he was 4 times as old as Al was. How old is each now? Al is 15 yr. His father is 45 yr.

3. A 20-kg object is 15 ft from the fulcrum, and balances a 30 kg object. How far is the 30 kg object from the fulcrum? 10 ft

4. George can paint a room in 12 h. Joe can paint a room in 15 h. How long will it take them if they work together? $6\frac{2}{3}$ h

5. Erin has 45 coins worth $9.65. There are some nickels, the rest are quarters. Find how many of each kind of coin Erin has. 37 quarters and 8 nickels

6. It takes 4 h for a boat to travel 64 mi downstream. The same boat can travel 35 mi upstream in 5 h. Find the rate of the boat in still water. $\frac{23}{2}$ mi/h

PROJECT

Conduct a survey. Choose any three sports. Ask students in your school to name the sport(s) they would participate in from your list. Draw a Venn diagram of the results and calculate the various probabilities. Check students' diagrams.

Probability: Compound Events

Objective: To solve problems involving independent, dependent, mutually exclusive, and inclusive events

LESSON PLAN

Vocabulary
Compound event
Dependent event
Inclusive event
Independent event
Mutually exclusive events

Materials/Manipulatives
Checkers
Colored paper
Teacher's Resource Book,
   Transparency 31

A **compound event** is made up of two (or more) events. Probability in compound events is influenced by the relationship between the separate events. A *tree diagram* can be used to show these relationships.

Suppose there are two checkers, red and black, in a box. Luanne picks one, looks at it, and puts it back. In this case does the probability of picking a red checker on the second pick depend upon whether she picked a red or a black checker the first time? Explain.

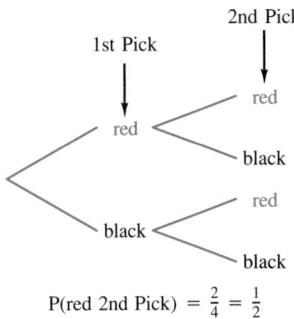

P(red 2nd Pick) $= \frac{2}{4} = \frac{1}{2}$

What happens if Luanne does not put that checker back after the first pick? Does the probability of picking a red checker the second time depend upon whether she picked a red or a black checker the first time? Explain.

BACKGROUND

In the Capsule Review, students review finding probabilities. You might want to remind students that the probability of an event that is impossible is 0. The probability of an event that is certain to happen is 1.

Critical Thinking
Classifying Use a dictionary to obtain a definition for each of the following words: independent, dependent, and exclusive. Independent is free from influence or control of others. Dependent means influenced or determined by something else. Exclusive is excluding all others; not shared or divided.

Capsule Review

In a box of colored pencils there are 4 red (R), 3 yellow (Y), 2 green (G), and 1 blue (B). Pick 1 pencil at random.

EXAMPLE $P(B) = \dfrac{\text{number of favorable outcomes}}{\text{total number of possible outcomes}} = \dfrac{1}{10}$

Find each probability.

1. $P(R)$ $\frac{2}{5}$ **2.** $P(G)$ $\frac{1}{5}$ **3.** $P(Y)$ $\frac{3}{10}$ **4.** $P(\overline{Y})$ $\frac{7}{10}$

5. $P(B \text{ or } G)$ $\frac{3}{10}$ **6.** $P(R \text{ or } G)$ $\frac{3}{5}$ **7.** $P(\text{a pencil})$ 1 **8.** $P(\text{a pen})$ 0

Independent events are events that do not influence one another. That is, each event occurs without changing the probability of the other event.

EXAMPLE 1 **Jason and Carl each own four pairs of jeans, one blue, white, tan, and gray pair. Find the probability that both will wear gray jeans today. Find $P(J \text{ and } C)$, where J and C are independent events.**

14.6 Probability: Compound Events **603**

- You might want to remind students that a "sample" space, the set of all possible outcomes, can be represented in a variety of ways, such as in a chart, a set of ordered pairs, or in a diagram, as in Example 1.
- In Example 2, point out that for the second pick, P(red) = $\frac{1}{5}$ because there are 5 socks left, and only one of the socks is red after the first pick.
- Have students conduct an experiment in variability. They can pull different colored socks from a sock drawer (or colored paper or checkers from a bag) similar to the event described in Ex. 2 or 3, do it several times, record the results, calculate the expected probability, and compare it with their results.

You may want to use Transparency 31 in the *Teacher's Resource Book* to record the results.

CHALKBOARD EXAMPLES

- **For Example 1**
  1. Petra and Cleo each own 5 dresses, two being the color red. What is the probability that both wear a red dress tomorrow? $\frac{4}{25}$

- **For Example 2**
  2. John has 4 brown socks and 8 black socks in his drawer. He chooses a sock at random, and it is brown. Find the probability that John will randomly select another brown sock without replacing the first. $\frac{3}{11}$

List the sample space to show all the possible combinations. Each boy's jeans are represented by blue, white, tan, and gray. The ordered pairs will be in the form Carl's choice, Jason's choice.

In the diagram, each dot stands for a possible pairing. The dots circled in black stand for pairings in which the boys choose the same color: (B, B), (W, W), (T, T), and (G, G). The dot circled in red, (G, G), stands for the pairing in which each boy chooses gray.

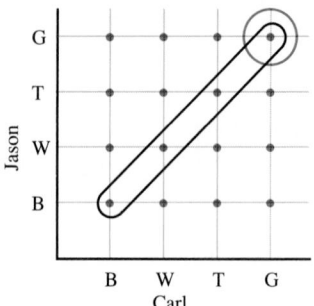

Of the 16 possible pairings, only one, (G, G), means that both Jason and Carl wear gray jeans on the same day. The probability of both selecting gray is $\frac{1}{16}$.

The probability for independent events can be considered another way:

Let $P(J)$ = the probability of Jason's wearing gray jeans today.
Let $P(C)$ = the probability of Carl's wearing gray jeans today.
$$P(J) = \frac{1}{4}, \; P(C) = \frac{1}{4}, \; P(J \text{ and } C) = \frac{1}{4} \cdot \frac{1}{4} = \frac{1}{16}$$

This suggests the following generalization.

> For two independent events A and B, $P(A \text{ and } B) = P(A) \cdot P(B)$.

Dependent events are events that influence each other. If one of the events occurs, it changes the probability of the other event.

EXAMPLE 2 **Beth has 2 red socks and 4 white socks in her sock drawer. Find the probability that she will randomly select one red sock and then, without replacing it, randomly select another red sock. Find P(red and red) for dependent events.**

First pick (6 socks)	Second pick (5 socks)
$P(\text{red}) = \frac{2}{6} = \frac{1}{3}$	$P(\text{red}) = \frac{1}{5}$, why?

$$P(\text{1st red and 2nd red}) = \frac{1}{3} \cdot \frac{1}{5} = \frac{1}{15}$$

> For two dependent events A and B, where B is influenced by A,
> $$P(A \text{ and } B) = P(A) \cdot P(B, \text{ given } A)$$

604   Chapter 14 Statistics and Probability

Mutually exclusive events are events that cannot happen at the same time.

EXAMPLE 3   Fred has 2 green, 4 blue, and 3 red shirts in a drawer. He chooses a shirt at random and does not want a red shirt. Find the probability that Fred will pick a green or blue shirt. Find P(g or b), for mutually exclusive events.

$$P(\text{green or blue}) = \frac{6}{9} = \frac{2}{3}$$

The probability can be calculated another way.

$$P(\text{green}) = \frac{2}{9}, P(\text{blue}) = \frac{4}{9}; P(\text{green or blue}) = \frac{2}{9} + \frac{4}{9} \text{ or } \frac{2}{3}.$$

For two mutually exclusive events A and B: $P(A \text{ or } B) = P(A) + P(B)$

Events which can occur at the same time are called **inclusive events**.

EXAMPLE 4   Of the 20 members of the bicycle club, 7 were in Race A, 8 were in Race B, and 3 were in both races. Find the probability of selecting at random a club member who was in Race A or in Race B. Find P(A or B) for mutually inclusive events.

Draw a diagram to find how many members were racing.

Begin with the 3 members who were in both races.
If 7 were in Race A, 7 − 3 or 4 were in Race A only.
If 8 were in Race B, 8 − 3 or 5 were in Race B only.
Count 4 + 3 + 5 = 12.

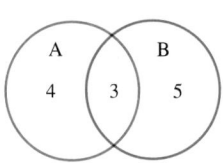

12 out of 20 members were in Race A or in Race B. $P(A \text{ or } B) = \frac{12}{20}$, or $\frac{3}{5}$.

It is not necessary to find out how many individual members were racing. The probability can be calculated in another way.

$$P(A) = \frac{7}{20} \qquad P(B) = \frac{8}{20} \qquad P(\text{both A and B}) = \frac{3}{20}$$

$$P(A \text{ or } B) = \frac{7}{20} + \frac{8}{20} - \frac{3}{20} = \frac{12}{20}, \text{ or } \frac{3}{5}$$

For two inclusive events A and B:

$$P(A \text{ or } B) = P(A) + P(B) - P(A \text{ and } B)$$

14.6 Probability: Compound Events   **605**

• **For Example 3**
   3. Jan has 3 green, 2 red, and 4 blue scarves in a drawer. She chooses a scarf at random and does not want a blue scarf. What is the probability that Jan will pick a red or green scarf. $\frac{5}{9}$

• **For Example 4**
   4. Of 30 members of the Yacht Club, 18 were in the yacht race, 10 in the regatta, and 3 were in both. Find the probability of selecting a club member that was in the yacht race or the regatta. $\frac{5}{6}$

Common Error
• Some students may have difficulty understanding the probability of a compound event. Encourage these students to use a tree diagram to help understand and solve the problem. An overhead projector may be helpful in demonstrating tree diagrams to the students.
• See *Teacher's Resource Book* for additional remediation.

LESSON FOLLOW-UP

Critical Thinking
Causal Explanation   In the formula for inclusive events A and B, P(A or B) = P(A) + P(B) − P(A and B). Explain what P(A and B) represents in the formula, and why it is subtracted from P(A) + P(B).   P(A and B) represents the probability of the overlapping events, A and B. Any outcomes contained in A and B have had their probabilities counted twice, once in P(A) and once in P(B); thus the probability of the overlapping outcomes is subtracted once by subtracting P(A and B).

Assignment Guide
- See p. 580B for assignments.
- See *Teacher's Resource Book,* for Reading and Writing in Algebra activity, p. 14.

Test Yourself
See *Teacher's Resource Book, Tests* pp. 147–148.

Lesson Quiz
A bag contains cards labeled with numbers. There are five 3's, two 4's, one 5, and two 6's. One card is randomly selected and then put back in the bag. Then another card is randomly selected. Find each probability.

1. P(1st 3 and 2nd 4) $\frac{1}{10}$

2. P(1st 3 and 2nd 3) $\frac{1}{4}$

3. P(1st even and 2nd even) $\frac{4}{25}$

One card is randomly selected, noted, and not replaced. Then another card is randomly selected. Find each probability.

4. P(1st 5 and 2nd 3) $\frac{1}{18}$

5. P(1st 5 and 2nd 5) 0

6. P(1st odd and 2nd odd) $\frac{1}{3}$

One card is randomly selected. Find the probability.

7. P(4 or 5) $\frac{3}{10}$

8. P(5 or 5) $\frac{1}{10}$

9. P(even or odd) 1

Enrichment
Of 20 students, 8 play football, 6 play baseball, and 3 play both. If two students are randomly selected, what is the probability that they both play only football? $\frac{1}{19}$

606

CLASS EXERCISES

A bag contains 5 red, 3 green, and 4 white marbles. One is selected randomly, replaced, and another is selected. Draw a tree diagram and find the probability. Check students' diagrams.

1. P(1st R and 2nd W) $\frac{5}{36}$ 2. P(1st R and 2nd R) $\frac{25}{144}$ 3. P(1st R and 2nd $\overline{\text{R}}$) $\frac{35}{144}$

A bag contains 5 red, 3 green, and 4 white marbles. One is selected randomly and not replaced, then another is selected. Draw a tree diagram and find the probability. See below.

4. P(1st R and 2nd W) $\frac{5}{33}$ 5. P(1st R and 2nd R) $\frac{5}{33}$ 6. P(1st R and 2nd $\overline{\text{R}}$) $\frac{35}{132}$

7. Of the 15 members in the stage band, 5 play saxophone, 7 play trumpet and 2 play both. If a member is chosen at random, what is the probability the member plays saxophone or trumpet? $\frac{2}{3}$

PRACTICE EXERCISES

A bag contains cards labeled with numbers. There are three 5s, one 4, two 3s, and two 2s. One card is randomly selected, noted, and replaced. Then another card is randomly selected. Find the probability.

A

1. P(1st 5 and 2nd 3) $\frac{3}{32}$ 2. P(1st 4 and 2nd 2) $\frac{1}{32}$ 3. P(1st 5 and 2nd 5) $\frac{9}{64}$

4. P(1st 3 and 2nd 3) $\frac{1}{16}$ 5. P(1st even and 2nd odd) $\frac{15}{64}$ 6. P(1st odd and 2nd odd) $\frac{25}{64}$

One card is randomly selected, noted, and not replaced. Then another card is randomly selected. Draw a tree diagram and find the probability. See Additional Answer section beginning p. 719.

7. P(1st 5 and 2nd 3) $\frac{3}{28}$ 8. P(1st 4 and 2nd 2) $\frac{1}{28}$ 9. P(1st 4 and 2nd 4) 0

10. P(1st 2 and 2nd 2) $\frac{1}{28}$ 11. P(1st even and 2nd even) $\frac{3}{28}$ 12. P(1st odd and 2nd even) $\frac{15}{56}$

One card is randomly selected; find the probability that the card chosen is:

13. P(4 or 5) $\frac{1}{2}$ 14. P(2 or 3) $\frac{1}{2}$ 15. P(3 or 5) $\frac{5}{8}$

16. P(2 or 4) $\frac{3}{8}$ 17. P(2 or 5) $\frac{5}{8}$ 18. P(3 or 4) $\frac{3}{8}$

B

A bag contains number cards and color cards. There are five 5s, three 3s, four red, and three green cards. One card is randomly selected, noted, and replaced. Then another card is randomly selected. What is the probability for each situation?

19. P(1st 5 and 2nd red) $\frac{4}{45}$ 20. P(1st 3 and 2nd green) $\frac{1}{25}$

21. P(1st number and 2nd color) $\frac{56}{225}$ 22. P(1st color and 2nd color) $\frac{49}{225}$

23. P(1st 3 and 2nd 3) $\frac{1}{25}$ 24. P(1st red and 2nd red) $\frac{16}{225}$

Additional Answers

4.

5.

6.

25. P(1st color and 2nd number) $\frac{56}{225}$

26. P(1st number and 2nd number) $\frac{64}{225}$

C **27.** Of 20 students, 6 read mysteries, 10 read science fiction, and 2 read both. If two students are picked at random, what is the probability they both read only mysteries? $\frac{3}{95}$

28. Of 28 students eating lunch, 8 eat salads, 12 eat sandwiches, and 5 eat both. If two students are randomly selected, what is the probability that each student chosen ate only a sandwich or only a salad? $\frac{5}{42}$

29. Of the 30 students in the class, 12 study Biology, 10 study Geometry, and 11 study neither. If two students are chosen at random, what is the probability that they both study Biology and not Geometry? $\frac{12}{145}$

30. Suppose 30% of couples surveyed purchased both a dishwasher and a microwave oven, and 10% purchased neither. If there were twice as many couples who purchased only a dishwasher as there were couples who purchased only a microwave, what is the probability that a couple selected at random purchased only a dishwasher? $\frac{2}{5}$ or 40%

Applications

31. Marketing Five people are chosen for product testing by lot from 15 men and 12 women. What is the probability, as a decimal to the nearest hundredth, that all will be men? that all will be women? that all will be men or all will be women? $\left(Hint: \text{ Probability that 2 women are selected is } \frac{12}{27} \cdot \frac{11}{26}.\right)$
0.04, 0.01, 0.05

32. Finance A wallet contains three $1 bills and four $5 bills. Two bills are taken from the wallet at random. What is the probability that $2 or $10 is taken? $\frac{3}{7}$

TEST YOURSELF

One box contains color tags: 3 red and 5 green. Another box contains number tags: four 2s and six 3s. A tag is selected at random from each box. Find each probability.

14.4, 14.6

1. P(red) $\frac{3}{8}$

2. P(2) $\frac{2}{5}$

3. P(blue) 0

4. P(2 or 3) 1

5. P(1st green and 2nd 2) $\frac{1}{4}$

6. P(1st red and 2nd 3) $\frac{9}{40}$

Solve.

7. Jan selects a red tag at random from the first box and keeps it. Find the probability of her selecting a second red tag. $\frac{3}{28}$

8. Of 30 people surveyed, 15 take a train to work, 20 drive a car to work, and 8 take both. If a person is selected at random, find the probability that the person only drives a car to work. $\frac{2}{5}$

14.6 Probability: Compound Events **607**

- See *Teacher's Resource Book, Spanish Chapter Summary and Review*, pp. 27–28.
- See *Extra Practice*, p. 668.

CHAPTER 14 SUMMARY AND REVIEW

Vocabulary

complementary events (597)	mode (582)
compound event (603)	mutually exclusive events (605)
dependent events (604)	odds (597)
equally likely (596)	outcome (596)
event (596)	probability (596)
frequency distribution (583)	range (590)
histogram (586)	sample space (596)
inclusive events (605)	standard deviation (591)
independent events (603)	statistics (582)
mean (582)	trial (596)
measure of central tendency (582)	variance (591)
median (582)	Venn diagram (600)

Finding Measures of Central Tendency   A **mode** of a set of data is a number in the set that occurs most frequently. A **median** of a set of data is the middle number in a set, or the mean of the two middle numbers, when the numbers are arranged in order from least to greatest. The **mean** of a set of data consisting of *n* numbers is the sum of the numbers in the set divided by *n*.   14.1

Find the mode, median, and mean. (A) (B) (C)

1. 7, 10, 24, 12, 7, 12 A: 7, 12 B: 11 C: 12

2. −2, 0, 1.5, 0.5, −5.5, 3.5, 3.8, 3.5 A: 3.5 B: 1 C: 0.66

A Histogram is a bar graph of a frequency distribution that plots data against their frequencies.   14.2

3. Construct a histogram to picture the distribution of the following 32 test scores. Group the scores in 5-point intervals. 75, 55, 69, 78, 88, 63, 73, 89, 66, 36, 44, 62, 57, 67, 70, 74, 58, 45, 95, 33, 65, 40, 80, 63, 69, 71, 57, 53, 67, 48, 69, 81 See below.

Finding Measures of Variability   The **range** of a set of data is the difference between the greatest number and the least number in the set. The **variance** is the mean of the sum of the squares of the deviations. The **standard deviation** is the square root of the variance.   14.3

4. Find the range of the data: 4.0, 5.0, 6.0, 4.5, 4.0, 6.0, 5.5. 2.0

5. To the nearest hundredth, find the variance and the standard deviation of the data: 4.0, 5.0, 6.0, 4.5, 4.0, 6.0, 5.5. variance = 0.64 std. deviation = 0.80

608   Chapter 14 Statistics and Probability

Additional Answers

3.

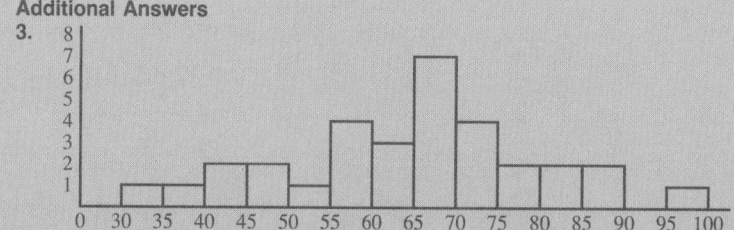

Determining Simple Probability and Odds   The **probability** $P(E)$ of an   14.4
event is the ratio of the number of favorable outcomes to the total number of
possible outcomes, $0 \leq P(E) \leq 1$. The **complement** $P(\overline{E})$ of an event is that
situation in which the event does not occur, $P(E) + P(\overline{E}) = 1$. Odds are a ratio
that compares the probability of an event to the probability of its complement.

**Four packs of tags, gold, red, white, and blue, each numbered 1–20,
make 80 tags in all. One tag is picked at random. Find the probability.**

6. $P(8)$ $\frac{1}{20}$ **7.** $P(\text{red})$ $\frac{1}{4}$ **8.** $P(\text{blue})$ $\frac{1}{4}$ **9.** $P(\text{blue 5})$ $\frac{1}{80}$

10. Odds in favor of rain on a day in June if the average number of rain
days in June over a 40-year period is 20. 2 to 1 for.

Determining the Probability of Two Events   Independent events   14.5–14.6
do not influence each other, but dependent events do. Mutually exclusive
events cannot occur at the same time, whereas inclusive events can.

For independent events A, B: $P(A \text{ and } B) = P(A) \cdot P(B)$

dependent events A, B: $P(A \text{ and } B) = P(A) \cdot P(B, \text{ given } A)$

mutually exclusive events A, B: $P(A \text{ or } B) = P(A) + P(B)$

inclusive events A, B: $P(A \text{ or } B) = P(A) + P(B) - P(A \text{ and } B)$.

**A box contains decorative disks: 3 gold, 6 red, 4 white, and 5 blue.
For Exercises 11 and 12 a disk is picked at random and replaced,
another disk is picked at random. For Exercises 13 and 14 only one disk
is picked. Find each probability.**

11. $P(\text{1st gold and 2nd red})$ $\frac{1}{18}$ **12.** $P(\text{1st gold and 2nd gold})$ $\frac{1}{36}$

13. $P(\text{red or white})$ $\frac{5}{9}$ **14.** $P(\text{white or blue})$ $\frac{1}{2}$

**The decorative disks, 3 gold, 6 red, 4 white, and 5 blue are mixed in a
bag. A disk is picked at random and not replaced. Another disk is
picked at random. Find each probability.**

15. $P(\text{1st gold and 2nd red})$ $\frac{1}{17}$ **16.** $P(\text{1st white and 2nd white})$ $\frac{2}{51}$

17. $P(\text{1st blue and 2nd gold})$ $\frac{5}{102}$ **18.** $P(\text{1st gold and 2nd gold})$ $\frac{1}{51}$

Solve.

19. Of the 20 students in class, 8 like science, 5 like math, and 3 like both.
If a student from class is randomly selected, what is the probability the
student will like science or math? $\frac{1}{2}$

See *Teacher's Resource Book.*
- *Tests,* pp. 149–152
- *Calculator Test,* pp. 27–28

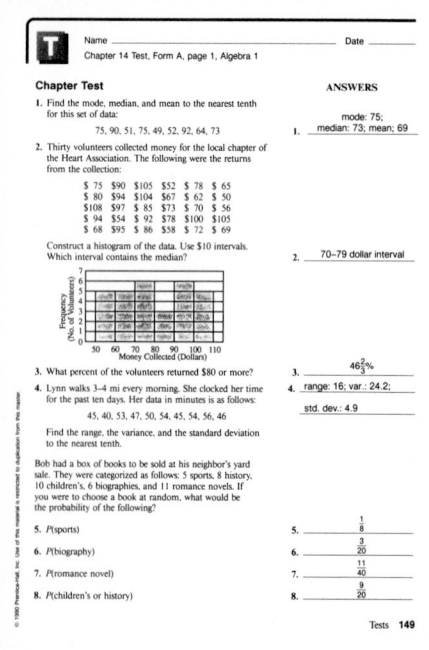

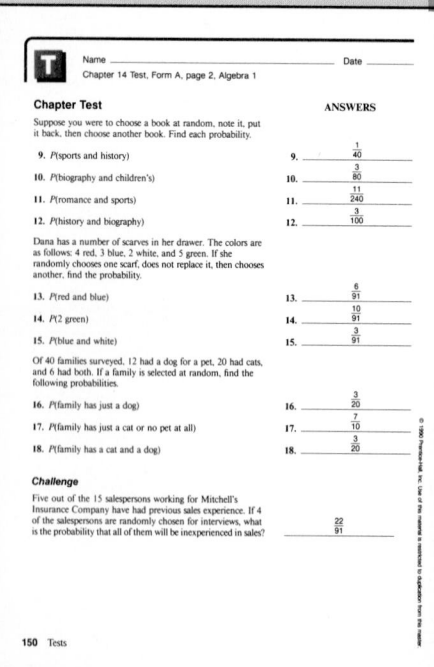

1. Find the mode, median, and mean, to the nearest tenth, for the set of data: 56, 58, 75, 70, 53, 90, 93, 70. mode: 70 median: 70 mean: 70.6

2. Construct a histogram of the following data: The heights (greater than 30 m) of redwood trees in a California Park. Use 10 m intervals. See below.

52	64	79	39	52	41
33	46	78	67	58	44
61	75	37	55	57	61
46	80	86	53	58	69
75	74	81	63	68	64

3. Find the range, the variance, and the standard deviation, to the nearest tenth, for the set of data: 8, 10, 10, 11, 12, 14, 14, 16, 16, 19. range: 11 variance: 10.4 std. deviation: 3.2

There are 4 sets of model boats. Each set is a different color: red (R), blue (B), yellow (Y), and green (G). There are 5 different models in each set—sailboat (S), paddle boat (P), motorboat (M), tugboat (T), and fireboat (F). Find each probability for models selected at random and put back each time.

4. $P(B)$ $\frac{1}{4}$

5. $P(T)$ $\frac{1}{5}$

6. $P(\overline{Y})$ $\frac{3}{4}$

7. $P(\text{any model})$ 1

8. Pick two: $P(\text{1st G and 2nd G})$ $\frac{1}{16}$

9. Pick two: $P(\text{1st S and 2nd F})$ $\frac{1}{25}$

10. Pick only one: $P(\text{R or B})$ $\frac{1}{2}$

11. Pick only one: $P(\text{M or T})$ $\frac{2}{5}$

12. Find the odds for rain on any day in April if there is an average of 12 rain days in the month. 2 to 3 for.

13. Jane and Sylvia each have 5 blouses. Each has 2 white ones. If both girls choose a blouse, what is the probability that they both will wear a white blouse today? $\frac{4}{25}$

14. Of the 60 people surveyed, 20 people travel to work by car, 37 people use public transportation, and 12 people use both. If a person from the survey is selected at random, what is the probability the person uses a car or public transportation? $\frac{3}{4}$

Challenge

In a group of coaches, there are 8 track coaches, 3 soccer coaches, and 1 football coach. If 3 coaches are selected at random to be on the Central Athletic Committee, what is the probability of selecting at least 1 soccer coach? $\frac{34}{55}$

Additional Answers   2.

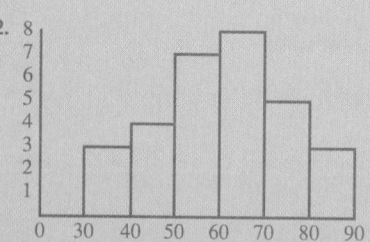

Directions: In each item you are to compare a quantity in Column 1 with a quantity in Column 2. Write the letter of the correct answer from these choices.

A. The quantity in Column 1 is greater than the quantity in Column 2.
B. The quantity in Column 2 is greater than the quantity in Column 1.
C. The quantity in Column 1 is equal to the quantity in Column 2.
D. The relationship cannot be determined from the given information.

Notes: Information centered over both columns refers to one or both of the quantities being compared. A symbol that appears in both columns has the same meaning in each column. All variables represent real numbers. Most figures are not drawn to scale.

Column 1	Column 2
1. 0.035 B	$\frac{7}{20}$
2. 80% of 45 C	36

$$a = 0,\ b = -1$$

Column 1	Column 2
3. $a^2b + ab^2$ A	$5b + 4a$

$$\frac{4}{7} = \frac{x}{21}$$

Column 1	Column 2
4. x A	10
5. $|5 - 4(3 - 6)|$ C	17
6. $\sqrt{16 + 9}$ B	$4 + 3$

$$9x + 1 \geq 2x - 6$$

Column 1	Column 2
7. x A	-2

Use this equation for questions 8–9:

$$2x^2 + 5x - 5 = 0$$

Column 1	Column 2
8. Discriminant A	50
9. Sum of the C roots.	Product of the roots.

Column 1	Column 2
10. $\frac{11}{12} \div \frac{7}{18}$ A	$2\frac{2}{7}$

This triangle
is isosceles.

Column 1	Column 2
11. x D	10
12. $\frac{2}{3} + \frac{1}{2}$ A	$\frac{3}{5}$

$$f(x) = 12x^2 - 3$$

Column 1	Column 2
13. $f(-1)$ C	$f(1)$

Column 1	Column 2
14. x B	57

Use this information for questions 15–16:

x and y are measures of
complementary angles.

Column 1	Column 2
15. $x + y$ B	180
16. x D	y

The individual comments provided about some problems can be helpful in guiding students to solve these problems.

3. Students should be encouraged to notice immediately that the value in Column 1 is 0, since $a = 0$ and a is a factor of each term.
6. Frequent exposure to the fact that $\sqrt{a^2 + b^2} \neq a + b$ might eliminate some occurrences of the error of thinking they are equal.
11. Too often, picture an isosceles triangle with its base in horizontal position. They need frequent exposures to other positions.

See *Teacher's Resource Book* for Preparing for Standardized Tests.

11.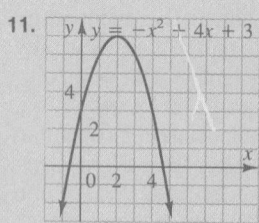

12.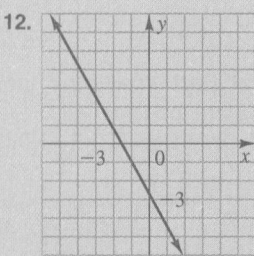

13.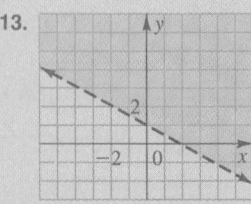

23.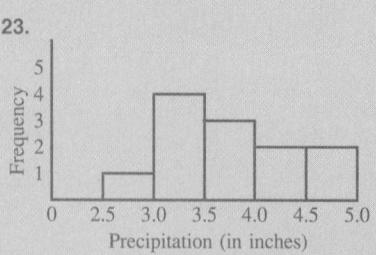

Replace each ? with $>$, $<$, or $=$ to make a true statement. 1.3, 5.7, 12.5, 12.6, 12.7

1. $-\dfrac{1}{2}$? $-\dfrac{1}{4}$ $<$

2. $\left(-\dfrac{1}{2}\right)^2$? $\dfrac{1}{4}$ $=$

3. $\sqrt{\dfrac{1}{4}}$? $\dfrac{1}{4}$ $>$

4. $\dfrac{2}{3}$? $\dfrac{16}{24}$ $=$

5. $\left|-\dfrac{2}{3}\right|$? $\sqrt{\dfrac{4}{9}}$ $=$

6. $4\sqrt{5}$? $\sqrt{20}$ $>$

7. $-\sqrt{\dfrac{9}{16}}$? $-\dfrac{3}{5}$ $<$

8. $\dfrac{2}{\sqrt{3}}$? $\dfrac{1}{3}\sqrt{6}$ $>$

9. $2\sqrt{16} - 3\sqrt{18}$? $\sqrt{2}$ $<$

10. $\sqrt{2}(3 + \sqrt{2})$? $3\left(\dfrac{2}{3} + \sqrt{2}\right)$ $=$

Graph. See side column. 5.2, 9.7

11. $y = -x^2 + 4x + 3$

12. $2x + y = -3$

13. $y > -\dfrac{1}{2}x + 1$

Perform the indicated operation. Simplify if possible. 12.5, 12.6, 12.7

14. $\sqrt{81} - (-\sqrt{36})$ 15

15. $-\sqrt{18} + \sqrt{50}$ $2\sqrt{2}$

16. $3\sqrt{8} \cdot 2\sqrt{3}$ $12\sqrt{6}$

17. $\dfrac{2\sqrt{3}}{1 + \sqrt{2}}$ $2\sqrt{3}(\sqrt{2} - 1)$

18. $\dfrac{2\sqrt{6}}{6\sqrt{3}}$ $\dfrac{\sqrt{2}}{3}$

19. $\dfrac{(-2\sqrt{2})^2}{\sqrt{6}\sqrt{2}}$ $\dfrac{4\sqrt{3}}{3}$

Solve. 10.5, 11.7, 12.8, 14.4

20. The diagonal of a square is $7\sqrt{2}$ cm. Find the length of the side of the square. 7 cm

21. Al's father is $2\dfrac{1}{4}$ times as old as Al is. 9 years ago he was 3 times as old as Al was. How old is each one now? Al is 24 yr. His father is 54 yr.

22. The number of days needed to do a job varies inversely as the number of people working on the job. It takes 12 days for 4 people to complete the job. If the job has to be finished in 8 days, how many people are needed? 6 people

23. The monthly normal precipitation (in inches) that falls in Houston, Texas is recorded in the chart below. These normals are based on records for the 30-year period 1951–1980 inclusive.

Jan.	Feb.	March	April	May	June	July	Aug.	Sept.	Oct.	Nov.	Dec.
3.2	3.3	2.7	4.2	4.7	4.0	3.3	3.7	4.9	3.7	3.4	3.7

a. Find the mean, mode, and median for the data. mean 3.7; mode 3.7; median 3.7
b. Draw a histogram to show the data. See side column.
c. Find the variance and standard deviation of the data. variance 0.37 standard deviation 0.61

SUMMARY

In Chapter 15, students are introduced to basic geometric figures. Students learn about different types of angles and triangles. They are introduced to the very important concepts of congruency and similarity. The lessons focus on special cases of right triangles, trigonometric ratios, and how many real world problems can be solved using them.

After this chapter is completed, students should be able to identify basic geometric figures and angles, and classify triangles according to the lengths of their sides and measures of their angles. Students will be able to identify and compute the sine, cosine, and tangent ratios, and read trigonometric tables.

CHAPTER OBJECTIVES

- To identify basic geometric figures, and to classify angles according to their measure
- To identify complementary and supplementary angles, and to solve word problems about them
- To classify triangles according to the measures of their angles and the lengths of their sides
- To find the measures of the angles of a triangle and to solve word problems involving the angles of a triangle
- To identify congruent figures and name the corresponding parts of congruent triangles
- To identify similar figures and name the corresponding vertices and sides of similar triangles
- To use proportions to solve problems concerning similar triangles
- To identify and compute the sine, cosine, and tangent ratios in any right triangle
- To use a trigonometric table to find the lengths of sides and the measure of angles of a right triangle

Problem Solving Strategy

To use trigonometric ratios to check for hidden assumptions.

CHAPTER HIGHLIGHTS

The *theme* of Chapter 15 is Architecture. The chapter's special features and applications demonstrate how architecture utilizes the concepts of lines, angles, and triangles.

PROBLEM SOLVING AND APPLICATIONS

Problem solving and applications form an integral part of each lesson. Students use their knowledge of geometric figures and angles to solve problems in real-world situations. In Lesson 15.7, the four step problem solving strategy of checking for hidden assumptions is used to simplify complex problems.

TECHNOLOGY

Calculator

Students learn how to find trigonometric ratios by using a calculator. They learn how to find the measure of an angle given its decimal approximation, and vice versa.

RESOURCES

Teacher's Resource Book

- Teaching Aid 18
- Transparency 32, 33

STUDENT TEXT

Chapter Content	Basic	Average	Enriched	R	P	E
15.1 Basic Geometric Figures	Omit	D: 616/1-19 odd, 24, 25 R: 616/2, 4, 6	D: 617/13-23 odd, 24, 25	1	2	3
15.2 Triangles	Omit	D: 621/1-25 odd, 29, 30 R: 616/6, 10, 18	D: 621/17-27 odd, 29, 30 R: 617/14, 20, 22	4	5	6
15.3 Congruence	Omit	D: 625/1-19 odd, 23, 24 R: Test Yourself	D: 625/1-21 odd, 23, 24 R: 621/18, 20, 26 Test Yourself	7	8	9
15.4 Similar Figures	Omit	Omit	D: 630/13-25 odd, 27 R: 625/14, 18, 20	10	11	12
15.5 Trigonometric Ratios	Omit	Omit	D: 635/19-27 odd, 28-31 R: 630/14, 20, 24	13	14	15
15.6 Using Trigonometric Ratios	Omit	Omit	D: 641/11-37 odd, 38-41 R: 635/22, 24, 26 641/12, 16, 20	16	17	18
15.7 Problem Solving Strategy: Check for Hidden Assumption	Omit	Omit	D: 646/1-13 odd MPSR 1-3 R: Test Yourself		19	20

D = Daily   R = Review   MPSR = Mixed Problem Solving Review   R = Reteaching   P = Practice   E = Enrichment

---

STUDENT TEXT

TEACHER'S RESOURCE BOOK

Reviewing	Test Yourself	627	Chapter Test	650	Spanish Chapter Summary and Review 29-30
And	Test Yourself	647	Prep. for Stan. Test	651	• Quizzes 157-160
Testing	Chapter Sum. and Rev.	648	Cumulative Review	652	• Chapter Test (Form A) 161-162
			Extra Practice	669	• Chapter Test (Form B) 163-164
					Calculator Test 29-30
Special	Geometry in Architecture	617	Extra	636	Applications—Chapter 15 21
Features	Algebra in Construction	622	Application	637	Critical Thinking 15
	Extra	632	Extra	642	Reading and Writing in Algebra 15
					Technology 28

15 Right Triangle Relationships

Triangular and rectangular shapes are used in many modern buildings. Architects arrange such shapes so that they are in logical relation to each other and are pleasing to the eye. The perspective of this photograph gives the appearance of a change in the shape of the structure.

613

BACKGROUND

For architects to design a building, they have to take into account various shapes and sizes. This requires many calculations involving the angles and lengths of sides of each figure. This chapter will demonstrate how geometric figures and calculations are integrated into real-world situations.

Vocabulary

Acute angle
Angle
Complementary angle
Geometry
Line
Line segment
Obtuse angle
Point
Ray
Right angle
Supplementary angle
Vertex

Materials/Manipulatives

Graph paper
Protractor
Straightedge
Overhead projector

BACKGROUND

In the Capsule Review, students graph sentences involving inequalities. Point out that each graph represents a line segment or a ray. Closed symbolism is used in all of the examples, that is, only the $\leq$ and $\geq$ symbols are used. When graphing line segments, students should represent the end points with a heavy dot. Also remind students to draw arrowheads on number lines and rays.

Critical Thinking

Discovering Relationships Establish criteria that can be used to distinguish between lines, rays, and segments. Answers may vary. Possible answers: Number of end points: line 0; ray 1; segment 2. Length: length is associated with segments, not with rays and lines. Segments and rays are subsets of lines.

15.1

Basic Geometric Figures

Objectives: To identify basic geometric figures, and to classify angles according to their measures
To identify complementary and supplementary angles, and to solve word problems about them

Geometry is a branch of mathematics that deals with sets of points. You have used dots to represent points on a number line as well as points in the coordinate plane. A point, however, is an abstract idea that has no size or shape, merely position. A set of points can represent a line or a geometric figure such as a triangle, a rectangle, or a circle.

Capsule Review

EXAMPLE   Graph $-2 \leq x \leq 5$.

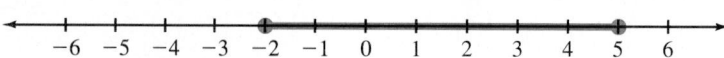

Graph each sentence. See below.

1. $-3 \leq x \leq 3$ **2.** $2x \leq 8$ **3.** $x \geq -3$ **4.** $-10 \geq 5x$

A **line** consists of infinitely many points extending without end in both directions. A *line* determined by points A and B is denoted by $\overleftrightarrow{AB}$ or $\overleftrightarrow{BA}$. The arrowheads show that the line extends infinitely in both directions.

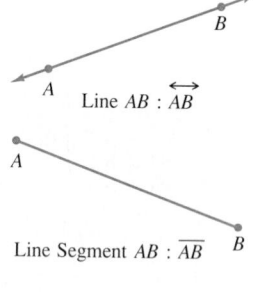
Line AB : $\overleftrightarrow{AB}$

A set of points on a line is a **line segment** if it consists of two points A and B called *endpoints* and all points in between them. Line segment AB is written as $\overline{AB}$ or $\overline{BA}$. The length or measure of a line segment is denoted AB.

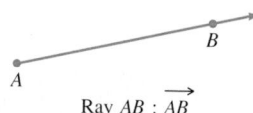
Line Segment AB : $\overline{AB}$

The part of $\overleftrightarrow{AB}$ that starts at point A and extends infinitely passing through point B is called **ray** AB and is denoted $\overrightarrow{AB}$. A is called the endpoint of $\overrightarrow{AB}$.

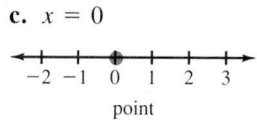
Ray AB : $\overrightarrow{AB}$

EXAMPLE 1   **Graph and tell whether the figure is a point, a line, a line segment, or a ray.**

a. $-2 \leq x \leq 3$ **b.** $x \geq 1$ **c.** $x = 0$

line segment   ray   point

614   Chapter 15 Right Triangle Relationships

Additional Answers

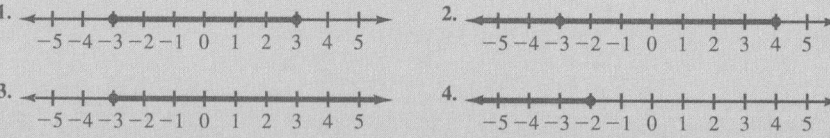

An **angle** is the union of two non-collinear rays with a common endpoint. The rays are the sides of the angle, and the common endpoint is the **vertex** of the angle. The angle at the right can be denoted as $\angle A$, $\angle CAB$, or $\angle BAC$.

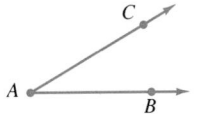

Angles are measured with a **protractor**. Using a protractor, you can see that the measure of $\angle CAB$ is 30°. This is written as $m\angle CAB = 30$.

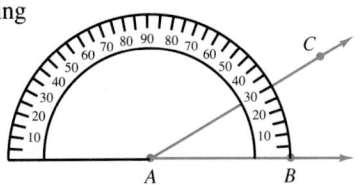

Angles are classified according to their measures.

> A **right angle** has a measure of 90°.
> An **acute angle** has a measure between 0° and 90°.
> An **obtuse angle** has a measure between 90° and 180°.

Some pairs of angles have special names.

> **Complementary angles** are two angles whose measures have a sum of 90°. Each angle is a complement of the other.
> **Supplementary angles** are two angles whose measures have a sum of 180°. Each angle is a supplement of the other.

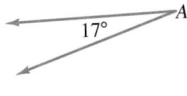 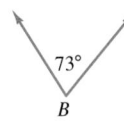 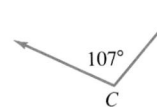

EXAMPLE 2 In the figure above, which pair of angles is complementary? Which pair of angles is supplementary?

$$m\angle A + m\angle B = 17 + 73 \qquad m\angle B + m\angle C = 73 + 107$$
$$= 90 \qquad\qquad\qquad = 180$$

So $\angle A$ and $\angle B$ are complementary, and $\angle B$ and $\angle C$ are supplementary.

EXAMPLE 3 Angles M and N are supplementary.
a. Find $m\angle N$ if $m\angle M = 35$.
b. Classify each angle as acute or obtuse.

a. $m\angle M + m\angle N = 180$ *The sum of the measures of supplementary*
         $35 + m\angle N = 180$ *angles is 180.*
         $m\angle N = 145$

b. $\angle M$ is acute and $\angle N$ is obtuse.

TEACHING SUGGESTIONS

- In this lesson, students are introduced to some of the basic geometric ideas and terminology. Point out how algebraic concepts are applied to solve geometric problems.
- An overhead projector may be helpful in demonstrating line segments, rays, and different types of angles.

CHALKBOARD EXAMPLES

- **For Example 1**

  Graph and tell whether the figure is a point, a line, a line segment, or a ray.

  1. $-1 \le x$ ray

  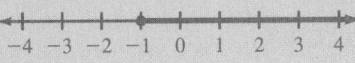

  2. $-1 \le a \le 2$ line segment

  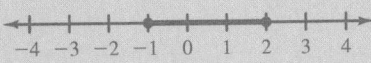

- **For Example 2**

  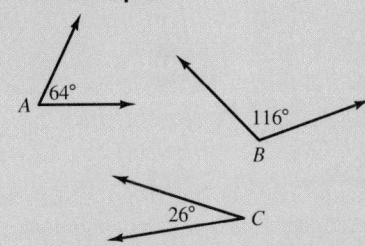

  3. In the figure above, which pair of angles is complementary?
  $\angle A$ and $\angle C$

  4. Which is supplementary?
  $\angle A$ and $\angle B$

- **For Example 3**

  Angles R and S are supplementary.

  5. Find $m\angle R$ if $m\angle S = 75$.
  $m\angle R = 105$

  6. Classify each angle. $\angle R$ is obtuse, $\angle S$ is acute.

- **For Example 4**

  The measure of an angle is 70 less than the measure of its supplement. Find the measure of the angle. 55°

615

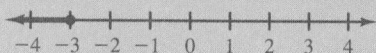
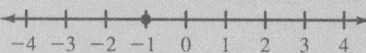
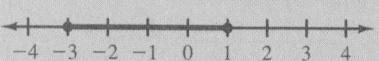
EXAMPLE 4 **The measure of an angle is 20 less than the measure of its supplement.**
  a. Find the measure of the angle.
  b. Find the measure of the supplement of the angle.
  c. Find the measure of the complement of the angle.

  a. Let x = the measure of the angle.
    Then $180 - x$ = measure of the supplement.
    $x = (180 - x) - 20$
    $2x = 160$
    $x = 80$

  b. The measure of the supplement is $180 - x$.
    $180 - x = 180 - 80 = 100$

  c. The measure of the complement is $90 - x$.
    $90 - x = 90 - 80 = 10$

So, the angle measures 80. The measure of the complement is 10 and the measure of the supplement is 100.

CLASS EXERCISES

Use the figure to the right for Exercises 1 and 2.

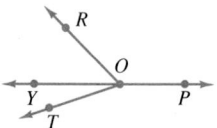

1. Name three different line segments.
  Answers may vary.
2. Name five different angles in the figure.
  $\angle ROY$, $\angle YOT$, $\angle ROT$, $\angle ROP$, $\angle POT$

Tell if each angle is acute, right, or obtuse.

3. 38° acute   **4.** 100° obtuse   **5.** 90° right   **6.** 145° obtuse

Find the complement of each angle.

7. 15° 75°   **8.** 75° 15°   **9.** 45° 45°   **10.** 89° 1°

Find the supplement of each angle.

11. 140° 40°   **12.** 10° 170°   **13.** 90° 90°   **14.** 150° 30°

PRACTICE EXERCISES

Graph each sentence on a number line, and state whether the figure represents a point, a line, a line segment, or a ray. See below.

A **1.** $x \leq 2$ ray   **2.** $x \geq 4$ ray   **3.** $x = 7$ point   **4.** $x = -3$ point

5. $4 \leq x \leq 7$ line segment   **6.** $0 \geq x \geq -5$ line segment   **7.** $6 > x$ or $x > 3$ line   **8.** $-1 \leq x$ or $x \leq 4$ line

State whether the given angles are complementary or supplementary.

9. 47°, 43° complementary   **10.** 12°, 78° complementary   **11.** 2°, 178° supplementary   **12.** 154°, 26° supplementary

616   Chapter 15 Right Triangle Relationships

Additional Answers

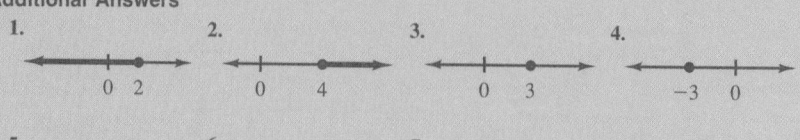

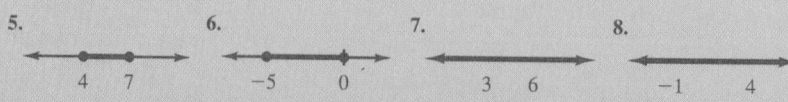

In Exercises 13–16, $\angle M$ and $\angle N$ are complementary, $\angle A$ and $\angle B$ are supplementary. Find the measure of the missing angle and classify the angle.

B 13. $m\angle M = 30$ 14. $m\angle N = 75$ 15. $m\angle A = 78$ 16. $m\angle B = 25$
$m\angle N = 60$; acute $m\angle M = 15$; acute $m\angle B = 102$; obtuse $m\angle A = 155$; obtuse

17. The measure of an angle is 40 more than that of its complement. Find the measure of the angle and its complement. 25°; 65°

18. The measure of an angle is 30 less than that of its complement. Find the measure of the angle and its complement. 30°; 60°

19. The measure of an angle is 50 less than that of its complement. Find the measure of the angle and its supplement. 20°; 160°

20. The measure of an angle is 10 more than that of its supplement. Find the measure of the angle and its supplement. 95°; 85°

C 21. The measure of the complement of an angle is 10 less than three times the measure of the angle. Find the measure of the angle and its supplement. 25°; 155°

22. The measure of the supplement of an angle is 45 less than four times the measure of the angle. Find the measure of the angle. 45°

23. Two times the measure of the supplement of an angle is five times the measure of the complement of the angle. Find the measure of the angle. 30°

Applications

24. **Construction**   A builder rests his 8-m ladder against the side of a building. The ladder forms a 28°-angle between itself and the ground. Find the complement and supplement of the angle formed. 62°; 152°

25. **Travel**   An airplane heading from California takes off and flys 65° NE. If the plane turns 90° to the right, what direction will the plane be heading in? 155° SE

GEOMETRY IN ARCHITECTURE

Geometry plays a key role in architecture through the incorporation of different shapes into various designs. Ludwig Mies Van der Rohe and Frank Lloyd Wright were probably two of the most famous architects of the twentieth century. Some basic geometric shapes in architecture include arches, circles, triangles, ellipses, parabolas, and domes. Many famous structures incorporate these shapes, including the White House and the Rose Bowl.

Investigate an unusual architectural design of your choice. Research the history of the structure and prepare a report of your findings for your class.
Check students' work.

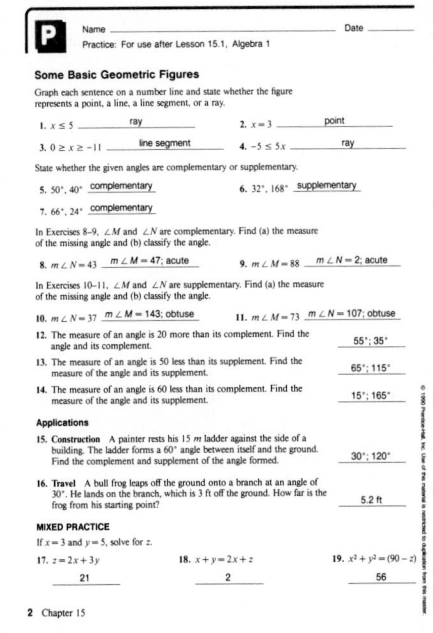

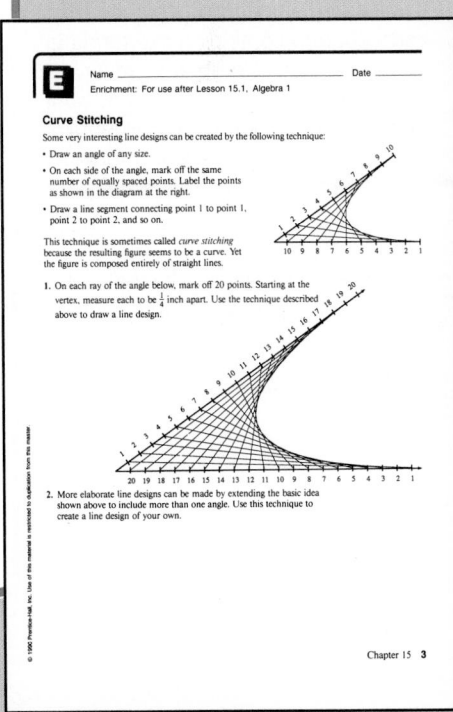

Vocabulary

Acute triangle
Equilateral triangle
Isosceles triangle
Obtuse triangle
Right triangle
Scalene triangle
Triangle

Materials/Manipulatives

Graph paper
Protractor
Straightedge
Overhead projector
Teacher's Resource Book,
Transparency 32

BACKGROUND

In the Capsule Review, the exercises involve solving equations by combining like terms and simplifying. Later in this lesson, students will extend their knowledge of combining like terms to solve geometric problems involving angles and triangles. You might want to point out to students that algebra is used as a tool to solve problems throughout the study of geometry.

Critical Thinking

Classifying Could a triangle be called a trilateral? A trigon? Explain.

Yes for both; tri comes from the Latin, Greek, or French tri, meaning 3. Trilateral or trigon would mean a figure (polygon) with 3 sides.

15.2

Triangles

Objectives: To classify triangles according to the measures of their angles and according to the lengths of their sides
To find the measures of the angles of a triangle and to solve word problems involving the angles of a triangle

The sides of the Transamerica Building in San Francisco are triangular in shape. A **triangle** is the figure formed by three segments joining three noncollinear points.

An architect can design a triangular side of a building by determining two angles that would be formed at the base of the building. Is it possible for the architect to find the measure of the third angle? Solving a problem of this type involves setting up the proper equation.

Capsule Review

To solve an equation in which the same variable occurs more than once:

- First combine like terms on each side.
- Use the addition or subtraction property for equations so that all variables are on one side and all constant terms are on the other.

EXAMPLE Solve: $3s + 7s = 15 - 5s$

$$10s = 15 - 5s$$
$$15s = 15$$
$$s = 1$$

Solve for the unknown.

1. $7b + 4b - 2b - 13 = 26 - 4b$ 3

2. $\frac{1}{2}x - 12 = \frac{3}{4}x - 36$ 96

3. $7w + 2w + 5 = w + 16$ $\frac{11}{8}$

4. $3x - 15 = x + 18 - 4x$ $\frac{11}{2}$

Triangle *TRN* can be written $\triangle TRN$.
Sides of $\triangle TRN$: $\overline{TR}$, $\overline{RN}$, $\overline{NT}$
Vertices of $\triangle TRN$: *T, R, N*
Angles of $\triangle TRN$: $\angle T$ ($\angle NTR$)
$\angle R$ ($\angle TRN$)
$\angle N$ ($\angle RNT$)

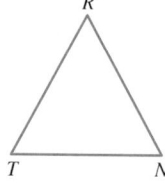

A triangle may be classified according to its angles.

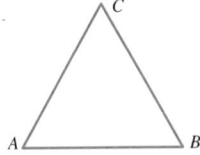

$\triangle ABC$ is an **acute triangle**
because each of its three
angles is acute.

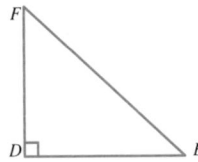

$\triangle DEF$ is a **right triangle**
because it has one
right angle.

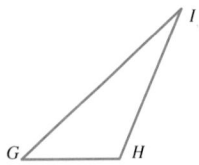

$\triangle GHI$ is an **obtuse triangle**
because it has one
obtuse angle.

A triangle may also be classified according to the lengths of its sides.

An **isosceles triangle**
has at least two sides
of equal length.

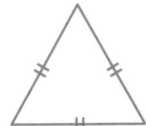

An **equilateral triangle**
has all sides of
equal length.

A **scalene triangle**
has no sides
of equal length.

In an isosceles triangle, the measures of the angles opposite the equal sides
are equal. In an equilateral triangle, the measures of all the angles are equal.
In a scalene triangle, the measures of the angles are not equal.

EXAMPLE 1   **Classify each triangle according to the measures of the angles and
according to the lengths of the sides.**

a.
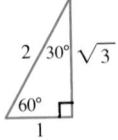

b.
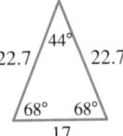

c.
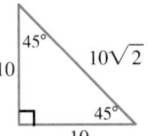

d.
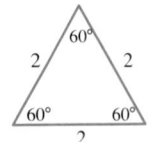

a. right triangle
scalene triangle

b. acute triangle
isosceles triangle

c. right triangle
isosceles triangle

d. acute triangle
equilateral triangle

The sum of the measures of the angles of a triangle is 180.

$$m\angle A + m\angle B + m\angle C = 180$$

15.2 Triangles   **619**

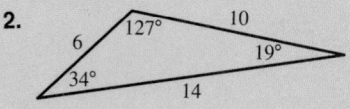

For Example 2
3. In $\triangle PQR$, $m\angle P = 38$ and $m\angle Q = 60$. Find $m\angle R$.
$m\angle R = 82$

- **For Example 3**
  4. If $\triangle TAN$ is isosceles, $TA = AN$, and $m\angle A = 48$, find $m\angle T$ and $m\angle N$. $m\angle T = m\angle N = 66$

- **For Example 4**
  5. In $\triangle JAM$, the measure of $\angle A$ is three times the measure of $\angle M$. The measure of $\angle J$ is six more than twice the measure of $\angle M$. Find the measure of each angle. $m\angle J = 64$; $m\angle A = 87$; $m\angle M = 29$

Common Error
- Students may translate word phrases into incorrect equations. Remind students of the key words used in word phrases. Encourage them to read each problem thoroughly.
- See *Teacher's Resource Book* for additional remediation.

LESSON FOLLOW-UP

Discussion

Is it possible to have a triangle with two obtuse angles? Why or why not?
no; the sum of the measures of the angles of a triangle is 180. Having more than one obtuse angle would result in a sum greater than 180.

Assignment Guide

See p. 612B for assignments.

See *Teacher's Resource Book,* for Reading and Writing in Algebra activity p. 15.

EXAMPLE 2   In $\triangle DES$, $m\angle D = 12$ and $m\angle E = 40$. Find $m\angle S$.

$$m\angle D + m\angle E + m\angle S = 180$$
$$12 + 40 + m\angle S = 180$$
$$52 + m\angle S = 180$$
$$m\angle S = 128$$

The sum of the measures of the angles of a triangle is 180.

EXAMPLE 3   If $\triangle RAN$ is isosceles, $RA = AN$, and $m\angle A = 32$, find $m\angle R$ and $m\angle N$. Draw a diagram. Since $RA = AN$, the angles opposite the equal sides are equal. So $m\angle R = m\angle N$.

$$m\angle A + m\angle R + m\angle N = 180$$
Let $x = m\angle R$. Then $x = m\angle N$.
So $32 + x + x = 180$
$$32 + 2x = 180$$
$$2x = 148$$
$$x = 74$$
So $m\angle R = 74$ and $m\angle N = 74$.

EXAMPLE 4   In $\triangle QRS$, the measure of $\angle Q$ is twice the measure of $\angle R$, and the measure of $\angle S$ is 15 more than the measure of $\angle Q$. Find the measure of each angle of the triangle.

Let $r = m\angle R$.
Then $m\angle Q = 2r$ and $m\angle S = 2r + 15$.
$$r + 2r + (2r + 15) = 180$$
$$5r + 15 = 180$$
$$5r = 165$$
$$r = 33$$
$$2r = 66$$
$$2r + 15 = 81$$
So $m\angle R = 33$, $m\angle Q = 66$, and $m\angle S = 81$.

CLASS EXERCISES

Classify each triangle according to the measures of the angles and according to the lengths of the sides.

1.

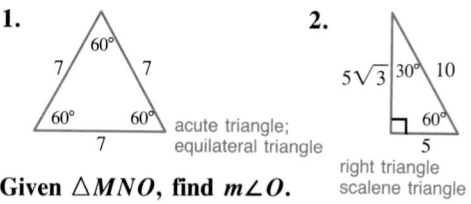

acute triangle;
equilateral triangle

2.

right triangle
scalene triangle

3.

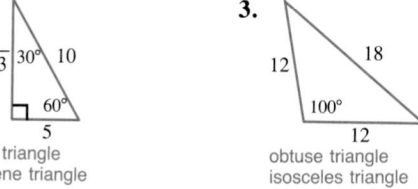

obtuse triangle
isosceles triangle

Given $\triangle MNO$, find $m\angle O$.

4. $m\angle M = 45$, $m\angle N = 30$ 105

5. $m\angle M = 90$, $m\angle N = 13$ 77

620   Chapter 15 Right Triangle Relationships

Use a protractor for Exercises 6 and 7.

6. Draw a large triangle. Find the measure of each angle with a protractor. Then find the sum of the measures. Check students' work.

7. Repeat Exercise 6 with two more types of triangles. What can you conclude about your results? Sum of the measures of three angles in a triangle is equal to 180°.

PRACTICE EXERCISES

Classify each triangle according to the measures of the angles and according to the lengths of the sides.

A

1.
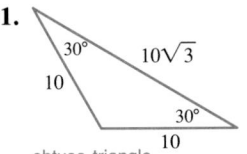
obtuse triangle
isosceles triangle

2.
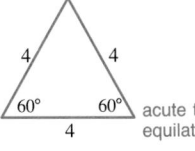
acute triangle
equilateral triangle

3.
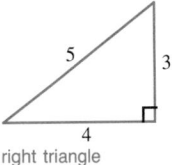
right triangle
scalene triangle

4.
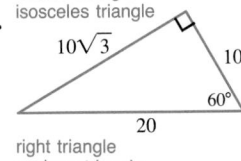
right triangle
scalene triangle

5.
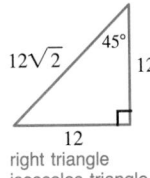
right triangle
isosceles triangle

6.
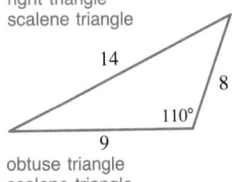
obtuse triangle
scalene triangle

Given △JKL, find $m\angle L$.

7. $m\angle J = 70$, $m\angle K = 40$ 70

8. $m\angle J = 30$, $m\angle K = 40$ 110

9. $m\angle J = 33$, $m\angle K = 80$ 67

10. $m\angle J = 50$, $m\angle K = 72$ 58

11. $m\angle J = 82$, $m\angle K = 73$ 25

12. $m\angle J = 42$, $m\angle K = 64$ 74

13. If △MNO is isosceles, $MN = NO$, and $m\angle N = 80$, find $m\angle M$. 50

14. If △WXY is isosceles, $m\angle Y = 24$, and $WY = XY$, find $m\angle X$. 78

15. If △ABC is a right isosceles triangle and $m\angle A = 90$, find $m\angle B$. 45

16. If △DEF is an equilateral triangle, find $m\angle E$. 60

B

17. In an isosceles triangle, one of the equal angles measures 33°. Find the measure of the remaining angles in the triangle. 33°, 114°

18. In an isosceles triangle, one of the equal angles measures 47°. Find the measure of the remaining angles. 47°, 86°

19. The measures of the angles of a triangle are consecutive integers. Find all the angles. 59°; 60°; 61°

20. The measures of the angles of a triangle are consecutive even integers. Find all the angles. 58°; 60°; 62°

15.2 Triangles **621**

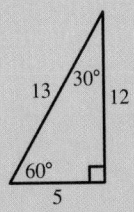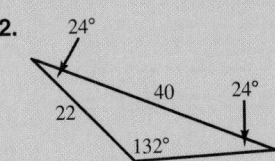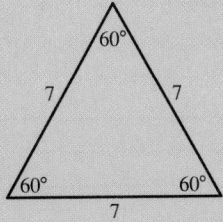
621

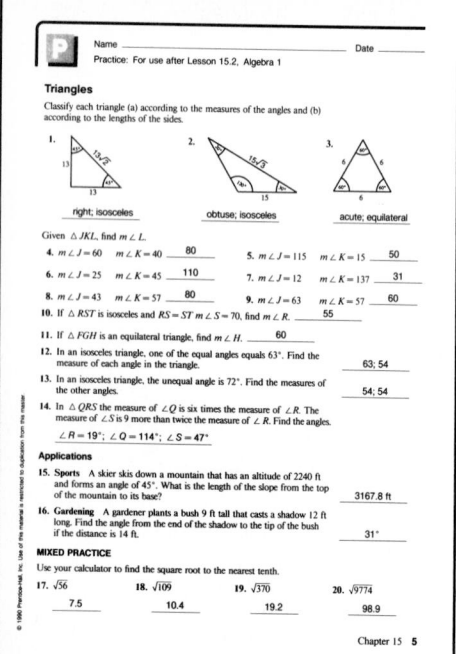

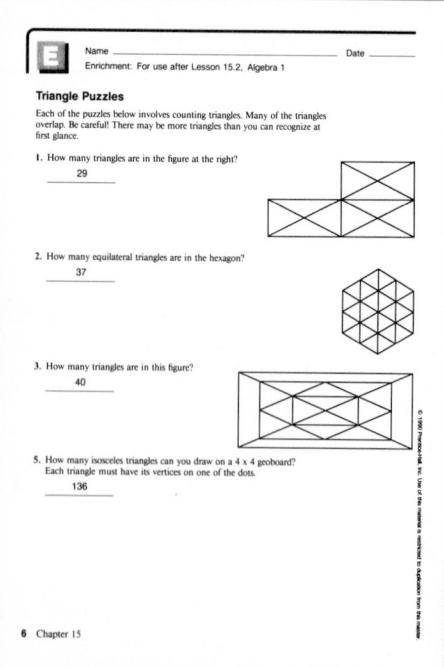

21. The measures of the angles of a triangle are in the ratio 2:3:4. Find all the angles. 40°; 60°; 80°

22. The measures of the angles of a triangle are in the ratio 3:4:5. Find all the angles. 45°; 60°; 75°

23. In $\triangle QRS$ the measure of $\angle Q$ is three times the measure of $\angle R$. The measure of $\angle S$ is 9 more than 5 times the measure of $\angle R$. Find the angles. $m\angle R = 19$; $m\angle Q = 57$; $m\angle S = 104$

24. In $\triangle ABC$ the measure of $\angle C$ is four times the measure of $\angle A$. The measure of $\angle B$ is 2 less than twice the measure of $\angle A$. Find the angles. $m\angle A = 26$; $m\angle B = 50$; $m\angle C = 104$

25. In $\triangle MNO$ the measure of $\angle N$ is 11 more than seven times the measure of $\angle M$. The measure of $\angle O$ is 5 times that of $\angle M$. Find the angles. $m\angle M = 13$; $m\angle N = 102$; $m\angle O = 65$

26. In $\triangle XYZ$ the measure of $\angle X$ is 53 and the measure of $\angle Z$ is 22 more than 6 times that of $\angle Y$. Find the angles. $m\angle Y = 15$; $m\angle Z = 112$

C 27. In $\triangle SUM$ the measure of $\angle M$ is 4 less than the measure of the supplement of $\angle U$. The measure of $\angle S$ is 30 less than $\frac{1}{2}$ the measure of $\angle U$. Find the angles. $m\angle S = 4$; $m\angle U = 68$; $m\angle M = 108$

28. In $\triangle FUN$ the measure of $\angle U$ is 8 more than $\frac{1}{3}$ the measure of the supplement of $\angle F$. The measure of $\angle N$ is 31 more than the complement of $\angle F$. Find the angles. $m\angle F = 27$; $m\angle U = 59$; $m\angle N = 94$

Applications

29. **Hobbies** Jason's kite is 30 ft above the ground. Draw a right triangle so that the angle formed between the kite string and the ground is 35°. Which side of the triangle represents the kite string? See below. The hypotenuse.

30. **Forestry** A forest ranger wishes to determine the height of a redwood tree. Draw a right triangle so that the line drawn from the ground to the top of the tree forms a 60° angle when the ranger is standing 50 ft from the base of the tree. See below.

ALGEBRA IN CONSTRUCTION

Becca and Steve work summers for the city recreation department. Their first "you're on your own" job was to design and build a sandbox for a playground. They made it in the shape of a right triangle with sides of one unit and b units, and hypotenuse AB.

The sandbox is very popular, so Becca was given the job of enlarging it. Because of the contour of the ground and location of other play equipment, she decided to build another right triangle, using the same hypotenuse AB. Another side is 2 units. How long is the third side? $\sqrt{b^2 - 3}$

622 Chapter 15 Right Triangle Relationships

Additional Answers

29.

30.

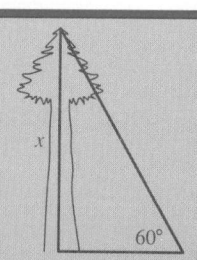

Congruence

15.3

Objective: To identify congruent figures and name the corresponding parts of congruent triangles

In the early 1940s, R. Buckminster Fuller introduced the idea of constructing buildings and other structures with a design based on equilateral triangles rather than rectangles. Note that the equilateral triangles are the same size and shape. The properties of equality for real numbers can also be applied to corresponding parts of triangles that are the same size and shape.

Capsule Review

For all real numbers a, b, and c, the following properties are true:
    Reflexive property: $a = a$
    Symmetric property: If $a = b$, then $b = a$.
    Transitive property: If $a = b$ and $b = c$, then $a = c$.

Which property of real numbers justifies each statement?

1. If $5 + x = -2$, then $-2 = 5 + x$ symmetric property

2. $15 - 5x = 15 - 5x$ reflexive property

3. If $a + 2 = 9$ and $9 = 7 + 2$, then $a + 2 = 7 + 2$. transitive property

Angles that have the same measure are called **congruent angles.** Line segments that have the same length are **congruent line segments.**
Congruent figures are figures that have the same size and shape.

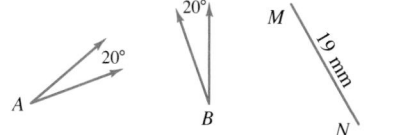

The symbol for "is congruent to" is ≅. Therefore, in the figure above
$\angle A \cong \angle B$ and $\overline{MN} \cong \overline{PQ}$.

15.3 Congruence   **623**

LESSON PLAN

Vocabulary
Congruent angles
Congruent figures
Congruent line segments
Corresponding angles
Corresponding parts
Corresponding sides
Corresponding vertices

Materials/Manipulatives
Graph paper
Protractor
Straightedge

BACKGROUND

In the Capsule Review, students determine which property of equality is used in the given statements. These exercises are designed to help students understand the similarity between congruence and equality.

Critical Thinking
Discovering Relationships Use a dictionary to find the derivation and the meaning of the word *congruent*. *Congruent* means *congruous* which is derived from the Latin *congruos,* meaning to come together or agree. Thus, congruent means "superposable so as to be coincident throughout."

CHALKBOARD EXAMPLES

• **For Example 1**

Name the length of each segment and tell whether the segments are congruent.

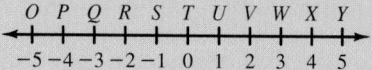

1. $\overline{RU}$ and $\overline{QT}$ $RU = QT = 3$; congruent

2. $\overline{OW}$ and $\overline{QX}$ $OW = 8$; $QX = 7$; not congruent

• **For Example 2**

Name the property of congruence that illustrates each statement.

3. If $\overline{PQ} \cong \overline{RS}$ then $\overline{RS} \cong \overline{PQ}$ symmetric property

4. If $\angle ABC \cong \angle XYZ$ and $\angle XYZ \cong \angle MNO$, then $\angle ABC \cong \angle MNO$ transitive property

5. $\overline{OK} \cong \overline{OK}$ reflexive property

• **For Example 3**

Given $\triangle CAR = \triangle HOP$.

6. Name the corresponding sides.
$\overline{CA} \longleftrightarrow \overline{HO}$; $\overline{AR} \longleftrightarrow \overline{OP}$; $\overline{CR} \longleftrightarrow \overline{HP}$

7. Is it correct to say $\triangle ARC \cong \triangle OPH$?   yes

---

EXAMPLE 1   **Find the length of each segment and tell whether the segments are congruent.**

a. $\overline{BE}$ and $\overline{DH}$ **b.** $\overline{FD}$ and $\overline{CA}$

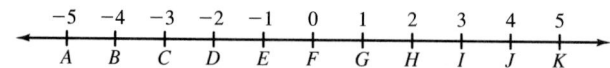

a. $BE = 3$ and $DH = 4$. So $\overline{BE}$ and $\overline{DH}$ are not congruent.

b. $FD = 2$ and $CA = 2$. So $\overline{FD} \cong \overline{CA}$.

The properties for equality will also be true for congruent angles and line segments. For example, the symmetric property for congruent angles would state

"If $\angle A \cong \angle B$, then $\angle B \cong \angle A$."

For congruent line segments, the symmetric property would state

"If $\overline{AB} \cong \overline{CD}$, then $\overline{CD} \cong \overline{AB}$."

EXAMPLE 2   **Name the property of congruence that illustrates each statement.**
   a. If $\angle WXY \cong \angle XYW$, then $\angle XYW \cong \angle WXY$.
   b. $\angle BND \cong \angle BND$
   c. If $\overline{PQ} \cong \overline{QR}$ and $\overline{QR} \cong \overline{ST}$, then $\overline{PQ} \cong \overline{ST}$.

   a. symmetric property   **b.** reflexive property   **c.** transitive property

If two triangles such as $\triangle ABC$ and $\triangle XYZ$ are congruent, you could mentally superimpose one over the other. In congruent triangles there are three types of **corresponding parts.**

Corresponding Vertices
$A \leftrightarrow X$ $B \leftrightarrow Y$ $C \leftrightarrow Z$

Corresponding Angles
$\angle A \leftrightarrow \angle X$ $\angle B \leftrightarrow \angle Y$ $\angle C \leftrightarrow \angle Z$

Corresponding Sides
$\overline{AB} \leftrightarrow \overline{XY}$ $\overline{BC} \leftrightarrow \overline{YZ}$ $\overline{AC} \leftrightarrow \overline{XZ}$

In congruent figures, corresponding parts are named in the same order. So, $\triangle ABC \cong \triangle XYZ$.

EXAMPLE 3 $\triangle RAT \cong \triangle MOP$
   a. Name the corresponding sides.
   b. If $\triangle RAT \cong \triangle MOP$ then is it true that $\triangle ART \cong \triangle OPM$?

624   Chapter 15 Right Triangle Relationships

a. If $\triangle RAT \cong \triangle MOP$, the following vertices correspond:

$R \leftrightarrow M \qquad A \leftrightarrow O \qquad T \leftrightarrow P$

Therefore, the following sides correspond:

$\overline{RA} \leftrightarrow \overline{MO} \qquad \overline{AT} \leftrightarrow \overline{OP} \qquad \overline{TR} \leftrightarrow \overline{PM}$

b. If $\triangle ART \cong \triangle OPM$, then the following vertices correspond:

$A \leftrightarrow O \qquad R \leftrightarrow P \qquad T \leftrightarrow M$

But this is not the same as the correspondence defined by $\triangle RAT \cong \triangle MOP$. So, $\triangle ART$ is not necessarily congruent to $\triangle OPM$.

CLASS EXERCISES

Refer to the number line below. Find the length of each line segment given and tell whether the segments are congruent.

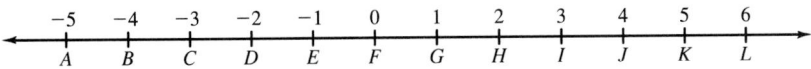

$\begin{array}{cccccccccccc} -5 & -4 & -3 & -2 & -1 & 0 & 1 & 2 & 3 & 4 & 5 & 6 \\ A & B & C & D & E & F & G & H & I & J & K & L \end{array}$

1. $\overline{AE}$ and $\overline{EI}$ 4; 4; congruent **2.** $\overline{DF}$ and $\overline{JL}$ 2; 2; congruent **3.** $\overline{CG}$ and $\overline{EJ}$
4; 5; not congruent

Use the indicated property of equality or congruence to complete each statement.

4. reflexive property: $\overline{AC} \cong \underline{\ \ \overline{AC}\ \ }$

5. symmetric property: If $m\angle G = 90$, then $\underline{\ \ 90\ \ } = m\angle G$.

6. transitive property: If $m\angle K = m\angle M$ and $\underline{\ \ m\angle M\ \ } = m\angle N$, then $m\angle K = m\angle N$.

7. transitive property: If $\overline{XY} \cong \underline{\ \ \overline{ZA}\ \ }$ and $\overline{ZA} \cong \overline{YZ}$, then $\overline{XY} \cong \overline{YZ}$.

8. symmetric property: If $\overline{TP} \cong \overline{AB}$, then $\underline{\ \ \overline{AB}\ \ } \cong \overline{TP}$.

Given $\triangle ABC \cong \triangle TOD$:

9. Name the corresponding vertices.
$A \leftrightarrow T; B \leftrightarrow O; C \leftrightarrow D$
10. Name the corresponding sides.
$\overline{AB} \leftrightarrow \overline{TO}; \overline{BC} \leftrightarrow \overline{OD}; \overline{AC} \leftrightarrow \overline{TD}$
11. Name the corresponding angles.
$\angle A \leftrightarrow \angle T; \angle B \leftrightarrow \angle O; \angle C \leftrightarrow \angle D$

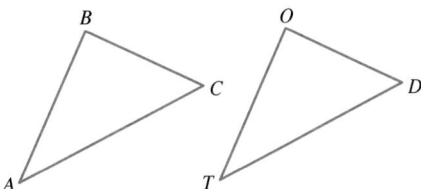

PRACTICE EXERCISES

Refer to the number line below. Find the length of each segment and then tell whether the segments are congruent.

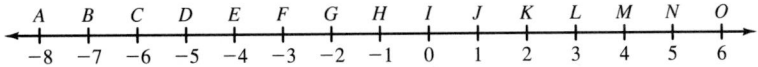

$\begin{array}{ccccccccccccccc} A & B & C & D & E & F & G & H & I & J & K & L & M & N & O \\ -8 & -7 & -6 & -5 & -4 & -3 & -2 & -1 & 0 & 1 & 2 & 3 & 4 & 5 & 6 \end{array}$

A **1.** $\overline{BF}$ and $\overline{KO}$ 4; 4; congruent **2.** $\overline{CH}$ and $\overline{IN}$ 5; 5; congruent **3.** $\overline{EI}$ and $\overline{KM}$
4; 2; not congruent
4. $\overline{AF}$ and $\overline{CE}$ **5.** $\overline{JM}$ and $\overline{DG}$ 3; 3; congruent **6.** $\overline{BE}$ and $\overline{KN}$
5; 2; not congruent 3; 3; congruent

15.3 Congruence   **625**

Common Error

- Students often misidentify corresponding sides. If they have this problem, you might want to show them how to write out the corresponding vertices and then pair each of them together as shown below.

Given $\triangle ABC \cong \triangle DEF$. Write corresponding vertices:

$A \longleftrightarrow D \quad B \longleftrightarrow E \quad C \longleftrightarrow F$

Pair the first and second:

$A \longleftrightarrow D \quad B \longleftrightarrow E \quad C \longleftrightarrow F$

$\overline{AB} \qquad \overline{DE}$

Pair the second and third, and then pair the first and third:

$\overline{BC} \longleftrightarrow \overline{EF}$ and $\overline{AC} \longleftrightarrow \overline{DF}$

- See *Teacher's Resource Book* for additional remediation.

LESSON FOLLOW-UP

Discussion

Is it ever correct to state $\triangle ABC \cong \triangle ACB$? $\triangle ABC \cong \triangle ABC$?   Yes, when $\triangle ABC$ is an isosceles triangle, so that $AB = AC$. Yes it is always correct to state $\triangle ABC \cong \triangle ABC$; by the reflexive property of congruence, every triangle is congruent to itself.

Assignment Guide

See p. 612B for assignments.

Test Yourself

See *Teacher's Resource Book*, Tests, pp. 157–158.

625

For Exercises 1–3 below, name the length of each segment and then tell whether the segments are congruent.

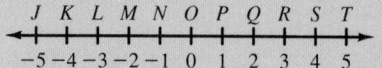

$$\begin{array}{ccccccccccc} J & K & L & M & N & O & P & Q & R & S & T \\ \end{array}$$
$$-5\ -4\ -3\ -2\ -1\ \ 0\ \ 1\ \ 2\ \ 3\ \ 4\ \ 5$$

1. $\overline{LN}$ and $\overline{PS}$ $LN = 2$; $PS = 3$;
not congruent

2. $\overline{LQ}$ and $\overline{OT}$ $LQ = OT = 5$;
congruent

3. $\overline{QT}$ and $\overline{JM}$ $QT = JM = 3$;
congruent

Name the property of congruence that illustrates each statement.

4. If $\angle NOP \cong \angle JKL$ and $\angle JKL \cong \angle PMN$, then $\angle NOP \cong \angle PMN$.
transitive property

5. $\overline{TP} \cong \overline{TP}$.   reflexive property

6. If the complement of $\angle A$ is congruent to $\angle B$, then $\angle B$ is congruent to the complement of $\angle A$.
symmetric property

For Exercises 7–8, $\triangle POT \cong \triangle PAN$.
7. Name the corresponding sides.
$\overline{PO} \longleftrightarrow \overline{PA}$; $\overline{PT} \longleftrightarrow \overline{PN}$; $\overline{OT} \longleftrightarrow \overline{AN}$

8. True or false: $\triangle OPT \cong \triangle ANP$.
false

Enrichment

Three times the measure of the complement of an angle is 60 more than the measure of the supplement of the angle. Find the measure of the angle.
15°

Name the property of equality or congruence that illustrates each statement.

7. $m\angle M = m\angle M$ reflexive

8. If $\angle J \cong \angle K$ and $\angle K \cong \angle L$, then $\angle J \cong \angle L$. transitive

9. If $\overline{AC} \cong \overline{BC}$, then $\overline{BC} \cong \overline{AC}$ symmetric

10. The length of $\overline{UV}$ is equal to itself. reflexive

11. If the complement of $\angle A$ is congruent to $\angle B$ and $\angle B$ is congruent to $\angle C$, then the complement of $\angle A$ is congruent to $\angle C$. transitive

12. If the supplement of $\angle M$ is congruent to $\angle M$, then $\angle M$ is congruent to its supplement. symmetric

B   **For Exercises 13–16, $\triangle TOP \cong \triangle CAR$.**

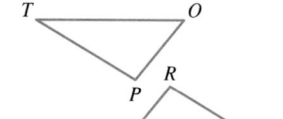

13. Name the corresponding angles.
$\angle T \leftrightarrow \angle C$; $\angle O \leftrightarrow \angle A$; $\angle P \leftrightarrow \angle R$
14. Name the corresponding sides.
$\overline{TO} \leftrightarrow \overline{CA}$; $\overline{OP} \leftrightarrow \overline{AR}$; $\overline{TP} \leftrightarrow \overline{CR}$
15. True or *false*? $\triangle ARC \cong \triangle OPT$
true
16. True or *false*? $\triangle RCA \cong \triangle OTP$
false

For Exercises 17–20, $\triangle PAL \cong \triangle DAN$.

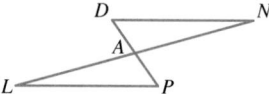

17. Name the corresponding sides.
$\overline{DA} \leftrightarrow \overline{PA}$; $\overline{AL} \leftrightarrow \overline{AN}$; $\overline{PL} \leftrightarrow \overline{DN}$
18. Name the corresponding angles.
$\angle DAN \leftrightarrow \angle PAL$; $\angle N \leftrightarrow \angle L$; $\angle D \leftrightarrow \angle P$
19. True or *false*? $\triangle LAP \cong \triangle AND$
false
20. True or *false*? $\triangle APL \cong \triangle ADN$
true

C   **21.** $RECT$ is a rectangle. $\overline{RC}$ and $\overline{ET}$ are diagonals of the rectangle. Name all triangles you think may be congruent to $\triangle RCT$. $\triangle ETC$; $\triangle CRE$; $\triangle TER$

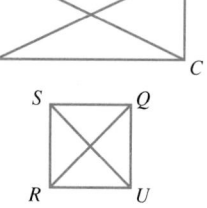

22. $SQUR$ is a square. $\overline{US}$ and $\overline{RQ}$ are diagonals of the square. Name all triangles you think may be congruent to $\triangle RSQ$. $\triangle SQU$; $\triangle QUR$; $\triangle URS$

Applications

23. Construction   A truss for a garage has two congruent sides and a vertical tie rod as shown in the diagram. Name two triangles that you think are congruent and their corresponding sides and angles.

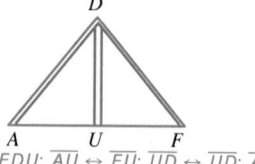

$\triangle AUD \cong \triangle FUD$; $\angle A \leftrightarrow \angle F$; $\angle AUD \leftrightarrow \angle FUD$; $\angle ADU \leftrightarrow \angle FDU$; $\overline{AU} \leftrightarrow \overline{FU}$; $\overline{UD} \leftrightarrow \overline{UD}$; $\overline{AD} \leftrightarrow \overline{FD}$

24. Construction The diagram at the right shows the cross section of a truss for a bridge. The vertical tie rods, ($\overline{TF}$, $\overline{UD}$, $\overline{SG}$), are equal in length and $\overline{BF}$, $\overline{FD}$, $\overline{DG}$, and $\overline{GE}$ are congruent. Name all triangles you think may be congruent.

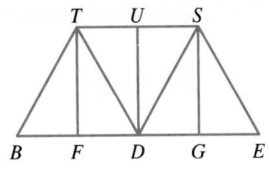

$\triangle BFT \cong \triangle DFT \cong \triangle TUD \cong \triangle SUD \cong \triangle DGS \cong \triangle EGS$; $\triangle BTD \cong \triangle SDT \cong \triangle DSE$

25. Construction A carpenter writes these six congruence statements. Complete correctly the statement about congruent triangles.

$$\angle P \cong \angle Q \qquad \overline{SP} \cong \overline{RQ}$$
$$\angle S \cong \angle R \qquad \overline{PT} \cong \overline{QU}$$
$$\angle T \cong \angle U \qquad \overline{ST} \cong \overline{RU}$$
$$\triangle \underset{PST}{\underline{\quad ? \quad}} \cong \triangle \underset{QRU}{\underline{\quad ? \quad}}$$

TEST YOURSELF

Graph the inequality and tell whether it is a point, a line, a line segment, a ray or none of these. See below.   **15.1**

1. $x \geq -2$ ray

2. $-3 \leq x \leq 0$ line segment   **3.** $x \geq -2$ or $x \leq 0$ line

4. If 10 more than $m\angle T$ is twice its complement, find $m\angle T$. $m\angle T = 56\frac{2}{3}$

5. If the complement of $\angle X$ is $\frac{1}{4}$ its supplement, find the measure of $\angle X$. $m\angle X = 60$

Classify each triangle according to the measures of the angles and according to the lengths of the sides.   **15.2**

6.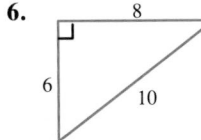

right triangle
scalene triangle

7.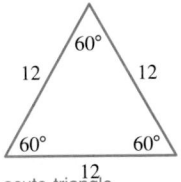

acute triangle
equilateral triangle

8.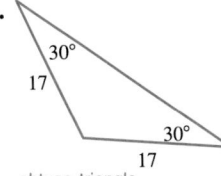

obtuse triangle
isosceles triangle

9. In $\triangle HIJ$, $\overline{HI} \cong \overline{JI}$, $m\angle I = 48$, find $m\angle H$ and $m\angle J$. 66, 66

Given $\triangle DEF \cong \triangle PAT$ **15.3**

10. $\angle D$ corresponds to $\angle P$, true or false? true

11. $\angle T$ corresponds to $\angle E$, true or false? false

12. $\overline{FD}$ corresponds to $\overline{AP}$, true or false? false

13. $\triangle FDE \cong \triangle TPA$, true or false? true

14. If $\angle D \cong \angle E$ and $\angle E \cong \angle A$ then $\angle D \cong \angle A$, true or false? true

15.3 Congruence   **627**

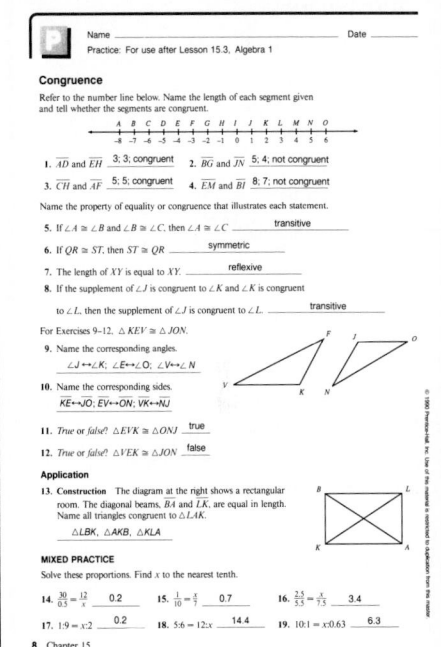
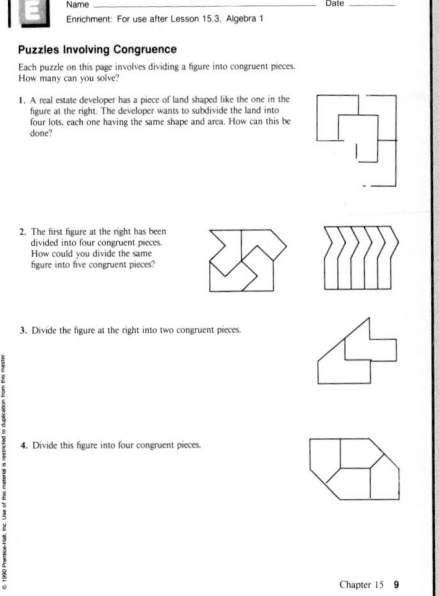
Additional Answers

1.

$-2 \quad 0$

2.

$-3 \quad 0$

3.

$-2 \quad 0$

Vocabulary
Similar triangles

Materials/Manipulatives
Graph paper
Protractor
Straightedge
Overhead projector

BACKGROUND

In the Capsule Review, students solve proportions by using the means and the extremes. Solving proportions is a key factor to success in solving the problems in the lesson.

15.4

Similar Figures

Objectives: To identify similar figures and name the corresponding vertices and sides of similar triangles
To use proportions to solve problems concerning similar triangles

When a photograph is enlarged, each object in the enlargement has the same shape as in the original photograph, but a different size.

The photographs are *similar* and the corresponding dimensions of each object are in proportion.

Capsule Review

A proportion is an equation that states that two ratios are equal. To solve a proportion, you use the fact that the product of the means equals the product of the extremes.

EXAMPLE $3 : x = 5 : 9$ (means / extremes) $\frac{3}{x} = \frac{5}{9}$; $5x = 27$; $x = \frac{27}{5} = 5.4$

Solve these proportions.

1. $\frac{5}{6} = \frac{10}{x}$ 12

2. $\frac{2}{3} = \frac{x}{18}$ 12

3. $\frac{51}{9} = \frac{n}{15}$ 85

4. $\frac{22}{7} = \frac{11}{x}$ $\frac{7}{2}$

5. $3 : 4 = x : 12$ 9

6. $5 : 7 = 15 : x$ 21

7. $21 : 7 = 3 : x$ 1

8. $1 : 6 = x : 3$ $\frac{1}{2}$

Similar figures have the same shape, but not necessarily the same size. Two triangles are **similar** if and only if their corresponding angles are congruent. Corresponding sides of similar triangles are in proportion.

The symbol for "is similar to" is ∼. In the figure, $\triangle ABC \sim \triangle XYZ$. Note that the corresponding vertices are named in the same order, and that the angles are congruent.

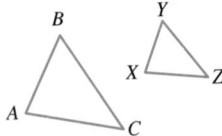

$\angle A \cong \angle X$ $\angle B \cong \angle Y$ $\angle C \cong \angle Z$

Corresponding sides are opposite congruent angles in similar triangles. For $\triangle ABC$ and $\triangle XYZ$ above, the corresponding sides are $\overline{AB}$ and $\overline{XY}$, $\overline{BC}$ and $\overline{YZ}$, and $\overline{AC}$ and $\overline{XZ}$.

628   Chapter 15 Right Triangle Relationships

EXAMPLE 1 **Is it true that $\triangle ABD \sim \triangle VWY$? If so, name the corresponding sides.**

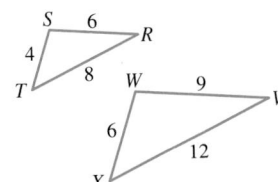

Since the sum of the angles of a triangle is 180°, the missing angle in both $\triangle ABD$ and $\triangle VWY$ is $180 - (35 + 50) = 95$. Therefore, the corresponding angles are congruent,

$\angle A \cong \angle V$, $\angle B \cong \angle W$, and $\angle D \cong \angle Y$

and the triangles are similar. The corresponding sides are $\overline{AB}$ and $\overline{VW}$, $\overline{BD}$ and $\overline{WY}$, and $\overline{AD}$ and $\overline{VY}$.

$\triangle TRS \sim \triangle XVW$, so the lengths of corresponding sides are in the same ratio or proportion.

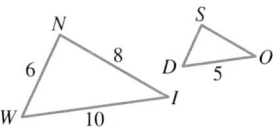

$$\frac{ST}{WX} = \frac{4}{6} = \frac{2}{3}; \frac{SR}{WV} = \frac{6}{9} = \frac{2}{3}; \frac{TR}{XV} = \frac{8}{12} = \frac{2}{3}$$

To find an unknown side using similar triangles, first find a pair of corresponding sides whose lengths are known. Then find the side that corresponds to the unknown side. Solve by writing a proportion.

EXAMPLE 2 **$\triangle WIN \sim \triangle DOS$, $WI = 10$, $IN = 8$, $WN = 6$, and $DO = 5$. Find the lengths of $\overline{DS}$ and $\overline{OS}$.**

Use the lengths of corresponding sides $\overline{WI}$ and $\overline{DO}$ to write a known ratio, $10:5$. Then show that the lengths of corresponding sides are in proportion.

$$\frac{WI}{DO} = \frac{WN}{DS} \qquad \frac{10}{5} = \frac{6}{DS} \qquad \text{and} \qquad \frac{WI}{DO} = \frac{IN}{OS} \qquad \frac{10}{5} = \frac{8}{OS}$$
$$30 = 10(DS) \qquad\qquad\qquad\qquad 40 = 10(OS)$$
$$3 = DS \qquad\qquad\qquad\qquad\quad 4 = OS$$

15.4 Similar Figures **629**

- In this lesson, students are introduced to identifying similar figures and naming the corresponding parts of similar triangles.
- To help students better understand the concept of similarity, you might want to have them use a protractor and a straightedge to construct two triangles of different sizes, but with congruent angles. Then have them measure the corresponding sides and show that they are in proportion. An overhead projector may be useful in demonstrating this procedure.

Critical Thinking

Causal Explanation Explain the meaning that "$\cong$" conveys in the statement $\triangle ABC \cong \triangle XYZ$. Be more explicit than to say "$\cong$" means "congruent." $\triangle ABC \cong \triangle XYZ$ means two triangles are the same shape ($\sim$) *and* the same size ($=$).

630

CHALKBOARD EXAMPLES

- **For Example 1**
  1. Is △RKO similar to △WHY? If so, name the corresponding sides.

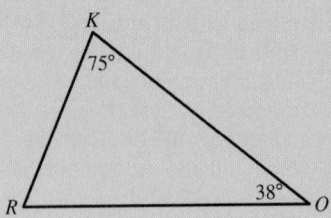

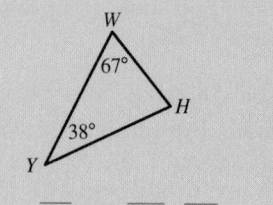

  yes; $\overline{RK} \longleftrightarrow \overline{WH}$; $\overline{KO} \longleftrightarrow \overline{HY}$; $\overline{RO} \longleftrightarrow \overline{WY}$

- **For Example 2**
  2. Given that △CAT ~ △DOG, CA = 18, CT = 9, AT = 24, and DO = 6, find OG and DG.
  OG = 8; DG = 3

  3. Given that △ROB ~ △JAT, RO = 48, RB = 60, OB = 30, and JT = 6, find AT and AJ.
  AT = 3; AJ = 4.8

LESSON FOLLOW-UP

Discussion

Are congruent triangles similar? Yes; congruent triangles have congruent angles, so the triangles are similar.

Assignment Guide

See p. 612B for assignments.

Extra

Have students work in pairs or groups to discuss the information given in the problem, and then solve.

630

CLASS EXERCISES

For Exercises 1–7, △GFE ~ △MNO.

1. Name the corresponding angles
∠G → ∠M; ∠F → ∠N; ∠E → ∠O

2. Name the corresponding sides.
$\overline{GF}$ → $\overline{MN}$; $\overline{FE}$ → $\overline{NO}$; $\overline{GE}$ → $\overline{MO}$

3. *True* or *false*? △FGE ~ △MNO.
false

4. *True* or *false*? △EGF ~ △OMN.
true

5. Complete the proportion: $\frac{FE}{NO} = \frac{FG}{?}$ NM

Write a proportion involving the following lengths.

6. *EG* and *MN*. $\frac{EG}{OM} = \frac{GF}{MN}$

7. *NO* and *GF*. $\frac{NO}{FE} = \frac{GF}{MN}$

Tell whether the triangles are similar, not similar, or not possible to determine.

8.

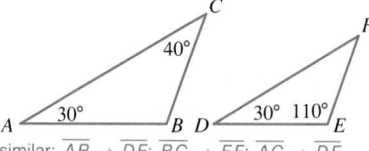

similar

9.

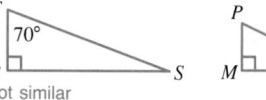
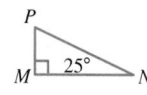

similar

10. Two isosceles triangles, each with one of their angles equal to 20°.
not possible to determine

11. Two right triangles, each with a 30° angle. similar

PRACTICE EXERCISES

Tell whether or not the triangles are similar. If similar, name the corresponding sides.

A 1.

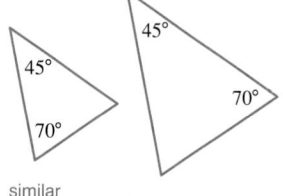

similar; $\overline{AB}$ → $\overline{DE}$; $\overline{BC}$ → $\overline{EF}$; $\overline{AC}$ → $\overline{DF}$

2.

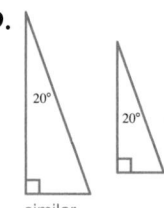

not similar

3.

similar; $\overline{EQ}$ → $\overline{ED}$; $\overline{EP}$ → $\overline{EL}$; $\overline{PQ}$ → $\overline{LD}$

4.

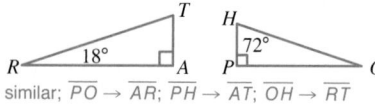

similar; $\overline{PO}$ → $\overline{AR}$; $\overline{PH}$ → $\overline{AT}$; $\overline{OH}$ → $\overline{RT}$

If △ABC ~ △XYZ, find the lengths of the two missing sides.

5. $AB = 4$, $BC = 7$; $AC = 5$; $XY = 8$ $YZ = 14$; $XZ = 10$

6. $AB = 18$; $BC = 36$; $AC = 21$; $XY = 6$ $YZ = 12$; $XZ = 7$

7. $XY = 4$, $YZ = 8$; $XZ = 10$; $AC = 7.5$ $AB = 3$; $BC = 6$

8. $XY = 3$, $YZ = 2.5$, $XZ = 4$; $BC = 7.5$ $AB = 9$; $AC = 12$

In Exercises 9–12, △DEF ~ △MNO. Find the lengths of the two missing sides.

9. $DE = 7$, $EF = 4$; $MO = 18$; $NO = 12$. $MN = 21$; $DF = 6$

10. $EF = 18$, $DF = 54$; $MN = 45$; $NO = 15$. $DE = 54$; $MO = 45$

11. $DF = 4$, $DE = 2.4$; $NO = 5$; $MN = 6$. $MO = 10$; $EF = 2$

12. $MO = 3.6$, $MN = 7.2$, $EF = 8$; $DE = 12$. $NO = 4.8$; $DF = 6$

For Exercises 13–16, △BAC ~ △PAR. Find the lengths of the missing sides.

B

13. $AB = 12$, $BC = 21$, $AC = 15$, and $AP = 20$. Find PR and AR
$PR = 35$; $AR = 25$

14. $AP = 30$, $PR = 50$, $AR = 40$, and $AB = 20$. Find BC and AC.
$BC = 33\frac{1}{3}$; $AC = 26\frac{2}{3}$

15. $AC = 8$, $AP = 16$, $BC = 12$, and $AR = 20$. Find AB and PR.
$AB = 6.4$; $PR = 30$

16. $AB = 28$, $AR = 63$, $BC = 54$, and $PR = 81$. Find AC and AP.
$AP = 42$; $AC = 42$

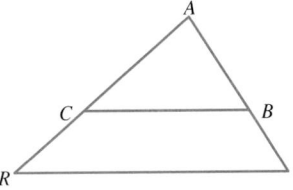

For Exercises 17–18, △JAR ~ △TOP. Find the lengths of the missing sides if the triangles are isosceles: ($JA = AR$ and $TO = OP$)

17. $JR = 3.6$, $OP = 5.6$, $\dfrac{JA}{TO} = \dfrac{3}{4}$
$AR = AJ = 4.2$; $TP = 4.8$

18. $TP = 11$, $AR = 33$, $\dfrac{JA}{TO} = \dfrac{3}{22}$
$OP = TO = 242$; $JR = 1.5$

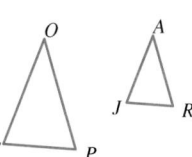

Find x. Assume that each figure shows a pair of similar triangles.

C

19.

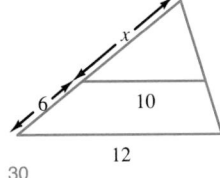

20.

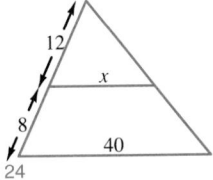

15.4 Similar Figures **631**

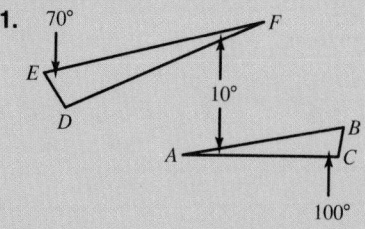
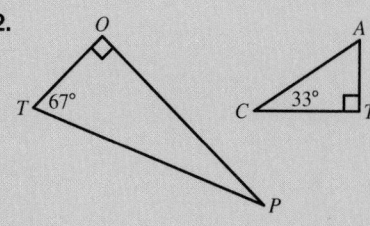
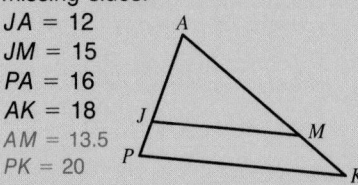
631

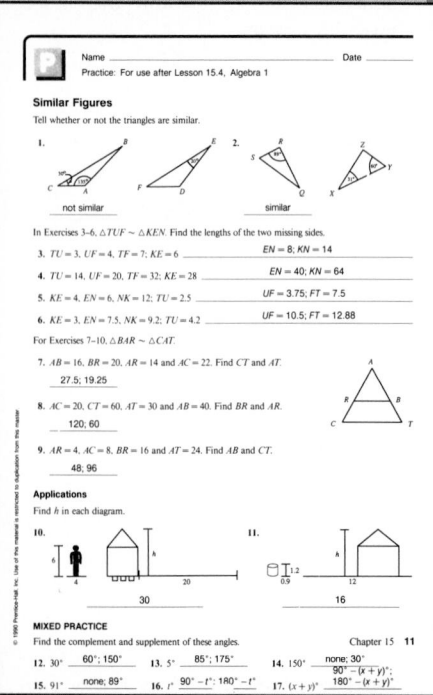

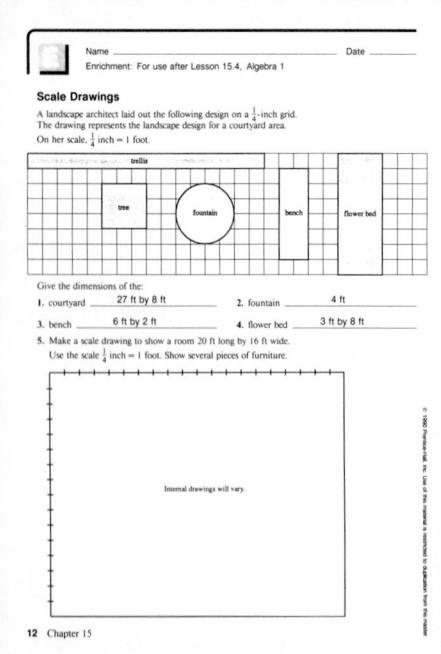

21.

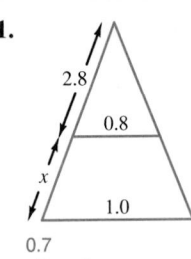

2.8

0.8

x

0.7

1.0

22.

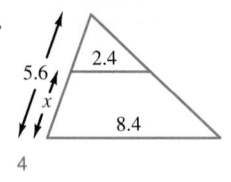

5.6

2.4

x

8.4

4

Applications

Surveying Find *h*. Assume the triangles in each exercise are similar.

23.

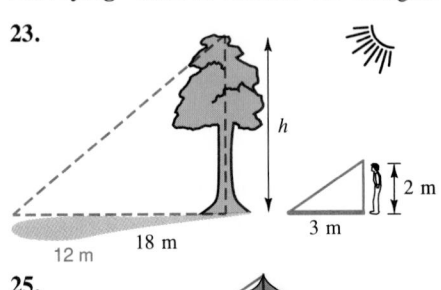

h

2 m

12 m   18 m   3 m

24.

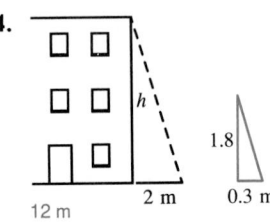

h

1.8

12 m   2 m   0.3 m

25.

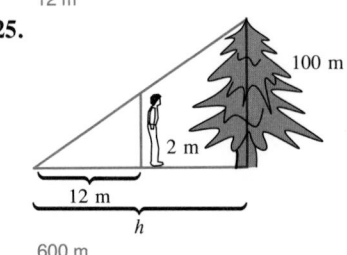

100 m

2 m

12 m

h

600 m

26.

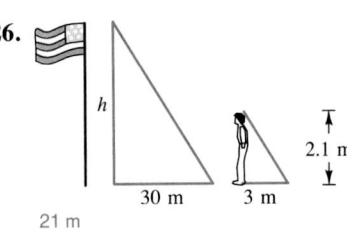

h

2.1 m

30 m   3 m

21 m

27. Gardening A triangular flower garden in a park has a sidewalk around it. The sides of the triangle around the outside of the sidewalk are 60 ft, 45 ft, and 20 ft. The smallest side of the garden is 14.5 ft long. How much will it cost to put a fence around the garden if the fencing costs $15.00 per yard? $453.13

EXTRA

Barry has a summer job as a carpenter's helper at Kid World, a local amusement park. The work crew is building picnic shelters. Barry's job is to cut rafters so that the ends make a vertical join at the peak of the shelter. What size angle will he measure before cutting? *Hint:* If two rafters are joined vertically, the angle formed between them is 90°. 90°

632   Chapter 15 Right Triangle Relationships

Trigonometric Ratios

Objective: To identify and compute the sine, cosine, and tangent
ratios in any right triangle

The word **trigonometry** is based on Greek words that mean "triangle
measurement." In similar triangles, ratios of corresponding sides are equal.
In trigonometry, some of these ratios are given special names when the
triangles are right triangles. In such triangles the measures of the acute angles
are related to the ratios of the lengths of the sides.

Capsule Review

A ratio with a radical in the denominator can be changed to simplest form by
rationalizing the denominator.

EXAMPLE Write $\dfrac{2}{\sqrt{3}}$ in simplest form with a rational denominator.

$$\frac{2}{\sqrt{3}} = \frac{2}{\sqrt{3}} \cdot \frac{\sqrt{3}}{\sqrt{3}} = \frac{2\sqrt{3}}{3}$$

Write each ratio in simplest form with a rational denominator.

1. $\dfrac{1}{\sqrt{5}}$ $\frac{\sqrt{5}}{5}$

2. $\dfrac{3}{\sqrt{2}}$ $\frac{3\sqrt{2}}{2}$

3. $\dfrac{1}{3\sqrt{2}}$ $\frac{\sqrt{2}}{6}$

4. $\dfrac{5}{\sqrt{10}}$ $\frac{\sqrt{10}}{2}$

5. $\dfrac{\sqrt{3}}{\sqrt{6}}$ $\frac{\sqrt{2}}{2}$

6. $\dfrac{\sqrt{2}}{\sqrt{5}}$ $\frac{\sqrt{10}}{5}$

7. $\dfrac{\sqrt{3}}{\sqrt{50}}$ $\frac{\sqrt{6}}{10}$

8. $\dfrac{\sqrt{7}}{\sqrt{21}}$ $\frac{\sqrt{3}}{3}$

Recall that in right triangle ABC, the side
opposite the right angle $\angle C$, is called the
hypotenuse and is labeled c. The other two
sides are called *legs*. Notice that a is the leg
opposite $\angle A$, and b is opposite $\angle B$. You can
also say that b is *adjacent to* $\angle A$ and a is
adjacent to $\angle B$.

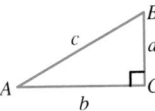

For any right triangle, there are three **trigonometric ratios** of the lengths of
its sides.

LESSON PLAN

Vocabulary
Cosine
Sine
Tangent
Trigonometric ratios
Trigonometry

Materials/Manipulatives
Calculators
Teacher's Resource Book,
  Teaching Aid 18,
  Transparency 33

BACKGROUND

In the Capsule Review, students review rationalizing denominators of
fractions. In the lesson which follows,
students will need to use this procedure after they have applied the Pythagorean theorem to find the length
of a side of a right triangle.

Critical Thinking

Discovering Relationships Use a
dictionary and the definition of the
functions to explain the relation between the sine and cosine. Cosine
comes from the New Latin *co sinus,* which
is an abbreviation of *complimenti sinus,*
meaning "the sine of the compliment of an
angle." In right triangle ABC with right
angle at C, the definitions of sine and co-
sine tell us that $\frac{b}{c}$ is the cosine of $\angle A$, and
also, the sine of $\angle B$. Thus, sine and co-
sine are cofunctions of complementary
angles.

CHALKBOARD EXAMPLES

- **For Example 1**

  1. For right $\triangle MNP$, $m\angle N = 90$, find $\sin M$, $\cos M$, $\tan M$, $\sin P$, $\cos P$, and $\tan P$.

  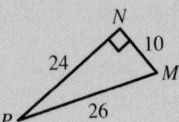

  $\sin M = \frac{12}{13}$, $\sin P = \frac{5}{13}$, $\cos M =$
  $\frac{5}{13}$, $\cos P = \frac{12}{13}$, $\tan M = \frac{12}{5}$,
  $\tan P = \frac{5}{12}$

- **For Example 2**

  2. For right $\triangle QRS$, $QR = 6$, $QS = 8$, and $m\angle R = 90$. Use the Pythagorean theorem to find RS. Then, find $\sin Q$, $\cos Q$, and $\tan Q$.

  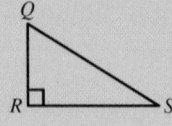

  $RS = 2\sqrt{7}$, $\sin Q = \frac{\sqrt{7}}{4}$, $\cos Q = \frac{3}{4}$, $\tan Q = \frac{\sqrt{7}}{3}$

The trigonometric ratios for right triangle ABC with acute angles A and B and right angle C:

$$\textbf{sine of } \angle A = \frac{\text{length of leg opposite } \angle A}{\text{length of hypotenuse}}; \ \sin A = \frac{a}{c}$$

$$\textbf{cosine of } \angle A = \frac{\text{length of leg of adjacent } \angle A}{\text{length of hypotenuse}}; \ \cos A = \frac{b}{c}$$

$$\textbf{tangent of } \angle A = \frac{\text{length of leg opposite } \angle A}{\text{length of leg adjacent } \angle A}; \ \tan A = \frac{a}{b}$$

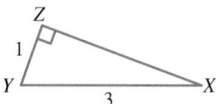

EXAMPLE 1 **For $\triangle ABC$, $m\angle C = 90$. Find $\sin A$, $\cos A$, $\tan A$, $\sin B$, $\cos B$, and $\tan B$.**

$$\sin A = \frac{6}{10} = \frac{3}{5} \qquad \sin B = \frac{8}{10} = \frac{4}{5}$$

$$\cos A = \frac{8}{10} = \frac{4}{5} \qquad \cos B = \frac{6}{10} = \frac{3}{5}$$

$$\tan A = \frac{6}{8} = \frac{3}{4} \qquad \tan B = \frac{8}{6} = \frac{4}{3}$$

EXAMPLE 2 **In $\triangle XYZ$, $YX = 3$, $YZ = 1$, and $m\angle Z = 90$. Use the Pythagorean theorem to find XZ. Then find the sine, cosine, and tangent of $\angle X$.**

$$YX^2 = YZ^2 + XZ^2$$
$$3^2 = 1^2 + XZ^2$$
$$9 = 1 + XZ^2$$
$$8 = XZ^2$$
$$2\sqrt{2} = XZ$$

Therefore, $\sin X = \frac{1}{3}$; $\cos X = \frac{2\sqrt{2}}{3}$; $\tan X = \frac{1}{2\sqrt{2}} = \frac{1 \cdot \sqrt{2}}{2\sqrt{2} \cdot \sqrt{2}} = \frac{\sqrt{2}}{4}$.

CLASS EXERCISES

Find the value of each trigonometric ratio. Express radicals in simplest form.

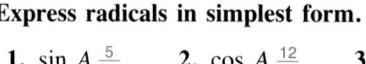

1. $\sin A \ \frac{5}{13}$ 2. $\cos A \ \frac{12}{13}$ 3. $\tan A \ \frac{5}{12}$
4. $\sin B \ \frac{12}{13}$ 5. $\cos B \ \frac{5}{13}$ 6. $\tan B \ \frac{12}{5}$

7. $\sin M \ \frac{\sqrt{5}}{5}$ 8. $\cos M \ \frac{2\sqrt{5}}{5}$ 9. $\tan M \ \frac{1}{2}$
10. $\sin N \ \frac{2\sqrt{5}}{5}$ 11. $\cos N \ \frac{\sqrt{5}}{5}$ 12. $\tan N \ 2$

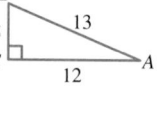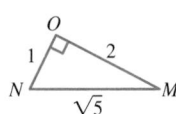

Additional Answers · Practice Exercises

7. $\sin A = \frac{5}{13}$ $\sin B = \frac{12}{13}$ $\cos A = \frac{12}{13}$ $\cos B = \frac{5}{13}$ $\tan A = \frac{5}{12}$ $\tan B = \frac{12}{5}$

8. $\sin A = \frac{24}{25}$ $\sin B = \frac{7}{25}$ $\cos A = \frac{7}{25}$ $\cos B = \frac{24}{25}$ $\tan A = \frac{24}{7}$ $\tan B = \frac{7}{24}$

9. $\sin A = \frac{12}{37}$ $\sin B = \frac{35}{37}$ $\cos A = \frac{35}{37}$ $\cos B = \frac{12}{37}$ $\tan A = \frac{12}{35}$ $\tan A = \frac{35}{12}$

PRACTICE EXERCISES

Find the value of each trigonometric ratio.

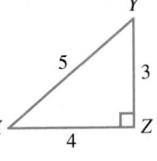

A
1. $\sin X$ $\frac{3}{5}$ **2.** $\cos X$ $\frac{4}{5}$ **3.** $\tan X$ $\frac{3}{4}$

4. $\sin Y$ $\frac{4}{5}$ **5.** $\cos Y$ $\frac{3}{5}$ **6.** $\tan Y$ $\frac{4}{3}$

Find the values for the sine, cosine, and tangent of $\angle A$ and $\angle B$.

See below pp. 634–635.

7. 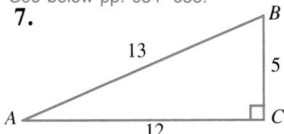 **8.** 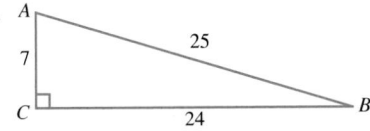 **9.**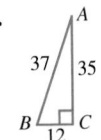

10. 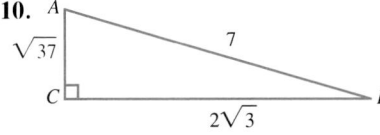 **11.** 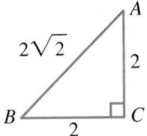 **12.**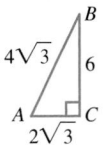

Use the Pythagorean Theorem to find the length of the missing side. Then find the sine, cosine, and tangent of $\angle Q$ and $\angle T$.

See Additional Answer section beginning p. 719.

B
13. 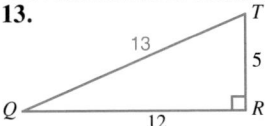 **14.** 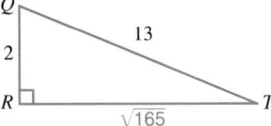 **15.**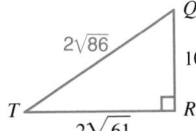

16. 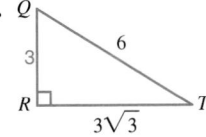 **17.** 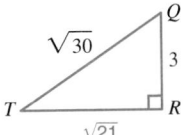 **18.**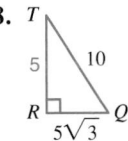

$\triangle JKL$ is a right triangle with $m\angle L = 90$. Show that each of the following is true.

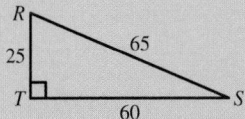

C
19. $\cos J = \sin K$ $\frac{k}{l} = \frac{k}{l}$ **20.** $\cos K = \sin J$ $\frac{j}{l} = \frac{j}{l}$

21. $(\sin J)^2 + (\cos J)^2 = 1$ **22.** $\tan K = \frac{\sin K}{\cos K}$

21. $(\sin J)^2 + (\cos J)^2 = \left(\frac{j}{l}\right)^2 + \left(\frac{k}{l}\right)^2 = \frac{j^2 + k^2}{l^2} = \frac{l^2}{l^2} = 1$ **22.** $\frac{\sin K}{\cos K} = \frac{\frac{k}{l}}{\frac{j}{l}} = \frac{k}{j} = \tan K$

15.5 Trigonometric Ratios   **635**

10. $\sin A = \frac{2\sqrt{3}}{7}$ $\sin B = \frac{\sqrt{37}}{7}$ $\cos A = \frac{\sqrt{37}}{7}$ $\cos B = \frac{2\sqrt{3}}{7}$ $\tan A = \frac{2\sqrt{111}}{37}$

$\tan B = \frac{\sqrt{111}}{6}$

11. $\sin A = \frac{\sqrt{2}}{2}$ $\sin B = \frac{\sqrt{2}}{2}$ $\cos A = \frac{\sqrt{2}}{2}$ $\cos B = \frac{\sqrt{2}}{2}$ $\tan A = 1$ $\tan B = 1$

12. $\sin A = \frac{\sqrt{3}}{2}$ $\sin B = \frac{1}{2}$ $\cos A = \frac{1}{2}$ $\cos B = \frac{\sqrt{3}}{2}$ $\tan A = \sqrt{3}$ $\tan B = \frac{\sqrt{3}}{3}$

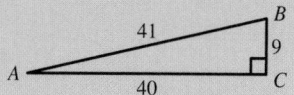

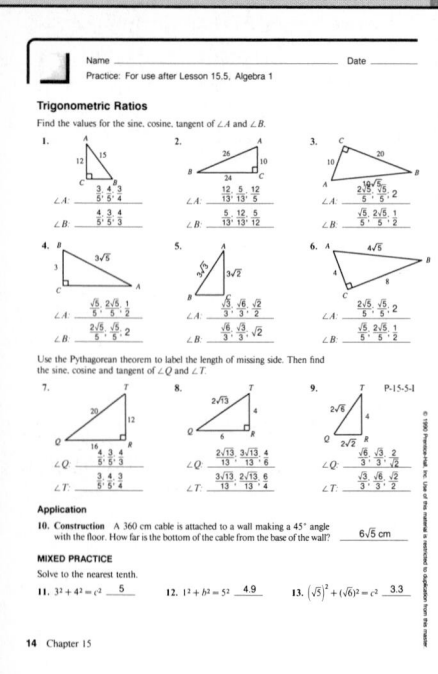

Evaluate each expression, use the table on page 671.

23. $\dfrac{\sin 30° + \cos 60°}{\sin 60° + \cos 30°}$ 0.5774

24. $\dfrac{2 \times \sin 15°}{2 \times \cos 15°}$ 0.2680

25. $\dfrac{1 - \sin 45°}{1 + \tan 45°}$ 0.1465

26. $\dfrac{\tan 60° - \tan 30°}{\tan 45°}$ 1.1547

27. $\dfrac{(\sin 75°)^2 + (\cos 75°)^2}{1 - (\tan 35°)^2}$ 1.9617

28. $\dfrac{\tan 30° - \cos 60° + \sin 45°}{\tan 45° + \cos 30° - \sin 60°}$ 0.7845

Applications

29. **Navigation** A submarine travels 36 miles diving at an angle of 32°. Which ratio would be used to find out how deep the submarine is? tangent

30. **Geometry** A rectangle has a length of 8 m and a width of 6 m. Find the length of the diagonal. What is the sine, cosine, and tangent for the angle formed by the diagonal and the length? $\sin x = \frac{3}{5}$; $\cos x = \frac{4}{5}$; $\tan x = \frac{3}{4}$

31. **Navigation** A boat sails 15 mi east, then 10 mi north. Find the distance from the boat to its starting point. Which trigonometric ratio is used to find the angle of the boat's straight-line course? tangent

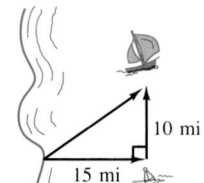

32. **Architecture** A 35-ft roof slopes at an angle 35° to the floor. Which trigonometric ratio would be used to find the width of the floor? cosine

EXTRA

Making a Tent
Celia has a large rectangular piece of tent cloth 5 m long. She wants to build a tent with a front and back opening in the shape of a triangle and with sides of equal length. So that she can stand comfortably in the tent, she decides to have a height of 1.7 m. Celia needs enough floor space to place two sleeping bags side by side with a walkway between them around the poles. Is this possible? no

Rule of Thumb
Hold your thumb vertically, at arm's length. You now have a tool for estimating the height of most buildings. You are missing one fact. What is it?
distance from the building

636   Chapter 15 Right Triangle Relationships

APPLICATION:
Networks

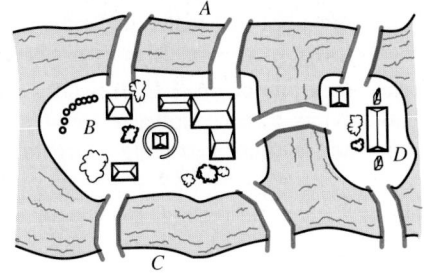

Did you know that geometry has been applied to problems in designing telephone and communications systems, transportation connections, and linking computer stations? These design problems often can be represented by a *network*. A **network** consists of a set of vertices and the connecting paths between them.

One of the most famous network problems occurred in the sixteenth century in Königsberg, Prussia. The town was on two islands in the middle of a river. The town was connected by seven bridges which crossed the river as shown in the sketch. The question was whether a person could plan a walk, starting anywhere, so that all seven bridges could be crossed without crossing the same bridge twice.

Leonhard Euler (pronounced *OY luhr*), a Swiss mathematician, first studied this problem in 1735. Here is Euler's approach to the problem:

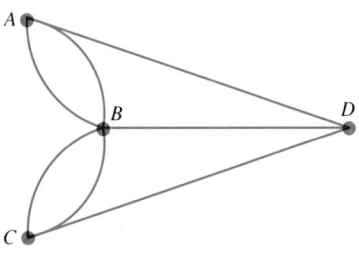

Euler began by redrawing the map so that the four areas of land were represented by four points A, B, C, and D. He then connected the four points with seven lines to represent the bridges. The Königsberg problem can now be restated as follows: Given four distinct vertices, try to draw a continuous path from one vertex to another, without retracing a previously drawn path.

Euler discovered that such a network can only be drawn if one of two conditions are true:

1. There are exactly 2 vertices with an odd number of paths leading from them.

2. All vertices have an even number of paths leading from them.

Application

These problems on *networks* afford the students the opportunity to review basic geometric figures. They learn how geometry and algebra are integrated into many real-world situations.

See *Teacher's Resource Book,* Follow-up Application, p. 21.

Since vertex *B* has 5 paths, and vertices *A*, *C*, and *D* all have three paths, it is impossible to cross each bridge only once.

Trace each one of these figures on a separate piece of paper. Then try to draw a copy of each figure without picking your pencil up from the paper and without retracing a previously drawn path.

Check students' graphs. Exercise 4 cannot be done.

1.

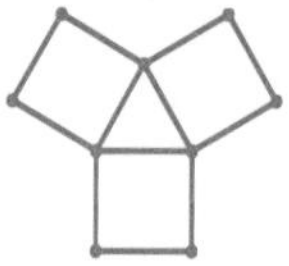

2.

3.

4.

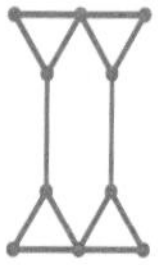

5.

6.

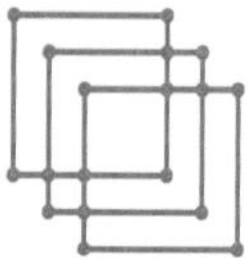

A set of problems similar to the Königsberg Bridge problem concerns closed geometric figures. The object is to cross each segment of the figure exactly once without picking the pencil up from the paper. Copy each figure on a separate piece of paper. Then draw a continuous path through each segment. Keep track of the following information:

> **The number of segments in the figure or figures.**
> **Starting on the outside, does the path end on the inside or outside?**
> **Starting on the inside, does the path end on the inside or outside?**

Check students' work.

7.

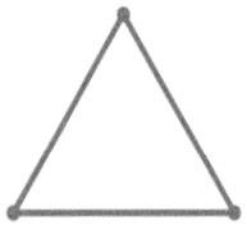

inside

8.

outside

9.

outside

10.

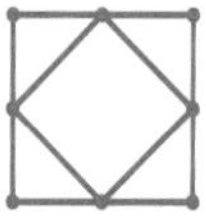

not possible

11.

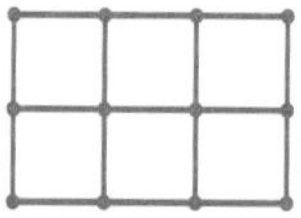

outside

12.

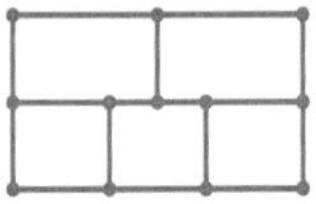

not possible

13. Using the problem solving strategies studied in this book, develop a set of rules concerning the figures that can be solved in Exercises 7–12.
Answers may vary.

14. Research network problems further and investigate a branch of mathematics known as topology. Check students' work.

Using Trigonometric Ratios

15.6

Objective: To use a trigonometric table to find the lengths of sides and the measures of angles of a right triangle

When architects design access ramps, the angle of inclination must be small enough to allow easy access. If a ramp rises 5 ft vertically over a horizontal distance of 100 ft, the architect can use a trigonometric table to determine the angle of inclination.

Capsule Review

In right triangle ABC, $m\angle C = 90$.

$\sin A = \dfrac{a}{c}$, $\cos A = \dfrac{b}{c}$, and $\tan A = \dfrac{a}{b}$.

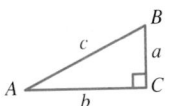

For right triangle ABC, use the Pythagorean theorem to find the length of the missing side. Then find the sine, cosine, and tangent of $\angle A$ and $\angle B$.

1. $a = 4, b = 3$ **2.** $b = 2, c = 3$ **3.** $a = 2\sqrt{5}, b = 2\sqrt{6}$

$5; \dfrac{4}{5}, \dfrac{3}{5}, \dfrac{4}{3}, \dfrac{3}{5}, \dfrac{4}{5}, \dfrac{3}{4}$ $\sqrt{5}; \dfrac{\sqrt{5}}{3}, \dfrac{2}{3}, \dfrac{\sqrt{5}}{2}, \dfrac{2}{3}, \dfrac{\sqrt{5}}{3}, \dfrac{2\sqrt{5}}{5}$ $2\sqrt{11}; \dfrac{\sqrt{55}}{11}, \dfrac{\sqrt{66}}{11}, \dfrac{\sqrt{30}}{6}, \dfrac{\sqrt{66}}{11}, \dfrac{\sqrt{55}}{11}, \dfrac{\sqrt{30}}{5}$

The three right triangles shown are similar. If the measures of angles A, D and G are equal to $60°$ then the sine of $60°$ will be the same since the ratios of the length of the corresponding sides are equal.

$\triangle ABC$	$\triangle DEF$	$\triangle GHI$
$\dfrac{\sqrt{3}}{2}$	$\dfrac{2\sqrt{3}}{4} = \dfrac{\sqrt{3}}{2}$	$\dfrac{3\sqrt{3}}{6} = \dfrac{\sqrt{3}}{2}$

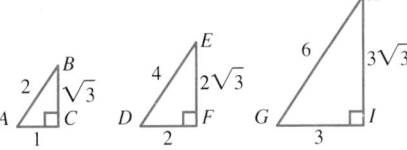

The equivalent of $\dfrac{\sqrt{3}}{2}$ is approximately 0.8660, so $\sin 60° = 0.8660$.

Trigonometric tables have been developed for angles from $0°$ to $90°$. Most values listed are approximations. For convenience, you can use $=$ when you write a trigonometric ratio. The following is a portion of the table found on page 671.

Angle	sin	cos	tan
58°	0.8480	0.5299	1.6003
59°	0.8572	0.5150	1.6643
60°	0.8660	0.5000	1.7321

LESSON PLAN

Materials/Manipulatives
Calculators
Trigonometric table
Teacher's Resource Book, Teaching Aid 18

BACKGROUND

In the Capsule Review, students review finding the length of the missing side of a triangle using the Pythagorean theorem, and then finding the appropriate values of trigonometric ratios. You may want to review the procedure for rationalizing denominators before introducing this lesson.

- Show students how to use a trigo-nometric table to find the decimal approximation for the sine, cosine, and tangent of an angle. Using several examples illustrate how to find the missing sides of a triangle using trigonometric ratios and re-ferring to the table.
- Have students use a calculator with trigonometric functions to find decimal approximations. Some students may need help in finding the inverse function when finding the measure of an angle whose trigonometric ratio is known.

CHALKBOARD EXAMPLES

- **For Example 1**
  1. Find sin 43° 0.6820
  2. Find cos 72° 0.3090

- **For Example 2**
  3. Find m∠x if cos x = 0.9272.
     22
  4. Find m∠A if sin A = 0.7880.
     52

- **For Example 3**
  5. In the right △GEM, m∠E = 90, GE = 42, and m∠M = 34. Find EM and GM to the nearest whole number.
     EM = 75; GM = 62

- **For Example 4**
  6. In right △GRD, m∠D = 90, GR = 52, and RD = 12. Find m∠G and m∠R. m∠G = 13; m∠R = 77

Critical Thinking

Observation How are Examples 3 and 4 of this lesson alike? Different?
In both, trigonometric ratios are used to solve for the measures of the missing parts. Example 3 gives the measure of an angle, and its trigonometric ratios are de-termined from the table. Example 4 re-verses the process.

To find a trigonometric ratio of an angle, first find the angle in the left-hand column. Then look across the row until you are under the column with the appropriate heading. When using a calculator, enter the degree measurement and press either the sine, cosine or tangent key.

EXAMPLE 1   **Find cos 62°.**

cos 62° = 0.4695

Angle	sin	cos	tan
61°	0.8746	0.4848	1.8040
62°	0.8829	0.4695	1.8807
63°	0.8910	0.4550	1.9626

To find an angle when given its trigonometric ratio, first find the column headed with the trigonometric ratio. Then look down the column until you find the closest decimal. On some calculators you can find the angle by entering the decimal and pressing the $\sin^{-1}$, $\cos^{-1}$, or $\tan^{-1}$ key.

EXAMPLE 2   **Find the measure of ∠x if sin x = 0.8572.**

x = 59°

Angle	sin	cos	tan
58°	0.8480	0.5299	1.6003
59°	0.8572	0.5150	1.6643
60°	0.8660	0.5000	1.7321

When you know one acute angle and one side in a right triangle, you can use a trigonometric table to find the other two sides.

EXAMPLE 3   **In right triangle JET, m∠E = 90, JE = 28, and m∠J = 78. Find TE and JT to the nearest whole number.**

$$\tan 78° = \frac{TE}{28} \qquad \cos 78° = \frac{28}{JT}$$

$$4.7046 = \frac{TE}{28} \qquad 0.2079 = \frac{28}{JT}$$

$$TE = 4.7046(28) \qquad JT = \frac{28}{0.2079}$$

$$TE = 131.7288 \qquad JT = 134.6801$$

$$TE ≈ 132. \qquad JT ≈ 135.$$

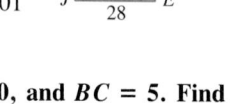

EXAMPLE 4   **In right triangle ABC, m∠C = 90, AC = 100, and BC = 5. Find m∠A and m∠B to the nearest whole number.**

$$\tan A = \frac{5}{100} = 0.05$$

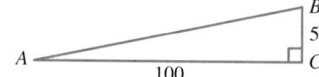

By referring to the trigonometric table, you find that m∠A = 3, to the nearest whole number. So, m∠B = 90 − 3 = 87.

CLASS EXERCISES

Use the table on page 671 to find the value of each trigonometric ratio.

1. cos 45° 0.7071 **2.** sin 15° 0.2588 **3.** tan 30° 0.5774 **4.** cos 53° 0.6018

5. sin 41° 0.6561 **6.** tan 17° 0.3057 **7.** sin 81° 0.9877 **8.** cos 71° 0.3256

Find the measure of ∠x.

9. cos x = 0.5000 60° **10.** sin x = 0.7071 45° **11.** tan x = 0.4663 25°

12. sin x = 0.9336 69° **13.** tan x = 1.8807 62° **14.** cos x = 0.8387 33°

Tell which trigonometric ratio you would use to find x.

15.

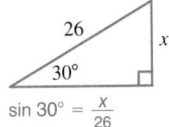

$$\sin 30° = \frac{x}{26}$$

16.

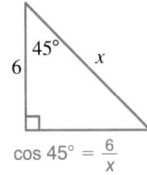

$$\cos 45° = \frac{6}{x}$$

17.

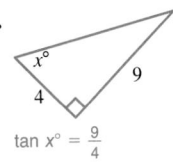

$$\tan x° = \frac{9}{4}$$

PRACTICE EXERCISES

Use the table on page 671 to find the values of each.

A **1.** cos 5° 0.9962 **2.** sin 23° 0.3907 **3.** tan 57° 1.5399 **4.** tan 16° 0.2867

5. sin 73° 0.9563 **6.** cos 82° 0.1392 **7.** cos 66° 0.4067 **8.** sin 2° 0.0349

9. tan 88° 28.6363 **10.** tan 65° 2.1445 **11.** sin 55° 0.8192 **12.** cos 43° 0.7314

Find the measure of ∠x to the nearest degree.

13. cos x = 0.8660 30° **14.** sin x = 0.3420 20° **15.** tan x = 1.000 45°

16. tan x = 3.7321 75° **17.** sin x = 0.8192 55° **18.** cos x = 0.2924 73°

19. cos x = 0.9511 18° **20.** sin x = 0.6561 41° **21.** tan x = 0.0349 2°

Refer to △ABC with m∠C = 90. Find the measures of the other sides to the nearest whole number.

B **22.** m∠A = 40, BC = 5   **23.** m∠A = 32, AB = 42
AC = 6, AB = 8   BC = 22, AC = 36
24. m∠B = 71, AC = 17   **25.** m∠B = 5, BC = 50
AB = 18, BC = 6   AB = 50, AC = 4

Refer to right △XYZ, with m∠Y = 90. Find the measures of the other sides to the nearest whole number.

26. m∠X = 50, XY = 50   **27.** m∠X = 22, YZ = 32
XZ = 78; YZ = 60   XY = 79; XZ = 85
28. m∠Z = 71, XZ = 34   **29.** m∠Z = 14, XY = 15
XY = 32; YZ = 11   XZ = 62; YZ = 60

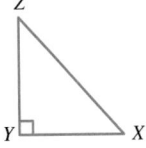

15.6 Using Trigonometric Ratios **641**

Common Error

- Students make errors in finding the trigonometric ratio of an angle. Review all the trigonometric ratios with the students. Encourage them to draw an accurate drawing of the problem and label all the given information.
- See *Teacher's Resource Book* for additional remediation.

LESSON FOLLOW-UP

Discussion

The ratios in the trigonometric tables are approximations. Are any ratios exact? yes: sin 30°, cos 60°, and tan 45° and the given ratios for 0° and 90°.

Assignment Guide

See p. 612B for assignments.

Lesson Quiz

Use the table on p. 671 to find the values of each.
  1. cos 36° 0.8090 **2.** sin 72° 0.9511
  3. tan 49° 1.150 **4.** tan 22° 0.4040
  5. cos 85° 0.0872 **6.** sin 13° 0.2250

Find x.
  7. cos x = 0.3907 67°
  8. tan x = 0.2126 12°
  9. sin x = 0.0175 1°
  10. △ABC is a right triangle, with m∠B = 90, m∠A = 15, and AC = 25. Find the other sides to the nearest whole number. AB = 24; BC = 6

Enrichment

△XYZ is a right triangle with m∠Z = 90. Find the measures of the length of the requested side to the nearest hundredth:

1. tan ∠X = 0.3057, XZ = 42. Find XY. 43.92
2. tan ∠Y = 3.4874, YZ = 22. Find XY. 79.82

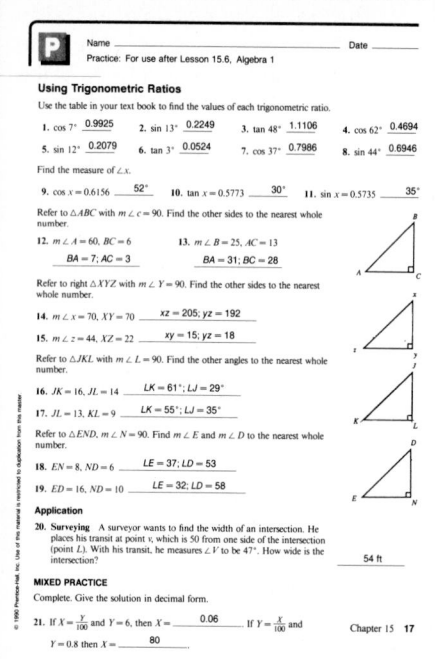

Refer to $\triangle JKL$, with $m\angle L = 90$. Find the other angle measures to the nearest whole number.

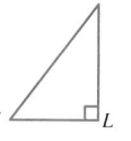

30. $JK = 13$, $JL = 12$ **31.** $JK = 5$, $KL = 3$
    $m\angle K = 67$; $m\angle J = 23$ $m\angle K = 53$; $m\angle J = 37$

32. $KL = 7$, $JL = 12$ **33.** $KL = 9$, $JL = 3$
    $m\angle K = 60$; $m\angle J = 30$ $m\angle K = 18$; $m\angle J = 72$

$\triangle ABC$ is a right triangle with $m\angle A = 90$. Find the length of the requested side to the nearest tenth.

C

34. $\cos \angle B = 0.4226$, $BC = 18$. Find AC.   16.3

35. $\sin \angle B = 0.6157$, $BC = 25$. Find AB.   19.7

36. $\tan \angle C = 0.2867$, $AB = 12$. Find BC.   43.5

37. $\tan \angle C = 4.7046$, $AC = 22$. Find BC.   105.8

Applications

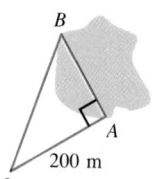

38. Surveying   A surveyor wants to find the width of a lake. She places her transit at point L, which is 200 m from one side of the lake (point A). With a transit, she measures $\angle L$ to be $37°$. How wide is the lake?   151 m

39. Architecture   An architect is designing an access ramp which forms an angle of $5°$ with the ground. The ramp will rise 5 ft, how long will the ramp be?   57 ft

40. Engineering   To support a pole, a cable is drawn tight between the pole and the ground. The cable is 4 m from the base of the pole. When the cable is attached it makes a $47°$ angle with the ground. How tall is the pole?   4 m

41. Hobbies   Benjamin is flying a kite. If he knows that the kite string is 60 m and that the angle the string makes with the ground is $65°$, how high above the ground is his kite?   54 m

EXTRA

Walking Distance

Elise walks by several large buildings as she goes from home to school to her after-school job, so she can't take a direct route. She travels 500 m east, 400 m north, 400 m east, and then 800 m north.

If Elise can take a straight path home from her job, how long is her return route?
  ≈1500 m

Problem Solving Strategy:
Check for Hidden Assumptions

LESSON PLAN

Vocabulary
Angle of depression
Angle of elevation

Materials/Manipulatives
Calculators
Protractor
Trigonometric table
*Teacher's Resource Book,
Teaching Aid 18*

When solving mathematical problems, it is important to check for any concepts that might be hidden within a problem. These are known as *hidden assumptions*, and they may or may not be true.

Before proceeding with a problem, be sure you clearly state what your assumptions are. This is important in order not to make an incorrect assumption about the problem. Such faulty reasoning can deter you from obtaining the correct solution.

In this lesson, certain assumptions are being made in order to apply the mathematics you know. These assumptions include:

1. Any triangle formed will be a right triangle.
2. When solving a problem involving navigation or surveying, vertical lines are perpendicular to the horizon or ground.

EXAMPLE 1 **At a point 100 ft from a tree a forest ranger measures the angle of elevation to the top of the tree to be 62°. How tall is the tree?**

Understand
the Problem

What are the given facts?
You are told that the forest ranger is 100 ft from the tree and that the angle of elevation is 62°.

What is the hidden assumption?
The triangle formed is a right triangle and the ground is level.

Plan Your
Approach

Choose a strategy.

You are asked to determine the height of the tree. Draw a diagram. Fill in all the given information. The **angle of elevation** is the angle formed by the line of sight and the horizon.

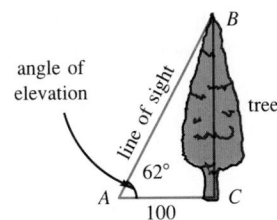

There are several approaches to take in solving this problem. For example use trigonometric functions and the Pythagorean theorem.

BACKGROUND

A key to success in solving the problems involving angles of elevation and depression is for students to understand the concepts of trigonometric functions and the Pythagorean theorem. Before beginning this lesson, you may want to review the trigonometric ratios and the use of a trigonometric table.

15.7 Problem Solving Strategy: Check for Hidden Assumptions **643**

- This problem solving lesson focuses on solving real-world problems using trigonometric ratios and tables. Many problems have a diagram to show a picture of the situation. You might want to remind students that a reasonably accurate diagram is helpful in the solution of word problems.
- Point out that students should use a calculator or a trigonometric table to facilitate calculations.

Critical Thinking

Classifying In your own words explain what "angle of depression" and "angle of elevation" are. Answers may vary.

Error Analysis Classification

1. *Misunderstanding*
   Came to the wrong hidden assumption
   Failed to understand the meaning of angle of elevation and/or angle of depression
2. *Misapplied Strategy*
   Wrote an incorrect trigonometric ratio
   Did not interpret the results correctly
   Failed to complete the solution

CHALKBOARD EXAMPLES

- **For Example 1**
   A roofer needs to retile the roof on an old building. She does not know how high the building is, but if she stands 5 feet from the wall, the angle of elevation to the roof is 68°. How high is the roof to the nearest foot?   12 ft

---

Complete the Work   Determine the measures of the angles of the triangle.

$\angle A + \angle B + \angle C = 180$ *The sum of the angles in a triangle is 180*
$62 + \angle B + 90 = 180$
$\angle B = 28°$

To find side BC two approaches may be used.

Approach One	Approach Two
$\tan A = \dfrac{\text{opp}}{\text{adj}}$	$\sin\angle B = \dfrac{\text{opp}}{\text{hyp}}$
$\tan 62° = \dfrac{BC}{100}$	$\sin 28° = \dfrac{100}{AB}$
$\tan 62°(100) = BC$	$\sin 28°(AB) = 100$
$1.881(100) = BC$	$0.4695(AB) = 100$
Therefore, $BC = 188$	$AB = 213$

Use the Pythagorean theorem, $a^2 + b^2 = c^2$, to find BC.
$a^2 + 100^2 = 213^2$
$a = 188$
Therefore, $BC = 188$

Interpret the Results   If the ground between the ranger and the tree is level and a right triangle is formed, then the tree is 188 ft tall.

It is also important to make certain assumptions and create an accurate drawing when solving the problem. This following example illustrates how to calculate the distance to an object using trigonometry.

EXAMPLE 2   **An observer in a lighthouse 225 ft above sea level spots a ship in the harbor. The angle of depression from the observer to the ship is 48°. Determine how far the ship is from the shore.**

Understand the Problem   **What are the given facts?**

You are told that the lighthouse is 225 ft above sea level, and that the angle of depression is 48°.

What are the hidden assumptions?

1. The line of center of the lighthouse forms a 90° angle with the ground.
2. A right triangle can be formed by the ship, the observer, and the base of the lighthouse.

644   Chapter 15 Right Triangle Relationships

Plan Your Approach

Choose a strategy.

The problem asks to determine the distance between the ship and the lighthouse. Draw a diagram.

Fill in all the given information keeping in mind that the **angle of depression** is the angle formed by the line of sight and the horizontal plane. Notice that the angle of depression to the ship is equal to the angle of elevation from the ship.

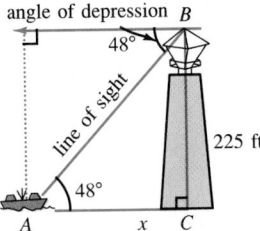

Complete the Work

$$\angle A + \angle B + \angle C = 180 \qquad \text{The sum of the angles in a triangle is } 180°.$$
$$48 + \angle B + 90 = 180$$
$$\angle B = 42°$$

Find the length of $\overline{AC}$ using $\tan B$.

$$\tan B = \frac{AC}{BC}$$

$$\tan 42° = \frac{x}{225}$$

$$x = 203$$

Interpret the Results

The distance between the lighthouse and the boat is 203 ft.

CLASS EXERCISES

For Discussion Answers may vary.

1. What is the meaning of the word *assumption?* A fact that is taken for granted.

2. Do problem solvers make hidden assumptions intentionally or unintentionally? probably both.

3. Can a hidden assumption make a solution to a problem incorrect? yes

4. Why are hidden assumptions not helpful to a problem solver? They can lead to incorrect solutions.

5. Why must a problem solver be careful in using drawings to help with the solution of a problem? Drawings may be based on hidden assumptions.

15.7 Problem Solving Strategy: Check for Hidden Assumptions **645**

- **For Example 2**
  An airplane is making an approach. The tower sees the plane and tells the pilot that the plane is 2 mi away from the tower. The pilot reads his altimeter and sees that he is 485 ft above the ground. What is the angle of depression from the plane to the base of the tower to the nearest degree?   3°

Mixed Problem Solving Review
- The following skills and concepts are reviewed:
  Solving problems involving systems of equations (Ex. 2)
  Solving problems involving inequalities (Ex. 3)
- The following problem solving strategies may be appropriate:
  Writing an equation (Ex. 1–3)

LESSON FOLLOW-UP

Discussion

What sciences make use of mathematics? What careers use trigonometry?   Answers may vary. Possible answers: Physics, Chemistry, Biology, etc.; architects, engineers, construction workers, etc.

Assignment Guide

See p. 612B for assignments.

Test Yourself

See *Teacher's Resource Book,* Tests, pp. 159–160.

Project

Have students work in groups to find the angle of elevation of an object they wish to measure. They need to measure the distance to the base of the object and use the appropriate trigonometric ratio to calculate the height.

Find each answer to the nearest whole number.

1. Find the length of the road. 132 m

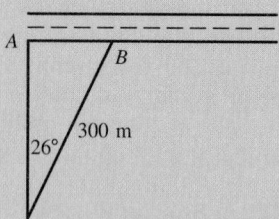

2. Find the height of the balloon. 56 m

3. Find the height of the building if the angle of elevation is 35° and the length of its shadow is 122 ft. 85 ft

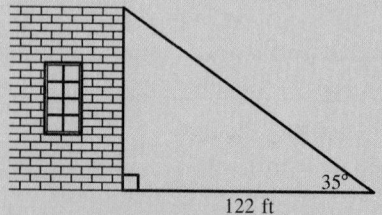

4. Find the angle of depression from the parachutist to the tree if it is 360 m from the tree and 500 m above the ground. 54°

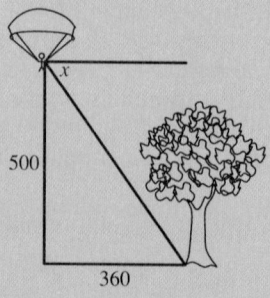

PRACTICE EXERCISES

A **For each situation, does the assumption made change the conditions of the problem? Write *yes* or *no*.**

1. In a problem about any positive real numbers a, b, c, and d, it is assumed that $a < 0 < b$. yes

2. In a problem about any two lines in a coordinate plane having slopes m_1 and m_2, it is assumed that $m_1 \cdot m_2 = -1$. yes

3. In a problem about any system of linear equations, it is assumed that the system is an independent system. yes

4. In a problem involving a circle of diameter d it is assumed that d_1 is another diameter and that $d = d_1$. yes .

To write each equation, state an assumption that has been made about the drawing.

5.

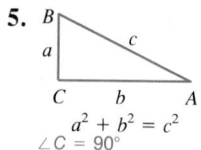

$$a^2 + b^2 = c^2$$
$$\angle C = 90°$$

6.

$$P = 4s$$
The figure is square.

For each problem, draw a diagram of the situation. State what assumptions are made and find each answer to the nearest whole number.

B **7.** The length of a tree's shadow is 13 m. The angle of elevation of the sun is 37°. What is the height of the tree? Assuming a right triangle (level land); 10 m

8. José is standing at a point 75 m from a base of the building. The angle of elevation from where he stands to the top of the building is 77°. How high is the building? Assuming a right triangle (level land); 325 m

9. A jet flying at an altitude of 8700 m spotted another aircraft flying at the same altitude. A pedestrian who was standing on the ground directly under the jet spotted the other aircraft at an angle of elevation of 38°. How far was the jet from the other aircraft? Assuming a right triangle (level land); 11,135 m

10. A sailboat was passing directly under a bridge where Lloyd was standing to watch his friend windsurf. If the angle of depression from Lloyd to his friend was 68° and he was 380 m above the water, how far was the sailboat from his friend? Assuming a right triangle (level land); 154 m

11. A plane is flying at an altitude of 10,000 ft. The airport is 112 miles ahead. What is the angle of depression from the plane to the airport? Assuming a flat earth; assuming 112 mi ahead means horizontal distance; 10°

12. A truck traveled 1600 m down a hill. If it is now 64 m below the starting point, what is the angle of depression from the starting point to the truck? Assuming a constant slope for the hill; 2°

13. An air-traffic controller is in a 78-meter-high tower and sees a plane, which is 7500 m away, at an angle of elevation of 38°. What is the altitude of the airplane? Assuming a flat earth; 5938 m

Mixed Problem Solving Review

1. The length of a rectangle is four times its width. The number of square feet in its area is four times the number of feet in its perimeter. What are the dimensions of the rectangle? $l = 40$ ft; $w = 10$ ft

2. The difference between two integers is 12. If twice the first integer is added to the second the sum is 84. Find the two integers. 32; 20

3. Rob received grades of 85, 78, 80, and 94 on his first four exams. What is the lowest possible test score he can receive to have an average greater than 85? 89

PROJECT

A definition of a term in mathematics gives a precise meaning to the term. A mathematical term is a name for a concept, such as a triangle, solution, or irrational number. Make a list of three definitions given in this chapter. Then change the definitions. Can an unintentional change made in a definition introduce a hidden assumption into a problem? yes

TEST YOURSELF

1. Given $\triangle ABC \sim \triangle AJN$, $AC = 10$, $AB = 12$, and $AJ = 4$, then $AN = \underline{?}$ $3\frac{1}{3}$ 15.4

2. In right triangle XYZ, $YX = 3$, $YZ = 5$ and $m\angle Y = 90$. Use the Pythagorean theorem to find XZ. Then find $\sin X$, $\cos X$ and $\tan X$. $\sqrt{34}$; $\frac{5\sqrt{34}}{34}$, $\frac{3\sqrt{34}}{34}$, $\frac{5}{3}$ 15.5

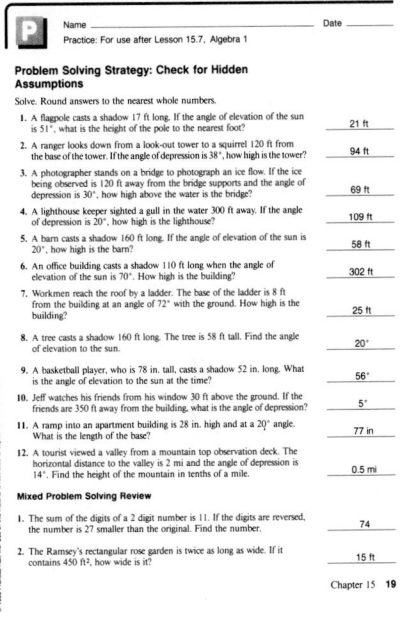

3. In right triangle ABC $m\angle C = 90$, $AC = 12$ and $BC = 4$. Find $m\angle A$ and $m\angle B$ to the nearest whole number. 18, 72 15.6

4. A lighthouse is 246 ft tall. Find the angle of depression to the nearest degree if a ship is 3 mi from the base of the lighthouse. 1° 15.7

15.7 Problem Solving Strategy: Check for Hidden Assumptions **647**

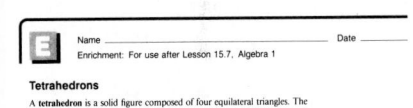
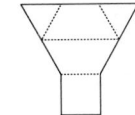

- See *Teacher's Resource Book, Spanish Chapter Summary and Review,* pp. 29–30.
- See Extra Practice, p. 669.

CHAPTER 15 SUMMARY AND REVIEW

Vocabulary

acute angle (615)
acute triangle (619)
angle (615)
angle of depression (645)
angle of elevation (643)
complementary angles (615)
congruent angles (623)
congruent line segments (623)
corresponding parts (624)
cosine (634)

equilateral triangle (619)
geometry (614)
isosceles triangle (619)
line (614)
line segment (614)
obtuse angle (615)
obtuse triangle (619)
protractor (615)
ray (614)
right angle (615)

right triangle (618)
scalene triangle (619)
similar triangles (628)
sine (634)
supplementary angles (615)
tangent (634)
trigonometry (633)
trigonometric ratios (633)
vertex (615)

Basic Geometric Figures   Angles can be classified as follows: A **right angle** has a measure of 90°. An **acute angle** has a measure between 0° and 90°. An **obtuse angle** has a measure between 90° and 180°. **Complementary angles** are two angles whose measures have a sum of 90°. **Supplementary angles** are two angles whose measures have a sum of 180°.

15.1

1. If $\angle M$ and $\angle N$ are supplementary, find $m\angle N$ if $m\angle M = 67$. 113

2. The measure of an angle is 20 more than the measure of its complement. Find the measure of the angle and its complement. 55°; 35°

Triangles   Triangles can be classified as follows: A **right triangle** has one right angle. An **acute triangle** has all acute angles. An **obtuse triangle** has one obtuse angle. An **isosceles triangle** has at least two sides of equal length. An **equilateral triangle** has all sides of equal length. A **scalene triangle** has no sides of equal length.

15.2

The sum of the measures of the angles of a triangle is 180.

3. Classify $\triangle RST$ according to the measures of its angles and according to the lengths of its sides.
right triangle; isosceles triangle

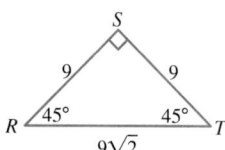

4. Given $\triangle MOP$, find $m\angle M$ if $m\angle O = 55$ and $m\angle P = 63$. $m\angle M = 62$

Congruence   **Congruent angles** are angles that have the same measure. **Congruent line segments** are line segments that have equal length. **Congruent figures** are figures that have the same size and shape.

15.3

$\triangle PAD \cong \triangle CAR.$

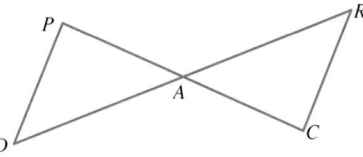

5. Name the corresponding angles.
$\angle P \leftrightarrow \angle C; \angle A \leftrightarrow \angle A; \angle D \rightarrow \angle R$

6. Name the corresponding sides.
$PA \leftrightarrow CA; AD \leftrightarrow AR; PD \leftrightarrow RC$

7. True or *false*? $\triangle DAP \cong \triangle ARC$
false

Similar Figures   In **similar triangles,** corresponding angles are congruent   15.4
and corresponding sides are proportional.

8. $\triangle DOG \sim \triangle CAT.$ Find the lengths of the two missing sides if
$DO = 4$, $GO = 3$, $CA = 10$, and $CT = 15$. $DG = 6; AT = 7.5$

9. $\triangle ABC \sim \triangle ADE$, $AB = 15$, $AD = 25$, $DE = 50$, and $AC = 32$. Find
AE and BC. $BC = 30; AE = 53\frac{1}{3}$

Trigonometric Ratios   **Trigonometric ratios** for right $\triangle ABC$ are as   15.5
follows:

$$\text{sine of } \angle A = \frac{\text{length of leg opposite } \angle A}{\text{length of hypotenuse}}; \sin A = \frac{a}{c}$$

$$\text{cosine of } \angle A = \frac{\text{length of leg adjacent } \angle A}{\text{length of hypotenuse}}; \cos A = \frac{b}{c}$$

$$\text{tangent of } \angle A = \frac{\text{length of leg opposite } \angle A}{\text{length of leg adjacent } \angle A}; \tan A = \frac{a}{b}$$

10. Use the Pythagorean theorem to find the
length of $\overline{AB}$. Find the values for $\sin A$,
$\cos A$, $\tan A$, $\sin B$, $\cos B$, and $\tan B$.
$\sin A = \frac{3}{5}$; $\sin B = \frac{4}{5}$; $\cos A = \frac{4}{5}$; $\cos B = \frac{3}{5}$; $\tan A = \frac{3}{4}$;
$\tan B = \frac{4}{3}$

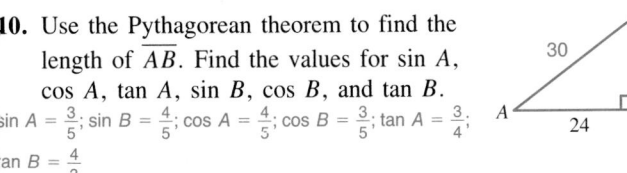

Use the table on page 671.   15.6

11. Find $\cos 29°$. 0.8746

12. Find x if $\tan x = 0.5774$. 30°

13. Given right $\triangle XYZ$, $m\angle Y = 90$. Find the other sides to the nearest
whole number if $m\angle X = 34$, $XY = 40$. $XZ = 48; YZ = 27$

For Exercises 14–15, refer to the problem below.   15.7

An 8-meter ladder rests against the side of a house. If the foot of the ladder
is 2 m from the house, find the angle the ladder makes with the ground.

14. Draw a diagram of a right triangle to represent the situation. Answers may vary.

15. Give the trigonometric ratio that relates the known sides of the right
triangle to the unknown angle. Find the angle to the nearest degree.
$\cos A = \frac{2}{8}$; $m\angle A = 76$

Summary and Review   **649**

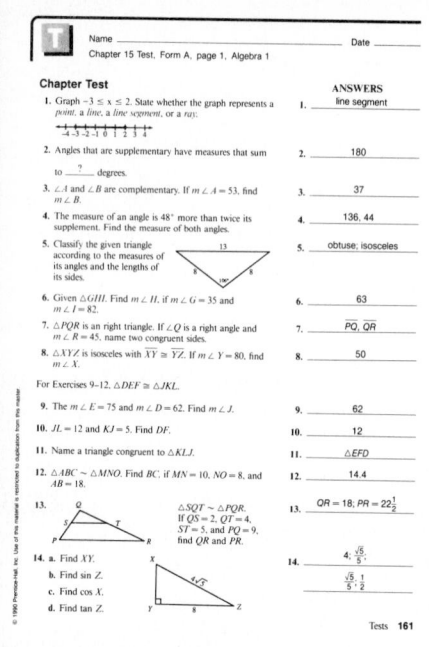

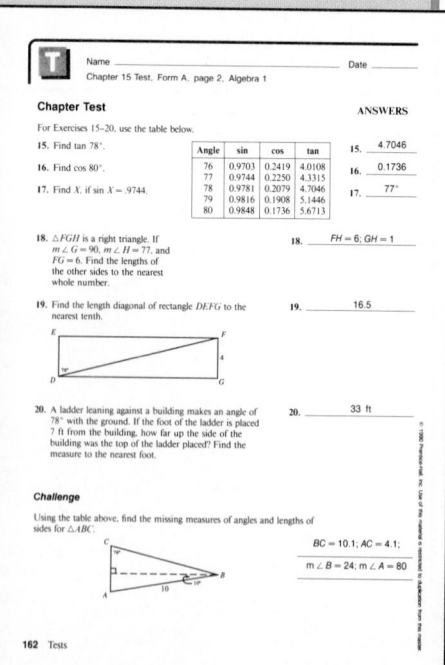

CHAPTER 15 TEST

1. Graph $x \leq 2$ on a number line and state whether the figure represents a point, a line, a line segment, or a ray. 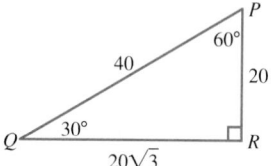 ray

2. *True* or *false*? Angles with measures of $72°$ and $18°$ are complementary. True

3. If $\angle M$ and $\angle N$ are complementary, find $m\angle N$ if $m\angle M = 71$. 19

4. The measure of an angle is $18°$ more than the measure of its supplement. Find the measure of the angle and its supplement. 99; 81

5. Classify $\triangle PRQ$ (a) according to the measures of its angles and (b) according to the lengths of its sides.
right triangle; scalene triangle

6. Given $\triangle BOG$, find $m\angle B$ if $m\angle O = 35$ and $m\angle G = 21$. 124

7. $\triangle MNO$ is isosceles, $m\angle N = 100$, and $MN = NO$. Find $m\angle M$. 40

For Exercises 8–9, $\triangle RIG \cong \triangle TIN$.
$GI \leftrightarrow NI$; $GR \leftrightarrow NT$; $IR \leftrightarrow IT$
8. Name the corresponding angles and sides.
$\angle R \leftrightarrow \angle T$; $\angle I \leftrightarrow \angle I$; $\angle G \leftrightarrow \angle N$
9. *True* or *false*? $\triangle GIR \cong \triangle NIT$.
true

10. $\triangle HIT \sim \triangle POS$. Find the lengths of the missing sides if $HI = 6$, $PO = 9$, $HT = 5$, and $SO = 15$. $IT = 10$; $PS = 7.5$

11. $\triangle JAM \sim \triangle JFT$, $JA = 12$, $JF = 18$, $AM = 15$, and $JT = 10$. Find FT and JM. $FT = 22.5$; $JM = 6\frac{2}{3}$

12. Use the Pythagorean theorem to find the length of $\overline{AB}$. Find the values for $\sin A$ and $\sin B$. $\sin A = \frac{8}{17}$; $\sin B = \frac{15}{17}$; $\cos A = \frac{15}{17}$; $\cos B = \frac{8}{17}$; $\tan A = \frac{8}{15}$; $\tan B = \frac{15}{8}$

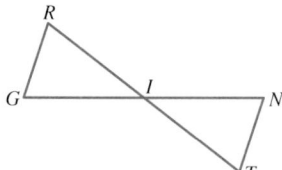

Use the table on page 671 for Exercises 13–14.

13. Find $\cos 71°$. 0.3256

14. Find x if $\tan x = 2.7475$. 70

15. Given right $\triangle XYZ$, $m\angle Y = 90$, find the other sides to the nearest whole number if $m\angle X = 68$ and $XY = 10$. $XZ = 25$; $YZ = 27$

Challenge

Find the acute angle that is formed by the line $y = \frac{1}{4}x - 3$ and the x-axis. $\approx 14°$

The individual comments provided about some problems can be helpful in guiding students to solve these problems.

Select the best choice for each question.

1. Solve the equation:
C $x^2 - 6x - 5 = 0$.
 A. 5, 1 **B.** $-1, -5$
 C. $3 \pm \sqrt{14}$ **D.** $-3 \pm \sqrt{14}$
 E. $\dfrac{6 \pm \sqrt{58}}{2}$

2. Find $f(-2)$ if $f(x) = 3x^2 + 5x + 1$.
C **A.** 23 **B.** 21 **C.** 3 **D.** 2 **E.** 1

3. The graph of $y = x^2 - 4x + 3$ is
B a parabola intersecting the y-axis at a point whose coordinates are:
 A. (3, 0) **B.** (0, 3) **C.** (0, 2)
 D. (1, 0) **E.** (0, 1)

4. Factor $6x^2 + 5x - 6$.
A **A.** $(3x - 2)(2x + 3)$
 B. $(3x + 2)(2x - 3)$
 C. $(3x + 3)(2x - 2)$
 D. $(6x + 1)(x - 6)$
 E. $(6x - 1)(x + 6)$

Use this information for questions 5–8.

The heights of 11 students were recorded in inches as 57, 52, 61, 57, 49, 54, 61, 57, 53, 51, and 53.

5. The mean is:
B **A.** 54 **B.** 55 **C.** 56 **D.** 57 **E.** 61

6. The median is:
A **A.** 54 **B.** 55 **C.** 56 **D.** 57 **E.** 61

7. The mode is:
D **A.** 54 **B.** 55 **C.** 56 **D.** 57 **E.** 61

8. The range is:
E **A.** 4 **B.** 6 **C.** 8 **D.** 10 **E.** 12

9. What is the conjunction of these
A two inequalities?
$$x < 5,\ x > -2$$
 A. $-2 < x < 5$
 B. $-2 < x$ or $x < 5$
 C. $-2 > x > 5$
 D. $x > 5$ or $x < -2$
 E. $x > 5$ and $x < -2$

10. What is $\frac{3}{4}\%$ of 64?
C **A.** 48 **B.** 4.8 **C.** 0.48
 D. 0.048 **E.** 0.0048

11. Ira bought two pens at $1.66 each,
D a box of pencils for $1.89, and a package of paper for $2.99. If the sales tax rate is 5%, what was the total Ira paid for these items?
 A. $7.56 **B.** $7.57 **C.** $7.61
 D. $8.61 **E.** $8.62

12. What is the probability that in a
D throw of a die, a multiple of two will appear?
 A. $\frac{1}{12}$ **B.** $\frac{1}{6}$ **C.** $\frac{1}{3}$ **D.** $\frac{1}{2}$ **E.** $\frac{2}{5}$

13. What is the slope of a line that is
A the graph of $5x - 2y = 8$?
 A. $\frac{5}{2}$ **B.** $-\frac{5}{2}$ **C.** $\frac{2}{5}$ **D.** $-\frac{2}{5}$ **E.** -4

14. Solve for x:
D $(x - 2)(x + 3) - 5 = (x - 1)(x + 1)$
 A. -12 **B.** -10 **C.** 8
 D. 10 **E.** 12

15. The probability of a particular event
E happening is $\frac{2}{7}$. What are the odds *against* it occurring?
 A. 7:5 **B.** 7:2 **C.** 5:7
 D. 2:5 **E.** 5:2

10. Estimation is helpful in this type of problem. Since 1% of 64 is 0.64, $\frac{3}{4}\%$ of 64 must be $\frac{3}{4}$ of 0.64 and the only choice near this value is 0.48.

12. If students have a mental picture of the sample space for the toss of two dice, then problems of this type become relatively easy.

15. It might be helpful to think of the sample space as having only 7 elements. Then, 2 of them are successes and 5 of them are failures, and the odds against are 5 to 2.

See *Teacher's Resource Book,* for Preparing for Standardized Tests.

See *Teacher's Resource Book.*
- *Semester Test,* pp. 165–172
- *Final Test,* pp. 173–180

Find the distance between each pair of points.   **12.10**

1. $A(2, 3)$ and $B(5, 7)$ 5

2. $X(-1, -2)$ and $Y(7, 4)$ 10

3. $M(3, -2)$ and $N(6, 1)$ $3\sqrt{2}$

4. $C(5, -4)$ and $D(-3, 1)$ $\sqrt{89}$

5. $R(-1, 2)$ and $T(3, 6)$ $4\sqrt{2}$

6. $J(-2, -5)$ and $K(2, 1)$ $2\sqrt{13}$

Simplify. Assume that no variable equals zero.   **2.4, 6.8, 7.6, 12.5, 12.6**

7. $|2 - (3\sqrt{2})^2|$ 16

8. $\sqrt{3}(2 + \sqrt{6})$ $2\sqrt{3} + 3\sqrt{2}$

9. $3\sqrt{12} + 3\sqrt{18} - 2\sqrt{27}$ $9\sqrt{2}$

10. $a - 3(a - 2)$ $-2a + 6$

11. $\sqrt{20c^2 d^3}$ $2cd\sqrt{5d}$

12. $(2b^3 - 1)^2$ $4b^6 - 4b^3 + 1$

13. $(2z - 6)(3z + 2)$ $6z^2 - 14z - 12$

14. $(2\sqrt{3} - 1)^2$ $13 - 4\sqrt{3}$

15. $(2r^2 t)^3 (3rt^3)$ 6.3, 8.3, 8.5, 8.7 $24r^7 t^6$

16. $\dfrac{(8m^3 n^5)^2}{(-4m^4 n^3)^2}$ $\dfrac{4n^4}{m^2}$

17. $\dfrac{2\sqrt{3}}{3 + \sqrt{2}}$ $\dfrac{6\sqrt{3} - 2\sqrt{6}}{7}$

18. $\dfrac{3x - 7}{x - 2} - \dfrac{3 - 2x}{5}$ $\dfrac{5}{}$

19. $\dfrac{24d^6}{\sqrt{5}} \cdot \dfrac{45}{\sqrt{6d^2}}$ $36d^4\sqrt{30}$

20. $\dfrac{4x^2 - 9}{x + 2} \div \dfrac{2x + 3}{x^2 - 4}$ $(2x - 3)(x - 2)$

21. $\dfrac{2x^2 + 2x}{x^2 - 9} + \dfrac{x + 1}{3 - x}$ $\dfrac{x + 1}{x + 3}$

22. $(2.5 \times 10^6)(0.3 \times 10^{-2})$ 7.5×10^3

23. $7(3c - 2) + 6 - 5c$ $8(2c - 1)$

24. $(2 \div 3)2^2 + 8 \div 3$ $\dfrac{16}{3}$

25. $(2\sqrt{3} + 3\sqrt{2})(3\sqrt{3} - 2\sqrt{2})$ 4.2, 6.4 $6 + 5\sqrt{6}$

26. $-\dfrac{2}{3}g^2 h(12gh^3 - 3h)$ $2g^2 h^2 - 8g^3 h^4$

27. $(8x^3 + 27) \div (2x + 3)$ $4x^2 - 6x + 9$

28. $(9p^2 - 3p + 1)(3p + 1)$ $27p^3 + 1$

29. $(2a^2 b - 3c)(2ab^2 + 3c)$ $4a^3 b^3 + 6a^2 bc - 6ab^2 c - 9c^2$

30. $\dfrac{36w^5 - 48w^3 + 12w^2}{-12w^2}$ $-3w^3 + 4w - 1$

31. $\dfrac{8m^2 - 6mn - 9n^2}{12m^2 + mn - 6n^2}$ $\dfrac{2m - 3n}{3m - 2n}$

Write an equation, inequality, or system for each problem. Solve.   **11.6**

32. The sum of the digits of a two-digit number is 13. If the digits are reversed then new number is 27 more than the original. Find the original number. $t + u = 13$; $10u + t = 10t + u + 27$; 58

33. Find the first of three consecutive integers. The product of the first and the second is 34 less than the square of the third. $x(x + 1) = (x + 2)^2 - 34$; 10, 11, 12   **7.11**

34. Thirty mL of a 15% acid solution is to be changed to a 10% acid solution by adding water. How much water is to be added? $4.5 = 0.10(30 + x)$; 15 mL   **4.7**

35. Mae's scores on three math tests are 81, 92, and 86. What is the lowest she can get on the fourth test to have an average greater than 85? $\dfrac{x + 81 + 92 + 86}{4} > 85$; 82   **5.8**

Factor completely. If the polynomial cannot be factored, write "prime." 7.1–7.6

36. $16x^2 - 9y^2$
$(4x - 3y)(4x + 3y)$

37. $t^2 + 2t - 35$
$(t + 7)(t - 5)$

38. $c^2 - 13c + 36$
$(c - 9)(c - 4)$

39. $2m^2 + m - 15$
$(2m - 5)(m + 3)$

40. $6m^2 + 5m - 6$
$(3m - 2)(2m + 3)$

41. $6a^3 - 24ab^2$
$6a(a - 2b)(a + 2b)$

42. $8a^3b + 12a^2b^2 - 4a^2b$
$4a^2b(2a + 3b - 1)$

43. $rt^2 - 9r + t^3 - 9t$
$(t - 3)(t + 3)(r + t)$

Solve each equation, inequality, or system. If there is no solution, state that fact. 2.3, 3.1, 4.2, 4.6, 5.2
5.6, 5.7, 7.5, 8.6,
11.4, 11.5, 12.5, 12.8, 13.1, 13.2

44. $0.2x + 3.9 = 1.5$
-12

45. $\frac{3}{5}r + 10 = 19$ 15

46. $2 - 3(a - 4) = 2a - 1$
3

47. 18% of $m = 90$ 500

48. $2y^2 - 3y = 27$ $-3, \frac{9}{2}$

49. $c^2 + 5c = 5c + 4$
$2, -2$

50. $8 - 5t > 13$ $t < -1$

51. $|d - 7| = 3$ 10, 4

52. $\sqrt{3n} + 1 = 10$ 27

53. $|p| + 6 = 5$ no solution

54. $|4 - 3x| \leq 10$
$-2 < x < \frac{14}{3}$

55. $\sqrt{b^2} + 2 = b - 2$
no solution

56. $\frac{u}{u + 1} = 2 - \frac{3}{u + 1}$
1

57. $\begin{cases} 2x + 3y = 5 \\ 5x + 3y = 11 \end{cases}$ $\left(2, \frac{1}{3}\right)$

58. $\frac{2h}{h^2 - 4} + 3 = \frac{3h}{h + 2}$
$\frac{3}{2}$

59. $|w - 5| > 1$ $w > 6$ or $w < 4$

60. $9x^2 = 18$ $x = \pm\sqrt{2}$

61. $|a - 2| \leq 3$
$-1 \leq a \leq 5$

62. $\begin{cases} b = 2a + 1 \\ a + 3b = 30 \end{cases}\left(\frac{27}{7}, \frac{61}{7}\right)$

63. $(m - 2)^2 = 36$ 8, -4

64. $\begin{cases} 6r + 7t = 24 \\ 2r - 3t = -8 \end{cases}\left(\frac{1}{2}, 3\right)$

65. $d^2 - 6d = 16$
$8, -2$

66. $3x^2 = 2x + 5$ $\frac{5}{3}, -1$

67. $5a^2 = 20(a + 3)$
$6, -2$

68. $p - 5(p - 2) + (p - 3) = 2$ $\frac{5}{3}$

69. $5 + \sqrt{3a} - 2 = 9$ 12

Evaluate $b^2 - 4ac$ for each equation, then state the nature of the solutions. 13.7

70. $2x^2 - x + 1$
-7; no real solutions

71. $x^2 + 3x - 2$
17; 2 real solutions

72. $x^2 - 2x - 1$
8; 2 real solutions

Write a quadratic equation with the given roots. 13.8

73. 2, 5 $x^2 - 7x + 10 = 0$

74. $\frac{1}{3}$, 2 $3x^2 - 7x + 2 = 0$

75. $-3, \frac{1}{2}$ $2x^2 + 5x - 3 = 0$

Find the mode, median, mean, and range for each set of data. 14.1

76. 6, 8, 8, 9, 14, 15
mode: 8; median: 8.5; mean: 10; range: 9

77. 21, 32, 63, 21, 35, 32
mode: 21 & 32; median: 32; mean: 34; range: 42

78. Gloria scored the following number of runs in 5 games: 4, 2, 0, 4, 5.
Find the range, variance, and standard deviation.
range: 5; variance: 3.2; standard deviation: 1.8

There are 4 green, 5 red, and 3 yellow cards in a box. Find each probability. One card is picked at random. 14.4

79. $P(\text{green})$ $\frac{1}{3}$

80. $P(\text{green or red})$ $\frac{3}{4}$

81. $P(\text{blue})$ 0

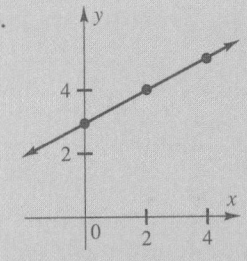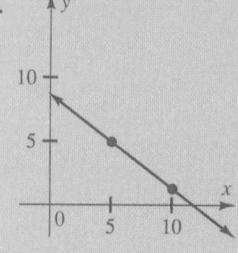
One card is picked, replaced, and another card is picked.   14.6

82. P(1st green and 2nd green) $\frac{1}{9}$ 83. P(1st green and 2nd not green) $\frac{2}{9}$

One card is picked, not replaced, and another card is picked.

84. P(1st green and 2nd green) $\frac{1}{11}$ 85. P(1st red and 2nd green) $\frac{5}{33}$

86. The measure of an angle is 20 less than its complement. Find the   15.2
    measure of the angle and its complement. 35°; 55°

87. In triangle ABC, the measure of angle B is twice $m\angle A$. The measure of
    angle C is 20 more than $m\angle A$. Find the measure of each angle.
    $m\angle A = 40$; $m\angle B = 80$; $m\angle C = 60$

88. The length of a tree's shadow is 8 ft. The angle of elevation of the sun   15.7
    is 33°. What is the height of the tree? 5 ft

89. Find the area of a rectangle whose length is $3\sqrt{x}$ cm and width is
    $2\sqrt{x}$ cm. 6x cm²

90. A square lot has an area of 625 square feet. How many feet of fencing
    is needed to enclose the lot? 100 ft

Find the slope of a line that contains the given points.   9.4

91. $A(3, 2)$; $B(4, 6)$ 4   92. $C\left(-\frac{1}{2}, 0\right)$; $D\left(\frac{3}{4}, 1\right)$ $\frac{4}{5}$

Through the given point, draw a line with the given slope. See side column.

93. $m = \frac{1}{2}$; $T(4, 5)$ 94. $m = -\frac{3}{5}$; $S(10, 2)$

Find the solution set of each sentence. The replacement set is   2.7
{−2, 0, 1, 3, 4}.

95. $3x - 1 = 8$ {3}   96. $z + 5 = -3$ no solution   97. $2m - 5 = 3$ {4}

98. $y - 1 < 5$ {−2, 0, 1, 3, 4} 99. $s + 2 > 3$ {3, 4}   100. $3 > 2y + 1$ {−2, 0}

101. A department store finds that its profit for selling x units of a certain   13.7
     product is given by the equation $p = x^2 - 30x + 125$. For which
     values of x is the profit zero? 5, 25

102. The length of a rectangle is 5 m longer than its width. What are the   6.8
     dimensions if its area is 36 m²? $l = 9$ m; $w = 4$ m

Chapter 1   Real Numbers

Evaluate each expression if $u = -5$, $w = \frac{4}{3}$, $x = 3$, $y = -\frac{1}{2}$, $z = -4.1$ **1.1–1.8**

1. $w + 6$ $\frac{22}{3}$

2. $(wx) - 1$ 3

3. $(9w) \div 4$ 3

4. $3 + z$ −1.1

5. $y + z$ −4.6

6. $|x + y|$ $2\frac{1}{2}$

7. $y - x$ $-3\frac{1}{2}$

8. $5 - (y - z)$ 1.4

9. $|z| - |y|$ 3.6

10. $(xyw) + z$ −6.1

11. $w[x + (6y)]$ 0

12. $\left(\dfrac{y}{w}\right) - (2z)$ 7.825

13. $u + z - 11.3$ −20.4

14. $(uw) - z + 0.3$ $-2.2\overline{6}$

15. $\dfrac{|(6w) - (4y)|}{-0.5}$ −20

Write an algebraic expression for each phrase.   **1.1**

16. The sum of a number i and five $i + 5$ **17.** 55 decreased by a number n $55 - n$

18. The number of miles traveled m divided by the number of hours h elapsed $\frac{m}{h}$

For Exercises 19–26, refer to the number line below.   **1.2**

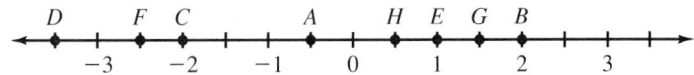

Give the coordinate of each point.

19. D $-3\frac{1}{2}$

20. A $-\frac{1}{2}$

21. B 2

22. G $1\frac{1}{2}$

Name the graph of each number.

23. 1 E

24. -2 C

25. $-2\frac{1}{2}$ F

26. 0.5 H

Show that each number is a rational number.   **1.2**

27. -7 $\frac{-7}{1}$

28. 0 $\frac{0}{1}$

29. $3\frac{2}{3}$ $\frac{11}{3}$

30. -1.26 $\frac{-126}{100}$

Simplify.   **1.3, 1.7**

31. $-(-3)$ 3

32. $-[-(-8)]$ −8

33. $(-7)(-9)\left(\frac{1}{3}\right)$ 21

34. $\frac{2}{5}(10)(-x)$ −4x

Replace each __?__ with >, <, or = to make a true statement.   **1.3–1.6**

35. -2 __?__ 0 <

36. -4 __?__ -3 <

37. $-\frac{1}{2}$ __?__ $-\frac{1}{3}$ <

38. -2.1 __?__ -2.1 =

39. $-11.1 + (-4.6) + 2.3$ __?__ $11.1 + (-4.6) - (+2.3)$ <

40. $0.56 + 2.12 + (-2.12)$ __?__ $-0.56 + (-2.21) + 2.21$ >

41. The temperatures at sunrise for 1 week were: $-1.5°$F, $-3.1°$F, $2.2°$F, $0.4°$F, $-1.1°$F, $3.6°$F, and $0.5°$F; what was the average temperature at sunrise? 0.1°F

Chapter 2 Algebraic Expressions

Evaluate each expression if $a = 4$, $b = -2$, $c = 0$, $d = -5$, $e = 8$.   **2.1–2.2**

1. $2b - e$ -12

2. $e - \dfrac{a}{c}$ no solution

3. $3[a - 2(4b - 3e) + 3c]$ 204

4. $\dfrac{-c + d}{2ae}$ $-\dfrac{5}{64}$

5. $5b^3 - 2d^2$ -90

6. $(2 - ab)(e - c) \div (2d + a)$ $-\dfrac{40}{3}$

7. $\dfrac{e^2 - a^2}{(e - a)^4}$ $\dfrac{3}{16}$

8. $4ac(2e + b)$ 0

9. $-4(2d^2 + b) \div (c^2 - e^2)$ 3

Which property of real numbers justifies each statement?   **2.3**

10. $-7(a + 11) = -7(a) + (-7)(11)$
distributive

11. $(-3 + 9) + 7 = -3 + (9 + 7)$
assoc., addition

12. $5(j + k) = 5(k + j)$ commut., addition

13. $-2(3x + y) = (3x + y)(-2)$
commut., mult.

Simplify.   **2.4–2.5**

14. $5r^2 - 2r + r^2 - r^3 - r$ $-r^3 + 6r^2 - 3r$

15. $j^2k^2 + 3jk^2 - j^2k^2 + 5j^2k + jk$
$5j^2k + jk + 3jk^2$

16. $5m^2 - [2m^2 - m(2m + 1)]$ $5m^2 + m$

17. $3x - 2[x^2 - x - x^2 + 3x(x + 2)]$
$-6x^2 - 7x$

18. $2g - [(-h + g) - (g^2 - h) - g^2 + (h + g)]$ $2g^2 - h$

Translate each word expression to an algebraic expression.   **2.6**

19. Three less than a number $n - 3$

20. The product of five and a number squared $5 \cdot n^2$

21. Eight times the sum of a number squared and one $8(n^2 + 1)$

Write an algebraic expression for each phrase.

22. Let s be Sarah's age now.
  a. What was Sarah's age 5 years ago? $s - 5$
  b. Greg is 6 years younger than Sarah. Represent Greg's age now. $s - 6$
  c. What was Greg's age 5 years ago? $s - 11$

Write an algebraic equation for each sentence.   **2.9**

23. Thirteen reduced by a number n is -24. $13 - n = -24$

24. The product of a number and -6 reduced by 2 is 10. $(-6n) - 2 = 10$

25. Thirty-eight increased by the quotient of 7 and some number is 50. $38 + \dfrac{7}{n} = 50$

26. Adult tickets cost $10 and children's $7.50. The total value of the tickets is $1520. $10a + 7.5c = 1520$

Find each solution set for a replacement set $\left\{-3, 1, 0, \dfrac{1}{3}\right\}$.   **2.7**

27. $-2 > 3y + 5$ $\{-3\}$ **28.** $-2y = 1$ $\emptyset$ **29.** $y + 2 > -4$ $\left\{-3, 1, 0, \dfrac{1}{3}\right\}$

Chapter 3 Equations in One Variable

Solve each equation.   **3.1–3.3**

1. $a + 26 = 31$ 5

2. $98 = 14m$ 7

3. $\frac{1}{2}y = -17$ -34

4. $4.5 + b = 11.2$ 6.7

5. $\frac{f}{8} = -3$ -24

6. $-\frac{2}{3} = \frac{5}{3} + c$ $-\frac{7}{3}$

7. $-2.23 + s = 0$ 2.23

8. $0 = -\frac{9}{4}r$ 0

9. $3.45 - (-t) = 2.82$
-0.63

10. $d - 4.2 = -3.1$ 1.1

11. $-9.6 = -h$ 9.6

12. $-8.21 + e = -8.21$
0

13. $4k + 3 = 11$ 2

14. $-4 + \frac{m}{6} = 2$ 36

15. $6.4p - 1.5 = -0.22$
0.2

16. Find a number n if this number reduced by 11 is -15. -4 **3.4, 3.7, 3.8**

17. Find a number n if $\frac{7}{8}$ of this number is 49. 56

18. Find a number n if 0.25 of this number decreased by 7 is -9. -8

19. Jan's father is 56 years old. If he is $3\frac{1}{2}$ times as old as Jan, how old is Jan? 16

20. Prove that for all real numbers a, b, and c, if $a = b$, then $c - a = c - b$. **3.5**

Proof:

Statements	Reasons
1. $c = c$	1. Refl. prop.
2. $c - a = c - a$	2. Subtr. prop.
3. $a = b$	3. Given
4. $c - a = c - b$	4. Subst. prop.

21. Prove that for all real numbers a, b, and c, $c \neq 0$, if $\frac{a}{c} = \frac{b}{c}$, then $a = b$.

Proof:

Statements	Reasons
1. $\frac{a}{c} = \frac{b}{c}$	1. Given
2. $\frac{a}{c} = \frac{1}{c} \cdot a;\ \frac{b}{c} = \frac{1}{c} \cdot b$	2. Def. of division
3. $\frac{1}{c} \cdot a = \frac{1}{c} \cdot b$	3. Subst. prop.
4. $c \cdot \frac{1}{c} \cdot a = c \cdot \frac{1}{c} \cdot b$	4. Mult. prop. for equations
5. $a = b$	5. Ident. prop. for mult.

22. If $P = 2l + 2w$, find l when $P = 48$ and $w = 11$. 13   **3.6**

23. $V = \pi r^2 h$. Find h if $r = 4$, $\pi \approx 3.14$, and $V = 251.2$. 5

24. $A = \frac{1}{2}h(a + b)$. Find b if $A = 60.4$, $h = 2.0$, and $a = 3.8$. 56.6

Chapter 4   More Equations in One Variable

Solve and check.   **4.1, 4.2, 4.4**

1. $-3a + 5a = 14$ 7

2. $-15 = 4b - 7b + 3$ 6

3. $3c + 2(c + 2) = -6$ –2

4. $-4(5d + 6) = 2$ $-\frac{13}{10}$

5. $5e + 1 = 7e + 7$ –3

6. $3(4f + 6) = -2f + 18$ 0

7. $2g + 4(3 - g) = 5g + 19$ –1

8. $-h + 2(h + 8) = -2(1 - 3h) + 3$ 3

9. $-3(2a + 5) = 9$ –4

10. $11k - 2k + 4 = 15 - 2k$ 1

11. $-0.5l + 0.7 = 1.4 - 0.4l$ –7

12. $0.03(2m - 3) + 0.05 = 5$ 84

13. Write three consecutive odd integers starting with odd integer i. $i, i + 2, i + 4$ **4.3**

14. Write the two consecutive integers preceding integer c. $c - 1, c - 2$

15. Find five consecutive integers if the sum of the first and the third is -28.
$-15, -14, -13, -12, -11$

16. What is 45% of 350? 157.5

17. What percent of 108 is 24? $22.\overline{2}$%   **4.5**

18. 0.15 is 30% of what number? 0.5

19. What percent of $50,000 is $5?
0.01%

20. What is the new price of a $12.50 item reduced by 30%? $8.75   **4.6**

21. If a haircut cost $12 last year and now costs $15.60, by what percent has the price increased? 30%

22. After a 20% weight loss, Gemma now weighs 124 lb. What was her original weight? 155 lb

23. How many mL of water should be added to 15 mL of a 20% solution of   **4.7**
    formic acid in water to produce a 5% solution? 45 mL

24. How many grams of ester must be added to 25 g of a 10% ester solution in alcohol in order to make a 25% solution? 5 g

Solve each equation for the underlined variable.   **4.8**

25. $p = r + \underline{s} + t$
$s = p - r - t$

26. $5\underline{a}c = 3d$ $a = \frac{3d}{5c}$

27. $2(\underline{p} - 3q) = 5\underline{p}$
$p = -2q$

Make a sketch and a table to solve these problems.   **4.9–4.10**

28. Two planes traveling at 540 mi/h and at 630 mi/h start from the same place at the same time and fly in opposite directions. How long will it take for the two planes to be 1755 mi apart? 1.5 h

29. Robin can ride at an average rate of 25 km/h. She sets out to overtake a cyclist averaging 20 km/h. If the second cyclist has a 1 h headstart, how long will it take Robin to overtake the first cyclist? 4 h

30. A truck and a car leave the same town and travel in the same direction. The car travels at 40 mi/h and the truck at 55 mi/h. How many minutes will it take before they are 10 mi apart? 40 min

Chapter 5 Inequalities in One Variable

Draw the graph of each inequality.   **5.1**

1. $x > -2$ 2. $y \leq 3$ 3. $z = 0$ 4. $v < -0.5$ 5. $w \neq -1$

Solve. Then draw the graph of each inequality.   **5.2–5.5**

6. $a + 11 > -6$ $a > -17$ 7. $4b \leq -15$ $b \leq -\frac{15}{4}$ 8. $-2c + 5 + 3c < 7$ $c < 2$

9. $-\frac{2}{3} \geq d + \frac{1}{6}$ $d \leq -\frac{5}{6}$ 10. $-\frac{5}{3} > -\frac{5}{4}e$ $e > \frac{4}{3}$ 11. $3(2f - 1) - 5f \leq 7$ $f \leq 10$

12. $-2g \geq 0$ $g \leq 0$ 13. $-0.12 + j \leq -1.002$ $j \leq -0.882$ 14. $h - 2h < -1.5$ $h > 1.5$

15. $5l - 10 > 16 - 8l$ $l > 2$ 16. $4 - (1 - t) \geq 2t - 3$ $t \leq 6$ 17. $3(1 - m) > -9m$ $m > -\frac{1}{2}$

18. $-6n > 3$ or $-5 \geq -5n + 20$ $n < -\frac{1}{2}$, or $n \geq 5$ 19. $8(2 - p) > 0$ and $p \leq -2$ $p \leq -2$

20. $-5 + 3q \geq 4$ or $6 - 5q > -9$ all real numbers   21. $-7 < 5 - 3r < 2$ $1 < r < 4$

Solve. Then draw the graph of each equation or inequality.   **5.6–5.7**

22. $|x| = 1.1$ {$-1.1, 1.1$}   23. $|z - 2| = 3$ {$-1, 5$}   24. $9 = |3v + 6|$ {$-5, 1$}

25. $-3 + |2w - 1| = 1$ $\left\{-\frac{3}{2}, \frac{5}{2}\right\}$ 26. $-6|1 - 2p| = -3$ $\left\{\frac{1}{4}, \frac{3}{4}\right\}$ 27. $-\left|\frac{2g}{3}\right| = 19$ no solution

28. $|m| < 0.5$ {$-0.5 < m < 0.5$} 29. $14 \leq |n + 8|$ {$n \geq 6$ or $n \leq -22$} 30. $|3l - 5| \leq 0$ $\left\{\frac{5}{3}\right\}$

31. $-3|2h + 1| < 0$ {all real numbers except $-\frac{1}{2}$} 32. $-2(3 - |1 - 2e|) < 3$ $\left\{-\frac{7}{4} < e < \frac{11}{4}\right\}$ 33. $5 + |2 - g| \geq 6$ {$g \leq 1$ or $g \geq 3$}

Write the inequality represented by each graph.   **5.2–5.7**

34.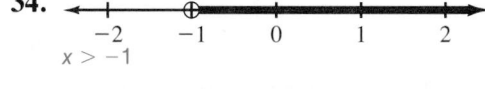
$x > -1$

35.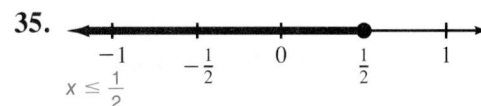
$x \leq \frac{1}{2}$

36.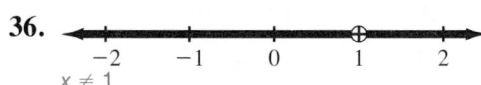
$x \neq 1$

37.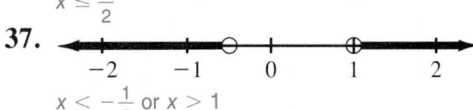
$x < -\frac{1}{2}$ or $x > 1$

38.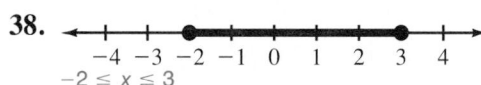
$-2 \leq x \leq 3$

39.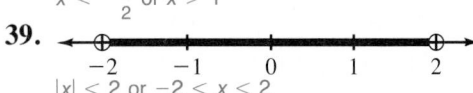
$|x| < 2$ or $-2 < x < 2$

Write and solve an inequality for each problem.   **5.8**

40. If Mark must not spend more than $15 for stamps and the stamps cost $0.35 each, what is the greatest number he can buy? 42

41. If the circumference of a round plate must be less than 36 in., what can be said about the plate's radius? must be less than 5.73 in.

42. To meet design specifications, the perimeter of a photograph must be at least 150 cm. If the width is 19 cm, what restrictions must be placed upon the length? length must be at least 56 cm

Chapter 6   Polynomials

Simplify. Assume that no variable equals zero.   **6.1–6.3**

1. $-2h^4 \cdot 11h^3$ $_{-22h^7}$

2. $(1.5 \times 10^8)(2.0 \times 10)$ $_{3.0 \times 10^9}$

3. $5jk^2 \cdot (-7j^2k^2)$ $_{-35j^3k^4}$

4. $\dfrac{b}{b^4}$ $_{\frac{1}{b^3}}$

5. $\dfrac{-14c^3d^2}{7c^2d^3}$ $_{\frac{-2c}{d}}$

6. $\dfrac{1.8 \times 10^4}{0.3 \times 10}$ $_{6 \times 10^3}$

7. $-f^0$ $_{-1}$

8. $(a^2)^4$ $_{a^8}$

9. $(-3bc^4)^2$ $_{9b^2c^8}$

10. $\dfrac{5ef^7}{-15e^4f^2g}$ $_{\frac{f^5}{-3e^3g}}$

11. $\left(\dfrac{2c^2}{d}\right)^3$ $_{\frac{8c^6}{d^3}}$

12. $\dfrac{(-5gh^3)^2}{20g^2h}$ $_{\frac{5h^5}{4}}$

Evaluate if $x = 3$, $y = -2$, and $z = -\dfrac{1}{2}$.

13. $5x^3(yz^5)$ $_{8\frac{7}{16}}$

14. $\dfrac{-7x^2 \cdot (4z^3)^2}{9y^2}$ $_{-0.4375}$

15. $\dfrac{-5y^5}{(-z^7)^2}$ $_{2,621,440}$

Rewrite each in scientific notation.   **6.4**

16. 0.00814 $_{8.14 \times 10^{-3}}$

17. $23,100,000$ $_{2.31 \times 10^7}$

18. 0.012×10^{-3} $_{1.2 \times 10^{-5}}$

19. $(0.7 \times 10^2)^2$ $_{4.9 \times 10^3}$

20. $(3.4 \times 10^{-2})(4.2 \times 10)$ $_{1.428 \text{ or } 1.428 \times 10^0}$

21. $\dfrac{1.9 \times 10^2}{38 \times 10^2}$ $_{5.0 \times 10^{-2}}$

Simplify. Then write in descending order with respect to x.   **6.5–6.6**

22. $-xy^2 + 2x^2y^2 + 3xy^2 - 7$ $_{2x^2y^2 + 2xy^2 - 7}$

23. $-2(ax^2 - 3a^2x^3) + 5ax^2$ $_{6a^2x^3 + 3ax^2}$

24. $\begin{array}{r} -8x^3 + 5x^2 + x - 11 \\ + 5x^3 + x^2 - x + 6 \\ \hline -3x^3 + 6x^2 - 5 \end{array}$

25. $\begin{array}{r} 6x^4 - 7x^3 - 2x^2 + x - 9 \\ - (-2x^4) + 9x^3 + 2x^2 + 2x + 9 \\ \hline 8x^4 - 16x^3 - 4x^2 - x - 18 \end{array}$

26. $(2d - 7x) + (d - 5x)$ $_{-12x + 3d}$

27. $(x^4 + 2x^3 - x + 5) - (3x^3 + 2x^2)$ $_{x^4 - x^3 - 2x^2 - x + 5}$

Multiply. Simplify, if possible.   **6.7–6.8**

28. $3y(-2y^2 + y - 3)$ $_{-6y^3 + 3y^2 - 9y}$

29. $(7z^3 - z^2 + 10)(-2z^3)$ $_{-14z^6 + 2z^5 - 20z^3}$

30. $-2a^2b(8ab^2 - 7a^3 + b)$ $_{-16a^3b^3 + 14a^5b - 2a^2b^2}$

31. $w(6w^2 - 5w) + 2w^2(7w - 8)$ $_{20w^3 - 21w^2}$

32. $(2x + 3)(x + 5)$ $_{2x^2 + 13x + 15}$

33. $(c - 7)(c + 11)$ $_{c^2 + 4c - 77}$

34. $(5t - 2)(2t - 5)$ $_{10t^2 - 29t + 10}$

35. $(4p + 7)(3p^2 - p + 2)$ $_{12p^3 + 17p^2 + p + 14}$

36. $(2a + b)(3a - 7b)$ $_{6a^2 - 11ab - 7b^2}$

37. $(5d^3 - 2d^2 - d)(3d^2 - 4)$ $_{15d^5 - 6d^4 - 23d^3 + 8d^2 + 4d}$

38. If the width of a rectangle is 6 cm shorter than its length l, write a polynomial to express its area. $_{l^2 - 6l}$

Write as a polynomial.   **6.9**

39. $(12x + 7)^2$ $_{144x^2 + 168x + 49}$

40. $(4a - 1)(4a + 1)$ $_{16a^2 - 1}$

41. $(-2b + c)^2$ $_{4b^2 - 4bc + c^2}$

42. $(5c^2 - 2d^3)^2$ $_{25c^4 - 20c^2d^3 + 4d^6}$

43. $(13x^2 - y)(13x^2 + y)$ $_{169x^4 - y^2}$

44. $(11 - 3e^3)^2$ $_{121 - 66e^3 + 9e^6}$

45. Use a pattern to find an algebraic expression that can be used to find the sum of the first n positive even integers. $_{n(n + 1)}$ **6.10**

Chapter 7   Factoring Polynomials

Give the prime factorization of each number.   **7.1**

1. 48
$2^4 \cdot 3$
2. 720
$2^4 \cdot 3^2 \cdot 5$
3. 41
prime
4. 960
$2^6 \cdot 3 \cdot 5$
5. 4375
$5^4 \cdot 7$
6. 1119
$3 \cdot 373$

Factor each polynomial completely, if possible.   **7.2–7.8**

7. $12m^2 + 27m^3 - 3m - 6$
$3(4m^2 + 9m^3 - m - 2)$
8. $8r^5 - 4r^4 + 32r^3 + 6r$
$2r(4r^4 - 2r^3 + 16r^2 + 3)$

9. $-3a^2b + 15a^3b^2 - 18ab^3$
$-3ab(a - 5a^2b + 6b^2)$
10. $14xy^2 - 21x^4 + 35y^2 - 28$
$7(2xy^2 - 3x^4 + 5y^2 - 4)$

11. $y^2 + 7y + 12$
$(y + 4)(y + 3)$
12. $b^2 - 6b + 8$
$(b - 4)(b - 2)$
13. $x^2 - 25x + 144$
$(x - 16)(x - 9)$

14. $n^2 + 17n + 72$
$(n + 8)(n + 9)$
15. $j^2 - 22j + 121$
$(j - 11)^2$
16. $s^2 + 7sk + 12k^2$
$(s + 4k)(s + 3k)$

17. $t^2 + t - 2$
$(t + 2)(t - 1)$
18. $r^2 - 5r - 150$
$(r + 10)(r - 15)$
19. $m^2 + 11m - 42$
$(m + 14)(m - 3)$

20. $b^2 - 9b - 6$
prime
21. $x^2 - 5xy + 6y^2$
$(x - 2y)(x - 3y)$
22. $m^2 + 14mn - 72n^2$
$(m + 18n)(m - 4n)$

23. $2h^2 + 3h + 1$
$(2h + 1)(h + 1)$
24. $5m^2 - 6m + 1$
$(5m - 1)(m - 1)$
25. $2t^2 - 5t + 2$
$(2t - 1)(t - 2)$

26. $3n^2 + 2n - 1$
$(3n - 1)(n + 1)$
27. $4k^2 + 3k - 1$
$(4k - 1)(k + 1)$
28. $7l^2 + 12l + 5$
$(7l + 5)(l + 1)$

29. $2x^2 + 5x - 12$
$(2x - 3)(x + 4)$
30. $6y^2 - 13y + 5$
$(2y - 1)(3y - 5)$
31. $4z^2 + 11z + 6$
$(4z + 3)(z + 2)$

32. $10x^2 - x + 6$
not factorable
33. $16q^2 + q - 15$
$(16q - 15)(q + 1)$
34. $4g^2 + 13gh - 12h^2$
$(4g - 3h)(g + 4h)$

35. $39k^2 + 37k + 8$
$(13k + 8)(3k + 1)$
36. $6a^2b^2 - ab - 40$
$(3ab - 8)(2ab + 5)$
37. $5c^2 - 7c - 15$
prime

38. $25y^2 - 9$
$(5y - 3)(5y + 3)$
39. $4w^2 + 4w + 1$
$(2w + 1)^2$
40. $9u^2 - 6ur + r^2$
$(3u - r)^2$

41. $1 - 49a^2$
$(1 - 7a)(1 + 7a)$
42. $4m^2 + 2mn - 2n^2$
$2(2m - n)(m + n)$
43. $a^2b^4 - c^6$
$(ab^2 - c^3)(ab^2 + c^3)$

44. $196 - 121b^2$
$(14 - 11b)(14 + 11b)$
45. $36 - 60v + 25v^2$
$(5v - 6)^2$
46. $81x^2 - 234x + 169$
$(9x - 13)^2$

47. $16q^2 + 48$
$16(q^2 + 3)$
48. $3a^4 - 3a^2$
$3a^2(a - 1)(a + 1)$
49. $7x^2 + 14xy + 28y^2$
$7(x^2 + 2xy + 4y^2)$

50. $1 - x - y + xy$
$(1 - y)(1 - x)$
51. $2p^3 + 3p^2 - 20p$
$p(2p - 5)(p + 4)$
52. $5 - 40w^2 + 80w^4$
$5(1 - 2w)^2(1 + 2w)^2$

53. $a^2 + 2a + 1 - b^2$
$(a + 1 - b)(a + 1 + b)$
54. $(3x - 2)^2 - 4y^2$
$(3x - 2 + 2y)(3x - 2 - 2y)$
55. $162 - 2d^4$
$-2(d^2 + 9)(d - 3)(d + 3)$

Solve and check.   **7.9**

56. $(2y + 3)(3y - 2) = 0$ $-\frac{3}{2}, \frac{2}{3}$
57. $5m - 6m^2 = 0$ $0, \frac{5}{6}$

58. $v^2 + 10v + 25 = 0$ -5
59. $j^2 - 6j = 7$ $-1, 7$

60. $3x^2 - 2x - 1 = 0$ $-\frac{1}{3}, 1$
61. $(2a + 4)(a - 1) = 20$ $-4, 3$

62. $3a^3 + 6a^2 + 3a = 0$ $-1, 0$
63. $36x^2 - 49 = 0$ $-\frac{7}{6}, \frac{7}{6}$

64. The square of a number reduced by three times the number gives 28.   **7.10**
Find the number. -4 or 7

65. The height of a triangle is 5 m less than its base. If its area is 33 m^2,
find its dimensions. base 11 m; height 6 m

66. Find three consecutive integers such that the square of twice the first is
30 more than three times the product of the second and third.
12, 13, 14 or $-3, -2, -1$

Chapter 8 Rational Expressions

Give the values of the variable for which each expression is undefined.   **8.1**

1. $\dfrac{5}{4x}$ 0

2. $\dfrac{-3y}{y+1}$ −1

3. $\dfrac{a+3}{a^2+3a}$ −3, 0

4. $\dfrac{z^2-1}{z^2-2z+1}$ 1

Simplify each expression if possible. Assume that no denominator is zero.

5. $\dfrac{15v}{27v^3}$ $\frac{5}{9v^2}$

6. $\dfrac{d+3}{d-3}$ imposs.

7. $\dfrac{a-b}{b-a}$ −1

8. $\dfrac{2x^2-5x-3}{x-3}$
$2x+1$

Multiply or divide. Express your answer in simplest form.   **8.2–8.3**

9. $-\dfrac{5m^2}{2n}\cdot\dfrac{6n^4}{10m}$ $-\frac{3mn^3}{2}$

10. $\dfrac{x-3}{x+5}\cdot\dfrac{2x+10}{3-x}$ −2

11. $\dfrac{2v+3}{2v^3}\cdot\dfrac{v^3+4v^2}{3+2v}$ $\frac{v+4}{2v}$

12. $\dfrac{2y^2-3y-2}{3y^2}\cdot\dfrac{12y^2-6y}{y-2}$ $\frac{8y^2-2}{y}$

13. $\dfrac{-14c^2}{d}\div\dfrac{21c^3}{d^2}$ $-\frac{2d}{3c}$

14. $\dfrac{9h^2+3h}{h+1}\div(6h+2)$ $\frac{3h}{2h+2}$

15. $\dfrac{5j-15}{6j}\div\dfrac{6-2j}{9j^2}$ $-\frac{15j}{4}$

16. $\dfrac{x^3-4x}{3x}\cdot\dfrac{x-5}{x+2}\div\dfrac{x-2}{x+5}$ $\frac{x^2-25}{3}$

Add or subtract. Express your answer in simplest form.   **8.4–8.6**

17. $\dfrac{2}{3ab}-\dfrac{5}{2a^2b}+\dfrac{6}{a^2b^2}$ $\frac{4ab-15b+36}{6a^2b^2}$

18. $\dfrac{y}{x-y}-\dfrac{x}{y-x}$ $\frac{y+x}{x-y}$

19. $\dfrac{d^2+3d+2}{d^2-4}-\dfrac{1}{2-d}$ $\frac{d+2}{d-2}$

20. $\dfrac{2n^2+2mn}{m^2-n^2}+1$ $\frac{m+n}{m-n}$

21. $\dfrac{\frac{1}{x}-\frac{3}{x^2}}{2x-\frac{1}{x^3}+1}$ $\frac{x^2-3x}{2x^4+x^3-1}$

22. $\dfrac{1-\frac{2}{c}-\frac{3}{c^2}}{\frac{2}{c}+\frac{2}{c^2}}$ $\frac{c-3}{2}$

Divide.   **8.7**

23. $(5j^2-10jk^2l+25j^2kl^2-30kl)\div 20jkl$ $\frac{j}{4kl}-\frac{k}{2}+\frac{5jl}{4}-\frac{3}{2j}$

24. $(3x^3-2x^2+3x-5)\div(x-2)$ $3x^2+4x+11+\frac{17}{x-2}$

25. $(y^3-27)\div(y-3)$ y^2+3y+9

Express as a ratio in simplest form.   **8.8**

26. $39:169$ 3:13

27. 3 m:20 cm 15:1

28. 3.25 h:20 min 39:4

Solve and check.   **8.9**

29. $\dfrac{1}{6}x^2+\dfrac{1}{3}x=\dfrac{5}{2}$ −5, 3

30. $\dfrac{8}{t^2-t}+\dfrac{t}{1-t}=\dfrac{7}{2}$ $-1,\frac{16}{9}$

31. If Sue walks 2 km/h faster, she can cover 16 km in the same time it   **8.10**
takes to walk 12 km at her present rate. How fast is she walking? 6 km/h

Chapter 9   Linear Equations

Plot each point in the coordinate plane. Tell its quadrant or axis.

9.1 1–5.

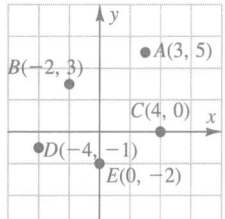

1. $A(3, 5)$ **2.** $B(-2, 3)$ **3.** $C(4, 0)$ **4.** $D(-4, -1)$ **5.** $E(0, -2)$
1st quadrant   2nd quadrant   x-axis   3rd quadrant   y-axis

Determine whether the ordered pairs are solutions of the equation.

9.2

6. $3y - 2x = 0$: $(3, 2)$, $\left(-\frac{3}{2}, -\frac{2}{3}\right)$, $(-2, -3)$, $\left(\frac{5}{4}, \frac{5}{6}\right)$, $\left(-4, -\frac{8}{3}\right)$
yes   no   no   yes   yes

From the graph of $x + y = -1$, determine whether the ordered pairs given are solutions of the equation $x + y = -1$. Check your answers.

7. $(2, -1)$ no   **8.** $(-1, 0)$ yes

9. $(0, -1)$ yes   **10.** $(1, 1)$ no

The cost c ($\$$) of w (oz) of milk is given by $c = 0.015w + 0.20$. Graph this equation and answer the following questions.

9.3 11.

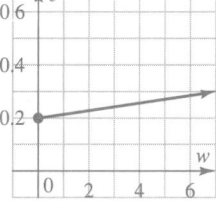

11. Approximately how much does 24 oz of milk cost? $0.56

12. Approximately how much milk can be purchased for $2? 120 oz

Find the slope of a line containing the given points.

9.4

13. $(-4, 3)$; $(2, -5)$ $-\frac{4}{3}$ **14.** $(7, -3)$; $(7, 1)$ **15.** $\left(-\frac{3}{2}, -1\right)$; $\left(\frac{4}{3}, -\frac{1}{5}\right)$
                                    no slope $\frac{24}{85}$

Through each given point, draw a line with the given slope.

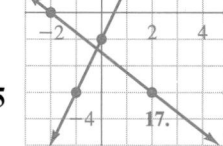

16. $(-1, -3)$; 2   **17.** $(-2, 0)$; $-\frac{3}{4}$ **18.** $(5, -3)$; no slope

Find the slope and y-intercept of each equation. Then graph the equation.

9.5

19. $3x + y = -2$ **20.** $2x - 5y = 0$ **21.** $-\frac{1}{3}x + \frac{1}{2}y = -\frac{3}{2}$
$m = -3$; $b = -2$ $m = \frac{2}{5}$; $b = 0$ $m = \frac{2}{3}$; $b = -3$

Determine if the graphs of each pair of equations are parallel lines.

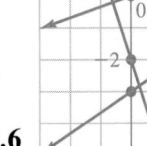

22. $y = -2x + 4$; $4x + 2y = 0$ yes   **23.** $y = -\frac{4}{3}x + \frac{3}{5}$; $15y - 20x = 0$ no

Write an equation in standard form for each line described.

9.6

24. The line contains points $P(-2, 6)$ and $Q(3, -4)$. $2x + y = 2$

25. The line has a zero slope and contains point $S(-6, 4)$. $y = 4$

Graph each inequality in a coordinate plane. See Solutions Manual.

9.7

26. $y > -2x + 3$ **27.** $5x + 2y \leq -10$ **28.** $3x + 12 < 0$

2. a. $(-1, -1)$, $\left(0, -\frac{1}{2}\right)$, $(1, 0)$, $\left(2, \frac{1}{2}\right)$, $(3, 1)$ **2. b.** Domain: $\{-1, 0, 1, 2, 3\}$;   Range: $\left\{-1, -\frac{1}{2}, 0, \frac{1}{2}, 1\right\}$

Chapter 10   Relations, Functions, and Variation

1c.

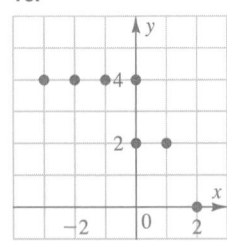

1. Given the mapping shown: 10.1–10.3
   a. State the ordered pairs of the relation.
     (−3, 4), (−2, 4), (−1, 4), (0, 4), (0, 2), (1, 2), (2, 0)
   b. Give the domain and range.
     Domain: {−3, −2, −1, 0, 1, 2}; Range: {0, 2, 4}
   c. Graph the relation.

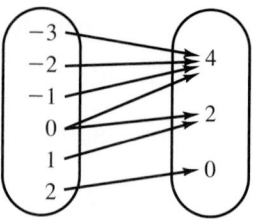

   d. Tell whether the relation is a function.
     no

2. Given the graphed relation:
   a. State the ordered pairs of the relation.

   b. Give the domain and range.

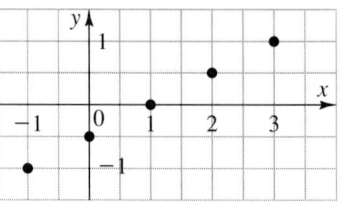

   c. Tell whether the relation is a function.
     yes

3a.

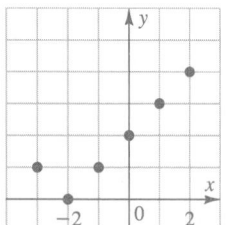

3. Given the relation $y = |x + 2|$. Domain: $\{-3, -2, -1, 0, 1, 2\}$.
   a. Graph the relation.
   b. Tell whether the relation is a function.
     yes

4. Given the graphed relation:
   a. Give three ordered pairs of the relation.
     Answers may vary; (0, 2), (1, 2), (−2, 2)
   b. Give the domain and range.
     Domain: all real numbers; Range: {2}
   c. What kind of function is this relation?
     constant
   d. Give the equation of this function.
     $y = 2$

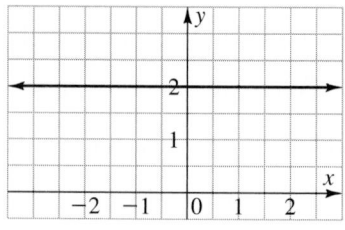

If $f(x) = -3x + 5$ and $g(x) = \frac{1}{10}x$, evaluate the following.   **10.2**

5. $f(0)$ 5   **6.** $f\left(-\frac{1}{3}\right)$ 6   **7.** $g(-20)$ −2   **8.** $g(0.2)$ .02

9. $f(g(9))$ $\frac{23}{10}$ **10.** $g(f(0))$ $\frac{1}{2}$ **11.** $f(1) \cdot g\left(\frac{1}{2}\right)$ $\frac{1}{10}$ **12.** $g(5) + f\left(-\frac{5}{3}\right)$
                                                                                $\frac{21}{2}$

For the data shown in the given tables, tell whether y varies directly   **10.4, 10.5**
as x, inversely as x, or neither of these. If there is direct or inverse   indirect variation
variation, give the constant of proportionality and the equation. $k = 48; y = \frac{48}{x}$

13.

| x | 4 | 18 | 6 | 10 | direct variation
|---|---|---|---|---|
| y | 6 | 27 | 9 | 15 |

$k = \frac{3}{2}; y = \frac{3}{2}x$

14.

x	3	12	2	8
y	16	4	24	6

15. If y varies directly as x and $y = 69$ when $x = 3$, find y when $x = 5$. 115

16. If y varies inversely as x and $y = 12$ when $x = 4$, find y when $x = 6$. 8

If $C = \frac{5}{9}(F - 32)$ is the formula for converting degrees F to degrees C;   **10.6**
find:

17. The temperature in degrees Celsius equivalent to 5°F −15°C

18. The temperature in degrees Fahrenheit equivalent to 100°C 212°F

Chapter 11 Systems of Linear Equations

Graph each system and give its solution set. See Solutions Manual.   **11.1**

1. $\begin{cases} x - 2y = 0 \\ 3x + y = -7 \end{cases}$
   $\{(-2, -1)\}$

2. $\begin{cases} 3y - 2x = 6 \\ y = \frac{2}{3}x + 1 \end{cases}$ ∅

3. $\begin{cases} 5x + 2y = 4 \\ 5x - 4 = -2y \end{cases}$
   $\{(x, y): 5x + 2y = 4\}$

Solve each system by an appropriate algebraic method.   **11.2, 11.4, 11.5**

4. $\begin{cases} x + 5y = -4 \\ -3x + 2y = 12 \end{cases}$ $(-4, 0)$

5. $\begin{cases} 2a - 3b = 18 \\ -4a + 3b = -24 \end{cases}$
   $(3, -4)$

6. $\begin{cases} -c = 10 - 5d \\ -2c + 5d = -5 \end{cases}$
   $(15, 5)$

7. $\begin{cases} 5x + 7y = 11 \\ 14y = 13 - 10x \end{cases}$ ∅

8. $\begin{cases} 4x = 3y - 4 \\ 5y - 2x = 9 \end{cases}$ $\left(\frac{1}{2}, 2\right)$

9. $\begin{cases} 3 = 4j - 9k \\ 5j + 12k = -4 \end{cases}$
   $\left(0, -\frac{1}{3}\right)$

10. $\begin{cases} 3u - 4v = 6 \\ u = 2 + \frac{4}{3}v \end{cases}$
    $\{(u, v): 3u - 4v = 6\}$

11. $\begin{cases} 8(r - t) = \frac{7}{2} - 5t \\ t = -0.5 \end{cases}$ $\left(\frac{1}{4}, -\frac{1}{2}\right)$

12. $\begin{cases} -\frac{1}{2}q + \frac{1}{3}p = p + 2 \\ \dfrac{p - q}{2} = p + 1 \end{cases}$
    $(-6, 4)$

Write a system of linear equations and solve.

13. The sum of two numbers is 22 and one is 1 more than twice the other. Find the two numbers. 7, 15   **11.3**

 20.

14. Belinda invested $1200 in two accounts. One paid 7.5% simple annual interest and the other 8.5%. At the end of one year, the total interest was $96.50. How much was invested in each account? $550 at 7.5%; $650 at 8.5%

15. The sum of the digits of a two-digit number is 10. The number with the digits reversed is 18 less than the original. Find the original number. 64   **11.6**

16. Lonnie is 6 yr younger than his sister. In 13 yr his age will be $\frac{4}{5}$ of hers. What are their present ages? 11 yr, 17 yr   **11.7**   21.

17. A combination of forty $1 and $5 bills is worth $144. How many of each kind of bill are there? 26 $5 bills; 14 $1 bills   **11.8**

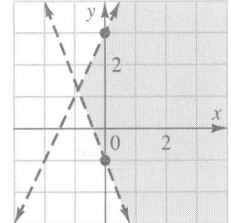

18. Sunflower seeds priced at $2.35/lb are mixed with peanuts at $1.85/lb to make a 16 lb mixture valued at $32.40. How many pounds of each are used? 5.6 lb sunflower seeds, 10.4 lb peanuts

19. A boat going downstream traveled 15 mi in 3 h but took $3\frac{3}{4}$ h for the return trip. What was the speed of the current? $\frac{1}{2}$ mi/h   **11.9**   22.

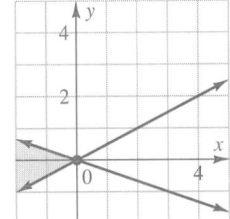

Graph each system of inequalities on a coordinate plane.   **11.10**

20. $\begin{cases} 2y + 5x > -2 \\ y < 2x + 3 \end{cases}$

21. $\begin{cases} x + 3y \le 0 \\ y \ge \frac{1}{2}x \end{cases}$

22. $\begin{cases} x < -1 \\ y \ge 1 \end{cases}$

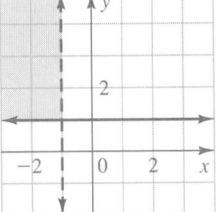

Chapter 12 Radicals

Express in simplest form. Assume variables are positive. 12.1, 12.4–12.7

1. $-\sqrt{225}$ –15

2. $\sqrt{\dfrac{5}{9}}$ $\frac{\sqrt{5}}{3}$

3. $\sqrt{96}$ $4\sqrt{6}$

4. $\sqrt{50x^3}$ $5x\sqrt{2x}$

5. $3\sqrt{12} - \sqrt{3} + 2\sqrt{5}$ $5\sqrt{3}+2\sqrt{5}$

6. $(3\sqrt{3a})(5\sqrt{a})$ $15a\sqrt{3}$

7. $\sqrt{0.0001b^4}$ $0.01b^2$

8. $\dfrac{1}{\sqrt{27}}$ $\frac{\sqrt{3}}{9}$

9. $\dfrac{\sqrt{2}}{2} + 3\sqrt{8} - \sqrt{32}$ $\frac{5}{2}\sqrt{2}$

10. $\dfrac{\sqrt{40c^3d}}{\sqrt{10cd}}$ $2c$

11. $\sqrt{288xy^2z^3}$ $12yz\sqrt{2xz}$

12. $(2 + 3\sqrt{5})(4\sqrt{5})$ $8\sqrt{5}+60$

13. $(5\sqrt{3} + 3\sqrt{2})^2$ $93 + 30\sqrt{6}$ 14. $(7\sqrt{5} - 1)(7\sqrt{5} + 1)$ 244 15. $\dfrac{-6}{3\sqrt{3} - 2}$ $\frac{-18\sqrt{3}-12}{23}$

Simplify. Use the square root table on p. 670 when necessary. 12.2

16. $\sqrt{51}$ 7.141

17. $\sqrt{94}$ 9.695

18. $\sqrt{7}$ 2.646

19. $\sqrt{145}$ 12.042

Use the divide-and-average method to approximate each square root to the nearest tenth.

20. $\sqrt{11}$ 3.3

21. $\sqrt{241}$ 15.5

22. $\sqrt{87.9}$ 9.4

23. $\sqrt{459.6}$ 21.4

Express each rational number as a decimal. 12.3

24. $-\dfrac{3}{8}$ –0.375

25. $\dfrac{25}{3}$ $8.\overline{3}$

26. $-\dfrac{7}{25}$ –0.28

27. $\dfrac{5}{7}$ $0.\overline{714285}$

Express each decimal as a rational number in the form $\dfrac{m}{n}$, where m and n are integers and $n \neq 0$.

28. 0.13 $\frac{13}{100}$

29. $-0.\overline{4}$ $-\frac{4}{9}$

30. 9.01 $\frac{901}{100}$

31. $3.\overline{12}$ $\frac{103}{33}$

Solve and check. 12.8

32. $7 + 3\sqrt{x} = 9$ $\frac{4}{9}$

33. $\sqrt{5 - 2x} = -2$ no solution 34. $2\sqrt{1 - 2v} = 3\sqrt{v}$ $\frac{4}{17}$

Given right $\triangle ABC$ with right $\angle C$. Use the table on p. 670 or a calculator to find the remaining side to the nearest tenth. 12.9

35. $a = 12$, $b = 16$ $c = 20$

36. $a = 7$, $c = 25$ $b = 24$

37. $b = 11.4$, $c = 14.5$ $a = 9.0$

The lengths of three sides of a triangle are given. Is it a right triangle? Write *yes* or *no*.

38. $1.0, 2.4, 2.6$ yes

39. $6\sqrt{3}, 3\sqrt{3}, 9$ yes

40. $7, 12, 13$ no

Find the distance between each pair of points. 12.10

41. $A(-1, 3)$, $B(2, 7)$ 5

42. $C(2, -5)$, $D(-3, -10)$ $5\sqrt{2}$

Find the lengths of the sides of a triangle with the following vertices.

43. $P(-2, 1)$, $Q(-2, 13)$, $R(-7, 1)$
$PQ = 12$, $QR = 13$, $PR = 5$

44. $H(5, 12)$, $K(0, 0)$, $L(-3, -4)$
$HK = 13$, $KL = 5$, $HL = 8\sqrt{5}$

Chapter 13 Quadratic Equations and Functions

Solve.   13.1

1. $z^2 = 225$ **2.** $3y^2 = 81$ **3.** $(x - 5)^2 = 98$ **4.** $(2b + 1)^2 = 4$
±15   ±3√3   5 ± 7√2 $-\frac{3}{2}, \frac{1}{2}$

Solve each equation by completing the square.   13.2

5. $r^2 - 4r - 96 = 0$ –8, 12 **6.** $q^2 - q = 2$ –1, 2   **7.** $2p^2 + 4p = 7$
$-1 \pm \frac{3\sqrt{2}}{2}$

Use the quadratic formula to solve each equation.   13.3

8. $x^2 - 6x + 4 = 0$ 3 ± √5 **9.** $6y^2 + 11y = 10$ $-\frac{5}{2}, \frac{2}{3}$ **10.** $9z^2 - 12z = 1$ $\frac{2 \pm \sqrt{5}}{3}$

Use the most appropriate method to solve each equation.   13.4

11. $t^2 - t - 110 = 0$ **12.** $(3m - 4)^2 = 50$ $\frac{4 \pm 5\sqrt{2}}{3}$ **13.** $16m^2 = 49$ $\pm\frac{7}{4}$
–10, 11
14. $10b^2 + 21b = 10$ $-\frac{5}{2}, \frac{2}{5}$ **15.** $c^2 + 2c - 1 = 0$ **16.** $d^2 - 6d + 10 = 0$
$-1 \pm \sqrt{2}$ no solution
17. If the product of two consecutive even integers is 288, find the   13.2–13.4
two integers. 16 and 18; −18 and −16

Find the vertex point and graph each function.   13.5

18. $f(x) = -x^2$ v(0, 0)   **19.** $y = 2x^2 + 3$ v(0, 3)   **20.** $f(x) = (x + 2)^2$
v(−2, 0)
21. $y = x^2 - 6x + 6$ v(3, −3) **22.** $y = -3x^2 + 12x + 1$ **23.** $f(x) = 2x^2 + 8x$
v(2, 13)   v(−2, −8)

Find the value of the discriminant and state the nature of the solutions.   13.6

24. $m^2 + 12m + 36 = 0$ **25.** $4n^2 - 8n + 1 = 0$ **26.** $3k^2 - 2k + 5 = 0$
1 real solution   2 real solutions   no real solutions

Find the number of x-intercepts of each function without graphing.

27. $f(x) = x^2 + 2x + 1$ **28.** $y = -2x^2 + x - 2$ **29.** $f(x) = 3x^2 - x - 1$
one   none   two

Use the sum and product of the solutions to write quadratic equations   13.7
with the given solutions.

30. −7, 11   **31.** $-\frac{2}{3}$, 5   **32.** $\frac{4}{5}, -\frac{1}{2}$ **33.** $-3 \pm \sqrt{2}$
$x^2 - 4x - 77 = 0$ $3x^2 - 13x - 10 = 0$ $10x^2 - 3x - 4 = 0$ $x^2 + 6x + 7 = 0$
34. A ski lodge cook keeps track   13.8
of the number of people at
breakfast and the amount of
oatmeal cooked in three days.

No. people n	12	20	35
No. cups oatmeal c	4.8	8	14

(12, 4.8) and (20, 8) give the same slope as (20, 8)
and (35, 14); $c = \frac{2}{5}n$.

a. Show that this is a linear function, and write the function.

b. Tell the meaning of the slope and intercepts. Slope $\frac{2}{5}$ means the average person uses
$\frac{2}{5}c$ of oatmeal per breakfast. The n- and c-intercepts, both zero, mean that no oatmeal is used if
no one is at breakfast.

18.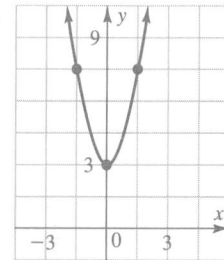

19.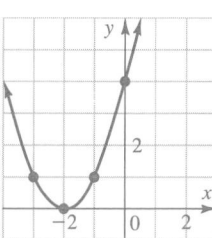

20.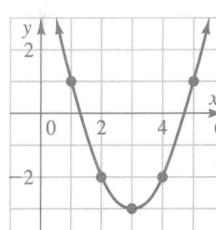

21.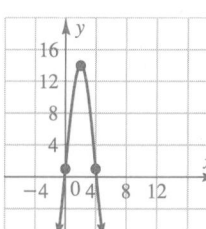

22.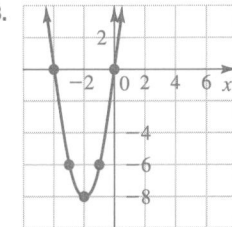

23.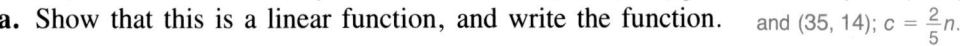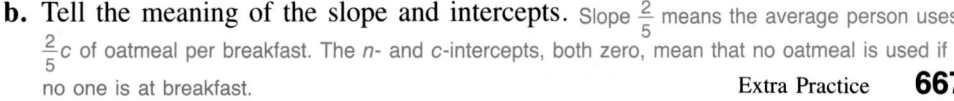

Chapter 14   Statistics, Probability, and Logic

Find the mode, median, and mean for each set of data.   14.1

1. $-3, -3, -2, 0, 1, 3, 4$
mode -3; median 0; mean 0

2. $-4.0, -2.3, -1.1, 2.7, 3.8, 4.2$
mode none; median 0.8; mean 0.55

Distances from home to school were compiled for a class of 30, and a histogram was constructed.

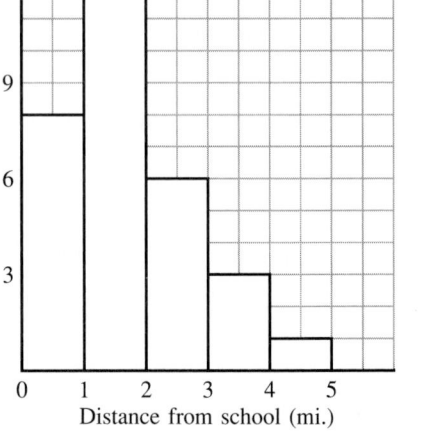
14.2

3. What percent of students live more than 2 mi away? 33.$\overline{3}$%

4. In what interval is the median distance? 1–2 mi

5. What is the mean distance to the nearest tenth of a mile? *Hint:* Use the middle of the interval as the distance; e.g., 0.5 mi, 1.5 mi, etc. 1.7 mi

The number of stray dogs taken by an animal shelter over a 12-mo period is shown below.   14.3

Jan	Feb	Mar	Apr	May	Jun	Jul	Aug	Sep	Oct	Nov	Dec
3	2	2	4	3	6	9	13	11	5	0	2

For the animals taken per month, find:

6. The mean
5

7. The range
13

8. The variance
14.83

9. The standard deviation
3.85

A letter is chosen at random from the word PROBABILITY. Find the probability of choosing: 14.4

10. $P(\text{vowel})$ $\frac{4}{11}$ **11.** $P(B)$ $\frac{2}{11}$ **12.** $P(J)$ 0   **13.** $P(B \text{ or } I)$ $\frac{4}{11}$

Of a class of 30 students, 5 have motor scooters, 19 have bicycles, and 4 have both. Make a Venn diagram and find the probability that a student chosen at random has: 14.5

14. Just a motor scooter $\frac{1}{30}$ **15.** A motor scooter or a bicycle $\frac{2}{3}$

16. Neither a bicycle nor a motor scooter $\frac{1}{3}$

A bag contains lettered, colored cards of the following type: 5 red As, 4 blue As, 3 red Bs, and 2 blue Bs. One card is randomly chosen, noted, and replaced. Then a second card is randomly selected. What is the probability of each event?   14.6

17. $P(\text{both red Bs})$ $\frac{9}{196}$ **18.** $P(\text{both blues})$ $\frac{9}{49}$ **19.** $P(\text{both cards same letter})$ $\frac{53}{98}$

Chapter 15   Right Triangle Relationships

Given the plane figure shown, find: **15.1**

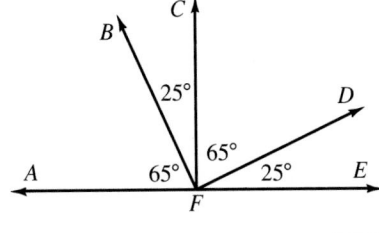

1. $m\angle BFE$ 115   2. $m\angle BFA$ 65   3. $m\angle AFD$ 155

4. Two right angles   5. Two obtuse angles
   $\angle CFE, \angle BFD, \angle AFC$ $\angle BFE, \angle AFD$
6. Three pairs of supplementary angles
   $\angle EFD, \angle AFD; \angle AFB, \angle BFE; \angle AFC, \angle CFE$
7. If an angle measures 15 more than half its
   supplement, find the angle and its supplement.
   70, 110

Complete.   **15.2**

8. In an isosceles triangle if the unequal angle has a measure of 74, then
   the angles opposite the congruent sides have measures of _?_ . This is a(n) _?_
   triangle.   53   acute

9. In right $\triangle ABC$, $m\angle C = 90$ and the measure of $\angle B$ is $\frac{1}{5}$ that of $\angle A$.
   Find the measures of $\angle A$ and $\angle B$. 75, 15

Given $\triangle JKL \cong \triangle PQR$:   **15.3**

10. Name the corresponding angles.   11. Name the corresponding sides.
    $\angle J$ and $\angle P$; $\angle K$ and $\angle Q$; $\angle L$ and $\angle R$ $\overline{JK}$ and $\overline{PQ}$; $\overline{JL}$ and $\overline{PR}$; $\overline{KL}$ and $\overline{QR}$
12. True or false? $\triangle KJL \cong \triangle QPR$? true

13. In $\triangle LMN$, $m\angle M = 75$ and $m\angle N = 33$. In $\triangle RST$, $m\angle S = 72$ and   **15.4**
    $m\angle T = 33$. Show that the triangles are similar. Write the similarity.
    $m\angle L = m\angle S = 72$; $m\angle M = m\angle R = 75$. $\triangle LMN \sim \triangle SRT$
14. $\triangle ABC \sim \triangle DEF$, $AB = 12$, $BC = 16$, and $EF = 12$. Find DE. 9

In $\triangle ABC$, $\angle B$ is a right angle. In terms   **15.5**
of a, b, and c, find:

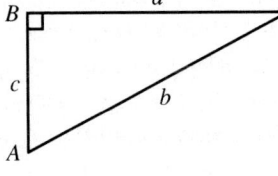

15. $\sin C \frac{c}{b}$ 16. $\cos C \frac{a}{b}$ 17. $\tan A \frac{a}{c}$

In right triangle GHK, $m\angle K = 90$, $GH = 4$,
and $HK = 2\sqrt{3}$. Find:

18. GK 2   19. $\sin G \frac{\sqrt{3}}{2}$ 20. $\tan H \frac{\sqrt{3}}{3}$

Use the trigonometric table on p. 671 to find: **15.6**

21. If $m\angle A = 23$ (a) $\sin A$ (b) $\tan A$ (c) $\cos A$
                          0.3907   0.4245   0.9205
22. If $\cos B = 0.9903$ (a) $m\angle B$ (b) $\tan B$ (c) $\sin B$
                          8°   0.1405   0.1392
23. In $\triangle ABC$, $m\angle C = 90$, $AB = 25$, and $BC = 15$. To the nearest whole
    number, find: (a) $m\angle A$ 37°   (b) $m\angle B$ 53°   (c) AC 20

24. From a lighthouse 350 ft high, the angle of a depression to a ship at sea   **15.7**
    is 12°. How far is the ship from shore? Are there hidden assumptions in
    this problem? 1647 ft to nearest ft; One assumes the lighthouse stands at the edge of the water.

Squares and Approximate Square Roots

Number n	Square n^2	Positive Square Root $\sqrt{n}$	Number n	Square n^2	Positive Square Root $\sqrt{n}$	Number n	Square n^2	Positive Square Root $\sqrt{n}$
1	1	1.000	51	2,601	7.141	101	10,201	10.050
2	4	1.414	52	2,704	7.211	102	10,404	10.100
3	9	1.732	53	2,809	7.280	103	10,609	10.149
4	16	2.000	54	2,916	7.348	104	10,816	10.198
5	25	2.236	55	3,025	7.416	105	11,025	10.247
6	36	2.449	56	3,136	7.483	106	11,236	10.296
7	49	2.646	57	3,249	7.550	107	11,449	10.344
8	64	2.828	58	3,364	7.616	108	11,664	10.392
9	81	3.000	59	3,481	7.681	109	11,881	10.440
10	100	3.162	60	3,600	7.746	110	12,100	10.488
11	121	3.317	61	3,721	7.810	111	12,321	10.536
12	144	3.464	62	3,844	7.874	112	12,544	10.583
13	169	3.606	63	3,969	7.937	113	12,769	10.630
14	196	3.742	64	4,096	8.000	114	12,996	10.677
15	225	3.873	65	4,225	8.062	115	13,225	10.724
16	256	4.000	66	4,356	8.124	116	13,456	10.770
17	289	4.123	67	4,489	8.185	117	13,689	10.817
18	324	4.243	68	4,624	8.246	118	13,924	10.863
19	361	4.359	69	4,761	8.307	119	14,161	10.909
20	400	4.472	70	4,900	8.367	120	14,400	10.954
21	441	4.583	71	5,041	8.426	121	14,641	11.000
22	484	4.690	72	5,184	8.485	122	14,884	11.045
23	529	4.796	73	5,329	8.544	123	15,129	11.091
24	576	4.899	74	5,476	8.602	124	15,376	11.136
25	625	5.000	75	5,625	8.660	125	15,625	11.180
26	676	5.099	76	5,776	8.718	126	15,876	11.225
27	729	5.196	77	5,929	8.775	127	16,129	11.269
28	784	5.292	78	6,084	8.832	128	16,384	11.314
29	841	5.385	79	6,241	8.888	129	16,641	11.358
30	900	5.477	80	6,400	8.944	130	16,900	11.402
31	961	5.568	81	6,561	9.000	131	17,161	11.446
32	1,024	5.657	82	6,724	9.055	132	17,424	11.489
33	1,089	5.745	83	6,889	9.110	133	17,689	11.533
34	1,156	5.831	84	7,056	9.165	134	17,956	11.576
35	1,225	5.916	85	7,225	9.220	135	18,225	11.619
36	1,296	6.000	86	7,396	9.274	136	18,496	11.662
37	1,369	6.083	87	7,569	9.327	137	18,769	11.705
38	1,444	6.164	88	7,744	9.381	138	19,044	11.747
39	1,521	6.245	89	7,921	9.434	139	19,321	11.790
40	1,600	6.325	90	8,100	9.487	140	19,600	11.832
41	1,681	6.403	91	8,281	9.539	141	19,881	11.874
42	1,764	6.481	92	8,464	9.592	142	20,164	11.916
43	1,849	6.557	93	8,649	9.644	143	20,449	11.958
44	1,936	6.633	94	8,836	9.695	144	20,736	12.000
45	2,025	6.708	95	9,025	9.747	145	21,025	12.042
46	2,116	6.782	96	9,216	9.798	146	21,316	12.083
47	2,209	6.856	97	9,409	9.849	147	21,609	12.124
48	2,304	6.928	98	9,604	9.899	148	21,904	12.166
49	2,401	7.000	99	9,801	9.950	149	22,201	12.207
50	2,500	7.071	100	10,000	10.000	150	22,500	12.247

Tables

Trigonometric Ratios

Angle	sin	cos	tan	Angle	sin	cos	tan
0°	0.0000	1.0000	0.0000	45°	0.7071	0.7071	1.0000
1	0.0175	0.9998	0.0175	46	0.7193	0.6947	1.0355
2	0.0349	0.9994	0.0349	47	0.7314	0.6820	1.0724
3	0.0523	0.9986	0.0524	48	0.7431	0.6691	1.1106
4	0.0698	0.9976	0.0699	49	0.7547	0.6561	1.1504
5	0.0872	0.9962	0.0875	50	0.7660	0.6428	1.1918
6	0.1045	0.9945	0.1051	51	0.7771	0.6293	1.2349
7	0.1219	0.9925	0.1228	52	0.7880	0.6157	1.2799
8	0.1392	0.9903	0.1405	53	0.7986	0.6018	1.3270
9	0.1564	0.9877	0.1584	54	0.8090	0.5878	1.3764
10	0.1736	0.9848	0.1763	55	0.8192	0.5736	1.4281
11	0.1908	0.9816	0.1944	56	0.8290	0.5592	1.4826
12	0.2079	0.9781	0.2126	57	0.8387	0.5446	1.5399
13	0.2250	0.9744	0.2309	58	0.8480	0.5299	1.6003
14	0.2419	0.9703	0.2493	59	0.8572	0.5150	1.6643
15	0.2588	0.9659	0.2679	60	0.8660	0.5000	1.7321
16	0.2756	0.9613	0.2867	61	0.8746	0.4848	1.8040
17	0.2924	0.9563	0.3057	62	0.8829	0.4695	1.8807
18	0.3090	0.9511	0.3249	63	0.8910	0.4540	1.9626
19	0.3256	0.9455	0.3443	64	0.8988	0.4384	2.0503
20	0.3420	0.9397	0.3640	65	0.9063	0.4226	2.1445
21	0.3584	0.9336	0.3839	66	0.9135	0.4067	2.2460
22	0.3746	0.9272	0.4040	67	0.9205	0.3907	2.3559
23	0.3907	0.9205	0.4245	68	0.9272	0.3746	2.4751
24	0.4067	0.9135	0.4452	69	0.9336	0.3584	2.6051
25	0.4226	0.9063	0.4663	70	0.9397	0.3420	2.7475
26	0.4384	0.8988	0.4877	71	0.9455	0.3256	2.9042
27	0.4540	0.8910	0.5095	72	0.9511	0.3090	3.0777
28	0.4695	0.8829	0.5317	73	0.9563	0.2924	3.2709
29	0.4848	0.8746	0.5543	74	0.9613	0.2756	3.4874
30	0.5000	0.8660	0.5774	75	0.9659	0.2588	3.7321
31	0.5150	0.8572	0.6009	76	0.9703	0.2419	4.0108
32	0.5299	0.8480	0.6249	77	0.9744	0.2250	4.3315
33	0.5446	0.8387	0.6494	78	0.9781	0.2079	4.7046
34	0.5592	0.8290	0.6745	79	0.9816	0.1908	5.1446
35	0.5736	0.8192	0.7002	80	0.9848	0.1736	5.6713
36	0.5878	0.8090	0.7265	81	0.9877	0.1564	6.3138
37	0.6018	0.7986	0.7536	82	0.9903	0.1392	7.1154
38	0.6157	0.7880	0.7813	83	0.9925	0.1219	8.1443
39	0.6293	0.7771	0.8098	84	0.9945	0.1045	9.5144
40	0.6428	0.7660	0.8391	85	0.9962	0.0872	11.4301
41	0.6561	0.7547	0.8693	86	0.9976	0.0698	14.3007
42	0.6691	0.7431	0.9004	87	0.9986	0.0523	19.0811
43	0.6820	0.7314	0.9325	88	0.9994	0.0349	28.6363
44	0.6947	0.7193	0.9657	89	0.9998	0.0175	57.2900
45	0.7071	0.7071	1.0000	90	1.0000	0.0000	

Symbols

Symbol	Meaning	Page
( )	parentheses—a grouping symbol	3
⋯	"and so on"	7
{ , }	encloses the numbers of a set	7
−	negative	7
+	positive	7
π	pi, a number approximately equal to $\frac{22}{7}$ or 3.14	8
=	equals, is equal to	12
>	is greater than	12
<	is less than	12
$-a$	opposite or additive inverse of a	13
$|a|$	absolute value of a	14
$\frac{1}{n}$	reciprocal of a number	35
[ ]	brackets—a grouping symbol	37
×, ·	multiply	42
a^b	exponent, a is used as a factor b times	55
≈	is approximately equal to	66
≠	is not equal to	78
∅, { }	empty set, null set	79
$\stackrel{?}{=}$	is this statement true?	137
%	percent	152
a_b	subscript, for descriptive discrimination	160
≥	is greater than or equal to	187
≤	is less than or equal to	187
$a:b$	ratio $\frac{a}{b}$	346

Symbol	Meaning	Page
(a, b)	ordered pair whose first component is a and second component is b	370
$P(x, y)$	point P with coordinates x, y	370
$f(x)$	f of x, the value of f at x	418
$F: x \rightarrow x + 1$	the function F that takes x into $x + 1$	418
$\pm$	positive or negative	494
$\sqrt{}$	principal square root	494
$0.6\overline{6}$	repeating decimal	500
σ	sigma, standard deviation	591
$P(A)$	probability of event A	596
$P(\overline{A})$	probability of the complement of A	597
$\overleftrightarrow{AB}$	a line containing points A and B	614
$\overline{AB}$	a line segment with two endpoints A and B	614
$\overrightarrow{AB}$	a ray with endpoint A passing through point B	614
AB	length or measure of line segment AB	614
$\angle A$	angle A	615
$m\angle A$	measure of angle A	615
$\triangle ABC$	triangle ABC	618
⦜	right angle, 90°	619
≅	is congruent to	623
~	is similar to	628
$\cos A$	$\dfrac{\text{length of leg adjacent to } \angle A}{\text{length of hypotenuse}}$	634
$\sin A$	$\dfrac{\text{length of leg opposite } \angle A}{\text{length of hypotenuse}}$	634
$\tan A$	$\dfrac{\text{length of leg opposite } \angle A}{\text{length of leg adjacent to } \angle A}$	634

Chapter 1 Real Numbers

Practice Exercises, pages 5–6 **1.** 27 **3.** 6

5. 2 **7.** 24 **9.** 15 **11.** $\dfrac{1}{300}$ **13.** 6

15. 7 **17.** $3 + x$ **19.** $t - 1.07$

21. $\dfrac{9}{8}$ **23.** $\dfrac{1}{4}$ **25.** 1 **27.** 0 **29.** $\dfrac{17}{6}$

31. $\dfrac{9}{2}$ **33.** $\dfrac{3}{8}j$ **35.** $\dfrac{6.4}{b}$ **37.** 23

39. 5 **41.** 8 **43.** $\dfrac{m}{g}$

Practice Exercises, pages 10–11 **1.** -1.0

3. 0.2 **5.** -1.2 **7.** 1.2 **9.** G

11. A **13.** I **15.** D **17.** $\dfrac{7}{1}$

19. $-\dfrac{3012}{1000}$ **21.** $\dfrac{47}{4}$ **23.** $\dfrac{-1}{1}$

25.
$-1\ 0\ 1\ 2\quad\ 4$

27.
$-4\qquad -1.5\ 0\qquad\ 2\ 2.5$

29.
$-1\frac{1}{4}\ -\frac{1}{2}\ \ 0\qquad \frac{3}{4}1$

31. natural numbers; whole number; integer; rational number; real number **33.** whole number; integer; rational number; real number **35.** rational number; real number **37.** Yes. The number line extends indefinitely in both directions, and all real numbers, rational and irrational, can be graphed on it. **39.** 71 **41.** 4 **43.** 15 **45.** when x is an integer

Practice Exercises, pages 15–16

1.
$-4\qquad -1\ 0\qquad\ 2\ 3$

3.
$-2\frac{1}{2}\ \ -\frac{1}{2}0\quad\ 2\ 2\frac{1}{2}$

5. $<$ **7.** $>$ **9.** $=$ **11.** $>$ **13.** 3.1

15. $-\dfrac{2}{5}$ **17.** 6.2 **19.** $-3\dfrac{1}{5}$ **21.** 13 **23.** 5

25. $\left\{\dfrac{1}{7}, \dfrac{1}{6}, \dfrac{1}{5}\right\}$ **27.** $\left\{-1\dfrac{3}{4}, -1\dfrac{2}{3}, -\dfrac{5}{4}\right\}$

29. $\{-0.1041, -0.104, -0.1\}$ **31.** -14 **33.** $-\dfrac{3}{8}$

35. -21 **37.** 12 **39.** 7 **41.** -7

43. -6.1 **45.** $3\dfrac{7}{20}$ **47.** false **49.** true

51. -20; 20°C below freezing

53. $+3\dfrac{1}{4}$; $3\dfrac{1}{4}$ lb weight gain

55. $+55$; 55 ft above sea level

57. -785.95; loss of \$785.95

Practice Exercises, pages 20–21 **1.** -5 **3.** -6

5. 1 **7.** -7 **9.** -8 **11.** -3.5

13. -8.0 **15.** -6 **17.** 1 **19.** 6

21. -6 **23.** -17 **25.** -6.5 **27.** $-2\dfrac{1}{2}$

29. $\dfrac{7}{3}$ **31.** $<$ **33.** $<$

35. $5 + (-17) = -12$; -12°C

37. $-3 + (-3) + (-3) + (-3) = -12$; 12 yd loss

39. $-3\dfrac{1}{8} + 4\dfrac{5}{8} = 1\dfrac{1}{2}$; up $1\dfrac{1}{2}$ points

Practice Exercises, pages 24–26 **1.** -500

3. -453 **5.** 4.61 **7.** -1.709 **9.** $-\dfrac{4}{7}$

11. $-\dfrac{5}{8}$ **13.** $\dfrac{1}{14}$ **15.** 0 **17.** 8.6

19. -8 **21.** 8 **23.** $\dfrac{17}{24}$ **25.** $1\dfrac{49}{75}$

27. 23.98 **29.** $3\dfrac{1}{3}$ **31.** -13 **33.** -25

35. 59 **37.** 15 **39.** 7 **41.** 1

43. $19 + 6 + (-8) = 17$; 17°C

45. $1000 + (-60) + 2200 + (-200) + 1700 = 4640$; 4640 m **47.** 15 **49.** 5.07 **51.** 72

Practice Exercises, pages 29–30 **1.** 4.1

3. -0.75 **5.** -8 **7.** -13 **9.** 3.7

11. 9.5 **13.** 17 **15.** 18 **17.** $\dfrac{7}{9}$

19. 46 **21.** 27 **23.** 0.3 **25.** 1.9

27. -3.6 **29.** $-\dfrac{13}{8}$ **31.** -5.65 **33.** $-14\dfrac{1}{3}$

35. $30\dfrac{9}{10}$ **37.** -17 **39.** 64 **41.** -24.3

43. -7.2 **45.** 3 **47.** -5 **49.** 0.4

Test Yourself, page 30 **1.** 22.3 **3.** 76

5.
$-4\,-3\,-2\,-1\ \ 0\ \ 1$ **7.** $>$ **9.** -1

11. $4\dfrac{1}{2}$ **13.** -4.42

Practice Exercises, pages 33–34 **1.** -30

3. -0.468 **5.** 65 **7.** 2.22 **9.** 30

11. -45 **13.** 120   **15.** 200   **17.** -1200
19. -900 **21.** -18 **23.** -6
25. 55,555.5   **27.** $-11,111.1111$
29. -1558.788 **31.** 15   **33.** 17
35. -12 **37.** -18 **39.** -3 **41.** 4
43. $(-7) \times 2 = -14$: $-14°$

Practice Exercises, pages 38–40   **1.** $\frac{1}{5}$ **3.** $\frac{1}{75}$

5. -5 **7.** $-\frac{10}{9}$ **9.** -7 **11.** -12

13. $\frac{15}{2}$ **15.** $-\frac{1}{2}$ **17.** 0

19. not possible   **21.** 2   **23.** $-\frac{1}{6}$

25. $-\frac{1}{16}$ **27.** -7 **29.** 3   **31.** -1

33. 2   **35.** 3   **37.** -2.909088 **39.** -587.22

41. 1800   **43.** -8 **45.** $-7\frac{1}{2}$ **47.** true

49. true   **51.** 80   **53.** 190 cm
55. 1.5 km; no   **57.** 89.6°F
59. 0.01   **61.** -2.5

Practice Exercises, pages 44–45   **1.** $m - 2$

3. $s + 500$ **5.** $p + 0.06p$ **7.** $\frac{a + b + c}{3}$

9. $2x - 1$ **11.** Yes, since one can be a simplified form of the other.   **13.** $-| 2x + 1 |$
15. True. $x - y$ and $y - x$ are opposites, but the absolute values of opposites are equal.

Test Yourself, page 45   **1.** -34 **3.** 8   **5.** 0

7. -6 **9.** 8   **11.** $-\frac{1}{9}$ **13.** -9 **15.** $\frac{3}{2}$

Summary and Review, pages 46–47   **1.** 3.5

3. 12   **5.** 32   **7.** $\frac{1}{8}$ **9.** $x + 18$

11. $a - b$
13.
15.
17. $>$ **19.** -4.31 **21.** -9 **23.** -1.2
25. -11.7 **27.** -5.92 **29.** 150   **31.** -120
33. 0   **35.** $+2.5$ yd

Maintaining Skills, page 50   **1.** 3.3147   **3.** 42.807
5. 0.9   **7.** 3.7   **9.** 14.94   **11.** 280.5
13. 2.8   **15.** 8.2   **17.** 0.452   **19.** -7
21. -28 **23.** 14   **25.** -15 **27.** -4
29. -42 **31.** 456 mi   **33.** 65 packages

Chapter 2   Algebraic Expressions

Practice Exercises, pages 53–54   **1.** -5 **3.** 130
5. 50   **7.** 23   **9.** 7   **11.** 13

13. $-\frac{39}{31}$ **15.** 54   **17.** -33 **19.** $\frac{76}{13}$

21. -90 **23.** $6.25

Practice Exercises, pages 57–58   **1.** 25   **3.** $\frac{1}{4}$

5. -16 **7.** 16   **9.** -16 **11.** -16 **13.** 98
15. 2209   **17.** 363   **19.** 44944   **21.** 216
23. -33
25. 0.09   **27.** 0.000000001   **29.** 100   **31.** 100
33. 5   **35.** 56   **37.** 64   **39.** 400   **41.** -15
43. -9 **45.** -226 **47.** 7776   **49.** -231.3441

Practice Exercises, pages 61–62   **1.** 68   **3.** 134

5. $\frac{1}{7}$ **7.** 5130   **9.** 2325   **11.** -24.75 **13.** 2

15. Distributive property   **17.** Commutative property for multiplication   **19.** Symmetric property
21. $(2)(3x) - (2)(11)$

23. $\left(-\frac{3}{4}\right)\left(\frac{2}{3} x\right) - \left(-\frac{3}{4}\right)(8)$ **25.** $(12 - 3)a$

27. False   **29.** False   **31.** False   **33.** $13.47

Practice Exercises, pages 64–66   **1.** like
3. unlike   **5.** like   **7.** unlike   **9.** unlike
11. like   **13.** $8x$ **15.** $-12t$ **17.** $2t + 15$
19. $12g^2$ **21.** $7x^2 + 7x$ **23.** $12g - h + 2$
25. $9ab$ **27.** $5ab^2$ **29.** $4m + 13$
31. $-6x + 7y - 14$ **33.** $3x + 11$ **35.** $5r - 2$
37. $6x + 7$ **39.** $-15c^2 + 16c$ **41.** $8x^3 - x^2$
43. $155r + 295$ **45.** $7m + 7n$ **47.** $6x^2 - 6y$
49. $3t^2 + 7t$ **51.** $6x^2y^2 + 3x^2y - 9xy^2$

53. $4a$ **55.** $\frac{5}{8} y$ **57.** $-23c + 24d$

59. $1.518b - 0.69$ **61.** $n + (n + 1) + (n + 2)$;
$3n + 3$ **63.** $5(7w) + 2(7w)$; $49w$

Test Yourself, page 66   **1.** -9 **3.** 1   **5.** 8
7. 192   **9.** 56.52
11. Associative property for multiplication
13. Commutative property for addition
15. $11hk - 5hk^2 - 5h^2k$ **17.** $2x^2 + 7$

Practice Exercises, pages 69–71   **1.** $g - 8$
3. $-2a + 13$ **5.** $3t^2 - 9$ **7.** $-2x - 1$
9. $ab^2c - 3abc^2$ **11.** -27 **13.** -3 **15.** 26
17. 5   **19.** $2x^2yz + x^2yz^2$ **21.** $-6x + 14$
23. $21r - 153$ **25.** 21   **27.** 41   **29.** $-5m - 1$
31. $a - 2$ **33.** $-36x + 37$ **35.** 18 cm^2
37. $2(a + 6) + 4(3a)$; $14a + 12$ **39.** 13.19
41. 5   **43.** 40

Practice Exercises, pages 76–77 **1.** $n - 7$
3. $n + 5$ **5.** $8n - 1$ **7.** $5n^2$ **9.** $\dfrac{n^2}{3}$

11. $6(n + 3)$
17. a. $m - 4$ **b.** $m - 4$ **c.** $m - 8$
19. a. l **b.** $l - 7$ **c.** $l^2 - 7l$ **d.** $4l - 14$
21. $9t + 36$ dollars; $2t - 36$ dollars
23. $p + 1 = 3c$

Practice Exercises, pages 80–81 **1.** $\{1\}$ **3.** $\{0\}$
5. $\{-1.0, 1\}$ **7.** $\{-1, 1\}$ **9.** $\{0\}$ **11.** $\{-1, 0, 1\}$
13. $\{-1\}$ **15.** $\{-1, 0\}$ **17.** $\emptyset$ **19.** $\left\{\dfrac{1}{2}\right\}$
21. $\{-1\}$ **23.** $\{-1\}$ **25.** $\{-1\}$ **27.** $\emptyset$
33. Any negative number.
35. Negative five is greater than negative seven.
37. Six subtracted from a is greater than zero.

Practice Exercises, pages 83–84
1. no solution **3.** 0 **5.** -2 **7.** -3 **9.** 1
11. 15 **13.** 33 **15.** $m + 50 = 2m$; $50, $100
17. $n + (n + 6) = -8$; -7
19. $l(32 - l) = 252$; 18 ft $\times$ 14 ft

Practice Exercises, pages 87–89 **1.** $x - 3 = 18$
3. $x + 4 = 27$ **5.** $5x - 2 = 18$ **7.** $8x^2 = 56$
9. $\dfrac{5}{3x} = 10$ **11.** $6(x + 9) = 132$
13. a. $b - 6$ **b.** $b - 1$ **c.** $b - 7$
d. $(b - 6) + (b - 7) = 35$; 24
15. a. $45n$ **b.** $45n + 35$ **c.** $45n + 35 = 485$; 10
21. $3j + 5 = 2(j + 5)$
23. $25e + 10(6 + e) = 235$
25. $13{,}250 = 2c + 150$; What was the cost of the old
car? **27.** $110 = 35 + 5p$; How much was a monthly
payment? **29.** $s = 100 + 2(1200)$; How much
tuition did Sheila pay?
31. $55 = \dfrac{1}{2}b(4b + 2)$; What are the base and height

of the triangle?

Test Yourself, page 89 **1.** $-2r - 12$
3. $-m^2 + n$; -11 **5.** $\dfrac{n}{9} - 8$ **9.** $\emptyset$
11. $n - (-2) = 11$

Summary and Review, pages 90–91 **1.** 12
3. -0.0001 **5.** 7 **7.** Distributive property
9. Associative property for addition
11. Associative property for multiplication
13. $-2c + 5 + 4c^2$ **15.** $4mn^2 - 3mn$

17. $2h^2$ **19.** $-24 + 26p$; 28 **21.** $2[n + (-2)]$
23. $5n$ **25.** $\{2\}$ **27.** $\{-2\}$ **29.** $\{-1, 1\}$
31. $2x - 2 = 1$

Cumulative Review, page 94
1. $-1.5, -1, 0, 2, 2.5$ **3.**
5. 0.8 **7.** $1\dfrac{1}{2}$ **9.** 14 **11.** -4.1 **13.** -4
15. $\dfrac{1}{4}$ **17.** 16 **19.** 18 **21.** $6x - 3y$
23. $-2a + 6$ **25.** $2c + 8$ **27.** -3 **29.** 8
31. 44 **33.** $\dfrac{1}{3}$ **35.** 14 **37.** $2n - 3$ **39.** $2w + 1$

Chapter 3 Equations in One Variable

Practice Exercises, pages 98–99 **1.** 13.01 **3.** 8.3
5. 8.1 **7.** $6\dfrac{2}{3}$ **9.** $2\dfrac{2}{3}$ **11.** $4\dfrac{2}{3}$ **13.** -30 **15.** 5
17. 44 **19.** -3.6 **21.** -6.1 **23.** -7
25. 19.019
27. 1.062 **29.** $2\dfrac{2}{3}$ **31.** 5 **33.** 27 **35.** -5.8
37. no solution **39.** 5 **41.** no solution **43.** 26
45. 12 **47.** $\{3\}$ **49.** $\{9\}$

Practice Exercises, pages 104–105 **1.** -8 **3.** -7
5. -5 **7.** -3 **9.** -7 **11.** -21 **13.** -12
15. 55 **17.** 20 **19.** 24 **21.** 35
23. $m = 10.5 \times 15$ **25.** $t = \dfrac{55.5 \times 11}{5}$
27. $r = \dfrac{24.6 \times 6}{-5}$ **29.** -18 **31.** -9 **33.** $\dfrac{2}{3}$
35. -0.118 **37.** 9.2 **39.** 20 **41.** $\{-12, 12\}$
43. $\left\{-\dfrac{2}{3}, \dfrac{2}{3}\right\}$ **45.** $m = 4.5 \times 33$; 148.5
47. $y = 6 \times 0.89$; 5.34
49. $m = 62.4 \div 81.23$; 0.77

Practice Exercises, pages 108–109 **1.** $\dfrac{8}{3}$ **3.** 3
5. $\dfrac{11}{3}$ **7.** 17 **9.** 76 **11.** $-\dfrac{15}{2}$ **13.** $\dfrac{15}{2}$ **15.** $\dfrac{1}{4}$
17. $-\dfrac{7}{9}$ **19.** 113 **21.** 117 **23.** $\dfrac{3}{2}$ **25.** $-4, 4$
27. $-2, 2$ **29.** $-1, 1$ **33.** 7 **33.** 6
35. $r = \dfrac{2.79 - 23.58}{583}$; -0.04
37. $x = (-0.14 + 0.03)0.24$; -0.03

Test Yourself, page 109   **1.** -7 **3.** $\frac{13}{4}$ **5.** -60
7. 3   **9.** 0

Practice Exercises, pages 111–112
1. $7x + 3 = 24$; 3 albums
3. $5x = 40$; books; 0 left over
5. $4e + 5 = 25$; $5 per hour

Practice Exercises, pages 115–116
1. Statements: **2.** $\frac{a}{c}$ **3.** $\frac{b}{c}$

Reasons: **1.** Given   **3.** Substitution property

Statements	Reasons
3. 1. $a = b$	**1.** Given
2. $a - c = a - c$	**2.** Reflex. prop.
3. $a - c = b - c$	**3.** Substit. prop.

Statements	Reasons
5. 1. $a + [b + (-a)]$	
$\quad = a + [(-a) + b]$	**1.** Comm. prop. add.
2. $\quad = [a + (-a)] + b$	**2.** Assoc. prop. add.
3. $\quad = 0 + b$	**3.** Add.inv.prop.
4. $\quad = b$	**4.** Ident. prop. add

Statements	Reasons
7. 1. $a = b$	**1.** Given
2. $a - d = a - d$	**2.** Reflex. prop.
3. $\quad = b - d$	**3.** Substit. prop.
4. $\quad = b + (-d)$	**4.** Def. of subtrac.
5. $\quad = -d + b$	**5.** Commut. prop. of add.
6. $\quad = -d - (-b)$	**6.** Def. of subtrac.
7. $\quad = (-1)(d) - (-1)(b)$	**7.** Prop. of -1 for mult.
8. $\quad = (-1)(d - b)$	**8.** Dist. prop.
9. $\quad = -(d - b)$	**9.** Prop. of -1 for mult.

9. transitive, symmetric   **11.** symmetric

Practice Exercises, pages 118–119   **1.** 3.5 units
3. $h = 5.9$ **5.** $r = 7$ **7.** $h = 3$ **9.** $w = 110$
13. 95.5 km/h   **15.** 71.02 m^2

Practice Exercises, pages 122–123   **1.** $10 = \frac{1}{3}x$
3. $2w + 3 = 7$ **5.** $n - 92 = -28$; 64
7. $11x = -165$; -15
9. $n + 7.13 = 2.09$; -5.04
11. $\frac{2}{5}x = 16$; 40 yr   **13.** $3n + 11 = 50$; 13
15. $21 + 2(12) = 54$; 15 cm   **17.** $\frac{3}{5}p = 245.97$;
$409.95   **19.** $4.50x + 117(2.50) = 733.50$; 98
21. $\frac{1}{2}x + \frac{1}{10}x + \frac{1}{20}x + 35{,}000 = x$; $100,000

Practice Exercises, pages 128–129   **1.** 3   **3.** -5
5. 9   **7.** 75   **9.** $21.98   **11.** 22 yr   **13.** -425
15. 7.7   **17.** 18 m   **19.** 3.2 h   **21.** 11 in.
23. $300   **25.** $-4°$F

Test Yourself, page 129   **1.** -216

Statements	Reasons
3. 1. $m = r$; $n \neq 0$	**1.** Given
2. $\frac{m}{n} = \frac{m}{n}$	**2.** Reflex. prop.
3. $\frac{m}{n} = \frac{r}{n}$	**3.** Subst. prop.

5. $h = 10$

Summary and Review, pages 130–131   **1.** 21
3. -32 **5.** 5   **7.** $\frac{36}{5}$ **9.** 5   **11.** -12 **13.** 1
15. 8   **17.** $w = 8$ **19.** $r = 0.04$ **21.** For all real
numbers x, y, and z, if $x = y$, then $x + z = y + z$
23. $3x + 500 = 12{,}200$; 3900 lb **25.** $2x + 14.95 =$
809.45; $397.25   **27.** $54 = 2(12) + 2(x)$;
15 cm   **29.** $2x = 210$; 105 lb

Maintaining Skills, page 134   **1.** $-2b + 35$
3. $y + 5$ **5.** $-4m + 4$ **7.** 0.20   **9.** 0.06
11. 0.1   **13.** 75%   **15.** 7%   **17.** 38.5%
19. 25%   **21.** 70%   **23.** 37.5%   **25.** $\frac{7}{20}$ **27.** $\frac{3}{8}$
29. $\frac{1}{12}$ **31.** $1\frac{1}{2}$ h   **33.** 95°F

Chapter 4   More Equations in One Variable

Practice Exercises, pages 138–139   **1.** 2   **3.** 4
5. 2   **7.** -3 **9.** 0   **11.** 7   **13.** 7   **15.** 9
17. -2 **19.** 10   **21.** 1   **23.** -2 **25.** -6 **27.** 5
29. 0.2   **31.** -1.5 **33.** $-9\frac{1}{2}$ **35.** $-5\frac{9}{11}$ **37.** 7
39. -10 **41.** -20 **43.** $-4\frac{3}{4}$ **45.** 2   **47.** 7
49. $2w + 2(2w - 10) = 118$; $w = 23$ ft, $l = 36$ ft

Practice Exercises, pages 142–143   **1.** -3 **3.** 1
5. 0   **7.** 10   **9.** $\frac{10}{3}$ **11.** 22   **13.** -2
15. 4   **17.** $1\frac{2}{3}$ **19.** 5   **21.** $-\frac{5}{4}$ **23.** $-1\frac{3}{10}$
25. $\frac{5}{4}$ **27.** 1   **29.** $-\frac{1}{29}$ **31.** 9   **33.** -3 **35.** $\frac{5}{2}$
37. $\frac{11}{15}$ **39.** $-\frac{6}{13}$ **41.** $\frac{1}{2}$ **43.** $\frac{3}{4}$ **45.** $9\frac{1}{4}$
47. $5\frac{1}{3}$ sq units

Practice Exercises, pages 146–147

1. $x + (x + 1) + (x + 2) = 99$; 32, 33, 34
3. $x + (x + 2) + (x + 4) + (x + 6) = -124$; $-34, -32, -30, -28$
5. $x + (x + 8) = 3(x + 6) - 2$; $-8, -6, -4, -2, 0$
7. $x + (x + 1) = 105$; 52, 53 **9.** $x + (x + 1) + x + 2) = -354$; $-119, -118, -117$
11. $x + (x + 2) = -54$; $-28, -26$
13. $x + (x + 2) + (x + 4) = -45$; $-17, -15, -13$
15. $(x + 1) + (x + 3) = 48$; 22, 23, 24, 25
17. $2(x + 2) + x = 85$; 27, 29
19. $x + (x + 1) + (x + 2) = 39 - x$; 9, 10, 11
21. $x + (x + 1) + (x + 2) = 4x - 9$; 12, 13, 14
23. $x + (x + 5) + (x + 10) + (x + 15) = 90$; 15, 20, 25, 30 **25.** $2(x + 1) = x + (x + 2)$; any three consecutive integers **27.** $3[x + (x + 1)] - [(x + 2) + (x + 3)] = 70$, 18, 19, 20, 21

Practice Exercises, pages 150–151 **1.** 9.5 **3.** 24
5. 18.72 **7.** $\frac{3}{2}$ **9.** 3 **11.** -10 **13.** $-\frac{1}{5}$ **15.** 1
17. 2 **19.** 6 **21.** 0 **23.** 106 **25.** 1400
27. -1.077 **29.** -0.4 **31.** 960 **33.** $-\frac{16}{5}$
35. $-\frac{11}{2}$ **37.** 0 **39.** $2\frac{2}{3}$ **41.** 19 **43.** 0.2
45. ≈ -0.46 **47.** ≈ 0.37
49. 3 **51.** $l = 26$ m; $w = 16$ m

Test Yourself, page 151 **1.** 14 **3.** 2 **5.** $-1\frac{2}{3}$
7. $i + 2, i + 4$ **9.** 11, 13, 15, 17 **11.** 34.95

Practice Exercises, pages 154–155 **1.** 0.98
3. 375 **5.** 20% **7.** $66\frac{2}{3}\%$ **9.** 15 **11.** 35
13. $3500 **15.** 2.5% **17.** 54 **19.** 250%
21. 7.2 **23.** $133\frac{1}{3}\%$ **25.** $90 **27.** $25 **29.** 8%
31. 100 **33.** 275 **35.** 8.25%

Practice Exercises, pages 157–159 **1.** $147; 25% (dec.) **3.** $82.86; $111.86 **5.** $26 (inc.); 2.9% (inc.) **7.** $78.75; $5.25 (dec.) **9.** $22,425
11. 12.6% **13.** 11.1% **15.** 1.4% **17.** old price: 60¢; new price: 70¢ **19.** $10,398.40 **21.** 33.7%
23. 66¢ **25.** 17.1% **27.** 96.9¢ **29.** 74
31. $22.92

Practice Exercises, pages 163 **1.** $16\frac{2}{3}\%$
3. $11.\overline{3}\%$ **5.** 6.7 mL **7.** 2.9 g **9.** 53.3 gal

Practice Exercises, pages 166–167 **1.** $x = y - 10$
3. $c = d + 3$ **5.** $d = \frac{2y}{a}$ **7.** $n = \frac{8}{3}k$

9. $m = \frac{2j}{kl}$ **11.** $y + \frac{12 - 3x}{4}$ **13.** $y = 4t$
15. $a = \frac{-11b - 7}{3}$ **17.** $m = \frac{2l - h}{4}$
19. $w = \frac{A}{l}$; 7 **21.** $b = p - 2a$; 20 **23.** $b = \frac{V}{h}$; $346\frac{2}{3}$ **25.** $y = \frac{-7x - 14z}{4}$ **27.** $r = \frac{158 - q}{115}$
29. $w = \frac{16}{3}t$ **31.** $q = \frac{-5v - 9}{2}$
33. $h = \frac{16i - l}{3}$ **35.** $C = \frac{5F - 160}{9}$; -20
37. $t = \frac{A - p}{pr}$; 5 **39.** $n = \frac{L - a + d}{d}$
41. $l = \frac{2S - na}{n}$ **43.** $c = \frac{a + 2b}{12b}$
45. $d = rt$; $r = \frac{d}{t}$; 5.14 km/h

Practice Exercises, pages 170– 171
1. $45t = 55(t - 1)$ **3.** $550(t + 2) = 625t$
5. $3(r + 20)$; $4r$ **7.** $5\frac{1}{2}$ **9.** $14\frac{2}{3}$ **11.** 90

13.

	Rate	× Time =	Distance
Car 1	40	$t + 1$	$40(t + 1)$
Car 2	55	t	$55t$

15.

	Rate	× Time =	Distance
Going	50	t	$50t$
Return	55	$t - \frac{1}{2}$	$55\left(t - \frac{1}{2}\right)$

17. $2\frac{2}{3}$ h; hiker 1: 7 mi/h, hiker 2: 4 mi/h; 275 mi

Practice Exercises, pages 175–177 **1.** 9h **3.** 4h
5. $3\frac{1}{2}$ h **7.** 1st bus 50 mi/h; 2nd bus 45 mi/h
9. 60 km **11.** $4\frac{2}{3}$ mi **13.** Bus 24 mi/h; Car 36 mi/h **15.** $9\frac{2}{3}$ h **17.** 2:15 AM **19.** 10:00 AM
21. $3\frac{5}{7}$ h **23.** 1000 m

Test Yourself, page 177 **1.** 0.75 **3.** 300%
5. 5% **7.** 6.25% **9.** $a = 2b + 3$ **11.** 3h

Summary and Review, pages 178–179 **1.** -9
3. $-12\frac{3}{4}$ **5.** -2.82 **7.** $z + 8, z + 10, z + 12$, $8z + 14$ **9.** 2.85 **11.** $1350 **13.** 108 students
15. 37.5 mL **17.** $n = \frac{15m - p}{5}$

19. $a = \frac{p-b}{2}; \frac{11}{2}$ 21. 1650 mi 23. $2\frac{2}{3}$ km

Cumulative Review, pages 182–184 1. $-\frac{1}{2}$

3. $\frac{3}{4}$ 5. -2 7. $\frac{1}{12}$ 9. $-\frac{29}{24}$ 11. $-\frac{7}{6}$

13. $\frac{7}{10}$ 15. $\frac{2}{3}$ 17. 7 19. -20 21. $2x - 6$

23. $2h + 9$ 25. $5mn - 1$ 27. 0 29. 56

31. 16 33. 8 35. -1 37. $m - 2$

39. $m + (m-2) = 30$ 41. 5 43. -9 45. $\frac{1}{9}$

47. -14 49. $-\frac{1}{10}$ 51. -1 53. 2 55. 4

57. 32 59. 8 61. 25 63. $42 = 21 + 2(6)$; 15 cm

65. $n + (n + 1) = 49$; 24, 25

67. $a = 0.15(40)$; 6 71. $48 = 0.12c$; 400

75. $4 = 0.08c$; 50 79. $15 = r(50)$; 30%

83. $5 = 0.20x$; 25 87. $x = 0.375(96)$; 36

91. $30 = 1.50x$; 20 95. $x = 0.005(200)$; \$1

97. $y = x - 9$ 99. $g = 2h - 6$ 103. $c = 3d$

105. $q = \dfrac{2p - 40}{3}$ 107. 20% 109. $8h$

Chapter 5 Inequalities in One Variable

Practice Exercises, pages 188–189

1. -3;

3. 1;

9.

11.

17.

19. $\{0\}$ 21. $\{$all real numbers$\}$

23. $\{$all real numbers except $-1\}$

25. -5;

27. $\frac{5}{2}$;

33.

35.

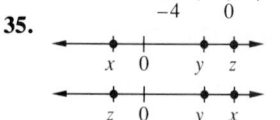

37. all real numbers 39. all real numbers where a and b are additive inverses

Practice Exercises, pages 192–193

1. $m > -2$

3. $a < 1\frac{1}{2}$;

9. $x < 12$

11. $a > 4$

17. $\{$all integers less than $-\frac{5}{2}\}$ 19. $\{$all integers less than 0$\}$ 21. $\{$all integers less than $-2\}$ 23. $\emptyset$

25. $t < -0.2$

27. $x > 10\frac{1}{2}$

29. $\{7, 8, 9, \ldots\}$ 31. $\{3, 4, 5, \ldots\}$

33. Answers may vary. An example: $5 > 4$, $-2 > -4, 5 - (-2) \overset{?}{=} 4 - (-4), 7 < 8$

35. False 37. $k - 6 < -6; k < 0$

Practice Exercises, page 197

1. $x < 5$

3. $a < 7$

9. $a > -7$

11. $b < 32$

17. $x \geq 5$

19. $z \leq 10$

25. $x \leq -40$

29. $m \geq 3$

33. $k < 9.6$

37. $\frac{3}{4}y > -18; y > -24$

Practice Exercises, pages 200–201

1. $y > -3$

3. $x \geq -2$

7. $\{x: x > 3\}$ 9. $\{b: b \leq 9\}$ 11. $\{y: y \leq -5\}$

13. $\{a: a < \frac{2}{3}\}$ 15. $\{d: d \geq 4\}$ 17. $\{y: y < -\frac{20}{3}\}$

19. $\{y: y > -15\}$ 21. $\{k: k > -\frac{1}{6}\}$

23. $\{n: n \geq -23\}$ 25. $\{m: m \geq 1\}$

27. $\{w: w$ is a real number$\}$

29. $\{t: t > \frac{7}{6}\}$ 31. $\{x: x \neq -\frac{1}{4}\}$ 33. $\{w: w \leq 3\}$

35. $\{y: y > \frac{1}{4}\}$ 37. $\{a: a \geq -\frac{19}{11}\}$

39. $\{m: m$ is a real number$\}$ 41. $\frac{2}{3}y + 14 \geq 8$; $\{$all real numbers greater than or equal to $-9\}$

Test Yourself, page 201

1. -2 0 **3.** 0

5. {all real numbers greater than -1}

9. {a: $a < -12$} -12 0

Practice Exercises, page 205

1. 34 35 **3.** -1 1

9. -4 4 **11.** 0

17. -1 0 3 **19.** -1 2

25. 0 ; no solution

27. $\frac{3}{5}$ 2

31. $23 < c < 23.5$ **33.** $l \le 107$

Practice Exercises, pages 208–209   1. $-5, 3$

3. $\emptyset$ **5.** $-9, -3$ **7.** $-8, 1$ **9.** $-\dfrac{7}{3}, 1$

11. $-\dfrac{11}{5}, 3$ **13.** $-\dfrac{13}{7}, 3$ **15.** $\dfrac{16}{3}, 8$ **17.** $-2, 2$

19. $-10, 4$ **21.** $-\dfrac{1}{4}, \dfrac{5}{4}$ **23.** $-10, 8$ **25.** $-4, 2$

27. $-9, 11$ **29.** $-11, 19$ **31.** $\dfrac{3}{2}, \dfrac{9}{2}$ **33.** $\dfrac{3}{5}, 3$

35. $\dfrac{4}{3}$ **37.** $\dfrac{3}{5}, 1$ **39.** $|4 + x| = 16; -20, 12$

41. $|2x - x| = 33; -33, 33$

43. $2|2x - 2| - 4 = 24; -6, 8$

Practice Exercises, pages 212–213

1. $y < -2$ or $y > 10$

-2 10

5. $-12 < c < 6$ -12 6

9. $-1 < x < 7$ -1 7

13. $m < 4$ or $m > 5$ 4 5

17. $-\dfrac{7}{5} \le a \le \dfrac{11}{5}$ $-\frac{7}{5}$ $\frac{11}{5}$

21. $\dfrac{3}{2} \le x \le 3$ $\frac{3}{2}$ 3

25. $\dfrac{1}{2} \le z \le \dfrac{5}{2}$ $\frac{1}{2}$ $2\frac{1}{2}$

33. all real numbers **35.** {d: $d < 1$ or $d > 5$}

37. $\left\{ t: \dfrac{1}{3} \le t \le 3 \right\}$ **39.** {p: p is a real number}

41. {z: z is a real number} **43.** $\left\{ g: g > \dfrac{1}{4} \right\}$

45. {y: $y > 2$} **47.** $\emptyset$ **49.** $|t - 0| < 5$

Practice Exercises, pages 215–216   1. at most
$30,000 **3.** 90 **5.** at least 24 h **7.** 5 m
9. no more than 5 mi
11. bonds: at least $2500; stocks: at most $7500

Test Yourself, page 217

1. $p < -3$ or $p > -1$ -3 -1

5. $-1, 7$ **7.** $-\dfrac{5}{3}, \dfrac{1}{3}$

9. $y < -\dfrac{1}{2}$ or $y > \dfrac{1}{2}$ $-\frac{1}{2}$ $\frac{1}{2}$

13. $11 - \dfrac{1}{3}n > 5$; number less than 18

15. $\dfrac{13.1 + 12.8 + 13.0 + 13.3 + 12.7 + x}{6} <$
12.8; less than 11.9 s

Summary and Review, pages 220–221

1. -3 0 **3.** -2 0

9. $g < -3$ -3 0

13. $-5, 9$ **15.** $-5, 4$

17. {y: $y \le 2$ or $y \ge 6$} 2 6

19. $\dfrac{1}{2}x + 3 > 2; x > -2$

21. $\dfrac{94 + x}{6} \ge 20$; at least $26

Maintaining Skills, page 224   1. 100,000 **3.** 1

5. -64 **7.** 729 **9.** 1 **11.** 256 **13.** $\dfrac{1}{8}$ **15.** $\dfrac{3}{5}$

17. $\dfrac{5}{6}$ **19.** $-5x^2 + 5xy$ **21.** $-5cd$

23. $2p^2 - 4pq + 6q^2$ **25.** $3920 **27.** $378

Chapter 6   Polynomials

Practice Exercises, pages 228–229

1. $3 \cdot 3 \cdot 3 \cdot z \cdot z$ **3.** $-7 \cdot a \cdot a \cdot a \cdot b \cdot b \cdot b \cdot b$
5. yes **7.** no **9.** yes **11.** yes **13.** $15x^7y^3$
15. $18r^7s^6$ **17.** $20g^8$ **19.** 15×10^9
21. 3×10^9 **23.** 2.1×10^8 **25.** k^{m+4} **27.** b^{x+3}
29. 2^m **31.** $-2,476,099$ **33.** 130,321
35. $2r^{5x}d^x$ **37.** $-27z^{5a}y^{8m}$ **39.** 135 **41.** -27

43. 288 **45.** $\dfrac{1}{2}x^2$

Practice Exercises, pages 232–233   1. x^3

3. $\dfrac{1}{y^8}$ **5.** 1 **7.** 8 **9.** $\dfrac{1}{10^4}$ **11.** $\dfrac{3b^3}{a^4}$ **13.** $\dfrac{3c^5}{7a^2}$

15. $\dfrac{4h}{t}$ **17.** 4×10^3 **19.** 3×10 **21.** 1 **23.** -1

25. $\dfrac{1}{2}$ **27.** 3 **29.** $-\dfrac{a}{2b}$ **31.** $\dfrac{5y^2}{3x}$ **33.** $\dfrac{7y^3z^2}{3x^2}$

35. $-2q^2r^3$ **37.** 1.4×10^9 **39.** $-\dfrac{3}{5}$ **41.** x^{a-2}

43. $\dfrac{1}{y^{2k-1}}$ **45.** 6 **47.** 1 **49.** x^2

Practice Exercises, page 236 **1. a.** x^{30} **b.** z^{27}

3. -10^{10} **5.** $(-3)^4$ or 81 **7.** $\dfrac{-a^5}{b^{10}}$

9. 16×10^{12} **11.** $24x^{10}$ **13.** $\dfrac{-27a^3}{b^6}$ **15.** $\dfrac{16y^2}{25x^2}$

17. $\dfrac{-8k^{12}}{27j^9}$ **19.** $\dfrac{1}{81b^4}$ **21.** $4a^2b^6$ **23.** $-250m^6n^7$

25. $-3a^8$ **27.** $\dfrac{-1}{32x^5y^{15}}$ **29.** z^{4k} **31.** $-32k^{5m}$

33. a^{2m+4} **35.** $5184a^{12}b^4$ **37.** $46^2 = 2116$;
$47^2 = 2209$; $48^2 = 2304$; $49^2 = 2401$; $50^2 = 2500$;
$51^2 = 2601$; $52^2 = 2704$; $53^2 = 2809$; $54^2 = 2916$;
$55^2 = 3025$; $56^2 = 3136$; $57^2 = 3249$; $58^2 = 3364$;
$59^2 = 3481$; $60^2 = 3600$

Practice Exercises, page 239 **1.** no; 27 is greater
than 10 **3.** no; 0.009 is less than 1 **5.** 2×10^6
7. 7.65×10^{-3} **9.** 3.98×10^9
11. 2.092×10^{11} **13.** 9×10^6 **15.** 6×10^9
17. $1.\overline{3} \times 10^9$ **19.** 9.216×10^{12} **21.** 3.2×10^5
23. 4.8×10^{10}; 6.912×10^{13}; 2.52288×10^{16}

Test Yourself, page 239 **1.** no; expression has

2 terms **3.** yes **5.** $-12x^4$ **7.** -81 **9.** $\dfrac{-2}{x^3y}$

11. 3.12×10^{-4} **13.** 2.3×10^{-4}

Practice Exercises, pages 243–244 **1.** 1 **3.** 7
5. 0 **7.** 4 **9.** 5 **11.** $-4x^3y + 6x^2y^2 + 2xy^3$
13. $5x^2y^2 - 2xy^3$ **15.** $17x^3 - 25x^2 + 10$

17. $4x^2z - \dfrac{15}{8}xz^2$ **19.** $-\dfrac{23}{5}x^2z + 2xz^2$

21. $-\dfrac{1}{2}cd^2$ **23.** $21x^2 - 17$ **25.** $-2xy^2 + 8x^2y$

27. $-x^{3a} + x^{2a} + 2x^a$ **29.** $x^{2a} - x^a$ **31.** $-\dfrac{13}{4}$

33. $8w + 8$ **35.** $6x - 3$

Practice Exercises, pages 246–247 **1.** $5x^3 +$
$2x^2 - 9x + 2$ **3.** $7r + 6s - 5t$ **5.** $2x^3 + 9x^2 -$
$x + 2$ **7.** $5x^3 + 3x - 16$ **9.** $7r - 2s + t$
11. $2x^3 + 3x^2 + 3x - 2$ **13.** $5x^3 + 4x - 17$
15. $m^3 + 3$ **17.** $5c^3 - 4c$ **19.** $13a + b + 2c$
21. $9r + 6s + 10$ **23.** $j + k + 6m$ **25.** $x^2 + 5x$
27. $3x^4 - 13x^3 - 7x^2 - 3x$ **29.** $14a^2 + a + 7$
31. $10x^3 - x^2 + 6x - 1$ **33.** $4n + 6$

Practice Exercises, pages 249–250 **1.** $-5x^5 +$
$30x^4 - 40x^3 + 25x^2$ **3.** $-6p^7 + 4p^5 - 10p^3$
5. $12p^3q + 6p^2q^2 - 3p^2qr$ **7.** $2x^5 - 2x^3 + 6x^2$
9. $15m^4n^2 - 5m^2n^3 - 10mn^4 + 5mn^2p$

11. $49h^2k - 7hk^2 + 56hk$ **13.** $-a^2b^3 -$
$11a^3b^2 + 40a^2b$ **15.** $-2y^2 + 7y - 10$
17. $6m^3 - 6m^2 + 2m$ **19.** $6a^2b^3 - 4a^3b^2$
21. $15r^4s^4 - 10r^2s^6 + 5rs^5$ **23.** $-12a^3bc^4 -$
$3a^2b^2c^3 + 6ab^3c^6$ **25.** $-5m^3 + 7m^2 + 2m^2n$
27. $24a^{2x} - 8a^{x+2} + 16a^x$ **29.** $j^2 + 2j$
31. $w^2 + 2w$ **33.** $3l^2 - 10l$

Practice Exercises, pages 253–255 **1.** $a^2 - 3a -$
40 **3.** $h^2 - 6h - 7$ **5.** $3a^2 + 11a - 20$
7. $10m^2 - 33m - 54$ **9.** $7r^2 - 38r + 15$
11. $10x^2 - 31x + 24$ **13.** $4y^2 - 7yz - 2z^2$
15. $8j^2 - 10jk - 3k^2$ **17.** $-6b^2 - 5b + 21$
19. $-24y^4 + 18y^3 - 15y^2 + 6y$ **21.** $-10z^4 -$
$13z^3 + 11z^2 + 12z$ **23.** $x^3 + 5x^2 + x - 10$
25. $z^3 - 8z^2 + 3z + 36$ **27.** $c^3 - 3c^2 - 9c - 5$
29. $-k^3 + 4k^2 + 29k + 24$ **31.** $y^3 - 5y^2 +$
$7y - 3$ **33.** $9x^2 - 24x + 16$ **35.** $4a^2 - 12ab +$
$9b^2$ **37.** $6a^3 + a^2 + 13a + 10$ **39.** $-2c^3 +$
$9c^2 + c - 2$ **41.** $10g^3 - 9g^2 + 8g^2 - 3$
43. $x^4 - 6x^3 + 8x^2 - 15x$ **45.** $4y^4 - 8y^3 +$
$7y^2 - 6y$ **47.** $5t^4 + 4t^3 - 14t^2 - 4t$
49. $a^3 + b^3$ **51.** $y^4 + y^3 - 6y^2 + 3y + 9$
53. $x^3 + 9x^2 + 27x + 27$ **55.** $64b^3 - 48b^2 +$
$12b - 1$ **57.** $3x^5 - 4x^3 + 6x^2 + x - 2$
59. $10a^5 - 9a^4 + 4a^3 + 14a^2 - 6a + 3$
61. $n^2 + 3n + 2$ **63.** $2x^2 + 9x + 7$
65. $e^2 + 6e + 8$

Practice Exercises, pages 258–259
1. $9x^2 + 12xy + 4y^2$ **3.** $64m^2 + 32mn + 4n^2$
5. $16m^4 - 48m^2 + 36$ **7.** $49s^4 - 42s^2 + 9$
9. 576 **11.** 144 **13.** $x^2 - 16$ **15.** $y^2 - 25$
17. $16x^6 - 9$ **19.** $4t^2 - 4tu + u^2$
21. $d^4 + 2d^2e^2 + e^4$ **23.** $h^4 - j^4$
25. $1 - 24g^3h^2 + 144g^6h^4$ **27.** $25a^2b^6 +$
$60ab^3c^2d^4 + 36c^4d^8$ **29.** $3721x^6y^4z^2$
31. $16 - a^{2x}$ **33.** $x^{2a+2} + 2x^{a+2} + x^2$
35. $3^{4y+2} - 4(3^{2y+1}) + 4$ **37.** $a^2 + 2a + 1$
39. $4x^2 - 9$

Test Yourself, page 259 **1.** $3x^3 - 4x$ **3.** $2y^2 - 4$
5. $6y^3 - 2y^2$ **7.** $55a^5b^3 - 33a^4b^4 + 77a^3b^5$
9. $3r^2 + 40r + 77$ **11.** $24n^2 - 5n - 75$
13. $81y^2 + 54y + 9$ **15.** $25a^2 - 90ab + 81b^2$

Practice Exercises, pages 262–263 **1.** 100,000,
1,000,000, 10,000,000 **3.** 35, 48, 63 **5.** 4558

7. 6, 12, 18, 30, 48, 78, 126 **9.** $\dfrac{n(n + 1)}{2}$

11. It is twice as large. **13.** 233, 377, 610, 987,
1597, 2584, 4181, 6765, 10,946, 17,711
15. 1, 1, 2, 3, 5

Answers

Summary and Review, pages 264– 265   **1.** a^7
3. $-15a^4c^5$ **5.** x^2 **7.** 1   **9.** 3×10^4 **11.** 1
13. $\dfrac{25a^2}{c^8}$ **15.** 2.89×10^5 **17.** 1.6×10^6
19. 9.0×10^3 **21.** 1; 1   **23.** $3x^3 - x^2 + 5$
25. $9x + 2y$ **27.** $-y + 5$ **29.** $3x^3 + 6xy - 3x$
31. $-35x^3y^2 + 5x^2y^3$ **33.** $3b^2 - 17b + 24$
35. $d^2 - 18d + 81$ **37.** $25x^2 - 16$ **39.** 30, 39, 49

Cumulative Review, page 268   **1.** -0.5 **3.** 7
5. $-5x + 1$ **7.** $9m^2 - m + 2$ **9.** $4b^3 -$
$6ab^2 + 2b^2$ **11.** $6n^2 - 11n + 4$ **13.** 15   **15.** 8
17. $-4xy$ **19.** $6n^5$ **21.** $8p^6$ **23.** $\dfrac{m^2}{4}$ **25.** -14
27. -8 **29.** 20   **31.** 5   **33.** 11   **35.** 4
37. All real numbers less than -2 or greater than or
equal to zero   **39.** 20 km/h, 25 km/h

Chapter 7   Factoring Polynomials

Practice Exercises, page 272   **1.** $2 \cdot 13$ **3.** $2^2 \cdot 13$
5. $2 \cdot 7 \cdot 11$ **7.** $3 \cdot 5 \cdot 13$ **9.** $3 \cdot 5 \cdot 7$
11. $11 \cdot 13$ **13.** $5^2 \cdot 11 \cdot 13$ **15.** $5^3 \cdot 7 \cdot 11$
17. $3^2 \cdot 5 \cdot 7^2$ **19.** $2^5 \cdot 5 \cdot 11$ **21.** $2 \cdot 11^2$
23. $2^5 \cdot 3^2$ **25.** prime   **27.** $2^3 \cdot 5^3$ **29.** 59
31. 109   **33.** yes; $3x$ is the product of two primes
35. yes; $x \cdot x = x^2$ is the product of two primes.
41. yes; the maximum area is obtained when the
rectangle is a square.

Practice Exercises, pages 276–277   **1.** 7   **3.** 18
5. 25   **7.** 8   **9.** $2x^2y(x - 6y^3)$
11. $7cd^3(1 + 2c^2d^2)$ **13.** $13x^2y^2(y + 2)$
15. $6mn^3(2m^3n^2 - 3)$ **17.** $2jk(2j^2 - 3k + 4)$
19. $4ab(a + 2ab + 3)$ **21.** $12x^3y^4(1 + 3x - 5y)$
23. $3m^2n^2(8m + 7n - 13n^2)$
25. $x^3y^3(13x^2y - 11y + 17x)$
27. $6l^2m(7lm - 6m^4 - 9l^2)$
29. $33x^5y^7(1 - 3xy^2 - 2y)$
31. $r^2s^3(89s^6 + 113rs^4 + 73r^2)$
33. $-5a^2b^4(3a + 3a^2b + 11)$
35. $-5x^4y^4(23 + 45xy + 57^2y^2)$
37. $7c^4d^2e^3(11d^4 + 4ce)$ **39.** $18x^2y^2z^2(3y^3z - 2x)$
41. $r^2\left(\dfrac{\pi}{2} + 4\right)$ **43.** $2r^2(8 - \pi)$

Practice Exercises, pages 280–281
1. $(x + 9)(x + 1)$ **3.** $(a + 11)(a + 1)$
5. $(z + 29)(z + 1)$ **7.** $(y + 11)(y + 3)$
9. $(s - 6)(s - 1)$ **11.** $(m - 4)(m - 1)$
13. $(y - 2)(y - 11)$ **15.** $(z - 17)(z - 3)$
17. $(13 - b)(5 - b)$ **19.** $(12 - z)(3 - z)$

21. $(3 + y)(16 + y)$ **23.** $(9 - f)(8 - f)$
25. $(a + 9b)(a + 3b)$ **27.** $(x - 7y)(x - y)$
29. $(r + 3t)(r + 2t)$ **31.** $(m - 25n)(m - n)$
33. $(s + 9t)(s + 2t)$ **35.** $(y - 8z)(y - 2z)$
37. $(x - 25y)(x - 2y)$ **39.** $(r + 16t)(r + 4t)$
41. $(m - 24n)(m - 3n)$ **43.** $(m - 8n)(m + 2n)$
45. $(c^2 + 6)(c^2 + 2)$ **47.** $(y^2 - 3)(y^2 - 8)$
49. $(a + 2)(a + 8)$ **41.** x^2 **53.** $(2 - z)(11 - z)$
55. $(a^x + 1)(a^x + 2)$ **57.** $(x^{2n} - 3)(x^{2n} - 4)$;
$(x^{2n} - 3)(x^n + 2)(x^n - 2)$
59. length: $x + 4$; width: $x + 1$
61. length: $m + 3$; width: $m + 1$
63. length: $x + 2a$; width: $x + a$

Practice Exercises, page 284
1. $(x + 5)(x - 1)$ **3.** $(m - 10)(m + 1)$
5. $(x - 2)(x + 4)$ **7.** $(m - 6)(m + 2)$
9. $(x - 1)(x + 3)$ **11.** $(a - 1)(a + 6)$
13. $(m - 4)(m + 3)$ **15.** $(k - 15)(k + 2)$
17. $(x - 3y)(x + 2y)$ **19.** $(r - 7s)(r + 3s)$
21. $(x - 10y)(x + 4y)$ **23.** $(k - 9j)(k + 4j)$
25. $(x - 2y)(x + y)$ **27.** $(r - 2t)(r + 7t)$
29. $(y - 16z)(y + 2z)$ **31.** $(x - 10y)(x + 2y)$
33. $(r - 6t)(r + 9t)$ **35.** $(y - 20z)(y + 5z)$
37. $(y^2 - 2)(y^2 + 25)$ **39.** $(a - 9)(a + 3)$
41. $(x^k - 2)(x^k + 14)$
43. $(a + 35b)(a - 10b)$; 550 ft $\times$ 100 ft

Practice Exercises, pages 287– 288
1. $(3x + 2)(x - 8)$ **3.** $(5z + 2)(z - 3)$
5. $(2m + 5)(m + 1)$ **7.** $(5r + 3)(3r + 7)$
9. $(9l + 5)(9l + 3)$ **11.** $(6z + 5)(z - 1)$
13. $(2m - 9)(2m + 1)$ **15.** $(2x + 11)(x - 1)$
17. $(7d - 5)(2d + 3)$ **19.** $(8x - 5)(3x - 4)$
21. $(4z + 5)(5z + 6)$ **23.** $(13c - 5)(2c + 3)$
25. $(3x + 2y)(x - y)$ **27.** $(2r + t)(r + 7t)$
29. $(3a - b)(a - 5b)$ **31.** $(3n - 2p)(2n + p)$
33. $(5x - 2y)(x + 4y)$ **35.** prime
37. $(4x + 9y)(3x + 2y)$ **39.** $(7k - 3m)(2k - 11m)$
41. $(9a + 8b)(3a - 4b)$ **43.** $(4x + 11)(x + 4)$
45. $(4a - 9)(3a - 16)$ **47.** $(3x^k + 2)(2x^k + 7)$
49. $(5x^{2k+3} + 4)(2x^{2k+3} - 3)$
51. $(y - 12)(6y + 1)$ **53.** $5c + 17$

Test Yourself, page 288   **1.** $2 \cdot 5 \cdot 11$
3. $2^2 \cdot 3^2 \cdot 5$ **5.** $3 \cdot 7^2$ **7.** $14x(3 - x^2)$
9. $(a + 5)(a + 7)$ **11.** $(m - 10)(m - 6)$
13. $(y - 15)(y + 4)$ **15.** $(2x + 1)(x + 12)$
17. $(3x - 2)(x + 2)$

Practice Exercises, pages 290–291   **1.** yes   **3.** no
5. yes   **7.** $(x + 6)^2$ **9.** $(2d + 9)^2$
11. $(k + 10)^2$ **13.** $(9y - 2)^2$ **15.** $(5t + 1)^2$

Answers to Selected Exercises   **681**

17. $(10k^5 + 1)^2$ **19.** $(5y^4 + 1)^2$
21. $(a^5b^2 - 4)(a^5b^2 + 4)$ **23.** $(x^9y^5 - 6)(x^9y^5 + 6)$
25. yes **27.** yes **29.** no **31.** yes
33. $(12x^2y - 25)(12x^2y + 25)$ **35.** $(a^3bc^2 - d)$
$(a^3bc^2 + d)$ **37.** $(2p^2q^2r^4 - 9)(2p^2q^2r^4 + 9)$
39. $(7rs + 1)^2$ **41.** $9(2x^3y^2 - 1)^2$
43. $(e^{32}f^{50} - g^{72}h^{18})(e^{32}f^{50} + g^{72}h^{18})$
45. $2a + 1$ **47.** x^2
49. $(a + b - c)(a + b + c)$
51. $(3x + 4)^2$ **53.** $t^2 - rs$

Practice Exercises, pages 294–295
1. $5(a + 3)$ **3.** $4(x - 3)$ **5.** $(5x - 4)(x - 2)$
7. $19(j - 2)$ **13.** $-2(a - b)$ **15.** $5(a - b)$
17. $(6 - h^3)$ $(h - k)$ **19.** ??
21. $(3r + s)(t + w)$ **23.** $(c - 2)(a + 3b)$
25. $(6y - 3x - 4)(6y + 3x + 4)$
27. $(x + y)(x + z)$
29. $(3b + 4c)(5a - 3c)$
31. $(3r + 1)(2t - 5s)$
33. $(r + 4s + t)(r - 4s - t)$
35. $(a + 3 + c)(a + 3 - c)$
37. $(5y + 2x - 3)(5y - 2x + 3)$
39. $(x + 3z^{3r})(x^{2r} + y)$
41. $(m^r + n)(p + n^{2r})$
43. $(x^a + y^b + 1)(x^a + y^b - 1)$
45. $3(8y - 3x)(2y + x)$

Practice Exercises, pages 298–299
1. $5(x + 2)(x - 2)$ **3.** $3(k + 7)(k - 7)$
5. $4y(y - 3z)(y + 3z)$ **7.** $6x(x + 2y)(x - 2y)$
9. $2(x + 5)(x - 2)$ **11.** $6(k + 1)^2$
13. $5(2k + 1)(k + 3)$ **15.** $-4(x + 3)(x - 2)$
17. $-10(m + 3)(m - 7)$ **19.** $3x(5x - 1)^2$
21. $12x(x + 1)^2$ **23.** $4x^2y(2x + 3)(x - 1)$
25. $6r^2s^2(r + 1)(2r - 1)$
27. $3x^3y^3(3x + 2y)(2x - 3y)$
29. $4x^4y^4(2x - 3y)^2$ **31.** $-3m^5p^2(2m + 5p)^2$
33. $2x(x^4 - 5)(x^4 + 5)$
35. $2x(x^3 - 4)(x^3 + 4)$
37. $3m(m + 4)(m - 4)(m + 2)(m - 2)$
41. $3x^4y^5(8x - 3)^2$ **43.** $3(2a - 1)(a - 4)$
45. $5(a + 2)(a - 1)$
47. $(a + 3)(a - 3)(a + 2)^2$
49. $3a(a^8 + 5)^2$ **51.** $x^{k+7}(x^{k+7} + 1)^2$
53. $x(x + 2)(x + 1)$ **55.** $2a(a + 3)(a + 1)$

Practice Exercises, pages 302–303 **1.** $\frac{2}{3}, -4$
3. $3, -6$ **5.** $-\frac{3}{5}, 2$ **7.** $0, -4$ **9.** $0, 4$
11. $0, -3$ **13.** $-4, 2$ **15.** $-\frac{1}{3}, -1$ **17.** $-\frac{1}{4}, 3$

19. $10, -9$ **21.** $5, 3$ **23.** $4, -\frac{5}{3}$ **25.** $\frac{5}{3}, -3$
27. $-\frac{5}{2}, \frac{2}{3}$ **29.** $-\frac{3}{7}, \frac{5}{2}$ **31.** $-1, \frac{1}{12}$
33. $0, -7, 3$ **35.** $0, -\frac{4}{3}, \frac{5}{2}$ **37.** $0, -\frac{9}{2}, \frac{7}{4}$
39. $0, -\frac{9}{5}, \frac{5}{2}$ **41.** $0, -\frac{3}{2}, \frac{11}{6}$ **43.** $-2, -1$
45. $-7, -3, -1$ **47.** $0, -3, 3, -1, 1$
49. $n^2 + 5n = 24$ **51.** $2n^2 = n - 10$

Test Yourself, page 303
1. $2y(y - 7)(y + 7)$ **3.** $4a(a - 2)(a - 1)$
5. $3x(1 - y)$ **7.** $16(x^2 + 4)$ **9.** $-1, 10$

Practice Exercises, page 306
1. 14 ft $\times$ 10 ft **3.** 14 cm $\times$ 6 cm
5. $-8, -6$ or $6, 8$ **7.** $-9, -7$ or $7, 9$
9. 6 **11.** 27 m $\times$ 8 m **13.** 30 in. $\times$ 30 in.
15. 8 in. $\times$ 4 in.

Summary and Review, pages 310–311
1. prime **3.** composite **5.** $2^4 \cdot 3$ **7.** $2^3 \cdot 3 \cdot 5$
9. 5 **11.** $3ab^2(1 - 3a)$ **13.** $(x + 3)(x + 2)$
15. $(a + 11b)(a + b)$ **17.** $(y - 12)(y + 2)$
19. $(2m + 1)(m + 7)$ **21.** $(3x - 5)(2x + 3)$
23. $4(5m - 2n)(5m + 2n)$ **25.** $7(m - 2)(m + 2)$
27. $3a(2a^2 + 4a + 3)$ **29.** $5(x - y)$
31. $4x(3x - 1)^2$ **33.** $9(2x^2 - 5)$ **35.** $-8, 10$
37. $-28, -26$ or $26, 28$

Maintaining Skills, page 314 **1.** $\frac{1}{2}$ **3.** $\frac{1}{10}$ **5.** $\frac{6}{7}$
7. $\frac{25}{14}$ **9.** $\frac{5}{9}; \frac{6}{9}$ **11.** $\frac{10}{36}; \frac{21}{36}$ **13.** $\frac{25}{24}$ **15.** $\frac{43}{60}$
17. 40 in.^{2}

Chapter 8   Rational Expressions
Practice Exercises, pages 318–319   **1.** -4
3. $-\frac{2}{5}$ **5.** $-\frac{1}{3}, \frac{1}{3}$ **7.** $-3, 3$ **9.** $\frac{1}{4c}; c \neq 0$
11. $\frac{2a + 3}{4}$ **13.** $7; a \neq 2$ **15.** $-\frac{1}{3}; m \neq \frac{5}{2}$
17. $\frac{1}{2x - 1}; x \neq \frac{1}{2}, -3$
19. $\frac{1}{5x - 3}; x \neq \frac{3}{5}, -2$
21. $-\frac{c + 6}{3 + c}; c \neq -3, 3$

23. $\frac{y+3}{y-2}$; $y \neq -2, 2$

25. $\frac{m-2}{m-5}$; $m \neq -5, 5$ **27.** $\frac{5c^2}{3a^2}$; $\dot{0}$; 0

29. $\frac{3+2n}{7m^3n^3}$; 0;0 **31.** $\frac{7z+2}{z-1}$; 1; -3

33. $\frac{2c+3}{c-7}$; $-\frac{3}{2}$; 7 **35.** $\frac{4a^2+8a-5}{15-a-2a^2}$; -3; $\frac{5}{2}$

37. $\frac{9+2x}{x-11}$; -1; 11 **39.** $\frac{2r-5}{2r-1}$; $\frac{1}{2}$; $-\frac{1}{3}$

41. $\frac{a-3b}{a+4b}$; 2b; -4b **43.** $\frac{x-y}{x+3y}$; -y; -3y

45. $\frac{3r+4s}{2r-s}$; $\frac{4}{3}s$; $\frac{1}{2}s$ **47.** $\frac{6}{s}$

Practice Exercises, pages 322–323 **1.** $\frac{6}{5x^2y}$

3. $\frac{12}{5x^2y}$ **5.** $\frac{5x^2}{y^2}$ **7.** $\frac{6r^2}{5st}$ **9.** $\frac{6q^2}{pr^2}$

11. $24m^2n^3p$ **13.** $\frac{1}{2}$ **15.** $\frac{c-5}{3c-4}$ **17.** $\frac{b+2}{3(2b-3)}$

19. $-\frac{3r+2}{r}$ **21.** -1 **23.** $\frac{15r^2s^2}{2q^2t^3}$

25. $\frac{2(i-3)}{i^3}$ **27.** 1 **29.** $\frac{l+5}{2l-9}$ **31.** -1

33. $-\frac{2a+1}{7a+2}$ **35.** $\frac{(s-1)(s-4)}{2(s+2)(s+3)}$ **37.** 1

39. $\frac{7t-3u}{2t+9u}$ **41.** $\frac{(r-2e)(r+2e)}{(2r-e)(2r+e)}$ **43.** 36

45. -125 **49.** $\frac{2}{x+5}$

Practice Exercises, pages 326–327 **1.** $\frac{10}{b}$

3. $\frac{4}{d}$ **5.** $\frac{d}{6e}$ **7.** $\frac{3}{2z+5}$ **9.** $\frac{1}{x+1}$

11. $\frac{7(r-7)}{5(r+2)}$ **13.** $\frac{x+2}{x+6}$ **15.** $\frac{4a^2}{15b^2}$

17. 1 **19.** $\frac{3ac}{10b}$ **21.** $\frac{x}{5(y+6)}$ **23.** 6(4 - c)

25. $\frac{5h-2}{3h-4}$ **27.** $\frac{2t+3}{2t-2}$ **29.** $\frac{5(2x-5)}{x-5}$

31. $\frac{7y+3}{3(3y-2)}$ **33.** $\frac{3y-1}{4y+5}$ **35.** $\frac{x}{y+5}$

37. $\frac{(g-3h)(g-4h)}{3(h+g)(2h+g)}$ **39.** $\frac{(3c+2d)(c-3d)}{(3c-d)(2c+3d)}$

41. $3x-1$

Practice Exercises, pages 331–332 **1.** $10ab$
3. $42xy$ **5.** $42a^3b^2$ **7.** $18x^2y^3$
9. $3(n+1)(n+5)$ **11.** $6(r-9)(2r+5)$

13. $(t+6)(t-6)$ **15.** $\frac{5}{12mn^2}$; $\frac{9m^2n}{12mn^2}$

17. $\frac{5(y+3)}{7(y+1)(y+3)}$; $\frac{21}{7(y+1)(y+3)}$

19. $\frac{3y}{y^2-9}$; $\frac{2(y+3)}{y^2-9}$ **21.** $(x+3)(x+2)(x+5)$

23. $(3c+7)(4c-5)(c-6)$

25. $(x-3)(16x+5)(2x+1)(x+3)$

27. $\frac{9b^2}{6a^2b^2}$; $\frac{18a^2b}{6a^2b^2}$; $\frac{a(a+b)}{6a^2b^2}$

29. $\frac{-8n(3n+5)}{(3n-5)(3n+5)}$; $\frac{5n^2}{(3n-5)(3n+5)}$

31. $\frac{3d(d+1)}{2d(d-2)(d+1)}$; $\frac{2d(d+3)}{2d(d-2)(d+1)}$

33. $\frac{c(c+2)}{3(c+1)(c+2)}$; $\frac{3c^2}{3(c+1)(c+2)}$;

$\frac{9c(c+1)}{3(c+1)(c+2)}$

35. $(5x-7y)(3x+4y)(4x-3y)$

37. $72(a-b)^2(a^2-b^2)(a^2+b^2)$

39. $6(5m-4)(3m+2)(m-4)$

41. $6x^3$

Practice Exercises, pages 335–336 **1.** $\frac{4}{m}$

3. $\frac{1}{2x}$ **5.** 2 **7.** -1 **9.** $\frac{a+1}{2a^2}$ **11.** $\frac{1-5m}{3m^2}$

13. $\frac{10-a}{5(a+4)}$ **15.** $\frac{8l+7}{(l+4)(l-1)}$

17. $\frac{24}{(x-5)(x+5)}$ **19.** $\frac{11}{(r-3)(r+3)}$

21. $\frac{8y+4}{(y-1)(y+3)}$ **23.** $\frac{a-2}{a-1}$

25. $\frac{g^3+g^2+2g-4}{g(g+2)}$ **27.** $\frac{5b^2-3b+2}{6b^2}$

29. $\frac{5u^2-11u+42}{6(u+2)(u-2)}$ **31.** $\frac{a^2+9a+7}{(a-4)(a+3)}$

33. $-\frac{d+3}{d+4}$ **35.** $\frac{t^2-t-9}{(2t+3)(4t-1)(t+5)}$

37. $\frac{4n^2+3n+18}{(n+3)(n-2)(3n+4)}$

39. $\frac{14k^2+67k+45}{k(k-3)(k+3)(k+5)}$ **41.** $-\frac{8}{a(a+4)}$;

$\frac{6}{(h+1)(h-1)}$; $\frac{-3d+15}{(d-3)(d+3)}$

Practice Exercises, pages 339–340 **1.** $\frac{2x+3}{x}$

3. $\frac{3x-10}{x}$ **5.** $\frac{2z^2-z-1}{z}$ **7.** $\frac{4y^2-10y+3}{4y}$

9. $\frac{2d^2+2d-3}{2d+1}$ **11.** $\frac{u^2+4u-1}{u+2}$ **13.** 2

15. $\dfrac{2}{5}$ **17.** $\dfrac{mn+2}{2n^2-m}$ **19.** $\dfrac{a}{a-4}$ **21.** $\dfrac{3}{2}$ **23.** $u-1$

25. $\dfrac{3x^2-4x-3}{9x^2-15x-5}$ **27.** $\dfrac{3z^2-13z-10}{3z^2-5}$

29. $\dfrac{x^2+2x-3}{x+1}$ **31.** $\dfrac{a^2-a+1}{a+1}$

33. $\dfrac{2m^2-2m-23}{2m+5}$ **35.** $c+3$ **37.** $\dfrac{a-2}{a+4}$

39. $\dfrac{n+6}{n-3}$ **41.** $-\dfrac{2u}{u^2+1}$ **43.** $\dfrac{x^2+2}{4x-1}$

45. $\dfrac{4a^2-2a-6}{3a^2-3a-18}$ **47.** $\dfrac{3a+9}{a(3a^2+a+3)}$

Test Yourself, page 340

1. $\dfrac{m+6}{3m}$ **3.** $\dfrac{3}{10ab^2}$; $\dfrac{4a^2b}{10ab^2}$

5. $\dfrac{3m+10}{6m}$ **7.** $\dfrac{3y-1}{3}$

Practice Exercises, page 344 **1.** $2x+1-\dfrac{1}{3x}$

3. $x^2-18x+3-\dfrac{7}{x}$ **5.** y^3-5y^2+

$7y+2-\dfrac{3}{y}$ **7.** $n-5$. **9.** $k+5-\dfrac{12}{k+6}$

11. $3j+16+\dfrac{43}{j-3}$ **13.** $5m+12$

15. $d-4-\dfrac{8}{d-3}$ **17.** $2b^2+2b+10+\dfrac{10}{b-1}$

19. $3x^2-3x+3-\dfrac{6}{x+1}$ **21.** $6s-17$

23. $2p^4q^2-6p^2q+3pq^3-1$ **25.** p^2+p-

$7+\dfrac{10}{p+2}$ **27.** $3h^2+h-5-\dfrac{2}{2h+1}$

29. $x^2+4x+13+\dfrac{57}{x-4}$

31. $3h^2+h-1+\dfrac{1}{3h-1}$ **33.** $9t^2+21t+49$

35. $3x+2y$ **37.** $2p+2q+\dfrac{2q^2}{3p+2q}$

39. $p=x-1$; $100

Practice Exercises, pages 348–349 **1.** $\dfrac{3}{4}$ **3.** $\dfrac{1}{6}$

5. $\dfrac{1}{5}$ **7.** $\dfrac{1}{2x}$ **9.** $\dfrac{5}{6}$ **11.** $\dfrac{4}{1}$ **13.** false **15.** true

17. true **19.** 36 **21.** 17 **23.** $\dfrac{3}{2}$ **25.** 4

27. $\dfrac{7}{2}$ **29.** $\dfrac{1}{3}$ **31.** -3 **33.** $-2, \dfrac{7}{6}$ **35.** $-6, 2$

37. $-6, 4$ **39. a.** $\dfrac{32}{7}$ **b.** $\dfrac{5}{12}$ **c.** $\dfrac{3}{4}$ **43.** 17 km

43. 8.5 h

Practice Exercises, pages 352–353 **1.** $\dfrac{9}{28}$ **3.** $\dfrac{4}{35}$

5. 4 **7.** no solution **9.** 7 **11.** $\dfrac{2}{5}$ **13.** -2

15. $-\dfrac{1}{3}$ **17.** $\dfrac{1}{2}$ **19.** 5 **21.** no solution **23.** 2, -3

25. $-\dfrac{3}{2}, 4$ **27.** $\dfrac{2}{3}, -\dfrac{3}{5}$ **29.** 1, 4 **31.** -14

33. 3, -3 **35.** 3, -1 **37.** $-\dfrac{6}{5}, -1$ **39.** $260

Practice Exercises, pages 356–357

1. $\dfrac{12}{7}$ h **3.** $2\dfrac{2}{9}$ h

5. Rhoda: 55 mi/h; Van: 48 mi/h

7. $62\dfrac{1}{2}$ mi/h **9.** 12 h **11.** 11 h 20 min

Practice Exercises, pages 359–360 **1.** $9276.69

3. $p=\dfrac{15\times(500)^2-7500u-ut}{500}$; $5835.00

5. $t=r(5.50)+s(4.50)$ **7.** $t=\dfrac{10v+7u}{uv}$

9. $r=(n-3)\left(\dfrac{200}{n}+2\right)$

11. $p=15n-15u-uc$

Test Yourself, page 361 **1.** $6-\dfrac{1}{y}+\dfrac{5}{y^2}$ **3.** $\dfrac{1}{25}$

5. 1300 m **7.** 14, 2 **9.** $b=$ number bought,

$n=$ number sold; $p=n\left(\dfrac{25}{b}+1.50\right)-25$

Summary and Review, pages 362–363

1. $\dfrac{b}{3}$, $b\neq0$ **3.** $\dfrac{1}{m+2}$; $m\neq-2, 1$ **5.** $\dfrac{16z}{5z}$

7. $\dfrac{a-1}{a-2}$ **9.** $\dfrac{3n}{24m^3n^2}$; $\dfrac{10m^2}{24m^3n^2}$

11. $\dfrac{2x}{(x+3)(x-3)}$; $\dfrac{3(x-3)}{(x+3)(x-3)}$

13. $\dfrac{2c-13}{(c+1)(c-2)}$ **15.** $\dfrac{u^2+4u+3}{u+2}$

17. $y-x$ **19.** $2r^2+9r-5$ **21.** $\dfrac{5}{2}$ **23.** 10

25. 18 min

Cumulative Review, pages 366–368 **1.** -1

3. -2 **5.** $2\dfrac{1}{2}$ **7.** $-3\dfrac{1}{2}$ **9.** $\{x: x\geq-1\}$

11. $\{x: x\neq-2\}$ **13.** $\{x: x\leq-1 \text{ or } x>0\}$

15. -3 **17.** $t\geq6$ **19.** no solution **21.** 8

23. 2 **25.** $-2 \le p \le 3$ **27.** 12 **29.** 3 **31.** 7

33. 6×10^6 **35.** 1.28×10^4 **37.** -5 **39.** 35

41. -1 **43.** -8 **45.** 4 **47.** $-\dfrac{2}{3}$ **49.** -2

51. -4 **53.** $4b^6$ **55.** $\dfrac{x}{3y}$ **57.** -1 **59.** $\dfrac{1}{z-2}$

61. $3a^2 + 5a$ **63.** $3r - 15$ **65.** $(h + 3)(h + 1)$

67. $\dfrac{(k-5)(k-2)}{(k+2)(k+5)}$ **69. a.** reflexive property

b. substitution property **c.** commutative property of
addition **71.** 24 oz **73.** $(a - 2b)$

75. $3c(2c - 3)$ **77.** $7p(3p^2 + 2p - 4)$

79. $(d + 4)^2$ **81.** $(g + 5)(g - 3)$

83. $(r - 6)(r - 4)$ **85.** $6a^3$ **87.** $3x(x + 1)$

89. $-\dfrac{2}{9}$ **91.** $\dfrac{5b + 6}{4b^2}$ **93.** $\dfrac{5h^2 + 11h + 3}{h + 2}$

95. 1 **97.** $4x^3y - 8x^2y^3 + 4x^2y$

99. $a^2 + 7a - 4$ **101.** $55.25 **103.** 3, 5, 7 or

$-3, -1, 1$ **105.** $66\dfrac{2}{3}$ min. **107.** $41\dfrac{2}{3}$ mi/h

Chapter 9 Linear Equations

Practice Exercises, pages 372–374

1. 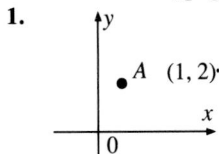 **7.**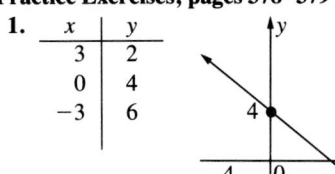

$G\ (-1, 5)$

13. 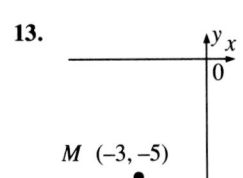 **15.** $P\left(-1, 1\dfrac{1}{2}\right)$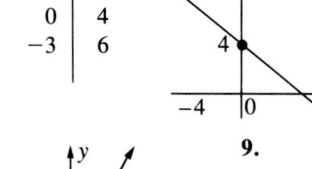

$M\ (-3, -5)$

17. $(-3, -7)$ **19.** $(3, 1)$ **29.** y-axis

31. Answers may vary; possible solutions are

$y = \dfrac{1}{2}x - \dfrac{7}{2}$, $y = 3x - 6$ **35.** $(-1, 4)$

37. parallel; perpendicular **39.** one; $(-2, 4)$

41. 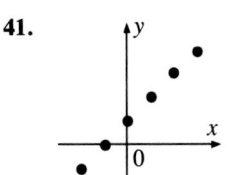 y-coordinate is one
more than x-coordinate;
$y = x + 1$

43. a. ordered pairs of (time, distance)
b. All are solutions except (0.5, 14).

Practice Exercises, pages 378–379

1.

x	y
3	2
0	4
-3	6

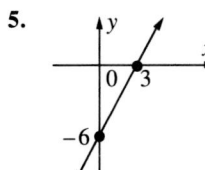

5.   **9.**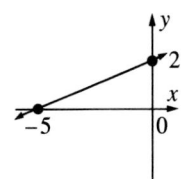

13. 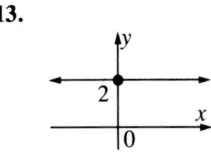 **15.**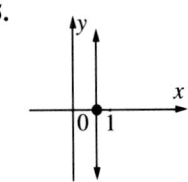

21. no **23.** yes **33.** 3 **35.** -3 **37.** $6a^2$

39. $8d^4 + 6$ **41.**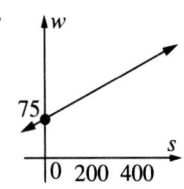

Practice Exercises, pages 381–383 **1.** $55; $70
3. $115 **5.** $102; $204 **7.** $306 **9.** 30; 36

11.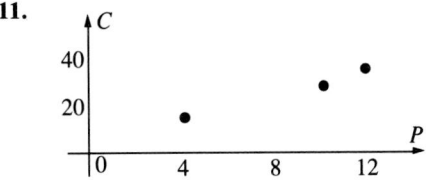

13. 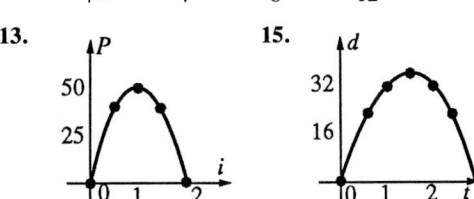 **15.**

Practice Exercises, pages 387–388 **1.** 2 **3.** $\dfrac{5}{3}$

5. $-\dfrac{3}{2}$ **7.** $-\dfrac{6}{5}$ **9.** -1 **11.** $-\dfrac{4}{5}$

13. 0; horizontal **15.** no slope; vertical

17. 0; horizontal

Answers

19.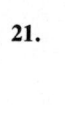

21.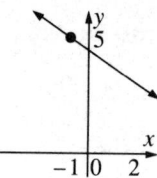

23. yes **25.** no **27.** no **29.** yes

31. $m_{AC} = -\dfrac{4}{5}$; $m_{BC} = -\dfrac{4}{3}$; $m_{AB} = 0$

33. 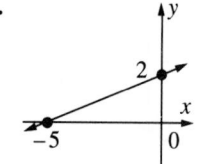 **35.**

37. 14 **39.** 1 **41.** $m_{AB} = 3$

43. $m_{RS} = \dfrac{1}{2}$; $m_{ST} = -\dfrac{4}{5}$; $m_{TO} = \dfrac{2}{7-x}$;

$m_{RO} = \dfrac{4}{-2-x}$

Test Yourself, page 388 1. yes
3.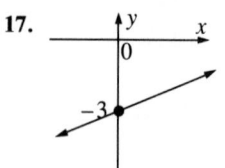

7.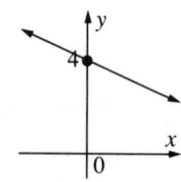

number of dogs

9. 66 lb **11.** $\dfrac{1}{2}$

Practice Exercises, pages 394–395 1. $-\dfrac{3}{2}$; 3

3. $\dfrac{1}{3}$; -3 **5.** -2; 0 **7.** 3; 6 **9.** $y = -2x$

11. $y = x + 3$ **13.** $y = \dfrac{2}{3} + 4$ **15.** $y = -1$

17. **19.**

25. not parallel **27.** parallel
29. $y = 2x$; $m = 2$, $b = 0$

31. $y = \dfrac{3}{5}x - 3$; $m = \dfrac{3}{5}$, $b = -3$

33. $y = \dfrac{5}{2}x$; $m = \dfrac{5}{2}$, $b = 0$

35. $y = 2x$; $m = 2$, $b = 0$

37. 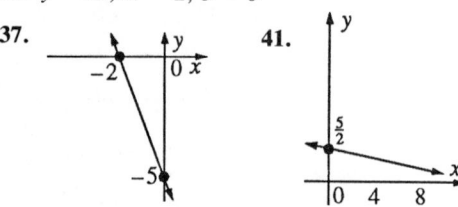 **41.**

45. -8 **47.** parallel **49.** perpendicular
51. No; parallel lines do not intersect.

53. $F = \dfrac{9}{5}C + 32$

55. a. 167°F **b.** 212°F **c.** 404°F

Practice Exercises, pages 398– 400

1. $y = \dfrac{3}{2}x - 3$ **3.** $-x + 2y = 0$

5. $2x + y = -1$ **7.** $5x + 4y = 8$

9. $-14x + 6y = -1$ **11.** $y = 5x - 2$

13. $y = 3x - 9$ **15.** $y = -3x + 8$

17. $y = -\dfrac{2}{3}x + 5$ **19.** $-3x + y = -9$

21. $2x + 5y = -4$ **23.** $-2x + y = -8$

25. $-x + y = -9$ **27.** $-2x + 2y = -1$

29. $-2x + 3y = 9$ **31.** $-3x + 5y = 15$

33. $-x + 3y = -17$ **35.** $y = 2gx + 7 - 4g$

37. $y = \dfrac{1}{n}x + \dfrac{2}{n} + 1$

Practice Exercises, pages 403–405 1. $(-6, 0)$
3. $(0, 0)$, $(3, 5)$ **5.** $y < -x + 2$ **7.** $y \le x$
9. $x \le 2$

13. 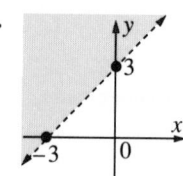 **15.**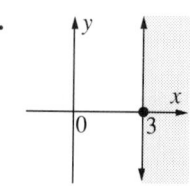

23. 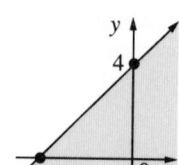 **25.**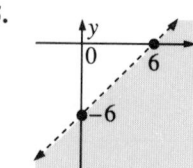

33. $y < \dfrac{5}{2}x - 3$ **35.** $y \ge \dfrac{1}{4}x + \dfrac{3}{4}$ **37.** $y \ge 1$

41.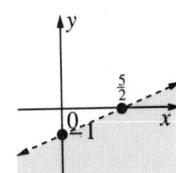

43.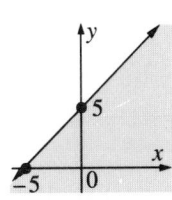

Test Yourself, page 405

3. $2x + y = 8$

7.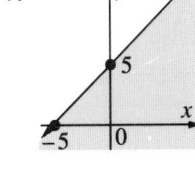

Summary and Review, pages 406–407

1. and 3. 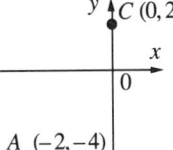 **5.** (2, 3).

7.

x	y
-2	2
0	1
2	0

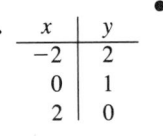

11.

t	F
0	39
40	79
80	119

13. $\dfrac{1}{2}$

17. $m = \dfrac{1}{2}; b = -4$ **19.** $m = -\dfrac{1}{2}; b = 3$

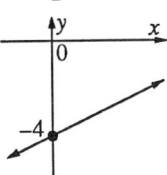 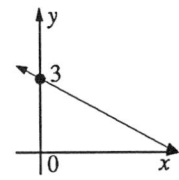

21. not parallel **23.** $-2x + 3y = -12$

25. 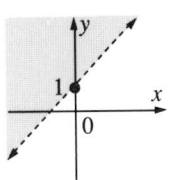 **27.**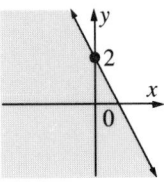

1. (2, 1)
3. (1, -3) **5.** (0, -2)

13. 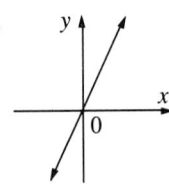 **15.**

17. -5 **19.** 12 **21.** -11 **23.** $\dfrac{5}{2}$ **25.** 0
27. 60 students

Chapter 10 Relations, Functions, and Variation

Practice Exercises, pages 414–416
1. $\{(-3, 5), (-1, 4), (1, 4), (3, -3)\}$;
$D = \{-3, -1, 1, 3\}; R = \{5, 4, -3\}$
3. $\left\{\left(\dfrac{1}{3}, -1\right), (0, 0), \left(\dfrac{1}{3}, 2\right), \left(\dfrac{1}{2}, 2\dfrac{1}{2}\right)\right\}$;
$D = \left\{\dfrac{1}{3}, 0, \dfrac{1}{2}\right\}; R = \left\{-1, 0, 2, 2\dfrac{1}{2}\right\}$
5. $\{(-3, -4), (1, 6), (4, 30), (5, 24)\}$;
$D = \{-3, 1, 4, 5\}; R = \{-4, 6, 24, 30\}$
7. $\{(-2, 0), (-1, 1), (0, 2), (1, 1), (2,0), (3, -1), (4, -2)\}; D = \{-2, -1, 0, 1, 2, 3, 4\}$;
$R = \{-2, -1, 0, 1, 2\}$
9. $R = \{2, 5, 11\}$

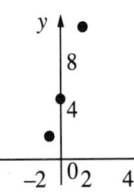

13. $R = \left\{\dfrac{1}{2}, 1, 2\right\}$

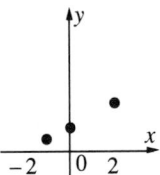

17. $\{(-1, 2), (-1, 8), (0, 4), (1, 4), (2, 6), (3, 4)\}$;
$D = \{-1, 0, 1, 2, 3\}; R = \{2, 4, 6, 8\}$
21. $R = \{-7, 0, 6\}$
23. $D = \{1, 2, 3, 4, 5\}; R = \{5000, 5200, 5400, 5600, 5800\}; \{(1, 5000), (2, 5200), (3, 5400), (4, 5600), (5, 5800)\}$ **25.** $D = \{1, 2, 3, 4, 5\}$;
$R = \{4, 5, 6, 7, 8\}; \{(1, 4), (2, 5), (3, 6), (4, 7), (5, 8)\}$

Practice Exercises, pages 419–421 **1.** a function
3. a function **5.** a function **7.** a function
9. not a function **11.** a function **13.** 5 **15.** -2

17. $R = \{-8, -5, 4, 13\}$; a function

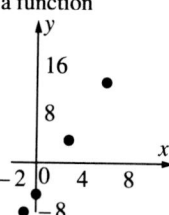

21. $R = \{$all real numbers greater than or equal to $-1\}$; a function

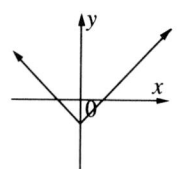

23. 2 **25.** -15 **27.** 3

Practice Exercises, page 424

3. yes; no; no

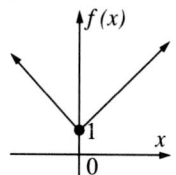

7. not a function

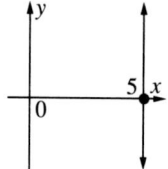

9. yes; yes; yes

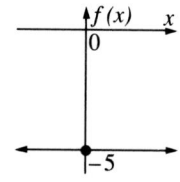

13. -1 **15.** -3 **17.** -1 **19.** 23
23. yes; no; no

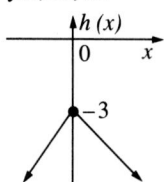

27. -8 **29.** 19 **31.** 2 **33.** -1 **35.** $\dfrac{29}{15}$

Test Yourself, page 424

3. $R = \left\{-\dfrac{7}{4}, -1, 0\right\}$

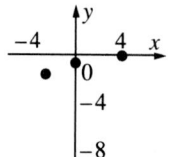

5. yes; no; no
9. yes; no; no

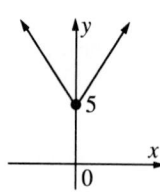

11. -7 **13.** 23

Practice Exercises, pages 428–429 **1.** yes **3.** no
5. yes; 4; $y = 4x$ **7.** yes; $\dfrac{1}{3}$; $y = \dfrac{1}{3}x$ **9.** 11

11. $5\dfrac{1}{3}$ **13.** 35 **15.** 12.8 **17.** 11.88 **19.** 52

21. 9 **23.** 20 **25.** 7.5 **27.** no **29.** $560

Practice Exercises, pages 432–433 **1.** yes; $xy = 12$
3. yes; $xy = -1.44$ **5.** 8 **7.** 4 **9.** 24 **11.** 6.3

13. 5.29 **15.** $\dfrac{36}{121}$ **17.** 21.03 **19.** 10 in.^{3}

21. 42 kg **23.** yes; $r_1t_1 = r_2t_2$ **25.** 35 mi/h
27. yes

Practice Exercises, pages 435–436 **1.** $A = s^2$

3. $V = C\left(1 - \dfrac{n}{N}\right)$ **5.** $V = \dfrac{4}{3}\pi r^3$ **7.** $40.32

9. $1.30 **11.** 18 **13.** 8 **15.** $4000 **17.** $0
19. $12,500 **21.** 6.79 **23.** 0.0218 **25.** 2.4

Test Yourself, page 439
1. yes; $y = -3x$; in the form $y = kx$

3. yes; $y = \dfrac{1}{2}x$; in the form $y = kx$

5. 6 **7.** yes; $xy = 14$ **9.** no **11.** 10
13. $44.90 **15.** $3000

Summary and Review, pages 438–439
1. $\{(2, -2), (5, -5), (2, 0), (-2, 1)\}$;
$D = \{-2, 2, 5\}$; $R = \{-2, -5, 0, 1\}$; not a function
3. a function; **7.** a function;
not a linear function   not a linear function

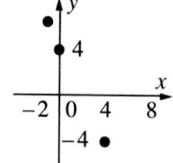
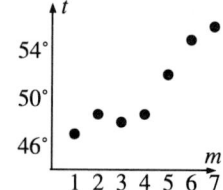

9. directly; $y = 4x$; 4 **11.** 11 **13.** $480 **15.** 8 m

Cumulative Review, page 442 **1.** -3 **3.** $-2, -6$

5. $3xy^2$ **7.** $\dfrac{7m + n}{7mn}$ **9.** 1 to 2 **11.** 1 to 5

13. $\dfrac{7x^2 + 5x - 3}{x}$ **15.** $\dfrac{3x}{x^2 + 4y}$

17. $(2x + 3)(2x - 5)$ **19.** $-3x - y = -3$
21. $x - 2y = 24$ **25.**

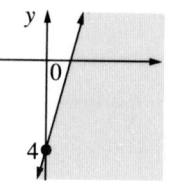

27. $R = \left\{0, -\dfrac{63}{4}, -7\right\}$ **29.** $\dfrac{2}{3} < t < \dfrac{14}{3}$

31. 11 h **33.** $l = 30\,\text{cm};\ w = 25\,\text{cm}$

Chapter 11 Systems of Linear Equations

Practice Exercises, pages 446–449

1. 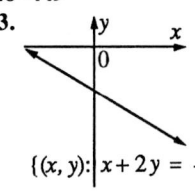 **3.**

$\{(x, y): x + 2y = -4\}$

13. independent and consistent; different graphs; one solution **15.** independent and inconsistent; different graphs; no solution **17.** dependent and consistent; same graph; more than one solution **19.** independent and consistent; different graphs; one solution **21.** dependent and consistent; same graph; more than one solution **23.** independent and inconsistent; different graphs; no solution **25.** intersecting lines; one solution **27.** parallel lines; no solution **29.** parallel lines; no solution

31. 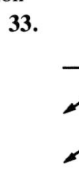 **33.**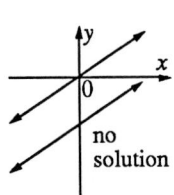

no solution

37. parallel lines; no solution **39.** parallel lines; no solution **41.** intersecting lines; one solution
47. $m_1 = m_2;\ b_1 \neq b_2$
49. $m_1 \neq m_2$ or $m_1 = m_2$ and $b_1 = b_2$

Practice Exercises, pages 453–454 **1.** (1, 1)
3. (5, −2) **5.** (3, 0) **7.** (−2, −1) **9.** (5, 2)
11. $\left(-\dfrac{13}{3}, \dfrac{56}{3}\right)$ **13.** (0, 4) **15.** $\left(-\dfrac{2}{3}, 2\right)$
17. $\left(11, \dfrac{13}{4}\right)$ **19.** no solution **21.** $\left(-\dfrac{4}{7}, \dfrac{6}{35}\right)$
23. $\left(\dfrac{1}{2}, -2\right)$ **25.** $\left(\dfrac{55}{9}, \dfrac{38}{9}\right)$ **27.** $\left(\dfrac{2}{5}, -\dfrac{3}{5}\right)$
29. (−4, −9) **31.** $\left(\dfrac{1}{3}, -6\right)$ **33.** $\left(\dfrac{3}{4}, \dfrac{1}{2}\right)$
35. (2, −3) **37.** $\left(-4, \dfrac{1}{7}\right)$
39. $\{(a, b): a - b = 2\}$ **41.** $\left(-\dfrac{7}{2}, -7\right)$
43. $\left(-\dfrac{10}{3}, -\dfrac{8}{3}\right)$ **45.** (1, 1)

47. $\left(-\dfrac{23}{41}, -\dfrac{50}{41}\right)$ **49.** (−2, 3)

Practice Exercises, pages 457–458
1. $l = 3w - 2$ **3.** $l + s = 48$
$2l + 2w = 68$ $\quad l - s = 12$
$l = 25\,\text{ft};\ w = 9\,\text{ft}$ $\quad 30, 18$
5. $f = 13 + 5s$ **7.** $x + y = 27$
$s + f = 247$ $\quad x = 3 + 2y$
Said 39; father 208 $\quad 8, 19$

9. $x = \dfrac{2}{3}y$ **11.** $x + y = 6000$
$0.075x + 0.08y = 469.75$
$y - x = 5$ $\quad \$3950$ at 8%; $\$2050$ at 7.5%
15, 10
17. $x + y = 18$
$x = 3 + \dfrac{1}{4}y$
6 blocks

Practice Exercises, pages 461–462 **1.** (2, 10)
3. (−3, 3) **5.** (−6, 4) **7.** (5, −6) **9.** (30, 6)
11. (−3, 1) **13.** (2, −3)
15. $\{(a, b): 2a - b = 1\}$
17. $\left(-\dfrac{5}{3}, -13\right)$ **19.** $\left(\dfrac{9}{2}, 7\right)$ **21.** (1, 0)
23. (−4, −5) **25.** $\left(-2, \dfrac{17}{2}\right)$ **27.** $\left(\dfrac{3}{4}, \dfrac{1}{2}\right)$
29. $\left(\dfrac{3}{2}, \dfrac{1}{2}\right)$ **31.** (−2, 8.5) **33.** (3, 8)
35. (4.1, 3.2) **37.** $\left(1, \dfrac{7}{9}\right)$ **39.** $\left(4, -\dfrac{3}{2}\right)$
41. $\left(\dfrac{75}{4}, -\dfrac{3}{2}\right)$ **43.** $\left(2, \dfrac{1}{3}\right)$ **45.** (−5, 1)
47. 25 acres **49.** $-\dfrac{1}{3}$ amp; 1 amp

Practice Exercises, pages 465–466 **1.** (−1, −1)
3. (3, 2) **5.** (−2, −3) **7.** (−22, −33) **9.** (4, 3)
11. (−3, −4) **13.** $\left(\dfrac{1}{2}, -\dfrac{1}{3}\right)$ **15.** (1, 2)
17. $\left(2, \dfrac{1}{2}\right)$ **19.** $\left(\dfrac{1}{2}, \dfrac{1}{3}\right)$ **21.** $\left(-\dfrac{4}{5}, -\dfrac{7}{5}\right)$
23. (1400, 450) **25.** no solution **27.** (−1, −2)
29. $\left(\dfrac{1}{4}, -\dfrac{1}{2}\right)$ **31.** $x = \dfrac{c(1 - b)}{1 - ab},\ y = \dfrac{c(1 - a)}{1 - ab}$
33. $\{(x, y): ax + y = c \text{ and } c = 0\}$ **35.** 25

Test Yourself, page 466 **1.** intersecting lines; one solution **3.** intersecting lines; one solution
5. (6, −4) **7.** (−2, 14) **9.** \$22,000; \$11,000

Practice Exercises, pages 468–469 **1.** 24 **3.** 39
5. 28 **7.** 82 **9.** 94 **11.** 83 **13.** 21
15. $t + u = 1$

Practice Exercises, pages 471–473 **1.** $c = 2b$; $c - 8 = 3(b - 8)$; Cordell 32 yr; Beth 16 yr

3. $m = 2 + 2n$; $n + 9 = \frac{2}{3}(m + 9)$; Nadia 5 yr; Mario 12 yr **7.** $a - 2 = 6(s - 2)$; $a + 3 = \frac{7}{3}(s - 14)$; Akhil 22 yr; Sarat 18 yr **11.** $(h - 6) + (c - 6) = 71$; $h = 27 + j$; Harvey 55 yr; Carol 28 yr

13. $m = 9 + s$; $m + 1 = 3(s + 1)$; Seth $3\frac{1}{2}$ yr; Mary $12\frac{1}{2}$ yr **15.** $s = 3r$; $\frac{1}{4}(s + r) = 8$; Randi 8 yr; Susan 24 yr **17.** Liz 1909; Bill 1927 **19.** Bill 59 yr; Ann 41 yr **21.** Spero $22\frac{1}{2}$ yr; Chris $27\frac{1}{2}$ yr

23. 20 yr **25.** Emma 20; Kim 32; Vangie 25 **27.** Mary 23 yr; Jim 48 yr; Grace 47 yr

Practice Exercises, pages 476–477
1. $n + d = 28$; $5n + 10d = 260$; 24 dimes; 4 nickels **3.** $c + a = 175$; $23 + 6a = 750$; 75 **5.** $p + r = 50$; $1.20p + 2.10r = 147(50)$; 35 lb peanuts; 15 lb raisins **7.** $x + y = 32{,}000$; $0.075x + 0.09y = 2670$; $18,000 **9.** $f + t = 124$; $5f + 10t = 840$; 44 tens; 80 fives **11.** $y = 2x$; $0.075y + 0.06x = 840$; $4000 at 6%; $8000 at 7.5% **13.** $x + y = 36$; $0.04x + 0.4y = 0.2(36)$; 16 gal cream; 20 gal milk **15.** $x + y = 350$; $2.25x + 1.00y = 600$; 150 children; 200 adults **17.** $w = p + 3$; $9.95w + 6.50p = 62.75$; 5 lb walnuts; 2 lb peanuts **19.** $p + n + d = 90$; $p + 5n + 10d = 285$; $p = 2(n + d)$; 60 pennies; 15 nickels; 15 dimes

Practice Exercises, pages 481–483 **1.** 216 mi/h **3.** 6 mi/h; 2 mi/h **5.** 9 km/h **7.** 540 km/h; 60 km/h **9.** $5\frac{1}{2}$ mi/h **11.** 17 h **13.** 385 mi/h

15. 16 km/h **17.** 2 mi/h; 0.8 mi/h **19.** 12 km/h
21. $\frac{2d}{t} - c = \frac{d}{t} + c$

Practice Exercises, pages 486–487
1. **7.**

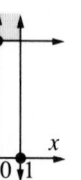

11.

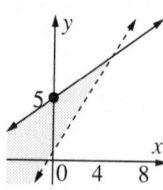

15.

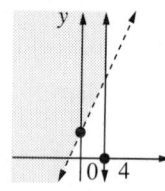

17.

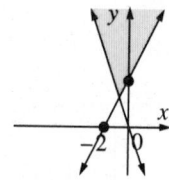

21.

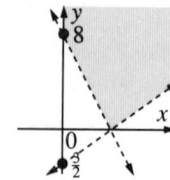

23.

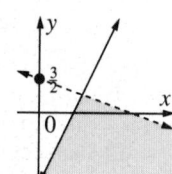

29.

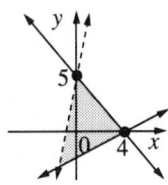

33.

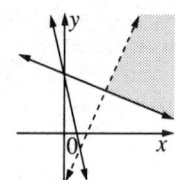

35.

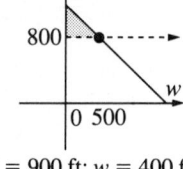

$l = 900$ ft; $w = 400$ ft
or
$l = 1000$ ft; $w = 300$ ft

Test Yourself, page 487 **1.** 56 **3.** Robert 23 yr; Dawn 19 yr **5.** 7 quarters; 45 dimes **7.** 40 mi/h
11.

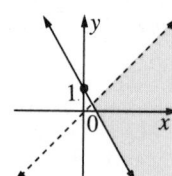

Summary and Review, pages 488–489
1. **3.**

(2, 1); 1 solution; lines intersect

no solution; parallel lines

5. $\left(\frac{27}{7}, \frac{45}{7}\right)$ **7.** 6 ft; 6 ft; 9 ft **9.** (3, 4)

11. $\left(-1, \frac{9}{2}\right)$ **13.** $\left(\frac{10}{3}, \frac{8}{3}\right)$

15. Sue 25 yr; Amy 10 yr **17.** 5 mi/h; 3 mi/h

19.

Maintaining Skills, page 492   1. 733.04
3. 215.91   **5.** 8   **7.** 52.7   **9.** 6   **11.** 25
13. 15   **15.** 0.3   **17.** $y^2 - 7y + 12$
19. $3b^2 - b - 10$ **21.** $12x^2 - 7x - 10$
23. 8 lb 1 oz

Chapter 12   Radicals

Practice Exercises, page 496   1. 5   **3.** -16
5. $\dfrac{2}{3}$ **7.** $-\dfrac{1}{12}$ **9.** $\pm\dfrac{4}{5}$ **11.** -100 **13.** 33
15. 0.1   **17.** 0.8   **19.** -1.4 **21.** 0.03   **23.** ±0.25
25. 0.36   **27.** $\dfrac{5}{3}$ **29.** $\dfrac{4}{5}$ **31.** 3   **33.** 5   **35.** 3 s

Practice Exercises, page 499   1. 2.2   **3.** 4.7
5. 9.1   **7.** 9.7   **9.** 5.2   **11.** 3.9   **13.** 9.9
15. 4.4   **17.** 12.2   **19.** 11.3   **21.** 8.5   **23.** 2.1
25. 200.25   **27.** 0.66   **29.** 6.93 ft

Practice Exercises, pages 501–502   1. 0.125
3. $2.\overline{3}$ **5.** -1.25 **7.** $0.\overline{4}$ **9.** -12.75 **11.** $0.1\overline{5}$
13. $\dfrac{233}{100}$ **15.** $\dfrac{1}{3}$ **17.** $\dfrac{3}{11}$ **19.** $\dfrac{11212}{9999}$ **21.** $\dfrac{325}{999}$
23. $\dfrac{1}{7}$ **25.** $\dfrac{2}{3}, \dfrac{1}{3}; 1$ **27.** $\dfrac{1}{18}, \dfrac{7}{18}; \dfrac{4}{9}$
29. The prime factors are all 2's or 5's.
31. A rational number represents a terminating decimal if the prime factors of its denominator consist of only the factors 2 and/or 5. A rational number represents a repeating decimal if the prime factors of its denominator include factors other than 2 and/or 5.

Practice Exercises, pages 505–506   1. $2\sqrt{2}$
3. $3\sqrt{3}$ **5.** $x \geq -\dfrac{7}{2}$ **7.** $x \leq -3$ **9.** $4\sqrt{3}$
11. $3\sqrt{6}$ **13.** $5\sqrt{6}$ **15.** $10\sqrt{10}$ **17.** $5x^2\sqrt{3}$
19. $10x^3\sqrt{3}$ **21.** $2y^6\sqrt{3}$ **23.** $d^3\sqrt{15d}$
25. $-5x^8\sqrt{5}$ **27.** $12p^4$ **29.** $x^2\sqrt{y}$ **31.** p^6q^5
33. $9x^6\sqrt{3x}$ **35.** $-5a^5\sqrt{6a}$ **37.** $10r^3\sqrt{5r}$
39. $\dfrac{6}{7}x^2\sqrt{xy}$ **41.** $0.3c^2\sqrt{c}$ **43.** $0.4m\sqrt{m}$
45. $3\sqrt{2}$ **47.** 10   **49.** $a - 3$ **51.** $64\sqrt{2}$ ft/s
53. π s

Practice Exercises, pages 510–511   1. $5\sqrt{5}$
3. $7\sqrt{10}$ **5.** $6\sqrt{3} + 12$ **7.** $5\sqrt{3} - 4\sqrt{5}$
9. $9\sqrt{2}$ **11.** $35\sqrt{2}$ **13.** $4\sqrt{x}$ **15.** $3\sqrt{3x}$
17. $21\sqrt{6}$ **19.** $-7x\sqrt{y}$ **27.** $11\sqrt{11} + 36\sqrt{2}$
29. $-\dfrac{1}{2}\sqrt{3}$ **31.** $-\dfrac{y}{6}\sqrt{5x}$ **33.** $ab\sqrt{ab}$
35. 0   **37.** $20\sqrt{5}$ cm

Practice Exercises, pages 514–515   1. 4   **3.** $2\sqrt{3}$
5. 7   **7.** 30   **9.** $-30\sqrt{2}$ **11.** $6\sqrt{21}$ **15.** 1
17. $12x\sqrt{6}$ **19.** $9n$ **21.** $4\sqrt{3} + 3$
23. $6 - 2\sqrt{6}$ **25.** $9 - 7\sqrt{2}$ **27.** 29
29. $6ab\sqrt{3}$ **31.** $cde\sqrt{e}$ **33.** $\dfrac{5a^2}{b}$
35. $67 + 12\sqrt{7}$ **37.** $12 + 3\sqrt{2} - 4\sqrt{3} - \sqrt{6}$
39. $x + 4\sqrt{xy} + 4y$ **41.** $8m - 10\sqrt{mn} - 3n$
43. $2\sqrt{6}$ m^2 **45.** $16x$ ft^2
47. $\sqrt{x^2} = 12$ **49.** $4\sqrt{3x} = 24$

Test Yourself, page 515   1. 6.71   **3.** $\dfrac{1}{3}$ **5.** 14
7. $\dfrac{5}{4}$ **9.** $-4\sqrt{3}$ **11.** $5x\sqrt{x}$ **13.** $5\sqrt{2} - 4\sqrt{7}$

Practice Exercises, pages 518–519   1. $\dfrac{\sqrt{22}}{11}$
3. $-\sqrt{2}$ **5.** $2\sqrt{6}$ **7.** -3 **9.** $\dfrac{5}{9}\sqrt{3}$ **11.** $-\dfrac{\sqrt{3}}{4}$
13. $\dfrac{4\sqrt{y}}{y}$ **15.** $\dfrac{2\sqrt{2x}}{x}$ **17.** $\dfrac{3\sqrt{a}}{a^2}$ **19.** $\dfrac{-2\sqrt{y}}{3y^2}$
21. $2c$ **23.** $ab\sqrt{b}$ **25.** $\dfrac{15 + 5\sqrt{2}}{7}$
27. $\dfrac{-3\sqrt{5} - 3}{4}$ **29.** $-2 + \sqrt{5}$
31. $\dfrac{2 + 2\sqrt{5} + \sqrt{3} + 15}{-4}$ **33.** $\dfrac{-\sqrt{11} + 1}{4}$
35. $\dfrac{3\sqrt{3} - 2 + 9\sqrt{21} + 6\sqrt{7}}{23}$ **39.** $\dfrac{x - \sqrt{xy}}{x}$
41. $\dfrac{2x - 5\sqrt{x} + 3}{x - 1}$ **43.** $\dfrac{\sqrt{5}}{4}$
45. all positive real numbers

Practice Exercises, pages 522–523   1. 64   **3.** 108
5. $\dfrac{1}{16}$ **7.** 12   **11.** 4   **13.** no solution   **15.** 4
17. $\dfrac{17}{5}$ **19.** $\dfrac{5}{3}$ **21.** 2   **23.** 6   **25.** 18   **27.** $\sqrt{7}$
29. 1   **31.** no solution   **33.** no solution   **35.** 7
37. 9   **39.** 170   **41.** Cubing a number does not
change its sign.   **43.** $\dfrac{38}{5}$ **45.** 144 ft

Practice Exercises, pages 526–527 **1.** 5 **3.** 16.2
5. 9.8 **7.** 8.3 **9.** no **11.** yes **13.** 1
15. $\dfrac{4}{15}$ **19.** 17 ft **21.** 8 cm **23.** 3, 4, 5

Practice Exercises, page 530 **1.** 5 **3.** $6\sqrt{2}$
7. 13 **7.** $\sqrt{29}$ **9.** $\sqrt{185}$ **11.** 13
13. $AB = 8$, $BC = 5$, $AC = 5$
15. $XY = 5$, $YZ = 2\sqrt{10}$, $XZ = \sqrt{85}$
17. $AB = 5$, $BC = 10$, $AC = 5\sqrt{5}$
19. $MN = 12$, $NP = 9$, $MP = 15$
21. 5 or -3 **23.** yes

Practice Exercises, pages 532–534 **1.** $(-5, 5)$
3. $(-6. 3)$ **5.** $\left(-3\dfrac{1}{2}, 2\right)$ **7.** $\left(\dfrac{3a}{2}, \dfrac{3b}{2}\right)$
9. $B(5, 5)$, $C(5, 0)$, $D(5, -5)$
11. a. $(6, 6)$ **b.** $6\sqrt{2}$ **c.** $6\sqrt{2}$ **d.** same length
13. $M_{BD} = M_{AC} = (3, 3)$
15. $AB = 5\sqrt{2}$; $AC = 3\sqrt{2}$; $BC = 4\sqrt{2}$; yes
because $(3\sqrt{2})^2 + (4\sqrt{2})^2 = (5\sqrt{2})^2$
17. a. $(4, 0)$ **b.** $(7, 8)$ **c.** $3\sqrt{2}$ **d.** $6\sqrt{2}$
f. $3\sqrt{2} = \dfrac{1}{2}(6\sqrt{2})$

Test Yourself, page 535 **1.** $\dfrac{\sqrt{2}}{2}$ **3.** $t + 3$
5. $-12\sqrt{5} - 15\sqrt{3}$ **7.** $\dfrac{4}{3}$ **9.** 7, 5
11. 13 **13.** $5\sqrt{2}$ **15.** $5\sqrt{10}$; $\left(5\dfrac{1}{2}, -2\dfrac{1}{2}\right)$

Summary and Review, pages 536–537 **1.** 5
3. $\dfrac{3}{2}$ **5.** 2.236 **7.** 9.434 **9.** 2.83 **11.** 5.20
13. -3.5 **15.** $0.8\overline{3}$ **17.** $\dfrac{2}{3}$ **19.** $2\sqrt{5}$
21. $7x\sqrt{2}$ **23.** $-3\sqrt{5} + 2\sqrt{6}$ **25.** $2\sqrt{6} - 5\sqrt{3}$
27. $\dfrac{\sqrt{15}}{5}$ **29.** $\dfrac{17}{3}$ **31.** 4 **33.** 1 **35.** $\sqrt{205}$

Cumulative Review, pages 540–542
1. $-2\sqrt{4}, 3, 6$ **3.** b **5.** a **7.** d
9. $a < 4$ **11.** 2 **13.** $(4, 2)$ **15.** 4 **17.** 6
19. $-5, 3$ **21.** \$15 **23.** 5 h **25.** 6
27. $\dfrac{1}{4}$ **29.** $6p^3q^4$ **31.** $-\dfrac{2a^2}{3b}$
33. $-\dfrac{1}{m + 2}$ **35.** $\dfrac{st}{3}$ **37.** $20 - 3\sqrt{3}$
39. $y = \dfrac{1}{2}x - 3$ **41.** $y = 3x + 1$

43. $3xy^2(4x - 3)$ **45.** prime
47. $3p(p^2 + 3p + 1)$ **49.** $(m + 2n)(3 - 2m)$
51.

53. 7 days **55.** -4 **57.** $2\sqrt{2}$ **59.** 1 **61.** 4
63. 4 **65.** -0.2 **67.** $9m^4n^6$ **69.** $\dfrac{p - 1}{p - 2}$
71. $\dfrac{c + 3}{c - 1}$ **73.** $3\sqrt{2} + 4\sqrt{5}$ **75.** $2r^2 + 6r - 1$
77. $xy^2 + 2xy$ **79.** $R = \{-7, -3, -1\}$
81. $R = \left\{5, 6, 6\dfrac{1}{2}\right\}$ **83.** \$2.15
85. crew: 7 mi/h; current: 2 mi/h
87. $l = 16$ ft; $w = 10$ ft **89.** $l = \dfrac{2}{w + 4}$

Chapter 13   Quadratic Equations
and Functions

Practice Exercises, pages 545–546
1. $\pm\dfrac{2}{5}$ **3.** ± 7 **5.** $\pm\sqrt{6}$ **7.** $\pm 2\sqrt{2}$
9. $\pm\sqrt{15}$ **11.** $\sqrt{3}$ **13.** no real solutions
15. ± 2 **17.** $\pm\sqrt{5}$ **19.** $-2, 4$
21. $-\dfrac{5}{2}, \dfrac{3}{2}$ **23.** $-1, 2$ **25.** $\pm\dfrac{3}{2}$
27. $1 \pm 6\sqrt{2}$ **29.** $-1, \dfrac{1}{3}$ **31.** $\dfrac{-2 \pm \sqrt{5}}{3}$
33. $-\dfrac{6}{5}, \dfrac{4}{5}$ **35.** $3 \pm \sqrt{7}$ **37.** $5 \pm 2\sqrt{6}$
39. $\dfrac{\pm\sqrt{2} + 5}{3}$ **41.** $\dfrac{\pm 3\sqrt{2} - 1}{2}$ **43.** $\dfrac{\pm\sqrt{15} - 3}{2}$
45. $\dfrac{1}{3} \pm \dfrac{\sqrt{2}}{4}$ **47.** $\dfrac{1}{2} \pm \dfrac{\sqrt{3}}{6}$ **49.** $-3, 7$
51. $-\dfrac{3}{2}, 0$ **53.** 4, 14 **55.** -7

Practice Exercises, pages 549–550
1. 16 **3.** 25 **5.** $-1, 5$ **7.** $-15, 3$
9. $-6, 2$ **11.** $-\dfrac{7}{2} \pm 2\sqrt{5}$

13. $\dfrac{3 \pm \sqrt{5}}{2}$ **15.** $-5, 0$ **17.** $-9, 1$

19. $-3, -2$ **21.** $-\dfrac{3}{2}, \dfrac{5}{2}$ **23.** $\dfrac{3 \pm \sqrt{11}}{4}$

25. $1 \pm \dfrac{\sqrt{5}}{5}$ **27.** $\dfrac{-1 \pm \sqrt{41}}{4}$

29. $\dfrac{-5 \pm \sqrt{31}}{2}$ **31.** $\dfrac{2}{3}, 2$ **33.** $\dfrac{-5 \pm \sqrt{17}}{4}$

35. $\dfrac{5 \pm \sqrt{145}}{6}$ **37.** $\dfrac{7 \pm \sqrt{17}}{4}$

39. $\dfrac{-b \pm \sqrt{b^2 - 4}}{2}$ **41.** $\dfrac{-b \pm \sqrt{b^2 - 4c}}{2}$

43. $-3, 1$

Practice Exercises, pages 552–553

1. $-3, -2$ **3.** $-2, 5$ **5.** $3, 6$ **7.** $\dfrac{3 \pm \sqrt{21}}{6}$

9. $\dfrac{3}{2}$ **11.** $\pm\sqrt{11}$ **13.** $-\dfrac{5}{3}, \dfrac{1}{2}$

15. $\dfrac{-3 \pm \sqrt{17}}{4}$ **17.** $\dfrac{2}{3}, 2$ **19.** $-3 \pm \sqrt{19}$

21. $\dfrac{-7 \pm \sqrt{29}}{2}$ **23.** $\dfrac{1 \pm \sqrt{11}}{2}$

25. $\dfrac{-11 \pm \sqrt{33}}{4}$ **27.** $\dfrac{3 \pm \sqrt{5}}{4}$ **29.** $\dfrac{3}{2}, 3$

31. $\dfrac{-5 \pm \sqrt{33}}{2}$ **33.** $\dfrac{7 \pm \sqrt{17}}{4}$ **35.** -3

37. $2 \pm \sqrt{4 + k^2}$ **39.** $\dfrac{-ac \pm \sqrt{ac(ac - 4b^2)}}{2bc}$

41. $3 - a, -2 - a$ **43.** $l = 4$ ft; $w = 3$ ft

Practice Exercises, pages 555–556

1. $-1, 2$ **3.** $\pm 2\sqrt{3}$ **5.** $1, 3$ **7.** $-1, \dfrac{1}{4}$

9. $0, \dfrac{2}{3}$ **11.** $-\dfrac{1}{2}, \dfrac{1}{3}$ **13.** $-3, 15$

15. $\dfrac{9 \pm \sqrt{17}}{4}$ **17.** $\dfrac{\pm\sqrt{10} + 2}{3}$

19. $\dfrac{1 \pm 3\sqrt{5}}{2}$ **21.** $\dfrac{3 \pm \sqrt{3}}{2}$ **23.** $-\dfrac{2}{5}, 1$

25. $2, 9$ **27.** $\dfrac{13}{5}, 3$ **29.** $\dfrac{1}{b}, \dfrac{1}{2b}$

31. $b - 1, b - 4$ **33.** $\dfrac{3b \pm 8}{12}$ **35.** 2 s

37. $l = 8$ ft; $w = 4$ ft **39.** 9 **41.** $0, \dfrac{2}{3}$

Test Yourself, page 556

1. $\pm 2\sqrt{2}$ **3.** $-2, 3$ **5.** $1 \pm \sqrt{6}$

7. $\pm\dfrac{3}{2}$ **9.** $-2, \dfrac{1}{3}$

Practice Exercises, pages 560–561

1. 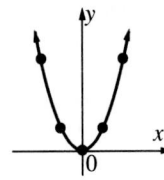 upward; minimum

5. 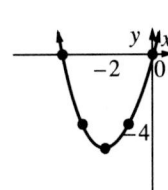 upward; minimum

7. 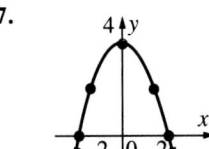 downward; maximum

15. $\left(-\dfrac{5}{2}, \dfrac{7}{4}\right)$; $x = -\dfrac{5}{2}$; none

17. $(-3, 16)$; $x = -3$; $-7, 1$

19. $\left(\dfrac{3}{4}, \dfrac{49}{8}\right)$; $x = \dfrac{3}{4}$; $\dfrac{5}{2}, -1$

21. $(0, -5)$; $= 0$; none **23.** $(0, 2)$; $x = 0$; none

25. $(-2, 0)$; $x = -2$; -2

27. $(-1, -5)$; $x = -1$; $-1 \pm \sqrt{5}$

29. $(-3, -4)$; $x = -3$; none

31. 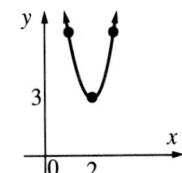 upward; minimum

35. 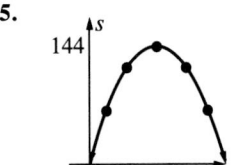 144 ft

Practice Exercises, page 566

1. 64; 2 real solutions **3.** 0; 1 real solution

5. 40; 2 real solutions **7.** -7; no real solutions

9. 25; 2 real solutions **11.** -71; no real solutions

13. 0; 1 real solution **15.** 13; 2 real solutions

17. $-\dfrac{61}{12}$; no real solutions **19.** 2 **21.** 2

23. 2 **25.** no

Answers

Practice Exercises, pages 569–571

1. linear function; $c = 0.80w + 55.6$; c-intercept 55.6 is the cost of producing zero ounces of silver; slope 0.80 is the increase ($) for each additional ounce of silver **3.** linear function; $c = 0.24h + 1.52$; c-intercept: 1.52 is the cost ($) for zero hours, perhaps a maintenance charge; h-intercept: no meaning—number of hours cannot be negative; slope: 0.24 is the increase ($) for each additional hour.

5. $c = 24.5m + 75$ **7.** $g = -\dfrac{1}{4}h + 55$

9. 3.5 h **11.** 15 bu per tree

13. 40 trees; 16 bushels per tree

15. $R(x) = (6 - 0.25x)(500 + 50x)$

17. $S(x) = (6 + 0.5x)(600 - 25x)$

Practice Exercises, pages 574–575

1. $x^2 - 4x + 3 = 0$ **3.** $x^2 - 4x - 12 = 0$

5. $x^2 + 6x + 5 = 0$ **7.** $x^2 + 5x = 0$

9. $5x^2 + 11x - 12 = 0$ **11.** $3x^2 - 5x + 2 = 0$

13. yes **15.** no **17.** $4x^2 - 25 = 0$

19. $6x^2 + x - 12 = 0$ **21.** $x^2 - 2x - 5 = 0$

23. yes **25.** no **27.** yes

29. $\dfrac{-b + \sqrt{b^2 - 4ac}}{2a} + \dfrac{-b - \sqrt{b^2 - 4ac}}{2a} =$

$\dfrac{-2b}{2a} = -\dfrac{b}{a}$ **31.** yes **33.** yes

Test Yourself, page 575 **1.** $(0, 0)$; $x = 0$

3. $(1, -1)$; $x = 1$ **5.** downward; maximum

7. -7; no real solutions **9.** 121; 2 real solutions

11. 27 or 13 people **13.** 0 or 40 people

15. $2; -2.5$

Summary and Review, pages 576–577 **1.** $\pm 2\sqrt{5}$

3. $-9, 3$ **5.** $3 \pm \sqrt{14}$ **7.** $\dfrac{-7 \pm \sqrt{13}}{6}$

9. no real solutions **11.** $\pm\sqrt{6}$ **13.** $\dfrac{5 \pm \sqrt{22}}{3}$

15. $-8, 3$

17.
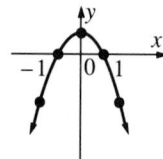
± 1; maximum; $x = 0$

19. 64; 2 real solutions **21.** -96; no real solutions

23. $x^2 + 11x + 30 = 0$ **25.** $6x^2 - 5x - 50 = 0$

Maintaining Skills, page 580 **1.** $-4, -3, -1, 2, 4$

3. $-3.1, -3.0, 2.08, 2.8, 2.88$

5. $-\dfrac{2}{3}, -\dfrac{3}{5}, -\dfrac{4}{7}, \dfrac{5}{6}, \dfrac{7}{8}$ **7.** 450 **9.** 200

11. 3.24 **13.** 6.76 **15.** -24.01 **17.** 26.01

19. -68.89 **21.** $\dfrac{3}{10}$ **23.** $\dfrac{7}{10}$

Chapter 14 Statistics and Probability

Practice Exercises, pages 584–585

1. mode: 71; median: 69; mean: 68.8

3. mode: none; median: 163; mean: 163

5. mode: 1.2, 1.4, 1.5; median: 1.4; mean: 1.5

7. mode: 2; median: 2; mean: 2

9. Change 16 to 12, or 19 to 12, or 12 to 8

11. 25

13. All three measures decrease by 8.

15. All three measures are halved.

17. 136.75 **19.** mode

Practice Exercises, pages 588–589

1.

Test Score	Tally	Frequency
45–49	I	1
50–54	I	1
55–59	III	3
60–64	III	3
65–69	$\bcancel{IIII}\,I$	6
70–74	IIII	4
75–79	$\bcancel{IIII}\,I$	6
80–84	II	2
85–89	II	2
90–94	II	2

3. 71 **5.** 16 students **7.** 40–49 **11.** 75.5%

13. 24.5%; 49%

17.
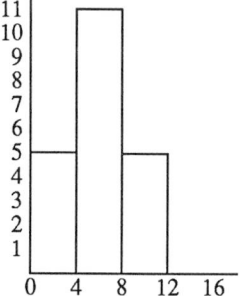

19.

Interval	Tally	Frequency
10,000–14,900	IIII	4
15,000–19,900	IIII	4
20,000–24,900	III	3
25,000–29,900		0
30,000–34,900	I	1
35,000–39,900	I	1

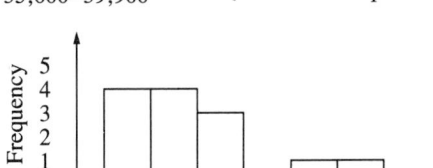

Depths in thousands (ft)

Practice Exercises, pages 592–593

1. variance: $3500; std. deviation: $59.16
3. mode: 8; median: 9; mean: 9; range: 7; variance: 4.6; std. deviation: 2.1 **5.** mode: 29.0, 29.4; median: 29.4; mean: 29.5; range: 1.1; variance: 0.2 F: 0.4 **7.** mode: none; median: $4.54; mean: $4.20; range: $4.69; variance: $2.46; std. deviation: $1.57
9. mean: $26,000; std. deviation: $3521.36

Test Yourself, page 593 **1.** 73.25
3.

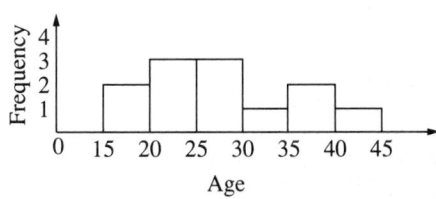

Age

Percentage under 25: 42%
5. mean: 71.9; std. deviation: 32.9

Practice Exercises, pages 598–599 **1.** $\frac{1}{3}$ **3.** $\frac{1}{8}$

5. $\frac{2}{3}$ **7.** $\frac{1}{4}$ **9.** $\frac{1}{4}$ **11.** $\frac{7}{8}$ **13.** $\frac{5}{31}$

15. 7 to 8 for **17.** $\frac{24}{31}$ **19.** $\frac{5}{9}$

21. $\frac{2}{9}$ **23.** $\frac{1}{3}$ **25.** 0 **27.** $\frac{1}{2}$ **29.** $\frac{2}{3}$

31. 3 to 1 against

Practice Exercises, pages 601–602

1. $\frac{1}{5}$ **3.** $\frac{10}{157}$ **5.** $\frac{1}{3}$

Practice Exercise, pages 606–607

1. $\frac{3}{32}$ **3.** $\frac{9}{64}$ **5.** $\frac{15}{64}$

Tree diagram for Exercises 7–12

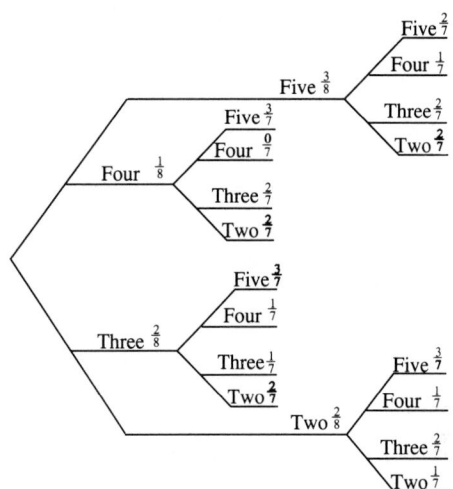

7. $\frac{3}{8} \times \frac{2}{7} = \frac{3}{28}$ **9.** $\frac{1}{8} \times 0 = 0$

11. $\frac{1}{8} \times \frac{0}{7} + \frac{1}{8} \times \frac{2}{7} = \frac{1}{28}$; $\frac{2}{8} \times \frac{1}{7} + \frac{2}{8} \times \frac{1}{7} = \frac{1}{14}$;

$\frac{1}{28} + \frac{1}{14} = \frac{3}{28}$ **13.** $\frac{1}{2}$

15. $\frac{5}{8}$ **17.** $\frac{5}{8}$ **19.** $\frac{4}{25}$ **21.** $\frac{56}{225}$ **23.** $\frac{1}{25}$

31. 0.04; 0.01; 0.05

Test Yourself, page 607 **1.** $\frac{3}{8}$ **3.** 0 **5.** $\frac{1}{4}$ **7.** $\frac{3}{28}$

Summary and Review, pages 608–609

1. mode: 7, 12; median: 11; mean: 12
3.

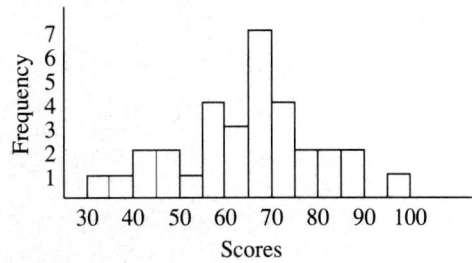

Scores

5. variance: 0.643; std. deviation: 0.802

7. $\frac{1}{4}$ **9.** $\frac{1}{80}$ **11.** $\frac{1}{18}$ **13.** $\frac{5}{9}$ **15.** $\frac{1}{17}$ **17.** $\frac{5}{102}$

19. $\frac{1}{2}$

Cumulative Review, page 612
1. < **3.** > **5.** = **7.** < **9.** <

11.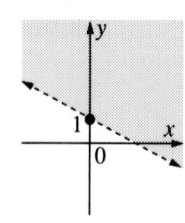

13.

15. $2\sqrt{2}$ **17.** $2\sqrt{3}(-1 + \sqrt{2})$ **19.** $\frac{4}{3}\sqrt{3}$

21. Father: 54 yr; Al: 24 yr   **23. a.** mean: 3.7; mode: 3.7; median: 3.7   **c.** variance: 0.37; standard deviation: 0.61

Chapter 15   Right Triangle Relationships

Practice Exercises, pages 616–617
 1. ray   **3.** point   **5.** line segment   **7.** line
 9. complementary   **11.** supplementary
13. $m\angle N = 60$; acute   **15.** $m\angle B = 102$; obtuse
17. 25°; 65°   **19.** 20°; 160°   **21.** 65°; 115°
23. 30°   **25.** 55° SE

Practice Exercises, pages 621–622
 1. obtuse triangle; isosceles triangle
 3. right triangle; scalene triangle
 5. right triangle; isosceles triangle
 7. 70   **9.** 67   **11.** 25   **13.** 50   **15.** 45
17. 33°, 114°   **19.** 59°; 60°; 61°   **21.** 40°; 60° 80°
23. $m\angle Q = 57$; $m\angle R = 19$; $m\angle S = 104$
25. $m\angle M = 13$; $m\angle N = 102$; $m\angle O = 65$
27. $m\angle S = 4$; $m\angle U = 68$; $m\angle M = 108$
29. the hypotenuse

Practice Exercises, pages 625–627
 1. 4; 4; congruent   **3.** 4; 2; not congruent
 5. 3; 3; congruent   **7.** reflexive
 9. symmetric   **11.** transitive
13. $\angle T \leftrightarrow \angle C$; $\angle O \leftrightarrow \angle A$; $\angle P \leftrightarrow \angle R$ **15.** true
17. $\overline{DA} \leftrightarrow \overline{PA}$; $\overline{AL} \leftrightarrow \overline{AN}$; $\overline{PL} \leftrightarrow \overline{DN}$ **19.** false
21. $\triangle ETC$; $\triangle TER$; $\triangle CRE$
23. $\triangle ROA$, $\triangle FOA$; $\overline{RO} \leftrightarrow \overline{FO}$; $\overline{RA} \leftrightarrow \overline{FA}$; $\overline{OA} \leftrightarrow \overline{OA}$; $\angle R \leftrightarrow \angle F$; $\angle O \leftrightarrow \angle O$; $\angle A \leftrightarrow \angle A$

Test Yourself, page 627   **1.** ray   **3.** line
 5. $m\angle X = 60$ **7.** acute; equilateral
 9. 66°, 66°   **11.** false   **13.** true

Practice Exercises, pages 630–632
 1. similar; $\overline{AB} \leftrightarrow \overline{DE}$; $\overline{BC} \leftrightarrow \overline{EF}$; $\overline{AC} \leftrightarrow \overline{DF}$
 3. similar; $\overline{EQ} \leftrightarrow \overline{ED}$; $\overline{EP} \leftrightarrow \overline{EL}$; $\overline{PQ} \leftrightarrow \overline{LD}$
 5. $YZ = 14$; $XZ = 10$ **7.** $AB = 3$; $BC = 6$

 9. $MN = 21$; $DF = 6$ **11.** $MO = 10$; $EF = 2$
13. $PR = 35$; $AR = 25$ **15.** $AB = 6.4$; $PR = 31$
17. $AR = AJ = 4.2$; $TP = 4.8$ **19.** 30   **21.** 0.7
23. 12 m   **25.** 600 m   **27.** \$453.13

Practice Exercises, pages 635–636   **1.** $\frac{3}{5}$ **3.** $\frac{3}{4}$

 5. $\frac{3}{5}$ **7.** $\sin A = \frac{5}{13}$; $\sin B = \frac{12}{13}$; $\cos A = \frac{12}{13}$; $\cos B = \frac{5}{13}$; $\tan A = \frac{5}{12}$; $\tan B = \frac{12}{5}$

 9. $\sin A = \frac{12}{37}$; $\sin B = \frac{36}{37}$; $\cos A = \frac{35}{37}$; $\cos B = \frac{12}{37}$; $\tan A = \frac{12}{35}$; $\tan B = \frac{35}{12}$

11. $\sin A = \frac{\sqrt{2}}{2}$; $\sin B = \frac{\sqrt{2}}{2}$; $\cos A = \frac{\sqrt{2}}{2}$; $\cos B = \frac{\sqrt{2}}{2}$; $\tan A = \frac{\sqrt{2}}{2}$; $\tan B = 1$

13. $\sin Q = \frac{5}{13}$; $\cos Q = \frac{12}{13}$; $\tan Q = \frac{5}{12}$; $\sin T = \frac{12}{13}$; $\cos T = \frac{5}{13}$; $\tan T = \frac{12}{5}$

15. $\sin Q = \frac{\sqrt{5246}}{86}$; $\cos Q = \frac{5\sqrt{86}}{86}$; $\tan Q = \frac{\sqrt{61}}{5}$; $\sin T = \frac{5\sqrt{86}}{86}$; $\cos T = \frac{\sqrt{5246}}{86}$; $\tan T = \frac{5\sqrt{61}}{61}$

17. $\sin Q = \frac{\sqrt{70}}{10}$; $\sin T = \frac{\sqrt{30}}{10}$; $\cos Q = \frac{\sqrt{30}}{10}$; $\cos T = \frac{\sqrt{70}}{10}$; $\tan Q = \frac{\sqrt{21}}{3}$; $\tan T = \frac{\sqrt{21}}{7}$

23. 0.5774   **25.** 0.1465   **27.** 1.9617
31. tangent ratio

Practice Exercises, pages 641–642   **1.** 0.9962   **3.** 1.539   **5.** 0.9563   **7.** 0.4067
 9. 28.6363   **11.** 0.8192   **13.** 30°   **15.** 45°
17. 55°   **19.** 18°   **21.** 2°   **23.** $BC = 22$; $AC = 36$
25. $AB = 50$; $AC = 4$ **27.** $XY = 79$; $XZ = 85$
29. $XZ = 62$; $YZ = 60$ **31.** $m\angle K = 53$; $m\angle J = 37$ **33.** $m\angle K = 18$; $m\angle J = 72$ **35.** 19.7
37. 105.8   **39.** 57 ft   **41.** 54 m

Practice Exercises, pages 646–647
 1. yes   **3.** yes   **5.** $m\angle C = 90$
 7.

assuming a right triangle (level land)
10m

h

37°

13 m

9.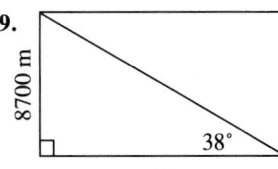
assuming a right triangle (level land) 11,135 m

11.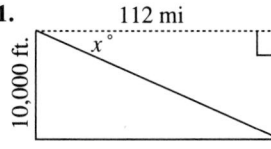
assuming a flat earth; assuming 112 mi ahead means horizontal distance; 1°

13.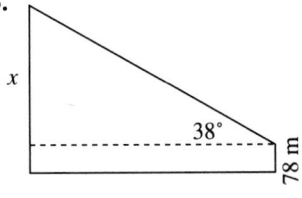
assuming a flat earth; 5938 m

Test Yourself, page 647

1. $3\frac{1}{3}$ **3.** $m\angle A = 18; m\angle B = 72$

Summary and Review, pages 648–649

1. 113   **3.** right triangle, isosceles triangle
5. $\angle P \leftrightarrow \angle C; \angle A \leftrightarrow \angle A; \angle D \leftrightarrow \angle R$
7. false   **9.** $AE = 53\frac{1}{3}; BC = 30$
11. 0.8746   **13.** $XZ = 48; YZ = 27$
15. $\cos A = \frac{2}{8}; m\angle A = 76$

Cumulative Review, pages 652–654

1. 5   **3.** $3\sqrt{2}$ **5.** $4\sqrt{2}$ **7.** 16   **9.** $9\sqrt{3}$
11. $2cd\sqrt{5d}$ **13.** $6z^2 - 14z - 12$ **15.** $24r^7t^6$
17. $\dfrac{6\sqrt{3} - 2\sqrt{6}}{7}$ **19.** $36d^4\sqrt{30}$ **21.** $\dfrac{x+1}{x+3}$
23. $8(2c + 1)$ **25.** $6 + 5\sqrt{6}$ **27.** $4x^2 - 6x + 9$
29. $4a^3b^3 + 6a^2bc - 6ab^2c - 9c^2$ **31.** $\dfrac{2m-3n}{3m-2n}$
33. $x(x + 1) = (x + 2)^2 - 34; 10$
35. 82   **37.** $(t + 7)(t - 5)$
39. $(2m - 5)(m + 3)$ **41.** $6a(a - 2b)(a + 2b)$
43. $(t - 3)(t + 3)(r + t)$ **45.** 15   **47.** 500
49. $-2, 2$ **51.** 4, 10   **53.** no solution
55. no solution   **57.** $\left(2, \dfrac{1}{3}\right)$ **59.** $w < 4$ or $w > 6$
61. $-1 \le a \le 5$ **63.** $-4, 8$ **65.** $-2, 8$
67. $-2, 6$ **69.** 12   **71.** 17; 2 real solutions
73. $x^2 - 7x + 10 = 0$ **75.** $2x^2 + 5x - 3 = 0$
77. mode: 21, 32; median: 32; mean: 34; range: 42
79. $\dfrac{1}{3}$ **81.** 0   **83.** $\dfrac{2}{9}$ **85.** $\dfrac{5}{33}$
87. $m\angle A = 40; m\angle B = 80; m\angle C = 60$
89. $6x \text{ cm}^2$ **91.** 4
93.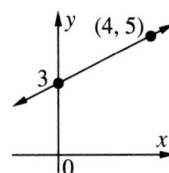

95. {3}   **97.** {4}   **99.** {3, 4}   **101.** 5, 25
103. yes; 7; $xy = 7$

The explanations given in this Glossary include definitions and brief descriptions of the key terms used in this book.

abscissa (p. 371)   The abscissa is the x-coordinate of an ordered pair.

absolute value (p. 14)   The absolute value of a number is its distance from zero on a number line.

acute angle (p. 615)   An angle that has a measure between $0°$ and $90°$.

acute triangle (p. 619)   A triangle that has all acute angles.

addition property for equations (p. 97)   If a, b, and c are any real numbers, and $a = b$, then $a + c = b + c$.

addition property for inequalities (p. 190)   For all real numbers a, b, and c: If $a > b$, then $a + c > b + c$; if $a < b$, then $a + c < b + c$.

additive identity (p. 59)   The sum of 0 and any real number a is equal to the number a. That is, $a + 0 = a$, so 0 is called an additive identity.

additive inverse (p. 27)   The opposite of a number is its additive inverse.

additive inverse property (p. 27)   For every real number n, there is exactly one real number $-n$ such that $n + (-n) = 0$ and $-n + n = 0$.

algebraic expression (p. 3)   An algebraic expression contains variable and/or numerical expressions.

angle (p. 615)   The union of two non-collinear rays with a common endpoint.

angle of depression (p. 645)   The angle formed by the line of sight and below the line of the horizon.

angle of elevation (p. 643)   The angle formed by the line of sight and above the line to the horizon.

ascending order (p. 242)   The degree of each term in a polynomial increases from left to right.

associative property for addition (p. 60)   For all real numbers a, b, and c, $(a + b) + c = a + (b + c)$.

associative property for multiplication (p. 60)   For all real numbers a, b, and c, $(a \cdot b) \cdot c = a \cdot (b \cdot c)$.

average (p. 39)   The sum of n numbers divided by n.

axis of symmetry (p. 559)   For a quadratic function, $f(x) = ax^2 + bx + c$, the axis of symmetry of the graph is $x = -\dfrac{b}{2a}$.

base (p. 55)   In the expression, a^n, a is the base.

binomial (p. 242)   A binomial is a polynomial with two terms.

boundary of two half-planes (p. 401)   The line which separates two half-planes is the boundary of each half-plane.

closed half-plane (p. 402)   If the inequality uses $\le$ or $\ge$, the boundary line is part of the graph and is drawn as a solid line. The graph is called a closed half-plane.

closure property for addition (p. 24)   For all real numbers m and n, $m + n$ is a unique real number.

closure property for multiplication (p. 33)   For all real numbers m and n, $m \cdot n$ is a unique real number.

Glossary

coefficient (p. 63) In the term $6x^2$, 6 is the coefficient or numerical coefficient.

collinear points (p. 386) A set of points that lie on the same line are collinear points.

combined inequality (p. 202) A conjunction or disjunction expressed using $>$, $<$, $\geq$, and/or $\leq$.

common factor (p. 274) The same factor for two or more integers is a common factor.

commutative property for addition (p. 59) For all real numbers a and b, $a + b = b + a$.

commutative property for multiplication (p. 59) For all real numbers a and b, $a \cdot b = b \cdot a$.

comparison property (p. 186) For all real numbers a and b, one and only one of the following is true: $a = b$, $a < b$, $a > b$.

complementary angles (p. 615) Two angles whose measures have a sum of $90°$.

complementary events (p. 597) In a random experiment, the two situations—that an event does occur and that the event does not occur—are complementary events.

completeness property (p. 497) A one-to-one correspondence between the real numbers and the points of a number line.

completing the square (p. 547) A method used to form a perfect square trinomial.

complex rational expression (p. 337) A rational expression whose numerator or denominator contains one or more rational expressions.

composite function (p. 423) A composite function combines two or more functions.

composite number (p. 270) A positive integer that has more than two positive integral factors is a composite number.

compound event (p. 603) A compound event is made up of two (or more) events.

conclusion (p. 114) The final statement of a proof or theorem is the conclusion.

conjugates (p. 517) The sum and difference of the same two terms are conjugates. For example, $a + \sqrt{b}$ and $a - \sqrt{b}$.

conjunction (p. 202) A sentence formed by joining two sentences with the word *and*.

congruent angles (p. 623) Angles that have the same measure are congruent angles.

congruent figures (p. 623) Figures that have the same size and shape.

congruent line segments (p. 623) Line segments that have the same length.

consecutive integers (p. 144) Integers that differ by one are consecutive integers.

consistent systems (p. 444) A system of equations with at least one solution.

constant function (p. 423) A linear function whose range contains only one element.

constant of proportionality (p. 426) The constant, k, in a direct variation, $y = kx$, or inverse variation, $xy = k$.

coordinate of a point on a number line (p. 8) The graph of a real number is a point on a number line.

coordinate of a point in a plane (p. 370) The two numbers paired with a given point.

corresponding parts (p. 624) The corresponding parts of congruent triangles are corresponding vertices, corresponding angles, and corresponding sides.

coordinate system (p. 370) Determined when two number lines in a plane are drawn so they intersect at right angles.

cosine (p. 634) In a right triangle, the cosine of an acute angle is the ratio of the length of the leg adjacent to the angle to the length of the hypotenuse.

data (p. 582) A collection of numerical information.

degree of a monomial (p. 241) The sum of the exponents of its variables.

degree of a polynomial (p. 242) The highest degree of any of the polynomial's terms.

density property (p. 498)   The density property states that between any two real numbers, there is another real number.

dependent events (p. 604)   If one event influences the other, they are dependent events.

dependent system (p. 445)   A linear system of equations where the graph of each equation is the same.

descending order (p. 242)   The degree of each term in a polynomial decreases from left to right.

difference of two squares (p. 290)   The product of two binomials that are the sum and difference of the same two numbers; $a^2 - b^2 = (a + b)(a - b)$.

direct proof (p. 114)   The reasoning that takes you from the hypothesis to the conclusion.

direct variation (p. 426)   A function in the form $y = kx$, $k \neq 0$, where it is said that y varies directly as x, or y is directly proportional to x.

discriminant (p. 564)   Determines the nature and number of solutions of a quadratic equation.

disjunction (p. 203)   A sentence formed by joining two sentences with the word *or*.

distance formula (p. 529)   For two points $P_1(x_1, y_1)$ and $P_2(x_2, y_2)$ in the coordinate plane, the distance d between the points is given by $d = \sqrt{(x_2 - x_1)^2 + (y_2 - y_1)^2}$.

distributive property (p. 60)   For all real numbers a, b, and c, $a(b + c) = ab + ac$ and $(b + c)a = ba + ca$.

divide-and-average method (p. 498)   A method for approximating irrational square roots.

division property for equations (p. 101)   For all real numbers a, b, and c, $c \neq 0$; if $a = b$, then $\dfrac{a}{c} = \dfrac{b}{c}$.

division property for inequalities (p. 195)   For all real numbers a, b, and c:

If $a > b$ and $c > 0$, then $\dfrac{a}{c} > \dfrac{b}{c}$,

If $a > b$ and $c < 0$, then $\dfrac{a}{c} < \dfrac{b}{c}$.

domain of a relation (p. 413)   The set of all the first elements or x-coordinates of a relation is called the domain.

empty set (p. 79)   The set with no members. Used when no member of the replacement set makes an open sentence true.

equally likely (p. 596)   The possible outcomes of an experiment which have the same chance of occurring.

equation (p. 78)   A mathematical sentence in which the symbol $=$ (equals) connects two numerical or variable expressions.

equilateral triangle (p. 619)   A triangle with three sides of equal length.

equivalent equations (p. 96)   Equations that have the same solution(s) for the same replacement set are equivalent equations.

equivalent systems (p. 463)   Linear systems that may look different but have the same solution are equivalent systems.

evaluate (p. 3)   To substitute a given number for each variable and simplify.

even integers (p. 144)   Integers that are exactly divisible by two are even integers.

event (p. 596)   Any of the possible outcomes for an experiment is an event.

exponents (p. 55)   Used to show how many times the factor is multiplied. In a^n, n is the exponent.

extraneous solution (p. 351)   An apparent solution which does not satisfy the original equation is an extraneous solution.

extremes (p. 346)   In the ratio $a:b = c:d$, a and d are the extremes.

factor (p. 55)   When two or more numbers are multiplied, each number is called a factor of the product.

factored completely (p. 296)   A polynomial is factored completely when it is written as a product of prime polynomials.

Fibonacci sequence (p. 261) The sequence of numbers, 1, 1, 2, 3, 5, 8, 13, 21, . . . , where each number, except the first two, is the sum of the two preceding numbers.

finite solutions (p. 82) The number of possible solutions can be counted.

FOIL (p. 251) Method used for multiplying two binomials: add the products of the First, Inside, Outside, and Last terms.

formula (p. 117) An equation that expresses a relationship among two or more quantities.

frequency distribution (p. 583) A summary of data where each number is matched with the number of times it occurs.

function (p. 417) A relation in which each element of the domain is paired with exactly one element of the range.

functional notation (p. 418) Notation used to specify a function, for example, the arrow notation, $f: x \rightarrow 2x + 1$, or the f of x notation, $f(x) = 2x + 1$.

Geometry (p. 614) A branch of mathematics that deals with sets of points.

graph of a number (p. 8) Drawings which show relations between numbers or sets of numbers.

greatest common factor (GCF) (p. 274) The greatest integer that is a common factor of two or more integers.

half-plane (p. 401) The regions formed when a boundary line divides a plane.

histogram (p. 586) A bar graph of a frequency distribution.

hypotenuse (p. 524) In a right triangle, the side opposite the right angle is the longest side and is called the hypotenuse.

hypothesis (p. 114) The given statement of a theorem or proof.

identity property for addition (p. 18) For every real number n, there is exactly one real number 0 such that $n + 0 = n$ and $0 + n = n$.

identity property for multiplication (p. 32) For every real number n, $n \cdot 1 = n$ and $1 \cdot n = n$.

inclusive events (p. 605) Two events which can occur at the same time.

inconsistent system (p. 445) A system of equations that has no solution.

independent events (p. 603) Two events that do not influence one another.

independent system (p. 444) A linear system of equations where the graph of each equation is different.

inequality (p. 78) A mathematical sentence in which $<$ (less than), $>$ (greater than), or $\neq$ (is not equal to) is used.

integers (p. 7) The set of numbers, $\{. . . , -2, -1, 0, 1, 2, . . .\}$.

intersection (p. 203) The graph of a combined inequality containing "and." The overlap of the graphs of the two inequalities.

inverse operations (p. 96) An inverse operation is used as an efficient method to solve an algebraic equation, addition and subtraction are inverse operations, as are multiplication and division.

inverse variation (p. 430) A function in the form $xy = k$, $k \neq 0$, where it is said that y varies inversely as x.

irrational numbers (p. 8) Numbers that cannot be written in the form $\frac{m}{n}$, where m and n are integers and $n \neq 0$.

isosceles triangle (p. 619) A triangle that has at least two congruent sides.

least common denominator (LCD) (p. 328) The smallest possible common denominator of two or more fractions.

leg (p. 524) A leg of a right triangle is one of the sides which form the right angle.

like terms (p. 63) Terms that are exactly the same or differ only in their numerical coefficients.

linear equation (p. 375)   An equation whose graph is a straight line.

linear function (p. 422)   A function whose graph is a straight line.

linear inequality (p. 401)   A linear expression with inequality signs.

line (p. 614)   A line consists of infinitely many points extending in both directions without end.

line segment (p. 614)   A set of points on a line consisting of A and B, and all points between A and B, is called the line segment AB.

literal equation (p. 164)   An equation in which constants or coefficients of the variables are expressed by letters.

mathematical model (p. 110)   Represents the known parts of a problem.

maximum point (p. 558)   The highest point of a parabola that opens downward.

mean (p. 582)   In a set of n numbers, the sum of the numbers divided by n.

measure of central tendency (p. 582)   A statistic (a number) that is in some way representative or typical of a set of data.

median (p. 582)   The middle number in the set, or the mean of the two middle numbers, when the numbers are arranged in order from least to greatest.

minimum point (p. 558)   The lowest point of a parabola that opens upward.

mixed expression (p. 337)   The sum or difference of a polynomial and a rational expression.

mode (p. 582)   A number in a set of data that occurs most often.

monomials (p. 226)   An expression that is either a real number, a variable, or a product of a real number and one or more variables.

multiplication property for equations (p. 101)   For all real numbers a, b, and c; if $a = b$ then $ac = bc$.

multiplication property for inequalities (p. 195)   For all real numbers a, b, and c, if $a > b$ and $c > 0$, then $ac > bc$. If $a > b$ and $c < 0$, then $ac < bc$.

multiplicative identity (p. 59)   The product of 1 and any real number a is equal to the number a. That is, $a \cdot 1 = a$, so 1 is called the multiplicative identity.

multiplicative inverse (p. 35)   For every nonzero real number n, there is exactly one real number $\dfrac{1}{n}$, such that $n \cdot \dfrac{1}{n} = 1$ and $\dfrac{1}{n} \cdot n = 1$.

mutually exclusive events (p. 605)   Two events that cannot happen at the same time.

negative exponents (p. 237)   For all real numbers a, $a \neq 0$, and for all positive integers n, $a^{-n} = \dfrac{1}{a^n}$.

negative numbers (p. 7)   Numbers to the left of the zero (0) on a number line.

numerical coefficient (p. 63)   The numeral part of a term. In the term $6x^2$, 6 is the numerical coefficient.

numerical expression (p. 3)   An expression that may contain one or more of the operations of addition, subtraction, multiplication, or division.

obtuse angle (p. 615)   An angle that has a measure between 90° and 180°.

obtuse triangle (p. 619)   A triangle that has one obtuse angle.

odd integers (p. 145)   Integers that are not exactly divisible by 2.

odds (p. 597)   A ratio that compares the probability of an event to the probability of its complement.

open half-plane (p. 402)   If the inequality uses $<$ or $>$, the boundary line is not part of the graph and is drawn as a dashed line. The graph is called an open half-plane.

open sentences (p. 79)   Equations and inequalities that contain variables.

opposites (p. 13)   Numbers whose graphs are the same distance from the origin but in opposite directions.

order of an inequality (p. 194)   The direction of the inequality.

ordered pairs (p. 379)   Each point in a coordinate plane is assigned a unique ordered pair of real numbers, (x, y).

ordinate (p. 371)   The ordinate is the y-coordinate of an ordered pair.

origin (p. 7)   The 0 (zero) point on a number line or coordinate plane.

outcome (p. 596)   The possible result of each trial or experiment.

parabola (p. 558)   A graph of a quadratic function $f(x) = ax^2 + bx + c, a \neq 0$.

parallel (p. 393)   Any lines that have the same slope.

percent (p. 152)   A percent means hundredth or per hundred.

percent decrease (p. 156)   The ratio of an amount of decrease to the previous amount, expressed as a percent.

percent increase (p. 156)   The ratio of an amount of increase to the previous amount, expressed as a percent.

perfect square (p. 544)   An algebraic expression which contains squares of integers and square algebraic expressions.

perfect square trinomial (p. 289)   The square of a binomial equals a perfect square trinomial. $(m + n)^2 = m^2 + 2mn + n^2$, and $(m - n)^2 = m^2 - 2mn + n^2$.

point (p. 186)   The graph of a real number on a number line is a point.

polynomial (p. 242)   A sum of monomials.

polynomial equation (p. 300)   An equation whose sides are both polynomials.

positive numbers (p. 7)   Numbers to the right of zero (0) on a number line.

postulates (p. 113)   Statements that are accepted as true without requiring a proof.

prime number (p. 263)   An integer greater than 1, whose only positive factors are itself and 1, is a prime number.

prime factorization (p. 271)   A composite number written as the product of prime numbers.

prime polynomial (p. 286)   A prime polynomial is a polynomial that has no polynomial factors with integral coefficients except itself and 1.

principal square root (p. 494)   The positive square root indicated by $\sqrt{y}$.

product property of square roots (p. 495)   For all real numbers m and n, where $m \geq 0$ and $n \geq 0$, $\sqrt{mn} = \sqrt{m} \cdot \sqrt{n}$.

probability (p. 596)   Measures the likelihood that a particular event will occur.

properties of real numbers (p. 59)   Properties of real numbers are statements that are true for all real numbers.

properties of equality (p. 61)   For all real numbers a, b, c:
Reflexive: $a = a$
Symmetric: If $a = b$, then $b = a$.
Transitive: If $a = b$ and $b = c$, then $a = c$.

property of exponents for division (p. 230)   For all real numbers a, $a \neq 0$, and for all positive integers m and n:
If $m > n$, then $\dfrac{a^m}{a^n} = a^{m-n}$.
If $m < n$, then $\dfrac{a^m}{a^n} = \dfrac{1}{a^{n-m}}$.
If $m = n$, then $\dfrac{a^m}{a^n} = a^0 = 1$.

property of exponents for multiplication (p. 227)   For all real numbers a, and for positive integers m and n:
$a^m \cdot a^n = a^{m+n}$.

property of −1 for multiplication (p. 67)   For every real number a: $-1 \cdot a = -a$ and $a \cdot -1 = -a$.

property of zero for multiplication (p. 32) For all real numbers n, $n \cdot 0 = 0$ and $0 \cdot n = 0$.

property of proportions (p. 346) In a proportion, the product of the means equals the product of the extremes.

proportion (p. 345) A statement that ratios are equal is called a proportion.

protractor (p. 345) A measuring device used for finding the size of angles.

Pythagorean theorem (p. 524) In a right triangle, the square of the length of the hypotenuse is equal to the sum of the squares of the lengths of the sides.

quadrants (p. 370) The four regions formed by the axes in a coordinate plane.

quadratic equation (p. 300) An equation of the form $ax^2 + bx + c = 0$, where a, b, and c are real numbers and $a \neq 0$.

quadratic formula (p. 552) If $ax^2 + bx + c = 0$, where a, b, and c are real numbers and $a \neq 0$, then
$$x = \frac{-b \pm \sqrt{b^2 - 4ac}}{2a}.$$

quadratic function (p. 557) A function given by the equation $f(x) = ax^2 + bx + c$, where a, b, and c are real numbers and $a \neq 0$.

radical equation (p. 520) An equation that contains radicals with variables in the radicand.

radical expression (p. 494) An expression in the form $\sqrt{a}$.

radical sign (p. 494) The radical sign is a symbol $\sqrt{}$ used to express a radical.

radicand (p. 494) The expression under the radical sign.

ratio (p. 345) The comparison of two quantities by division.

range (p. 590) The difference between the greatest number and the least number in a set.

range of a relation (p. 413) The set of all

the second elements or y-coordinates of a relation is called the range.

rational expression (p. 316) An expression that can be written in the form $\frac{p}{q}$, where p and q are polynomials, $q \neq 0$.

rational number (p. 8) A number that can be written in the form $\frac{m}{n}$, where m and n are integers, and $n \neq 0$.

rationalize a denominator (p. 516) To write an equivalent rational expression so the denominator is changed from an irrational expression to a rational expression.

ray (p. 614) A ray is a part of a line which starts at a point and extends infinitely passing through a second point.

real numbers (p. 7) The set of irrational numbers together with the set of rational numbers form the set of real numbers.

reciprocal (p. 35) Two numbers whose product is 1 are called reciprocals.

reflexive property of equality (p. 61) For all real numbers a, $a = a$.

relation (p. 413) A set of one or more pairs of numbers is a relation.

repeating decimal (p. 500) A decimal which repeats endlessly the same digit, or the same set of digits.

replacement set (p. 79) The set of numbers that may be substituted for the variable.

right angle (p. 615) An angle that has a measure of 90°.

right triangle (p. 619) A triangle that has one right angle.

sample space (p. 596) The set of all possible outcomes in an experiment.

scalene triangle (p. 619) A triangle with three sides of unequal length.

scientific notation (p. 238) A number expressed in the form $n \times 10^m$, where n is a real number such that $1 \leq n < 10$ and m is an integer.

sequence (p. 260)   A sequence is a set of numbers arranged in a pattern.

set-builder (p. 198)   Set-builder notation is a way of expressing a solution set, such as $\{x: x < -12\}$, read as: the set of all real numbers x such that x is less than -12.

similar triangles (p. 628)   Two triangles are similar if and only if the measures of their corresponding angles are equal. The measures of their corresponding sides are proportional.

simplest form of an expression (p. 317)   When the numerator and the denominator have no common factors other than 1.

simplify (p. 13)   To replace the expression with its simplest name.

simultaneous equations (p. 444)   Simultaneous equations are two (or more) linear equations using the same variables.

sine (p. 634)   In a right triangle, the sine of an acute angle is the ratio of the length of the leg opposite the angle to the length of the hypotenuse.

slope of a line (p. 384)   The slope of a line is the ratio of the change in y to the corresponding change in x. For any two points on a line, (x_1, y_1) and (x_2, y_2);
$$m = \frac{y_2 - y_1}{x_2 - x_1}.$$

slope-intercept form (p. 391)   A linear equation in the form $y = mx + b$, where m is the slope of the line and b is the y-intercept.

solution (p. 79)   Any value of the variable that makes the open sentence true.

solution set (p. 79)   The set of all the numbers from the replacement set that make the open sentence true.

standard deviation (p. 591)   Measures how much each value in the data differs from the mean of the data.

standard form of linear equations (p. 375)   An equation in the form $Ax + By = C$, where A, B, and C are integers and A and B are not both zero.

statistics (p. 582)   Statistics is the collection, organization, analysis, and interpretation of numerical information.

substitution (p. 114)   If $a = b$, then a may replace b and b may replace a.

subtraction property for equations (p. 97)   For all real numbers a, b, and c, if $a = b$, then $a - c = b - c$.

subtraction (p. 28)   For all real numbers m and n: $m - n = m + (-n)$.

supplementary angles (p. 615)   Two angles whose measures have a sum of $180°$.

square of a binomial (p. 257)   Square the first term, double the product of the two terms, square the last term, and write the sum as a perfect square trinomial.

square root (p. 494)   If $x^2 = y$, then x is called a square root of y.

square root property (p. 544)   If $x^2 = k$, then $x = +\sqrt{k}$ or $x = -\sqrt{k}$, for any real number k, $k \geq 0$.

symmetric property of equality (p. 114)   For all real numbers a and b, if $a = b$ then $b = a$.

systems of linear equations (p. 444)   Two (or more) linear equations using the same variables.

tangent (p. 634)   The tangent of an angle in a right triangle is the ratio of the length of the leg opposite the angle to the length of the leg adjacent to the angle.

terminating decimal (p. 500)   A decimal which ends at a finite number of places.

theorem (p. 114)   A general conclusion that is shown to be true by using postulates, definitions, given facts, and other proved theorems.

transitive property of equality (p. 114)   For all real numbers a, b, and c, if $a = b$ and $b = c$, then $a = c$.

tree diagram (p. 603)   A diagram used to show relationships in compound events.

trial (p. 596)   A repetition of a probability experiment.

triangle (p. 618)   A figure formed by three segments joining three noncollinear points.

trigonometric ratios (p. 634)   Ratios of the lengths of the sides of a right triangle, sine, cosine, and tangent.

trigonometry (p. 633)   A Greek word for triangle measurement.

trinomial (p. 242)   A trinomial is a polynomial with three terms.

uniform motion (p. 172)   An object that moves at a constant speed, or rate, is said to be in uniform motion.

unlike terms (p. 63)   Terms that are not exactly the same.

union (p. 204)   For a combined inequality involving *or,* the union contains both graphs of the inequalities.

variable (p. 2)   A symbol used to represent one or more numbers.

variable expression (p. 2)   An expression that contains one or more variables.

variability (p. 590)   A measure of the spread of the numbers in a set of data.

variance (p. 591)   The mean of the sum of the squares of the deviations from the mean is called the variance.

Venn diagram (p. 600)   A pictorial representation of sets.

vertex of an angle (p. 615)   The common endpoint of the two rays which form the sides of an angle.

vertex of a parabola (p. 559)   The minimum or maximum point of a parabola.

vertical line test (p. 418)   A method for determining whether a relation is a function.

***x*-axis** (p. 370)   The horizontal number line on the coordinate plane.

***x*-coordinate** (p. 371)   The first element in a set of ordered pairs.

***x*-intercept** (p. 376)   The x-coordinate of the point where a graph intercepts the x-axis.

***y*-axis** (p. 370)   The vertical number line on the coordinate plane.

***y*-coordinate** (p. 371)   The second element in a set of ordered pairs.

***y*-intercept** (p. 376)   The y-coordinate of the point where a graph intercepts the y-axis.

zero-product property (p. 300)   For all real numbers a and b, if $ab = 0$, then $a = 0$ or $b = 0$ or both a and $b = 0$.

Abscissa, 371
Absolute value, 14, 213
  equations, 206–208
  inequalities, 210–212
  on a number line, 14
Accounting, algebra in, 429
Acute angle, 615
Addition
  additive identity property,
    59
  additive inverse property, 27
  associative property for, 60
  closure property for, 24
  commutative property for,
    59
  distributive property, 60
  of fractions, 328, 333
  identity property for, 18
  on a number line, 17–19
  of polynomials, 245, 337
  of radicals, 509–510
  of rational expressions, 333–
    334, 337
  of real numbers, 22–24
  rules for, 22–23
  solving systems of equations
    by, 459–460
Addition/subtraction method,
  459–460
Addition property
  for equations, 97
  for inequalities, 190
Additive identity, 18
Additive inverse, 27
Algebra in
  accounting, 429
  aviation, 167
  bookkeeping, 469
  construction, 622
  demography, 585
  engineering, 159
  geometry, 71, 205, 299 (see
    also Geometry)
  health, 247, 344
  industry, 499
  mechanics, 213
  meteorology, 34
  physics, 336
  police science, 506
  recreation, 284

Algebra in (cont.)
  space technology, 255
  taxation, 416
  transportation, 143
Algebraic expression(s)
  evaluating, 3–4, 52–53,
    55–57, 67–69
  involving exponents, 55–57
  numerical, 3
  parentheses in, 3–4, 52–53,
    67–69
  simplifying, 13, 52–64
  translating word phrases
    into, 5, 74–75, 454
  value of, 3–4, 52
  variable, 2–5
  writing, 6, 105
Algebraic notation, 42 (see
  also Symbol)
Algebraic proof, 113–114
Angle(s), 615–616
  acute, 615
  complementary, 615–616
  congruent, 623
  corresponding, 624, 628–
    629
  of depression, 643–645
  of elevation, 643–644
  measure of, 615
  obtuse, 615
  right, 615
  sides of, 615
  supplementary, 615–616
  of a triangle, 619
  vertex of, 615
Applications (see also Problem
  solving)
  agriculture, 308–309
  break-even point, 450
  cost analysis, 425
  image formation, 507–508
  interest, 341
  marathon running, 218–
    219
  mean, 39
  messenger service, 160
  meteorology, 41
  networks, 637–638
  physics, 562–563
  radio waves, 389–390

Applications (cont.)
  scattergrams, 594–595
  technology, 240 (see also
    Technology)
Area
  of a circle, 276, 284, 299
  greatest, 272, 309
  of a rectangle, 71, 281,
    304, 353
  of a shaded region, 275–
    276, 299
  of a square, 256, 276, 299
  of a trapezoid, 70
  of a triangle, 118, 276, 462
Arrow notation, 418
Associative property
  for addition, 60
  for multiplication, 60
Average (see Mean)
Aviation, algebra in, 167
Axes, coordinate, 370–371
Axis of symmetry, 559

Base, 55
Binomial(s), 242
  difference of two squares,
    290
  dividing by, 342–343
  factoring products of, 289–
    290
  multiplying, 251–252, 256–
    258
  opposites, 318
  squaring, 256–257
Binomial factor, 275
Biography
  Gauss, Carl Friedrich, 21
  Hypatia, 273
  Noether, Amalie, 511
  Poncelet, Jean-Victor, 349
  Ramanujan, Srinivasa, 58
  Turing, Alan, 81
Bookkeeping, algebra in, 469
Boundary line of a half-plane,
  401–402
Brackets, 37, 52, 69

Calculator, 6
  calculation-ready form, 103–
    105, 109, 341

Calculator (*cont.*)
  change sign key, 26
  evaluating expressions with,
    323
  factoring with, 277, 291
  Fibonacci sequence and, 263
  graphing, 419–420, 448,
    454, 560
  input sequence, 323
  interest and, 341
  memory keys, 71, 317
  power key, 58, 229
  reciprocals and, 40
  scientific notation, 255, 238
  simplifying expressions
    with, 234
  solve equations with, 103,
    556
  square numbers with, 236
  square root, 494, 497–498,
    544–545
  statistics, 583, 592
  trigonometry and, 525–526,
    640
Capacity, formulas for, 308
Careers
  air traffic controller, 449
  computer designer, 81
  computer software
    developer, 77
  geophysicist, 483
  meteorologist, 41
  seismologist, 483
Challenge, 48, 92, 132, 180,
  222, 226, 312, 364, 408,
  440, 490, 538, 578, 610
Chapter Review (*see* Reviews)
Chapter Test (*see* Tests)
Circle, area of, 276, 284, 299
Closed half-plane, 402
Closure property
  for addition, 24
  for multiplication, 33
Coefficient, 63
Collinear points, 386
Combined inequalities, 202–
  204, 209, 213
Combining like terms, 63–64,
  136–138
Common factors, 274–275
Commutative property
  for addition, 59
  for multiplication, 59
Comparison property, 186
Complementary angles, 615–
  616
Complementary events, 597
Completeness property, 497

Completing the square, 547–
  549
Complex rational expression,
  337–338
Composite function, 423
Composite number, 270–271
Compound events, 603–605
Computer (*see also*
  Technology)
  ABS function, 30
  computer applications, 51,
    54, 72–73, 77, 81
  graphing, 189, 376, 395
  INT function, 11
  SUM function, 125
  using computer programs,
    54, 72–73, 125–126,
    189, 197, 217, 236, 240,
    247, 272, 277, 309, 376–
    377, 390, 395, 405, 469,
    478, 502, 530, 549, 562–
    563, 592
Conclusion, 114, 332
Conditional, 332
Congruence, properties of, 624
Congruent angles, 623
Congruent line segments, 623
Congruent triangles, 624–625
Conjugates, 517
Conjunction, 202
Consecutive integers, 144–
  145, 305
Consistent systems, 444
Constant, 164
  function, 425
  of proportionality, 426–428
  of variation, 426–428
Construction, algebra in, 622
Coordinate
  axes, 370–371
  plane, 370–372
  system, 370
Coordinate geometry, 531–532
Coordinate(s) of a point, 8,
  370–371
Coriolis force, 379
Corresponding angles, 624,
  628–629
Corresponding sides, 624, 628–
  629
Corresponding vertices, 624,
  628
Cosine, 634, 639–640
Counting numbers (*see* Natural
  numbers)
Critical Thinking
  analysis, 40
  classifying, 244

Critical Thinking (*cont.*)
  generalizing, 353
  predicting consequences,
    400
Cross-ratio, 349
Cubes, sum of two, 58
Cubic-root equations, 522
Cumulative Review (*see*
  Reviews)
Cylinder, volume of, 118

Decimal(s)
  coefficients, 148–149
  in equations, 98, 103
  expressed as fractions, 500–
    501
  as irrational numbers, 497–
    498
  on a number line, 8
  and percent, 152–154
  repeating, 500–501
  terminating, 500–501
Degree
  of a monomial, 241
  of a polynomial, 242
Demography, algebra in, 585
Denominator(s)
  adding or subtracting
    expressions with like and
    unlike, 334
  fractions with irrational, 516–
    517
  least common, 328–330
  rationalizing, 516–517
Density property, 498
Dependent events, 604
Dependent systems, 445
Depreciation
  annual rate of, 429
  linear, 434–435
Did You Know?, 81, 163,
  209, 233, 281, 379, 527,
  553
Difference of two squares, 290
Diophantine problem, 273
Direct proof, 114
Direct variation, 426–428
  graph of, 427
Discriminant, 564–565
Disjunction, 203
Distance formula, 528–529
  uniform motion, 119, 389,
    479–480, 483
Distributive property, 60
Divide-and-average method,
  498
Divisible, 270, 469

Division
  definition of, 36
  fraction form of, 4, 42, 52
  of fractions, 324
  of monomials, 230–231
  of polynomials, 342–343
  property of exponents for, 230
  of radicals, 516–517
  of rational expressions, 324–325, 327
  of real numbers, 35–37
  by zero, 37, 40, 291, 351
Division property
  for equations, 101
  for inequalities, 195
Domain
  of a function, 417
  of a relation, 413

Empty set, 79
Endpoint(s), 614
Engineering, algebra in, 159
Enrichment (*see* Challenge; Critical Thinking; Extra; Logical Reasoning; Math Club Activities; Projects; Puzzles)
Equal sign, 12, 42
Equality, properties of, 61, 114
Equally likely, 596
Equation(s), 78 (*see also* Solving equations)
  absolute value, 206–208
  addition property for, 97
  cubic-root, 522
  with decimal coefficients, 148
  decimals in, 98, 103
  division property for, 101
  equivalent, 96, 460
  fractions in, 97, 102-103, 107, 507–508
  and functions, 418–419, 422–423
  graphing, 186
  of inverse variations, 430–431
  of a line, 375, 396–398
  linear, 375 (*see also* Linear equation)
  literal, 164–165
  multiplication property for, 101
  with percent, 152–154

Equation(s) *(cont.)*
  polynomial, 300–302, 304–305
  as proportion, 345–347
  quadratic, 300 (*see also* Quadratic equation)
  radical, 520–521
  rational, 350–359
  simultaneous, 444
  solutions of (*see* Solution)
  standard forms of polynomial, 300
  subtraction property for, 97
  systems of linear, 444–446
  translating word statements to, 85–87, 139
  in two variables, 371–372
  writing, 110–111, 120–121
Equilateral triangle, 619
Equivalent equations, 96, 460
Equivalent expressions, 329–330
Equivalent systems of equations, 460, 463–464
Estimating from graphs, 380
Euclid's Algorithm, 277
Evaluating algebraic
  expressions, 3–4, 52–53
  involving exponents, 55–57
  parentheses in, 67–69
  rule for order of operations, 52
Evaluating formulas, 55–57, 117–118
Evaluating functions, 418–419, 423
Even integers, 144
Event, probability of, 596–597, 600–601
Exponent(s), 55
  ascending order of, 242
  descending order of, 242
  division with, 230–232
  evaluating expressions with, 55–57
  factored form of expressions with, 226
  multiplication with, 226–227
  negative, 237–238, 240
  order of operations with, 56
  positive integers as, 55
  in prime factorization, 271
  properties of, 227, 230, 234–235
  scientific notation, 237–238, 240
  simplifying expressions with, 55–56

Exponent(s) *(cont.)*
  in simplifying polynomials, 242–243
  in simplifying radicals, 504
  zero, 232
Exponential form, 227
Exponential notation, 240
Expressions (*see* Algebraic expression, Radical expression, Rational expression)
Extra, 155, 197, 250, 277, 319, 395, 433, 462, 473, 502, 519, 523, 589, 632, 636, 642
Extra Practice, 655–669
Extraneous
  solutions, 351–352, 521
Extremes of a proportion, 346

Factor(s), 270
  binomial, 275
  common, 274–275
  greatest common, 274–275, 277
  integral, 270–271
  missing, 274
  monomial, 275
  prime, 271
  square, 503
  variable, 226
Factored form, 226
Factoring
  applications of, 299, 308–309
  completely, 296–297
  a difference of two squares, 290
  by grouping, 292–293
  perfect square trinomials, 289
  polynomials, 274–276
  by removing a common binomial factor, 292–293
  solving polynomial equations by, 300–302, 304–305
  trinomials, 278–287
False statement, 82, 519
Fibonacci Sequence, 260–261
Figurate numbers, 496
FOIL method, 251
Formula(s), 117
  amount in savings account, 118

Formula(s) *(cont.)*
  area of a circle, 276
  area of a rectangle, 304
  area of a square, 256
  area of a trapezoid, 70
  area of a triangle, 118
  aspect ratio, 167
  capacity of a rectangular
    bin, 308
  capacity of a round bin, 308
  circular motion, 55
  cost of composition, 499
  depreciation, annual rate of,
    429
  depreciation, linear, 434–
    435
  diagonals in a polygon, 566
  distance, 528–529
  evaluating, 55–57, 117–118
  focal length, 507
  height of a rocket, 307
  interest, compound, 550
  interest, simple, 54, 154
  midpoint, 532
  monthly payments, 341
  perimeter, 117–118, 304
  in problem solving, 358–
    359, 434–435
  profit, 358–359
  quadratic, 551–552
  resistance, 336
  slope, 384
  speed, 506
  sum of *n* terms of arithmetic
    series, 118
  temperature conversion, 118
  uniform motion, 168–169,
    172–174, 479–481
  vision, 523
  volume of a cylinder, 118
  volume of a rectangular
    prism, 118
  volume of a sphere, 233
  writing, 358–359, 361
Fraction(s) (*see also* Rational
  expression)
  adding and subtracting, 328,
    333
  decimal form of, 500–501
  dividing, 324
  in equations, 97, 102–103,
    107, 507–508
  equivalent, 328
  with irrational denominator,
    516–517
  least common denominator
    of, 328
  mixed numbers, 337

Fraction(s) *(cont.)*
  multiplying, 320
  on a number line, 8
  ratio expressed as, 345
  reciprocal of, 324
  simplifying, 230
Frequency distribution, 583,
  586–587, 590
Function(s), 417
  applications of, 425, 429,
    562–563, 571
  arrow notation, 418
  composite, 423
  constant, 423
  defined by equations, 418–
    419, 422–423
  described in tables, graphs,
    and mappings, 417–419
  direct variation, 426–428
  domain of, 417
  evaluating, 418–419, 423
  graphing, 418, 423, 427,
    430, 557–560
  inverse variation, 430–431
  linear, 422–423, 567–568
  quadratic, 557–560, 568–
    569
  range of, 417
  trigonometric, 634
  vertical line test for, 418
Functional notations, 418
$f(x)$ notation, 418

Gauss, Carl Friedrich, 21
Geometry, 614
  algebra in, 71, 205, 299
  angles, 615–616 (*see also*
    Angle)
  applications of, 116, 281,
    353, 622, 637–638
  in architecture, 617
  area (*see* Area)
  capacity, 308
  congruent figures, 623–625
  coordinate, 531–532
  formulas (*see* Formula)
  lines, 614 (*see also* Line;
    Line segment)
  networks, 637–638
  perimeter, 71, 117–118,
    304, 353, 455–456
  points, 614 (*see also* Point)
  projective, 349
  similar triangles, 628–629
  triangles, 618–620 (*see also*
    Triangle)
  volume (*see* Volume)

Graph(s)
  and absolute value, 14, 206–
    207, 210–212
  bar, 586
  with a calculator, 419–420,
    448, 454, 560
  with computer programs,
    189, 376, 395
  of a direct variation, 427
  of an equation, 186
  estimating from, 380–381
  of functions, 418, 423, 427,
    430
  of a horizontal line, 377,
    385–386
  of a hyperbola, 430
  of inequalities, 187–188,
    205
  of intersecting lines, 444
  of an inverse variation, 430
  of a line, 375–378
  of linear equations, 375–
    378, 384–386, 391–393
  of linear inequalities, 401–
    403
  on a number line, 7–9, 186–
    188
  of opposites, 13
  of ordered pairs, 371–372
  of a parabola, 558
  of parallel lines, 393
  of quadratic functions, 557–
    560
  of relations, 412–414
  scattergram, 594–595
  of solution set of an
    equation, 186
  of solution sets of
    inequalities, 187–188,
    191, 195–196, 203–204
  of systems of linear
    equations, 444–445
  of systems of linear
    inequalities, 484
  of a vertical line, 377, 385–
    386
Greater than (>), 12, 42,
Greater than or equal to (≥),
  187, 215
Greatest common factor, 274–
  275, 277
Grouping
  factoring by, 292–293
  symbols, 52

Half-planes, 401–402
Health, algebra in, 247, 344

Histogram, 586–587
History, 77, 81, 163, 209, 233, 295, 496, 546
Horizontal number line, 370
Hypatia, 273
Hyperbola, 430
Hypotenuse, 524
Hypothesis, 114, 332

Identity
  additive, 59
  multiplicative, 59
Identity property
  for addition, 18
  for multiplication, 32
If-then statements, 332
Inclusive events, 605
Inconsistent systems, 445
Independent events, 603–604
Independent systems, 444
Industry, algebra in, 499
Inequality(ies), 78–80
  absolute value, 210–212
  addition property for, 190
  applications of, 209, 213
  combined, 202–204, 209, 213
  division property for, 195
  graphing, 187–188, 205
  linear, 401–403
  multiplication property for, 195
  solution sets of, 79–80, 187–188
  subtraction property for, 190
  systems of linear, 484
  transitive property of order for, 189
  writing, 214–215
Inequality symbols, 12, 42, 78, 187, 215
Integer(s), 7
  absolute value of, 14
  addition of, 17–19, 21
  consecutive, 144–145, 305
  even, 144
  negative, 7–8
  on a number line, 7–9
  odd, 145
  positive, 7–8
Integral factor, 270–271
Integral solution, 273
Interest
  compound, 550
  simple, 54, 154
Intersecting lines, 444
Intersection

Intersection *(cont.)*
  graph of combined inequality, 203
  point of, 444
  of sets, 600
Inverse(s)
  additive, 27
  multiplicative, 35
Inverse operations, 35, 96
Inverse variation, 430–431
  graphs of, 430
Irrational numbers, 8, 497–498
  on a number line, 9
Isosceles triangle, 619

Königsberg Bridge problem, 637–638

Least common denominator, 328–330
Less than (<), 12, 42,
Less than or equal to (≤), 187, 215
Lever, principle of, 431
Like radicals, 509–510
Like terms, 63
  combining, 64
  in equations, 136–138
Line(s), 614
  equation of, 375, 396–398
  graphing, 375–378
  horizontal, 385–386
  intersecting, 444
  parallel, 393, 445
  slant of, 385–386
  slope of, 384–386
  vertical, 385–386
  x-intercept of, 376
  y-intercept of, 376
Line segment(s), 614
  congruent, 623
  finding midpoint of, 531–532
Linear equation(s), 375
  applications of, 433, 458
  graphing, 375–378, 384–386, 391–393
  slope-intercept form of, 391–393
  standard form of, 375
  systems of (*see* Systems of linear equations)
Linear functions, 422–423, 567–568
Linear inequality(ies), 401–403

Linear inequality *(cont.)*
  graphing, 402–403
  systems of, 484
Literal equation(s), 164–165
  application of, 167
Logical reasoning, 26, 54, 116, 189, 236, 291, 327, 332, 530, 566

Maintaining Skills (*see* Reviews)
Mappings, 412–413, 417
Math Club Activities, 11, 147, 193, 229, 357, 374, 550, 561, 599
Mathematical model, 110
Maximum point, 558
Mean, 39, 41, 582–583, 585
Means of a proportion, 346
Measure of an angle, 615
Measures of central tendency, 582–583
Measures of variability, 590–592
Mechanics, algebra in, 213
Median, 582–583
Members of a set, 7
Mental computation, 238, 257
Meteorology
  algebra in, 34
  application, 41
Midpoint formula, 532
Minimum point, 558
Mixed expression, 337
Mode, 582–583
Monomial(s), 226
  degree of, 241
  dividing, 230–231
  division of a polynomial by, 342
  and exponents, 234–235
  multiplying, 227
  multiplying a polynomial by, 248–249
  terms of a polynomial, 242
Monomial factor, 275
Multiplication
  associative property for, 60
  of binomials, 251–252, 256–258
  closure property for, 33
  commutative property for, 59
  distributive property, 60
  of fractions, 320
  identity property for, 32
  of monomials, 227

Multiplication *(cont.)*
  of a polynomial by a
    monomial, 248–249
  of polynomials, 248–258
  property of exponents for,
    227
  property of −1, 67
  property of zero for, 32
  of radicals, 512–513
  of rational expressions, 320–
    321
  of real numbers, 31–33
  rules for, 31–32
  symbols for, 3, 42
  zero-product property, 300
Multiplication-addition/
  subtraction method, 463–
  464
Multiplication property
  for equations, 101
  for inequalities, 195
Multiplicative identity, 59
Multiplicative inverse, 35
Mutually exclusive events, 605

**Natural (counting) numbers,
  7**
  on a number line, 9
Negative direction on a
  number line, 17–18
Negative exponents, 237–238,
  240
Negative numbers, 7–9
Negative slope, 385
Newton's method, 502
Noether, Amalie, 511
Nomogram, 508
Number(s)
  absolute value of, 14
  comparing, 12
  composite, 270–271
  consecutive, 144–145
  corresponding to a point on
    a number line, 7–9
  decimals *(see* Decimal)
  Egyptian, 163
  even, 43, 144
  graphing, 7–9, 11
  integers, 7 *(see also*
    Integer)
  irrational, 8–9, 497–498
  natural, 7
  negative, 7–9
  odd, 145
  opposite of, 13
  ordered pairs of, 370–372
  patterns, 236, 260–263

Number(s) *(cont.)*
  positive, 7–9
  prime, 270–271
  prime factorization of, 271
  rational, 8–9, 316
  real, 7–9 *(see also* Real
    numbers)
  reciprocal of, 35
  square, 496
  square root of, 494–495
  squaring, 494
  triangular, 496
  whole, 7
Number line
  absolute value and, 14
  addition on, 17–19
  coordinate of a point on, 8
  direction on, 17–19
  distance on, 17–19, 206–
    208
  graphing on, 7–9, 11, 186–
    188
  horizontal, 370
  ordering numbers on, 12
  origin on, 7
  real numbers on, 7–9, 12–
    13
  vertical, 370
Numerical coefficient, 63
Numerical expression, 3

Obtuse Angle, 615
Obtuse triangle, 619
Odd integers, 145
Odds, 597
One as multiplicative identity,
  59
Open half-plane, 402
Open sentence(s), 79 *(see also*
  Equation; Inequality)
  replacement set of, 79–80,
    82–83
  solution of, 79–80
  solution set of, 79–80
Operations
  inverse (opposite), 35, 96
  order of, 52
Opposite(s)
  additive inverse, 27
  of a binomial, 318
  of a number, 13
  operations, 35, 96
Order
  of operations, 52
  of real numbers, 12
  transitive property of, 189
Ordered pair(s), 370–372

Ordered pair(s) *(cont.)*
  graph of, 371–372
  set of, 412–413
Ordinate, 371
Origin
  on a number line, 7
  in a plane, 370–371
Outcome, 596

**Palantine Anthology
  problem, 546**
Parabola, 558–560
  axis of symmetry, 559
  graph of, 558
  maximum point, 558
  minimum point, 558
  vertex, 559
  x-coordinate of the vertex
    of, 559
Parallel lines, 393, 445
Parentheses
  adding negative numbers
    with, 18
  algebraic expressions with,
    3–4, 52–53, 67–69
  equations with, 98, 137–138
Pattern(s), number
  Fibonacci sequence, 260–
    261
  look for, 260–261, 263
  Pascal's triangle, 263
  with squares of numbers,
    236
Percent, 152–154
  applications of, 159, 160,
    357, 416
  of change, 156–157
Perfect square, 544
Perfect square trinomial, 289
Perimeter, 71, 117–118, 304,
  353, 455–456
Physics
  algebra in, 336
  application of, 562–563
Pi (π), 8
Plane, coordinate, 370–372
  coordinates of points in,
    370–371
  distance between two points
    in, 528–529
  origin in, 370–371
  plotting points in, 371–372
  quadrants in, 370
  x-axis in, 370
  y-axis in, 370
Point(s), 614
  collinear, 386

Point(s) *(cont.)*
coordinate(s) of, 8, 370–371
distance between two, 206–208, 528–529
graph of, 186
of intersection, 444
maximum, 558
minimum, 558
on a number line, 7–9
plotting, 371–372
Police science, algebra in, 506
Polynomial(s), 241–242
adding, 245
ascending order of exponents in, 242–243
binomial factors of, 278–287
classifying, 244
degree of, 242
descending order of exponents in, 242
dividing, 342–343
equations, 300–302, 304–305
factoring, 274–276 (*see also* Factoring)
monomial factors of, 274–276
multiplying, 248–258
prime, 286
simplifying, 242–243
subtracting, 246
terms of, 242
Polynomial equation(s), 300 (*see also* Linear equation; Quadratic equation)
applications of, 307, 308–309
solutions (roots) of, 300–302
solving, by factoring, 300–302, 304–305
standard forms of, 300
Poncelet, Jean-Victor, 349
Positive direction on a number line, 17–18
Positive numbers, 7–9
Postulates, 113
Power(s)
multiplying by a power of 10, 148–149
of a number, 55
of a product, 234–235
of a quotient, 235
Preparing for Standardized Tests (*see* Tests)
Prime factorization, 271

Prime numbers, 263, 270–271, 295
Prime polynomial, 286
Principal square root, 494
Probability, 596
of two dependent events, 604
of an event, 596–597, 600–601
of two inclusive events, 605
of two independent events, 603–604
of two mutually exclusive events, 605
odds, 597
Problem solving (*see also* Application)
age, 470–471
angle of depression, 643–645
angle of elevation, 643–644
commission, 380
consecutive integers, 144–145, 305
digit, 467–468
linear depreciation, 434–435
mixed types, 127–129 (*see also* Reviews)
mixture, 161–163, 474–475
money, 474–475
percent of change, 156–157
perimeter, 455–456
probability, 600–601
profit, 358–359, 567–568
reminders, 121
steps, 43
trigonometry, 643–644
uniform motion, 168–169, 172–174, 355–356, 479–481
wind and water current, 479–481
work, 354–355
Problem solving strategies
account for all possibilities, 82–83
check for hidden assumptions, 643–645
draw a diagram, 600–601
estimate from graphs, 380
look for a pattern, 260–261
make a drawing or a table, 168–169
make a model, 110–111
select appropriate notation, 42–44
solve a simpler problem, 358–359

Problem solving strategies *(cont.)*
write an equation, 120–121
write an inequality, 214–215
write a linear system, 455–456
use an appropriate formula, 434–435
use coordinate geometry, 531–532
use a function, 567–569
use polynomial equations, 304–305
Product(s)
of binomials, 251–252, 256–257, 289–290
of means and extremes, 346
of monomials, 227
power of a, 235
of powers, 227
property of square roots, 495
of radicals, 512–513
of rational expressions, 320–321
of signed numbers, 31–33
of sum and difference of two terms, 257–258
Product property of square roots, 495
Projectile motion, 553
Projective geometry, 349
Projects, 45, 84, 112, 124, 171, 217, 263, 307, 361, 383, 436, 458, 535, 571, 602, 647
Proof, 113–114
Property(ies)
additive inverse, 27
associative, for addition, 60
associative, for multiplication, 60
closure, for addition, 24
closure, for multiplication, 33
commutative, for addition, 59
commutative, for multiplication, 59
comparison, 186
of completeness, 497
of congruence, 624
density, 598
distributive, 60
of equality, 61, 114
for equations, 97, 101
of exponents, 234–235

Property(ies) *(cont.)*
of exponents for division, 230
of exponents for multiplication, 227
identity, for addition, 18
identity, for multiplication, 32
for inequalities, 190, 195
multiplicative inverse, 35
of parallel lines, 393
product, of square roots, 495
of proportions, 346
quotient, of square roots, 495
reciprocal, 35
reflexive, 61, 624
square-root, 544
substitution, 114
symmetric, 61, 624
transitive, 61, 624
transitive, of order for $<$ and $>$, 189
of zero for multiplication, 32
zero-product, 300
Proportion(s), 345–347
property of, 346
and similar triangles, 628–629
Proportionality, constant of, 426–428
Protractor, 615
Pythagorean theorem, 524–525
applications of, 527, 622
converse of, 525
Puzzles, 16, 54, 100, 155, 473

Quadrants, 370
Quadratic equation(s), 300
application of, 553
involving perfect-square expressions, 544–545
solutions (roots) of, 564–565, 572–573
solving, by completing the square, 547–549
solving, by factoring, 300–302
solving, by using the quadratic formula, 551–552, 564–565
solving, by using the square-root property, 544–545
standard form of, 300

Quadratic formula, 551–552
Quadratic function(s), 557–560, 568–569
applications of, 562–563, 571
graphing, 557–560
Quotient(s)
power of a, 235
of powers, 230–231
property of square roots, 495
of radicals, 516–517
of signed numbers, 35–37
Quotient property of square roots, 495

Radical(s), 494
like, 509
unlike, 509
Radical equation(s), 520–521
applications of, 506, 523
Radical expression(s)
adding, 509–510
application of, 506
conjugates, 517
dividing, 516–517
in equations, 520–521
multiplying, 512–513
rationalizing the denominator of, 516–517
simplifying, 503–504, 509–517
subtracting, 509–510
with variables, 504
Radical sign, 494
Radicand, 494
Radio signals, 255, 389–390
Ramanujan, Srinivasa, 58
Random experiment, 596–597
Random survey, 124, 589, 600–602
Range
of a function, 417
of a relation, 413
of a set of data, 590
Ratio(s), 345
cross-ratio, 349
expressed as a fraction, 345
probability, 596–597
and proportion, 345–347
in simplest form, 345–346
slope of a line expressed as, 384
trigonometric, 633–634
Rational equations, 350–359
Rational expression(s), 316
adding, 333–334

Rational expression(s) *(cont.)*
complex, 337–338
dividing, 324–325, 327
in equations, 350–359
equivalent, 329–330
least common denominator of, 328–330
mixed expression, 337
multiplying, 320–321
in simplest form, 317
simplifying, 317–318, 338
subtracting, 333–334
undefined, 317
Rational number(s), 316
decimal forms for, 500–501
on a number line, 8–9, 11
Rationalizing the denominator, 516–517
Ray, 614
Reading in Algebra, 421
Real number(s), 7–9
adding, 22–24
application of, 41
dividing, 35–37
multiplying, 31–33
on a number line, 7–9, 12–13
opposite of, 13
order of, 12
properties (*see* Property)
rules for, 22–23, 31–32
subtraction of, 27–29
Reciprocal(s), 35
of a fraction, 324
Reciprocal property, 35
Recreation, algebra in, 284
Rectangle, area of, 71, 281, 304, 353
Rectangular prism, volume of, 118
Reflexive property, 61, 114, 624
Relation(s), 413 (*see also* Function)
domain of, 413
graphing, 414
range of, 413
Repeating decimal, 500–501
Replacement set, 79–80
finite, 82
infinite, 82
Reviews
Chapter Summary and, 46–47, 90–91, 130–131, 178–179, 220–221, 264–265, 310–311, 362–363, 406–407, 438–439, 488–489,

Reviews *(cont.)*
    536–537, 576–577, 608–609, 648–649
    Cumulative, 94, 182–184, 268, 366–368, 442, 540–542, 612, 652–654
    Extra Practice, 655–669
    Maintaining Skills, 50, 134, 224, 314, 410, 492, 580
    Mixed Problem Solving, 84, 112, 124, 171, 216, 263, 307, 361, 383, 436, 458, 571, 602, 647
Right angle, 615
Right triangle(s), 619
    applications of, 527, 622
    hypotenuse of, 524
    Pythagorean theorem, 524–525
        converse of, 525
    trigonometric ratios in, 633–634, 639–640
Root(s), 302, 564
    extraneous, 521
Rule for order of operations, 52

Sample space, 596
Scalene triangle, 619
Scattergram, 383, 594–595
Scientific notation, 237–238, 240
    application of, 240
Segment, line, 614
Self-test *(see* Tests)
Sentence(s)
    conjunction, 202
    disjunction, 203
    open, 78–80
Set(s)
    empty, 79
    intersection of, 600
    members of, 7
    of ordered pairs, 412–413
    of rational numbers, 8
    of real numbers, 7–9
    replacement, 79–80, 82–83
    solution, 79–80
Set-builder notation, 198–199
Set notation, 7, 42
Sides
    of an angle, 615
    corresponding, 624, 628–629
    of a triangle, 618
Similar terms, 63, 509
Similar triangles, 628–629

Simplest form
    of radical expressions, 503–504
    of rational expressions, 317
    of ratios, 345–346
Simplifying
    algebraic expressions, 13, 52–64
    expressions with parentheses, 67–69
    fractions, 230
    polynomials, 242–243
    products of radicals, 512–513
    quotients of radicals, 516–517
    rational expressions, 317–318, 338
    square roots, 503–504
    sums and differences of radicals, 509–510
Simultaneous equations, 444 *(see also* System of linear equations)
Sine, 634, 639–640
Slant of a line, 385–386
Slope of a line, 384–386, 400
Slope-intercept form of a linear equation, 391–393
Solution(s)
    of equations, 79, 96–98, 186, 300–302, 371–372
    extraneous, 351–352, 521
    integral, 273
    of open sentences, 79–80
    of quadratic equations, 564–565, 572–573
Solution set(s)
    of equations, 79, 97
    graphing *(see* Graph)
    of inequalities, 79–80, 187–188
    of open sentences, 79–80
    of systems of linear equations, 444–445
    of systems of linear inequalities, 484
Solving equations, 96–108
    by combining like terms, 136–138
    with decimal coefficients, 148–149
    by factoring, 300–302
    fractional, 507–508
    involving absolute value, 206–208

Solving equations *(cont.)*
    involving percent, 152–154, 156–157
    involving proportion, 346–347
    literal, 164–165
    parentheses in, 98, 137–138
    polynomial, 300–302, 304–305
    quadratic, 544–555, 564–565, 572–573
    radical, 520–521
    rational, 350–359
    shortcuts for, 148–149
    steps for, 141
    with the variable on both sides, 140–141
Solving inequalities, 190–199
    application of, 218–219
    combined, 202–204
    involving absolute value, 210–212
    systems of linear, 484
    using a computer program, 197
Solving systems of linear equations
    by the addition/subtraction method, 459–460
    by graphing, 444–446
    by the multiplication-addition/subtraction method, 463–464
    in problems, 455–456, 467–483
    by the substitution method, 451–452
Space technology, algebra in, 255
Sphere, volume of, 233
Square, area of, 256, 276, 299
Square(s)
    of a binomial, 256–257
    factoring the difference of two, 290
    factoring a perfect square trinomial, 289
    of a number, 494
    perfect, 544
Square factor, 503
Square numbers, 496
Square root(s), 494–495
    approximating, 497–498, 502
    irrational, 497–498, 516–517
    negative, 494

Square root(s) *(cont.)*
  positive, 494
  principal, 494
  product property of, 495
  property, 544
  quotient property of, 495
  simplifying, 503–504
  with variable expressions, 503–504
Standard deviation, 591–592
Standard form
  of a linear equation, 375
  of a polynomial equation, 300
  of a quadratic equation, 300
Standardized Tests (*see* Tests)
Statistics, 582
  applications of, 585, 594–595
  frequency distribution, 583, 586–587, 590
  graphing data, 586–587, 594–595
  measures of central tendency, 582–583
  measures of variability, 590–592
Substitution method, 451–452
Substitution property, 114
Subtraction
  definition of, 28
  distributive property, 60
  of a polynomial and a rational expression, 337
  of polynomials, 246
  of radicals, 509–510
  of rational expressions, 333–334
  of real numbers, 27–29
  solving systems of equations by, 459–460
Subtraction property
  for equations, 97
  for inequalities, 109
Summary and Review (*see* Reviews)
Supplementary angles, 615–616
Symbol(s)
  absolute value, 14, 42
  congruence, 623
  division, 4, 42, 52
  empty set, 79
  equality, 12, 42
  greater than, 12, 42
  greater than or equal to, 187, 215

Symbol(s) *(cont.)*
  grouping, 3–4, 37, 52
  inequality, 78
  less than, 12, 42
  less than or equal to, 187, 215
  multiplication, 3, 42
  parentheses, 3–4, 52
  positive and negative signs, 7, 42
  radical sign, 494
  for repeating digit, 500
  for a set, 7, 42
  is similar to, 628
  square root, 494
  table of, xii
Symmetric property, 61, 114, 624
Symmetry, axis of, 559
Systems of linear equations, 444–446 (*see also* Solving systems of linear equations)
  applications of, 450, 458, 473
  consistent, 444
  dependent, 445
  equivalent, 460, 463–464
  graphing, 444–445
  inconsistent, 444
  independent, 445
  solution sets of, 444–445
  writing, 455–456
Systems of linear inequalities, 484

Table(s)
  frequency distribution, 583, 586–587, 590
  of squares and square roots, 670
  of symbols, xii
  of trigonometric ratios, 671
Tangent, 634, 639–640
Taxation, algebra in, 416
Technology
  applications of, 240, 255, 562–563
  using spreadsheets, 72–73, 125–126, 217
Term(s), 63
  combining like, 64, 136–138
  like, 63
  of a polynomial, 242
  unlike, 63–64
Terminating decimal, 500–501

Tests
  Chapter, 48, 92, 132, 180, 222, 266, 312, 364, 408, 440, 490, 538, 578, 610, 650
  Preparing for Standardized, 49, 93, 133, 181, 223, 267, 313, 365, 409, 441, 491, 539, 579, 610, 651
  Test Yourself, 45, 66, 89, 109, 129, 151, 177, 217, 239, 259, 288, 303, 340, 361, 388, 405, 424, 437, 466, 487, 515, 535, 556, 575, 593, 607, 627, 647
Theorem, 114
  Pythagorean, 524–525
Tolerance, 213
Transitive property
  of congruence, 624
  of equality, 61, 114
  of order for < and >, 189
Translating word phrases into algebraic expressions, 5, 74–75, 454
Translating word statements to equations, 85–87, 139
Transportation, algebra in, 143
Trapezoid, area of, 70
Tree diagram, 603
Trial, 596
Triangle(s), 618–620
  acute, 619
  angles of, 619
  area of, 118, 276, 462
  congruent, 624–625
  corresponding parts, 624–625
  equilateral, 619
  isosceles, 619
  obtuse, 619
  right, 619 (*see also* Right triangle)
  scalene, 619
  sides of, 618
  similar, 628–629
  in trigonometry, 633–634, 639–640
  vertices of, 618
Triangular numbers, 496
Trigonometric ratios
  cosine, 634, 639–640
  sine, 634, 639–640
  tangent, 634, 639–640
Trigonometry, 633
  using a calculator in, 640
  using trigonometric ratios, 639–640, 643–645

Trigonometry *(cont.)*
  using trigonometric tables,
    639–640
Trinomial(s), 242
  factoring, 278–287
  perfect square, 289
True statement, 79, 82, 319,
  519

Undefined
  rational expression, 317
  slope, 386
Uniform motion, 168–169,
  172–174, 355–356, 479–
  481
    applications of, 255, 389–
      390, 483, 561
Union, graph of combined
  inequality, 204
Unit distance, 17–19
Units of measure
  bushel, 308
  cubit, 383
  em, 499
  foot, 383
  megahertz, 389
Unlike radicals, 509
Unlike terms, 63–64

Value(s)
  of an expression, 3–4, 52
  of a variable, 3–4, 317
Variability, 590

Variable(s), 2–5
  on both sides of an
    equation, 140–141
  value of, 3–4, 317
Variable expression, 2–4
Variable factor, 226
Variance, 591
Variation
  constant of, 426–428
  direct, 426–428
  inverse, 430–431
Velocity, 55, 143, 307, 370,
  506, 571
Venn diagram, 600–602
Vertex (vertices)
  of an angle, 615
  corresponding, 624, 628
  of a parabola, 559
  of a triangle, 618
Vertical line test, 418
Vertical number line, 370
Vocabulary, 46, 90, 130, 178,
  220, 264, 310, 362, 406,
  438, 488, 536, 576, 608,
  648
Volume
  of a cylinder, 118
  of a rectangular prism, 118
  of a sphere, 233

Whole numbers, 7
  on a number line, 9

Writing in Algebra, 6, 62,
  105, 119, 139, 323, 454

x-axis, 370
x-coordinate, 370
x-coordinate of the vertex of a
  parabola, 559
x-intercept, 376

y-axis, 370
y-coordinate, 370
y-intercept, 376, 396–397

Zero
  absolute value of, 14
  as additive identity, 59
  division by, 37, 40, 291,
    351
  as an exponent, 232
  as origin, 7
  product property, 300
  property for multiplication,
    32
Zero-product property, 300

Photo Credits

Chapter 1 **1:** Arjen Verkaik/The Stock Market. **2:** Ken Karp. **21:** The Bettmann Archive. **26:** Chris Sorensen/The Stock Market. **34:** Ted Kaufman/The Stock Market. **41:** Russ Kinne/Comstock.
Chapter 2 **51:** Brian Brake/Science Source/Photo Researchers. **55:** Chris Jones/The Stock Market. **58:** The Granger Collection. **77:** Ed Kashi. **78:** Arjen Verkaik/The Stock Market. **81:** The Science Museum.
Chapter 3 **95:** Mark E. Gibson/The Stock Market. **96:** Seaworld of Florida. **100:** Michal Heron/Woodfin Camp. **118:** Tom King/The Image Bank.
Chapter 4 **135:** Hank Morgan/Photo Researchers. **136:** Frank Whitney/The Image Bank. **143:** Cliff Feulner/The Image Bank. **160:** Roy Morsch/The Stock Market. **161:** DPI. **167:** Peter F. Runyon/The Image Bank.
Chapter 5 **185:** Bill Ross/Westlight/Woodfin Camp. **189:** Ken Karp. **194:** David Madison/Duomo. **202:** D. Strohmeyer/Focus West. **208:** Rutger's New Jersey Bowl/NJN.

209: Harvard College Observatory/Science Photo Library/Photo Researchers. **214:** Richard Steedman/The Stock Market. **218:** Paul Sutton/Duomo.
Chapter 6 **225:** NASA. **255:** NASA.
Chapter 7 **269:** DPI. **273:** The Bettmann Archive. **308:** Gary Cralle/The Image Bank.
Chapter 8 **315:** Henley & Savage/The Stock Market. **327:** Jay Freis/The Image Bank. **341:** Barry O'Rourke/The Stock Market. **345:** Obremski/The Image Bank. **354:** Gregory Heisler/The Image Bank.
Chapter 9 **369:** Brownie Harris/The Stock Market. **389:** Co. Rentmeester/The Image Bank.
Chapter 10 **411:** Robert Kristofik/The Image Bank. **425:** Jay Freis/The Image Bank.
Chapter 11 **443:** Michal Heron/Woodfin Camp. **449:** Walter Bibikow/The Image Bank. **455:** William Strode/Woodfin Camp. **478:** The Bettmann Archive. **479:** William Strode/Woodfin Camp. **481:** (t) Phillip Wallick/The Stock

Market. **481:** (b) Tom Leigh/Rainbow. **482:** Eddie Hironaka/The Image Bank. **483:** David Austen/Stock Boston. **487:** Joe Bator/The Stock Market.
Chapter 12 **493:** Gary Gladstone/The Image Bank. **494:** Sonya Jacobs/The Stock Market. **497:** Miguel/The Image Bank. **500:** Dan McCoy/Rainbow. **503:** Roger Ressmeyer/Starlight Photo Agency. **506:** George Anderson. **507:** Tom Stack & Associates. **520:** Duomo.
Chapter 13 **543:** Wes Thompson/The Stock Market. **544:** Charles West/The Stock Market. **557:** Jay Freis/The Image Bank. **562:** NASA.
Chapter 14 **581:** Jeff Lowenthal/Woodfin Camp. **582:** Robert Frerck/Odyssey Prod. **594:** John M. Roberts/The Stock Market. **596:** The Bettmann Archive.
Chapter 15 **613:** John Blaustein/Woodfin Camp. **618:** Paul Barton/The Stock Market. **623:** Murray & Assoc., Inc./The Stock Market. **628:** Russ Kinne/Comstock. **639:** Ken Karp.

Additional Answers

Chapter 2 Algebraic Expressions
Writing in Algebra, page 62
7. Addition, subtraction, multiplication, or division

8. Has no reciprocal

9. The symbol either for less than or greater than

Class Exercises, page 76
14. The product of 10 and a number squared, increased by 60; 10 times a number squared, plus 60.

Practice Exercises, page 76
13. Three times a number, decreased by five; Five less than three times a number

14. Seven times a number, increased by six; six more than seven times a number

15. w times the sum of w and three; The product of w and w plus three

Chapter 3 Equations in One Variable
Practice Exercises, page 112
11. In our place-value numeration system, the position of the digit determines its numeric value. Digits to the left of the decimal point represent whole numbers, digits to the right of the decimal point represent fractions.

12. Fill the 3-quart measure and pour it into the 5-quart measure. (2) Fill the 3-quart measure a second time and pour as much as you can into the 5-quart measure. This will leave 1 quart in the 3-quart measure. (3) Empty the 5-quart measure and pour the 1 quart into it. (4) Fill the 3-quart measure and pour it into the 5-quart measure. This will make 4 quarts.

Practice Exercises, page 115
4. Proof:

Statements	Reasons
1. $x = y$	1. Given
2. $z - x = z - x$	2. Reflex. prop.
3. $z - x = z - y$	3. Substit. prop.

5. Proof:

Statements	Reasons
1. $a + [b + (-a)]$ $= a + [-a + b]$	1. Commut. prop. for add.
2. $= [a + (-a)] + b$	2. Assoc. prop. for add.
3. $= 0 + b$	3. Add. inv. prop.
4. $= b$	4. Ident. prop. for add.

6. Proof:

Statements	Reasons
1. $x + [-(x + y)]$ $= x + [-1(x + y)]$	1. Prop. of -1 for mult.
2. $= x + [-1(x)$ $+ (-1)(y)]$	2. Dist. prop.
3. $= x + [-x + (-y)]$	3. Prop. of -1 for mult.
4. $= [x + (-x)] + (-y)$	4. Assoc. prop. for add.
5. $= 0 + (-y)$	5. Add. inv. prop.
6. $= -y$	6. Ident. prop. for add.

7. Proof:

Statements	Reasons
1. $a = b$	1. Given
2. $a - d$ $= a - d$	2. Reflex. prop.
3. $= b - d$	3. Substit. prop.
4. $= b + (-d)$	4. Def. of subtrac.
5. $= -d + b$	5. Commut. prop. for add.
6. $= -d - (-b)$	6. Def. of subtrac.
7. $= (-1)(d)$ $- (-1)(b)$	7. Prop. of -1 for mult.
8. $= (-1)(d - b)$	8. Dist. prop.
9. $= -(d - b)$	9. Prop. of -1 for mult.

Writing in Algebra, page 119
4.

Dan:	Rosita:
$3b - 2 = 19$	$3b - 2 = 19$
$b - \dfrac{2}{3} = \dfrac{19}{3}$	$3b = 19 + 2$
$b = \dfrac{19}{3} + \dfrac{2}{3}$	$3b = 21$
$b = \dfrac{21}{3}$	$b = 7$
$b = 7$	

Rosita's method is easier. It requires less steps.

Test Yourself, page 129
3. Proof:

Statements	Reasons
1. $m = r; n \neq 0$	1. Given
2. $\dfrac{m}{n} = \dfrac{m}{n}$	2. Reflex. prop.
3. $\dfrac{m}{n} = \dfrac{r}{n}$	3. Substit. prop.

Chapter Test, page 132
12. Proof:

Statements	Reasons
1. $ab + cb + d$ $= (a + c)b + d$	1. Distr. prop.
2. $= d + (a + c)b$	2. Comm. prop. for add.
3. $= d + b(a + c)$	3. Comm. prop. for mult.

Chapter 4 More Equations in One Variable
Class Exercises, page 149
7. Divide each side by 5: $2m - 3 = 3m$

8. Add 8 to each side. Then divide each side by 5: $p - 10 = 9$

Chapter 5 Inequalities in One Variable
Practice Exercises, pages 188–189

1.
$-3\ -2\ -1\ \ 0\ \ 1\ \ 2$

2.
$-3\ -2\ -1\ \ 0\ \ 1\ \ 2$

3.
$-2\ -1\ \ 0\ \ 1\ \ 2\ \ 3$

4.
$-3\ -2\ -1\ \ 0\ \ 1\ \ 2$

5.
$-1\ \ 0\ \ 1\ \ 2\ \ 3\ \ 4$

6.
$-2\ -1\ \ 0\ \ 1\ \ 2\ \ 3$

7.
$-2\ -1\ \ 0\ \ 1\ \ 2\ \ 3$

8.
$0\ \ 5\ \ 10\ \ 15\ \ 20\ \ 25$

9.
$-2\ -1\ \ 0\ \ 1\ \ 2\ \ 3$

10.
$-3\ -2\ -1\ \ 0\ \ 1\ \ 2$

11.
$-2\ -1\ \ 0\ \ 1\ \ 2\ \ 3$

12.
$-1\ \ 0\ \ 1\ \ 2\ \ 3\ \ 4$

13.
$-2\ -1\ \ 0\ \ 1\ \ 2\ \ 3$

14.
$-2\ -1\ \ 0\ \ 1\ \ 2\ \ 3$

15.
$-2\ -1\ \ 0\ \ 1\ \ 2\ \ 3$

16.
$-2\ -1\ \ 0\ \ 1\ \ 2\ \ 3$

17.
$-2\ -1\ \ 0\ \ 1\ \ 2\ \ 3$

18.
$-2\ -1\ \ 0\ \ 1\ \ 2\ \ 3$

31.
$-4\ -3\ -2\ -1\ \ 0\ \ 1$

32.
$-6\ -4\ -2\ \ 0\ \ 1\ \ 2$

33.
$-5\ -4\ -3\ -2\ -1\ \ 0$

34.
$-3\ -2\ -1\ \ 0\ \ 1\ \ 2$

35. a
$0\quad x\quad y\quad z$

b
$0\quad z\quad y\quad x$

Practice Exercises, pages 192–193

1.
$-3\ -2\ -1\ \ 0\ \ 1\ \ 2$

2.
$-3\ -2\ -1\ \ 0\ \ 1\ \ 2$

3.
$-2\ -1\ \ 0\ \ 1\ \ 2\ \ 3$

4.
$-2\ -1\ \ 0\ \ 1\ \ 2\ \ 3$

5.
$-2\ -1\ \ 0\ \ 1\ \ 2\ \ 3$

6.
$-10\ -8\ -6\ -4\ -2\ \ 0$

7.
$-3\ -2\ -1\ \ 0\ \ 1\ \ 2$

8.
$-2\ -1\ \ 0\ \ 1\ \ 2\ \ 3$

9.
$-12\ -6\ \ 0\ \ 6\ \ 12\ \ 18$

10.
$-1\ \ 0\ \ 1\ \ 2\ \ 3\ \ 4$

11.
$-2\ -1\ \ 0\ \ 1\ \ 2\ \ 3$

12.
$-3\ -2\ -1\ \ 0\ \ 1\ \ 2$

13.
$-2\ -1\ \ 0\ \ 1\ \ 2\ \ 3$

14.
$-15\ -10\ -5\ \ 0\ \ 5\ \ 10$

15.
$-20\ -10\ \ 0\ \ 10\ \ 20\ \ 30$

Practice Exercises, page 197

1.
$0\ \ 1\ \ 2\ \ 3\ \ 4\ \ 5$

2.
$-1\ \ 0\ \ 1\ \ 2\ \ 3\ \ 4$

3.
$-2\ \ 0\ \ 2\ \ 4\ \ 6\ \ 8$

4.
$-8\ -4\ \ 0\ \ 4\ \ 8\ \ 12$

5.
$-4\ \ 0\ \ 4\ \ 8\ \ 12\ \ 16$

6.
$-2\ \ 0\ \ 2\ \ 4\ \ 6\ \ 8$

7.
$-8\ -6\ -4\ -2\ \ 0\ \ 2$

8.
$-18\ -12\ -6\ 0\ \ 6\ \ 12$

9.
$-8\ -6\ -4\ -2\ \ 0\ \ 2$

10.
$-6\ -4\ -2\ \ 0\ \ 2\ \ 4$

11.
$-20\ -10\ 0\ \ 10\ \ 20\ \ 30$

12.
$-10\ -8\ -4\ \ 0\ \ 4\ \ 8$

13.
$-3\ -2\ -1\ \ 0\ \ 1\ \ 2$

14.
$-6\ -4\ -2\ \ 0\ \ 2\ \ 4$

15.
$-4\ -2\ \ 0\ \ 2\ \ 4\ \ 6$

16.
$-10\ -5\ \ 0\ \ 5\ \ 10\ \ 15$

17.
$-15\ -10\ -5\ \ 0\ \ 5\ \ 10$

18.
$-3\ \ 0\ \ 3\ \ 6\ \ 9\ \ 12$

19.
$-15\ -10\ -5\ \ 0\ \ 5\ \ 10$

20.
$-12\ -6\ \ 0\ \ 6\ \ 12\ \ 18$

21.
$-2\ \ 0\ \ 2\ \ 4\ \ 6\ \ 8$

22.
$-30\ -20\ -10\ 0\ \ 10\ \ 20$

23.
$-3\ -2\ -1\ \ 0\ \ 1\ \ 2$

24.
−5 −4 −3 −2 −1 0

25.
−80 −60 −40 −20 0 20

26.
−40 −20 0 20 40 60

27.
−3 −2 −1 0 1 2

28.
−30 −20 −10 0 10 20

29.
−1 0 1 2 3 4

30.
−2 −1 0 1 2 3

31.
−3 −2 −1 0 1 2

32.
−3 −2 −1 0 1 2

33.
−15 −10 −5 0 5 10

34.
−3 −2 −1 0 1 2

35.
−2 −1 0 1 2 3

36.
−15 −10 −5 0 5 10

Practice Exercises, page 200

1.
−3 −2 −1 0 1 2

2.
−6 −3 0 3 6 9

3.
−3 −2 −1 0 1 2

4.
−3 −2 −1 0 1 2

5.
−2 −1 0 1 2 3

6.
0 2 4 6 8 10

Test Yourself, page 201

6.
0 1 2 3 4 5

7.
−2 −1 0 1 2 3

8.
−3 −2 −1 0 1 2

9.
−12 −8 −4 0 4 8

10.
−3 −2 −1 0 1 2

11.
−3 −2 −1 0 1 2

12.
−20 −10 0 10 20 30

13. No Solution
0

Practice Exercises, page 205

7.
−6 −3 0 3 6 9

8.
−5 0 5 10 15 20

9.
−8 −4 0 4 8 12

10.
−2 −1 0 1 2 3

11.
0 1 2 3 4 5

12.
−2 −1 0 1 2 3

13.
−3 −2 −1 0 1 2

14.
−2 −1 0 1 2 3

15.
−2 −1 0 1 2 3

16.
−2 −1 0 1 2 3

17.
−2 −1 0 1 2 3

18.
−10 −5 0 5 10 15

19.
−2 −1 0 1 2 3

20.
−2 −1 0 1 2 3

21.
−4 −3 −2 −1 0 1

22.
−4 −3 −2 −1 0 1

23.
−4 −3 −2 −1 0 1

24.
−3 −2 −1 0 1 2

25. No Solution
0 1 2 3 4 5

26.
−2 −1 0 1 2 3

27.
−2 −1 0 1 2 3

28.
−2 −1 0 1 2 3

29.
−1 0 1 2 3 4 5

30.
−2 −1 0 1 2 3 4

Practice Exercises, pages 212–213

1.
−15 −10 −5 0 5 10

2.
−15 −10 −5 0 5 10

3.
−16 −12 −8 −4 0 4

4.
−12 −8 −4 0 4 8

5.
−12 −8 −4 0 4 8

6.
−15 −10 −5 0 5 10

7.
$$-2\ 0\ 2\ 4\ 6\ 8$$

8.
$$-6\ -3\ 0\ 3\ 6\ 9$$

9.
$$-2\ 0\ 2\ 4\ 6\ 8$$

$\{-3 < a < 7\}$

10.
$$-2\ 0\ 2\ 4\ 6\ 8$$

11. no solution

$\left\{-\dfrac{4}{3} < t < 2\right\}$

12.
$$-3\ -2\ -1\ 0\ 1\ 2$$

$\{m:\ m < 4\ \text{or}\ m > 5\}$

13.
$$0\ 1\ 2\ 3\ 4\ 5$$

$\left\{\text{all real numbers except } \dfrac{1}{4}\right\}$

14.
$$-2\ -1\ 0\ 1\ 2\ 3$$

$\left\{-\dfrac{9}{2} \le t \le \dfrac{3}{2}\right\}$

15.
$$-4\ -3\ -2\ -1\ 0\ 1$$

$\left\{-3 \le x \le \dfrac{7}{3}\right\}$

16.
$$-3\ -2\ -1\ 0\ 1\ 2$$

$\left\{-\dfrac{7}{5} \le a \le \dfrac{11}{5}\right\}$

17.
$$-2\ -1\ 0\ 1\ 2\ 3$$

$\left\{-\dfrac{3}{2} \le b \le \dfrac{5}{2}\right\}$

18.
$$-2\ -1\ 0\ 1\ 2\ 3$$

$\{a:\ a \le -10\ \text{or}\ a \ge 4\}$

19.
$$-12\ -8\ -4\ 0\ 4\ 8$$

$\{b \le -7\ \text{or}\ b \ge -3\}$

20.
$$-8\ -6\ -4\ -2\ 0\ 2$$

$\left\{\dfrac{3}{2} \le x \le \dfrac{5}{2}\right\}$

21.
$$-2\ -1\ 0\ 1\ 2\ 3$$

$\{-2 \le q \le 3\}$

22.
$$-4\ -2\ 0\ 2\ 4\ 6$$

$\{\text{all real numbers}\}$

23.
$$-2\ -1\ 0\ 1\ 2\ 3$$

$\{\text{all real numbers}\}$

24.
$$-2\ -1\ 0\ 1\ 2\ 3$$

$\left\{\dfrac{1}{2} \le z \le \dfrac{5}{2}\right\}$

25.
$$-2\ -1\ 0\ 1\ 2\ 3$$

$\{1 \le t \le 11\}$

26.
$$-3\ 0\ 3\ 6\ 9\ 12$$

$\{-2 \le x \le 10\}$

27.
$$-10\ -5\ 0\ 5\ 10\ 15$$

$\{5 > m > 7\}$

28.
$$-2\ 0\ 2\ 4\ 6\ 8$$

29. no solution

$\{\text{all real numbers}\}$

30.
$$-2\ -1\ 0\ 1\ 2\ 3$$

$\left\{\dfrac{1}{2} \le q \le \dfrac{7}{2}\right\}$

31.
$$0\ 1\ 2\ 3\ 4\ 5$$

Chapter 5 Test, page 222

1.
$$-2\ -1\ 0\ 1\ 2\ 3$$

2.
$$-2\ -1\ 0\ 1\ 2\ 3$$

3.
$$-4\ -2\ 0\ 2\ 4\ 6$$

4.
$$-12\ -6\ 0\ 6\ 12\ 18$$

5.
$$-2\ -1\ 0\ 1\ 2\ 3$$

6.
$$-2\ -1\ 0\ 1\ 2\ 3$$

7.
$$-2\ -1\ 0\ 1\ 2\ 3$$

11.
$$-8\ -4\ 0\ 4\ 8\ 16$$

12.
$$-4\ -2\ 0\ 2\ 4\ 6$$

13.
$$-10\ -8\ -6\ -4\ -2\ 0$$

1. no solution
$$0$$

2.
$$-4\ -3\ -2\ -1\ 0\ 1$$

Chapter 9 Linear Equations
Practice Exercises, pages 372–373

1–4.

$C\ (0, 4)$ $B\ (3, 4)$
$A\ (1, 2)$
$D\ (3, 0)$

5 – 8.

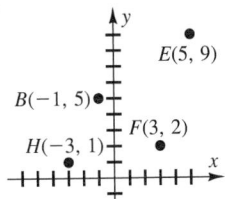

9 – 12.

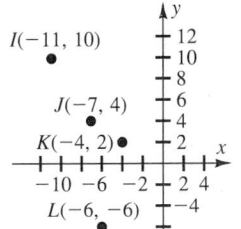

13 – 16.

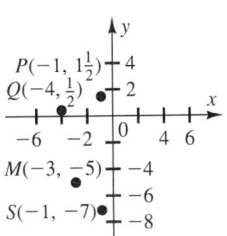

21.

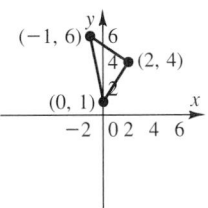

22.

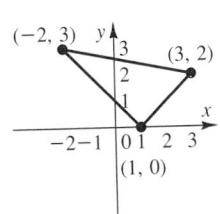

23.

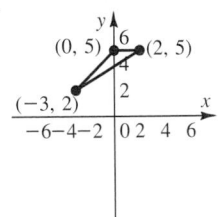

24.

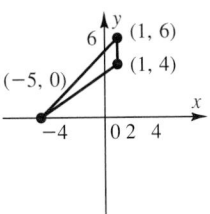

25.

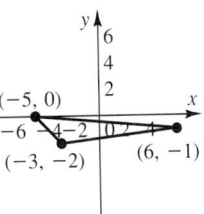

26.

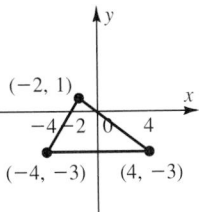

27.

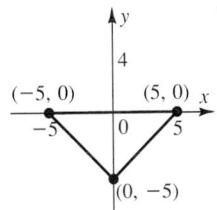

28.

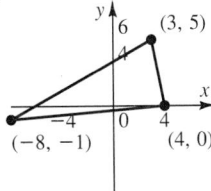

42.

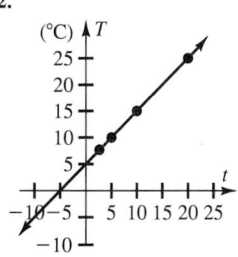

43.

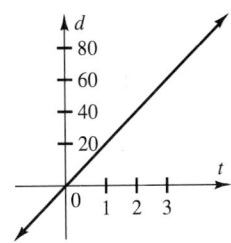

44.

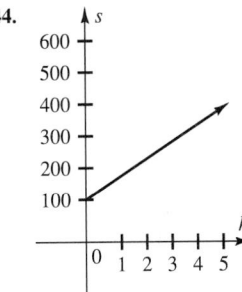

Practice Exercises, pages 378–379

5.

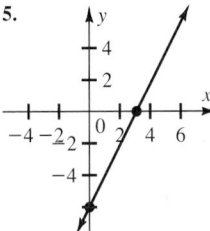

6.

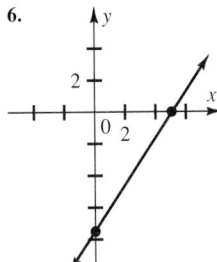

7.

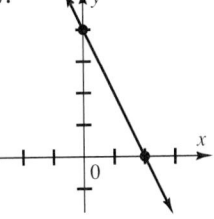

8.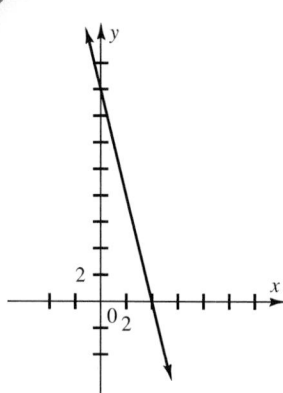

9.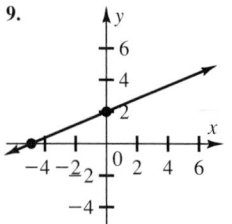

10.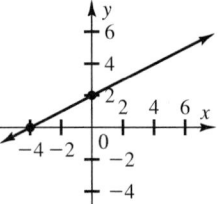

11.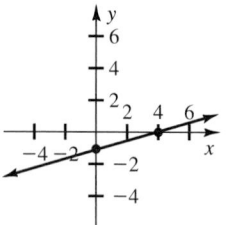

12.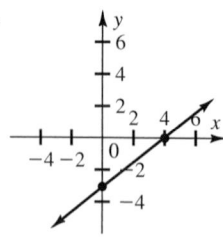

13.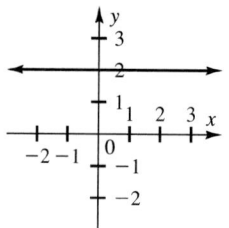

14.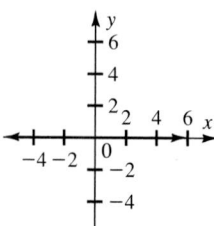

15.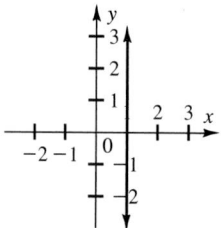

16.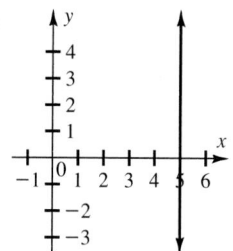

17.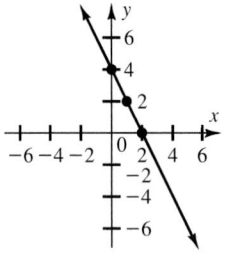

18.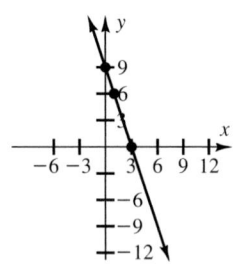

19.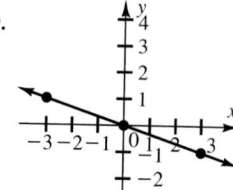

20.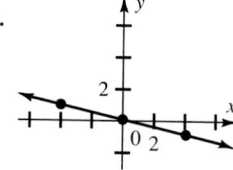

25.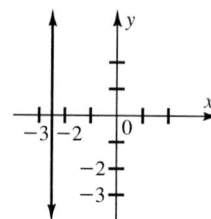

26.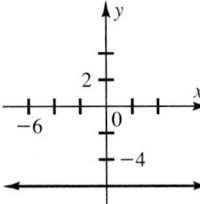

27.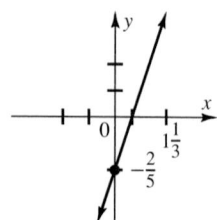

28.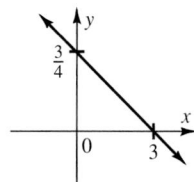

29.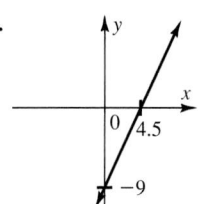

30.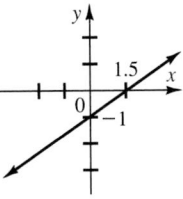

31.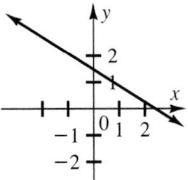

32.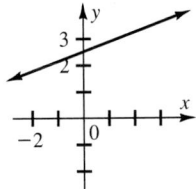

41.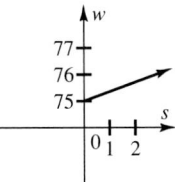

Practice Exercises, page 394

37.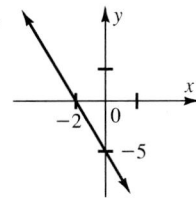

38.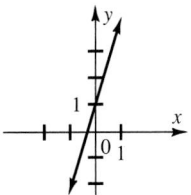

39.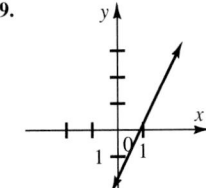

40.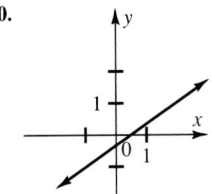

41.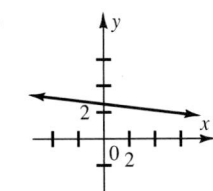

42.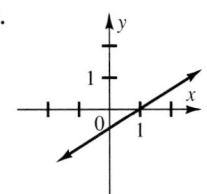

Practice Exercises, pages 404–405

11.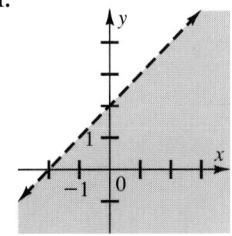

12.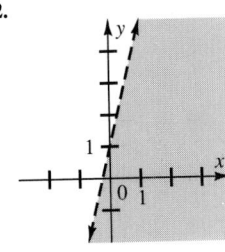

13.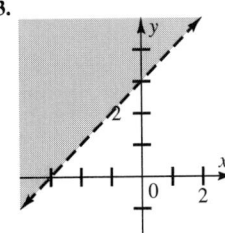

14.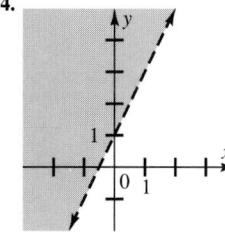

15.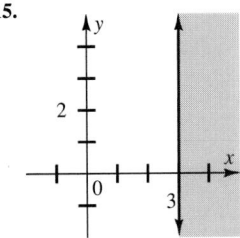

16.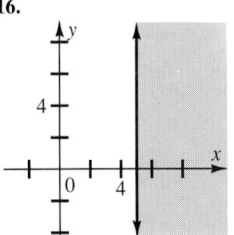

17.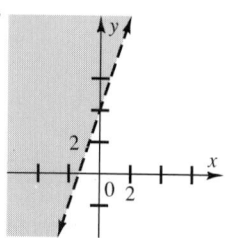

18.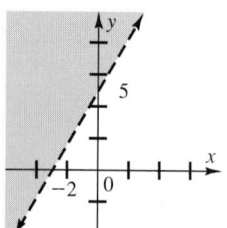

19.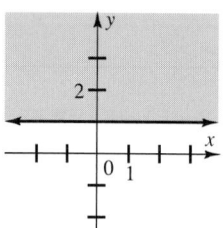

20.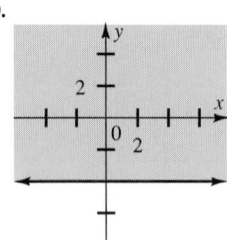

21.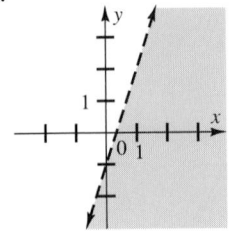

22.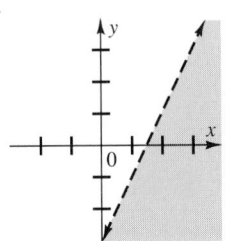

23.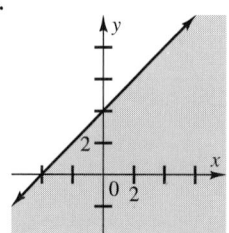

24.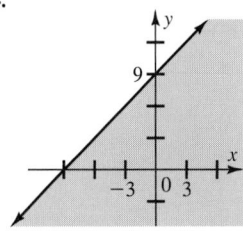

25.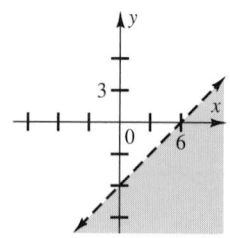

26.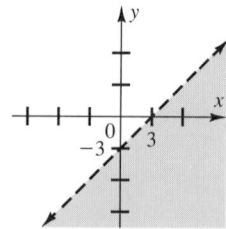

27.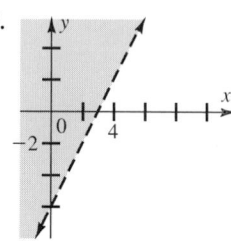

28.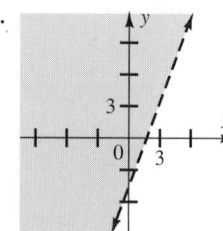

29.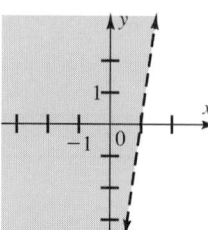

30.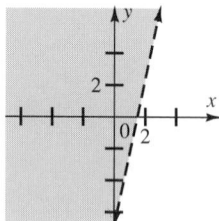

31.

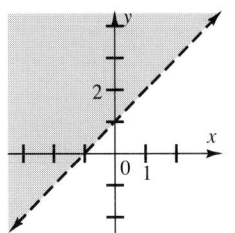

38.

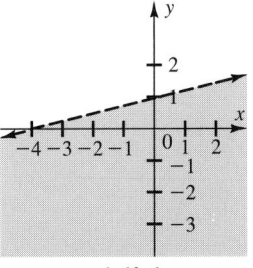

open half-plane

39.

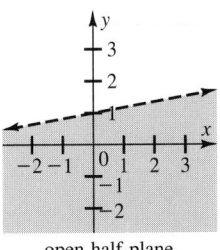

open half-plane

40.

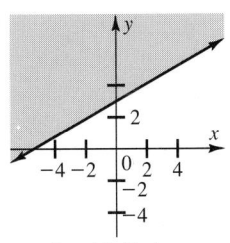

closed half-plane

41.

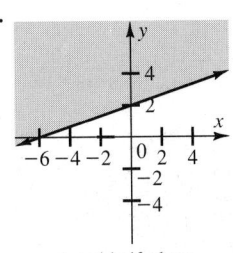

closed half-plane

42.

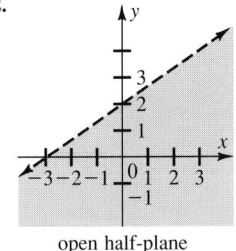

open half-plane

43.

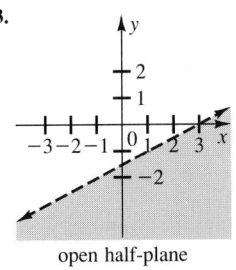

open half-plane

Test Yourself, page 405

5.

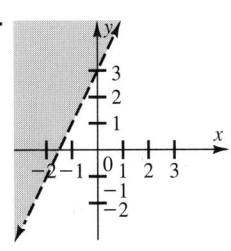

6.

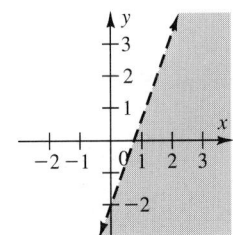

7.

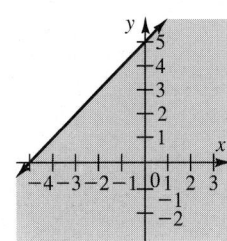

8.

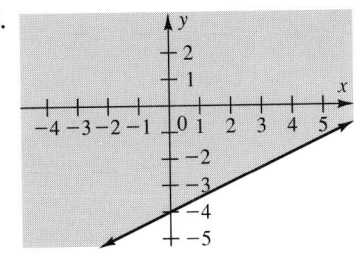

Chapter 9 Summary and Review, page 407

25.

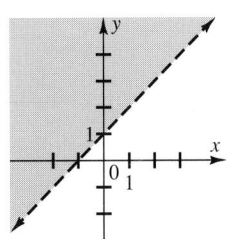

26.

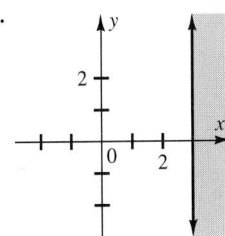

27.

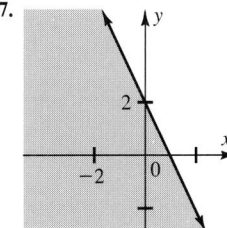

Chapter 11 Systems of Equations Capsule Review, page 444

1.

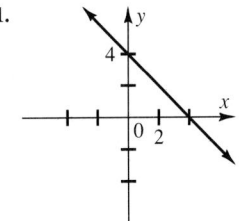

727

2.

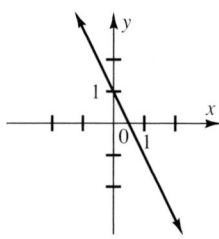

3.

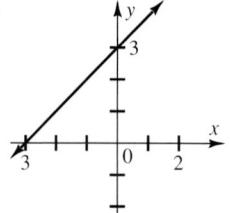

4.

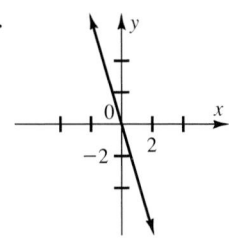

Practice Exercises, page 486

1.

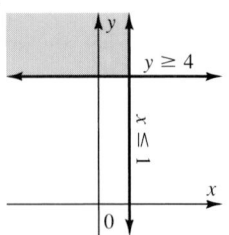

$y \geq 4$

$x \leq 1$

2.

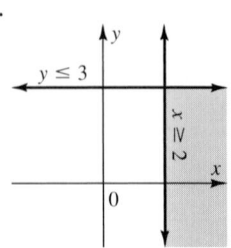

$y \leq 3$

$x \geq 2$

3.

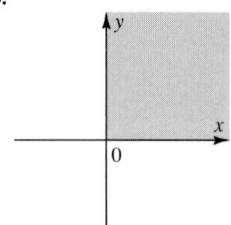

4.

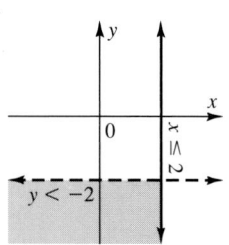

$y < -2$

$x \leq 2$

5.

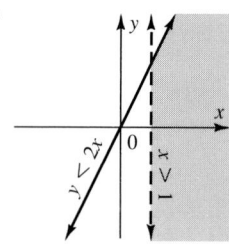

$y < 2x$

$x > 1$

6.

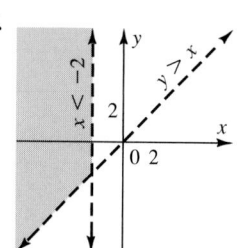

$x < -2$

$y > x$

7.

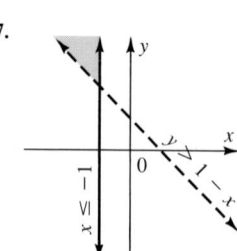

$x \geq 1$

$y > 1 - x$

8.

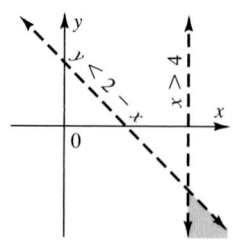

$y < 2 - x$

$x < 4$

9.

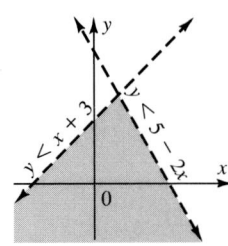

$y < x + 3$

$y < 5 - 2x$

10.

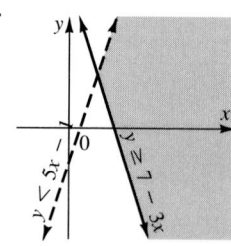

$y < 5x - 1$

$y \geq 7 - 3x$

11.

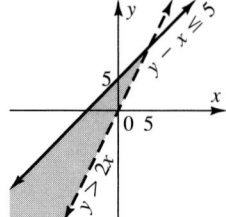

$y - x \leq 5$

$y \geq 2x$

12.

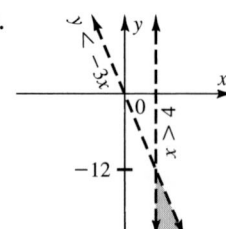

$y \geq -3x$

$x < 4$

13.

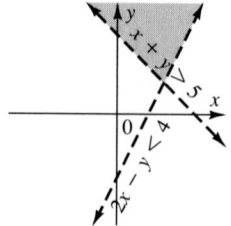

$x + y \geq 5$

$2x - y < 4$

14.
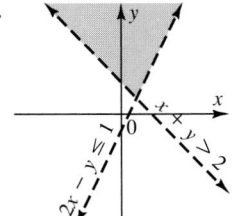

15.
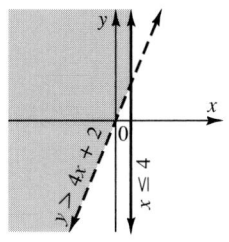

16.
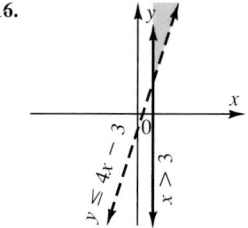

17.
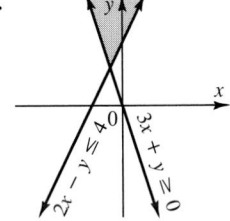

18.
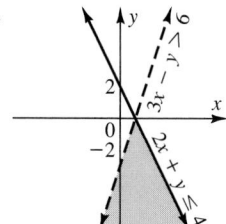

19.
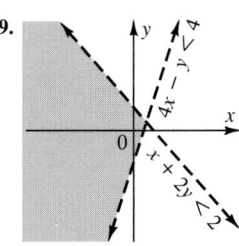

20.
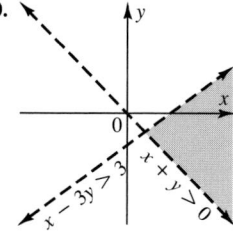

21.
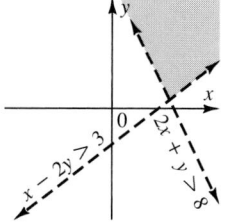

22.
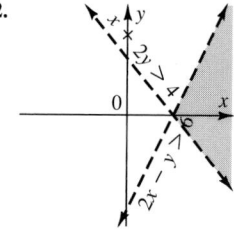

23.
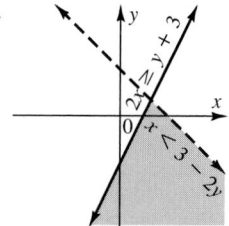

24.
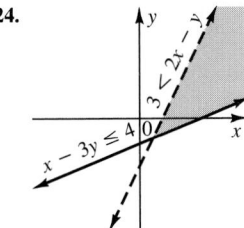

25.
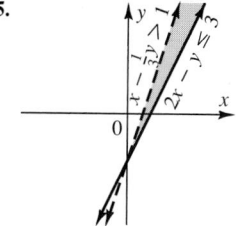

26.
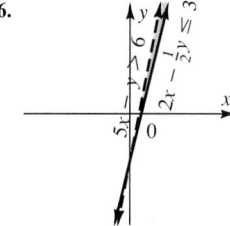

27.
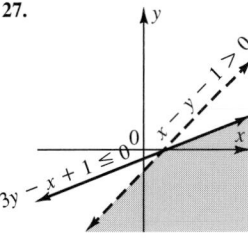

28.
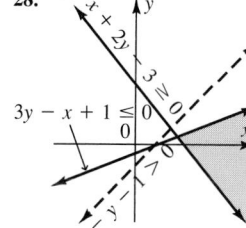

29.
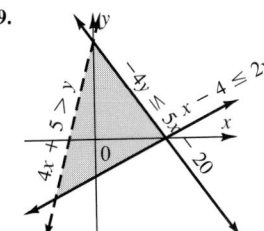

30.

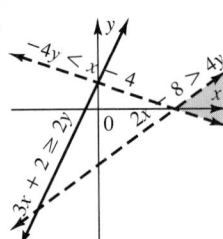

31.

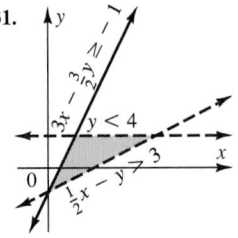

32.

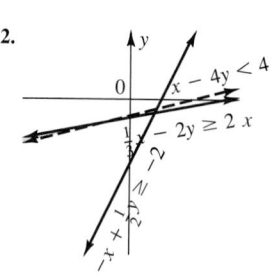

33.

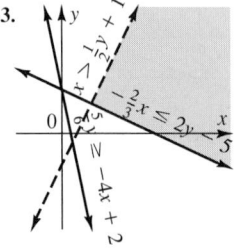

Test Yourself, page 487

9.

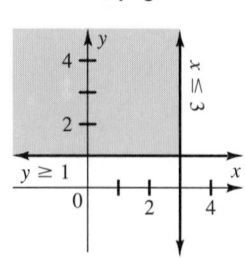

10.

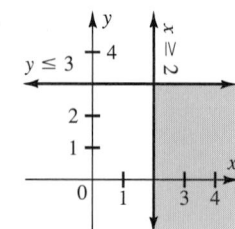

11.

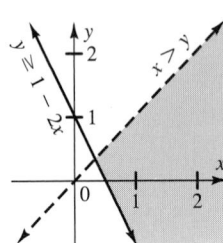

12.

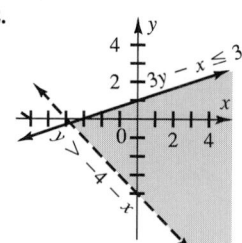

Chapter 11 Test, page 490

10.

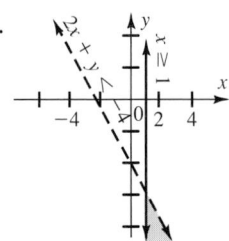

11.

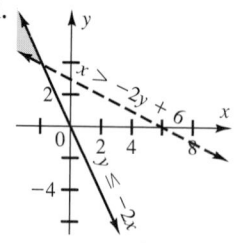

12.

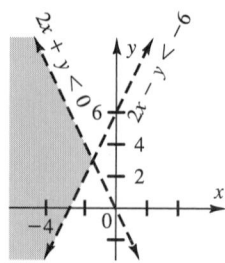

Chapter 12 Radicals
Capsule Review, page 497

1.

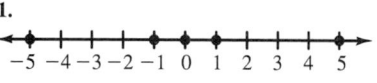

2.

3.

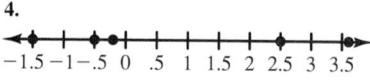

4.

5.

Chapter 13 Quadratic Equations and Functions
Capsule Review, page 557

1.

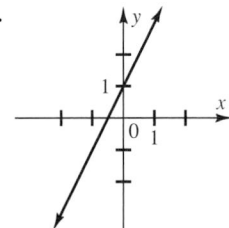

2.

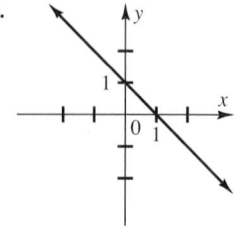

3.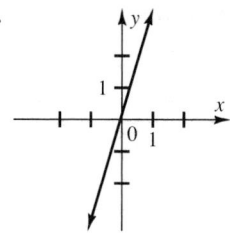

4.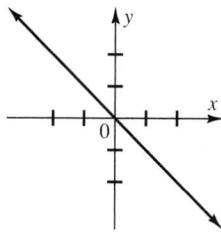

5.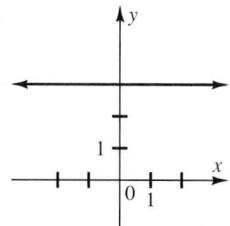

6.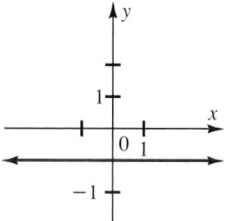

Practice Exercises, pages 560–561

1.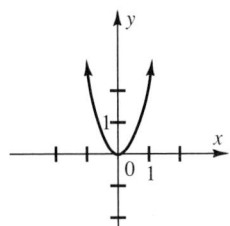

2.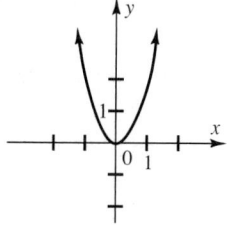

3.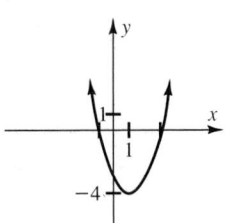

4.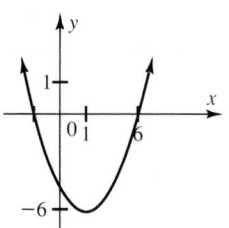

5.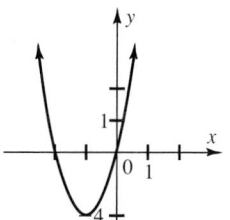

6.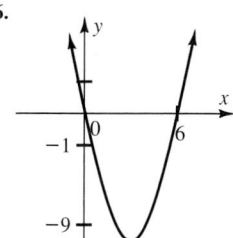

7.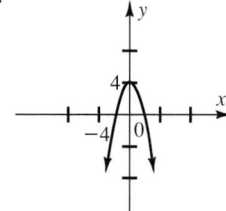

8.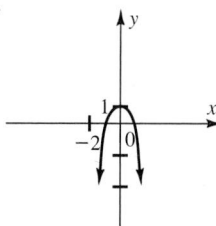

9.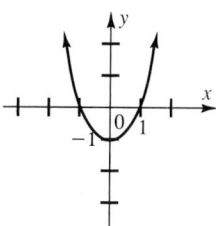

10.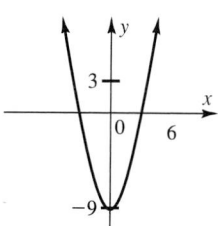

11.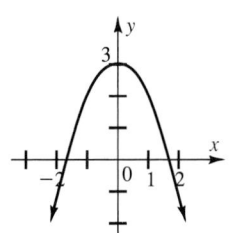

12.

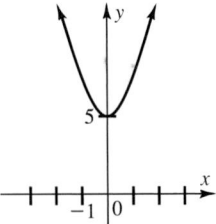

31.

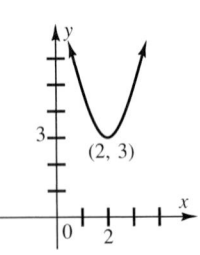

(2, 3)

32.

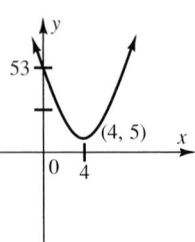

53

(4, 5)

0   4

33.

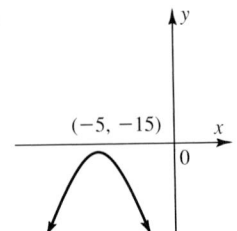

(−5, −15)

Practice Exercises, pages 588–589

6.

Interval	Frequency
10–19	3
20–29	7
30–39	7
40–49	10
50–59	4
60–69	4

9.

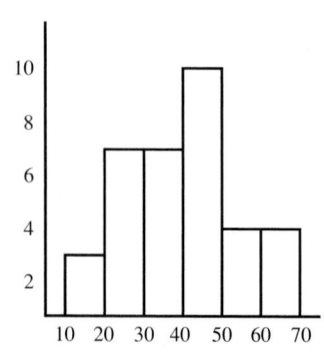

732

19.

Interval	Frequency
10,000–14,900	4
15,000–19,900	4
20,000–24,900	3
25,000–29,900	0
30,000–34,900	1
35,000–39,900	1

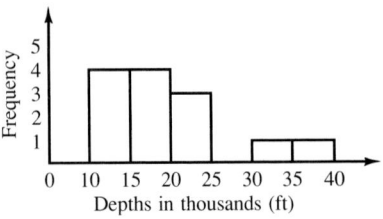

Depths in thousands (ft)

20.

Interval	Frequency
100–200	11
201–300	2
301–400	4
401–500	0
501–600	2
601–700	1

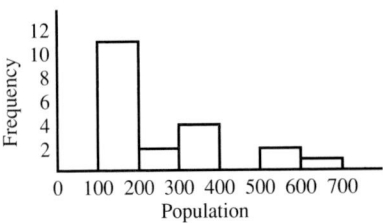

Population

Practice Exercises, page 606

7–12.

Five $\frac{3}{8}$
 — Five $\frac{2}{7}$
 — Four $\frac{1}{7}$
 — Three $\frac{2}{7}$
 — Two $\frac{2}{7}$

Four $\frac{1}{8}$
 — Five $\frac{3}{7}$
 — Four $\frac{0}{7}$
 — Three $\frac{2}{7}$
 — Two $\frac{2}{7}$

Three $\frac{2}{8}$
 — Five $\frac{3}{7}$
 — Four $\frac{1}{7}$
 — Three $\frac{1}{7}$
 — Two $\frac{2}{7}$

Two $\frac{2}{8}$
 — Five $\frac{3}{7}$
 — Four $\frac{1}{7}$
 — Three $\frac{2}{7}$
 — Two $\frac{1}{7}$

Chapter 15 Right Triangle Relationships

Practice Exercises, page 635

13. 13; $\sin Q = \frac{5}{13}$ $\cos Q = \frac{12}{13}$ $\tan Q = \frac{5}{12}$ $\sin T = \frac{12}{13}$ $\cos T = \frac{5}{13}$ $\tan T = \frac{12}{5}$

14. $\sqrt{165}$; $\sin Q = \frac{\sqrt{165}}{13}$ $\cos Q = \frac{2}{13}$, $\tan Q = \frac{\sqrt{165}}{2}$ $\sin T = \frac{2}{13}$ $\cos T = \frac{\sqrt{165}}{13}$ $\tan T = \frac{2\sqrt{165}}{165}$

15. $2\sqrt{86}$; $\sin Q = \frac{\sqrt{5246}}{86}$; $\cos Q = \frac{5\sqrt{86}}{86}$; $\tan Q = \frac{\sqrt{61}}{5}$; $\sin T = \frac{5\sqrt{86}}{86}$; $\cos T = \frac{\sqrt{5246}}{86}$; $\tan T = \frac{5\sqrt{61}}{61}$

16. 3; $\sin Q = \frac{\sqrt{3}}{2}$ $\cos Q = \frac{1}{2}$ $\tan Q = \frac{\sqrt{3}}{3}$ $\sin T = \frac{1}{2}$ $\cos T = \frac{\sqrt{3}}{2}$ $\tan T = \sqrt{3}$

17. $\sqrt{21}$; $\sin Q = \frac{\sqrt{70}}{10}$ $\cos Q = \frac{\sqrt{30}}{10}$ $\tan Q = \frac{\sqrt{21}}{3}$ $\sin T = \frac{\sqrt{30}}{10}$ $\cos T = \frac{\sqrt{70}}{10}$ $\tan T = \frac{\sqrt{21}}{7}$

18. 5; $\sin Q = \frac{1}{2}$ $\cos Q = \frac{\sqrt{3}}{2}$ $\tan Q = \frac{\sqrt{3}}{3}$ $\sin T = \frac{\sqrt{3}}{2}$ $\cos T = \frac{1}{2}$ $\tan T = \sqrt{3}$